SECOND-ORDER EFFECTS IN ELASTICITY, PLASTICITY
AND FLUID DYNAMICS

INTERNATIONAL UNION
OF THEORETICAL AND APPLIED MECHANICS

SECOND-ORDER EFFECTS

IN

ELASTICITY, PLASTICITY

AND

FLUID DYNAMICS

INTERNATIONAL SYMPOSIUM, HAIFA, ISRAEL, APRIL 23–27, 1962

CO-SPONSORED BY THE ISRAEL ACADEMY OF SCIENCES AND HUMANITIES,
AND THE TECHNION–ISRAEL INSTITUTE OF TECHNOLOGY, HAIFA

Edited by
MARKUS REINER
Member of the Israel Academy of Sciences and Humanities
Research Professor, Technion–Israel Institute of Technology, Haifa

and

DAVID ABIR
Associate Professor, Technion–Israel Institute of Technology, Haifa

International Symposium on Second-Order
Effects in Elasticity, Plasticity and
Fluid Dynamics, Haifa, 1962

A Pergamon Press Book

THE MACMILLAN COMPANY
NEW YORK
1964

1004703

CONTENTS

	Page
Preface	vii
IUTAM International Scientific Committee	xii
Local Organizing Committee	xii
List of Participants	xiii
Working Sessions	xv

GENERAL LECTURE

C. TRUESDELL, Second-Order Effects in the Mechanics of Materials	1

I. ELASTICITY

E. STERNBERG AND M. E. GURTIN, Further Study of Thermal Stresses in Viscoelastic Materials with Temperature-Dependent Properties	51
E. H. LEE AND T. G. ROGERS, Non-Linear Effects of Temperature Variation in Stress Analysis of Isothermally Linear Viscoelastic Materials	77
D. R. BLAND, On Shock Waves in Hyperelastic Media	93
H. ZORSKI, On the Equations Describing Small Deformations Superposed on Finite Deformation	109
A. SEEGER, The Application of Second-Order Effects in Elasticity to Problems of Crystal Physics	129
P. J. BLATZ, Finite Elastic Deformation of a Plane Strain Wedge-Shaped Radial Crack in a Compressible Cylinder	145
B. R. SETH, Generalized Strain Measure with Applications to Physical Problems	162
J. F. BELL, Experiments on Large Amplitude Waves in Finite Elastic Strain	173
C. TRUESDELL, Second-Order Theory of Wave Propagation in Isotropic Elastic Materials	187
A. J. M. SPENCER, Finite Deformations of an Almost Incompressible Elastic Solid	200
Z. KARNI AND M. REINER, The General Measure of Deformation	217
A. FOUX, An Experimental Investigation of the Poynting Effect	228
S. FERSHT, Examination of Quasi-Linear Elasticity	252
B. R. SETH, Survey on Second-Order Elasticity	261

II. PLASTICITY

W. OLSZAK AND J. RYCHLEWSKI, Geometrical Properties of Stress Fields in Plastically Non-Homogeneous Bodies under Conditions of Plane Strain	269
F. K. G. ODQVIST, On Theories of Creep Rupture	295
A. SLIBAR AND P. R. PASLAY, On the Analytical Description of the Flow of Thixotropic Materials	314
D. C. DRUCKER, Stress-Strain-Time Relations and Irreversible Thermodynamics	331
J. HULT, On the Stationarity of Stress and Strain Distributions in Creep	352
Z. SOBOTKA, Some Problems of Non-Linear Rheology	362
D. ROSENTHAL AND W. B. GRUPEN, Second-Order Effect in Crystal Plasticity: Deformation of Surface Layers in Face-Centered Cubic Aggregates	391
D. C. DRUCKER, Survey on Second-Order Plasticity	416

III. Fluid Dynamics

Page

J. Schurz, Non-Newtonian Flow and Coiling of Macromolecules 427

Z. Hashin, Bounds for Viscosity Coefficients of Fluid Mixtures by Variational Methods 434

A. Foux and M. Reiner, Cross-Stresses in the Flow of Air at Reduced Pressures .. 450

L. Rintel, Flow of Non-Newtonian Fluids at Small Reynolds Number Between Two Discs: One Rotating and the Other at Rest 467

M. Bentwich and M. Reiner, Second-Order Effects in the Torsional Flow of a Gas in Accordance with the Kinetic Theory 473

E. Bousso, Observations on the Self-Acting Thrust Airbearing Effect 483

R. G. Storer and H. S. Green, Kinetic Theory of Second-Order Effects in Fluids 493

K. Walters, Non-Newtonian Effects in Some General Elastico-Viscous Liquids .. 507

J. G. Oldroyd, Non-Linear Stress, Rate of Strain Relations at Finite Rates of Shear in So-Called "Linear" Elastico-Viscous Liquids 520

B. D. Coleman and W. Noll, Simple Fluids with Fading Memory 530

H. Giesekus, Statistical Rheology of Suspensions and Solutions with Special Reference to Normal Stress Effects 553

H. Markovitz and D. R. Brown, Normal Stress Measurements on a Polyisobutylene-Cetane Solution in Parallel Plate and Cone-Plate Instruments 585

M. N. L. Narasimhan, Flow of a Non-Newtonian Electrically Conducting Fluid Along a Circular Cylinder with Uniform Suction 603

M. K. Jain, Collocation Method to Study Problems of Cross-Viscosity 623

W. P. Graebel, The Hydrodynamic Stability of a Bingham Fluid in Couette Flow 636

A. B. Metzner, W. T. Houghton, R. E. Hurd and C. C. Wolfe, Dynamics of Fluid Jets: Measurement of Normal Stresses at High Shear Rates 650

R. S. Rivlin, Second and Higher-Order Theories for the Flow of a Viscoelastic Fluid in a Non-Circular Pipe 668

P. Lieber, The Mechanical Evolution of Clusters by Binary Elastic Collisions and Conception of a Crucial Experiment on Turbulence 678

J. G. Oldroyd, Survey on Second-Order Fluid Dynamics 699

IV. Papers Accepted but not Read

L. Finzi, On the Uniqueness of Solution in Statics of Continua with General Differential Stress–Strain Relations 715

Y. Yoshimura and Y. Takenaka, Strain History Effects in Plastic Deformation of Metals 729

J. Dvořák, Relaxation of Stresses in Flanged Joints of High-Pressure Steam Piping 751

W. Segawa, Rheological Equations of Generalized Maxwell Model and Voigt Model in Three-Dimensional, Non-Linear Deformation 758

L. Dintenfass, Micro-Rheological Classification and Analysis of Complex Multiphase Suspensions 764

A. Peterlin, Non-Newtonian Intrinsic Viscosity and Streaming Birefringence of Polymer Solutions 776

R. D. Bell and R. C. L. Bosworth, Normal Pressure Effects in the Shearing of Viscous Liquids 786

PREFACE

A symposium on second order effects in elasticity, plasticity and fluid dynamics was first proposed by me to the General Assembly of the Union of Theoretical and Applied Mechanics in 1958. A positive decision was taken at the meeting of the IUTAM Bureau at Stresa on September 1st, 1960. As a result, an International Scientific Committee was established, the composition of which is given on page xii. I succeeded in obtaining the sponsorship of the Symposium by the Israel Academy of the Sciences and the Technion–Israel Institute of Technology. It was decided to hold the symposium during the Easter vacation of 1962, some time between April 17th and April 30th. However, we had to consider the fact that business meetings could not be held during actual holiday celebrations. The following dates had therefore to be taken into account:

Wednesday,	April	18th	evening Jewish Passover Meal
Thursday,	”	19th	Jewish Passover feast
Friday,	”	20th	Good Friday
Sunday,	”	22nd	Easter Sunday
Monday,	”	23rd	Easter Monday
Wednesday,	”	25th	Jewish Passover feast
Saturday,	”	28th	Jewish day of rest
Sunday,	”	29th	Christian day of rest

In accordance with these dates a time table as described below was suggested and approved by the Scientific Committee:

The formal opening of the Symposium would take place in Jerusalem, the seat of the Academy. The business meetings would take place in Haifa, at the Technion.

The opening ceremony was fixed for Saturday night, April 21st, when the Jewish day of rest was over. There was to be a formal lunch given by the Academy on Sunday noon, April 22. This plan made it possible to arrange for sightseeing in Jerusalem. It was thought that it would be impossible to hold a scientific meeting in Israel, without a pilgrimage to Jerusalem, the holy city.

After the Sunday lunch, participants were to be transported to Haifa. They could choose to stay at the Students' hostels as the guests with full board of the Technion.

The business meetings were located at the Aeronautics building, which houses also the Rheological Laboratory and the Mechanics Department, at the Technion City of Haifa. This is placed in pleasant, semi-secluded surroundings.

The business sessions were to take place on four days, namely Monday, April 23, Tuesday, April 24, Thurday, April 26, and Friday, April 27. This left Wednesday, April 25, a Jewish holiday, for sightseeing, providing an interesting respite.

A local Organizing Committee was set up in Haifa. Its composition is given on page xii.

Participation at the Symposium was by invitation only and papers had to be accepted by the Scientific Committee for presentation.

A short program of the Symposium found its expression in the invitation which it was my privilege to address to prospective participants in the following words:

"The intention was to consider physical phenomena only, due to either (i) a variability of rheological parameters such as moduli of elasticity, coefficients of viscosity, etc., or (ii) a non-linear definition of the deformation or flow tensor in terms of the displacement or rate of displacement gradient, or (iii) a non-linear relation between the tensor of stress and the tensor of strain or flow. The Symposium was not be concerned with what may be called geometrical non-linearity, i.e. a non-linearity which appears when a structure is strained so that the displacements are finite while the stress-strain relation is linear and the strain itself is infinitesimal".

In accordance with this scheme it was possible to arrange the subject matter of the different contributions as belonging to one, or more, of the nine categories listed here:

	Parametrical	Deformational	Tensorial
		Non-linearity	
Elasticity	I	II	III
Plasticity	IV	V	VI
Fluid Dynamics	VII	VIII	IX

For the understanding of the term "geometrical" non-linearity, one may point to the example given by Timoshenko, which shows that "there are cases in which the displacements are not proportional to the loads, although the material of the body may follow Hooke's law". The example refers to two equal horizontal bars AC and CB hinged at A, B and C, subjected to the action of a vertical force P at C. Let A be the cross-sectional area of the bar and E be Young's modulus, then it is shown that the small vertical displacement δ of point C is equal to

$$\delta = l \sqrt[3]{P/AE}$$

where l is the length of $AC = CB$.

This is contrary to the statement which one sometimes finds, for instance, that in classical linear theory "a uniformly doubled load produces a doubled displacement".

In contradistinction to this "geometrical" non-linearity, the Symposium dealt with what may be called "physical" non-linearity. It is obvious that the rheological parameters of the material will be dependent in their magnitude upon the physical conditions of the field in which a phenomenon takes place, e.g. of the temperature. As is well known, changes in the temperature very much influence the magnitude of the coefficient of viscosity of any material. However, this was not what was meant by "parametrical" non-linearity. The "variability" of the parameter was meant to refer to the other quantities implicit in the constitutive (rheological) equation of the material. Taking for instance

$$s_{ij} = - p\delta_{ij} + \lambda_v f_{\alpha\alpha}\delta_{ij} + 2\eta\, f_{ij}$$

as the rheological equation of the classical viscous fluid with

$$f_{ij} = \tfrac{1}{2}(v_{i,j} + v_{j,i}),$$

the question is after the dependence of the parameters λ_v and η upon the velocity gradient $v_{i,j}$. The dependence of the coefficient of viscosity η upon the velocity gradient in colloidal solutions is a well-known and much investigated fact; this is a case of physical non-linearity. Such liquids have been named "non-Newtonian" or "generalized" Newtonian.

"Deformational non-linearity" takes place when the expression for the classical strain-tensor

$$\varepsilon_{ij} = \tfrac{1}{2}(u_{i,j} + u_{j,i})$$

is replaced, for instance, by the Almansi measure

$$^A e_{ij} = \tfrac{1}{2}\left(\frac{\partial u_i}{\partial x_j} + \frac{\partial u_j}{\partial x_i} - \frac{\partial u_\alpha}{\partial x_i}\frac{\partial u_\alpha}{\partial x_j} \right)$$

"Tensorial non-linearity" results from a rheological equation of the form

$$s_{ij} = -p\delta_{ij} + \aleph_0\delta_{ij} + \aleph_1 f_{ij} + \aleph_2 f_{i\alpha}f_{\alpha j}$$

This follows from the only condition that s is an isotropic function of f. Here the scalar coefficients $\aleph$ are functions of the principal invariants of the tensor f.

A similar equation has been postulated for the case of elasticity.

— · — · — · — · — · —

Invitations were issued on recommendation of the members of the Scientific Committee and of other scientists active in the field. The number of invitations was nearly one hundred. Of these some did not respond, and some submitted abstracts which, while indicating valuable scientific contributions, were found to fall outside the scope of the Symposium. Finally 46 papers were accepted for presentation. Unfortunately the authors of some of the accepted papers did not arrive in Israel for various reasons. These were sometimes financial, sometimes health and possibly others. Especially regrettable was the complete absence of participants from the U.S.S.R. Finally 80 scientists from 14 countries were present. Their names and addresses are listed on pages xiii to xiv. The numbers of participants from different countries were as follows: Israel 24, U.S.A. 18, France 8, U.K. 7, Germany 4, Sweden 4, Denmark 3, Australia 2, Austria 2, Czechoslovakia 2, India 2, Poland 2, Holland 1, Italy 1. The names of those participants whose papers were accepted, but who were not present, are listed on page vi.

Preprints of all accepted papers were sent in time to all participants.

The first session on Monday commenced with a one-and-half hour lecture by Professor Truesdell, which provided a survey of the whole field under discussion. This was followed by papers on Elasticity. Tuesday was given over to Plasticity and Fluid Dynamics. The latter occupied also Thursday. On Friday three review papers were given in the fields of elasticity by Professor Seth, in plasticity by Professor Drucker, and in fluid dynamics by Professor Oldroyd.

The program of the particular sessions is given on pages xv to xvi. The names of the chairmen of the relevant sessions are also indicated.

Participants were charged a registration fee of $ 20.— for themselves and $ 10.— for the accompanying ladies. In consideration of these payments they received a set of preprints and the present book, while a special program was arranged for the ladies.

IUTAM set aside the sum of $5000.— for the purpose of reimbursing participants for their travelling expenses and subsistence. We received from 14 participants statements of expenses with requests for $5642.—. It was decided by members of the Scientific Committee present at the Symposium to cover first all travelling expenses asked for and to divide the remainder in proportion.

After the Symposium a sightseeing tour was arranged which gave a significant cross section of the country.

The present book contains the proceedings of the conference, including papers which had been accepted but were not presented. It contains also such discussions as were supplied in writing.

Thanks are due to the sponsors and to those bodies and persons who helped to make the symposium a success. Special mention must be made to Professor A. Katzir, the Vice President of the Academy, Professor S. Irmai, the Vice President of the Technion, and Professor G. Racah, the Rector of the Hebrew University of Jerusalem, who attended some of our meetings, and last but not least to her Excellency Mrs. Golda Meir, the Israel Minister of Foreign Affairs, who took part at the farewell dinner on April 26, given by the Technion.

Thanks are also due to the members of the Department of Mechanics and the Rheological Laboratory of the Technion and Mrs. Singer, the organizing secretary, for their devoted help.

Haifa, May 1962.

M. REINER

IUTAM INTERNATIONAL SCIENTIFIC COMMITEE

LOCAL ORGANIZING COMMITEE

CONTENTS

Name	Address
ABELL D. F.	Lawrence Radiation Laboratory, California, *Livermore*, U.S.A.
ABIR D.	Technion – Israel Institute of Technology, *Haifa*, Israel
BEATRIX P.	Centre d'Etudes Nucleaires de Saclay, *Paris*, France
BELL J. F.	The Johns Hopkins University, *Baltimore*, Maryland, U.S.A.
BEN-ZVI, E.	Teconion – Israel Institute of Technology, *Haifa*, Israel
BERNIER H.	Centre d'Etudes Nucleaires de Saclay, *Paris*, France
BETSER A.	Technion – Israel Institute of Technology, *Haifa*, Israel
BLAND D. R.	The University of Manchester, *Manchester*, England
BLATZ P. J.	California Institute of Technology, *Pasadena*, California, U.S.A.
BOUSSO E.	Technion – Israel Institute of Technology, *Haifa*, Israel
BROER L. J. F.	Technische Hogeschool, *Eindhoven*, Holland
CABANNES H.	Université de Paris, *Paris*, France
COLEMAN B. D.	Mellon Institute, *Pittsburgh*, Pennsylvania, U.S.A.
DANZIGER A.	Technion – Israel Institute of Technology, *Haifa*, Israel
DRUCKER D. C.	Brown University, *Providence*, Rhode Island, U.S.A.
ETTENBERG M.	Technion – Israel Institute of Technology, *Haifa*, Israel
FERSHT S.	Technion – Israel Institute of Technology, *Haifa*, Israel
FOUX A.	Technion – Israel Institute of Technology, *Haifa*, Israel
GERMAIN P.	Institut Henri Poincaré, *Paris 5ème*, France
GIESEKUS H.	Farbenfabriken Bayer A.G., *Leverkusen*, West Germany
GÖRANSSON U.	The Royal Institute of Technology, *Stockholm* 70, Sweden
GRAEBEL W. P.	The University of Michigan, *Ann Arbor*, Michigan, U.S.A.
GREEN A. E.	University of Durham, *Newcastle-on-Tyne*, U.K.
GREEN H. S.	The University of Adelaide, Australia
HASHIN Z.	University of Pennsylvania, *Philadelphia*, Pennsylvania, U.S.A.
HULT J.	Chalmers University of Technology, *Gothenburg*, Sweden
IRMAY SH.	Technion – Israel Institute of Technology, *Haifa*, Israel
KARNI Z.	Technion – Israel Institute of Technology, *Haifa*, Israel
KATCHALSKI E.	Weizmann Institute of Science, *Rehovot*, Israel
KAYE A.	The College of Aeronautics, *Cranfield*, England
LANGE-HANSEN P.	Danmarks Tekniske Hojskole, *Copenhagen*, Denmark
LEDERER A.	Zichron Yaacov Street 8, *Tel-Aviv*, Israel.
LEE E. H.	Brown University, *Providence*, Rhode Island, U.S.A.
LEVI M.	Technion – Israel Institute of Technology, *Haifa*, Israel
LIEBER P.	University of California, *Berkeley* 4, California, U.S.A.
MAIER G.	Politecnico di Milano, *Milano*, Italy
MALINOVSKY R.	Technion – Israel Institute of Technology, *Haifa*, Israel
MARKOVITZ H.	Mellon Institute, *Pittsburgh*, Pennsylvania, U.S.A.
MEDWIN H.	Office of Naval Research, U.S.A. Embassy, *London W.* 1., England
METZNER A. B.	University of Delaware, *Newark*, Delaware, U.S.A.
MICHAUD L.	Centre d'Etudes Nucleaires de Saclay, *Paris* France

LIST OF PARTICIPANTS (CONTINUED)

Name	Address
MOREAU E.	Centre d'Etudes Nucleaires de Saclay, *Paris*, France
MURTHY S. N. B.	Purdue University, *Lafayette*, Indiana, U.S.A.
NIORDSON F.	The Royal Technical University, *Copenhagen*, Denmark
ODQVIST F. K. G.	Royal Institute of Technology, *Stockholm*, Sweden
OLDROYD J. G.	University College of Swansea, Wales, U.K.
OLSZAK W.	Polish Academy of Sciences, *Warsaw*, Poland
PARTOM Y.	Palmach Street 6, *Haifa*, Israel
PASLAY P. R.	Technische Hochschule, *Stuttgart*, Germany
PUST L.	Czechoslovak Academy, *Prague*, Czechoslovakia
RADOK J. R. M.	Dornbacherstrasse 115, *Vienna XVII*, Austria
RAM A.	Technion – Israel Institute of Technology, *Haifa*, Israel
REINER M.	Technion – Israel Institute of Technology, *Haifa*, Israel
RINTEL L.	Technion – Israel Institute of Technology, *Haifa*, Israel
RIVLIN R. S.	Brown University, *Providence*, Rhode Island, U.S.A.
ROSENTHAL D.	University of California, *Los Angeles*, California, U.S.A.
ROTEM Z.	Technion – Israel Institute of Technology, *Haifa*, Israel
SAIBEL E.	Rensselaer Polytechnic Institute, *Troy*, N.Y., U.S.A.
SAUNOIS M.	Centre d'Etudes Nucleaires de Saclay, *Paris*, France
SAVINS J. G.	Socony Mobil Oil Company, Inc., *Dallas* 21, Texas, U.S.A.
SCHURZ J.	University of Graz, Austria
SEEGER A.	Max-Planck-Institut für Metallforschung, *Stuttgart*, West Germany
SEEGER R. J.	National Science Foundation, *Washington*, D.C., U.S.A.
SETH B. R.	Indian Institute of Technology, *Kharagpur*, India
SHAHAR S.	Negev Research Institute, *Beer Sheba*, Israel
SHINNAR R.	Technion – Israel Institute of Technology, *Haifa*, Israel
SHKLARSKY E.	Technion – Israel Institute of Technology, *Haifa*, Israel
SHRAM R.	Tel-Aviv University, Israel
SLIBAR A.	Technische Hochschule, *Stuttgart*, West Germany
SOBOTKA Z.	Svedska 10, *Prague* 5 – Smichor, Czechoslovakia
SPENCER A. J. M.	The University of Nottingham, England
STERNBERG E.	Brown University, *Providence*, Rhode Island, U.S.A.
STORER R. G.	The University of Adelaide, South Australia
SUNDSTRAND A.	Saab Aircraft Co., *Linköping*, Sweden
TAUB I.	*Tel Aviv*, Israel
THOFT-CHRISTENSEN P.	Technical University of Denmark, *Copenhagen K*, Denmark
TRUESDELL C.	The Johns Hopkins University, *Baltimore*, Maryland, U.S.A.
DE VRIES A.	Centre de Recherche, Saint Gobain, *Antony* (Seine), France
WALTERS K.	University College of Wales, *Aberystwyth*, U.K.
ZASLAVSKY D.	Technion – Israel Institute of Technology, *Haifa*, Israel
ZORSKI H.	Polish Academy of Sciences, *Warsaw*, Poland

WORKING SESSIONS

First Meeting

Monday, April 23, 1962 — Morning Session

Chairman: B. R. Seth
Deputy Chairman: Z. Sobotka

9.00 – 10.30 Introductory General Lecture by C. Truesdell

Topic: *ELASTICITY*

10.30 – 10.50	Coffee break		11.40 – 12.00	Bland	II
10.50 – 11.20	Sternberg and Gurtin	I*	12.00 – 14.30	Break for lunch	
11.20 – 11.40	Lee and Rogers	I		and rest	

Second Meeting

Monday, April 23, 1962 — Afternoon Session

Chairman: B. D. Coleman
Deputy Chairman: M. Reiner

14.30 – 14.55	Zorski	II	16.45 – 17.25	Truesdell	III
14.55 – 15.20	A. Seeger	II	17.25 – 17.45	Spencer	III
15.20 – 15.40	Blatz	II	17.45 – 18.00	Karni and Reiner	II
15.40 – 16.00	Tea break		18.00 – 18.20	Foux	II
16.00 – 16.25	Seth	II	18.20 – 18.40	Fersht	II
16.25 – 16.45	Bell	II			

Topic: *PLASTICITY*

Third Meeting

Tuesday, April 24, 1962 — Morning Session

Chairman: H. Giesekus
Deputy Chairman: H. Markovitz

9.00 – 9.30	Olszak and Rychlewski	IV	11.05 – 11.30	Coffee break	
9.30 – 10.00	Odqvist	IV	11.30 – 11.50	Sobotka	VI
10.00 – 10.25	Slibar and Paslay	IV	11.50 – 12.10	Rosenthal and Grupen	IV
10.25 – 10.45	Drucker	VI	12.10 – 14.30	Break for lunch and rest	
10.45 – 11.05	Hult	VI			

Topic: *FLUID DYNAMICS*

Fourth Meeting

Tuesday, April 24, 1962 — Afternoon Session

Chairman: D. C. Drucker
Deputy Chairman: P. Lieber

14.30 – 15.00	Schurz	VII	16.30 – 17.00	Rintel	IX
15.00 – 15.30	Hashin	VII	17.00 – 17.30	Bentwich and Reiner	IX
15.30 – 16.00	Tea break		17.30 – 17.50	Bousso	VIII
16.00 – 16.30	Foux and Reiner	IX	17.50 – 18.10	Storer and Green	VIII

* Roman numerals refer to category of paper as explained in the Preface.

FIFTH MEETING

Thursday, April 26, 1962 — Morning Session

Chairman: F. K. G. ODQVIST

Deputy Chairman: A. E. GREEN

9.00– 9.20	WALTERS	IX	10.50–11.10	MARKOVITZ AND BROWN	IX
9.20– 9.40	OLDROYD	IX	11.10–11.50	NARASIMHAN; JAIN (read by SETH)	IX
9.40–10.00	COLEMAN AND NOLL	IX			
10.00–10.20	GIESEKUS	IX	11.50–12.10	GRAEBEL	VIII
10.20–10.50	Coffee break		12.10–14.30	Break for lunch and rest	

SIXTH MEETING

Thursday, April 26, 1962 — Afternoon Session

Chairman: W. OLSZAK

Deputy Chairman: A. B. METZNER

14.30–15.00	METZNER et al.	VIII	15.30–16.00	Tea break	
15.00–15.30	RIVLIN	IX	16.00–16.30	LIEBER	VII

SEVENTH MEETING

Friday, April 27, 1962 — Morning Session

Chairman: R. S. RIVLIN

Deputy Chairman: H. ZORSKI

8.30– 9.30 Survey Lecture on Elasticity — SETH
9.30–10.30 Survey Lecture on Plasticity — DRUCKER
10.30–10.45   Coffee break
10.45–11.45 Survey Leeture on Fluid Dynamics — OLDROYD

SECOND-ORDER EFFECTS IN THE MECHANICS OF MATERIALS

C. Truesdell

The Johns Hopkins University, Baltimore, Maryland, U.S.A.

CONTENTS

1. The meaning of "order"
2. The work of Reiner (1945–1948)
3. The work of Rivlin (1947–1949)
4. The work of Noll (1955–1958)
5. Second-order effects in simple elastic solids
6. The general theory of stress relaxation
7. Polar elastic solids
8. Second-order effects in hypo-elasticity
9. Second-order stresses and flows of simple fluids
10. The anistropic fluids of Ericksen
11. Fluid mixtures
12. Second-order memory
13. Effects of the second order in the natural time of a simple fluid
14. Non-linear continuum theories derived from molecular models
15. Concluding remarks

1. The meaning of "order".

If a function $f(x)$ can be approximated by a polynomial of several terms,

$$f(x) = ax + bx^2 + \dots, \tag{1}$$

we say that the terms bx and cx^2 are the contributions of first and second orders, respectively, in x. More generally, if $\mathscr{I}$ is a transformation or operation such that, in some sense,

$$f(x) = \mathscr{I}g(x) + \mathscr{I}^2 g(x) + \dots, \tag{2}$$

we say that $\mathscr{I}g(x)$ and $\mathscr{I}^2 g(x)$ are the contributions of first and second orders in the operator $\mathscr{I}$. The idea of "order" is mathematical, not physical; it has nothing to do with the phenomenon occurring, since it results only from the mathematical framework we choose in describing the phenomenon. Therefore, in order to discuss second-order effects rationally, we need first an exact theory for the phenomenon. Moreover, what is a second-order effect according to one theory may be a first-order effect according to another, and the same experimental facts may be consistent with both. For example, it is usually

1

said that the normal stresses needed in order to maintain a state of simple shear within the elastic range are effects of second-order because they are proportional to the square of the amount of shear. However, in a theory according to which stress arises in response not only to strain but also to differences of strain at neighboring points, every solution according to the classical theory of finite strain is a first-order solution only, so that in such a theory the occurrence of normal stresses in shear is a first-order effect. Since the particular strain is homogeneous, the results of the two kinds of theories will be identical for this problem, although they will differ for more complicated states of strain. This example should make it clear that even when two theories agree with each other and with experimental data in a particular case, the "orders" of a given effect may differ between them.

In summary, the concept of the order of an effect is purely theoretical, and it varies with the theorist. If we are to have any common ground in the symposium, we must first lay down some exact theories of materials, and we must agree on their value or at least their interest as models for the observed behavior of physical materials. On the other hand, not taking this necessity as license to give a lecture on the general principles alone, I shall discuss only those aspects of the foundations that bear on some classification of effects according to order.

2. The work of Reiner (1945–1948).

While some valuable work on the foundations of non-linear continuum mechanics was done in the last century and as late as 1913, the literature published between the two wars is for the most part futile from lack of direction. The necessity for deciding what is exact before one can give any objective meaning to the term "approximate" was not felt. Some non-linearity was desired since the linearized or linear theories did not allow effects like the variation of apparent viscosity in a tube viscometer, but, it seems, the authors at that time were content with the first non-linear term that came to mind, and in addition many suffered under a delusion that the universe has only one or two dimensions. Direction was given to the field by two classical papers of Reiner, published in 1945 and 1948. While these papers have become thoroughly known through repeated analysis and summary, it is a pleasure to be able to begin this conference, organized by Professor Reiner, with a somewhat different evaluation of them. The first [2] proposed a theory of non-linear viscosity of fluids which has since come to be regarded as too special to represent any physical fluid so far tested, except when it reduces to the Navier-Stokes theory. Looking back at this paper, we see now that it was the first to show the value of an explicit representation formula. In particular, starting from the assumption that the stress, **t**, is given by a tensor polynomial in the stretching, **d**, Reiner showed that for an isotropic fluid

$$\mathbf{t} = -p\mathbf{1} + \aleph_0\mathbf{1} + \aleph_1\mathbf{d} + \aleph_2\mathbf{d}^2 \tag{3}$$

where p is the pressure that would correspond to equilibrium and where $\aleph_\Gamma$ is a scalar function of the principal invariants I_d, II_d, III_d of **d**. We now know that the formula, as an algebraic theorem, was not new; we can prove it more efficiently and under far weaker assumptions; and also the fluid itself need not be assumed isotropic, because we can prove from Reiner's original assumption that it has to be. Nevertheless, the value of this paper remains, not only as the opener of the modern theory of continuum mechanics—I still remember the powerful effect this paper had on me when I first came across it, some time in 1948 or 1949, when I was struggling with similar problems by use of series expansions—, but also for some definite results. First, the painful groping after new effects by adding little terms here and there was shown to be unnecessary forever: A definite *concept*, independent of expansions and such impedimenta, entered the field and received a simple, finite expression that we can *understand*. Second, a rational basis for the order of various effects was laid down. Consider, for example, Reiner's classically lucid and easy analysis of simple shearing of amount κ. Since in this flow

$$\mathbf{d} = \kappa \begin{Vmatrix} 0 & 1 & 0 \\ 1 & 0 & 0 \\ 0 & 0 & 0 \end{Vmatrix}, \tag{4}$$

from (3) we have

$$\mathbf{t} = (-p + \aleph_0)\mathbf{1} + \kappa\aleph_1 \begin{Vmatrix} 0 & 1 & 0 \\ 1 & 0 & 0 \\ 0 & 0 & 0 \end{Vmatrix} + \kappa^2\aleph_2 \begin{Vmatrix} 1 & 0 & 0 \\ 0 & 1 & 0 \\ 0 & 0 & 0 \end{Vmatrix}. \tag{5}$$

Since $I_d = III_d = 0$ and $II_d = \kappa^2$, the response coefficients $\aleph_\Gamma$ are even functions of the shearing. From (5), then, we see that shear stress and shearing are related as follows:

$$t_{xy} = \kappa\aleph_1 = \text{odd function of } \kappa, \tag{6}$$

while there are deviatoric normal stresses following an independent as well as different rule:

$$t_{xx} - t_{zz} = t_{yy} - t_{zz} = \kappa^2 \, \aleph_2 = \text{even function of } \kappa \, . \tag{7}$$

Therefore, departure from the classical linear relation between shear stress and shearing is an effect of third or higher odd order in the shearing; the second-order effect in simple shearing is the occurrence of deviatoric normal pressures on the shearing planes, the planes normal to the flow, and the planes of shear. The magnitudes of the second-order effects, in this theory, are altogether independent of those of the first-order effects. These second-order effects, far from confirming any particular theory, are only natural in all theories of this kind; whatever are the values of the response coefficients $\aleph_\Gamma$, apart from the special case when $\aleph_2 = 0$, the normal-stress effect will occur and will be of second or higher even order in κ. Finally, for adequate description of simple shearing flow, long taken as a typical one-dimensional situation, *all three spatial dimensions* are needed.

Not long after the appearance of Reiner's paper some striking experimental results of various investigators were collected and published by Weissenberg [5]. The most widely noticed of these refer to the flow between rotating cylinders (Figure 1). The surface does not remain plane, as it should according to the theory of linear viscosity when the weight and surface tension of the fluid are negligible. While inertia tends to make the fluid rise on the outer cylinder, the experiments in many cases show that it climbs up the inner one. The diagrams in Weissenberg's note served to convince many persons that the Navier-Stokes equations are not the last word in fluid dynamics, and that shearing of a fluid is not always a one-dimensional phenomenon.

I wish I could tell you that the one-dimensional concept of rheology as a whole had been shot dead by this work; all I can say is that apparently this illusion, like some noxious weeds and insects, is so sturdy as to survive all the efforts of science.

Reiner's second paper [6] concerned finite elastic strain. Based upon the same algebraic representation formula, it showed us that a stored-energy function is not necessary for a simple and definite theory of elastic response, as has been confirmed recently by more detailed investigations. The theory of Reiner, which derives from ideas of Cauchy, may be called simply *elasticity*, while the special case employing a stored-energy function is called *hyperelasticity*, a theory deriving from ideas of Green. For isotropic elastic materials Reiner obtained a formula much like (3):

$$t = \beth_0 1 + \beth_1 m + \beth_2 m^2 \, , \tag{8}$$

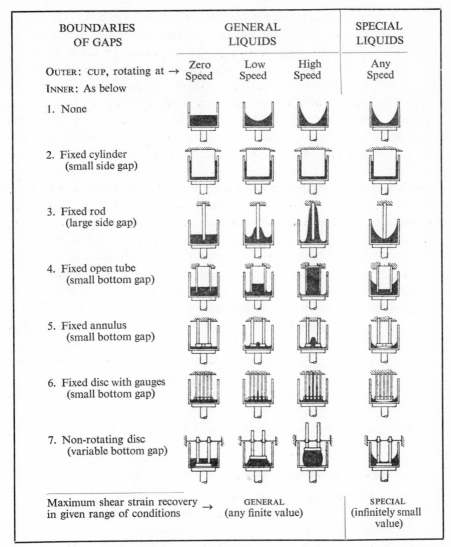

BOUNDARIES OF GAPS	GENERAL LIQUIDS			SPECIAL LIQUIDS
OUTER: CUP, rotating at → INNER: As below	Zero Speed	Low Speed	High Speed	Any Speed
1. None				
2. Fixed cylinder (small side gap)				
3. Fixed rod (large side gap)				
4. Fixed open tube (small bottom gap)				
5. Fixed annulus (small bottom gap)				
6. Fixed disc with gauges (small bottom gap)				
7. Non-rotating disc (variable bottom gap)				
Maximum shear strain recovery in given range of conditions →	GENERAL (any finite value)			SPECIAL (infinitely small value)

Figure 1

where **m** is a measure of finite strain in the deformed configuration. As he remarked, the theory is invariant under change of strain measure, as it ought to be: If we select any two different strain measures in the deformed state, either is an isotropic function of the other, so that a representation such as (8) is equally appropriate to each of them, and any two such representations may be interconverted. A difficulty arises in regard to the orders of various effects, however. Since distance is measured by a quadratic form, there is no strain measure that is a linear function of the deformation gradients. An effect that is of second-order in the principal extensions will fail to be of second order in most strain measures, and an effect that is of second order in one strain measure will fail to be of second order in others. Some of the older special theories of elasticity are linear in some particular quadratic strain measure; these theories never describe second-order effects correctly. For example, they all predict normal-stress effects, but the magnitudes of those effects are meaningless because they result from the choice of measure made in stating the assumed linearity. A definition of order fails to have physical value unless it is invariant under change of strain measure, since the choice of measure is arbitrary. If we are to get not merely arbitrary results from elasticity, we must abandon the old guessing at simplicity and consider the fully general theory. Much of the earlier work, influenced by the linearized theory, takes order as defined by the degree of expressions in the displacement gradients. Since for small extensions these are linear in the extensions, one gets a physically meaningful classification of effects, but at the cost of exactness: The general stress-strain relation if broken off after terms of the nth power in the displacement gradients is not a possible one for any material in large strain. Therefore, results interpreted in terms of this definition of order can never be exact, for any material, and if we are not careful, by too great confidence in such results we can get nonsensical predictions. This fact is well known and fairly well understood for the linearized theory, but the intuitive picture is not so clear in a second-order theory. There is insecurity in all considerations concerning this kind of order in elasticity, and we are better off if we can avoid them.

3. The work of Rivlin (1947–1949).

That expansions and approximations are often unnecessary was shown by the remarkable researches of Rivlin, which had already begun to appear in 1947. Although much of his work on the foundations led to rediscoveries, his approach to special problems was entirely original: While earlier authors had given up, it would seem, before starting an attack on solution for a particular flow or deformation, presuming that series and approximations were unavoidable, Rivlin saw that explicit, exact solutions to several basic problems could be gotten easily in the case of incompressible materials. He was the first to understand the far-reaching effect of incompressibility in mechanics, and a large part of the progress made to the present day has grown straight from his early work. For incompressible hyperelastic materials he found the exact solutions for torsion, inflation, and extension of a circular-cylindrical tube, and for bending of a rectangular block into a cylindrical segment [8] [11] [12] [13]. Comparison of these results and of the easier ones on homogeneous strains with the data from an experimental program [29] [30] made possible the tabulation of the elastic response coefficients for certain rubbers, and good correlation was found between the results for various classes of deformations. Thus began the modern theory of finite elastic strain, which now boasts several exclusive specialists, entire treatises, and a proliferous literature. For an incompressible fluid of Reiner's type, Rivlin obtained the exact solutions for simple shearing flow in a plane-parallel channel, flow in a cylindrical pipe, and flow between rotating cylinders [3] [7] [10]. These achievements gave the field of research on the foundations of continuum mechanics a directness and concreteness never seen before, and ever since then explicit and exact solutions for certain cases have been expected as a part of any satisfactory essay toward a new or more general theory of non-linear response.

After the researches of Reiner and Rivlin from 1945 to 1949, it became possible to see a certain order in the whole field and to place earlier researches in a general framework, as was attempted in my old survey, *The Mechanical Foundations* [16] [17].

4. The work of Noll (1955–1958).

A third major stream in the modern theory of materials grew from the thesis of Noll [18], published in 1955, the first work in which principles of invariance were clearly and explicitly recognized as the major tool for reducing constitutive assumptions to manageable form. The main and most commonly accepted requirement is the principle of *material indifference*, according to which a constitutive equation must have the same form for all observers, or, equivalently, must be insensitive to rigid motion of the body as a whole. Using this principle, Noll showed, for example, that if a fluid is defined as a material in which

$$t = f(v, w, d), \tag{9}$$

where v is the velocity and w is the spin, then necessarily such a relation must reduce to Reiner's form (3); that is, it is unnecessary to assume that translation and spin have no effect on viscosity, as Stokes had done, or to assume isotropy, as Reiner had done: It is impossible for translation and spin to affect the material response, and within the definition (9) there are no anisotropic fluids. While earlier researches had laid down as definitions of materials constitutive equations of particular functional forms, specifying how many derivatives were to occur, *etc.*, Noll's later work work [21] [22] succeeded in eliminating these unmotivated formalities. According to Noll's view, the defining properties of materials are statements of special kinds of invariance, and beyond them it suffices to lay down only a *principle of determinism:* The past experience of a material determines its present response. The major effort has concerned what Noll calls *simple materials.* The constitutive equation of such a material has the form

$$t = \mathop{\mathfrak{G}}_{s=0}^{\infty} \left(\mathbf{F}(t-s) \right), \tag{10}$$

where $\mathfrak{G}$ is a tensor-valued functional of its tensor argument and where $\mathbf{F}(t-s)$ is the gradient of the deformation from the reference configuration to that in which the particle found itself at time $t-s$. In virtue of the principle of material ndifference, $\mathfrak{G}$ must satisfy a certain functional equation; this equation, allow- ng us in effect to express explicitly the influence of the finite rotation, can be solved once and for all, and (10) may be replaced by the relation

$$\mathbf{F}t\mathbf{F}^{T} = \mathop{\bar{\mathfrak{G}}}_{s=0}^{\infty} \left(\mathbf{C}(t-s) \right), \tag{11}$$

where $\bar{\mathfrak{G}}$ is a different and now unrestricted functional, where the superscript T denotes transposition, and where $\mathbf{C}(t-s)$ is Green's tensor measuring the finite strain from the reference configuration to that at time $t-s$. According to this theory, then, the stress at a particle is determined by the cumulative deforma- tion history of that particle. (Mention should be made also of an essentially equivalent theory proposed earlier by Green and Rivlin [20] [23] [24] but expressed more elaborately.) If order is defined in terms of derivatives of the deformation, these theories are of first order only; nevertheless, they are extremely general in contrast to most others, since they represent properties of elasticity, viscosity, long-range and short-range memory, and stress relaxation, in any combination, and in generality.

The form of the functional $\bar{\mathfrak{G}}$ depends, in general, upon the reference configuration. Noll calls the group of all transformations under which the material properties represented by $\bar{\mathfrak{G}}$ are invariant the *isotropy group* of the material, with respect to the reference configuration. This group is always a subgroup of the unimodular group. Noll then lays down the following definitions:

   a.   A simple material is *isotropic* if there exists for it a reference configuration with isotropy group containing the proper orthogonal group.

b. A simple material is a *simple solid* if it has a reference configuration with isotropy group contained in the proper orthogonal group.

c. A simple material is a *simple fluid* if its isotropy group, for every reference configuration, is the full unimodular group.

We observe that in consequence of these definitions, all simple fluids are isotropic; that the isotropy group of an isotropic solid, relative to a suitable reference configuration, is the orthogonal group; that both solids and fluids may exhibit effects of visco-elasticity and stress relaxation; and that there are simple materials which are neither fluids nor solids. We note also that in statics, every simple material behaves as a perfectly elastic material, *i.e.*, the stress is a definite function of the deformation gradient, but the dynamic response of a material in general cannot be determined from its static properties. The classical theories of perfect fluids and perfectly elastic solids thus result by applying the so-called Principle of D'Alembert to the most general possible static equations for simple materials. The infinitely greater variety of possible dynamic response corresponds to a broad concept of "friction".

With this much background in the exact theory, we can approach rationally the problem of determining the second-order effects according to various schemes and in various materials. Some major results have been derived for very general classes of simple materials, which need be neither fluid nor solid, but the more concrete work, including explicit solutions to particular problems, has been confined mainly to two extremes: fluids and perfectly elastic solids. Despite the title of the symposium, I cannot say anything about plasticity. Apart from some limit theorems of hypo-elasticity [62] [63], I know of no successful attempt to connect the contents of treatises on plasticity with the general principles of the mechanics of materials. It is difficult to state clearly why it is that plasticity and the rest of mechanics have gone separate ways, but it is a fact that they have[1], and I cannot see that the foundations of plasticity are yet secure enough for us to give a sound definition of second-order effects within it. In contrast, a great deal has been learned, especially in the last three years, about simple materials in the sense of Noll, and this lecture is mainly a sketch of such of this work as leads to a classification of effects according to order, either in general or for particular solutions. On non-simple

---

[1] On the one hand, some of the theories of plasticity, such as the Prandtl-Reuss theory, are not properly invariant except subject to uncertain and dimly stated special assumptions about the deformation and motion we are expected to find by solving the equations. Those that are properly invariant, such as the St. Venant-Lévy-Mises theory, are rarely approached except subject to interpretation of velocities as displacements and to neglect of the inertia of the material in flow. If, as the enthusiasts of these theories state, their procedures are justified, the burden of proof lies upon them.

materials, after some early work ([9] [103], *cf.* also the summary of previous researches in [17]), the relatively little that has been done concerns theories in which the stress tensor need not be symmetric: polar elastic solids and certain of the anisotropic fluids(1), which will be mentioned later.

A detailed survey of the whole field, under the title, *The Non-linear Field Theories of Mechanics*, is being written for Flügge's *Encyclopedia of Physics*. In this lecture I cannot attempt to do more than repeat the results or outline the methods that seem to me definitive or fruitful for future research, making no attempt at completeness.

5.   Second-order effects in simple elastic solids.

Within the classical theory of finite elastic strain, we may take the principal extensions δ_i as the ordering parameters. Expanding the solutions(2) in powers of the δ_i, we may then say that the quadratic terms in these expansions give the second-order effects. As already mentioned, this definition of order is independent of the choice of tensor used to measure strain; the formulae so obtained, however, can never describe the exact response of any material; like the results of the linearized theory, they are valid in all materials for sufficiently small strain, but in none for sufficiently great strain. The literature on this subject, going back at least fifty years, is too voluminous even to list in a short survey of the present kind, so I shall make only a few remarks concerning it.

The definition of order used here restricts the results to cases not too different from those treated in the linearized theory, sacrificing altogether some of the most interesting features of elasticity. For example, instability results from the failure of the uniqueness presumed in order that a series expansion be possible. The stresses in a hemispherical cap turned inside out are not expressible as power series in the extensions, so that the phenomenon of eversion is not of any order at all.

A general method for solving problems not too different from those in the old books was worked out by Signorini [25] over thirty years ago. By series expansion, he reduced a problem of nth order to n problems in the linearized

---

(1) These materials do not fall under Noll's scheme as stated, because he presumes the stress symmetric. However, his scheme may be susceptible of generalization so as to include polar elastic solids and all kinds of anisotropic fluids.

(2) Not the stress-strain relations, since stress-strain relations of a specified order in the δ_i predict some, but not all, of the effects of higher order in the δ_i. An example is furnished by the Mooney-Rivlin theory of incompressible elastic materials, defined by taking the stored-energy function as exactly quadratic in the δ_i. In solutions according to this theory, the stresses are not necessarily linear functions of the δ_i, assigned surface tractions do not always yield a unique solution, *etc., etc.*

theory, for the same material. For the second-order theory a method of the same kind was later arranged by Rivlin [32] in such a way as to be intuitively natural. To find the solution of a second-order problem, Rivlin showed the following steps to be sufficient:

1. On the basis of the linearized theory, calculate the displacements arising from the given forces.

2. On the basis of the second-order theory, calculate the additional forces needed to maintain the displacements just found.

3. On the basis of the linearized theory, calculate the displacements corresponding to the additional forces just determined. These displacements, reversed, are the second-order displacements arising from the given forces.

By this method, the entire second-order problem in static elasticity is solved once and for all in principle, and an analogous arrangement of the perturbations may be made for arbitrary order [35]. The subject has been cultivated extensively by British and Italian authors, with diverse ends in mind. As Signorini [25] noticed very early, a condition of compatibility must be satisfied at each stage, and in general this condition has the effect of determining uniquely the infinitesimal rotation at the preceding stage. It will be recalled that in the classical linearized theory, solutions of the stress boundary-value problem are indeterminate to within an infinitesimal rotation, which is simply cast away. At the second-order, however, that linearized rotation is generally determined. Some years later Signorini [26] observed that for certain exceptional kinds of load, the second-order compatibility conditions fail to determine a unique rotation, or have no solution at all. He contended that in these cases the solution from the classical linearized theory is invalid, since it cannot be imbedded as the first step in the perturbation process he chose to consider. From this time onward the Italian school has directed its main effort toward discovering and classifying these incompatible cases; the literature has recently been summarized by Grioli [46]. The British school, on the other hand, not showing itself aware of the compatibility problem at all, has harvested an abundant ready crop of special solutions [33] [34] [37] [38] [39] [40] [41] and has set up other perturbation procedures, among which may be mentioned the important one starting from an arbitrary state of finite strain [27] [31] [37] [44] [45] [50] (*cf.* also [40] [48]), later put into an elegant and compact form by Toupin and Bernstein [42]. An extensive study of second-order effects in anisotropic materials, not necessarily hyperelastic, was made in 1949–1954 by Sheng [36]; his monograph includes numerous special solutions. Want of time forces me to omit even the most summary description of work on the fascinating connections between wave propagation, uniqueness, and stability in various kinds of problems of finite elastic strain.

Earlier, of course, numerous papers on second-order effects according to one or another special elastic theory had appeared, nor has the discovery of general methods discouraged subsequent authors from publishing as new results that follow straightaway from general solutions already in the literature. The first complete solution of a second-order problem is Murnaghan's calculation of the lengthening of circular cylinders in torsion [28]. If we turn to the general second-order theory as organized by Signorini and Rivlin, we see that their methods remain valid even if no stored-energy function exists. The second-order stress-strain relations for isotropic materials may then be written in the form

$$\frac{\mathbf{t}}{\mu} = \frac{\lambda}{\mu} I_{\mathbf{E}}\mathbf{1} + 2\mathbf{E} + (\alpha_3 I\overset{2}{\underset{\sim}{\mathbf{E}}} + \alpha_4 II \underset{\sim}{\mathbf{E}})\mathbf{1} +$$
$$+ \alpha_5 I \underset{\sim}{\mathbf{E}}\underset{\sim}{\mathbf{E}} + \alpha_6 \underset{\sim}{\mathbf{E}}^2, \tag{12}$$

where $\mathbf{E}$ is the St. Venant finite-strain tensor, $\underset{\sim}{\mathbf{E}}$ is the classical linearized strain tensor, and $\alpha_3, \alpha_4, \alpha_5, \alpha_6$ are the four dimensionless second-order elasticities. One of Rivlin's results, slightly generalized, is an expression for the mean fractional elongation $\bar{\delta}$ resulting from a twist of amount ψ applied to a cylinder whose cross-sectional area, polar moment of inertia, and torsional rigidity in the undeformed state are A_0, I_0 and S_0, respectively:

$$\bar{\delta} = \frac{\psi^2}{2A_0}\left[\frac{(1-2\sigma)\alpha_4 - (1-\sigma)\alpha_6}{4(1+\sigma)}S_0 - (I_0 - S_0)\right], \tag{13}$$

σ being Poisson's modulus. It will be seen that this elongation is indeed an effect of second order, and that its magnitude is determined by the second-order elasticities α_4 and α_6. The elastic properties of a material in the linear range aire altogether insufficient for determining whether the second-order effects will be large or small.

A number of explicit results of this kind have been calculated. A survey of them reveals that while of course all four of the second-order elasticities $\alpha_3, \alpha_4, \alpha_5, \alpha_6$ have their respective and independent effects upon the detailed, local distribution of stress and displacement, all the gross effects, such as second-order resultant normal forces or extensions, are independent of α_5. Now from (12) it is easy to see that a stored-energy function exists, as far as second-order terms are concerned, if and only if

$$\alpha_4 + \alpha_5 = 2\left(\frac{\lambda}{\mu} - 1\right). \tag{14}$$

Since this relation connects α_5 with other elasticities, and since, as I just said, the magnitudes of all gross second-order effects are independent of the value of α_5, we see that overall static measurements cannot show whether or not a given elastic material is hyperelastic.

So as to provide, among other things, an undulatory interpretation for (14), last year I constructed the general theory of weak waves in elastic materials and calculated the second-order effects within it [43]. My short communication [49] this afternoon will present an equivalent relation among speeds of transverse and longitudinal waves. The communication of Bell [47] shows that the general formulae for the speeds of propagation in prestressed materials are verified by experiment in far different circumstances, suggesting that the formulae hold in fact under assumptions weaker than those I had to use in deriving them.

6. The general theory of stress relaxation.

A broad extension for the results obtainable from the theory of elastic equilibrium was proposed by Rivlin [51–53]. He suggested that if a material is subjected to an assigned instantaneous deformation and then held fixed, the the stress should be related to that deformation by a purely elastic stress-strain relation, except that the response coefficients may depend upon time. That is, for a very general kind of material, the stress arising from a strain impulse will be of the form

$$F t F^T = \mathfrak{h}(C, t), \tag{15}$$

where C is Green's deformation tensor. In particular, for isotropic materials we shall have a formula just like (8), except that $\mathbf{J}_\Gamma$ will depend upon t as well as upon the strain invariants. Rivlin based his inference upon a constitutive equation having the form of a power series in an integral operator; recently [unpublished] Noll has shown that (15) follows easily from the more general equation (11) and thus gives the *general theory of stress relaxation* for a simple material subject to a strain impulse. This is, in fact, almost obvious, for at the outset the stress is assumed determined by the strain history, and in this case that history consists in a sudden jump from the value **1** to the value **C**; the only thing left that can vary is the time elapsed since the jump occured. All the solutions for static problems in elasticity thus hold also in any simple material undergoing stress relaxation of this kind; moreover, the general theory of waves in elastic materials can likewise be transferred entire to waves in any simple material subjected to a strain impulse.

Just before leaving to attend the symposium, I was shown an experiment verifying this result for impulsive simple extension of an incompressible material. The work was done at the U. S. National Bureau of Standards. The measurements are claimed to be consistent not only with the general theory but also with the special case obtained by considering only the first term in Green and Rivlin's expansion [20].

7. Polar elastic solids.

Despite widespread prejudice to the contrary, as well as a torrent of nonsense on the subject, it is not a law of mechanics that the stress tensor is symmetric. As has been known for nearly a century, the presence of couples, acting whether from without the material like body forces or upon contiguous portions of material like stresses, is sufficient to render the stress tensor unsymmetric. A recent general exposition of continuum mechanics [1], besides making this entirely obvious and explicit, recapitulates a generalized theory of elasticity, proposed by E. and F. Cosserat in 1909, in which couple stresses arise in response to inhomogeneity of strain. This theory was then immediately revived, put on a sounder mechanical footing, and generalized by Grioli [46] [58] [59], Mindlin [60], Toupin [61], and others. It is too soon to report in detail on the results of this interesting and entirely plausible theory of polar elastic media, especially since I have not yet seen some of the papers now being prepared for the press. I mention it so as to advertise that the theory is no longer just a curiosity, since a considerable body of special solutions is now at hand. For example, it turns out that waves of a given kind travelling in a polar medium, even for small strain, no longer have a common speed, since the presence of the couple stresses leads to dispersion. The occurrence of dispersion is an effect of first-order in the strain, not second; it is possible because a polar material has a characteristic length as well as a characteristic elasticity. However, even in the linearized case, the entire theory of polar elastic media may be considered as including second-order effects, since the couple stresses themselves arise in response to second rather than first derivatives of the deformation field. The ordering parameters are now the partial differential operators rather than the extensions. As I remarked at the outset, different definitions of "order" lead to different results. I do not wish to labor the point, which I do not regard as important; I wish only to summarize the more concrete of the recent fundamental researches in the field and yet stay within the scope laid down for the meeting.

Here should be mentioned also the continuum theory of "dislocations" in finite strain [54–57]. This theory may be regarded as a generalization of finite elasticity in that no natural state is assumed possible for the body as a whole although each element responds as to strain from such a state. In some presentations of this theory a polar medium is presumed. Current emphasis is laid on the purely geometrical foundation, and a correspondingly clear and general statement of the constitutive equations has not yet been given.

8. Second-order effects in hypo-elasticity.

When I proposed the theory of hypo-elasticity [17], I had in mind an alternative concept of purely elastic response that would agree with the theory of finite strain only for infinitesimal strains. The defining equations are of the form

$$\tilde{\mathbf{t}} = \mathbf{f}(\mathbf{t}, \mathbf{d}), \tag{16}$$

where $\mathbf{f}$ is linear in $\mathbf{d}$ and where $\tilde{\mathbf{t}}$ is any of the several invariant stress rates. We may regard the theory as representing a material in which the stress is built up by increments which at any instant obey a linear stress-strain relation with coefficients depending upon the present value of the stress. Noll [18] quickly showed that every isotropic elastic material is also hypo-elastic, but the converse is not true, nor does the result carry over to anisotropic materials; moreover, later researches by Bernstein [69] show clearly that (16) does not suffice to define a material. One of my objectives was to free the concept of elasticity from any connection with a natural or otherwise preferred state, so that the initial stress may be arbitrary. While this objective was reached, Bernstein showed that very different material responses can result from different initial stresses. In one of his examples, a fixed relation of the form (16) when integrated yields a finite stress-strain relation that defines a fluid if the initial stress is hydrostatic but a non-fluid if the initial stress is other than hydrostatic. These results show that hypo-elasticity allows greater flexibility than does elasticity, but here it is another aspect of the theory that interests us more, namely, that hypo-elasticity offers an entirely different method of ordering effects.

Recall in finite elasticity the difficulties in connection with choice of strain measure, resulting in the usual definition of order in terms of the degree of a polynomial approximation in the displacement gradients. The theory of nth-order elasticity, no matter how large is n, is an approximate one, not properly invariant and hence impossible as a model for the behavior of *any* material in finite strain. The difficulties arise from the fact that finite distances are involved, and these are determined by quadratic functions. In hypo-elasticity occurs as a strain measure only the stretching, $\mathbf{d}$, and it is linear in the velocity; essentially, only infinitesimal distances are involved. The dependence upon $\mathbf{d}$ in (16) can be rendered entirely explicit, but the dependence upon $\mathbf{t}$ remains arbitrary. By taking **f** as the most general polynominal of degree n in **t** we may define a hypo-elastic material of grade n. The theory so obtained may not happen to describe any physical material, but, in contrast to nth-order elasticity, there is no reason against its doing so, since it is properly invariant for all kinds of deformations. In this way we have an ordering of theories according to their increasing formal complexity, without committing ourselves to any scheme of mathematical approximation.

In proposing the theory of hypo-elasticity I had in mind also the objection, often voiced outside officially plastic circles, against yield conditions postulated *ad hoc*. It has always seemed to me that a yield condition should be the outcome, not the axiom, of a good theory of yielding. We have no experimental proof for yield conditions as assumed in theories of plasticity: indeed, in some simple tests a yield stress is approached or maintained, but the theories lay down the axiom that for all states of deformation some fixed yield function involving asix quantities shall remain constant. While the experiments do not forbid this extrapolation, neither do they dictate it. It seemed to me that a good theory of purely elastic response should predict yield-like phenomena without assuming a yield condition, and that the nature of these phenomena might well depend upon the particular test. Without too much contortion, one ought to be able to get a yield surface in shear, for example, different from that in extension. The first work on hypo-elasticity [62] revealed that even some materials of grade 1 do indeed exhibit yield-like phenomena, since the solutions break down in some way at a finite strain determined by the differential equations themselves: we find an asymptotic value for the stress, or a theoretical maximum, or two different regimes of deformation, according to the initial stress. Similar but more elaborate effects were found by Noll [18] in his theory of hygrosteric materials, which defines a properly invariant visco-elasticity of Maxwell-Zaremba type.

The most striking result of this kind is a second-order effect within the hypo-elastic scheme, since it occurs in a body of grade 2. In experimenting with particular materials, Thomas [63] proposed for study the special case when

$$\tilde{\sigma} = \mathbf{d} - \frac{1}{K^2} \operatorname{tr}(\mathbf{d}\sigma)\,\sigma, \tag{17}$$

where σ is the stress deviator measured in units of twice the elastic shear modulus, and where K is a dimensionless constant. I then showed [64] that in simple shear according to (17) the total stress intensity does approach asymptotically a finite value determined by K, so that a yield of Maxwell-v. Mises type occurs as a proved theorem, not an assumption, but that the yield values of the stress intensity and the shear stress are different. Normal-stress effects occur and at yield are of higher order of magnitude than the classical effects. The dimensionless stresses as functions of the angle of shear, in a particular case, are shown in Figure 2. From this standpoint we may say that at least some types of yield in some cases occur as second-order effects according to hypo-elasticity[1].

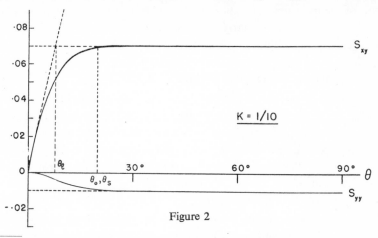

Figure 2

(1) *Note added in proof.* In view of some remarks made during the symposium by a well known expert in the common theories of plasticity, it appears necessary to explain more specifically the result illustrated in Figure 2. At the angle Θ_0, the shear stress overshoots its asymptotic value, attaining a maximum when $\Theta = \Theta_s$. When K is small, it follows that $\Theta_0 \approx \Theta_s$ and the maximum of s_{xy} is indistinguishable from its asymptotic value, as ought to be clear from the figure. Thus the particular hypo-elastic theory defined by (17) indicates yield *at a definite, predicted value of the shear.* The constant K is disposable, and when K is small, Θ_0 is small. In particular.

$$\Theta_0 = \arctan \left| \frac{K}{(\frac{1}{2} - K^2)^{\frac{1}{2}}} \quad \log \frac{1}{2K^2} \right|$$

$$\approx \quad -2\sqrt{2} \, K \log K. \quad .$$

The value of the yield stress *assumed* (not predicted) according to the corresponding Maxwell–v. Mises criterion is $2\mu K$, where μ is the elastic shear modulus. Thus the figure is drawn for a v. Mises yield stress of $1/5\mu$, which is very large. For smaller yield stress, the curve for s_{xy} would be still nearer to two straight lines connected by a small curved sector. No matter how small is the yield stress, however, *the whole effect disappears if the equations are linearized*, for if $\overset{\approx}{\sigma}$ is replaced by $\overset{\bullet}{\sigma}$, the usual (and hence non-invariant) stress rate, the definite yield points Θ_0 and Θ_s are lost altogether, and s_{xy} then fails to reach its yield value until $\Theta = \infty$. The difference between $\overset{\approx}{\sigma}$ and $\overset{\bullet}{\sigma}$, no matter how small it is, has the effect of changing the whole character of the curve of s_{xy}. Returning to the exact theory based on (17), we see that $\Theta_0/\Theta_1 \to \infty$ as $K \to 0$; that is, *for small yield stress the secant modulus of yield and the elastic tangent modulus differ from each other very much,* so that the softening prior to yield cannot be neglected, no matter how small is the yield stress.

While I have never claimed that any theory of hypo-elasticity adequately describes the behavior of any particular physical material, the rather scornful rejection of hypo-elasticity by the plastic experts, both orally and in print, does not appear to have been preceded by the pains necessary to understand what that theory does in fact predict.

In the nine years since the theory of hypo-elasticity was proposed, it has not lived up to the promise we first saw in it. Not enough particular solutions have been found, perhaps because those who cultivate this theory have laid weight on exact work and mathematical precision, being unwilling or unable to follow the lead of plasticity in throwing away inconvenient terms from physical intuition or mathematical frustration. Hypo-elasticity has served as a useful concept for theoretical organization, and some beautiful general theorems have been proved about it, particularly in connection with work and power [67–69], but these do not lie within our present scope of second-order effects.

9. Second-order stresses and flows of simple fluids.

The first kind of second-order effects in steady flow of simple fluids are those arising in cases for which exact solutions, really rendering unnecessary a discussion of order, are known. It may seem remarkable that any solution at all can be found for a material having long-range memory of almost arbitrary kind, but a little reflection shows that particular flow geometries may be such as to leave that memory scarcely anything to remember.

The problem of generalizing Rivlin's solutions for the Reiner-Rivlin theory was first attacked by Rivlin himself, working in a theory of intermediate generality [71]. From the result (7) derived from Reiner-Rivlin theory we see that in a simple shearing we have the universal relation

$$t_{xx} = t_{yy}, \tag{18}$$

whatever be the values of the response functions $\aleph_\Gamma$. That is, the normal pressure on the shearing planes is always equal to the normal pressure on the planes perpendicular to the flow. On the basis of arguments I have never been able to understand, Weissenberg [5] asserted that instead

$$t_{yy} = t_{zz} : \tag{19}$$

The normal pressures on all planes parallel to the flow are equal. Although experimental test of these relations is somewhat difficult to approach, it now seems that for the fluids known to exhibit normal-stress effects, neither relation is confirmed. Partly so as to obtain a theory of fluids not confined to either of these extremes, Rivlin and Ericksen [19] proposed an extended definition in which the stress may be influenced by the gradients of the accelerations up to any given order n. The nth Rivlin-Ericksen tensor $\mathbf{A}_n$ is defined as follows in terms of the nth material derivative of the squared element of arc:

$$\overset{(n)}{ds^2} = d\mathbf{x} \cdot (\mathbf{A}_n d\mathbf{x}).\tag{20}$$

By applying the principle of material indifference, Rivlin and Ericksen showed that the constitutive equation of a fluid according to their definition could be reduced to the form

$$\mathbf{t} + p\mathbf{1} = \mathbf{f}(\mathbf{A}_1, \mathbf{A}_2, ..., \mathbf{A}_n),\tag{21}$$

where $\mathbf{f}$ is an isotropic function. The Reiner-Rivlin relations (18) or the Weissenberg assertion (19) may now occur as special cases, but there is no reason to expect either of them. In the theory defined by (21), no idea of approximation need be involved, since (21) provides a suitably invariant definition of a fluid for all kinds of motions. We may call n the *complexity* of the Rivlin-Ericksen fluid. A fluid of complexity 1 is the Reiner-Rivlin fluid. It was for fluids defined by (21) that Rivlin then found the exact solutions for the viscometric flows. His solutions start from the observation that for these special flows $\mathbf{A}_3 = \mathbf{A}_4 = ... = 0$, so that it suffices to consider dependence on $\mathbf{A}_1$ and $\mathbf{A}_2$ only. In other words, the general Rivlin-Ericksen fluid is indistinguishable in viscometric measurements from the fluid of complexity 2. Rivlin's results were expressed in terms of eight material functions. Both Markovitz [75] and Ericksen [77] [81] noted that three material functions suffice.

The simple fluid of Noll is far more general than the Rivlin-Ericksen fluid, since it allows for stress-relaxation and long-range memory as well as for visco-elastic effects of the Meyer-Voigt type. Coleman and Noll [79] [80] observed that in a viscometric flow a fluid particle carries with it a constant strain history, which is in fact a quadratic function of the time measured backward from the present; for these flows, then, the cumulative memory effects are constant in time. Accordingly, Coleman and Noll were able to exhibit the exact solutions for all viscometric flows. *E.g.*, in a simple shearing of amount κ

$$\begin{aligned}
t_{xy} &= \tau(\kappa) = \kappa\mu(\kappa), \\
t_{xx} - t_{zz} &= \sigma_2(\kappa), \\
t_{yy} - t_{zz} &= \sigma_1(\kappa),
\end{aligned}\tag{22}$$

and all results for all the viscometric flows are expressed in terms of these same three functions $\mu(\ )$, $\sigma_1(\ )$, $\sigma_2(\ )$, all of which are even. For example, the discharge Q in a circular pipe of radius R, subject to driving force a, is given by

$$Q = \frac{8\pi}{a^3} \int_0^{\frac{1}{2}aR} \xi^2 \tau^{-1}(\xi) \, d\xi \qquad (23)$$

and hence is independent of normal-stress effects or other second-order effects. We may write $(22)_1$ in the form

$$\kappa = \frac{t_{xy}}{\mu} \zeta \left(\frac{\tau t_{xy}}{\mu} \right), \qquad (24)$$

where the constant μ is the shear viscosity at low shearing, where τ is a material constant having the dimension of time, and where $\zeta(\ )$ is an even dimensionless material function of its dimensionless argument. Thus we may write (23) in the form

$$Q = \frac{\pi a R^4}{2\mu} \int_0^1 u^3 \zeta \left(\frac{\frac{1}{2}aR\tau}{\mu} u \right) du$$

$$= \frac{\pi a R^4}{2\mu} \Phi \left(\frac{aR\tau}{\mu} \right), \qquad (25)$$

where $\Phi(\ )$ is an even dimensionless function such that $\Phi(0) = \frac{1}{4}$. Since $\mu(\kappa) > 0$, in order that $\Phi = $ const. it is necessary and sufficient that $\zeta = $ const. Thus the famous law of the fourth power is equivalent to the linearity of the shear viscosity function. Contrary to most statements regarding it in the literature, experimental test of this law is not at all a test of the Navier-Stokes equations. The efflux may satisfy exactly the Hagen-Poiseuille formula, yet the fluid may exhibit normal-stress effects and long-range memory effects, since these are governed by material functions unrelated to the shear-viscosity function. An example is furnished by the Rivlin-Ericksen fluid of grade 2, defined by (51), below. In the viscometric flows, the second-order effects do not alter the classical results for drag, discharge, *etc.*, being governed by independent material functions. In particular, from (25) we see at once that to within effects of second-order in the shearing, even the classical numerical coefficient, *viz* $\frac{1}{8}\pi$, remains unaffected.

Coleman and Noll have considered also oscillatory shearings:

$$\dot{x} = 0, \quad \dot{y} = v(x, t), \quad \dot{z} = 0, \tag{26}$$

where v is a periodic function. The solutions for these flows are determined by three scalar-valued functionals of the argument

$$\int_0^\tau \frac{\partial v(x, \tau - s)}{\partial x} ds.$$

Coleman and Noll exhibit the shear stress and the two normal-stress differences, and they prove that while the shear stress oscillates at the same frequency as does the velocity, the three normal stresses oscillate at twice that frequency.

A new class of exact solutions for simple fluids, including continual elongation of a cylinder at a rate proportional to its length, has just been discovered by Coleman and Noll [82]. In these solutions there is no such clear separation of effects of the first and second order. If the principal stretchings are d_1, d_2, d_3, the corresponding differences of normal stresses are given by the relations

$$t_1 - t_2 = (d_1 - d_2)h + (d_1^2 - d_2^2)l, \tag{27}$$
$$t_2 - t_3 = (d_1 - d_3)h + (d_1^2 - d_3^2)l,$$

where $h(\ )$ and $l(\ )$ are material functions which are not, in general, determined by the viscometric functions $\mu(\ )$, $\sigma_1(\ )$, and $\sigma_2(\ )$. In the theory of linear viscosity, $h(\ ) = 2\mu$ and $l(\ ) = 0$; thus the terms containing l represent second-order effects superimposed upon the first-order effects. This example suffices to show that the separation of effects of odd and even orders, which gave the beginnings of the theory of non-linear viscosity much of their dramatic appeal, is not general, being rather a special property of viscometric flows.

The results on fluids so far presented concern additional stresses required in order to maintain flows of certain classical types. For example, in order to maintain a flow in which the stream lines are coaxial circles in parallel planes, as between rotating cylinders, it is necessary to supply deviatoric and non-uniform normal pressures on those planes. If those non-uniform pressures be wanting, the fluid will rise or fall according as they ought to be positive or negative. This rising or falling, in turn, destroys the assumed flow. It is a secondary flow of this kind that makes the fluid rise on the inner of a pair of rotating cylinders, as reported by Weissenberg. I know of no calculation of this particular secondary flow.

A different kind of secondary flow was discovered by Ericksen [72] [78] (cf. also [74]). While a linearly viscous fluid may travel along straight streamlines

down a pipe of any cross-section, almost any kind of non-linear viscosity
suffices to make rectilinear motion impossible except in a circular pipe. Any
small perturbation of the parallel velocity field will tend to make the fluid mix
in spirals as it travels. Green and Rivlin [73] have made an approximate
calculation for a special type of fluid in a pipe having an elliptical cross-section;
according to their results, the axial planes of the elliptical cylinder divide it
into four sectors, within each of which the fluid swirls along in spirals
about a single straight streamline, the senses of rotation being opposite in
contiguous sectors (Figure 3). In his communication to this symposium [83a],
Rivlin confirms this result as being, in general, of exactly fourth order according to a certain method of expansion.

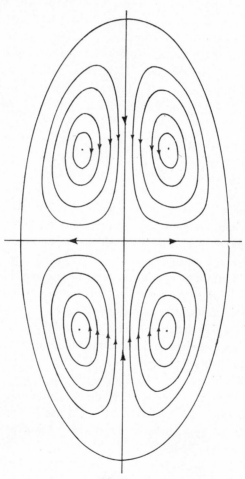

Figure 3

An apparatus demonstrating this effect has been designed and constructed by Kearsley at the U.S. Bureau of Standards. Other secondary flows have been determined approximately by Langlois [76]. Results of this kind should attract even those who do not yet know that they ought to be interested in non-linear viscosity. For a non-circular pipe, the instability associated with the magnitude of the Reynolds number need not be the first to occur; the magnitude of the normal-stress effect is independent of the Reynolds number, so that instability arising from secondary flow may set in at lower speeds than those predicted by a conventional analysis of stability according to the Navier-Stokes equations. It should be possible to distinguish fluids subject to this normal-stress instability, since the corresponding secondary flow does not occur in circular pipes or channels bounded by parallel planes.

10. The anisotropic fluids of Ericksen.

While all simple fluids, according to the definition of Noll, have been proved to be isotropic, it remains possible to find simple[1] or non-simple materials capable of flow yet not necessarily isotropic. Anisotropy results from the presence of preferred directions; in a substance capable of flowing, there can be no intrinsic preferred directions, but there may well be preferred directions that change in a way at least partially independent of the flow occurring. Such a fluid material must consist not only of points but also of directions associated with, but not bound to, those points.

The basic concept of an *oriented material*, which is an aggregate of points and associated vectors, was proposed by Duhem, and a kinematical theory for it was worked out by E. & F. Cosserat over fifty years ago. In our recent generalization of their work, Ericksen and I emphasized, as they had done, intended applications to rods and shells [1]. At about the same time, Günther [54] considered a similar theory for elastic initial stresses. The simplest kind of oriented material, however, may be realized in a three-dimensional point space with a single orientation vector or *director* **n** at each point. Under additional hypotheses expressing the possibility of flow, such a material furnishes the kinematical foundation of Ericksen's theory of anisotropic fluids [84–93]. To distinguish these materials more clearly from the simple fluids previously discussed, we might call them *subfluids*. Besides a constitutive equation for the stresses as functions both of **d** and of **n**, these theories lay down a law of change for **n**, of the type

$$\dot{\mathbf{n}} = \mathbf{g}\,(\mathbf{d}, \mathbf{n}). \tag{28}$$

---

(1) If such a material is simple, its isotropy group neither contains the orthogonal group nor is contained in it.

In addition, the moment of momentum and the energy arising from change of **n** have to be taken into account in the general conservation principles expressing the laws of mechanics. As in other recent theories, principles of invariance are used to reduce and render explicit the constitutive equations.

Ericksen has chosen to develop this theory by exploration of cases rather than by general theorems. He has succeeded in showing that the simplest kinds of subfluids, in which the dependence on **d** is linear, exhibit as a result of flow of orientation some effects very like those we have grown accustomed to regarding as second-order effects in simple fluids, or as plastic phenomena. Considering first a simple theory in which **n** is not allowed to change in length, he showed that in simple shearing the steady state value of the shear stress behaves like that in a so-called Bingham material, while the normal-stress differences are linear in the shearing. The experimental evidence here is not yet certain. While some of the data seems to favor this linear dependence of the normal-stress differences, not only the early experiments of Greensmith and Rivlin [70] but also the recent measurements of Eisenberg and of Markovitz and Brown [83], some of which are to be described later in this symposium, confirm for polyisobutylene the quadratic dependence typical of the simple fluid.

A measure of elasticity, even in incompressible subfluids, is attained in a theory general enough to allow the length of the director **n** to vary. Some subfluids of this type behave in a shearing flow just like Newtonian fluids for sufficiently small shearing, while for large shearings the entire stress system, including the normal stresses, becomes approximately linear in the shearing, as in the case when **n** is of constant length.

In flow in a pipe at sufficiently high speed, the classical type of velocity profile becomes impossible, and instead a central core of fluid moves rigidly, shearing an outer annulus of fluid between it and the walls [89]. A similar phenomenon occurs in a fluid confined between rotating cylinders [92].

All these effects are predicted, not assumed. Yield-like phenomena arise in the course of solution of certain problems defined by smooth and simple constitutive equations. Virtually everything done so far in these theories comes from the terms of lowest non-trivial order, namely, first order in **d**, and second order in **n**. The results illustrate my opening remark that the "order" of an effect is purely theoretical, depending upon the theory being used.

Since the director **n** represents a structure in the material, its fate in the course of flow may be of significance. In some flows of some of these subfluids it tends to orient itself in some fixed direction relative to the flow; in others, it oscillates; in one class of flows studied, the former effect reigns if the vorticity number is sufficiently low, while the latter occurs for highly rotational motions [87].

Although the various kinds of subfluids were first proposed with application to polymer solutions or liquid crystals in mind, some researches of Ericksen in the past few weeks have pointed to dramatic new possibilities. Dependence upon **n** through a coefficient varying with the magnitude of **n** may endow the material with apparent elasticity with respect to various orientations. The equations can be integrated to yield a relation between stress and finite strain in shear that is strikingly similar to those observed in experiments on plastic, work-hardening metals.

11. Fluid mixtures.

An effect that is of second order in a theory of pure fluids may turn out to be indistinguishable from, or at least closely similar to, an effect of first order in mixtures of fluids. The classical example here is the theory of absorption and dispersion of ultrasonic waves. In a pure fluid endowed with viscosity and heat conductivity, the absorption coefficient varies linearly with frequency at low frequencies, and there is no dispersion. For higher frequencies, however, there is an absorption peak as well as a steady increase of velocity, determined entirely by the two viscosities and the heat conductivity. It is difficult to summarize the experimental literature because it is so confused, but we can say that for reasons right or wrong the pure fluid theory was judged inadequate, and, in a classic paper, Einstein (1920) chose to consider a chemically pure fluid as dissociated into two components when excited by an ultrasonic wave. Neglecting viscosity and thermal conduction altogether, he showed that absorption and dispersion arose from diffusion, leading to coefficients that could be adjusted so as to place the peak wherever it was observed. The immense literature (*cf.* [97]) on "molecular relaxation" has grown from this idea. Unfortunately the persons who write on ultrasonics generally like to give the illusion that they construct a kinetic-molecular theory, while in fact they are working with at best a molecular motivation for continuum theories; their papers are made harder to read by being confined entirely to plane waves, so the constitutive equations are concealed rather than stated openly. Nevertheless, a critical reader easily sees that the whole field concerns the dissipative effects of dispersion in a mixture, as is shown by the more general theory of Sakadi [94] and Meixner [95].

Theories of diffusive flow are much older but are likewise in a state so primitive, from the standpoint of classical mechanics, as to be ridiculous. Authors working with them seem not to have felt any need to use the principles of mechanics as well as the definition of the diffusive forces, or to set

up and solve any concrete flow problems: their main activity seems to be
the naming of coefficients and allegedly determining their values by measurement. The general principles governing the transfer of mass, momentum,
and energy in a mixture of substances have been established recently [96].
Let mass, momentum, and energy be created in the constituent $\mathfrak{A}$ at the
rates $\hat{c}_{\mathfrak{A}}$, $\hat{\mathbf{p}}_{\mathfrak{A}}$, $\hat{\varepsilon}_{\mathfrak{A}}$, respectively. The conservation laws for the mixture of $\mathfrak{K}$
constituents then assume the forms

$$\sum_{\mathfrak{A}=1}^{\mathfrak{K}} \hat{c}_{\mathfrak{A}} = 0,$$

$$\sum_{\mathfrak{A}=1}^{\mathfrak{K}} \left[\hat{\mathbf{p}}_{\mathfrak{A}} + \hat{c}_{\mathfrak{A}} \mathbf{u}_{\mathfrak{A}} \right] = 0, \tag{29}$$

$$\sum_{\mathfrak{A}=1}^{\mathfrak{K}} \left[\hat{\varepsilon}_{\mathfrak{A}} + \hat{\mathbf{p}}_{\mathfrak{A}} \cdot \mathbf{u}_{\mathfrak{A}} + \hat{c}_{\mathfrak{A}} \left(\varepsilon_{\mathfrak{A}} + \tfrac{1}{2} u_{\mathfrak{A}}^2 \right) \right] = 0,$$

where $\mathbf{u}_{\mathfrak{A}}$ is the diffusion velocity and $\varepsilon_{\mathfrak{A}}$ is the internal energy of constituent
$\mathfrak{A}$. For a mixture there are two distinct kinds of constitutive equations: those
specifying the nature of the individual constituents, and those specifying the
action of one constituent upon another. Those of the second kind connect
the supplies $\hat{c}_{\mathfrak{A}}$, $\hat{\mathbf{p}}_{\mathfrak{A}}$, $\hat{\varepsilon}_{\mathfrak{A}}$ with kinematical variables. A simple and rational
theory of diffusion [1] [98] [99a] is obtained by supposing the supplies of
momentum result directly and proportionately from the relative diffusion of
the constituents:

$$\hat{\mathbf{p}}_{\mathfrak{A}} = \sum_{\mathfrak{B}=1}^{\mathfrak{K}} F_{\mathfrak{A}\mathfrak{B}}(\mathbf{u}_{\mathfrak{B}} - \mathbf{u}_{\mathfrak{A}}). \tag{30}$$

Fick's law, the Maxwell-Stefan theory, and Meixner's theory of diffusion
follow as special cases from this constitutive equation. A necessary and sufficient condition for it to be consistent with $(29)_2$ is

$$\sum_{\mathfrak{B}=1}^{\mathfrak{K}} \left(F_{\mathfrak{A}\mathfrak{B}} - F_{\mathfrak{B}\mathfrak{A}} \right) = 0. \tag{31}$$

The so-called Onsager relations, first proposed in this context by Stefan, are equivalent to the stronger condition

$$F_{\mathfrak{AB}} - F_{\mathfrak{BA}} = 0. \tag{32}$$

Whether these relations really hold or not is unknown. A rational basis for them is easily found, however, for it suffices to assume that $F_{\mathfrak{AB}}$ is independent of the concentrations of all constituents other than $\mathfrak{A}$ and $\mathfrak{B}$, and that $F_{\mathfrak{AB}} \to 0$ as the density of constituent $\mathfrak{A}$ approaches 0; under these assumptions, from (31) we may show that (32) follows [98] [99a].

Apart from such relations of symmetry, the theory itself remains in its infancy, from lack of concrete solutions. An enlightening case to consider would be that of flow in a pipe of a mixture of two fluids, one perfect and the other linearly viscous. The adherence of the viscous fluid to the walls, while the perfect fluid slips past, gives rise to diffusive drag and also to normal-stress effects.

Problems of this kind, again treated by questionable means, are found in the flow of liquid helium. A two-fluid theory of very special nature was proposed some years ago and was recently clarified and expressed in purely classical terms by Lin [99]. Lin favors the case when the superfluid has no entropy; the mean velocity, however, is not equal to the velocity of the normal fluid, so that the mean flow of entropy is not zero. The diffusion of entropy is thus described by a single vector, much like a director of an oriented material, and the theory is similar to that of one of Ericksen's subfluids.

What the theory of fluid mixtures lacks above all is the concreteness resulting from a few good specific examples rigorously solved.

12.   Second-order memory.

In a theory of any degree of complexity, a number of different schemes of order present themselves formally, and there is no reason to adopt one rather than another. In fact, one scheme may lead to approximations useful in one context, while a different expansion may be applicable to other circumstances. In a simple material, defined by (10), the stress arises in response to the entire deformation history; we may expect, for example, that the order of an effect in terms of strain magnitude may be different from what it is in terms of rate-of-strain magnitude, and that the extent to which either of these may influence the result will depend on how long ago the strain or straining occurred, and on how sensitive is the functional $\mathfrak{G}$ to events in the distant or recent past. In the case of a simple fluid, we may ask for the "second approximation," improving upon the laws of linear viscosity. The discussion of the Reiner-Rivlin and Weissenberg relations should make plain that answer to this question is not trivial. Another question of the same kind and level of difficulty is met when we seek to improve upon the classical theory of elastokinetics by allowing for friction or viscosity or more general kinds of damping.

This whole group of questions has been taken up and studied deeply by Coleman and Noll [100–103] [105] (*cf.* also [104]). In addition to the postulates used so far, they introduce a hypothesis of fading memory, according to which events in the distant past have less effect on material response than do more recent ones. (This class of problems had been approached earlier by Green and Rivlin and their collaborators [20] [23] [24], who approximated the constitutive functional by a series of repeated integrals over the history of the deformation.) It is the merit of Coleman and Noll to have seen that different measures of fading memory are most easily and naturally defined in terms of topologies in function spaces, and that the essence of the matter lies in the amount of smoothness presumed of the constitutive functional in such topologies. A part of their work is to be presented later in this symposium [105]; accordingly, I attempt no more than a brief summary of it. They call a positive real function $h(s)$ an influence function of order r if $s^r h(s) \to 0$ as $s \to \infty$. Thus an influence function or *obliviator* is one that vanishes sufficiently rapidly at ∞. For example, e^{-s} is an obliviator of arbitrarily high order. Given a history $\mathbf{A}(s)$ of a tensor $\mathbf{A}$, Coleman and Noll introduce a norm that may be called the *recollection* of $\mathbf{A}$ of order p:

$$\|\mathbf{A}\| \equiv \{\int_0^\infty h^p |\mathbf{A}|^p \, ds\}^{\frac{1}{p}}, \tag{33}$$

where $|\mathbf{A}|$ denotes the magnitude of $\mathbf{A}$, as usual: $|\mathbf{A}|^2 \equiv \mathrm{tr}\mathbf{A}\mathbf{A}^T$. A similar norm may be defined for $p = \infty$, but for most purposes the choice $p = 2$ is simplest([1]).

The recollection is a measure of the mean magnitude of $\mathbf{A}(s)$ omitting a set of times of measure 0 and weighting recent times far more heavily than long past times. The collection of tensor histories $\mathbf{A}(s)$ with finite norm $\|\mathbf{A}\|$ forms a Hilbert space, within which Fréchet differentiation is defined.

([1]) In their communication [105] to this symposium, Coleman and Noll discuss relations among results obtained by different choices of norm.

Write the constitutive equation (10) in the equivalent form

$$\bar{\mathbf{t}} = \mathbf{h}(\mathbf{C}) + \mathop{\mathfrak{F}}_{s=0}^{\infty} (\mathbf{G}_t\,(t - s)\,;\,\mathbf{C})\,, \qquad\qquad (34)$$

where

$$
\begin{aligned}
\bar{\mathbf{A}} &\equiv \mathbf{R}^T\mathbf{A}\,\mathbf{R} \quad \text{for any } \mathbf{A},\\
\mathbf{R} &= \text{rotation tensor},\\
\mathbf{C} &= \text{present value of the Green strain measure},\\
\mathbf{G} &\equiv \bar{\mathbf{C}} - \mathbf{1},
\end{aligned}
$$

$$\mathop{\mathfrak{F}}_{s=0}^{\infty} (0;\mathbf{C}) = 0\,.$$

If we now assume that there exists an obliviator h such that $\mathfrak{F}$ is Fréchet differentiable at $\mathbf{G} = 0$, then the fact that every continuous linear functional in Hilbert space is an inner product enables us to write (34) in the form

$$\bar{\mathbf{t}} = \mathbf{h}(\mathbf{C}) + \int_0^{\infty} \Gamma(s,\mathbf{C})\,\{\mathbf{G}(s)\}\,ds + o\,(\|\,\mathbf{G}\,\|)\,, \qquad\qquad (35)$$

where Γ operates linearly on $\mathbf{G}$ but may depend arbitrarily on $\mathbf{C}$. If we drop the error term and consider only infinitesimal strain, it is possible to derive from (35) the constitutive equations of the Boltzmann-Volterra theory of infinitesimal linear viscoelasticity. Now the more thoughtful students of mechanics have long refused to accept this theory for two reasons: It is not properly invariant if regarded as an exact theory, and its status as an approximation to some exact theory is unknown. Both objections are met to some extent by this result of Coleman and Noll. First, the infinitesimal theory results as an approximation to the general theory of simple materials if the strain has been small at all times. It still remains possible that this theory is internally inconsistent in that, for some particular case, the process of solution may come out with the prediction of a strain growing large in time, contrary to the assumption from which it was derived, so I do not think the theorem of Coleman and Noll gives the partisans of linear viscoelasticity the right to the kind of confidence we justly place in linearized static elasticity. The objection on the grounds of want of invariance may be met by refusing to linearize in the strain: If in (35) we simply drop the error term, the resulting equation is properly invariant for strains of all magnitudes and hence defines a possible theory of materials. We may conceive of a material obeying this equation of *finite linear viscoelasticity* in all circumstances, without approximation. Unfortunately, however, the process is not unique. There are infinitely many different strain measures $\mathbf{G}^*$ that vanish in the undeformed state, and choosing any one of these leads to a result of the form (35). For each, the error $o\left(\|\mathbf{G}^*\|\right)$ has, of course, a different meaning; for each, by dropping that error term we obtain a different theory of finite linear viscoelasticity. The difficulty is similar to one already mentioned for finite elasticity; there it was resolved by agreeing to take the extensions δ_i as natural measures of strain, by which choice it was recognized incidentally that no finite linear theory of elasticity can be generally correct. A similar conclusion holds here, too.

On the other hand, we may make $\|\mathbf{G}\|$ small by restricting attention to deformations that are small in the recent past. For example, we may define the *retardation* of a given history $\mathbf{G}(s)$ by the formula:

$$\mathbf{G}_\alpha(s) \equiv \mathbf{G}(\alpha s), \qquad (36)$$

where $0 < \alpha \leqq 1$. By calculating formulae in the limit as $\alpha \to 0$, with $\mathbf{G}$ held fixed, we get asymptotic expressions for a whole family of motions, obtained by describing a given motion more slowly. In this way, Coleman and Noll were the first to succeed in giving a definite meaning to the common old term, "slow motion," in terms of the retardation of a given process. It is not difficult show that

$$\lim_{\alpha \to 0} \left\| \mathbf{G}_\alpha(s) \right\| = 0. \qquad (37)$$

Thus the error term in (35) may be made small by considering, instead of a single process in which the strains are small, the retardation of any given process, in which the strain need not be small at all times. For sufficiently small values of α, the retarded motion will always have arbitrarily small strain in the sufficiently recent past.

Thus Coleman and Noll's theory of finite linear viscoelasticity, unlike the classical linearized one, enjoys a double range of validity: (1) for bodies that have never been deformed more than a very little, in which case it reduces to Boltzmann's linear viscoelasticity, and (2) for bodies deformed arbitrarily much altogether, but very little recently.

I have already warned against taking the results of Coleman and Noll as justifying, in the case of linearized viscoelasticity, the unquestioning return of every ostrich to his sand. A similar warning needs to be posted against the general idea of slow motions. The results obtained by Coleman and Noll for slow motions are asymptotic formulae. Like all other asymptotic formulae, they give us no information whatever about the behavior of a given specimen of material subject to given loads. Rather, they tell us that if we consider a given material in a given deformation process, by retarding that process sufficiently we may obtain another one in which the constitutive equation is indistinguishable from that of a linearly viscoelastic material subject to small deformation from a given state of strain. How much retardation is needed, *i.e.*, how small we have to take α, we don't know; even if we did, we have no assurance that neglect of a term of small norm in the constitutive equation does not lead to a large error when we solve the equations of motion. Objections of this kind always come in when an asymptotic formula is involved. Results derived from asymptotic formulae deserve to be regarded as no more than half truths. As such, they call for attention and respect, but we must beware of beatifying them.

Objections aside, we recognize the effectiveness of Coleman and Noll's method. Like any good approximation, it affords means of improving any given stage, and in this it is entirely different from the older literature on viscoelasticity, where at the word "approximation" the reader was expected to bow down and join the cult, since it was never stated what was being approximated. While the general results are elaborate, we can repeat here Coleman and Noll's formula for the stresses in the second-order theory of incompressible viscoelastic fluids:

$$\mathbf{t} + p\mathbf{1} = \int_0^\infty \mu(s)\, \mathbf{J}(s)\, ds + $$

$$+ \int_0^\infty \int_0^\infty [\alpha(s_1, s_2)\, \mathbf{J}(s_1)\, \mathbf{J}(s_2) + \beta(s_1, s_2)\, \mathbf{J}(s_2)\, \mathrm{tr}\, \mathbf{J}(s_1)]\, ds_1 ds_2, \tag{38}$$

where $\mathbf{J} \equiv \mathbf{C}_t(t-s) - \mathbf{1}$, where $\mu(s)$ is the usual shear-viscosity function, and where α and β are real material functions. Thus far the only application of this equation has been to the case of periodic shearing of small amplitude. Coleman and Noll [103] have obtained the surprizing result that one of the normal-stress differences is determined by the shear-viscosity function $\mu(s)$. It should be possible to test this dependence by experiment.

Another and still more important class of results is obtained by Coleman and Noll on the basis of a new general theorem of approximation in function spaces. Again using the retardation of a given motion, they are able to approximate $\mathbf{G}$ in (10), to within an error $o(\alpha^n)$, by a multilinear form in the first

n derivatives of the strain history, evaluated at $s = 0$. Thus a *functional* is approximated by a *function of the derivatives* of the argument function, enabling Coleman and Noll to show that a Rivlin-Ericksen material of complexity n may serve as the nth-order approximation to a simple fluid, in the sense of retardation.

This is not the end, however, for within the Rivlin-Ericksen theory of complexity n the approximation method permits further simplification. For example, for the second-order theory of incompressible simple fluids Coleman and Noll show that a particular Rivlin-Ericksen fluid of complexity 2 suffices as the general approximation:

$$t + p\mathbf{1} = 2\mu\mathbf{A}_1 + \beta\mathbf{A}_1^2 + \gamma\mathbf{A}_2, \tag{39}$$

μ being the shear viscosity and β, γ, the two cross-viscosities, all three being constants. It will be noted that in this *fluid of second grade*, neither the Reiner-Rivlin relations (18) nor the Weissenberg conjecture (19) need hold. Apparently based upon the relative ease of solving problems, a fairly abundant literature about the Reiner-Rivlin fluid with constant shear and cross-viscosities has sprouted. Neither has any physical fluid yet been found to obey the Reiner-Rivlin theory at all, let alone with constant response functions, nor, as shown by the results of Coleman and Noll, is there any theoretical reason to expect the Reiner-Rivlin theory to be valid past its domain of agreement with the Navier-Stokes equations. While the early work of Reiner and Rivlin has attracted much and deserved notice, it is a pity that most of the readers of those early papers have not been induced to follow the newer fundamental literature growing out of the lines of thought there introduced. We find ourselves in a curious period, when our subject is only some fifteen years old, yet most of what is published concerning it is naively out of date.

Coleman and Noll have pointed out that many interesting flows beyond the class of viscometric flows can be solved for incompressible fluids of second grade. Most of those that for the Navier-Stokes equations can be reduced to solution of the ordinary diffusion equation can be reduced for fluids of second grade to solution of a linear partial differential equation with constant coefficients. These are flows in which the convective acceleration is a lamellar field and hence can be eliminated by redefinition of the pressure. Consider, for example, a non-steady shearing flow:

$$\dot{x} = 0, \quad \dot{y} = v(x, t), \quad \dot{z} = 0. \tag{40}$$

For a fluid of second grade, the dynamical equations are equivalent to a single equation of diffusive type:

$$\frac{\partial v}{\partial t} = v \frac{\partial^2 v}{\partial x^2} + \frac{\gamma}{\rho} \frac{\partial^3 v}{\partial x^2 \partial t}.$$ (41)

Since separation of variables, Laplace and Fourier transforms, complex or hypercomplex potentials, and the other linear devices so dear to the older generation of "applied mathematicians" can be brought to bear on these problems of generalized diffusion, it is surprising that no literature yet adorns them. Perhaps there has not yet been sufficient time for diffusion of discovery from the highly vorticose but certainly not turbulent boundary-layer at the frontier of knowledge in modern mechanics. In (41) we may see the ovum of a chain reaction of doctorate theses. For our present purpose it is essential to know that the greater generality of the Rivlin-Ericksen theory — the very generality that enables it to escape the Reiner-Rivlin relation (18) — changes basically the nature of the second-order effects even in the relatively degenerate case here considered. According to the second-order Reiner-Rivlin theory, which is obtained by putting $\gamma = 0$, the velocity field itself is unaltered from that predicted by the Navier-Stokes equations, although maintenance of that same field requires deviatoric normal stresses; in the true second-order theory of fluids, the term multiplied by γ has the effect of changing the whole picture of diffusion of velocity and vorticity from a boundary, since the order of the governing differential equation is raised by one, and a new kind of instability becomes possible.

13.   Effects of second order in the natural time of a simple fluid.

The objection against use of Coleman and Noll's method of approximation for fluids because the results are asymptotic formulae may be removed in part by appeal to another method of ordering. The argument of Coleman and Noll falls into two distinct stages. The result of the first stage approximates a simple fluid by a Rivlin-Ericksen fluid of complexity n, while the second stage replaces the general Rivlin-Ericksen fluid of complexity n, which is specified by eight material functions of scalar invariants, by a particular one with finitely many, explicitly enumerated, constant coefficients. This particular fluid we call the Rivlin-Ericksen fluid of *grade n*. In the first stage, which involves replacing a functional approximately by a function, I do not see how asymptotic considerations can be avoided; this is the deeper part of the argument, and I cannot improve upon it. For the second and easier part, however, we may substitute a simple finite argument, starting from the fact that the Rivlin-Ericksen theory is a dynamically possible one for fluid motions of any kind, so that no idea of approximation is *necessarily* involved in it. This is a matter of principle so important it cannot be too often repeated: While the typical theories of elasticity, beginning with classical linearized elasticity and viscoelasticity, and going through n^{th}-order elasticity and the corresponding viscoelasticity, are *approximate theories*, not dynamically possible for *any* material except in a restricted class of deformations, the common theories of fluids, from the Navier-Stokes fluids through the Rivlin-Ericksen fluids and Ericksen's subfluids, present us self-consistent, properly invariant *special models* of fluid behavior, which, while perhaps not describing adequately the response of any known physical fluid, yet as theories do not in themselves force us to introduce any idea of mathematical approximation in order to interpret them. Therefore it becomes possible to order these fluids according to *material properties* rather than according to the circumstances in which they find themselves or according to some mathematical process.

The method I shall use rests upon a dimensional analysis such as I gave long ago for other theories of fluids [4] [9] [14] [15]. That this method is not more generally used, I can attribute only to my failure to explain it sufficiently clearly in earlier publications. Coleman and Noll were aware of the possibility of applying an argument of this kind, but they did not give it, although it seems to me to offer clear physical significance, closer to the conditions based upon estimates of the Reynolds number, Mach number, and Froude number in ordinary hydrodynamics, and therefore I shall present it expicitly.

Returning to (21), we observe that the relation cannot be complete, since it is not dimensionally invariant. In order to secure dimensional invariance we must assume dependence upon additional quantities. The only quantities that can be added without invalidating everything done so far are scalars independent of the deformation, since the presence or absence of such scalars will not affect any of the reasoning about invariance. Omitting consideration of the effects of temperature changes so as to simplify matters, we allow to the fluid only two independent dimension-bearing material constants:

μ, the natural viscosity, having the dimensions $ML^{-1}T^{-1}$

τ, the natural time, having the dimension T.

In any audience there are some persons who insist on talking about measuring things before it is known what they are; although it does some violence to the logic of the theory, I shall satisfy those persons by giving "operational" definitions of μ and τ. Our operationalist must procure himself a pair of infinite parallel plates (not difficult for an operationalist), the space between which, of breadth h, he fills with the fluid to be tested, while voiding the rest of the universe. After verifying operationally that his frame of reference is inertial, he must then pull one plate parallel to the other at uniform speed V, and he must measure the drag and the normal forces on these plates; he must also measure the force of fluid on fluid divided by a plane normal to the flow, which he will easily do by introducing a cut or small cavity such as is described in works in the operational foundations of electrostatics. Of course all these forces are infinite, but our operationalist will have no trouble in dividing them by the infinite areas of the planes and coming out with finite limits for quantities he will then feel justified in calling stresses. Setting $\kappa = V/h$, he will find relations of just the same form as Coleman and Noll's formulae (22), with the functions $\mu(\ )$, $\sigma_1(\ )$, and $\sigma_2(\ )$ empirically determined. If the operationalist now sets

$$\mu \equiv \mu(0),$$

$$\tau \equiv \frac{1}{2\mu} \lim_{\kappa \to 0} \frac{\sqrt{[\sigma_1(\kappa) + \sigma_2(\kappa)]^2 + [\sigma_1(\kappa) - \sigma_2(\kappa)]^2}}{\kappa}, \tag{42}$$

he will see that μ and τ are operationally defined constants having the dimensions of viscosity and time, respectively. Moreover he will have the comfort of finding that μ is the same number as the viscosity he read about in his first course in physics; since it is a fixed number measured in a fixed experiment, it cannot possibly be one of those mystifying things called "apparent", "frequency-dependent", etc., in the rheological literature. According to the freshman physics book, the natural time τ will come out to be zero, but our operationalist is not allowed to read any books before starting to make measurements. He will get a positive number for τ if he had the foresight to choose a polyisobutylene solution when he was laying in his infinite supply of fluid preparatory to voiding the universe. We have to caution him here; should he choose water and so destroy all our stock of polyisobutylene, not only would he get the value of 0 for τ, but also he would annihilate experimental rheology. Fortunately, even so, the theory can continue unaffected.[1]

---

[1] The argument given now, like all operational presentations, is circular. From the logical standpoint, one has to assume the existence of τ in order to formulate the theory to start with; otherwise one cannot state (10) in dimensionally invariant form, and without (10) one cannot get Coleman and Noll's formulae (22). Moreover, it is possible that τ as defined by $(42)_2$ will come out to be zero (i.e., there will be no normal-stress effects in shearing), yet (10) will not reduce to a relation (such as the constitutive equations of linear viscosity or finite elasticity) in which no time constant is needed for dimensional invariance. In this case, a different definition of τ is needed. For example, a fluid without normal-stress effects but endowed with a non-linear shear viscosity function $\mu(\varkappa)$ must have a non-zero natural time; if $\mu''(0) \neq 0$, we may take as the definition

$$\tau_\mu \equiv \sqrt{\frac{|\mu''(0)|}{2\mu}},$$

where the subscript μ serves as a reminder that $\tau_\mu \neq \tau$ in general. Even if $\mu(\varkappa) = \text{const.}$ and $\sigma_1 = \sigma_2 = 0$, so that the viscometric behavior of the fluid is entirely described by the Navier-Stokes equations, a natural time must enter the constitutive equation if memory effects are to be represented by it.

The difficulty arising from the possible failure of one or another particular definition of the natural time results only from the demand for immediate explanation of theoretical quantities in experimental terms. It is easily avoided in a consistent mathematical presentation.

Thinking it would be impressive to give now a numerical value for τ as measured in polyisobutylene, I asked Dr. Markovitz for the relevant data, but he replied that the measurements at low shearings are not accurate enough for this purpose. We shall have to rest content, for the time being, with the operational value of τ.

With this important point settled, we are permitted to return to the theory, replacing (21) by

$$\mathbf{t} + p\mathbf{1} = \mathbf{f}(\mathbf{A}_1, \mathbf{A}_2, ..., \mathbf{A}_n, \mu, \tau) \tag{43}$$

as the full definition of a Rivlin-Ericksen fluid of complexity n, where $\mathbf{f}$ is an isotropic function of its n tensor arguments. The dimensional matrix of a typical component of (43) is [1]:

	L	T	M	
$t_{km} + pg_{km}$	-1	-2	1	
$\mathbf{A}_1$	0	-1	0	(6 rows)
$\mathbf{A}_2$	0	-2	0	(6 rows)
$\vdots$	$\vdots$	$\vdots$	$\vdots$	$\vdots$
$\mathbf{A}_n$	0	$-n$	0	(6 rows)
μ	-1	-1	1	
τ	0	1	0	

The rank of this $3 \times (6n + 3)$ matrix is 2. Since $6n + 3 - 2 = 6n + 1$, the typical component of (43) must be equivalent to a dimensionless relation connecting $6n + 1$ dimensionless ratios formed from the quantities in the column at the left-hand side of the matrix. Such a set of $6n + 1$ ratios is easily seen to be

$$\tau(t_{km} + pg_{km})/\mu, \tau\mathbf{A}_1, \tau^2\mathbf{A}_2, ..., \tau^n\mathbf{A}_n.$$

Since the reasoning may be applied in turn to each of the six components of (43), we have shown that (43) is equivalent to a relation of the form

---

[1] A statement and rigorous proof of the π-theorem is given by L. Brand, *Arch. Rational Mech. Anal.*, **1**, (1957/58), (1957) 34–45.

$$\mathbf{t} + p\mathbf{1} = \frac{\mu}{\tau}\mathbf{F}(\tau\mathbf{A}_1, \tau^2\mathbf{A}_2, ..., \tau^n\mathbf{A}_n), \tag{44}$$

where $\mathbf{F}$ is a dimensionless isotropic function of its n arguments.

It might seem that nothing is accomplished by such simple reasoning, but that is not true. In the initially assumed relation (43), nothing is presumed regarding the dependence on τ, but in the result (44) that dependence is shown to be special in form, determined by the nature of the dependence on the kinematic tensors $\mathbf{A}_k$. For example, if the dependence of stress upon kinematic quantities is assumed to be of polynomial type, from (44) it follows that *the stress is also a polynomial in the natural time*. In this way a scalar ordering parameter appears.

Henceforth we assume that $\mathbf{t} + p\mathbf{1}$ is a polynomial, possibly of very high degree, in the Rivlin-Ericksen tensors $\mathbf{A}_1$, $\mathbf{A}_2$, ..., $\mathbf{A}_n$. By collecting terms of a fixed power in τ, from (44) we now conclude that

$$\mathbf{t} + p\mathbf{1} = \mu\sum_q \tau^{q-1}\mathbf{F}_q(\mathbf{A}_1, \mathbf{A}_2, ..., \mathbf{A}_n), \tag{45}$$

where $\mathbf{F}_q$ is the most general isotropic polynomial of degrees α_1, α_2, ..., α_n such that

$$\alpha_1 + 2\alpha_2 + 3\alpha_3 + ... + n\alpha_n = q. \tag{46}$$

The sum in (45) runs far enough that the total degree of (45) equals that of (44). The coefficients of the polynomial $\mathbf{F}_q$ are absolute, dimensionless constants.

Now consider a given flow, and consider the response to this flow of the various fluids in common the same dimensionless coefficients of all the polynominals $\mathbf{F}_q$ and the same viscosity μ. These fluids differ from one another only in the values of their natural times τ. If we let $\mathbf{t}^{(q)}$ stand for the result of truncating (45) after the term of degree $q-1$ in τ, then

$$|\mathbf{t} - \mathbf{t}^{(q)}| = o(\tau^{q-1}) \text{ as } \tau \to 0. \tag{47}$$

If we call the substance defined by $\mathbf{t}^{(q)}$ a *Rivlin-Ericksen fluid of grade q*, we see that as $\tau \to 0$ the response of the fluid of grade q becomes a steadily better approximation, and the more so the greater is q, to that of the general Rivlin-Ericksen fluid.

While the method of Coleman and Noll compares the responses of the same fluid to more and more severe retardation of a given motion, the present method compares the responses to the same deformation of different fluids having smaller and smaller natural times, but otherwise identical. Although the ideas and mathematical processes are different, the resulting scheme of approximation is the same in each case.

If we set $q = 1$, from (46) we see that $\alpha_1 = 1$ and $\alpha_2 = \alpha_3 = \ldots = 0$. Therefore $t + p\mathbf{1}$ is a linear isotropic function of $\mathbf{A}_1$, so that by (42) we have

$$t + p\mathbf{1} = \mu\alpha\mathbf{A}_1. \tag{48}$$

For consistency with $(42)_1$ it is necessary that $\alpha = 1$; thus the Rivlin-Ericksen fluid of grade 1 is the classical fluid with linear viscosity. The natural time τ has cancelled out of the first-order theory, and from $(42)_2$ we may say, if we like, that the Newtonian fluid is one whose natural time is zero.

Now set $q = 2$. From (46) we see that $\alpha_3 = \alpha_4 = \ldots = 0$, while for α_1 and α_2 we have only the following possible combinations beyond the one present in the Newtonian fluid: $(0, 1), (2, 0)$. Hence for the fluid of second grade

$$t + p\mathbf{1} = \mu[\mathbf{A}_1 + \tau(\beta\mathbf{A}_1^2 + \beta'\mathbf{A}_2)]. \tag{49}$$

In view of (42), one of the coefficients β, β' is supernumerary. If we introduce the *normal-stress ratio*,

$$r_n \equiv \frac{\sigma_1 - \sigma_2}{\sigma_1 + \sigma_2}, \tag{50}$$

σ_1 and σ_2 being the constants to which the normal-stress functions in (21) reduce in the present approximation, then (49) may be written in the form

$$t + p\mathbf{1} = \mu\left\{\mathbf{A}_1 + \frac{\tau}{\sqrt{1 + r_n^2}}\left[(1 + r_n)\mathbf{A}_1^2 - r_n\mathbf{A}_2\right]\right\}. \tag{51}$$

Thus the coefficients in the constitutive equation of the fluid of second grade are expressed entirely in terms of the effects measurable in viscometric flows: the linear shear viscosity, the natural time, and the dimensionless normal-stress ratio. The ratio r_n is a dimensionless measure of the relative magnitudes of the normal-stress effects: The Reiner-Rivlin relation (18) is equivalent to $r_n = 0$; the Weissenberg conjecture (19) is equivalent to $r_n = 1$; there is no reason to expect either of these special relations to hold, and little simplicity gained if either of them does.

The fluid of second grade has a remarkable property in common with the classical linearly viscous one: for these fluids *viscometric measurements suffice to determine the form of the constitutive equation for all flows.* We may put this result in another way: The effects of second order in the shearing in viscometric measurements on a simple fluid suffice to determine the general second-order approximation to its constitutive equation. This property does not carry over to the next stage of approximation, for the incompressible fluid of third grade may be shown to have a constitutive equation of the form obtained by adding to the right-hand side of (51) the terms

$$\mu\tau^2 [\gamma\,(\mathrm{tr}\,\mathbf{A}_1^2)\mathbf{A}_1 + \gamma'(\mathbf{A}_1\mathbf{A}_2 + \mathbf{A}_2\mathbf{A}_1) + \gamma''\mathbf{A}_3], \tag{52}$$

where γ, γ', and and γ'' are dimensionless constants. In a viscometric flow, the formulae for the normal stresses are the same as for a fluid of second grade, but we now obtain a correction to the shear viscosity, of third order in the shearing:

$$\mu(\kappa) = \mu[1 + 2\tau^2(\gamma + \gamma')\kappa^2]. \tag{53}$$

Viscometric data can determine $\gamma + \gamma'$ but can give no further information about the three third-order viscosities; in particular, the term whose coefficient is γ'' never manifests itself, since $\mathbf{A}_3 = 0$ in a viscometric flow. Thus it is precisely at the effects of third order in the shearing that viscometric tests begin to fail us as a means of determining the material properties of fluids.

14. Non-linear contiuum theories derived from molecular models.

So far I have spoken exclusively of phenomenological theories, but of course it is desirable to connect these with the molecular structure of materials. The disadvantage of the molecular theories lies in their mathematical complexity: Their greater accuracy in principle is sacrificed in practice, either from compromise with a greatly oversimplified molecule, or from mathematical approximations so drastic as to destroy grounds for confidence in the result, or, more usually, from both. However, the value of molecular theories as models is great, for they show us how a substance *might* behave, even if no real material with so simple a structure happens to exist.

The kinetic theory of rubber elasticity [121] is a case in point. The earliest efforts produced an overly simple stress-strain relation of roughly the right kind, but a great deal of elaborate later study has not succeeded in getting a stored-energy function sufficiently general to fit the experimental data, while the continuum theory has triumphed again and again. What a molecular model can do but the continuum theory does not do is to relate some of the simpler coefficients to the temperature and other parameters of state and composition.

More progress has been made in the kinetic theory of moderately rarefied monatomic gases. Maxwell himself proved that the Navier-Stokes equations cannot be exact according to the kinetic theory, and he showed how stresses can arise from inequalities of temperature. The simplest molecular picture of a gas, then, yields an elaborate constitutive equation not included in the theory of simple fluids based upon (10). There has been much argument regarding what the kinetic theory really does predict (*cf.* [120] [117]). Using the simplest of all models, the Maxwellian gas, Galkin [116] and I [118] obtained the first exact solutions representing dissipative flows (*cf.* also the extension of these results by Galkin [119]). For a class of flows including a kind of simple shearing, in turns out that the constitutive equations reduce to those of one of Noll's hygrosteric materials, but a material without a natural time. The resulting problem, with temperature-dependent viscosity and heat conductivity and with all moduli numerically determined from the molecular model, is fully thermomechanical; it is in fact the equation of energy that plays the central part. In this theory, Weissenberg's assertion (18) is verified, in the sense that any departure from it is damped out according to the classical relaxation law for a Maxwellian gas, with the same relaxation time as for the shear stress in a gas grossly at rest. The second-order effects are much the same as for a simple fluid, but for very high shearing the normal-stress effects dominate the whole phenomenon. However, contrary to widespread misconception, the Maxwellian gas is basically different from the fluids considered in most theories of nonlinear viscosity in that *it has no natural time:* In the kinetic theory, relaxation effects arise only in connection with compressibility, not controlled by any material parameter having the dimension T.

There is much literature on approximate constitutive equations for more general kinetic theories of fluids. A contribution to this problem will be presented to the symposium by Storer and Green [122].

15. Concluding remarks.

While this has been a long lecture, I have not had time to summarize the valuable and interesting researches on second-order effects arising from non-mechanical interactions. I refer, among other things, to Toupin's researches on electrostriction, magnetostriction, and elasto-optics, and to various studies of non-linear thermoelasticity and thermofluidity [9] [16] [41] [106–115] (*cf.* also [118]).

Confining attention to the major results on purely mechanical effects, and emphasizing those more immediately connected with experiment, I hope I have succeeded in linking the various concepts of order and of showing how they fit into the general scheme of rational mechanics. Looking back over what I have been able to include, I trust everyone will see that the field opened by the researches of Reiner scarcely more than fifteen years ago has reached a certain level of maturity, witnessed by some extraordinary concrete results, and has now established a general rationale as well as standards against which future achievement must be measured. I hope that my summary will assist you in the organization and critique of the particular contributions to be presented in the course of the meeting.

It is a pleasure to thank Messrs. Coleman, Ericksen, Noll, and Toupin for their advice and criticism. The investigation reported here was supported in part by the U.S. National Science Foundation and by the U.S. National Bureau of Standards.

SELECTED BIBLIOGRAPHY

As is the lecture itself, the bibliography is selective, confined to works mentioned in the lecture. A full bibliography will accompany the forthcoming survey of the foundations by W. NOLL and C. TRUESDELL, *The Non-linear Field Theories of Mechanics*, Flügge's Encyclopedia of Physics **3**, Part 3.

General reference:

[1] C. TRUESDELL AND R. TOUPIN, *The Classical Field Theories*, with an Appendix on *Invariants* by J. L. ERICKSEN, Flügge's *Encyclopedia of Physics* **3**, Part 1, (1960), 226–858

Early work on the foundations:
  [2] M. REINER, A mathematical theory of dilatancy, *Am. J. Math.* **67,** (1945), 350–362.
  [3] R. S. RIVLIN, Hydrodynamics of non-Newtonian fluids, *Nature* **160,** (1947), 611–613.
  [4] C. TRUESDELL AND R. N. SCHWARTZ, *The Newtonian Mechanics of Continua*, U.S
        Naval Ordnance Lab. Memo. No. 9223, 18 July 1947.
  [5] K. WEISSENBERG, A continuum theory of rheological phenomena, *Nature* **159,** (1947),
        310–311.
  [6] M. REINER, Elasticity beyond the elastic limit, *Am. J. Math.* **70,** (1948), 433–446.
  [7] R. S. RIVLIN, The hydrodynamics of non-Newtonian fluids I, *Proc. Roy. Soc. London*
        A **193,** (1948), 260–281.
  [8] R .S. RIVLIN, Large elastic deformations of isotropic materials IV. Further developments
        in the general theory, *Phil. Trans. Roy. Soc. London* A **241,** (1948), 379–397.
  [9] C. TRUESDELL, On the differential equations of slip flow, *Proc. Nat. Acad. Sci. U.S.A.*
        34, (1948), 342–347.
 [10] R. S. RIVLIN, The hydrodynamics of non-Newtonian fluids II, *Proc. Cambr. Phil. Soc.*
        45, (1949), 88–91.
 [11] R. S. RIVLIN, Large elastic deformations of isotropic materials V, The problem of
        flexure, *Proc. Roy. Soc. London* A **195,** (1949), 463–473.
 [12] R. S. RIVLIN, Large elastic deformations of isotropic materials VI. Further results in
        the theory of torsion, shear and flexure, *Phil. Trans. Roy. Soc. London* A **242,** (1949),
        173–195.
 [13] R. S. RIVLIN, A note on the torsion of an incompressible highly elastic cylinder, *Proc.
        Cambr. Phil. Soc.* **45,** (1949), 485–487.
 [14] C. TRUESDELL, A new definition of a fluid I. The Stokesian fluid, *Proc. 7th Intern.
        Congr. Appl. Mech.* (1948) **2,** (1949), 351–364.
 [15] C. TRUESDELL, A program of physical research in classical mechanics, *Z. Angew.
        Math. Phys.* **3,** (1952), 79–95.
 [16] C. TRUESDELL, The mechanical foundations of elasticity and fluid dynamics, *J. Ra-
        tional Mech. Anal.* **1,** (1952), 125–300.
 [17] C. TRUESDELL, Corrections and additions to "The mechanical foundations of
        elasticity and fluid dynamics", *J. Rational Mech. Anal.*, **2,** (1953), 593–616.

General theories of the mechanical behavior of materials:
 [18] W. NOLL, On the continuity of the solid and fluid states, *J. Rational Mech. Anal.*,
        4, (1955), 3–81.
 [19] R. S. RIVLIN AND J. L. ERICKSEN, Stress-deformation relations for isotropic ma-
        terials, *J. Rational Mech Anal.*, **4,** (1955), 323–425.
 [20] A. E. GREEN AND R. S. RIVLIN, The mechanics of non-linear materials with memory,
        I, *Brown Univ. Rep. No.* C 11–17 (1956) = *Arch. Rational Mech. Anal.*, **1,** (1957/8),
        (1957), 1–21.
 [21] W. NOLL, On the foundations of the mechanics of continuous media, *Carnegie Inst.
        Tech. Rep. No. 17, Air Force Off. Sci. Res.*, 1957.
 [22] W. NOLL, A mathematical theory of the mechanical behavior of continuous media,
        Arch. Rational Mech. Anal., **2,** (1958/9), (1958), 197–226.
 [23] A. E. GREEN, R. S. RIVLIN AND A. J. SPENCER, The mechanics of non-linear ma-
        terials with memory, Part II, *Arch. Rational Mech. Anal.*, **3,** (1929), 82–90.
 [24] A. E. GREEN AND R. S. RIVLIN, The mechanics of non-linear materials with memory,
        Part III. *Arch. Rational Mech. Anal.*, **4,** (1959/60), (1960), 387–404.

Second-order effects in elasticity:

[25] A. Signorini, Sulle deformazioni termoelastiche finite, *Proc. 3rd Internat. Congr. Appl. Mech.*, **2,** (1930), 80–89.

[26] A. Signorini, Transformazioni termoelastiche finite, caratteristiche dei sistemi differenziali, onde di discontinuità, in particolare, onde d'urto e teoria degli esplosivi, *Atti. XXIV Riun. Soc. Ital. Progr. Sci.*, **3,** (1936), 8–25.

[27] A. E. Green and R. T. Shield, Finite extension and torsion of cylinders, *Phil. Trans. Roy. Soc. London* A **244,** (1951), 47–86.

[28] F. D. Murnaghan, *Finite Deformation of an Elastic Solid*, New York, John Wiley and Sons, 1951.

[29] R. S. Rivlin and D. W. Saunders, Large elastic deformations of isotropic materials, VII. Experiments on the deformation of rubber, *Phil. Trans. Roy. Soc. London* A **243,** (1951), 251–288.

[30] A. N. Gent and R. S. Rivlin, Experiments on the mechanics of rubber, *Proc. Phys. Soc.* B **65,** (1952), 118–121, 487–501, 645–648.

[31] A. E. Green, R. S. Rivlin and R. T. Shield, General theory of small elastic deformations superposed on finite elastic deformations, *Proc. Roy. Soc. London* A **211,** (1952), 128–154.

[32] R. S. Rivlin, The solution of problems in second-order elasticity theory, *J. Rational Mech. Anal.*, **2,** (1953), 53–81.

[33] A. E. Green and E. B. Spratt, Second-order effects in the deformation of elastic bodies, *Proc. Roy. Soc. London* A **224,** (1954), 347–361.

[34] A. E. Green, A note on second-order effects in the torsion of incompressible cylinders, *Proc. Cambr. Phil. Soc.*, **50,** (1957), 488–490.

[35] R. S. Rivlin and C. Topakoglu, A theorem in the theory of finite elastic deformation, *J. Rational Mech. Anal.*, **3,** (1954), 581–589.

[36] P. L. Sheng, *Secondary Elasticity*, Chin. Assoc. Adv. Sci. Mono., **1,** Taipei, 1955.

[37] J. L. Ericksen and R. A. Toupin, Implications of Hadamard's condition for elastic stability with respect to uniqueness theorems, *Canad. J. Math.*, **8,** (1956), 432–436.

[38] J. E. Adkins and A. E. Green, Plane problems in second-order elasticity theory, *Proc. Roy. Soc. London* A **239,** (1957), 557-576.

[39] W. S. Blackburn and A. E. Green, Second-order torsion and bending of isotropic elastic cylinders, *Proc. Roy. Soc. London* A **240,** (1957), 408–422.

[40] A. J. M. Spencer, On finite deformations with a perturbed strain-energy function, *Q. J. Mech. Appl. Math.*, **12,** (1959), 129–145.

[41] A. E. Green and J. E. Adkins, *Large Elastic Deformations and Non-linear Continuum Mechanics*, Oxford, Clarendon Press, 1960.

[42] R. A. Toupin and B. Bernstein, Sound waves in deformed perfectly elastic materials; the acoustoelastic effect, *J. Acoust. Soc. Am.*, **33,** (1961), 216–225.

[43] C. Truesdell, General and exact theory of waves in finite elastic strain, *Arch. Rational Mech. Anal.*, **8,** (1961), 263–296.

[44] M. Hayes and R. S. Rivlin, Surface waves in deformed elastic materials, *Arch. Rational Mech. Anal.*, **8,** (1961), 358–380.

[45] T. C. Woo and R. T. Shield, Fundamental solutions for small deformations superposed on finite biaxial extension of an elastic body, *Arch. Rational Mech. Anal.*, **9,** (1962), 196–224.

[46] G. Grioli, *Mathematical Theory of Elastic Equilibrium (Recent Results)* Ergebnisse der angewandten Mathematik, Berlin-Göttingen-Heidelberg, J. Springer, 1962.

[47] J. F. BELL, Experiments on large amplitude waves in finite elastic strain, *Proc. Internat. Symp. Second-order Effects*, Haifa, 1962, 173–186.

[48] A. J. M. SPENCER, Finite deformations of an almost incompressible elastic solid, *Proc. Internat. Symp. Second-order Effects*, Haifa, 1962, 200–216.

[49] C. TRUESDELL, Second-order theory of wave propagation in isotropic elastic materials, *Proc. Internat. Symp. Second-order Effects*, Haifa, 1962, 187–199.

[50] H. ZORSKI, On the equations describing small deformations superposed on finite deformation, *Proc. Internat. Symp. Second-order Effects*, Haifa, 1962, 109–128.

Stress relaxation:

[51] R. S. RIVLIN, Stress relaxation in incompressible elastic materials at constant deformation, *Q. Appl. Math.*, **14**, (1956), 83–89.

[52] R. S. RIVLIN, The constitutive equations for certain classes of deformations, *Arch. Rational Mech. Anal.*, **3**, (1959), 304–311.

[53] R. S. RIVLIN, Constitutive equations for classes of deformations, *Viscoelasticity: Phenomenological aspects*, N.Y., Academic Press, (1960), 93–108.

Continuum theory of dislocations in finite strain:

[54] W. GÜNTHER, Zur Statik und Kinematik des Cosseratschen Kontinuums, *Abh. Braun-Braunschw. Wiss. Gess.*, **10**, (1958), 195–213.

[55] E. KRÖNER AND A. SEEGER, Nicht-lineare Elastizitätstheorie der Versetzungen und Eigenspannungen, *Arch. Rational Mech. Anal.*, **3**, (1959), 97–119.

[56] E. KRÖNER, Allgemeine Kontinuumstheorie der Versetzungen und Eigenspannungen, *Arch. Rational Mech. Anal.*, **4**, (1959/60), (1960), 273–334.

[57] B. A. BILBY, Continuous distributions of dislocations, *Progr. Solid Mech.*, **1**, (1961), 329–398.

Polar elastic solids:

[58] G. GRIOLI, Elasticità asimmetrica, *Annali di mat. pura applic.*, (4), **50**, (1960), 389–418.

[59] G. GRIOLI, Onde di discontinuità ed elasticità asimmetrica, *Rend. Accad. Lincei Cl. Sci. Mat. Fis. Nat.*, (8), **29**, (1960), (1961), 309–312.

[60] R. D. MINDLIN, Effects of couple-stresses in linear elasticity, *Arch. Rational Mech. Anal.*, to appear in 1962.

[61] R. A. TOUPIN, On perfectly elastic materials with couple-stresses, *Arch. Rational Mech. Anal.*, to appear in 1962.

Hypo-elasticity:

[62] C. TRUESDELL, Hypo-elasticity, *J. Rational Mech. Anal.*, **4**, (1955), 83–133, 1019–1020.

[63] T. Y. THOMAS, Combined elastic and Prandtl-Reuss stress-strain relations, *Proc. Nat. Acad. Sci.*, **41**, (1955), 720–726.

[64] C. TRUESDELL, Hypo-elastic shear, *J. Applied Phys.*, **27**, (1956), 441–447.

[65] A. E. GREEN, Hypo-elasticity and plasticity, *Proc. Roy. Soc. London*, A, **234**, (1956), 46–59.

[66] A. E. GREEN, Hypo-elasticity and plasticity II, *J. Rational Mech. Anal.*, **5**, (1956), 725–734.

[67] J. L. ERICKSEN, Hypo-elastic potentials, *Q. J. Mech. Appl. Math.*, **11**, (1958), 67–72.

[68] B. BERNSTEIN AND J. L. ERICKSEN, Work functions in hypo-elasticity, *Arch. Rational Mech. Anal.*, **1**, (1958), 396–409.

[69] B. BERNSTEIN, Hypo-elasticity and elasticity, *Arch. Rational Mech. Anal.*, **6**, (1960), 89–104.

Second-order stresses and flows of simple fluids:

[70] H. W. GREENSMITH AND R. S. RIVLIN, The hydrodynamics of non-Newtonian fluids, III. The normal stress effect in high-polymer solutions, *Phil. Trans. Roy. Soc. London*, **245**, (1953), 399–428.

[71] R. S. RIVLIN, Solution of some problems in the exact theory of visco-elasticity, *J. Rational Mech. Anal.*, **5**, (1956), 179–188.

[72] J. L. ERICKSEN, Overdetermination of the speed in rectilinear motion of non-Newtonian fluids, *Q. Applied Math.*, **14**, (1956), 318–321.

[73] A. E. GREEN AND R. S. RIVLIN, Steady flow of non-Newtonian fluids through tubes, *Q. Applied Math.*, **14**, (1956), 299–308.

[74] D. E. STONE, On non-existence of rectilinear motion in plastic solids and non-Newtonian fluids, *Q. Applied Math.*, **15**, (1957), 257–262.

[75] H. MARKOVITZ, Normal stress effect in polyisobutylene solutions, II. Classification and application of rheological theories, *Trans. Soc. Rheology*, **1**, (1957), 37–52.

[76] W. LANGLOIS, Doctoral dissertation, Brown Univ., 1957.

[77] W. O. CRIMINALE, Jr., J. L. ERICKSEN AND G. L. FILBEY, Jr., Steady shear flow of non-Newtonian fluids, *Arch. Rational Mech. Anal.*, **1**, (1957/8), (1958), 410–417.

[78] J. L. ERICKSEN, Secondary flow phenomena in non-linear fluids, *Tappi*, **42**, (1959), 773–775.

[79] B. D. COLEMAN AND W. NOLL, On certain steady flows of general fluids, *Arch Rational Mech. Anal.*, **3**, (1959), 289–303.

[80] B. D. COLEMAN AND W. NOLL, Helical flow of general fluids, *J. Applied Phys.*, **30**, (1959), 1508–1512.

[81] J. L. ERICKSEN, The behavior of certain visco-elastic materials in laminar shearing motions, *Visco-elasticity: Phenomenological Aspects*, N. Y., Academic Press, (1960), 77–91.

[82] B. D. COLEMAN AND W. NOLL, Steady extension of incompressible simple fluids, in press.

[83] H. MARKOVITZ AND D. R. BROWN, Normal stress measurements on a polyisobutylene-cetane solution in parallel plate and cone-plate instruments, *Proc. Internat. Sympos. Second-order Effects*, Haifa, 1962.

[83a] R. S. RIVLIN, Second and higher-order theories for the flow of a viscoelastic fluid in a non-circular pipe *Proc. Internat. Sympos. Second-Order Effects*, Haifa, 1962.

Anisotropic fluids:

[84] J. L. ERICKSEN, Transversely isotropic fluids, *Kolloid Z.*, **173**, (1960), 117–122.

[85] J. L. ERICKSEN, Anisotropic fluids, *Arch. Rational Mech., Anal.*, **4**, (1960), 231–237.

[86] J. L. ERICKSEN, Theory of anisotropic fluids, *Trans. Soc. Rheol.*, **4**, (1960), 29–39.

[87] J. L. ERICKSEN, A vorticity effect in anisotropic fluids, *J. Polymer Sci.*, **47**, (1960), 327–331.

[88] G. L. HAND, A theory of dilute suspensions, *Arch. Rational Mech. Anal.*, **7**, (1961), 81–86.

[89] J. L. ERICKSEN, Poiseuille flow of certain anisotropic fluids, *Arch. Rational Mech Anal.*, **8**, (1961), 1–8.

[90] J. L. ERICKSEN, Kinematics of macromolecules, *Arch. Rational Mech. Anal.*, **9**, (1962), 1–8.

[91] J. L. ERICKSEN, Hydrostatic theory of liquid crystals, *Arch. Rational Mech. Anal.* **9**, (1962), 371–378.

[92]   P. D. S. Verma, Couette flow of certain anisotropic fluids, *Arch. Rational Mech. Anal.*, **10**, (1962), 101–107.

[93]   J. L. Ericksen, Nilpotent energies in liquid crystal theory, *Arch. Rational Mech. Anal.*, **10**, (1962), 189–196.

Fluid mixtures:

[94]   Z. Sakadi, On the dispersion of sound wave considering the effects of heat conduction and viscosity, *Proc. Phys. Math. Soc. Japan*, **23**, (1941), 208–213.

[95]   J. Meixner, Allgemeine Theorie der Schallabsorption in Gasen und Flüssigkeiten unter Berücksichtigung der Transporterscheinungen, *Acustica*, **2**, (1952), 101–109.

[96]   C. Truesdell, Sulle basi della termomeccanica, *Rend. Accad. Linc.*, (8), **22**, (1957), 33–38, 158–166.

[97]   H. Kneser, Schallabsorption und dispersion in Gasen, Flügge's *Encyclopedia of Physics*, **11**$_1$, (1961), 129–201.

[98]   C. Truesdell, Una teoria meccanica della diffusione, *Celebraz. Archimed. del Sec. XX* (1961), Siracusa, forthcoming.

[99]   C. C. Lin, *Hydrodynamics of Liquid Helium II*, Lectures at Int. School of Physics, Varenna, 1961, forthcoming.

[99a] C. Truesdell, Mechanical basis of diffusion *J. Chem. Phys.*, fortchoming.

Second-order memory effects:

[100] B. D. Coleman and W. Noll, An approximation theorem for functionals, with applications in continuum mechanic, *Arch. Rational Mech. Anal.*, **6**, (1960), 355–370.

[101] B. D. Coleman and W. Noll, Recent results in the continuum theory of visco-elastic fluids, *Annals N. Y. Acad. Sci.*, **89**, (1961), 672–714.

[102] B. D. Coleman and W. Noll, Foundations of linear visco-elasticity, *Rev. Mod Phys.*, **33**, (1961), 239–249.

[103] B. D. Coleman and W. Noll, Normal stresses in second-order visco-elasticity *Trans. Soc. Rheol.*, **5**, (1961), 41–46.

[104] A. C. Pipkin and R. S. Rivlin, Small deformations superposed on large deformations in materials with fading memory, *Arch. Rational Mech. Anal.*, **8**, (1961), 297–308.

[105] B. D. Coleman and W. Noll. Simple fluids with fading memory, *Proc. Internat. Sympos. Second-order Effects*, Haifa, 1962.

Thermomechanical and electromechanical theories:

[106] C. Truesdell, A new definition of a fluid II, The Maxwellian fluid, *J. Math. Pures Appl.*, **30**, (1951), 111–158.

[107] R. A. Toupin, The elastic dielectric, *J. Rational Mech. Anal.*, **5**, (1956), 849–915.

[108] B. D. Coleman and W. Noll, On the thermostatics of continuous media, *Arch. Rational Mech. Anal.*, **4**, (1958/9), (1959), 97–128.

[109] A. C. Pipkin and R. S. Rivlin, The formulation of constitutive equations in continuum physics, I, *Arch. Rational Mech. Anal.*, **4**, (1959), 129–144.

[110] R. A. Toupin, Piezoelectric relations and the radial deformation of a polarized sperical shell, *J. Acoust. Soc.*, **31**, (1959), 315–318.

[111] A. C. Pipkin and R. S. Rivlin, Electrical conduction in deformed isotropic materials, *J. Math. Phys.*, **1**, (1960), 127–130.

[112] R. S. RIVLIN, The formulation of constitutive equations in continuum physics, II, *Arch. Rational Mech. Anal.*, **4**, (1960), 262–272.

[113] A. H. ENGLAND AND A. E. GREEN, Steady-state thermoelasticity for initially stressed bodies, *Phil. Trans. Roy. Sc. London* A, **253**, (1961), 517–542.

[114] J. N. FLAVIN AND A. E. GREEN, Plane thermo-elastic waves in an initially stressed medium. *J. Mech. Phys. Solids*, **9**, (1961), 179–190.

[115] R. A. TOUPIN, Dynamical theory of elastic dielectrics, *J. Engr. Sci.*, forthcoming. Non-linear continuum theories derived from molecular models:

[116] V. S. GALKIN, OB ODNOM RESHENII KINETICHESKOGO URAVNENIIA BOL'CHMANA, PRIKL. MAT. MEKH. **20**, (1956).

[117] C. IKENBERRY AND C. TRUESDELL, On the pressures and the flux of energy in a gas according to Maxwell's kinetic theory, I, *J. Rational Mech. Anal.*, **5**, (1956), 3–54.

[118] C. TRUESDELL, On the pressures and the flux of energy in a gas according to Maxwell's kinetic theory, II, *J. Rational Mech. Anal.*, **5**, (1956), 55–128.

[119] V. S. GALKIN, OB ODNOM KLASSE RESHENII URAVNENIIA KINETICHESKIKH MOMENTOV GRADA, PRIKL. MAT. MEKH. **22**, (1958), 386–389. English transl., *J. Appl Math. Mech.*, **22**, (1958), 532–536.

[120] H. GRAD, Principles of the kinetic theory of gases, Flügge's *Encyclopedia of Physics*, **12**, (1958), 205–294.

[121] L. R. G. TRELOAR, *The Physics of Rubber Elasticity*, 2nd ed., Oxford, 1958.

[122] R. G. STORER AND H. S. GREEN, Kinetic theory of second-order effects in fluids, *Proc. Internat. Sympos. Second-order Effects*, Haifa, 1962.

I. ELASTICITY

FURTHER STUDY OF THERMAL STRESSES
IN VISCOELASTIC MATERIALS WITH
TEMPERATURE-DEPENDENT PROPERTIES*

ELI STERNBERG AND M. E. GURTIN

Brown University, Providence, R. I., U.S.A.

ABSTRACT

This paper deals with the quasi-static analysis of transient thermal stresses in the linear theory of homogeneous and isotropic viscoelastic solids with temperature-dependent properties. The underlying constitutive law rests on the temperature-time equivalence hypothesis originally proposed by Leaderman. Accordingly, the instantaneous stresses at each material point of the solid are functionals of the entire preceding local strain and temperature history, the dependence on the temperature being nonlinear. The present investigation is a continuation of earlier work by Morland and Lee and by Muki and Sternberg.

1. Introduction.

The effect of temperature-dependent mechanical properties upon thermal stresses in viscoelastic materials has attracted repeated attention during recent years. A consistent formulation of such problems, set within the framework of linear viscoelasticity theory and based upon the temperature-time equivalence hypothesis originally proposed by Leaderman [1]([1]), was initiated by Morland and Lee [2]. In [2] the postulate of thermo-rheologically simple behavior([2]) was applied to the two-dimensional analysis of the stresses in an incompressible hollow circular cylinder which is exposed to a stationary radial temperature field and is subjected to a suddenly imposed internal pressure.

More recently, Muki and Sternberg [4] explored the consequences of the temperature-time equivalence hypothesis in circumstances which involve time-dependent temperature fields by deducing exact solutions to two specific problems of this type. The first of these concerns the termal stresses in an infinite slab which, in the absence of loading, is confined to a purely transverse motion, the stress-inducing temperature field being permitted to vary

---

* The results communicated in this paper were obtained in the course of an investigation conducted under Contracts Nonr-562(30) and Nonr-562(25) of Brown University with the Office of Naval Research in Washington, D. C.

([1]) Numbers in brackets refer to the list of publications at the end of this paper.

([2]) This terminology is due to Schwarzl and Staverman [3].

arbitrarily with the thickness coordinate and the time. The second application considered in [4] aims at the stresses generated in a sphere by an arbitrary transient radial temperature distribution.

It is the purpose of the present paper to examine further the implications of thermo-rheologically simple behavior in the context of the quasi-static linear theory of viscoelastic solids. Section 2 contains a résumé of the appropriate governing field equations, boundary conditions, and initial conditions for three-dimensional problems. In Section 3 we discuss the analogous two-dimensional theory and establish the connection between the plane-strain and the generalized plane-stress solutions associated with one and the same plane problem. Section 4 deals with generalizations of certain theorems of ordinary thermoelasticity theory, including results concerning temperature fields that fail to cause thermal stresses.

Section 5, finally, is devoted to the particular problem of a spherical shell of arbitrary thickness. The underlying temperature field, as well as the accompanying boundary conditions (which may involve given surface tractions or surface displacements) are required to posses polar symmetry about the center of the shell, whereas the dependence upon time of the corresponding prescribed functions is left essentially unrestricted. Similarly, no artificial restrictions are placed upon the deviatoric response of the material (which may be of the general linear hereditary type) or on the (thermo-rheologically simple) temperature-dependence of this response. In contrast, the dilatational response of the material is assumed to be purely elastic, but compressibility is taken into account. As a special case of the solution obtained, we recover the results appropriate to the solid sphere, deduced previously in [4] by less systematic means.

2.   Résumé of the governing equations.

We now summarize the basic equations governing the quasi-static linear theory of homogeneous and isotropic, thermo-rheologically simple, viscoelastic media in the absence of thermo-mechanical coupling[3].

Thus, let $u_i(x,t)$, $\varepsilon_{ij}(x,t)$, and $\sigma_{ij}(x,t)$ be the cartesian components of displacement, strain and stress, x denoting the triplet of rectangular cartesian coordinates (x_1, x_2, x_3) and t the time. Further, let $F_i(x,t)$ stand for the components of the body-force density and let $T(x,t)$ be the temperature field. In the usual indicial notation[4] the *displacement-strain relations* take the form

---

[3] A detailed exposition of this theory may be found in [2], [4].
[4] Throughout this paper Latin subscripts have the range of the integers (1, 2, 3) and summation over repeated subscripts is implied.

$$\varepsilon_{ij} = \frac{1}{2}\left(\frac{\partial u_i}{\partial x_j} + \frac{\partial u_j}{\partial x_i}\right) , \tag{2.1}$$

while the *stress equations of equilibrium* become

$$\frac{\partial \sigma_{ij}}{\partial x_j} + F_i = 0. \tag{2.2}$$

With a view toward stating alternative forms of the *stress-strain relations* we introduce the deviatoric components of strain and stress through

$$e_{ij} = \varepsilon_{ij} - \tfrac{1}{3}\delta_{ij}\varepsilon, \quad s_{ij} = \sigma_{ij} - \tfrac{1}{3}\delta_{ij}\sigma, \quad \varepsilon = \varepsilon_{kk}, \quad \sigma = \sigma_{kk}, \tag{2.3}$$

where δ_{ij} is Kronecker's delta. The *relaxation integral law* may then be written as

$$\left.\begin{aligned}
s_{ij}(x, t) &= \int_{-\infty}^{t} G_1(\xi - \xi') \frac{\partial}{\partial t'} e_{ij}(x, t')dt', \\[2ex]
\sigma(x, t) &= \int_{-\infty}^{t} G_2(\xi - \xi') \frac{\partial}{\partial t'} \left[\varepsilon(x, t') - 3\alpha_0\Theta(x, t')\right]dt'.
\end{aligned}\right\} \tag{2.4}$$

Here $G_1(t)$ and $G_2(t)$ are the relaxation moduli in shear and isotropic compression, measured at the fixed reference temperature T_0. The function $\Theta(x, t)$ is a "pseudo-temperature" defined by

$$\Theta(x, t) = \frac{1}{\alpha_0} \int_{T_0}^{T(x,t)} \alpha(T')dT', \quad \alpha_0 = \alpha(T_0), \tag{2.5}$$

in which $\alpha(T)$ is the (temperature-dependent) coefficient of linear thermal expansion. Finally,

$$\xi = f(x, t) = \int_0^t \varphi[T(x, t')]\, dt', \quad \xi' = f(x, t'), \tag{2.6}$$

where $\varphi(T)$ is the shift-factor which characterizes the temperature dependence of the material's mechanical response and must conform to

$$\varphi(T_0) = 1, \quad \varphi(T) > 0, \quad \frac{d\varphi}{dT} > 0 \tag{2.7}$$

throughout the relevant temperature range. The analogous generalization of the *creep integral law* is given by

$$
\left.
\begin{aligned}
e_{ij}(x,t) &= \int_{-\infty}^{t} J_1(\xi-\xi') \frac{\partial}{\partial t'} s_{ij}(x,t') dt', \\
\varepsilon(x,t) &= \int_{-\infty}^{t} J_2(\xi-\xi') \frac{\partial}{\partial t'} \sigma(x,t') dt' + 3\alpha_0 \Theta(x,t),
\end{aligned}
\right\}
\tag{2.8}
$$

provided $J_1(t)$ and $J_2(t)$ denote the creep moduli in shear and isotropic compression, referred to the base temperature T_0. In connection with the hereditary laws (2.4) and (2.8) we stipulate that

$$
G_\beta(t) = 0, \quad J_\beta(t) = 0 \text{ for } -\infty < t \leq 0 \ (\beta = 1,2).
\tag{2.9}
$$

If the medium happens to exhibit a finite and discrete spectrum of relaxation and retardation times, the foregoing integral laws admit an equivalent representation in differential-operator form, which need not be cited here explicitly[5].

As is apparent from (2.4), the instantaneous stresses at each material point of the body are, in general, functionals of the entire preceding local strain and temperature history; these functionals are linear in the strains but nonlinear in the temperature. If $T(x,t) \equiv T_0$, so that the body is permanently maintained at the uniform base temperature T_0, (2.5), (2.6), (2.7) imply that $\Theta(x,t) = 0$, $\xi = t$, $\xi' = t'$, and (2.4), (2.8) reduce to their familiar counterparts in the isothermal theory.

The field equations (2.1), (2.2), and (2.4) or (2.8), which must hold throughout the region D occupied by the medium, are to be supplemented by appropriate initial and boundary conditions. We shall henceforth suppose the body to be initially undisturbed in the sense that

$$
u_i(x,t) = \sigma_{ij}(x,t) = 0, \quad T(x,t) = T_0 \text{ in } D(-\infty < t \leq 0).
\tag{2.10}
$$

On the other hand, the boundary conditions for the standard mixed boundary-value problem take the form

$$
\left.
\begin{aligned}
u_i &= U_i(x,t) \text{ on } B_1 \ (0 < t < \infty), \\
\sigma_{ij} n_j &= S_i(x,t) \text{ on } B_2 \ (0 < t < \infty),
\end{aligned}
\right\}
\tag{2.11}
$$

---

[5] See [2], [4] for this generalization of the conventional isothermal differential-operator law.

where B_1 and B_2 are complementary portions of the boundary B of D, n_j are the components of the unit outward normal of B, whereas $U_i(x, t)$ and $S_i(x, t)$ are prescribed surface displacements and surface tractions, respectively.

The stress-strain relations (2.4) and (2.8) involve the time t through $\xi = f(x, t)$, as well as explicitly. It is occasionally advantageous to eliminate the physical time t from these equations in favor of the "reduced time" ξ. To this end we note from (2.6), (2.7) that $\xi = f(x, t)$, for fixed (x_1, x_2, x_3), is a monotone increasing function of t. Hence $f(x, t)$ in (2.6) may be inverted with respect to t, so that

$$t = g(x, \xi), \quad t' = g(x, \xi'), \tag{2.12}$$

while from (2.6), (2.12),

$$\frac{\partial \xi}{\partial t} \equiv \frac{\partial}{\partial t} f(x, t) = \varphi[T(x,t)], \quad \frac{\partial t}{\partial \xi} \equiv \frac{\partial}{\partial \xi} g(x, \xi) = \left(\frac{\partial \xi}{\partial t}\right)^{-1}. \tag{2.13}$$

If $Q(x,t)$ is any function of position and time, we shall consistently write

$$Q(x,t) = \hat{Q}(x,\xi) = Q[x, g(x,\xi)]. \tag{2.14}$$

We now use the second of (2.12) to change the variable of integration in (2.4), (2.8) from t' to ξ' and, with the notation adopted in (2.14), thus obtain

$$\left.\begin{aligned}
\hat{s}_{ij}(x,\xi) &= \int_{-\infty}^{\xi} G_1(\xi - \xi') \frac{\partial}{\partial \xi'} \hat{e}_{ij}(x,\xi') d\xi', \\[2mm]
\hat{\sigma}(x,\xi) &= \int_{-\infty}^{\xi} G_2(\xi - \xi') \frac{\partial}{\partial \xi'} [\hat{\varepsilon}(x,\xi') - 3\alpha_0 \hat{\Theta}(x,\xi')] d\xi',
\end{aligned}\right\} \tag{2.15}$$

$$\left.\begin{aligned}
\hat{e}_{ij}(x,\xi) &= \int_{-\infty}^{\xi} J_1(\xi - \xi') \frac{\partial}{\partial \xi'} \hat{s}_{ij}(x,\xi') d\xi', \\[2mm]
\hat{\varepsilon}(x,\xi) &= \int_{-\infty}^{\xi} J_2(\xi - \xi') \frac{\partial}{\partial \xi'} \hat{\sigma}(x,\xi') d\xi' + 3\alpha_0 \hat{\Theta}(x,\xi).
\end{aligned}\right\} \tag{2.16}$$

For future convenience we recall here also the familiar connection between the relaxation and the creep moduli. This connection may be confirmed by taking the Laplace transform with respect to ξ in (2.15), (2.16) and by invoking (2.9), as well as the relevant convolution theorem. Using the notation

$$Q^*(x,\eta) = \mathcal{L}\{Q(x,t);\eta\} = \int_{-\infty}^{\infty} Q(x,t)\exp(-\eta t)dt, \qquad (2.17)$$

in which $Q(x,t)$ is once again an arbitrary (suitably restricted) function of position and time, one has

$$G_\beta^*(\eta) = \frac{1}{\eta^2 J_\beta^*(\eta)} \qquad (\beta = 1,2). \qquad (2.18)$$

Finally, we cite the relations linking the relaxation modulus in extension $\bar{E}(t)$ and the (time-dependent) Poisson ratio $\bar{v}(t)$ of a linear viscoelastic material to its relaxation and creep moduli in shear and isotropic compression[6]:

$$\left.\begin{array}{l} \bar{E}^*(\eta) = \dfrac{3G_1^*(\eta)G_2^*(\eta)}{G_1^*(\eta) + 2G_2^*(\eta)} = \dfrac{3}{\eta^2\left[2J_1^*(\eta) + J_2^*(\eta)\right]}, \\[2ex] \bar{v}^*(\eta) = \dfrac{G_2^*(\eta) - G_1^*(\eta)}{\eta[G_1^*(\eta) + 2G_2^*(\eta)]} = \dfrac{J_1^*(\eta) - J_2^*(\eta)}{\eta[2J_1^*(\eta) + J_2^*(\eta)]}. \end{array}\right\} \qquad (2.19)$$

The particular forms assumed by the various response functions for certain special viscoelastic materials were listed in [4]. At present it will be sufficient to note merely that for the *elastic solid*

$$\left.\begin{array}{l} G_1(t) = 2\mu H(t), \quad G_2(t) = 3kH(t), \\[2ex] J_1(t) = \dfrac{1}{2\mu}H(t), \quad J_2(t) = \dfrac{1}{3k}H(t), \\[2ex] \bar{E}(t) = EH(t), \quad \bar{v}(t) = vH(t), \end{array}\right\} \qquad (2.20)$$

provided the constants μ, k, E, and v (in this order) designate the shear modulus, the bulk modulus, Young's modulus, and Poisson's ratio of the material, while $H(t)$ is the Heaviside unit step-function given by

---

(6) Explicit definitions of $\bar{E}(t)$ and $\bar{v}(t,)$ based on the relaxation test at constant strain, may be found in [4], where the following relations are deduced.

$$H(t) = \begin{cases} 1 \text{ for } 0 < t < \infty \\ 0 \text{ for } -\infty < t \leq 0. \end{cases} \tag{2.21}$$

Accordingly, the second of (2.4) and of (2.8) are to be replaced with

$$\sigma(x,t) = 3k[\varepsilon(x,t) - 3\alpha_0 \Theta(x,t)], \tag{2.22}$$

in the event that the dilatational response of the medium is assumed to be purely elastic.

3. Plane strain and generalized plane stress.

We now consider the plane problem and assume for this purpose that D is a prismatic or cylindrical (not necessarily simply connected) region of space with the *lateral* boundary B. Suppose that the generators of B are parallel to the x_3-axis, let $x_3 = 0$ coincide with the middle plane of the body and let its terminal cross-sections be at $x_3 = \pm h$. The mixed plane problem for D is then governed by the field equations (2.1), (2.2), and (2.4) or (2.8), where at present

$$T = T(x_1, x_2, t), \quad F_\beta = F_\beta(x_1, x_2, t) \quad (\beta = 1, 2), \quad F_3 = 0. \tag{3.1}$$

These equations are subject to the initial conditions (2.10) in conjunction with the lateral boundary conditions (2.11), restricted by

$$\begin{aligned} U_\beta &= U_\beta(x_1, x_2, t) \quad (\beta = 1, 2), \quad U_3 = 0, \\ S_\beta &= S_\beta(x_1, x_2, t) \quad (\beta = 1, 2), \quad S_3 = 0, \end{aligned} \tag{3.2}$$

and with the terminal boundary conditions

$$\sigma_{3i} = 0 \text{ on } x_3 = \pm h. \tag{3.3}$$

Turning first to the *plane-strain solution* associated with the foregoing (three-dimensional) plane problem, we set

$$u_\beta = u_\beta(x,t), \quad u_3 = 0, \tag{3.4}$$

it being understood that Greek subscripts henceforth take on the values (1,2) and that for the remainder of this section the single argument x stands for (x_1, x_2). In view of (3.4), equations (2.1), (2.2), (2.3), (2.15) now yield

$$\varepsilon_{3i} = 0, \quad \sigma_{31} = \sigma_{32} = 0, \tag{3.5}$$

$$\varepsilon_{\beta\gamma} = \frac{1}{2}\left(\frac{\partial u_\beta}{\partial x_\gamma} + \frac{\partial u_\gamma}{\partial x_\beta}\right), \tag{3.6}$$

$$\frac{\partial \sigma_{\beta\gamma}}{\partial x_\gamma} + F_\beta = 0, \tag{3.7}$$

$$\hat{\sigma}_{\beta\gamma}(x, \xi) = \int_{-\infty}^{\xi} G_1(\xi - \xi')\frac{\partial}{\partial \xi'}\hat{\varepsilon}_{\beta\gamma}(x, \varsigma')d\xi' \; +$$

$$+ \; \delta_{\beta\gamma}\int_{-\infty}^{\xi} M(\xi - \xi')\frac{\partial}{\partial \xi'}\hat{\varepsilon}_{\lambda\lambda}(x,\xi')d\xi' \; +$$

$$+ \; \alpha_0\delta_{\beta\gamma}\int_{-\infty}^{\xi} G_2(\xi - \xi')\frac{\partial}{\partial \xi'}\hat{\Theta}(x,\xi')d\xi', \tag{3.8}$$

where
$$M(t) = \frac{1}{3}[G_2(t) - G_1(t)]. \tag{3.9}$$

In order to establish the relation between σ_{33} and the remaining normal stresses, we take $i = j = 3$ in the first of (2.15) and apply the (two-sided) Laplace transform with respect to the reduced time ξ to the resulting stress-strain relation. Bearing in mind that $\varepsilon_{33} = 0$ and by virtue of (2.3), (2.9), (2.17), we thus obtain

$$2\hat{\sigma}_{33}^*(x,\eta) - \hat{\sigma}_{\beta\beta}^*(x,\eta) = -\eta G_1^*(\eta)\hat{\varepsilon}^*(x,\eta). \tag{3.10}$$

Similarly, from the second of (2.15),

$$\hat{\sigma}^*(x,\eta) = \eta G_2^*(\eta)[\hat{\varepsilon}^*(x,\eta) - 3\alpha_0\hat{\Theta}^*(x,\eta)]. \tag{3.11}$$

Eliminating $\hat{\varepsilon}^*$ among (3.10), (3.11), and subsequently making use of (2.19), we find that

$$\hat{\sigma}^*_{33}(x,\eta) = \eta\bar{v}^*(\eta)\hat{\sigma}^*_{\beta\beta}(x\,\eta) - \alpha_0\eta\bar{E}^*(\eta)\hat{\Theta}^*(x,\eta). \tag{3.12}$$

Finally, taking the inverse transform of (3.12), we arrive at

$$\hat{\sigma}_{33}(x,\xi) = \int_{-\infty}^{\xi} \bar{v}(\xi - \xi')\frac{\partial}{\partial \xi'}\hat{\sigma}_{\beta\beta}(x,\xi')d\xi' +$$

$$- \alpha_0 \int_{-\infty}^{\xi} \bar{E}(\xi - \xi')\frac{\partial}{\partial \xi'}\hat{\Theta}(x,\xi')d\xi'. \tag{3.13}$$

In the special case of an elastic solid with $\alpha(T) = \alpha_0$ the relation (3.13) evidently reduces to the familiar result

$$\sigma_{33} = v\sigma_{\beta\beta} - \alpha_0 E(T - T_0) \tag{3.14}$$

of ordinary thermoelasticity theory[7].

For the purpose at hand it is useful to record also an alternative form of the stress-strain relations (3.8), which is obtained by solving (3.8) for the strains in terms of the stresses. This is readily accomplished with the aid of the Laplace transform and, because of (2.18), (2.19), (3.9), results in

$$\hat{\varepsilon}_{\beta\gamma}(x,\xi) = \int_{-\infty}^{\xi} J_1(\xi - \xi')\frac{\partial}{\partial \xi'}\hat{\sigma}_{\beta\gamma}(x,\xi')d\xi' +$$

$$+ \delta_{\beta\gamma} \int_{-\infty}^{\xi} L(\xi - \xi')\frac{\partial}{\partial \xi'}\hat{\sigma}_{\lambda\lambda}(x,\xi')d\xi' +$$

$$+ \alpha_0\delta_{\beta\gamma}[\hat{\Theta}(x,\xi) + \int_{-\infty}^{\xi} \bar{v}(\xi - \xi')\frac{\partial}{\partial \xi'}\hat{\Theta}(x,\xi')d\xi'], \tag{3.15}$$

provided

$$L^*(\eta) = \frac{J_1^*(\eta)[J_2^*(\eta) - J_1^*(\eta)]}{[2J_1^*(\eta) + J_2^*(\eta)]} \tag{3.16}$$

Suppose now that Π designates the cross-section of the cylindrical or prismatic body under consideration and let C be the boundary of the (two-dimensional) region Π. As is apparent, the determination of the desired plane-strain solution requires the solution of the subsidiary two-dimensional boundary-

---

[7] See, for example, [5], p. 103.

value problem for $u_\beta(x,t)$, $\varepsilon_{\beta\gamma}(x,t)$, $\sigma_{\beta\gamma}(x,t)$, governed by (3.6), (3.7), and (3.8) or (3.15), which must hold throughout Π and are subject to the initial conditions

$$u_\beta(x,t) = \sigma_{\beta\gamma}(x,t) = 0, \quad T(x,t) = T_0 \text{ in } \Pi(-\infty < t \leq 0) \qquad (3.17)$$

together with the boundary conditions

$$\left.\begin{aligned}
u_\beta &= U_\beta(x,t) \text{ on } C_1 \ (0 < t < \infty), \\
\sigma_{\beta\gamma}n_\gamma &= S_\beta(x,t) \text{ on } C_2 \ (0 < t < \infty),
\end{aligned}\right\} \qquad (3.18)$$

Here n_γ stands for the components of the outward unit normal to C, while C_1, C_2 are complementary portions of C corresponding to B_1, B_2 in (2.11). The values of u_β, $\varepsilon_{\beta\gamma}$, $\sigma_{\beta\gamma}$ thus determined are to be supplemented by the values of u_3, ε_{3i}, σ_{3i} in accordance with (3.5), (3.13). The plane-strain solution reached in this manner meets all conditions of the plane problem stated earlier, except for the requirement $\sigma_{33} = 0$ on $x_3 = \pm h$, which is ordinarily violated; it is, however, the exact solution to the modified three-dimensional problem obtained by replacing the foregoing requirement on σ_{33} with $u_3 = 0$ on $x_3 = \pm h$.

We turn next to the associated *generalized plane-stress solution*, which characterizes the thickness averages of u_β, $\varepsilon_{\beta\gamma}$, $\sigma_{\beta\gamma}$ appropriate to the solution of the plane problem on the approximative assumption that

$$\sigma_{33}(x_1,x_2,x_3,t) = 0 \text{ in } D(0 < t < \infty). \qquad (3.19)$$

Let the averaged (generalized) field quantities in question be denoted by

$$\underset{\sim}{u}_\beta(x,t) = \frac{1}{2h} \int_{-h}^{h} u_\beta(x_1,x_2,x_3,t)dx_3, \text{ etc.} \qquad (3.20)$$

Further, to avoid ambiguity, suppose temporarily that $\underline{J}_1(t)$, $\underline{J}_2(t)$ and $\underset{\sim}{\Theta}(x,t)$ designate the creep moduli (at the base temperature T_0) and the pseudo-temperature, respectively.

A formal application of the foregoing averaging procedure to the field equations (2.1), (2,2), (2.16), in view of (2.3) and (3.1), (3.19), then leads to

$$\underset{\sim}{\varepsilon}_{\beta\gamma} = \frac{1}{2}\left(\frac{\partial \underset{\sim}{u}_\beta}{\partial x_\gamma} + \frac{\partial \underset{\sim}{u}_\gamma}{\partial x_\beta}\right), \qquad (3.21)$$

$$\frac{\partial \tilde{\sigma}_{\beta\gamma}}{\partial x_\gamma} + F_\gamma = 0, \tag{3.22}$$

$$\hat{\tilde{\varepsilon}}_{\beta\gamma}(x,\xi) = \int_{-\infty}^{\xi} \underline{J}_1(\xi - \xi') \frac{\partial}{\partial \xi'} \hat{\tilde{\sigma}}_{\beta\gamma}(x,\xi')d\xi' \; +$$

$$+ \delta_{\beta\gamma} \int_{-\infty}^{\xi} \underline{N}(\xi - \xi') \frac{\partial}{\partial \xi'} \hat{\tilde{\sigma}}_{\lambda\lambda}(x,\xi')d\xi' + \alpha_0 \delta_{\beta\gamma} \hat{\underline{\Theta}}(x,\xi), \tag{3.23}$$

where

$$\underline{N}(t) = \frac{1}{3}[\underline{J}_2(t) - \underline{J}_1(t)], \tag{3.24}$$

while the accompanying initial and boundary conditions take the form

$$\underline{u}_\beta(x,t) = \underline{\sigma}_{\beta\gamma}(x,t) = 0, \quad T(x,t) = T_0 \text{ in } \Pi \; (-\infty < t \leqq 0), \tag{3.25}$$

$$\left. \begin{aligned} \underline{u}_\beta &= U_\beta(x,t) \text{ on } C_1 \; (0 < t < \infty), \\ \underline{\sigma}_{\beta\gamma}n_\gamma &= S_\beta(x,t) \text{ on } C_2 \; (0 < t < \infty), \end{aligned} \right\} \tag{3.26}$$

where Π, C_1, C_2 and n_γ have the same meaning as in (3.17), (3.18). Equations (3.21) to (3.26) completely characterize the generalized plane-stress solution associated with the mixed plane problem under consideration.

A comparison of (3.6), (3.7), (3.15), (3.17), (3.18) with (3.21), (3.22), (3.23), (3.25), (3.26), by virtue of (3.16) and (3.24), permits certain conclusions concerning the connection between the plane-strain and the generalized plane-stress solutions associated with a plane problem for a given domain, given surface data and body forces, as well as given thermal properties. Thus consider a plane problem with fixed $\Pi, C_1, C_2, \; U_\beta(x,t), \; S_\beta(x,t), \; F_\beta(x,t), \; \alpha_0, \; T_0,$ sand $\varphi(T)$. Then *the field quantities* $u_\beta(x,t), \; \varepsilon_{\beta\gamma}(x,t), \; \sigma_{\beta\gamma}(x,t)$ *of the plane-strain solution coincide with the corresponding average field quantities* $\underline{u}_\beta(x,t),$ $\underline{\varepsilon}_{\beta\gamma}(x,t), \; \underline{\sigma}_{\beta\gamma}(x,t)$ *of the generalized plane-stress solution if*

$$\underline{J}_1(t) = J_1(t), \; \underline{J}_2^*(\eta) = \frac{J_1^*(\eta)[4J_2^*(\eta) - J_1^*(\eta)]}{2J_1^*(\eta) + J_2^*(\eta)} \tag{3.27}$$

$$\underline{\hat{\Theta}}(x, \xi) = \hat{\Theta}(x, \xi) + \int_{-\infty}^{\xi} \bar{v}(\xi - \xi') \frac{\partial}{\partial \xi'} \hat{\Theta}(x,\xi')d\xi'. \tag{3.28}(^8)$$

---

(8) See (2.19) for the relation between $\bar{v}(t)$ and $J_1(t), J_2(t)$.

For the special case of an elastic solid, in accordance with (2.20), we have $J_1(t) = H(t)/2\mu$, $J_2(t) = H(t)/3k$, $\underline{J}_1(t) = H(t)/2\underline{\mu}$, $\underline{J}_2(t) = H(t)/3\underline{k}$. Also, $\Theta = T - T_0$ and $\underline{\Theta} = \underline{T} - T_0$ when $\alpha(T)$ is constant. Since

$$k = \frac{2\mu(1 + v)}{3(1 - 2v)}, \qquad \underline{k} = \frac{2\underline{\mu}(1 + \underline{v})}{3(1 - 2\underline{v})} \qquad (3.29)$$

we gather readily that (3.27), (3.28) in the present circumstances reduce to

$$\underline{\mu} = \mu, \ \underline{v} = \frac{v}{1 - v}, \quad \underline{T} - T_0 = (1 + v)\,(T - T_0), \qquad (3.30)$$

in agreement with ordinary thermoelasticity theory[9]. The relations (3.27), (3.28), which are a generalization of (3.30) and establish the connection between "plane strain" and "generalized plane stress" in the linear theory of thermo-rheologically simple viscoelastic solids, are apt to be of interest also under isothermal conditions. In particular, it is worth noting from (3.27) that elastic behavior in dilatation is ordinarily not preserved in the transition from plane strain to generalized plane stress.

4. Extension of certain theorems of ordinary thermoelasticity theory.

In the present section we generalize certain theorems of classical thermoelasticity to the quasi-static linear theory of thermo-rheologically simple viscoelastic solids. In this connection we aim first at some conclusions regarding temperature distributions that fail to induce thermal stresses[10].

Returning to the three-dimensional theory summarized in Section 2, we consider once again a medium occupying a region of space D with the boundary B, which is initially undisturbed in the sense of (2.10). *Then, in the absence of body forces and surface tractions, the medium is free from stresses if and only if the temperature distribution conforms to*

$$\Theta(x,t) = \lambda_0(t) + \lambda_i(t)x_i \ \text{in} \ D\,(0 < t < \infty), \qquad (4.1)$$

where $\Theta(x,t)$ is the pseudo-temperature defined in (2.5). In case the coefficient of linear thermal expansion is constant, (4.1) is equivalent to

$$T(x,t) - T_0 = \lambda_0(t) + \lambda_i(t)x_i, \qquad (4.2)$$

---

[9] See, for example, [6], p. 762.
[10] See [5], Art. 3.9 and [7], Ch. 3 for analogous results in thermoelasticity theory.

so that in this instance the *actual* temperature field is a linear function of the cartesian coordinates with time-dependent coefficients. We now turn to the proof of the preceding assertion, which is an elementary generalization of the corresponding arguments in thermoelasticity theory.

To establish the *necessity*[11] of condition (4.1) we observe on the basis of (2.3), (2.8) that $\sigma_{ij}(x,t) \equiv 0$ implies

$$\varepsilon_{ij}(x,t) = \alpha_0 \delta_{ij} \Theta(x,t). \tag{4.3}$$

Substitution from (4.3) into the strain equations of compatibility yields

$$\gamma_{imp} \gamma_{jnq} \delta_{mn} \frac{\partial^2 \Theta}{\partial x_p \partial x_q} = 0, \tag{4.4}$$

provided γ_{ijk} are the components of the usual alternator. From (4.4) one draws readily

$$\delta_{ij} \nabla^2 \Theta - \frac{\partial^2 \Theta}{\partial x_i \partial x_j} = 0, \tag{4.5}$$

so that

$$\frac{\partial^2 \Theta}{\partial x_i \partial x_j} = 0, \tag{4.6}$$

and thus (4.1) follows.

Conversely, to demonstrate the *sufficiency* of (4.1), we assume that (4.1) holds and consider the following field of displacement, strain, and stress, defined in $D + B$ for $0 < t < \infty$:

$$\left. \begin{array}{l} u_i(x,t) = \overset{\circ}{u}_i(x,t) + \alpha_0[\lambda_0(t)x_i - \tfrac{1}{2}\lambda_i(t)x_k x_k + \lambda_k(t)x_k x_i] \\[2mm] \varepsilon_{ij}(x,t) = \alpha_0 \delta_{ij}\Theta(x,t), \quad \sigma_{ij}(x,t) = 0, \end{array} \right\} \tag{4.7}$$

where

$$\overset{\circ}{u}_i(x,t) = a_i(t) + \gamma_{ijk}\omega_j(t)x_k \tag{4.8}$$

represents a rigid displacement field. It is easily verified by direct substitution that $u_i(x,t)$, $\varepsilon_{ij}(x,t)$, and $\sigma_{ij}(x,t)$, so defined, satisfy (2.1), (2.2), (2.4), as well as the boundary conditions (2.11), provided $F_i(x,t) = S_i(x,t) = 0$ and $B = B_2$.

---

(11) An indication of this part of the proof is contained in a note by Hilton [8]. Although the deviatoric stress-strain relations used in [8] might be interpreted to include the first of (2.8), the dilatational response assumed there is highly restricted and fails to encompass the solids under present consideration. The claim that the constitutive law underlying [8] is "the most general" is clearly untenable and is, in fact, not meaningful.

Further, according to a uniqueness theorem which will be communicated elsewhere[12], there cannot exist more than one (sufficiently regular) solution of the field equations which meets the boundary conditions (2.11) and the initial conditions (2.10), if the   relaxation moduli $G_1(t)$, $G_2(t)$ are suitably restricted. This completes the proof.

The foregoing conclusions have a counterpart in the two-dimensional theory of generalized plane stress discussed in Section **3**, Thus, let the cross-sectional domain Π appropriate to a plane problem be *simply connected* and suppose that the medium is initially undisturbed. *Then the thickness averages of the stresses in the associated generalized plane-stress solution vanish identically, when the body forces and surface tractions are absent, if and only if the temperature distribution conforms to*

$$\nabla^2 \Theta(x,t) = 0 \text{ in } \Pi \ (0 < t < \infty). \tag{4.9}$$

Equation (4.9) is equivalent to the requirement that the actual temperature $T(x,t)$ be a harmonic function of the cartesian coordinates (x_1, x_2) when $\alpha(T)$ is constant.

The *necessity* of (4.9) is immediate since $\sigma_{\beta\gamma}(x,t) \equiv 0$, by virtue of (3.23), implies

$$\varepsilon_{\beta\gamma}(x,t) = \alpha_0 \delta_{\beta\gamma} \Theta(x,t), \tag{4.10}$$

so that the compatibility condition

$$\frac{\partial^2 \varepsilon_{11}}{\partial x_2^2} + \frac{\partial^2 \varepsilon_{22}}{\partial x_1^2} = 2 \frac{\partial^2 \varepsilon_{12}}{\partial x_1 \partial x_2} \tag{4.11}$$

belonging to (3.21) reduces to (4.9). Conversely, (4.9) are also *sufficient*. For, if (4.9) hold, (4.11), (3.22), (3.23), as well as the boundary conditions (3.26), are evidently met by

$$\varepsilon_{\beta\gamma}(x,t) = \alpha_0 \delta_{\beta\gamma} \Theta(x,t), \ \sigma_{\beta\gamma}(x,t) = 0 \tag{4.12}$$

in Π for $0 < t < \infty$, provided $F_\beta(x,t) = S_\beta(x,t) = 0$ and $C = C_2$. Moreover, (4.11), (3.22), (3.23), (3.26), together with the initial conditions (3.25), in the presence of suitable regularity assumptions and of appropriate restrictions

---

[12] This uniqueness theorem is an extension of results due to Breuer and Onat [9] that apply to the isothermal theory.

upon the creep moduli, uniquely determine $\underset{\sim}{\varepsilon}_{\beta\gamma}$ and $\underset{\sim}{\sigma}_{\beta\gamma}$ when Π is simply connected. The proof is now complete. In a strictly analogous manner one finds that *in the same circumstances the stresses* $\sigma_{\beta\gamma}(x,t)$ *of the associated plane-strain solution vanish identically if and only if the temperature distribution conforms to*

$$\nabla^2\left[\Theta(x,t) + \int_{-\infty}^{\xi(x,t)} \bar{v}(\xi - \xi') \frac{\partial}{\partial \xi'} \hat{\Theta}(x,\xi')d\xi'\right] = 0 \text{ in } \Pi(0 < t < \infty). \quad (4.13)$$

In this case, as is apparent from (3.13),

$$\hat{\sigma}_{33}(x,\xi) = -\alpha_0 \int_{-\infty}^{\xi} \bar{E}(\xi - \xi') \frac{\partial}{\partial \xi'} \hat{\Theta}(x,\xi')d\xi'. \quad (4.14)$$

Finally, we deduce a formula for the change in volume, due to a given surface traction, body force, and temperature distribution, of an arbitrary (not necessarily viscoelastic) solid which has a linearly elastic dilatational response and is in a state of infinitesimal deformations. If D, with the boundary B, is the region occupied by the undeformed body and ΔV designates the volume change in question, we have from (2.22), (2.3),

$$\Delta V = \int_D \varepsilon dV = \frac{1}{3k} \int_D \sigma_{ii} dV + 3\alpha_0 \int_D \Theta dV. \quad (4.15)$$

Thus and by (2.2),

$$\Delta V = \frac{1}{3k} \int_D \left[\frac{\partial}{\partial x_j}(\sigma_{ij}x_i) + F_i x_i\right]dV + 3\alpha_0 \int_D \Theta dV, \quad (4.16)$$

so that from the divergence theorem

$$\Delta V = \frac{1}{3k}\left[\int_B S_i x_i dA + \int_D F_i x_i dV\right] + 3\alpha_0 \int_D \Theta dV, \quad (4.17)$$

where S_i again denotes the components of the surface traction on B. In particular, if $S_i(x,t) = F_i(x,t) = 0$, (4.17) leads to

$$\Delta V = 3\alpha_0 \int_D \Theta dV, \quad (4.18)$$

which is a well-known result of classical thermoelasticity theory[13]. Formula (4.18) was deduced by Hieke [10] and Goodier [11] on the basis of

---

(13) See, for example, [5], Art. 9.15

alternative extensions of Betti's reciprocal theorem. The present method of derivation of (4.17) which generalizes a scheme employed by Sokolnikoff [12] (p. 395), confirms the intuitively obvious claim that (4.17), and hence (4.18), is valid regardless of the nature of the material's deviatoric response.

5. Spherical symmetry. The problem of the spherical shell.

Our current objective is to apply the general theory of Section **2** to the special case of spherical symmetry. Specifically, we seek to recover in a more systematic manner and to generalize the solution of the problem of the sphere established in [4].

Let (r,θ,ϕ) be spherical coordinates defined by

$$\left.\begin{array}{c} x_1 = r\sin\theta\cos\phi, \;\; x_2 = r\sin\theta\sin\phi, \;\; x_3 = r\cos\theta, \\[2mm] 0 \leqq r < \infty, \;\; 0 \leqq \theta \leqq \pi, \;\; 0 \leqq \phi < 2\pi \end{array}\right\} \qquad (5.1)$$

In the presence of polar symmetry about the origin $x_i = 0$, the spherical components of displacement become

$$u_r = u(r,t), \;\; u_\theta = u_\phi = 0, \qquad (5.2)$$

while the temperature field has the special form

$$T = T(r,t). \qquad (5.3)$$

Because of (5.2) the strain-displacement relations (2.1), referred to spherical coordinates, appear as

$$\varepsilon_{rr} = \frac{\partial u}{\partial r}, \, \varepsilon_{\theta\theta} = \varepsilon_{\phi\phi} = \frac{u}{r}, \, \varepsilon_{r\theta} = \varepsilon_{\theta\phi} = \varepsilon_{\phi r} = 0. \qquad (5.4)$$

From (5.4) and the stress-strain relations (2.4), by virtue of (2.3), follow the restrictions

$$\sigma_{\theta\theta} = \sigma_{\phi\phi}, \, \sigma_{r\theta} = \sigma_{\theta\phi} = \sigma_{\phi r} = 0 \qquad (5.5)$$

upon the spherical components of stress. In addition, (2.3), (2.4) yield

$$\sigma_{rr}(r,t) = \int_{-\infty}^{t} G_1(\xi - \xi') \frac{\partial}{\partial t'} \varepsilon_{rr}(r,t') dt' + \Lambda(r,t),$$

$$\sigma_{\theta\theta}(r,t) = \int_{-\infty}^{t} G_1(\xi - \xi') \frac{\partial}{\partial t'} \varepsilon_{\theta\theta}(r,t') dt' + \Lambda(r,t), \qquad (5.6)$$

where

$$\Lambda(r,t) = \frac{1}{3} \int_{-\infty}^{t} [G_2(\xi - \xi') - G_1(\xi - \xi')] \frac{\partial}{\partial t'} [\varepsilon_{rr}(r,t') + 2\varepsilon_{\theta\theta}(r,t')] dt' +$$

$$- \alpha_0 \int_{-\infty}^{t} G_2(\xi - \xi') \frac{\partial}{\partial t'} \Theta(r,t') dt'. \qquad (5.7)$$

Alternatively, (2.3), (2.8) in the present instance imply

$$\varepsilon_{rr}(r,t) = \int_{-\infty}^{t} J_1(\xi - \xi') \frac{\partial}{\partial t'} \sigma_{rr}(r,t') dt' + \Omega(r,t),$$

$$\varepsilon_{\theta\theta}(r,t) = \int_{-\infty}^{t} J_1(\xi - \xi') \frac{\partial}{\partial t'} \sigma_{\theta\theta}(r,t') dt' + \Omega(r,t), \qquad (5.8)$$

where

$$\Omega(r,t) = \frac{1}{3} \int_{-\infty}^{t} [J_2(\xi - \xi') - J_1(\xi - \xi')] \frac{\partial}{\partial t'} [\sigma_{rr}(r,t') + 2\sigma_{\theta\theta}(r,t')] dt' +$$

$$+ \alpha_0 \Theta(r,t). \qquad (5.9)$$

In view of (5.5), the stress equations of equilibrium (2.2) in spherical coordinates reduce to the single equation

$$\frac{\partial \sigma_{rr}}{\partial r} + \frac{2}{r} (\sigma_{rr} - \sigma_{\theta\theta}) = 0, \qquad (5.10)$$

if the body forces vanish. Finally, we record the compatibility condition

$$\frac{\partial \varepsilon_{\theta\theta}}{\partial r} + \frac{1}{r} (\varepsilon_{\theta\theta} - \varepsilon_{rr}) = 0 \qquad (5.11)$$

associated with (5.4).

in connection with (5.6) to (5.9) it should be noted that the reduced time ξ, because of (5.3) and (2.6), is now a function of r and t alone. Thus (2.6) are to be replaced with

$$\xi = f(r,t) = \int_0^t \varphi[T(r,t')]dt', \quad \xi' = f(r,t') \tag{5.12}$$

and

$$\left. \begin{array}{l} t = g(r,\xi), \quad t' = g(r,\xi'), \\[2mm] Q(r,t) = \hat{Q}(r,\xi) = Q[r,g(r,\xi)] \end{array} \right\} \tag{5.13}$$

take the place of (2.12), (2.14),

Upon elimination of the strains and stresses among (5.4), (5.6), and (5.10), one obtains, after elementary manipulations, the subsequent displacement equation of equilibrium in terms of the radial displacement $u(r,t)$:

$$\frac{2}{r^3} \frac{\partial}{\partial r} \int_{-\infty}^t G_1(\xi-\xi') \frac{\partial}{\partial t'} \left[r^4 \frac{\partial}{\partial r} \left(\frac{u}{r} \right) \right]_{(r,t')} dt' +$$

$$+ \frac{\partial}{\partial r} \int_{-\infty}^t G_2(\xi-\xi') \frac{\partial}{\partial t'} \left[\frac{1}{r^2} \frac{\partial}{\partial r} (r^2 u) \right]_{(r,t')} dt'$$

$$= 3\alpha_0 \frac{\partial}{\partial r} \int_{-\infty}^t G_2(\xi-\xi') \frac{\partial}{\partial t'} \Theta(r,t')dt'. \tag{5.14}$$

Similarly, the elimination of the strains and of $\sigma_{\theta\theta}$ among (5.8), (5.10), and (5.11) leads to an equation involving $\sigma_{rr}(r,t)$ alone. Writing temporarily $s(r,t)$ in place of $\sigma_{rr}(r,t)$ we thus arrive at

$$\frac{1}{r^3} \frac{\partial}{\partial r} \int_{-\infty}^t J_1(\xi-\xi') \frac{\partial}{\partial t'} \left[r^4 \frac{\partial s}{\partial r} \right]_{(r,t')} dt' +$$

$$+ 2\frac{\partial}{\partial r} \int_{-\infty}^t J_2(\xi-\xi') \frac{\partial}{\partial t'} \left[\frac{1}{r^2} \frac{\partial}{\partial r} (r^3 s) \right]_{(r,t')} dt' = -6a_0 \frac{\partial \Theta}{\partial r}. \tag{5.15}$$

Comparing (5.15) with (5.14) we observe that both u/r and s are governed by integro-differential equations of the same structure.

Equations (5.14) and (5.15) become integrable if the dilatational response of the material is purely elastic. On this assumption we may write[14]

$$G_1(t) = G(t), \qquad J_1(t) = J(t)$$
$$G_2(t) = 3kH(t), \qquad J_2(t) = \frac{1}{3k}H(t). \tag{5.16}$$

Consequently (5.14), (5.15) reduce to

$$\frac{\partial}{\partial r} \int_{-\infty}^{t} G(\xi - \xi') \frac{\partial}{\partial t'} \left[r^4 \frac{\partial}{\partial r}\left(\frac{u}{r}\right) \right]_{(r,t')} dt' + \frac{3k}{2} \frac{\partial}{\partial r}\left[r^4 \frac{\partial}{\partial r}\left(\frac{u}{r}\right) \right]$$
$$= \frac{9}{2} k\alpha_0 r^3 \frac{\partial \Theta}{\partial r}, \tag{5.17}$$

$$\frac{\partial}{\partial r} \int_{-\infty}^{t} J(\xi - \xi') \frac{\partial}{\partial t'}\left[r^4 \frac{\partial s}{\partial r} \right]_{(r,t')} dt' + \frac{2}{3k} \frac{\partial}{\partial r}\left[r^4 \frac{\partial s}{\partial r} \right] = -6\alpha_0 r^3 \frac{\partial \Theta}{\partial r}. \tag{5.18}$$

As is apparent, (5.18) passes over into (5.17) if we make the replacements indicated by

$$s(r,t) \to \frac{1}{r}u(r,t), \quad J(t) \to G(t), \quad k \to \frac{4}{9k}, \quad \alpha_0 \to -\frac{3\alpha_0 k}{4}. \tag{5.19}$$

We now turn to the problem of a spherical shell which occupies the region D characterized by $r_1 \leq r \leq r_2$ $(0 < r_1 < r_2)$. Adhering to the assumption of polar symmetry, we take the temperature field in the form (5.3) and suppose the body forces to vanish identically. The initial conditions (2.10) then appear as

$$u(r,t) = s(r,t) = \sigma_{\theta\theta}(r,t) = 0, \quad T(r,t) = T_0$$
$$(r_1 \leq r \leq r_2, \quad -\infty < t \leq 0). \tag{5.20}[15]$$

Considering first the case of given surface tractions, the boundary conditions (2.11) presently become

$$s(r_1,t) = s_1(t), \quad s(r_2,t) = s_2(t) \quad (0 < t < \infty), \tag{5.21}$$

where $s_1(t)$ and $s_2(t)$ are prescribed functions.

---

[14] Recall (2.20).
[15] Recall that $s(r, t) = \sigma_{rr}(r, t)$.

We are therefore required to solve (5.18) subject to (5.20), (5.21). Integrating (5.18) once with respect to r and setting

$$\omega(r,t) = r^4 \frac{\partial s}{\partial r}, \quad \Phi(r,t) = -6\alpha_0 \int_{r_1}^{r} \rho^3 \frac{\partial}{\partial \rho} \Theta(\rho,t)\, d\rho, \qquad 5.22$$

there results

$$\int_{-\infty}^{t} J(\xi - \xi') \frac{\partial}{\partial t'} \omega(r,t')\, dt' + \frac{2}{3k} \omega(r,t) = \Phi(r,t) + c(t), \quad (5.23)$$

in which $c(t)$ is arbitrary. Further, referring (5.23) exclusively to the reduced time ξ, and taking account of (5.12), (5.13), we reach

$$\int_{-\infty}^{\xi} J(\xi - \xi') \frac{\partial}{\partial \xi'} \hat{\omega}(r,\xi')\, d\xi' + \frac{2}{3k} \hat{\omega}(r,\xi) = \hat{\Phi}(r,\xi) + \hat{c}(r,\xi). \quad (5.24)$$

Equation (5.24) is an integral equation of Volterra's second kind for the unknown function $\hat{\omega}(r,\xi)$. Since the corresponding kernel is of the convolution type, this equation may be solved by means of the Laplace transform. Indeed, taking the transform with respect to ξ in (5.24), and using once again the notation introduced in (2.17), we obtain

$$\hat{\omega}^*(r,\xi) = \eta R^*(\eta)[\hat{\Phi}^*(r,\eta) + \hat{c}^*(r,\eta)], \qquad (5.25)$$

in which $R^*(\eta)$ is the transform of the auxiliary response function defined by

$$R(t) = \mathcal{L}^{-1}\left\{ \frac{3k}{2\eta + 3k\eta^2 J^*(\eta)}; t \right\}, \qquad (5.26)$$

$\mathcal{L}^{-1}$ denoting the inverse transform. Inverting (5.25) and referring the resulting equation to the actual time t, we find on account of (5.20), (5.23), and the first of (5.22) that for $0 < t < \infty$,

$$\frac{\partial s}{\partial r} = \frac{1}{r^4} \int_{0-}^{t} R(\xi - \xi') \frac{\partial}{\partial t'}[\Phi(r,t') + c(t')]\, dt'. \qquad (5.27)$$

Integrating (5.27) with respect to r and invoking the second boundary condition in (5.21), we are led to the following result for $s(r,t) \equiv \sigma_{rr}(r,t)$:

$$\sigma_{rr}(r,t) = \int_{r_2}^{r} \frac{1}{\rho^4} \int_{0-}^{t} R[\xi(\rho,t) - \xi(\rho,t')] \frac{\partial}{\partial t'} [\Phi(\rho,t') + c(t')] \, dt' d\rho + s_2(t).$$

$$(5.28)$$

Further, on applying the first boundary condition in (5.21), we gather that $c(t)$ must satisfy the integral equation

$$\int_{0-}^{t} K(t,t') \frac{d}{dt'} c(t') \, dt' = P(t) \quad (0 < t < \infty),$$

$$(5.29)$$

in which

$$K(t,t') = \int_{r_1}^{r_2} \frac{1}{r^4} R[\xi(r,t) - \xi(r,t')] \, dr,$$

$$P(t) = s_2(t) - s_1(t) - \int_{r_1}^{r_2} \frac{1}{r^4} \int_{0-}^{t} R[\xi(r,t) - \xi(r,t')] \frac{\partial}{\partial t'} \Phi(r,t') \, dt' dr,$$

$$(5.30)$$

The normal stress $\sigma_{rr}(r,t)$ is completely determined by (5.28), (5.12), once $R(t)$ has been found from (5.26) and $c(t)$ has been established consistent with (5.29), (5.30), (2.5), and the second of (5.22). Postponing the discussion of the determination of $R(t)$ and $c(t)$, we observe with the aid of (5.10) that

$$\sigma_{\theta\theta}(r,t) = \sigma_{rr} + \frac{r}{2} \frac{\partial \sigma_{rr}}{\partial r}.$$

$$(5.31)$$

Finally, once $\sigma_{rr}(r,t)$ and $\sigma_{\theta\theta}(r,t)$ are known, the desired radial displacement $u(r,t)$ is immediate from the second of (5.8) and (5.9), since $u(r,\theta) = r\varepsilon_{\theta\theta}(r,\theta)$ according to (5.4).

The auxiliary response function $R(t)$, introduced in (5.26), was previously encountered in [4]. It follows from (2.18), (2.19), (5.16), (5.26) that $R(t)$ admits the alternative representations

$$R(t) = \mathcal{L}^{-1} \left\{ \frac{3kG^*(\eta)}{3k + 2\eta G^*(\eta)}; t \right\}$$

$$(5.32)$$

and

$$R(t) = \frac{2E}{3} \mathcal{L}^{-1} \left\{ \frac{\bar{E}^*(\eta)}{E + (1 - 2v)\eta \bar{E}^*(\eta)}; t \right\},$$

$$(5.33)$$

where

$$E = \bar{E}(0+), \quad v = \bar{v}(0+)$$

$$(5.34)$$

Explicit formulas for $R(t)$ appropriate to the elastic solid, the Maxwell solid, and the Kelvin solid, are given in [4]. For the *elastic solid*

$$R(t) = \frac{H(t)E}{3(1-v)}. \tag{5.35}$$

The determination of $R(t)$ for an *actual* viscoelastic material was illustrated in [4] on the basis of available measurements of $\bar{E}(t)$ and v for polymethyl methacrylate. The procedure adopted in this connection turned out to be highly laborious. It involved first the construction of a convenient analytica approximation to the empirical values of $\bar{E}(t)$ from which the transform $\bar{E}^*(\eta)$ was computed. The corresponding approximate values of $R(t)$ were then found from (5.33) by means of two asymptotic inversions, one applicable to small, the other to large time values. Since then Lee and Rogers [13] have used a more economical and considerably more accurate numerical scheme for determining $R(t)$ directly from the measured values of $\bar{E}(t)$ and v. This scheme, the wider usefulness of which is also discussed in [13], rests on the observation([16]) that (5.33) is equivalent to

$$y(t) + \kappa \int_0^{t-} \left[\frac{dh}{dt}\right]_{(t-t')} y(t')dt' = h(t), \tag{5.36}$$

provided

$$y(t) = \frac{2(1-v)}{E} R(t), \quad h(t) = \frac{2\bar{E}(t)}{3E}, \quad \kappa = \frac{3(1-2v)}{4(1-v)}, \tag{5.37}$$

and relies on the step-wise numerical solution of the integral equation (5.36) which is readily accomplished on an electronic computer.

With regard to the determination of the function $c(t)$ appearing in (5.28) we note that (5.29) is a Volterra integral equation of the first kind. Because of the structure of its kernel $K(t,t')$, which is ordinarily not of the convolution type, (5.29) is amenable to an analytical treatment, based on the Laplace transform, only in exceptional circumstances. However, a numerical treatment of this integral equation by the method employed in [13] presents no difficulties.

([16]) See [13] for details.

An explicit solution of (5.29) becomes feasible if the temperature field depends on position alone. In this event we have from (5.12)

$$\xi = t\psi(r), \quad \psi(r) = \varphi[T(r)],$$ (5.38)

so that, according to (5.29), (5.30),

$$\int_{0-}^{t} \bar{K}(t - t') \frac{d}{dt'} c(t')dt' = P(t),$$ (5.39)

where

$$\bar{K}(t) = \int_{r_1}^{r_2} \frac{1}{r^4} R[t\psi(r)] \, dr.$$ (5.40)

Consequently,

$$c(t) = \int_{0-}^{t} C(t - t')P(t')dt'.$$ (5.41)

with

$$C(t) = \mathfrak{L}^{-1} \left\{ \frac{1}{\eta \bar{K}^*(\eta)}; t \right\}.$$ (5.42)

For the *elastic solid* (5.29), (5.30), (5.35) yield

$$c(t) = \frac{r_1^3 r_2^3}{r_1^3 - r_2^3} \left\{ \frac{9(1 - v)}{E} [s_1(t) - s_2(t)] + 3 \int_{r_1}^{r_2} \frac{\Phi(r,t)}{r^4} \, dr \right\},$$ (5.43)

and (5.28) is found to reduce to a well-known result in the classical theory of thermoelasticity[17].

We have so far dealt only with the case of given surface tractions, governed by the boundary conditions (5.21). If instead the surface displacements are prescribed, (5.21) give way to

$$u(r_1, t) = u_1(t), \quad u(r_2, t) = u_2(t) \quad (0 < t < \infty).$$ (5.44)[18]

---

[17] See, for example, [5], Art. 9.14.
[18] Note that $u_\beta(t)$ are at present given surface values of the radial displacement, rather than cartesian displacement components.

In these circumstances we need to solve (5.17) subject to (5.20), (5.44). It is clear from the discussion following (5.17), (5.18) that $u(r,t)/r$ in the present instance is given by the right-hand member of (5.28), provided we make the replacements (5.19) in (5.26), as well as in the second of (5.22), and write $u_\beta(t)/r_\beta$ (no sum) in place of $s_\beta(t)$. Integral representations for the associated stresses then follow readily from (5.4), (5.6), and (5.16).

The preceding problem of the spherical shell was also treated in a recent paper by Aggarwala [14], who restricted the analysis to the special case of the standard linear viscoelastic solid and supposed the surface tractions to vanish identically. In [14] the four parameters which govern the mechanical behaviour of this particular solid are assumed to be arbitrary functions of the temperature. Such an assumption is inconsistent with the temperature–time equivalence hypothesis underlying the present investigation.

Finally, consider a solid sphere of radius r_0 which, in the absence of body forces, is exposed to the temperature field (5.3) and is subjected to the surface tractions

$$s(r_0,t) \equiv \sigma_{rr}(r_0,t) = s_0(t) \quad (0 < t < \infty). \tag{5.45}$$

Further, let the medium (whose dilatational response is once again required to be elastic) be initially undisturbed in the sense of (5.20). Proceeding as in the analogous problem of the spherical shell discussed earlier, it is at once apparent that (5.22), (5.28) remain valid if we write $0, r_0, s_0(t)$ in place of $r_1, r_2, s_2(t)$ and take $c(t) = 0$. Thus, for the solid sphere,

$$\left. \begin{array}{l} \Phi(r,t) = -6\alpha_0 \int_0^r \rho^3 \, \dfrac{\partial}{\partial\rho} \, \Theta(\rho,t)d\rho, \\[20pt] \sigma_{rr}(r,t) = \int_{r_0}^r \dfrac{1}{\rho^4} \int_{0-}^t R[\xi(\rho,t) - \xi(\rho,t')]\dfrac{\partial}{\partial t'} \, \Phi(\rho,t')dt'd\rho + s_0(t), \end{array} \right\} \tag{5.46}$$

where $R(t)$ is still given by (5.26). The values of $\sigma_{\theta\theta}(r,t)$ then again follow from (5.31).

In contrast to the problem of the shell, an especially convenient representation of the associated radial displacement in the present problem follows directly from the theorem established at the end of Section **4**. Indeed, on applying (4.17) to a spherical region D, contained within and concentric with the sphere under consideration, we find at once that

$$u_r(r,t) = \frac{r}{3k}\sigma_{rr}(r,t) + \frac{3\alpha_0}{r^2}\int_0^r \rho^2\Theta(\rho,t)d\rho, \qquad (5.47)$$

from which, in particular,

$$u_r(r_0,t) = \frac{r_0}{3k}s_0(t) + \frac{3\alpha_0}{r_0^2}\int_0^{r_0}\rho^2\Theta(\rho,t)d\rho. \qquad (5.48)$$

Also, it is clear from the manner in which (5.47) has been obtained that its validity is independent of the material's deviatoric response.

The foregoing solution to the problem of the sphere, for $s_0(t) = 0$ (zero surface tractions), coincides with results deduced in [4] by considerably less direct means. Further, if the material displays Maxwell behavior in shear, this solution reduces to earlier results of Rongved [15]. In conclusion we mention that, as in the problem of the shell, (5.19) may be used to adapt the present solution to the case in which the boundary condition (5.45) is replaced with the specification of the surface displacements.

REFERENCES

[1] H. LEADERMAN, *Elastic and creep properties of filamentous materials*, Textile Foundation, Washington, D.C., (1943), 175.

[2] L. W. MORLAND AND E. H. LEE, Stress analysis for linear viscoelastic materials with temperature variation, *Transactions of the Society of Rheology*, **4**, (1960), 233.

[3] F. SCHWARZL AND A. J. STAVERMAN, Time-temperature dependence of linear viscoelastic behavior, *Journal of Applied Physics*, **23**, (1952), 838.

[4] R. MUKI AND ELI STERNBERG, On transient thermal stresses in viscoelastic materials with temperature-dependent properties, *Journal of Applied Mechanics*, **28**, (1961), 193.

[5] BRUNO A. BOLEY AND JEROME H. WEINER, *Theory of Thermal Stresses*, John Wiley and Sons, Inc., New York, (1960).

[6] R. D. MINDLIN AND M. G. SALVADORI, Analogies, *Handbook of Experimental Stress Analysis*, Edited by M. Hetényi, John Wiley and Sons, Inc., New York, (1950).

[7] E. MELAN AND H. PARKUS, *Wärmespannungen*, Springer-Verlag, Vienna, (1953).

[8] H. H. HILTON, Thermal distributions without thermal stresses in nonhomogeneous media, *Journal of Applied Mechanics*, **26**, (1959), 1, 137.

[9] S. BREUER AND E. T. ONAT, *On uniqueness in linear viscoelasticity*, Technical Report No. 23 Contract Nonr-562(20), Brown University, June 1961.

[10] M. HIEKE, Eine indirekte Bestimmung der Airyschen Fläche bei unstetigen Wärmespannungen, *Zeitschrift für Angewandte Mathematik und Mechanik*, **35**, (1955), 285.

[11] J. N. GOODIER, *Formulas for overall thermoelastic deformation*, Proceedings of the Third U.S. International Congress of Applied Mechanics, Brown University, (1958), 343.

[12]   I. S. SOKOLNIKOFF, *Mathematical Theory of Elasticity*, Second Ed., McGraw Hill
       Book Company, Inc., New York, (1956).

[13]   E. H. LEE AND T. G. ROGERS, *Solution of viscoelastic stress analysis problems using
       measured creep or relaxation functions*, Interim Technical Report No. 1, Grant DA-
       ARO(D)-31-124-G54, Brown University, August 1961.

[14]   B. D. AGGARWALA, Thermal stresses in spherical shells of viscoelastic materials,
       Zeitschrift fur Angewandte Mathematik und Mechanik, **40**, (1960), 482.

[15]   L. RONGVED, *Residual stress in glass spheres*, Technical Report No. 16, Contract Nonr
       266(09), Columbia University, July 1954.

DISCUSSION

See discussion at end of next paper by E. H. LEE AND T. G. ROGERS.

NON-LINEAR EFFECTS OF TEMPERATURE VARIATION IN STRESS ANALYSIS OF ISOTHERMALLY LINEAR VISCOELASTIC MATERIALS*

E. H. LEE AND T. G. ROGERS

Brown University, Providence, R. I., U.S.A.

ABSTRACT

The form of the equations for viscoelastic stress analysis including the influence of temperature variation is discussed. Thermo-rheologically simple material behavior is assumed, for which temperature change produces a non-linear translation of viscoelastic characteristic functions and spectra on a log-time or log-frequency plot. The advantages and disadvantages of utilizing a reduced time variable in place of real time are assessed. The equations for spherically symmetrical thermal stress fields in a solid sphere or spherical shell are presented, and expressed in the form of Volterra integral equations for the radial stress gradient. A method of numerical treatment of these for various boundary value problems with fixed or moving boundaries is presented. As a particular example the thermal stresses in a sphere of polymethyl-methacrylate are computed, when ablation of the surface at constant temperature occurs.

1. Introduction.

The effect of a change in temperature on the response to stress of certain isothermally linear viscoelastic materials is to produce a simple shift, without change of shape, of all viscoelastic characteristic functions plotted on a log (time) abscissa. Thus, for example, an increase in temperature causes a shift of the relaxation spectrum to shorter times, so that the relaxation time for every component of the spectrum is decreased in a constant ratio. Such material behavior has been termed by Schwarzl and Staverman [1], thermo-rheologically simple. In general this shift is a markedly non-linear function of the temperature, increasing rapidly as the temperature rises. Such behavior is exhibited by many polymers, and this paper is concerned with stress analysis for materials of this type.

A generalization of this property to include the effect of variation of the temperature with time was suggested by Morland and Lee [2], and is convenient-

---

* The results communicated in this paper were obtained in the course of an investigation conducted under contract Nonr 562(30) between the Office of Naval Research in Washington, D.C. and Brown University.

77

ly expressed by replacing the real time t at each material point by the reduced time ξ according to:

$$\xi(x,t) = \int_0^t \phi[T(x,t')]dt' \tag{1}$$

where x denotes the triplet of rectangular cartesian coordinates (x_1,x_2,x_3), $T(x,t)$ the temperature field, and $\phi(T)$ the exponential of the shift function of the viscoelastic characteristics on a $\log(t)$ abscissa. The integrand $\phi(T)$ in (1) introduces the variation due to temperature of the rate of relaxation, being greater than unity for T elevated above the standard temperature T_0, so that, in terms of the reduced time ξ, whatever the temperature variation, relaxation processes occur as at the standard temperature in terms of the real time t. Thus, if $G(t)$ is the relaxation modulus in shear at the standard temperature T_0, the stress deviator $s_{ij}(x,t)$ is given in terms of the strain deviator $e_{ij}(x,t)$ by the standard temperature isothermal linear viscoelastic law for an isotropic material undisturbed at $t = 0$:

$$s_{ij} = \int_0^t 2G(t-t')\frac{\partial e_{ij}}{\partial t'}dt' \tag{2}$$

in the form

$$\hat{s}_{ij}(x,\xi) = \int_0^\xi 2G(\xi-\xi')\frac{\partial \hat{e}_{ij}}{d\xi'}(x,\xi')d\xi' \tag{3}$$

Here, following Muki and Sternberg [3], $\hat{s}_{ij}$ and $\hat{e}_{ij}$ denote the stress and strain deviators as functions of position x and the reduced time ξ, which using (1) can be expressed in terms of the real time t for general temperature variation:

$$s_{ij}(x,t) = \int_0^t 2G[\xi(x,t) - \xi(x,t')]\frac{\partial e_{ij}}{\partial t'}(x,t')dt' \tag{4}$$

where $s_{ij}(x,t) \equiv \hat{s}_{ij}[x,\xi(x,t)]$, $\xi(x,t)$ being given by (1). This change of variable notation is used throughout the paper.

The integral operator form of viscoelastic law (2) has been utilized since, in general, temperature variation leads to a wide equivalent frequency band for the loading function in terms of the reduced time, and the integral operator relation naturally covers such a requirement through the range of t for which the relaxation modulus $G(t)$ is specified at standard temperature T_0. This

could be measured directly or inferred from measurements at a range of temperatures. In contrast, the commonly used low-order differential operator relations are satisfactory only over a relatively narrow frequency band, as for
example determined in [4] for polyisobutylene. With temperature differences
between parts of the viscoelstic body, the corresponding range of ξ over the
body at a given time t introduces widely varying frequencies in terms of the
reduced time ξ for a simple transient stress variation $s_{ij}(x, t)$. Thus high-
order differential operators would be needed for satisfactory material representation, with the corresponding difficulty of determining the many material
constants. Moreover, as pointed out by Muki and Sternberg [3], considering
temperature variation, the representation in terms of real time of the constitutive differential relation corresponding to the integral operator law (4)
becomes extremely complicated.

The much simpler mathematical form of (3), a convolution integral, compared with (4), suggests the use of reduced time ξ in formulating stress analysis problems. However, the equilibrium equations and the expressions for
strain components in terms of displacements are much simpler in their familiar
form based on real time. The equilibrium equations containing the stress
derivatives $\left(\dfrac{\partial \sigma_{ij}}{\partial x_j}\right)_t$ at fixed real time t take the form:

$$\left(\frac{\partial \sigma_{ij}}{\partial x_j}\right)_t + f_i = 0 \tag{5}$$

assuming the usual summation of terms for $j = 1,2,3$ associated with the
repeated index j. The change of variable in (5) from t to ξ gives:

$$\left(\frac{\partial \hat{\sigma}_{ij}}{\partial x_j}\right)_\xi + \left(\frac{\partial \hat{\sigma}_{ij}}{\partial \xi}\right)_x \left(\frac{\partial \xi}{\partial x_j}\right)_t + f_i = 0 \tag{6}$$

Similarly the representation of the infinitesimal strain components ε_{ij} in terms
of the displacement components u_i:

$$\varepsilon_{ij}(x,t) = \frac{1}{2}\left[\left(\frac{\partial u_i}{\partial x_j}\right)_t + \left(\frac{\partial u_j}{\partial x_i}\right)_t\right] \tag{7}$$

becomes:

$$\hat{\varepsilon}_{ij}(x,\xi) = \frac{1}{2}\left[\left(\frac{\partial \hat{u}_i}{\partial x_j}\right)_\xi + \left(\frac{\partial \hat{u}_i}{\partial \xi}\right)_x\left(\frac{\partial \xi}{\partial x_j}\right)_t + \left(\frac{\partial \hat{u}_j}{\partial x_i}\right)_\xi + \left(\frac{\partial \hat{u}_j}{\partial \xi}\right)_x\left(\frac{\partial \xi}{\partial x_i}\right)_t\right] \tag{8}$$

In view of the highly non-linear character of the shift function $\phi(T)$ in the definition of ξ (see eqn. (1)), (6) and (8) containing the reduced time ξ will be much more difficult to solve than the corresponding equations (5) and (7) in terms of the real time t. The choice of (3), (6) and (8) in terms of reduced time, or (4), (5) and (7) in real time has been avoided in solutions presented in the literature, by the selection of problems in which time integrals of (3) and space integrals of (5) and (7) can be evaluated separately and subsequently combined to determine the thermo-viscoelastic stress distributions. Thus the simpler forms of constitutive, equilibrium, and strain-displacement equations are all utilized. Such an example is presented in this paper.

Use of the integral operator representations (3) or (4) can reduce the stress analysis problem to the solution of integral equations as discussed by Lee and Rogers [5], in which it is shown that finite-difference numerical integration can provide a convenient and accurate method of solution. Since the kernel function $G(t)$ is determined experimentally, numerical manipulation is more directly applicable than the standard analytical approach for convolution integral equations, which is through application of the Laplace transform. Quite apart from ease of evaluation, the use of the Laplace transform, an integral from 0 to ∞ in t, limits the boundary conditions to remain of the same type at each surface point, and the shape of the body to remain unchanged with time (apart from the infinitesimal displacements associated with the strains); for otherwise the transform of boundary conditions or dependent variables at a fixed material point is not meaningful. The case of an ablating boundary, which violates this restriction but is amenable to analysis by numerical solution of integral equations, is presented below.

2.   The spherically symmetric stress field.

A body in the form of a solid sphere or spherical shell is considered, loaded uniformly over each surface and subject to a radially symmetrical temperature distribution $T(r,t)$, where r is the radius. A development based on the work of Muki and Sternberg [3], modified to include the ablating boundary problem, is presented. Symmetry determines the principal stresses to be the radial stress σ_r and the circumferential stress σ_θ repeated. The sum of the principal stresses is therefore:

$$\sigma = \sigma_r + 2\sigma_\theta \tag{9}$$

The single non-trivially satisfied equilibrium equation is:

$$\frac{\partial \sigma_r}{\partial r} + \frac{2}{r}(\sigma_r - \sigma_\theta) = 0 \tag{10}$$

Symmetry determines a single independent stress deviator component, and corresponding strain deviator component, which for convenience can be replaced by principal stress and strain differences. With $u(r,t')$ as the radial displacement, the equivalent of (3) then becomes:

$$\hat{\sigma}_\theta(r,\xi) - \hat{\sigma}_r(r,\xi) = \int_0^\xi 2G(\xi - \xi')\frac{\partial}{\partial \xi'}\left[\frac{\hat{u}}{r} - \frac{\widehat{\partial u}}{\partial r}\right]d\xi' \tag{11}$$

which, using (10), can be written in the form:

$$\frac{\widehat{\partial \sigma_r}}{\partial r} = -\int_0^\xi 4G(\xi - \xi')\frac{\partial}{\partial \xi'}\left[\widehat{\frac{\partial}{\partial r}\left(\frac{u}{r}\right)}\right]d\xi' \tag{12}$$

where $\dfrac{\widehat{\partial \sigma_r}}{\partial r}$ denotes $\left(\dfrac{\partial \sigma_r}{\partial r}\right)_t$ expressed in (r,ξ) variables through (1), and similarly for $\widehat{\dfrac{\partial}{\partial r}\left(\dfrac{u}{r}\right)}$ which is expressed in primed time variables. The term σ_θ can be eliminated from (9) and (10) to give

$$\frac{\partial}{\partial r}(r^3\sigma_r) = r^2\sigma \tag{13}$$

Elastic dilatational response is assumed, and thermal expansion with constant coefficient α, giving:

$$\sigma = 3k\left[\frac{\partial u}{\partial r} + \frac{2u}{r} - 3\alpha\Theta\right] \tag{14}$$

where k is the bulk modulus and Θ the increase in temperature over the base temperature T_0. Integration of (13) at constant real time, and substitution for σ from (14), yields

$$r^3\sigma_r(r,t) - a^3\sigma_r(a,t) = 3k[r^2u(r,t) - a^2u(a,t) - 3\alpha\int_a^r \rho^2\Theta(\rho,t)d\rho] \tag{15}$$

where $a(t)$ is a boundary radius, and substitution of u from (15) into (12) gives:

$$\frac{\widehat{\partial \sigma_r}}{\partial r} = -4\int_0^\xi G(\xi - \xi')\frac{\partial}{\partial \xi'}\left[\frac{1}{3k}\frac{\partial \sigma_r}{\partial r} + \frac{3a^3}{r^4}\left(\frac{\sigma_r(a,t')}{3k} - \frac{u(a,t')}{a}\right) +\right.$$

$$\left. + \frac{3\alpha}{r^4}\left(\int_a^r \rho^3\frac{\partial\Theta}{\partial\rho}d\rho + a^3\Theta(a)\right)\right]d\xi' \tag{16}$$

where the space derivatives and integral inside the square brackets are to be evaluated at real time t', followed by a change of variable to ξ' to form the integrand of the reduced time integral.

(16) is a Volterra integral equation of the second kind and of convlution type for $\partial\hat{\sigma}_r/\partial r$, and can be most conveniently treated using the associative property of convolutions as discussed by Tricomi [6]. Writing the convolution:

$$\int_0^\xi \phi(\xi - \xi')\psi(\xi')d\xi' \equiv \phi*\psi \tag{17}$$

(16) can be written in the form:

$$\frac{\partial\hat{\sigma}_r}{\partial r} + \frac{4}{3k} G* \frac{\partial}{\partial\xi'}\left(\frac{\partial\hat{\sigma}_r}{\partial r}\right) = -4G* \frac{\partial}{\partial\xi'}\left[\frac{3a^3}{r^4}\left(\frac{\sigma_r(a,t')}{3k} - \frac{u(a,t')}{a}\right) + \right.$$
$$\left. + \frac{3\alpha}{r^4}\left(\int_a^r \rho^3 \frac{\partial\Theta}{\partial\rho}d\rho + a^3\Theta(a)\right)\right] \tag{18}$$

It is convenient to utilize the auxiliary function $\hat{R}(\xi)$ introduced by Muki and Sternberg, which satisfies the related equation:

$$R + \frac{4}{3k} G* \frac{\partial}{\partial\xi'}(R) = 2G \tag{19}$$

Then, because of the associative property:

$$\phi*(\psi*\chi) = (\phi*\psi)*\chi$$

$$\frac{\partial\hat{\sigma}_r}{\partial r} = R* \frac{\partial}{\partial\xi'}\left[-\frac{6a^3}{r^4}\left(\frac{\sigma_r(a,t')}{3k} - \frac{u(a,t')}{a}\right) - \frac{6\alpha}{r^4}\int_a^r \rho^3 \frac{\partial\Theta}{\partial\rho}d\rho + a^3\Theta(a)\right] \tag{20}$$

will satisfy (18). $\hat{R}$ has been computed [5] for polymethylmethacrylate by the numerical finite-difference solution of (19).

To consider the case of the solid sphere, take $a = 0$, and (20) becomes:

$$\frac{\partial\hat{\sigma}_r}{\partial r} = R* \frac{\partial}{\partial\xi'}\left[-\frac{6\alpha}{r^4}\int_0^r \rho^3 \frac{\partial\Theta}{\partial\rho}d\rho\right] \tag{21}$$

As described in [5] care must be taken to take the range of integration in (21) to be 0^- to ξ^+, since the step in R at $\xi = 0$ must be included. Separating out the resulting discontinuities, and integrating by parts to obtain a more convenient form for numerical integration yields the expression:

$$\frac{\hat{\partial}\sigma_r}{\partial r} = -\frac{6\alpha}{r^4}\left[\int_{0+}^{\xi^-}\int_0^r \rho^3\frac{\partial\Theta(\rho,t')}{\partial\rho}d\rho R'(\xi-\xi')d\xi' + R(0)\int_0^r \rho^3\frac{\partial\Theta}{\partial\rho}(\rho,t)\,d\rho\right] \quad (22)$$

where $R'(\xi) \equiv \dfrac{dR(\xi)}{d\xi}$.

The temperature variation $\Theta(r,t)$ is obtained as the solution of a heat conduction problem, neglecting the coupling between heat energy and mechanical energy dissipated in viscoelastic flow. Since Θ is thus expressed in terms of real time, it is convenient to express (22) as an integral in real time:

$$\frac{\partial\sigma_r}{\partial r} = -\frac{6\alpha}{r^4}\left[\int_{0+}^{t^-}\int_0^r \rho^3\frac{\partial\Theta(\rho,t')}{\partial\rho}d\rho\, R'(\xi(r,t)-\xi(r,t'))\frac{d\xi}{dt'}(r,t')\,dt' + \right.$$

$$\left. + R(0)\int_0^r \rho^3\frac{\partial\Theta}{\partial\rho}(\rho,t)\,d\rho\right] \quad (23)$$

With $R(\xi)$ determined by numerical integration of the integral equation (19), (23) can be evaluated numerically. In terms of t, (23) is not a convolution type integral, so that it could not be evaluated by means of the Laplace transform with respect to t, but this consideration does not influence the finite-difference numerical integration procedure suggested.

We consider a solid sphere with ablating surface given by:

$$r = b(t), \quad \sigma_r(b(t),t) = f(t) \quad (24)$$

where $f(t)$ is a prescribed variation of applied pressure. Then σ_r is given by numerical integration of $\partial\sigma_r/\partial r$ evaluated from (23) for a range of r values, to yield:

$$\sigma_r(r,t) - f(t) = \int_{b(t)}^r \frac{\partial\sigma_r}{\partial\rho}(\rho,t)\,d\rho \quad (25)$$

$\sigma_\theta(r,t)$ is then given by (10). It will be observed that this approach is not influenced by the process of ablation which rules out the more common analysis through use of the Laplace transform. (23) is integrated at constant radius r, and has significance only for $t \leqq t_1$, $r = b(t_1)$, since thereafter material at this radius has been ablated. (25) is integrated at constant t, and is only meaningful for $r \leqq b(t)$, since at this time the layers beyond this radius have been removed. Both these restrictions rule out the possibility of taking a Laplace transform of the stresses since it would call for integration with respect to t over the range zero to infinity.

We next consider a hollow sphere with ablating inner radius

$$r = a(t), \ \sigma_r(a(t),t) = f_1(t) \tag{26}$$

and outer radius

$$r = b(t), \ \sigma_r(b(t),t) = f_2(t) \tag{27}$$

It is convenient to use the inner radius $a(t)$ as the integration limit $a(t)$ in (20), which then becomes:

$$\frac{\hat{\partial}\sigma_r}{\partial r} = -\frac{6\alpha}{r^4}R^* \frac{\partial}{\partial \xi'}\left[f_3(t') + \int_{a(t')}^{r} \rho^3 \frac{\partial \Theta}{\partial \rho}(\rho,t')\,d\rho + a(t')^3\Theta(a(t'),t') \right] \tag{28}$$

where:

$$f_3(t') = \frac{a(t')^3}{\alpha} \left(\frac{\sigma_r(a(t'),t')}{3k} - \frac{u(a(t'),t')}{a(t')} \right) \tag{29}$$

Note that the terms in the square brackets in (28) are to be considered transformed to functions of r and ξ before evaluation of the convolution. In numerical integration $f_3(t)$ will be determined by the boundary conditions on σ_r. For each time step $f_3(t)$ will appear as a constant in the expression (28) for $\partial \sigma_r / \partial r$ at each value of the radius. Integration of $\partial \sigma_r / \partial r$ from $a(t)$ to $b(t)$ will give:

$$\int_{a(t)}^{b(t)} \frac{\partial \sigma_r}{\partial \rho}(\rho,t)\,d\rho = f_2(t) - f_1(t) \tag{30}$$

in terms of the boundary pressures prescribed in (26) and (27). For each time increment, (30) will determine the value of the constant $f_3(t)$, so that $\partial \sigma_r / \partial r$, σ_r and σ_θ will be determined by (28), (25) and (10). For fixed boundaries, this approach is equivalent to that of Sternberg and Gurtin [7].

It is interesting to note the form of the coupling between the radius and time coordinates. (21) shows that for a solid sphere, $\partial\sigma_r/\partial r$ is determined at each radius in terms of the temperature field at this radius and inside this spherical shell, independently of the stresses at other values of r. The coupling through the radial coordinate is simply through integration of this stress gradient, and its influence on σ_θ through (10). However, for a hollow sphere a more involved coupling arises through the function $f_3(t)$ which appears in the expressions for the radial stress gradient at all values of the radius. (30) is then an integral equation for determining $f_3(t)$ which can be simply treated in the numerical finite difference solution utilized, as described above.

3. Thermal stresses in an ablating solid sphere.

As an example of the theory discussed in the previous section, the thermal stresses in a solid sphere ablating with constant surface tempeiature and zero external pressure, are presented below. Polymethyl-methacrylate material behavior is assumed, so that the auxiliary function $R(\xi)$, defined by (19) and evaluated in [5], can be utilized.

Since we wish to present a meaningful example without excessive computation we select as simple a temperature field as we could devise, appropriate to the ablation problem. A somewhat artificial, but suitable, solution of the heat conduction equation is obtained by turning to the correspondence between heat flow in a slab and spherically symmetrical flow ([8] p. 286).

$$u(r,t) = r\Theta(r,t) \tag{31}$$

will satisfy the slab heat conduction equation, with r representing depth in the slab, so that Θ can be determined in the form

$$\Theta(r,t) = u(r,t)/r \tag{32}$$

The initial slab temperature field shown in Figure 1, leads to a temperature variation $u(r,t)$ which will eventually approach $2\Theta_1 r$. At $t = 0^+$, the slab temperature at $r = b$ will be $b\Theta_1$, and $u(r,t) = r\Theta_1$ will give a curve

$$r = b(t), \; b(0) = b \tag{33}$$

On this curve:

$$\Theta(r,t) = u(r,t)/r = \Theta_1 \tag{34}$$

and this can serve as an ablating boundary at constant temperature for the spherical analogue. The temperature variation for the sphere based on the initial slab distribution shown in Figure 1 is given by:

$$\Theta(r,t) = \frac{2\Theta_1}{r}\sqrt{\frac{\kappa t}{\pi}}\left(e^{-\frac{(b-r)^2}{4\kappa t}} - e^{-\frac{(b+r)^2}{4\kappa t}}\right) +$$

$$+ \Theta_1\left(\text{erfc}\,\frac{b-r}{2\sqrt{\kappa t}} + \text{erfc}\,\frac{b+r}{2\sqrt{\kappa t}}\right) \tag{35}$$

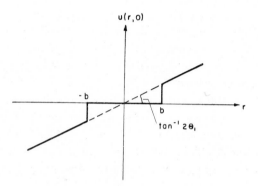

Figure 1
Initial slab temperature distribution

where κ is the diffusivity. Figure 2 shows the resulting boundary motion. The boundary ablation velocity is approximately constant at first, but gradually increases as the centre is approached, until the velocity approaches infinity as the radius reduces to zero. Figure 3 shows the resulting temperature distribution in the sphere, $r \leqq b(t)$, for four values of the time. For $t = 0^+$, the outer skin only is heated, but as the ablating boundary moves in, the temperature rises throughout the sphere and finally approaches the constant value Θ_1.

Although Θ_1 is unrestricted for the solution of the linear heat conduction problem, a particular value must be selected for the computation of the viscoelastic response through the shift function $\phi(T)$ and auxiliary function $R(\xi)$.

The temperature range used by Muki and Sternberg [3] was adopted: $\Theta_1 = 30°C$ with a base temperature of $80°C$.

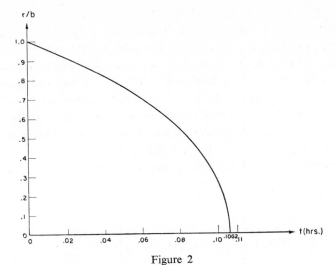

Figure 2

Position of ablating boundary plotted against time

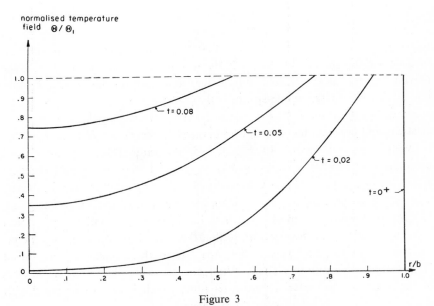

Figure 3

Temperature variations in the ablating sphere

The thermal stresses $\sigma_r(r,t)$ and $\sigma_\theta(r,t)$ are determined by numerical integration of the relations presented in the previous section: (23) and (25), and substitution into (10). Simpson's rule was used for the integrations over r, apart from the increments adjacent to the limits for which the trapezoidal rule was employed. Steps of $\Delta s = \Delta r/b = 0.05$ were found satisfactory, since doubling this step changed the stress magnitudes computed by only a few per cent. Integration of (23) with respect to time was carried out by replacing it by a finite sum, as for the similar expression in the integration of the integral equation for $R(\xi)$ in [5]. For the interval (t_n, t_{n+1}) a mean value expression for the space integral was used, the remainder comprising an increment of R as follows:

$$
\frac{\partial \sigma_r}{\partial r} = \frac{6\alpha}{r^4} \left\{ - R(0) \int_0^r \rho^3 \frac{\partial \Theta}{\partial \rho}(\rho,t)d\rho + \sum_1^{j-1} \frac{1}{2} \left[\int_0^r \rho^3 \frac{\partial \Theta}{\partial \rho} (\rho, t_n) \, d\rho \right. \right.
$$

$$
\left. + \int_0^r \rho^3 \frac{\partial \Theta}{\partial \rho} (\rho, t_{n+1}) \, d\rho \right]
$$

$$
\times \left[R(\xi(r,t) - \xi(r,t_{n+1})) - R(\xi(r,t) - \xi(r,t_n)) \right] \right\} \tag{36}
$$

where $t_1 = 0$ and $t_j = t$. For $b^2/\kappa = 0.5$, the value selected for the present problem, a step length of $\Delta t = .02b^2/\kappa$ was found to be satisfactory, since halving this for $\Delta r = 0.1b$ had only a small influence on the results. The annihilation time for the whole sphere is $0.2125\, b^2/\kappa$.

Selection of a value for b^2/κ relates the time effects associated with viscoelasticity and heat conduction, and the choice of 0.5 gives a significant coupling between these influences. For $b^2/\kappa \ll 0.5$, the rate of heat diffusion, and corresponding rate of ablation, would be so rapid that the viscoelastic characteristics of the material would have insufficient time to influence the stresses, and the material would deform essentially elastically. On the other hand, $b^2/\kappa \gg 0.5$ determines an ablation time longer than the dominant relaxation time characteristics of the material, so that thermal relaxation stresses will continuously relax to small magnitudes, apart from the influence of the initial temperature discontinuity. These initial stresses will relax away in a time of the order of the material relaxation time, which is small compared with the total duration considered in the problem.

The solution obtained for prescribed b^2/κ will formally apply for a range of spheres of varying b and κ, but fixed viscoelastic material characteristics. This arises since in all such spheres the temperature variation at a prescribed dimensionless radius $s = r/b$ will be identical. In [3] κ for polymethyl-methacrylate is given as 8 cm²/hr, which determines $b = 2$ cms for the present problem.

Figures 4a, b, c and d show the distributions of σ_r and σ_θ at four times. The normalised stress plotted is defined as $\sigma/6\alpha E\Theta_1$ where σ denotes σ_r and σ_θ, and E is the instantaneous elastic Young's modulus. The full lines show the solutions for polymethyl-methacrylate using the $R(\xi)$ evaluated in [5] from experimental relaxation measurements. The broken lines were evaluated by substituting:

$$R(\xi) = R(0) = 0.51282$$

and thus correspond to an elastic body with the properties of polymethyl-methacrylate for instantaneous loading.

Figure 4a for $t = 0^+$ shows the situation immediately after the surface skin has been raised to the temperature Θ_1, before any appreciable conduction of heat into the sphere has taken place. The heated skin is constrained from expanding by the body of the sphere at the base temperature, and a compressive circumferential thermal stress results of normalized magnitude -0.2564. Because the skin has infinitesimal thickness at $t = 0^+$, the thermal stress in it produces only infinitesimal stresses in the rest of the sphere.

Figure 4b shows the stress distributions at $t=0.02$ hrs. The circumferential compressive stress region has spread ahead of the ablating boundary with the diffusion of heat into the sphere. This now results in tensile hoop stresses towards the centre, and a field of radial tensile stress. The maximum hoop compressive stress occurs some distance ahead of the ablating boundary, because the higher temperature near the surface leads to more rapid relaxation of stress there in view of the influence of temperature on viscoelasticity. This latter effect does not arise for the elastic solution which gives maximum thermal stress at the surface where the temperature is also a maximum. In general the stresses in the elastic case are larger, because no relaxation occurs. For $t=0^+$, Figure 4a, the two solutions are identical, since only instantaneous elastic response of the viscoelastic material occurs.

At $t=0.05$ hrs., Figure 4c, increased relaxation due to viscoelastic material response has occurred. The thermal stresses for the elastic problem have also decreased due to the influence of heat conduction in smoothing out the temperature field, as illustrated in Figure 3.

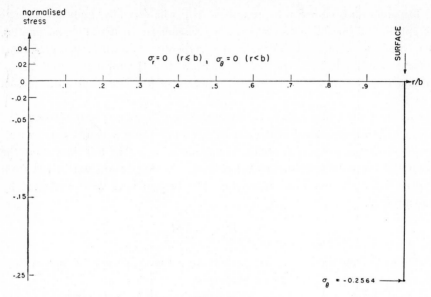

Figure 4a
Stress distribution at $t = 0^+$

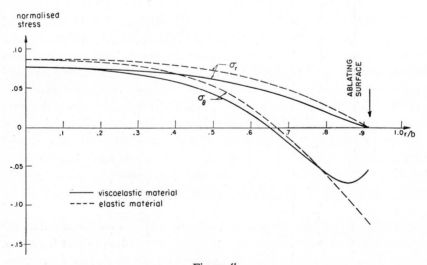

Figure 4b
Stress distribution at $t = 0.02$ hrs.

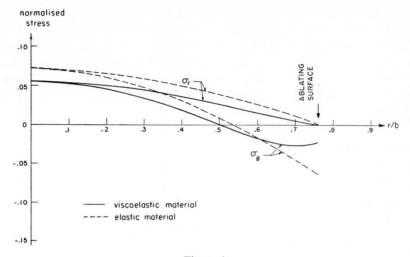

Figure 4c
Stress distribution at $t = 0.05$ hrs.

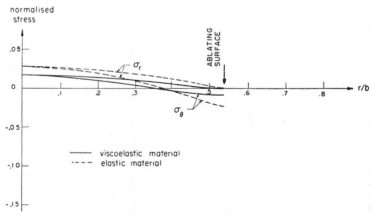

Figure 4d
Stress distribution at $t = 0.08$ hrs.

At $t=0.08$, when ablation has reduced the radius to about half its initial value, the viscoelastic thermal stresses have fallen to low magnitudes, with the corresponding elastic stresses of about twice this magnitude.

The solution presented in Figure 4 illustrates the application of the integral operator representation of viscoelastic response to a problem with non-linear temperature influence, and a time varying body geometry due to ablation of the surface. The details of the numerical treatment illustrate the convenience of this approach, and the theory presented indicates the applicability to a broader range of problems which fall outside previously published analytical approaches.

Acknowledgment.

The authors wish to acknowledge the valuable assistance rendered by the Staff of the Brown University Computing Laboratory in programming and carrying out the computations presented in this paper.

REFERENCES

[1]　F. SCHWARZL AND A. J. STAVERMAN, *J. Appl. Phys.*, **23,** (1952), 838.

[2]　L. W. MORLAND AND E. H. LEE, *Trans. Soc. of Rheology*, **4,** (1960), 233.

[3]　R. MUKI AND E. STERNBERG, *J. Appl. Mech.*, **28,** (1961), 193.

[4]　D. R. BLAND AND E. H. LEE, *J. Appl. Mech.*, **23,** (1956), 416.

[5]　E. H. LEE AND T. G. ROGERS, Brown University Technical Report DA-G-54/1, (1961), To appear in *J. Appl. Mech.*

[6]　F. G. TRICOMI, *Integral Equations*, Interscience Publishers, Inc., New York, (1957).

[7]　E. STERNBERG AND M. E. GURTIN, Brown University Technical Report 562 (30)/2 to be presented at this Symposium.

[8]　H. S. CARSLAW AND J. C. JAEGER, *Conduction of Heat in Solids*, Clarendon Press, Oxford (1947).

DISCUSSION

E. H. LEE AND E. STERNBERG replied to comments by B. D. COLEMAN AND R. S. RIVLIN:

We do not know of any quantitative measurements of the effect of strain on thermal conductivity. However, such an effect can hardly be appreciably compared with the major influence of the temperature dependence of viscoelastic properties demonstrated in the two papers. The suggestion by Professor Rivlin that highly filled materials are most likely to exhibit such a strain sensitive conductivity, means that such a complication is not likely to arise with the present theory, since highly filled materials are not likely to obey an isothermally linear viscoelastic relation with a temperature dependent shift function.

ON SHOCK WAVES IN HYPERELASTIC MEDIA

D. R. BLAND

Department of Mathematics, University of Manchester, U.K.

ABSTRACT

This paper considers the propagation of plane surfaces, across which one or more components of stress are discontinuous, through hyperelastic media. Thermal effects are included; compressible and incompressible materials are treated separately. Possible types of shock in particular media are investigated and, for shocks of small amplitude, a detailed study is made of whether or not the necessary condition of non-negative entropy change is satisfied.

1. Introduction.

Shock waves in compressible hyperelastic media have been considered in four notes by Jougert [1], of which the last two include entropy change. He derives the condition that the entropy change is at least third order in the displacement gradient for small shocks and finds the leading term for the entropy change.

This paper amplifies Jougert's results and extends the theory to include incompressible hyperelastic media. I have found it more convenient to present a uniform treatment for both types of media rather than continually refer back to Jougert's work for the compressible case. The governing equations are given in section 2 and simplified in section 3. Section 4 considers the types of shock that may occur in isotropic materials, section 5 the two types of small shocks in compressible isotropic media and section 6 the one type in incompressible media. Section 7 discusses the value of the isentropic approximation.

2. Foundations.

I define a compressible hyperelastic material as a material for which i) the six independent components γ_{ij} of the Green strain tensor and the temperature T form a complete and independent set of variables of state and for which ii) any state can be reached from any other state by a reversible path. The definition of an incompressible hyperelastic material is identical except that the γ_{ij} must satisfy the condition of incompressibility, namely $|\delta_{ij} + 2\gamma_{ij}| = 1$. The material is assumed to be homogeneous throughout this paper.

93

The work done per unit mass by the external forces acting on the material in any small reversible change is[1] $\delta W = \rho_0^{-1} K_{ij} d\gamma_{ij} + \delta K$ where ρ_0 is the density in the natural state, K_{ij} the components of the Kirchhoff stress tensor and δK the increase in kinetic energy. The first two laws of thermodynamics state that there exist functions of state, the internal energy U and the entropy S such that $dU = \delta Q + \delta W - \delta K$ and $T dS \geqq \delta Q$, the equality in this last relation holding only for reversible changes. It follows that, for reversible changes, $dU = T dS + \bar{\rho}_0^{1} K_{ij} d\gamma_{ij}$. But U, S and γ_{ij} are variables of state and therefore the last equation is true for all small changes, reversible or irreversible.

Since S is a variable of state, $S = S(T, \gamma_{ij})$; hence $T = T(S, \gamma_{ij})$ and we may take, when convenient, S and the γ_{ij} as our basic variables of state. It follows that $U = U(S, \gamma_{ij})$ and

$$dU = \frac{\partial U}{\partial S} dS + \frac{\partial U}{\partial \gamma_{ij}} d\gamma_{ij}.$$

For a compressible material S and the γ_{ij} are independent, therefore

$$T = \frac{\partial U}{\partial S} \quad \text{and} \quad K_{ij} = \rho_0 \frac{\partial U}{\partial \gamma_{ij}}. \tag{1}$$

If a_i and x_i are the initial and current coordinates of a particle, referred to rectangular Cartesian axes fixed in space, then for an incompressible material[2]

$$\frac{\partial a_i}{\partial x_r} \frac{\partial a_j}{\partial x_r} d\gamma_{ij} = 0.$$

Hence

$$T = \frac{\partial U}{\partial S} \quad \text{and} \quad K_{ij} = \rho_0 \frac{\partial U}{\partial \gamma_{ij}} - p \frac{\partial a_i}{\partial x_r} \frac{\partial a_j}{\partial x_r}, \tag{2}$$

where p is an arbitrary scalar parameter. A negative sign is placed before p in equation (2) so that the term can be interpreted as a hydrostatic pressure p.

We consider a plane surface of discontinuity moving through a hyperelastic media. The axes are orientated so that the normal to the surface, taken in the sense from behind the surface to in front, is in the direction of the positive 1-axis. Restrict consideration to cases where the displacements of particles at

---

[1] See e.g. reference [2], chapter 9, eqn. (4.10).
[2] reference [2], chapter 10, eqn. (3.2).

any time are of the form $u_i = x_i - a_i = u_i(a_1, t)$. Rayleigh-type waves are examples of waves excluded by this form for the u_i. The current density ρ is given by

$$\rho_0 = \rho J \begin{pmatrix} x_1 & x_2 & x_3 \\ a_1 & a_2 & a_3 \end{pmatrix} = \rho(1 + m_1), \tag{3}$$

where $m_i = \dfrac{\partial u_i}{\partial a_1}$. $\tag{4}$

Let the surface be across particles a_1 with 1-coordinate x_1 at time t and across particles $a_1 + \delta a_1$ with 1-coordinate $x_1 + \delta x_1$ at time $t + \delta t$, then V_a and V_s are defined by

$$V_a = \lim_{\delta t \to 0} \frac{\delta a_1}{\delta t} \quad \text{and} \quad V_s = \lim_{\delta t \to 0} \frac{\delta x_1}{\delta t}. \tag{5}$$

V_s is the velocity of the surface with respect to axes fixed in space. Let positive and negative suffixes denote values of quantities just ahead of and just behind the surface of discontinuity respectively and let $[f] = f_- - f_+$, $\tag{6}$ the jump in f due to the passage of the surface. Then, since $x_1 = x_1(a_1, t)$,

$$V_s = \left(\frac{\partial x_1}{\partial a_1}\right)_t V_a + \left(\frac{\partial x_1}{\partial t}\right)_{a_1}$$

or

$$V_s = (1 + m_{1+})V_a + v_{1+} = (1 + m_{1-})V_a + v_{1-}, \tag{7}$$

the positive suffixes occurring when the derivatives are evaluated just ahead of the wavefront, the negative just behind. v_i is the material velocity, i.e. the time derivative of x_i or u_i at constant a_i. Note that for motion into a media at rest in its natural state, $m_{1+} = v_{1+} = 0$ and $V_s = V_a$. In this case V will be used to denote either V_s or V_a.

For material continuity the displacement u_i must be continuous everywhere. The lowest order discontinuities that can occur across the surface of discontinuity are in the time and spacial derivatives of the components of displacement. Such discontinuities imply discontinuities in the components of stress. In these circumstances the surface, provided it is moving, is referred to as a 'shock wave'[3].

---

[3] If the discontinuities are in the second derivatives of the components of displacement the first being continuous, the discontinuities are called 'acceleration waves' [3, 4].

Since the shock wave is of zero thickness, the jumps across the shock surface take place instantaneously with no loss or gain of heat from the surrounding material. The equations of momentum and of energy, the kinematic condition and the entropy condition are[4]

$$[\sigma_{i1}] = -\rho_0 V_a[v_i],\tag{8}$$

$$-[\sigma_{i1}\, v_i] = \tfrac{1}{2}\rho_0 V_a[v_i{}^2] + \rho_0 V_a[U],\tag{9}$$

$$[v_i] + V_a[m_i] = 0\tag{10}$$

and $$[S] \geqq 0,\tag{11}$$

where σ_{ij} is the Eulerian stress tensor. When $u_i = u_i(a_1,t)$ the relations between the σ_{ij} and the K_{ij} are

$$\sigma_{ij} = (1 + m_1)^{-1} (K_{ij} + m_j K_{i1} + m_i K_{j1} + m_i m_j K_{11}),\tag{12}$$

in particular $\sigma_{i1} = K_{i1} + m_i K_{11},\tag{13}$

and the components of the Green strain tensor are given by

$$\gamma_{11} = m_1 + \tfrac{1}{2}m_i{}^2,\ \gamma_{12} = \tfrac{1}{2}m_2,\ \gamma_{13} = \tfrac{1}{2}m_3,\ \gamma_{22} = \gamma_{33} = \gamma_{23} = 0.\tag{14}$$

3. Simplification of the equations.

If we introduce $\partial U/\partial m_i$, defined by

$$\frac{\partial U}{\partial m_i} = \frac{\partial U}{\partial \gamma_{jk}} \frac{\partial \gamma_{jk}}{\partial m_i},\tag{15}$$

then substitution from equations (14) gives

$$\frac{\partial U}{\partial m_i} = \frac{\partial U}{\partial \gamma_{i1}} + m_i \frac{\partial U}{\partial \gamma_{11}}.\tag{16}$$

For compressible materials substitute in equation (13) from equations (1) and (16):

$$\sigma_{i1} = \rho_0 \frac{\partial U}{\partial m_i}.\tag{17}$$

---

[4] The standard reference is [5].

Eliminate $[\sigma_{i1}]$ and $[v_i]$ between equations (8), (10) and (17),

$$\left[\frac{\partial U}{\partial m_i}\right] = V_a^2\left[\, m_i \,\right].$$ (18)

The energy equation (9) can be written

$$-[\sigma_{i1}][v_i] - v_{i+}[\sigma_{i1}] - \sigma_{i1+}[v_i] = \tfrac{1}{2}\rho_0 V_a[v_i^2] + \rho_0 V_a v_{i+}[v_i] + \rho_0 V_a[U].$$ (19)

On substitution from equations (8) and (10),

$$\tfrac{1}{2}V_a^2[m_i]^2 + \rho_0^{-1}\sigma_{i1+}[m_i] = [U].$$ (20)

The three equations (18), equation (20) and $U = U(m_i, S)$ are five equations for the six unknowns m_{i-}, V_a, U_- and S_-; the conditions ahead of the shock are assumed to be known. Since there is one more unknown than equation the solutions contain one parameter, which is a measure of the strength of the shock.

If the shock is propagating into a media at rest in its natural state, $S_+ = m_{i+} = U_+ = \sigma_{i1+} = 0$ and equations (18) and (19) can be written

$$\frac{\partial U}{\partial m_i} = V^2 m_i$$ (21)

and

$$2U = V^2 m_i^2,$$ (22)

where all variables are to be evaluated just behind the shock front.

For incompressible materials, from equation (3), $m_1 = 0$ everywhere. From equations (8), (10) and (13) with $i = 1$, $[v_1] = [\sigma_{11}] = [K_{11}] = 0$. When $m_1 = 0$,

$$\frac{\partial a_i}{\partial x_r}\frac{\partial a_j}{\partial x_r} = \delta_{ij} - m_i\delta_{ij} - m_j\delta_{1i} + m_i m_j.$$ (23)

From equations (2) and (23),

$$K_{11} = \rho_0 \frac{\partial U}{\partial \gamma_{11}} - p$$

whence

$$[p] = \rho_0\left[\frac{\partial U}{\partial \gamma_{11}}\right],$$ (24)

and
$$K_{i1} = \rho_0 \frac{\partial U}{\partial \gamma_{i1}} + m_i p, \quad i = 2 \text{ or } 3.$$

From equation (13) and (16),

$$\sigma_{i1} = \rho_0 \frac{\partial U}{\partial m_i}, \quad i = 2 \text{ or } 3. \tag{25}$$

Except for the range of the suffix, equation (25) is identical with equation (17). Equations (18), (20), (21) and (22) are therefore valid for incompressible as well as for compressible materials, the only difference being that

whereas
$$\left.\begin{array}{l} i = 1, 2 \text{ or } 3 \text{ for compressible materials} \\ i = 2 \text{ or } 3 \text{ only for incompressible materials.} \end{array}\right\} \tag{26}$$

4. Possible shocks in particular media.

Let us first investigate whether purely dilatational shocks, $[m_2] = [m_3] = 0$, can propagate in particular compressible media. Assuming a shock of some sort propagates, the axes can always be rotated about the 1-direction so that $[m_3] = 0$. Then by equation (18), $[\partial U/\partial m_3] = 0$. If U and the state of the media ahead of the shock is symmetrical with respect to the directions 2 and 3, then, because $[m_3] = [\partial U/\partial m_3] = 0$ satisfies equation (18) with $i = 3$, $[m_2] = [\partial u/\partial m_2] = 0$ are possible solutions for $i = 2$. In these circumstances a dilatational shock satisfying

$$\left[\frac{\partial U}{\partial m_1}\right] = V_a^2 [m_1] \tag{27}$$

and

$$\tfrac{1}{2} V_a^2 [m_1]^2 + \rho_0^{-1} \sigma_{11+} [m_1] = [U] \tag{28}$$

may propagate. In particular cases it must be verified that V_a^2 is positive and that $[S] > 0$ for the shock to exist.

Now consider non-dilatational shocks propagating into a compressible media at rest in its natural state. A necessary existence condition is from equation (21) with $i = 1$, that $\partial U/\partial m_1 = 0$ when $m_1 = 0$. For isotropic media

$$\frac{\partial U}{\partial m_1} = \sum_{l=1}^{3} \frac{\partial U}{\partial I^{(l)}} \frac{\partial I^{(l)}}{\partial \gamma_{jk}} \frac{\partial \gamma_{jk}}{\partial m_1},$$

where the $I^{(l)}$ are any three independent invariants of γ_{ij}. Choosing

$$I^{(1)} = \gamma_{ii}, \; I^{(2)} = \gamma_{ij}\gamma_{ij} = \text{and } I^{(3)} = \gamma_{ij}\gamma_{jk}\gamma_{ki}, \tag{29}$$

$$\frac{\partial U}{\partial m_1} = (1+m_1)\left(\frac{\partial U}{\partial I^{(1)}} + 2(m_1 + \tfrac{1}{2}m_i^2)\frac{\partial U}{\partial I^{(2)}} + 3\{(m_1 + \tfrac{1}{2}m_i^2)^2 + \tfrac{1}{4}m_2^2 + \tfrac{1}{4}m_3^2\}\frac{\partial U}{\partial I^{(3)}}\right).$$
$$\tag{30}$$

For $\partial U/\partial m_1$ to be zero when $m_1 = 0$ for arbitrary m_i^2, $\partial U/\partial I^{(1)} = \partial U/\partial I^{(2)} = \partial U/\partial I^{(3)} = 0$ when $m_1 = 0$ and $m_i^2 \neq 0$. This implies U is constant and we no longer have a hyperelastic material. We therefore conclude that non-dilatational shocks cannot propagate into a compressible isotropic media at rest in its natural state.

The considerations of the last paragraph do not apply to shocks, necessarily non-dilatational, in incompressible media because equation (21) no longer holds for $i = 1$; the corresponding equation is equation (24) which determines the jump in p. For incompressible media the axes can again be orientated so that $[u_3] = 0$. Then $[\partial U/\partial m_3] = 0$. The shock satisfies

$$\left[\frac{\partial U}{\partial m_2}\right] = V_a^2 [m_2] \tag{31}$$

and

$$\tfrac{1}{2} V_a^2 [m_2]^2 + \rho_0^{-1} \sigma_{21+}[m_2] = [U]. \tag{32}$$

Note the formal resemblance of equations (31) and (32) to equations (27) and (28).

In the isentropic classical elasticity theory, U is a homogeneous quadratic in the m_i and equations (18) reduce to $A_{ij}[m_j] = V_a^2[m_i]$ with $A_{ij} = A_{ji}$. If the eigen-values are distinct, then there are only three eigen-vectors $[m_i]$. For the more general hyperelastic media, it is therefore to be expected that $[m_i]$ will only have a prescribed direction in certain special cases.

5.   Shocks of small amplitude in compressible media.

In the rest of this paper, it is assumed that U can be expanded as a generalised Taylor series in the γ_{ij} and S; attention will be confined to isotropic materials and to shocks propagating into a media at rest in its natural state. In the natural state we take $U = S = 0$, $T = T_0$, $\gamma_{ij} = K_{ij} = 0$. Then for compressible isotropic materials, using equations (1),

$$U = T_0 S + \lambda \gamma_{ii}^2 + \mu \gamma_{ij} \gamma_{ij} + \eta S^2 + \kappa S \gamma_{ii} + \text{third and higher order terms.} \qquad (33)$$

The deviatoric strain tensor γ'_{ij} is defined by

$$\gamma'_{ij} = \gamma_{ij} - \tfrac{1}{3} \gamma_{kk} \delta_{ij}, \qquad (34)$$

whence

$$U = T_0 S + (\lambda + \tfrac{1}{3}\mu)\gamma_{ii}^2 + \mu \gamma'_{ij} \gamma'_{ij} + \eta S^2 + \kappa S \gamma_{ii} + 0(S,\gamma_{ij})^3. \qquad (35)$$

If the media is deformed isentropically from its natural state $\delta W > 0$. Hence $U > 0$ for $S = 0$ for all small γ_{ij}. Since γ_{ii} and $\gamma'_{ij}\gamma'_{ij}$ can be varied independently this implies

$$\lambda + \tfrac{1}{3}\mu > 0 \quad \text{and} \quad \mu > 0. \qquad (36)$$

If the media is heated from its natural state under no external force, the temperature rises and the body expands or contracts uniformly, i.e. $T > 0$ and $\gamma_{ij} = \Delta \delta_{ij}$ when $S > 0$ and $K_{ij} = \partial U/\partial \gamma_{ij} = 0$ for small Δ. $K_{ij} = 0$ gives $\kappa S = -(6\lambda + 2\mu)\Delta$ and $T - T_0 = \{2\eta - 3\kappa^2(6\lambda + 2\mu)^{-1}\}S$.

Hence

$$\eta > \kappa^2 \{4(\lambda + \tfrac{1}{3}\mu)\}^{-1} \qquad (37)$$

and $\kappa < 0$ or $\kappa > 0$ according as the media expands or contracts on heating.

We first find the order of the entropy increase for shocks of small amplitude. Multiply equation (21) by m_i and subtract equation (22):

$$m_i \frac{\partial U}{\partial m_i} - 2U = 0. \qquad (38)$$

Since $S \to 0$ as $|m_i| \to 0$, $T_0 S$ is of lower order in $|m_i|$ than any other term containing S in both U and $m_i(\partial U/\partial m_i)$. The first approximation to $2T_0 S$ is therefore given by the lowest order terms in $m_i(\partial U^*/\partial m_i) - 2U^*$ which are non-zero, where $U^* = U(S = 0)$. If U_n^* denotes the terms of degree n in m_i in the series for U^*, then $U_1^* = 0$ and, by Euler's theorem for homogeneous functions

$$m_i \frac{\partial U^*}{\partial m_i} - 2U^* = \sum_{n=3}^{\infty} (n-2)U_n^*. \tag{39}$$

Terms of degree n in m_i are of order $\geq n$ in $|m_i|$. The inequality can arise when the components m_1, m_2 and m_3 are not of the same order. Hence

$$S = 0(|m_i|^N) \text{ where } N \geq 3 \text{ as } |m_i| \to 0, \tag{40}$$

and the first approximation to $2T_0S$ is given by the lowest order terms on the right-hand side of equation (39). A necessary condition for the shock to exist physically is that the sum of these terms is non-negative.

Now consider dilatational shocks. Correct to third order in $|m_i|$, equation (33) gives

$$U = T_0S + \lambda\gamma_{ii}^2 + \mu\gamma_{ij}\gamma_{ij} + \alpha\gamma_{ii}^3 + \beta\gamma_{ii}\gamma_{jk}\gamma_{kj} + v\gamma_{ij}\gamma_{jk}\gamma_{ki}. \tag{41}$$

For a dilatational shock, $\gamma_{11} = m_1 + \frac{1}{2}m_1^2$, all other $\gamma_{ij} = 0$.

$$\therefore U = T_0S + (\lambda + \mu)m_1^2 + (\lambda + \mu + \alpha + \beta + v)m_1^3 + 0(m_1^4).$$

Hence

$$2T_0S = (\lambda + \mu + \alpha + \beta + v)m_1^3 + 0(m_1^4). \tag{42}$$

By equation (27),

$$\left.\begin{array}{l}
V = \left(\dfrac{1}{m_1}\dfrac{\partial U}{\partial m_1}\right)^{\frac{1}{2}} = (2(\lambda + \mu) + 3(\lambda + \mu + \alpha + \beta + v)m_1 + 0(m_1^2))^{\frac{1}{2}} \\[3mm]
V = (2(\lambda + \mu))^{\frac{1}{2}}(1 + \frac{3}{4}(\lambda + \mu + \alpha + \beta + v)(\lambda + \mu)^{-1}m_1 + 0(m_1^2)) \\[3mm]
\text{or} \\[2mm]
V = (2(\lambda + \mu))^{\frac{1}{2}}\left(1 + \dfrac{3T_0S}{2(\lambda + \mu)m_1^2} + 0(m_1^2)\right)
\end{array}\right\} \tag{43}$$

Conditions (36) ensure that V is real. If $\lambda + \mu + \alpha + \beta + v > 0, S > 0$ when $m_1 > 0$, i.e. for shocks producing expansion, and $S < 0$ for shocks producing compression; hence only expanding shocks are physically permissible and, for these shocks, equations (42) and (43) show that the shock velocity increases with amplitude. If $\lambda + \mu + \alpha + \beta + v < 0$, then it is the compressive shock which is physically possible. The material velocity and stress behind the shock are given in terms of m_1 by substitution in equations (10) and (8). If $\lambda + \mu + \alpha + \beta + v = 0$, then fourth powers of m_1 must be considered.

For shocks in which m_1 and m_2 are non-zero, with the axes orientated so that $m_3 = 0$,

$$\gamma_{11} = m_1 + \tfrac{1}{2}(m_1^2 + m_2^2), \ \gamma_{12} = \gamma_{21} = \tfrac{1}{2}m_2 \text{ and all other } \gamma_{ij} = 0.$$

Substituting in equation (41),

$$\Omega = T_0 S + (\lambda + \mu)m_1^2 + \tfrac{1}{2}\mu m_2^2 + (\lambda + \mu + \alpha + \beta + v)m_1^3 +$$
$$+ (\lambda + \mu + \tfrac{1}{2}\beta + \tfrac{3}{4}v)\cdot m_1 m_2^2 + 0(|m_i|^4).$$

By equation (21)

$$\frac{\partial U}{\partial m_1} = \frac{m_1}{m_2}\frac{\partial U}{\partial m_2},$$

whence

$$(2\lambda + \mu)m_1 + (\lambda + \mu + \tfrac{1}{2}\beta + \tfrac{3}{4}v)m_2^2 + (\lambda + \mu + 3\alpha + 2\beta + \tfrac{3}{2}v)m_1^2 + 0(|m_i|^3) = 0.$$

For small $|m_i|$,
$$m_1 = -\frac{\lambda + \mu + \tfrac{1}{2}\beta + \tfrac{3}{4}v}{2\lambda + \mu}m_2^2 + 0(m_2^3) \tag{44}$$

and
$$U_3^* = -(2\lambda + \mu)^{-1}(\lambda + \mu + \tfrac{1}{2}\beta + \tfrac{3}{4}v)^2 m_2^4 + 0(m_2^6). \tag{45}$$

We thefore consider whether any terms in U_4^* are of order m_2^4. Since $S = 0(m_2^4)$, $\gamma_{ii} = 0(m_2^2)$, $\gamma_{ij}\gamma_{ij} = 0(m_2^2)$ and $\gamma_{ij}\gamma_{jk}\gamma_{ki} = 0(m_2^4)$, equation (41) will be correct to order 4 in m_2 if a term $\xi(\gamma_{ij}\gamma_{ij})^2$ is added to the right hand side. Substituting for the γ_{ij} and arranging in powers of m_2,

$$U = T_0 S + \tfrac{1}{2}\mu m_2^2 + (\lambda + \mu)(m_1^2 + m_1^2 m_2^2 + \tfrac{1}{4}m_2^4) + (\tfrac{1}{2}\beta + \tfrac{3}{4}v)m_1 m_2^2 +$$
$$+ (\tfrac{1}{4}\beta + \tfrac{3}{8}v)m_2^4 + \tfrac{1}{4}\xi m_2^4 + 0(m_2^5). \tag{46}$$

$$\therefore \ m_i\frac{\partial U_4^*}{\partial m_i} - 2U_4^* = 2U_4^* = (\tfrac{1}{2}(\lambda + \mu) + \tfrac{1}{2}\beta + \tfrac{3}{4}v + \tfrac{1}{2}\xi)m_2^4 + 0(m_2^5). \tag{47}$$

On summing equations (45) and (47),

$$2T_0 S = \{\tfrac{1}{2}\xi - \tfrac{1}{4}\mu - (2\lambda + \mu)^{-1}(\tfrac{1}{2}\mu + \tfrac{1}{2}\beta + \tfrac{3}{4}v)^2\}m_2^4 + 0(m_2^5). \tag{48}$$

The entropy change is positive for small m_2 if

$$\xi > \tfrac{1}{2}\mu + (\lambda + \tfrac{1}{2}\mu)^{-1}(\tfrac{1}{2}\mu + \tfrac{1}{2}\beta + \tfrac{3}{4}v)^2. \tag{49}$$

From equations (22), (44), (46) and (48), the velocity of the shock can be shown to be

$$V = \mu^{\frac{1}{2}}\left(1 + \frac{2T_0 S}{\mu m_2^2} + 0(m_2^3)\right) \tag{50}$$

Equation (36) ensures that V is real. It is seen that the condition for the existence of the shock, eqn. (49), is quite restrictive. ξ, the coefficient of the term $(\gamma_{ij}\gamma_{ij})^2$ in the expansion of U must be greater than a positive function of the coefficients of terms of lower degree. Since $m_1/m_2 \to 0$ as $m_2 \to 0$ this shock tends to the rotational shock wave of classical theory. It should be noted that if U^* is exactly given by $U^* = \lambda\gamma_{ii}^2 + \mu\gamma_{ij}\gamma_{ij}$, then the entropy condition (49) cannot be satisfied. For real shocks, the velocity increases with amplitude.

6. Shocks of small amplitude in incompressible media.

For shocks propagating into a material at rest in its natural state, the axes can be orientated so that $m_3 = 0$ and equations (21) and (22) become

$$\frac{\partial U}{\partial m_2} = V^2 m_2 \quad \text{and} \quad 2U = V^2 m_2^2. \tag{51}$$

The γ_{ij} are $\gamma_{11} = \tfrac{1}{2}m_2^2$, $\gamma_{12} = \gamma_{21} = \tfrac{1}{2}m_2$ with all other components zero. In the natural state $U = S = 0$, $T = T_0$, $\gamma_{ij} = K_{ij} = 0$. Then, using equations (2) and remembering p is arbitrary, for an isotropic material
$U = T_0 S + \phi\gamma_{ii} + \lambda\gamma_{ii}^2 + \mu\gamma_{ij}\gamma_{ij} + \eta S^2 + \kappa S\gamma_{ii} +$ third and higher order terms. Since γ_{ii} and $\gamma_{ij}\gamma_{ij}$ are even in m_2, U is even[5] in m_2. If V^2 is eliminated from equations (51),

$$m_2 \frac{\partial U}{\partial m_2} - 2U = 0.$$

---

[5] There are only two independent invariants of γ_{ij} for an incompressible material.

Since $S \to 0$ as $m_2 \to 0$, $T_0 S$ is lower order in m_2 than any other term containing S in both $m_2\,(\partial U/\partial m_2)$ and U. The m_2^2 term vanishes in $m_2\,(\partial U/\partial m_2) - 2U$ and therefore $S = 0(m_2^4)$ as $m_2 \to 0$.

The terms in the expansion of U, which make a contribution up to the fourth degree in m_2, are $T_0 S + \phi\gamma_{ii} + \lambda\gamma_{ii}^2 + \mu\gamma_{ij}\gamma_{ij} + \beta\gamma_{ii}\gamma_{jk}\gamma_{kj} + \xi(\gamma_{ij}\gamma_{ij})^2$. Substituting for the γ_{ij},

$$U = T_0 S + \tfrac{1}{2}(\phi + \mu)m_2^2 + \tfrac{1}{4}(\lambda + \mu + \beta + \xi)m_2^4 + 0(m_2^6)$$

and

$$2T_0 S = \tfrac{1}{2}(\lambda + \mu + \beta + \xi)m_2^4 + 0(m_2^6).$$

The shock is real for small m_2 if

$$\lambda + \mu + \beta + \xi > 0. \tag{52}$$

The velocity is given by

$$V = (2U)^{\frac{1}{2}}m_2^{-1} = (\phi + \mu)^{\frac{1}{2}}(1 + \frac{2T_0 S}{(\phi + \mu)m_2^2} + 0(m_2^4)). \tag{53}$$

$\phi + \mu$ can be shown to be positive: the condition of incompressibility can be written as $\gamma_{ii} = \gamma_{ij}\gamma_{ij} + 0(\gamma_{ij})^3$, then $U = T_0 S + (\phi + \mu)\gamma_{ij}\gamma_{ij} + 0(\gamma_{ij})^3$; for isentropic deformation from the natural state, $S = 0$, $\delta W > 0$ and $\delta Q = 0$, hence $U > 0$ for all small γ_{ij} and $\phi + \mu > 0$. For real shocks the velocity again increases with amplitiude. Note i) that, for the second type of small amplitude shock for compressible materials and for the small amplitude shock for incompressible materials, the velocity is stationary with respect to amplitude at zero amplitude and ii) that the entropy condition (52) for incompressible media is far less restrictive than the corresponding condition (49) for compressible media.

7. The isentropic approximation.

In elementary treatments of dynamic elasticity, entropy changes are assumed to be zero. The energy equation (9) no longer plays an essential role, it is only used after other calculations are complete to evaluate the temperature changes if these are required. The role of the internal energy, U, is taken by the strain energy $U^*(\gamma_{ij})$, equal to U with S put equal to zero, and equation (1) for compressible materials is replaced by

$$K_{ij} = \rho_0 \frac{\partial U^*}{\partial \gamma_{ij}}. \tag{54}$$

Equations (3) to (8), (10) and (12) to (24) are unaltered. It is quite clear from the previous sections of this paper that these equations will give many bogus solutions for shock waves, solutions that violate the second law of thermodynamics. The entropy change for small amplitude waves is of the order of the third or fourth power of the amplitude and therefore tends to zero more rapidly than the amplitude. This however is not enough, the second law requires that the entropy change must be positive and therefore it must tend to zero from above. The nature of the isentropic approximation is such that it is impossible to determine the sign of the entropy change and therefore whether or not a particular solution is physically admissible.

Before rejecting all solutions for shock waves with negative entropy change as valueless, it is reasonable to ask whether such a solution may be an approximation to an actual physical situation. If so, even though the solution itself is physically inadmissable, it may act as a guide to the correct solution. If a stress, discontinuous in time, is applied at the surface of the media, it will be propagated either as a shock, i.e. a discontinuous change, or as a region of rapidly changing stress with the width of the region probably increasing with distance propagated. The solution in the latter case will be governed solely by the differential form of the equations of motion, to which it may not be possible to find an explicit solution. The bogus shock solution may provide the first step in some procedure for solution by successive approximation.

List of Symbols.

a_i	= initial coordinates
$I^{(e)}, l = 1,2,3.$	= invariants of γ_{ij}
K_{ij}	= components of the Kirchhoff stress tensor.
m_i	= defined by equation (4)
p	= scalar parameter, introduced by equation (2)

S	= entropy per unit mass
t	= time
T	= absolute temperature
T_0	= absolute temperature in natural state
u_i	= components of displacement
U	= internal energy per unit mass, generally a function of S and γ_{ij}
U^*	= U with S put equal to zero
v_i	= particle velocity
V_a, V_s	= defined by equation (5)
V	= equal to V_a or V_s when $V_a = V_s$
x_i	= current coordinates
γ_{ij}	= components of Green strain tensor
δ_{ij}	= Kronecker delta
ρ	= density
ρ_0	= density in natural state
σ_{ij}	= components of Eulerian stress tensor
$\phi, \lambda, \mu, \eta, \kappa, \alpha, \beta, \gamma, \xi$	= constants in the expansion of U
suffix $-$	= e.g. f_- means f evaluated immediately behind the shock
suffix $+$	= e.g. f_+ means f evaluated immediately ahead of the shock
$[f]$	= $f_- - f_+$

REFERENCES

[1] E. JOUGERT, *Comptes Rendues*, **171**, (1920), 461, 512, 789, 904.

[2] W. PRAGER, *Introduction to Mechanics of Continua*, Ginn and Co., (1961).

[3] J. L. ERICKSON, *J. Rat. Mech. Anal.*, **2**, (1953), 329.

[4] C. TRUESDELL, *J. Rat. Mech. Anal.*, **8**, (1961), 263.

[5] J. HADAMARD, *Leçons sur la propagation des ondes*, Reprinted by Chelsea (1949).
ADDITIONAL REFERENCE ADDED IN PROOF:

[6] J. DEWEY, "Strong shocks and stress-strain relations in solids", Report No. 1074, April 1959, Ballistic Research Laboratories, Aberdeen Proving Ground, Maryland, U.S.A.

DISCUSSION

L. J. BROER: 1. Shock solutions as given by Dr. Bland can be considered as asymptotic solutions of equations including dissipation. It is required only that there exists some mechanism for dissipation. The nature of this dissipation is not relevant here.

2. Negative entropy shocks have been used to construct approximate solutions in gas dynamics (expansion Mach waves). However these approximations are not uniform, they have a limited region of validity.

P. GERMAIN: It seems to me that, strictly speaking, we may have a shock wave only if no dissipation process is present in the material outside the shock. If some dissipation is present (for instance, heat conduction), one can still consider shock waves, but only in an asymptotic sense. In such cases, extra terms may appear in the shock conditions, even for a plane shock moving in a medium at rest when the shock velocity is not a constant.

S. IRMAY: Another case with a solution that seems to violate the second law of thermodynamics has been described elsewhere (S. Irmay, Dynamic Behavior of Linear Rheological Bodies Under Periodic Stresses, Quart. J. Mech. & Appl. Math., v. 7, pt. 4, 1954, pp. 400–409). It is shown that under periodical shearing stresses, the power expended has the sign of $(L - R)$, where R = time of relaxation, L = time of retardation. Two cases are possible: (1) Either $L > R$, which is a thermodynamic limitation of the rheological coefficients; (2) or $L < R$, the dissipation seems to be negative, which is in apparent contradiction with the second law. This is possible when the body undergoes internal structural and physico-chemical changes, accompanied by the liberation of sufficient amounts of energy, so as to compensate for the negative "dissipation".

D. R. BLAND's Reply: As Professors Broer and Germain point out, I have omitted from the left hand side of equation (9) the term $[Q_1]$, where Q_i is the heat flux vector. If we assume $Q_i = -k(\partial T/\partial a_i)$, where k is the coefficient of heat conductivity, then equation (9) as written is only strictly accurate if either $k = 0$ or $[(\partial T/\partial a_i)] = 0$. In particular the latter condition is satisfied wherever conditions both ahead of and behind the shock are uniform. When neither of these conditions is satisfied but $[Q_1]$ is small compared to the other terms in equation (9), the neglect of $[Q_1]$ should introduce no appreciable error—

except possibly in the sign of [S], which is critical, if the absolute magnitude of [S] is small. An exact solution for non-zero [Q_1] would be extremely difficult not only because the exact form of the relationship between Q_i and $(\partial T/\partial a_i)$ is unknown, but also because such a solution would almost certainly involve the continua equations instead of (or as well as) the jump conditions.

Professor Broer's second comment reinforces the remarks in the last paragraph of my paper. I think that he, Professor Irmay and I are agreed that shocks with negative entropy change only have meaning as solutions in so far as they can be used to construct approximate solutions over a limited physical range.

ON THE EQUATIONS DESCRIBING SMALL DEFORMATIONS SUPERPOSED ON FINITE DEFORMATION

HENRYK ZORSKI

Warszawa, Wiktorska 49/53 m. 4

ABSTRACT

The general displacement equations of small deformations superposed on finite deformation are investigated. Conditions of ellipticity and strong ellipticity are derived and particular cases for simple initial deformations (uniform extension, simple shear, extension and torsion of circular cylinder, are discussed in detail. Inequalities restricting the form of the potential function and ensuring the possibility of a general formulation of the problem yield those derived previously by Truesdell and Ericksen, and certain additional relations. The following example is typical. For an elastic body the potential function of which depends only on first powers of strain invariants, under a uniform extension, the conditions of existence of small deformations are

$$\frac{\partial W}{\partial J_1} + (1 + \delta_i)^2 \frac{\partial W}{\partial J_2} > 0; \quad \tau^{11}, \tau^{22}, \tau^{33} > 0.$$

If the first set is satisfied, but, say, $\tau^{11} < 0$ the equation for the stress function in a particular case has the form

$$\left(c_1^2 \nabla^2 - \frac{\partial^2}{\partial t^2} \right) \left(c_2^2 \nabla^2 + \frac{\partial^2}{\partial t^2} \right) \phi = 0$$

and the usual formulation of the stable boundary value problem is impossible.
   The energy integral, Betti's law, etc. are examined (the operator is not self-conjugate, the body being more general that anisotropic and non-homogeneous). Various examples of mechanical and thermal vibrations illustrate the above derived results (thermal vibrations of a finitely strained right circular cylinder, uniformly extended body, simple shear, etc.).

Introduction.

   In this paper we propose to investigate some properties of the linear system of partial differential equations describing the motion of an initially finitely deformed body. The requirement that the velocities of elastic waves be real is equivalent to the property of strong ellipticity of the considered system of equations, which leads to the positive definiteness of the differential operator defined on a linear manifold of functions. These conditions impose certain restrictions on the form of the potential energy (or the free energy) of the body and on the initial finite deformation; a part of the relevant necessary conditions are identical with the conditions introduced by Truesdell [6] and examined also by other authors. It is proved that the condition of strong ellipticity ensures both the uniqueness and existence of the first boundary value problem (displacements described on the boundary); these results can easily be extended to include the second and the third (mixed) boundary value problems.

The condition of stability (the second variation of the energy is greater or equal to zero) is equivalent to the condition of positiveness of the considered differential operator; this is a condition weaker than strong ellipticity.

1. The equilibrium equations.

To derive the eqilibrium equations for small deformations superposed on finite deformation (displacement equations) consider the equilibrium equations of a finitely deformed body in convected coordinates[1]

$$\nabla_i \tau^{ij} = 0. \tag{1.1}$$

Now, replace

$$\tau^{ij} \text{ by } \tau^{ij} + \varepsilon \left(\frac{\partial \tau^{ij}}{\partial \gamma_{pq}} \gamma'_{pq} + \frac{\partial \tau^{ij}}{\partial T} \theta \right) \tag{1.2}$$

and

$$\Gamma^k_{ij} \text{ by } \Gamma^k_{ij} + \varepsilon g^{kp} \nabla_i \nabla_j w_p \tag{1.3}$$

where

$$\gamma'_{pq} = \nabla_{(p} w_{q)} \tag{1.4}$$

and ε is a small parameter. w_i is the vector of the additional displacement and θ the increment of temperature. Substituting from (1.2), (1.3) and (1.4) into the equilibrium equations in the final state (they are identical with (1.1) and taking into account (1.1) we arrive at the required equilibrium equations in displacements

$$A^{iprs} \nabla_p \nabla_r w_s + \nabla_p K^{iprs} \cdot \nabla_r w_s = - \nabla_p (\alpha^{ip} \theta) + \rho w^i_{,tt}. \tag{1.5}$$

Here

$$\alpha^{ij} = \frac{\partial \tau^{ij}}{\partial T}$$

and the terms of order ε^2 and higher have been neglected. The tensorial coefficients of the equation have the form

---

(1) We use almost everywhere the notations of A. E. Green and W. Zerna, *Theoretical Elasticity*, Oxford (1954).

$$K^{iprs} = \tfrac{1}{2}\left(\frac{\partial \tau^{ip}}{\partial \gamma_{rs}} + \frac{\partial \tau^{ip}}{\partial \gamma_{sr}}\right); \qquad A^{iprs} = K^{iprs} + 2g^{s(i}\tau^{p)r}. \tag{1.7}$$

Our system (1.5) can be written in the form

$$\nabla_p(\bar{A}^{iprs}\nabla_r w_s) = -\nabla_p(\alpha^{ip}\theta) + \rho w^i_{,tt}. \tag{1.8}$$

The tensor $t^{pi} = \bar{A}^{iprs}\nabla_r w_s$ is a non-symmetric stress tensor introduced in the general case by Urbanowski [3].

The system of equations (1.5) is a system of partial differential equations of second order; separating the second derivatives we can write it in the form (setting for the time being $\theta = 0$)

$$A^{iprs}\partial_p\partial_r w_s + M^i(w_m, \partial_n w_m) = \rho w^i_{,tt} \tag{1.9}$$

where

$$M^i(w_m, \partial_n w_m) = -\left[A^{iprs}(\delta^m_p\Gamma^n_{rs} + \delta^n_s\Gamma^m_{pr} + \delta^m_r\Gamma^n_{ps}) - \nabla_p K^{ipmn}\right]\partial_m w_n -$$

$$-\left[A^{iprs}(\partial_p\Gamma^n_{rs} - \Gamma^m_{pr}\Gamma^n_{ms} - \Gamma^m_{ps}\Gamma^n_{rm}) + \nabla_p K^{iprm}\Gamma^n_{rm}\right]w_n.$$

The system (1.9) contains only the symmetric part of A^{iprs} with respect to the second and third indices. This tensor is also symmetric with respect to the first two indices; in the general case of the finite deformation the above are the only algebraic relations connecting its components. Our system contains besides the deformation tensor $\nabla_{(i}w_{j)}$ also the rotation tensor $\nabla_{[i}w_{j]}$, it is therefore (even without considering the operator M^i) much more general than the displacement equations for the classical anisotropic body. The condition of absence of the tensor $\nabla_{[i}w_{j]}$ is

$$A^{ip[rs]} = 0$$

i.e., from (1.7)

$$g^{i[s}\tau^{r]p}_r + g^{p[s}\tau^{r]i}_r = 0$$

or

$$\tau^{ij} = \tfrac{1}{3}g_{pq}\tau^{pq}g^{ij}. \tag{1.10}$$

This condition constitutes a severe restriction on the state of stress (it can for instance be shown that in the case of homogeneous tension this condition is satisfied only when $\lambda_1 = \lambda_2 = \lambda_3$). If (1.10) is satisfied it can easily be verified that A^{iprs} satisfies the condition of the tensor of elastic coefficients appearing in the Hooke law

$$A^{iprs} = A^{pirs} = A^{ipsr} = A^{rsip}.$$

(1.10) is also a necessary condition of the validity of the last relations.

In this paper we confine ourselves to the case of an initially isotropic body. Expressing the stress τ^{ij} by the derivatives of the potential function with respect to the three invariants $I_1 = \overset{\circ}{g}{}^{pq}g_{pq}$, $I_2 = \overset{\circ}{g}_{pq}g^{pq}I_3$, $I_3 = g/\overset{\circ}{g}$ we have

$$\tau^{ij} = \Phi\overset{\circ}{g}{}^{ij} + \Psi B^{ij} + pg^{ij}, \quad B^{ij} = g_{pq}(\overset{\circ}{g}{}^{ij}\overset{\circ}{g}{}^{pq} - \overset{\circ}{g}{}^{ip}\overset{\circ}{g}{}^{jq})$$

and from (1.7) after transformations

$$A^{iprs} = \frac{1}{4\sqrt{I_3}}(W_{,ip,rs} + W_{,pi,rs} + W_{,ip,sr} + W_{pi,sr}) + g^{is}\tau^{pr} +$$

$$+ g^{ps}\tau^{ir} - g^{rs}\tau^{ip}$$

$$W_{,ip,rs} = \frac{\partial^2 W}{\partial\gamma_{ip}\partial\gamma_{rs}}, \quad \text{etc.}$$

or

$$A^{i(pr)s} = a^{iprs} + \Psi\overset{\circ}{c}{}^{iprs} + pc^{iprs} + g^{is}\tau^{pr} \tag{1.11}$$

where

$$a^{iprs} = (\overset{\circ}{g}{}^{i(p}\overset{k}{\alpha} + B^{i(p}\overset{k}{\beta} + g^{i(p}\overset{k}{\gamma})\,\underset{k}{i}{}^{r)s},$$

$$c^{iprs} = g^{i(p}g^{r)s} - g^{is}g^{pr},$$

$$\overset{\circ}{c}{}^{iprs} = \overset{\circ}{g}{}^{i(p}\overset{\circ}{g}{}^{r)s} - \overset{\circ}{g}{}^{is}\overset{\circ}{g}{}^{pr},$$

the tensor a^{iprs} containing only the second derivatives of $W(I_p)$ with respect to I_p.

The following notations have been introduced:

$$\overset{k}{\alpha} = (A,F,E), \quad \overset{k}{\beta} = (F,B,D), \quad \overset{k}{\gamma} = (EI_3, DI_3, CI_3)$$

$$A = \frac{2}{\sqrt{I_3}}W_{11}, \quad B = \frac{2}{\sqrt{I_3}}W_{22}, \quad C = \frac{2}{\sqrt{I_3}}W_{33}, \quad D = \frac{2}{\sqrt{I_3}}W_{23},$$

$$E = \frac{2}{\sqrt{I_3}}W_{13}, \quad F = \frac{2}{\sqrt{I_3}}W_{12}; \quad W_{11} = \frac{\partial^2 W}{\partial I_1^2}, \quad \text{etc.}$$

$$\underset{1}{i}{}^{ij} = 2\overset{\circ}{g}{}^{ij}, \quad \underset{2}{i}{}^{ij} = 2I_3\overset{\circ}{g}_{pq}(g^{pq}g^{ij} - g^{p(i}g^{j)q}), \quad \underset{3}{i}{}^{ij} = 2I_3 g^{ij}.$$

Before proceeding to investigate the properties of the equilibrium equations let us derive the equation of heat conduction (c.f. [9]). Thus, we have, assuming isotropy and point symmetry

$$- T \frac{DS}{Dt} = \sqrt{I_3} \nabla_i Q^i$$

(1.12)

where

$$Q^i = - \lambda^{ip} \nabla_p \theta, \quad \lambda^{ir} = g^{pr}(M_1 \delta_p^i + M_2 \gamma_p^i + M_3 \gamma_q^i \gamma_p^q),$$

(1.13)

$\gamma_p^i = \mathring{g}^{iq} \gamma_{pq}$ and M_1, M_2, M_3 are functions of the invariants. Taking into account that $S = - \dfrac{\partial F}{\partial T}$, F being the free energy,

$$\frac{DS}{Dt} = - \varepsilon \left(\frac{\partial^2 F}{\partial T \partial I_p} \frac{DI_p^1}{Dt} + \frac{\partial^2 F}{\partial T^2} \frac{D\theta}{Dt} \right)$$

where I_p' are the increments of the invariants due to the displacement w^i, i.e $I_1' = \mathring{g}^{pq} g_{pq}' = 2 \mathring{g}^{pq} \nabla_{(p} w_{q)}$, $I_2' = \mathring{g}_{pq}(I_3 g'^{pq} + I_3' g^{pq})$, $I_3' = I_3 g^{pq} g_{pq}'$. Substituting and introducing the notations

$$\sqrt{\mathring{g}/g} \, T \frac{\partial^2 F}{\partial T^2} = - \frac{M_1}{\kappa}, \quad \sqrt{\mathring{g}/g} \, T \frac{\partial^2 F}{\partial T \partial I_p} = \eta_p M_1$$

we finally obtain

$$\nabla_p(\lambda^{pq} \nabla_q \theta) + M_1 \eta_p \frac{DI_p'}{Dt} = \frac{M_1}{\kappa} \frac{D\theta}{Dt}$$

(1.14)

The term $M_1 \eta_p \dfrac{DI_p'}{Dt}$ accounts for the influence of the rate of deformation on the distribution of temperature. In the case of classical (infinitesimal) theory it has the form $\eta \dfrac{D}{Dt}(\nabla^p w^p)$. It is readily observed that it contains the second derivatives of the displacement with respect to time and spatial variables. The system (1.14) can be written in the form

$$\lambda^{pq} \partial_p \partial_q \theta + v_r^p \partial_p \frac{\partial w^r}{\partial t} + N \left(\theta, \partial_p \theta, w^m, \partial_n w^m, \frac{\partial w^m}{\partial t} \right) = \frac{M_1}{\kappa} \frac{\partial \theta}{\partial t},$$

(1.15)

in which the second derivatives of the temperature and the displacement have been separated out. If the coupling is absent ($\partial^2 F / \partial T \partial I_p \equiv 0$) equation (1.15) is considerably simplified

$$\lambda^{pq}\partial_p\partial_q\theta + N(\theta,\partial_p\theta) = \frac{M_1}{\kappa}\frac{\partial\theta}{\partial t} \qquad (1.16)$$

The system of equations (1.9)—(1.15) is a system of four second order equations with four unknown functions. In the case $\partial^2 F/\partial T\partial I_p \equiv 0$ (only this case will be considered in this paper) we have a system of three equations in displacements and a separate equation for temperature (1.16). In order that the latter equation be parabolic the coefficients λ^{ij} must satisfy certain relations (assuming that $M_1/\kappa > 0$; the other case is of no physical significance and, moreover, it would only change the sign of the inequalities for λ_{ij}). Thus, the quadratic form

$$\lambda^{pq}\xi_p\xi_q > 0 \ , \ \xi_p\xi^p = 1$$

i.e. λ^{ij} must satisfy the inequalities

$$\lambda^{11} > 0, \quad \lambda^{11}\lambda^{22} - (\lambda^{12})^2 > 0$$

$$\det \lambda^{ij} > 0$$

which also imply that $\lambda^{22} > 0$ and $\lambda^{33} > 0$. According to (1.13), the above inequalities restrict the form of the three functions of invariants M_p and the deformation γ_{ij}.

2. Properties of the displacement equations. Strongly elliptic systems.

In the case of one equation of second order the coefficients of the second derivatives decide whether the equation is elliptic, hyperbolic or parabolic, i.e. whether under prescribed boundary and initial conditions the boundary value problem has a solution, and whether the latter is unique and stable. In the case of systems of equations the counterpart of the elliptic equation is the strongly elliptic system; the requirement of ordinary ellipticity can turn out to be too weak.

Consider the left-hand side of the system (1.9). The system

$$A^{iprs}\partial_p\partial_r w_s + M^i(w_m, \partial_n w_m) = 0$$

is said to be elliptic if

$$\det a^{ij} > 0 \qquad (2.1)$$

where $a^{ij} = A^{ipqj}\xi_p\xi_q$ and ξ_p is an arbitrary non-vanishing vector. This system is strongly elliptic[2] if the quadratic form with the coefficients a^{ij} is positive definite, i.e.

$$A^{ipqj} \xi_p \xi_q \zeta_i \zeta_j > 0 \qquad (2.2)$$

for arbitrary non-vanishing ξ_p and ζ_i. A strongly elliptic system is also an elliptic system[3].

To illustrate the difference consider the Lamé equations. Here we have

$$A^{1111} = \lambda + 2\mu, \ A^{1221} = \mu, \ A^{1122} = A^{1212} = \frac{\lambda + \mu}{2}, \ A^{1133} = A^{1313} = \frac{\lambda + \mu}{2},$$

$$A^{1331} = \mu, \ A^{2121} = A^{2211} = \frac{\lambda + \mu}{2}, \ A^{2112} = \mu, \ A^{2222} = \lambda + \mu, \ A^{2232} = A^{2322} =$$

$$= \frac{\lambda + \mu}{2}, \ A^{2332} = \mu, \ A^{3131} = A^{3311} = \frac{\lambda + \mu}{2}, \ A^{3232} = A^{3322} = \frac{\lambda + \mu}{2},$$

$$A^{3113} = \mu, \ A^{3223} = \mu, \ A^{3333} = \lambda + 2\mu$$

In the case of three dimensions (the case of two dimensions yields the same results)

$$\det \alpha^{ij} = (\alpha^2 + \beta^2 + \gamma^2)^6 \mu^2 (\lambda + 2\mu)$$

α, β, γ being the components of ξ_i.

The ellipticity conditions yields the inequality

$$\lambda + 2\mu > 0$$

while the condition of strong ellipticity leads to the following result:

$$\alpha^2(\lambda + 2\mu) + (\beta^2 + \gamma^2)\mu > 0$$

for arbitrary α, β, γ. Hence

$$\lambda + 2\mu > 0 \quad \text{and} \quad \mu > 0$$

and two more conditions which do not give any new results. Since the squares of the velocities of elastic waves are given by the formulae

$$c_1^2 = \frac{\lambda + 2\mu}{\rho}, \quad c_2^2 = \frac{\mu}{\rho}$$

---

[2] The corresponding system with the right-hand side $\varrho w_{i,tt}$ may then be called strongly hyperbolic

[3] In Petrovski's sense. (2.2) implies (2.1).

we observe that the condition of strong ellipticity is essential, since it ensures that the above velocities are real. The requitement of simple ellipticity is too weak. In the general case therefore (for arbitrary initial finite deformation) we shall impose the condition (1.18).

The necessary and sufficient conditions for A^{iprs} ensuring the fulfiment of (1.18) constitute a very complicated system of non-linear inequalities; for instance in the two-dimensional case we have the following results. Regarding the expression $A^{ipqi}\xi_p\xi_q\zeta_i\zeta_j$ as the quadratic form with the coefficients $A^{ipqi}\xi_p\xi_q$ and demanding that the two principal determinants be positive (which con-stitutes the necessary and sufficient condition of definiteness of the considered quadratic form) we obtain

$$A^{1pq1}\xi_p\xi_q > 0, \qquad B^{prqs}\xi_p\xi_r\xi_q\xi_s > 0$$

where

$$B^{pqrs} = A^{1pr1}A^{2qs2} - A^{1pr2}A^{1qs2}.$$

Already the first condition leads to non-linear inequalities

$$A^{1111} > 0, \quad A^{1111}A^{1221} - (A^{1121})^2 > 0$$

while the second yields even more complicated relations. The three-dimensional case is even more complicated since there appear forms of sixth order.

Non-linear inequalities of the above form are hardly of any practical use. We shall therefore confine ourselves to necessary linear relations. Linear suf-ficient (but not necessary) conditions can also be derived by known methods c.f. [11]). Setting in turn $\xi_i = (1,0,0)$, $(0,1,0)$, $(0,0,1)$ we obtain nine con-ditions

$$A^{ijji} > 0 \qquad \text{(no summation)} \tag{2.3}$$

Neglecting for the time being the second derivatives of $W(I_p)$ (i.e. $a^{iprs} = 0$) we have

$$W_2[(\mathring{g}^{ij})^2 - \mathring{g}^{ii}\mathring{g}^{jj}] + I_3 W_3[(g^{ij})^2 - g^{ii}g^{jj}] + \frac{\sqrt{I_3}}{2}g^{ii}\tau^{jj} > 0 \tag{2.4}$$

or, substituting for τ^{jj}

$$W g^{ii}\mathring{g}^{jj} + W_2[(\mathring{g}^{ij})^2 - \mathring{g}^{ii}\mathring{g}^{jj} + g^{ii}g_{pq}(\mathring{g}^{pq}\mathring{g}^{jj} - \mathring{g}^{jp}\mathring{g}^{jq}) + I_3 W_3(g^{ij})^2 > 0. \tag{2.5}$$

For $i = j$ we have

$$g^{ii}\tau^{jj} > 0 \tag{2.6}$$

and since the metric of the space is positive definite

$$\tau^{ii} > 0 \tag{2.7}$$

Thus, for bodies the potential energy of which contains only the first powers of the invariants (e.g. for the Mooney material) all normal stresses must be positive. For $i \neq j$, after simple transformations, setting without loss of generality $g^{ij} = \delta^{ij}$ we obtain

$$\overset{\circ}{g}{}^{ii}W_1 + [\overset{\circ}{g}{}^{ii}\overset{\circ}{g}{}^{jj} - (\overset{\circ}{g}{}^{ij})^2]W_2 > 0. \tag{2.8}$$

In the general case when $W(I_p)$ does contain higher powers of I_p our inequalities take the form

$$a^{iiii} + g^{ii}\tau^{ii} > 0 \tag{2.9}$$

$$a^{ijji} + \overset{\circ}{g}{}^{ii}W_1 + [\overset{\circ}{g}{}^{ii}\overset{\circ}{g}{}^{jj} - (\overset{\circ}{g}{}^{ij})^2]W_2 > 0.$$

The above inequalities restricting the form of the potential energy and the finite deformation of the elastic body, constitute a necessary condition for the velocities of elastic body to be real. In the next section we shall investigate the relation between the property of strong ellipticity and the existence, uniqueness and stability of the solution.

Examples.

(a) *Homogeneous tension and compression*

In this well-known case we have

$$g^{ij} = \left(\frac{1}{\lambda_i}\right)^2 \overset{\circ}{g}{}^{ij} \qquad \text{(no summation)}$$

$$\tau^{11} = \frac{1}{\lambda_1}[\lambda_1\Phi + \lambda_1(\lambda_2 + \lambda_2)\Psi + p],$$

$$\tau^{22} = \frac{1}{\lambda_2}[\lambda_2\Phi + \lambda_2(\lambda_1 + \lambda_3)\Psi + p],$$

$$\tau^{33} = \frac{1}{\lambda_3}[\lambda_3\Phi + \lambda_3(\lambda_1 + \lambda_2)\Psi + p], \quad \tau^{12} = \tau^{13} = \tau^{23} = 0.$$

From the formula (1.11) we obtain

$$A^{iprs} = \mu^{is}(\delta^{ir}\delta^{ps} + \delta^{is}\delta^{pr}) + \lambda^{is}\delta^{ip}\delta^{rs} \quad \text{(no summation)}$$

where

$$\mu^{is} = \frac{1}{\lambda_s}[\Phi + (I_1 - \lambda_i - \lambda_s)\Psi]$$

$$\tfrac{1}{2}\lambda^{is} = \left[\overset{1}{\alpha} + \frac{1}{\lambda_s}\overset{2}{\alpha}\left(I_2 - \frac{1}{\lambda_s}I_3\right) + \frac{1}{\lambda_s}I_3\overset{3}{\alpha}\right] + (I_1 - \lambda)\left[\overset{1}{\beta} + \right.$$

$$\left. + \frac{1}{\lambda_q}\overset{2}{\beta}\left(I_2 - \frac{1}{\lambda_q}I_3\right) + \frac{1}{\lambda_q}\overset{3}{\beta}I_3\right] + \quad \text{(no summation)}$$

$$+ \frac{1}{\lambda_i}\left[\overset{1}{\gamma} + \frac{1}{\lambda_q}\overset{2}{\gamma}\left(I_2 - \frac{1}{\lambda_q}I_3\right) + \frac{1}{\lambda_q}\overset{3}{\gamma}I_3\right] - \frac{1}{2\lambda_q}\Phi + \left(1 - \frac{I_1 - \lambda_i}{2\lambda_q}\Psi\right) +$$

$$+ \frac{1}{2\lambda_i\lambda_q}p$$

The equilibrium equations take the form

$$[\mu^{is}(\delta^{ir}\delta^{ps} + \delta^{is}\delta^{pr}) + \lambda^{is}\delta^{ip}\delta^{rs}]\partial_p\partial_r w_s = \rho w^i_{,tt} - \partial_p(\alpha^{ip}\theta) \qquad (2.10)$$

(no summation inside the square brackets).

The necessary condition of strong ellipticity of the above system (2.3) take the form (for $a^{iprs} = 0$)

$$W_1 + (1 + \delta_i)^2 W_2 > 0,$$

$$\tau^{ii} > 0, \quad \text{i.e.} \quad W_1 + [(1 + \delta_i)^2 + (1 + \delta_j)^2]W_2 + \frac{I_3}{(1+\delta_k)^2}W_3 > 0 \qquad \text{\{(2.11)}$$

$$i \neq j \neq K$$

where $\lambda_i = 1 + \delta_i$. The first three conditions are known (see e.g. [6]).

The simplest case occurs obviously for $\lambda_1 = \lambda_2 = \lambda_3 = \lambda$. This is the case of "isotropy", since the equilibrium equations take the form

$$[\mu_L(\delta^{ir}\delta^{ps} + \delta^{is}\delta^{pr}) + \lambda_.\delta^{ip}\delta^{rs}]\partial_p\partial_r w_s = \rho w^i_{,tt} - \partial_p(\alpha^{ip}\theta) \qquad (2.12)$$

Here, in the case $a^{iprs} = 0$, $\mu_L = \frac{1}{\lambda^2}\Phi + \Psi$, $\lambda_. = -\frac{1}{\lambda^2}(\Phi - p/\lambda^2)$. Our conditions are considerably simpler. In fact,

$$\mu_L > 0, \quad \lambda_L + 2\mu_L > 0. \qquad (2.13)$$

It is evident from (2.12) that they are conditions of reality of the velocities of elastic waves. Introducing the displacement functions, in the case $\alpha^{ij} = 0$ we obtain

$$w_1 = \left[\mu_L \frac{\partial^2}{\partial x^2} + (\lambda_L + 2\mu_L) \left(\frac{\partial^2}{\partial y^2} + \frac{\partial^2}{\partial z^2} \right) - \rho \frac{\partial^2}{\partial t^2} \right] \psi_1 +$$

$$+ (\lambda_L + \mu_L) \frac{\partial}{\partial x} \left(\frac{\partial \psi_2}{\partial y} + \frac{\partial \psi_3}{\partial z} \right), \text{ etc.,}$$

and the equations for ψ_i:

$$\left(c_1^2 \nabla^2 - \rho \frac{\partial^2}{\partial t^2} \right) \left(c_2^2 \nabla^2 - \rho \frac{\partial^2}{\partial t^2} \right) \psi_i = 0$$

where

$$c_1^2 = \frac{\mu_L}{\rho} = \frac{1}{\rho \lambda^2} [W_1 + (1 + \delta)^2 W_2],$$

$$c_2^2 = \frac{\lambda_L + 2\mu_L}{\rho} = \Phi + 2\lambda\Psi + p/\lambda.$$

The analogy with the Lamé equations is obvious (it is to be borne in mind, however, that in the latter case the initial stresses vanish; moreover, above we have neglected W_{11}, W_{12},...).

For the Mooney material where

$$W = C_1(I_1 - 3) + C_2(I_2 - 3),$$

$$\tau^{ii} = \frac{2}{\sqrt{I_3}} [(C_1 + C_2(\gamma_{jj} + \gamma_{kk})]$$

our inequalities take the form

$$C_1 + C_2(\gamma_{jj} + \gamma_{kk}) > 0$$

$$C_2 > 0$$

The first inequality should be satisfied for arbitrary deformations, Hence, finally

$$C_1 > 0, \quad C_2 > 0,$$

$$\gamma_{jj} + \gamma_{kk} > 0, \quad j \neq k.$$

(2.14)

(b)   Circular cylinder

As the next example we consider a generalization of the problem examined by A. E. Green [7]. Thus, a circular cylinder of initial radius a_0 is homogeneously deformed so that the new radius is $a = va_0$ and the ratio of the final to the initial length is v'. Assuming that the convected coordinates coincide with the polar coordinate system in the deformed body let us imagine that the deformed cylinder undergoes small vibrations such that the point (r, z) moves to $(r + u, + \phi, z + w)$ and the increment of temperature is θ. The usual calculations in the case of axial symmetry lead to the following system of equilibrium equations

$$(a^{1111} + \tau^{11})\left[u_{,rr} + \left(\frac{u}{r}\right)_{,r}\right] + \frac{2v'}{v^2}(F_1 + v^2 F_2)u_{,zz} +$$

$$+ [a^{1133} + 2v'(F_2 + v^2 F_3)]w_{,rz} = \rho u_{,tt} - \alpha_1 \theta_{,r}$$

$$(F_1 + v'^2 F_2)\left(\psi_{,rr} + \frac{3}{r}\psi_{,r}\right) + \left(\frac{v'}{v}\right)^2 (F_1 + v^2 F_2)\psi_{,zz} = \rho \psi_{,tt}$$

$$[a^{3311} + 2v'(F_2 + v^2 F_3)]\left(u_{,rz} + \frac{1}{r}u_{,z}\right) +$$

$$+ \frac{2}{v'}(F_1 + v^2 F_2)(w_{,rr} + \frac{1}{r}w_{,r}) + (a^{3333} + \tau^{33})w_{,zz} = \rho w_{,tt} - \alpha_3 \theta_{,z}$$

where $F_1 = \dfrac{\partial F}{\partial I_1}$, etc. Thus, the angle $\psi(r,z)$ satisfies a separate differential equation while the displacements $u(r,z)$ and $w(r,z)$ satisfy a system of two equations. The fundamental inequalities can be deduced from the general formulae (2.3) or directly from the system (2.15). The first group has the form

$$F_1 + v^2 F_2 > 0$$

and from the equation for $\psi(r,z)$

$$F_1 + v'^2 F_2 > 0.$$

The second group is the following:

$$a^{1111} + \tau^{11} > 0, \quad a^{3333} + \tau^{33} > 0.$$

If we require that the curved surface of the cylinder be free of tractions, then $\tau^{11} = 0$ and

$$F_1 + (v^2 + v'^2)F_2 + v^2 v'^2 F_3 = 0$$

— a relation between v and v'. Assuming, moreover, that $u = w \equiv 0$ we arrive at the results of A. E. Green [7].

It is interesting to note that in this simple case our necessary conditions of strong ellipticity are identical with the conditions of simple ellipticity.

This is due to the fact of separation of the equation for $\psi(r,z)$. In fact, the condition of ellipticity (det $a^{ij} > 0$) of the system of equations for $u(r,z)$ and $w(r,z)$ has the form

$$(F_1 + v^2 F_2)(a^{1111} + \tau^{11}) > 0,$$

$$(F_1 + v^2 F_2)(a^{3333} + \tau^{33}) > 0,$$

Now, from the equation for $\psi(r,z)$ we have the condition of ellipticity or strong ellipticity (in the case of one equation they are identical)

$$(F_1 + v^2 F_2) > 0, \quad (F_1 + v'^2 F_2) > 0.$$

Hence we have immediately $a^{1111} + \tau^{11} > 0$, $a^{3333} + \tau^{33} > 0$, i.e. the conditions of strong ellipticity.

(c) Simple shear

Consider as the last example simple shear of an elastic space in the plane (x_1, x_2), independent of x_3. Here the point (x, y, z) passes into the point $(x + Ky, y, z)$, K being a constant. The stresses are the following:

$$\tau^{11} = \Phi + (2 + K^2)\Psi + (1 + K^2)p,$$

$$\tau^{22} = \Phi + 2\Psi + p,$$

$$\tau^{33} = \Phi + (2 + K^2)\Psi + p,$$

$$\tau^{12} = -K(\Psi + p),$$

$$\tau^{13} = \tau^{23} = 0.$$

Confining ourselves to the case of $W(I_p)$ containing only the first powers of I_p we obtain after transformations the following eight inequalities (the ninth is identical with the third):
the first group

$$\tau^{11} > 0, \quad \text{i.e.} \quad \Phi + (2 + K^2)\Psi + (1 + K^2)p > 0,$$

$$\tau^{22} > 0, \quad \text{i.e.} \quad \Phi + 2\Psi + p > 0,$$

$$\tau^{33} > 0, \quad \text{i.e.} \quad \Phi + (2 + K^2)\Psi + p > 0,$$

the second group

$$\Phi + (1 + K^2)\Psi + K^2 p > 0$$

$$\Phi + (1 + K^2)\Psi > 0$$

$$\Phi + \Psi > 0$$

$$(1 + K^2)\Phi + (1 + 2K^2)\Psi + K^2 p > 0$$

$$(1 + K^2)\Phi + [(1 + K^2)^2 + K^2]\Psi > 0.$$

Thus, in the case $a^{iprs} = 0$ the normal stresses again must be positive.

Let us now return to the general displacement equations (1.8). Confining ourselves without loss of generality to the Cartesian coordinates, we can derive by the simple integration by parts the following counterpart of the Betti formula from the classical elasticity:

$$\int_V [\overset{2}{w}_i \partial_p(\bar{A}^{iprs}\overset{1}{\mu}_{rs}) - \overset{1}{w}_i \partial_p(\bar{A}^{iprs}\overset{2}{\mu}_{rs})] \, dV =$$

$$= \int_S (\overset{2}{w}_i \overset{1}{\mu}_{rs} - \overset{1}{w}_i \overset{2}{\mu}_{rs}) n_p \bar{A}^{iprs} dS - \qquad (2.15)$$

$$- \int_V (\bar{A}^{pirs} - \bar{A}^{srip})\overset{1}{\mu}_{rs}\overset{2}{\mu}_{ip} dV.$$

Here $\mu_{ij} = \partial_i w_j$. Introducing the operators

$$\mathfrak{R}^i(w) = \partial_p(\bar{A}^{iprs}\mu_{rs}), \qquad \mathfrak{M}^i(w) = \partial_p(\bar{A}^{srpi}\mu_{rs}),$$

$$\overset{s}{\mathfrak{R}}{}^{ip}(w) = \bar{A}^{iprs}\mu_{rs}, \qquad \overset{s}{\mathfrak{M}}{}^{ip}(w) = \bar{A}^{srpi}\mu_{rs},$$

we can write the above integral identity in the form

$$\int_V [\overset{2}{w}_i \mathfrak{R}^i(\overset{1}{w}) - \overset{1}{w}_i \mathfrak{M}^i(\overset{2}{w})] \, dV =$$

$$= \int_S [\overset{2}{w}_i \overset{s}{\mathfrak{R}}{}^{ip}(\overset{1}{w}) - \overset{1}{w}_i \overset{s}{\mathfrak{M}}{}^{ip}(\overset{2}{w})] \, n_p dS \qquad (2.16)$$

Observe that

$$\bar{A}^{pirs} - \bar{A}^{srip} = g^{ip}\tau^{rs} - g^{rs}\tau^{ip}$$

and, consequently, this expression does not vanish in the general case. The operator $\mathfrak{R}^i(w)$ therefore is not self-adjoint, $\mathfrak{R}^i \neq \mathfrak{M}^i$. Only in the case (cf. condition (1.10) of absence of the rotation tensor in the equilibrium equations)

$$\tau^{ij} = \tfrac{1}{3} g_{pq} \tau^{pq} g^{ij}$$

(homogeneous extension with equal extensions λ_i) we have $\mathfrak{R}^i = \mathfrak{M}^i$.

We shall see later (Sec. 3) that by formulating the problem in material coordinates, it is described by a self-adjoint operator.

3. Formulation in material coordinates. Uniqueness, existence and stability.

Denoting by u^α the displacement referred to a Cartesian coordinate system
and by $W(u^\alpha_{,\beta})$ the energy referred to the unit volume of undeformed body,
we have the equations of equilibrium ,[2],

$$\left(\frac{\partial W}{\partial u^\alpha_{,\beta}}\right)_{,\beta} = 0 \tag{3.1}$$

Setting $u^\alpha = v^\alpha + w^\alpha$ where w^α is the additional small displacement, after simple
transformations we arrive at the system of equations corresponding to (1.9)
(we neglect the inertia and temperature terms)

$$- L_w = A_{\alpha..\mu}^{\beta\lambda} w^\mu_{,\alpha\beta} + (A_{\alpha..\mu}^{\beta\lambda})_{,\beta} w^\mu_{,\lambda} = (A_{\alpha..\mu}^{\beta\lambda} w^\mu_{,\lambda})_{,\beta} = 0 \tag{3.2}$$

where

$$A_{\alpha..\mu}^{\beta\lambda} = \tfrac{1}{2}\left(\frac{\partial^2 W}{\partial v^\alpha_{,\beta}\partial v^\mu_{,\lambda}} + \frac{\partial^2 W}{\partial v^\alpha_{,\lambda}\,\partial v^\mu_{,\beta}}\right). \tag{3.3}$$

The above important tensor satisfies the algebraic conditions

$$A_{\alpha..\mu}^{[\beta\lambda]} = A_{[\alpha..\mu]}^{\beta\lambda} = 0 \tag{3.4}$$

Integrating by parts we obtain the Betti formula

$$\int_V [(\overset{1}{w}{}^\mu_{,\lambda}A_{\alpha..\mu}^{\beta\lambda})_{,\beta}\,\overset{2}{w}{}^\alpha - (\overset{2}{w}{}^\mu_{,\lambda}A_{\alpha..\mu}^{\beta\lambda})_{,\beta}\overset{1}{w}{}^\alpha]\,dV =$$

$$= \int_S n_\beta [\overset{2}{w}{}^\alpha(\overset{1}{w}{}^\mu_{,\lambda}A_{\alpha..\mu}^{\beta\lambda}) - \overset{1}{w}{}^\alpha\,\overset{2}{w}{}^\mu_{,\lambda}A_{\alpha..\mu}^{\beta\lambda})]\,dS$$

$$= \int_S (\overset{1}{t}{}_\alpha\overset{2}{w}{}^\alpha - \overset{2}{t}{}_\alpha\overset{1}{w}{}^\alpha)\,dS \tag{3.5}$$

where

$$t_\alpha = n_\beta A_{\alpha..\mu}^{\beta\lambda} w^\mu_{,\lambda} \tag{3.6}$$

is the stress vector on the surface S of the body. Thus, the operator L is self-
adjoint. The functional the variation of which leads to equation (3.2) (as the
Euler equarion of the variational problem) can be written in the form

$$\int_V (-Lw \cdot w) dV = \int_V (A_{\alpha..\mu}^{\beta\lambda} w_{,\lambda}^{\mu})_{,\beta} w^{\alpha} dV = \tag{3.7}$$

$$= - \Phi + \int_S t_{\alpha} w^{\alpha} dS$$

where

$$\Phi = \int_V w_{,\beta}^{\alpha} w_{,\lambda}^{\mu} A_{\alpha..\mu}^{\beta\lambda} dV. \tag{3.8}$$

The condition of strong ellipticity of the system $A_{\alpha..\mu}^{\beta\lambda} \xi^{\alpha}\xi^{\mu}\zeta_{\beta}\zeta_{\lambda} > 0$ (identical with Hadamard's condition) and the condition of positiveness of the functional (3.8)

$$\mathfrak{F} \geq 0 \tag{3.9}$$

which according to (3.7) ensures the positiveness of the operator L,

$$(Lw, w) = \int_V (-Lw, w) dV \geq 0 \tag{3.10}$$

are decisive for the problems of existence and uniqueness of small deformations superposed on a finite deformation, and for the stability of the latter. We now proceed to consider in more detail these problems, making use of M. I. Vishik's results on strongly elliptic systems of equations, [4].

Introduce a linear manifold Ω_L of functions possessing first generalised derivatives, vanishing on the boundary S of V, on which the operator L is defined, in the space of functions with summable squares. Further, introduce the scalar product([5]).

$$(u, v) = \int_V u_{\alpha} v^{\alpha} dV \tag{3.11}$$

constructing in this way the Hilbert space $H(V)$. The operator L for $w \in \Omega_L$ is symmetric, i.e.

$$(Lu, v) = (u, Lv) \tag{3.12}$$

This property, according to (3.7) holds for the functions satisfying instead of the condition $w^{\alpha} = 0$ on S the condition $t_{\alpha} = 0$ or, more generally,

$$w^{\alpha} = 0 \text{ on } S_1 \text{ and } t_{\alpha} = 0 \text{ on } S_2, \quad S_1 + S_2 = S.$$

We first examine the case of constant $A_{\alpha..\mu}^{\beta\lambda}$. We shall prove that for $w^{\alpha} \in \Omega$ the property of strong ellipticity of the operator L is equivalent to the inequality

$$(Lu, u) = \Phi \geq \mu' \left(\frac{\partial u}{\partial u} , \frac{\partial u}{\partial x} \right) = \mu' \sum_{i,j=1}^{3} \int_V \left(\frac{\partial u_i}{\partial x_j} \right)^2 dV, \tag{3.14}$$

$$\mu' > 0,$$

([5]) Elements of Ω_L are denoted by u, v, w.

which in the classical elasticity is called the Korn inequality. Since

$$\left(\frac{\partial u}{\partial x}, \frac{\partial u}{\partial x}\right) \geq \mu''(u,u) \quad (6)$$

the operator L is then positive-definitive, i.e.

$$(Lu,u) \geq \mu(u,u). \tag{3.15}$$

To carry out the proof consider the Fourier transform of the function $u(x_i) \in \Omega$

$$u(x) = \left(\frac{1}{2\pi}\right)^{\frac{3}{2}} \int_{-\infty}^{\infty}\int\int e^{i(\lambda x)} U(\lambda)d\lambda$$

where $(\lambda x) = \lambda_1 x_1 + \lambda_2 x_2 + \lambda_3 x_3$, $d\lambda = d\lambda_1 d\lambda_2 d\lambda_3$. Simple transformations lead to the formula

$$Lu_\alpha(x) = \left(\frac{1}{2\pi}\right)^{\frac{3}{2}} \int_{-\infty}^{\infty}\int\int A_{\alpha..\mu}^{\beta\lambda}\lambda_\beta\lambda_\lambda U^\mu(\lambda)e^{i(\lambda x)}d\lambda.$$

Making use of the Parseval formula we obtain

$$(Lu,u) = \int_{-\infty}^{\infty}\int\int A_{\alpha..\mu}^{\beta\lambda}\lambda_\beta\lambda_\lambda U^\alpha U^\mu d\lambda. \tag{3.16}$$

The condition of strong ellipticity implies that there exists a constant $\mu > 0$ such that for arbitrary λ_α and ζ_α

$$A_{\alpha..\mu}^{\beta\lambda}\lambda_\beta\lambda_\lambda\zeta^\alpha\zeta^\mu \geq \mu\lambda_\alpha\lambda^\alpha\zeta_\beta\zeta^\beta.$$

Applying the latter inequality to the integrand in (3.16) we obtain

$$(Lu,u) \geq \mu \int_{-\infty}^{\infty}\int\int \lambda_\lambda\lambda^\alpha U_\beta U^\beta d\lambda.$$

---

(6) The proof is elementary. See for instance R. Courant and D. Hilbert, *Methoden der Mathematischen Physik*, v. II, Springer Verlag, Berlin (1931).

It can easily be verified that the right-hand side of the last relation is equal to $\left(\dfrac{\partial u}{\partial x}, \dfrac{\partial u}{\partial x}\right)$. This leads to (3.14) and completes the proof. Similarly, it can be shown that (3.14) implies strong ellipticity.

In the general case of a non-constant $A_{\alpha..\mu}^{\beta\lambda}$ the equivalence has been proved only for sufficiently small regions V; generally it can only be proved that (3.14) implies strong ellipticity. However, it follows from Vishik's considerations that for sufficiently smooth functions $A_{\alpha..\mu}^{\beta\lambda}$ the equivalence holds also in the general case.

The following result concerning the existence and uniqueness of solution is very important. The trivial boundary value problem ($w^{\alpha} = 0$ on S and homogeneous equation) for the system (3.2) has only trivial solutions, provided condition (3.14) is satisfied. Since the operator L is self-adjoint and the Fredholm alternative is valid, this implies that there exists in Ω_L (the domain of definition of L) a unique solution of the non-homogeneous equation

$$Lw = f \tag{3.17}$$

for an arbitrary $f \in H(V)$, or for the corresponding non-homogeneous boundary condition (w^{α} prescribed on S). Passing from one to the other of these problems is accomplished by introducing the appropriate particular solution of (3.17). Observe that for uniqueness, condition (3.15) is sufficient.

Consider now the condition of stability of finite deformation

$$\Gamma = \delta^2 \int_V W \, dV \geqq 0 \tag{3.18}$$

for $\delta u^{\alpha} = w^{\alpha} = 0$ on S. Simple transformations yield the relation

$$\Gamma = \int_V \delta^2 u_{,\beta}^{\alpha} \frac{\partial W}{\partial u_{,\beta}^{\alpha}} \, dV + \int_V w_{,\beta}^{\alpha} w_{,\lambda}^{\mu} \frac{\partial^2 W}{\partial u_{,\beta}^{\alpha} \, \partial u_{,\lambda}^{\mu}} \, dV.$$

Making use of the equilibrium equations (3.1) and the boundary condition it can easily be shown that the first integral vanishes. Consequently, taking into account (3.8) we obtain

$$\Gamma = \Phi = \int_V w_{,\beta}^{\alpha} w_{,\lambda}^{\mu} A_{\alpha..\mu}^{\beta\lambda} \, dV \tag{3.19}$$

and the condition of stability is (3.9) or (3.10)

$$\Phi = (Lw,w) \geqq 0. \tag{3.20}$$

The difference between this condition and the condition of strong ellipticity (or the equivalent condition (3.14)) is essential. In fact, first of all Φ, according to (3.20) can vanish even for $w^\alpha \neq 0$; moreover, even if in accordance with Kelvin's suggestion (see e.g. [2]) we separate the case of neutral stability $\Phi = 0$ and we demand that

$$\mathfrak{F} > 0 \quad \text{for } w_\alpha \neq 0 \tag{3.21}$$

this condition is equivalent to the positive definiteness of the operator (3.15). This latter however is weaker than (3.14). Thus, the condition of stability is weaker than the condition of strong ellipticity of the system. Condition (3.21) (or (3.15)) does not ensure existence but ensures uniqueness, if the solution exists; the last statement can be proved very easily. In fact, if w_1 and $w_2 \in \Omega_L$ are solutions of $Lw = f \in H(V)$, then $L(w_1 - w_2) = 0$ whence $(L(w_1 - w_2), w_1 - w_2) = 0$ and this implies that $w_1 = w_2$.

As concerns the spectra let us observe that the eigenvalues of a strongly elliptic operator are always positive whereas for the positive operator the zero is a point of the continuous spectrum of the operator.

Similarly to the classical elasticity the condition of strong ellipticity (3.14) makes it possible to apply variational methods to all static problems (all three boundary value problems).

REFERENCES

[1] C. Truesdell, Das ungelöste Hauptproblem der endlichen Elastizitätstheorie, *ZAMM*, **36**, (1956), 97.

[2] J. L. Ericksen and R. A. Toupin, Implications of Hadamard's conditions for elastic stability with respect to uniqueness theorem, *Canad. J. of Math.*, **7**, (1956), 432.

[3] W. Urbanowski, Deformed body structure, *Archiwum Mechaniki Stosowanej*, **13**, (1961), 277.

[4] M. I. Vishik, O silno ellipticheskikh sistemakh differentsyalnykh uravnenyi (in Russian) (On strongly elliptic systems of differential equations), *Matematitcheskii Sbornik*, **29**, (71), No. 3 (1951), 615.

[5] R. Hill, On Uniqueness and stability in the theory of finite elastic strain, *J. of Mech. and Ph. of Solids*, **5**, (1957), 229.

[6] C. Truesdell, The mechanical foundations of elasticity and fluid dynamics, *J. of Rat. Mech. and Analysis*, **1**, (1952), 125.

[7] A. E. Green, Torsional vibrations of initially strained circular cylinder, *Problems of Continuum Mechanics*, Contributions in the honour of 70th Birthday of N. I. Muskhelishvili, Philadelphia, (1961).

[8] J. Hadamard, *Leçons sur la Propagation des Ondes et les Equations de l'Hydrodynamique*, Paris, (1903).

[9] M. Hayes and R. S. Rivlin, Propagation of plane wave in an isotropic elastic material subjected to pure homogeneous deformation, *Arch. for Rat. Mech. and Analysis*, **8,** (1961), 15.

[10] A. E. Green and J. E. Adkins, *Large Elastic Deformation*, Oxford, Clarendon Press, (1960).

[11] M. Parodi, *La localisation des valeur caractéristiques des matrices et ses applications*, Paris, Gauthier-Villars, (1959).

THE APPLICATION OF SECOND-ORDER EFFECTS
IN ELASTICITY TO PROBLEMS OF CRYSTAL PHYSICS

Alfred Seeger

Max-Plank-Institut für Metallforschung, Stuttgart, and Institut für theoretische und angewandte Physik der Technischen Hochschule Stuttgart, Germany

ABSTRACT

Crystal physics offers a number of outstanding possibilities for applications of second-order elasticity. It is true that macroscopic crystals deform plastically or rupture at strains which are too small to exhibit easily measurable second-order effects. The non-elastic behaviour of crystals is, however, due to the movement of imperfections. These are imbedded in a perfect matrix, which follows the laws of elasticity up to strains of the order 10^{-1}. In the theory of these imperfections it is often advantageous to apply second-order elasticity, in particular to problems in which the linear theory of elasticity gives a vanishing result. Examples for such problems are the effect of dislocations (internal stresses) on the macroscopic density and the scattering of elastic waves from imperfections or from other lattice waves.

The general methods that have been developed to handle these problems are outlined, and a number of specific applications to crystal physics are discussed. The advantage of using second-order elasticity over techniques based on the concept of a crystal as a lattice of atoms is particularly apparent with respect to obtaining numerical results. Whereas up to now it has not been possible to obtain the higher order coupling constants between atoms in crystals, a number of experimental methods are available to measure the third-order elastic constants of both isotropic and anisotropic elastic media.

1. Introduction.

This paper is devoted to a discussion of the application of second-order effects in elasticity to problems in crystal physics. The majority of these applications will be on imperfections in crystals, in particular on dislocations, the imperfection responsible for the plastic properties of crystals. The use of elasticity in the theory of dislocations is rather old; as a matter of fact, it is older than the scientific study of imperfections in *crystals*. Whereas the theory of crystal defects has come into prominence only during the past three decades, the mathematical foundations for the theory of dislocations (as a concept in the theory of *self-strained elastic bodies*, not as imperfections in crystals) where laid at the beginning of the century by the work of Weingarten [1], Volterra [2] and Timpe [3].

At first sight it might appear surprising that an imperfection which plays such a dominant rôle in our present physical picture of the *plasticity* of crystals should be amenable to a useful analysis in terms of the theory of *elasticity*. The solution of this apparent paradox lies in the fact that the imperfections are imbedded in a perfect matrix that obeys the macroscopic laws of elasticity to a very good approximation. The plastic properties of the crystals come about by the movement of the dislocations under an applied stress, and it is these *movements* of the crystalline imperfections that cause the laws of elasticity to break down on a macroscopic scale even at small or moderate stresses and strains. Under normal conditions the imperfections occupy a very small fraction of the volume of the crystalline body.

From the view-point of the theory of elasticity the imperfections in crystals are described as *singularities* in the stresses or strains. The determination of the magnitude of the singulatities lies outside the scope of the theory of elasticity and must be obtained from crystal physics. To give an example, in elasticity theory a dislocation line is most simply described as a line singularity, characterized by its Burgers vector. Crystal physics restricts the possible Burgers vectors of (so-called complete) dislccations to lattice vectors, i.e. vectors connecting the positions of equivalent atoms in the crystal.

In regions sufficiently far from the singularities, the stresses and strains are small and may be adequately described by the linear theory of elasticity. On the other hand, close to the singularities the strains become very large, and it is obvious that the linear theory of elasticity can no longer be valid. If disloations are described as line singularities, the linear theory predicts stresses and strains that vary as the inverse first power of the distance from the dislocations and therefore may grow beyond all bounds. The infinities in the stresses and strains can be avoided by considering continuous distributions of dislocations of infinitesimal strength (dislocation strength = modulus of the Burgers vector) and by distributing the total dislocation strength over a tube of a cross section of atomic dimensions (the dislocation core) as suggested by crystal physics. However, been so the strains reach magnitudes of the order one tenth to unity. They are therefore too large to be treated adequately by the linear theory of elasticity. Nevertheless, on account of its simplicity, the linear theory of elasticity is an indispensable tool in the theory of defects in crystals and has had considerable success, e.g. in the study of the far-reaching stresses around dislocations, the interaction between distant imperfections, and in the calculations of defect energies. (As an illustration, dislocation energies are stored to about 9/10 in the long-range stress fields; only about ten percent of the dislocation energy is due to the dislocation core).

From the preceding discussion it might appear that the most important application of the theory of finite elasticity would be to the dislocation core, or, in the case of other imperfections such as atoms on interstitial sites, to the centre of the defect. However, up to now the theory of finite elasticity has not yet found any important applications to such problems, presumably for two reasons: firstly, in problems associated with the centres of the defects the atomistic nature of the defects is just as important as the deviations from Hooke's law, so that a continuum theory, even if carried through exactly, could not give a complete description of the central region of the defects. Secondly, for really large strains, i.e. strains of the order unity, the stress-strain relations for those materials which are of interest in crystal physics are not known. The stress–strain relations for crystalline materials are usually in the form of expansions of the elastic energy in terms of powers of stresses or strains. At present complete sets of the coefficients of these expansions are at best known up to third powers, corresponding to quadratic stress-strain relations. These quadratic relations are of course not adequate to describe strains of the order unity in crystals, since they do not allow for the fact that the potential energy of a crystal is a periodic function of the relative displacement of two neighbouring crystal planes. It might be mentioned that the so-called Peierls dislocation model (Peierls [4]—see also Seeger [5]) allows in a limited way for this periodicity. However, it does not employ finite elasticity in the proper sense, since all the non-linearit̀es occur in one plane only, the so-called glide plane of the dislocation.

For the reasons outlined in the preceding paragraph the most important applications of finite elasticity theory in crystal physics have been made to problems involving rather small strains, in which, however, the linear theory is inadequate. There are two simple prototypes of such situations: we may be interested in a quantity for which the linear theory happens to give a vanishing result, or the linear theory fails because of the validity of the super-position principle. (Of course, problems of the second kind may also be reckoned under the first group.) An example for the first prototype is furnished by the average values of stresses or strains in a self-strained elastic body. Albenga [6] has shown that static equilibrium requires the average of any stress component over a self-stressed body to be zero. For an elastically homo-geneous body obeying Hooke's law it follows that the average values of all strain components are zero, too. This has the interesting consequence that the linear theory of elasticity predicts a vanishing effect of dislocations on the macroscopic density of crystals, although experimentally dislocations are known to give a positive volume expansion. The best known example for the second prototype (inadequacy of the superposition principle) is the scattering of elastic waves from crystal imperfections (or indeed any strain field). Within the framework of the linear theory the superposition principle holds, and therefore the static strain field of the imperfection and the dynamic solution of an elastic wave superimpose without perturbing each other, i.e. without scattering of the wave. On the other hand, any inhomogeneity in an elastic body must scatter elastic waves. This scattering is known to be of importance in the low temperatures heat resistivity of insulating crystals, in which the heat transport occurs by the propagation of elastic waves.

The preceding examples belong to the class of problems considered by Reiner [7] in which the first order effects are zero and in which the second-order effects may not be neglected, although the strains involved are infinitesimal. Such problems are relatively simple from the computational point of view, since in order to obtain a satisfactory answer it often suffices to concentrate on the second-order effects and to neglect all higher powers in the stress-strain relations. A calculation consistent up to second-order may be carried out by the use of perturbation theory, starting from the solutions of linear elasticity as a first approximation. This is the approach which has been used in the examples to be discussed in the following paragraphs. It means that although we are dealing with non-linear problems, we do not actually have to find solutions to *non-linear* partial differential equations but can exploit fully the well-known techniques for solving the *linear* differential equations of mathematical physics.

2.   The effect of dislocations on the macroscopic density of crystals.

Among the problems posed by crystal physics to the theory of second-order elasticity we have introduced in section **1** the effect of dislocations (or of any other kind of internal strain) on the average density of macroscopic bodies. For isotropic media this problem was solved in general form by Zener [8], although without the explicit use of second-order elasticity. The physical argument of Zener may be described as follows: The energy of an elastic body is given by the sum of products of elastic moduli and quadratic invariants of the strain components. The elastic moduli are known to decrease with increasing specific volume of an elastic medium. For given strains the elastic energy may be lowered by an over-all expansion of the body. The expression for the average dilatation is therefore expected to contain the volume derivatives of the elastic moduli, which are special combinations of the third-order elastic constants. Making use of thermodynamic arguments in order to relate the dilatation connected with shear to the change of the shear modulus due to a dilatation, Zener finds the following expression for the average dilatation:

$$\bar{\Theta} = \frac{1}{K} \left[\left(- \frac{d\ln G}{d\ln V} - 1 \right) W_s + \left(- \frac{d\ln K}{d\ln V} - 1 \right) W_d \right]. \qquad (2.1)$$

In eqn. (2.1) V denotes the specific volume of the body, G and K are shear and bulk modulus, and W_s and W_d are defined as the reversible work done per unit volume in establishing the shear strains (W_s) and the dilatational strains (W_d). From the experimental viewpoint it is important that to a good approximation (for details see Seeger and Haasen [9]) W_s and W_d may be replaced by the energies stored during the isothermal generation of the internal strains in cold-working experiments, say. Furthermore, the variations of the elastic constants with volume may be expressed by the variations with an hydrostatic pressure p according to

$$- \frac{d \ln G}{d \ln V} = \frac{K}{G} \frac{dG}{dp}; \quad - \frac{d \ln K}{d \ln V} = \frac{dK}{dp} . \qquad (2.2a,b)$$

The pressure derivatives of the elastic constants have been measured for a number of materials. A comparison between the measured volume expansion due to dislocations and the stored energy of dislocations is therefore possible. The agreement between experiment and theory is good, although certainly not perfect [10].

Zener's expression equation (2.1) can be generalized to anisotropic media. The generalization to cubic crystals is particularly straightforward (Seeger [10]). Let K denote the bulk modulus, and C' and C'' the two shear moduli of cubic crystals. The corresponding terms in the expression for the elastic energies in terms of strains are W_d, W_s', and W_s''. The total elastic energy may therefore be written in the form

$$W = W_d + W_s' + W_s'' . \qquad (2.3)$$

The average dilation is then given by

$$\bar{\Theta} = \frac{1}{K}\left[\left(- \frac{d \ln K}{d \ln V} - 1\right) W_d + \left(- \frac{d \ln C'}{d \ln V} - 1\right) W_s' + \left(- \frac{d \ln C''}{d \ln V} - 1\right) W_s''\right].$$
$$(2.4)$$

Eqn. (2.1) and eqn. (2.4) have the form that we would expect from a calculation based on second order elasticity: the average dilatation is expressed as a quadratic form of the strain components, with coefficients that are linear combinations of the third-order elastic constants. For the present approximation it suffices to insert on the right hand side of eqns. (2.1) and (2.4) the strains as derived from the linear theory.

Eqn. (2.4) has also been derived from second order elasticity theory by Toupin and Rivlin [11]; the special case of eqn. (2.1) was obtained independently from second order elasticity by Pfleiderer, Seeger and Kröner [12]. The approaches used in these two papers are rather different. The approach of Pfleiderer, Seeger and Kröner [12] has also been applied to other dislocation problems and will be discussed in more detail in the next section.

3.   The calculation of second order internal strains.

In section **2** we have reported on a problem in second order elasticity that could be solved without employing the formal theory of finite elasticity. The simplified treatment was possible because we were interested only in the average of the dilatation over the whole body under consideration. If we wish to know the local value of the dilatation or of any other component of strain (or of the stresses), we have to use the full machinery of second order elasticity. It has been developed in essentially two different forms. The formalism based on the use of *displacement gradients* is described in the books by Murnaghan [13] and Green and Adkins [14], and in review articles by Rivlin [15], [16]. The alternative method is due to Kröner and Seeger [17] and employs *stress functions* (even for three dimensional problems), thereby avoiding (for isotropic media) the use of displacements and of displacement gradients. The latter method is particularly adapted to problems of internal strain, if the coordinates of the deformed body are used. The reasons for this are twofold: in problems of internal strain we have no external forces, and in final coordinates the conditions of static equilibrium are the same in finite elasticity and in infinitesimal elasticity, namely the vanishing of the divergence of the stress tensor.

In the absence of external forces, the "sources" of the internal strains are dislocations which may be continuously distributed. In the infinitesimal theory continuous distributions of dislocations are described by the dislocation density tensor α first introduced by Nye [18]. α relates the normal vector df of a surface element to the resulting Burgers vector db of the dislocations threading that element:

$$db = df \cdot \alpha \tag{3.1}$$

Kondo [19], Bilby [20], and Bilby, Bullough and Smith [21] have shown how to generalize this concept to finite strains by employing non-Riemannian geometry. The appropriate generalization of the dislocation density tensor α turns out to be Cartan's antisymmetric rank three torsion tensor. The fundamental geometrical equation of the theory is the vanishing of the Riemann curvature tensor, which expresses the fact that the deformed crystal is embedded in the three-dimensional Euclidian space and that it does not contain any inserted matter. These fundamental geometrical relations are the generalization of the St.Venant compatibility conditions to finite strains and to the presence of dislocations. In a medium containing dislocations the compatibility equations are in general violated. In the infinitesimal theory the degree of violation is measured by a second-order tensor, the incompatiblity tensor $\boldsymbol{\eta}$, which is derived from $\boldsymbol{\alpha}$ by differentiation.

The non-linear elastic theory of Kröner and Seeger [17] proceeds by satisfying the equations of equilibrium in final coordinates in the usual way by introducing stress functions and by relating the second derivatives of the stress function tensor (i.e. the stress tensor) through the strain-stress relations to the strains or the metric tensor. The fundamental geometrical equations furnish non-linear fourth order partial differential equations for the components of the stress function tensor. For the applications of interest in this paper it is convenient to solve this equation in an approximate way by perturbation theory, starting from the solution of the linear theory. The equations for such an iteration procedure are given explicitly by Pfleiderer, Seeger and Kröner [12] for straight dislocation lines. Second-order solutions of these equations were obtained for edge and screw dislocations lying along the axes of cylindrical tubes of circular cross sections. For details of the procedure reference is made to the original literature. We confine ourselves to a few remarks on the determination of the local dilatation in final coordinates intended mainly to illustrate the discussion of section **2**.

In an isotropic medium the dilatation Θ in final coordinates must be expressible in terms of the first and second invariants σ_I and σ_{II} of the stress tensor in the general form

$$\Theta = s_1\sigma_I + s_2\sigma_I^2 + s_3\sigma_{II}, \tag{3.2}$$

provided we confine ourselves to the second-order effects. The coefficients s_i are related to the elastic constants. They may be obtained by writing Θ in terms of the invariants of the strain tensor and by replacing the strain invariants through the stress-strain relations by the stress invariants. If K' and G' denote the pressure derivatives of K and G at zero pressure, Pfleiderer *et al.* [12] find

$$s_1 = \frac{1}{3K}$$

$$s_2 = \frac{1}{18K^2}(K'-1) + \frac{1}{6G^2}\left(G' - \frac{G}{K}\right) \tag{3.3}$$

$$s_3 = -\frac{1}{2G^2}\left(G' - \frac{G}{K}\right)$$

Restricting ourselves to a state of internal strain, we may apply Albenga's theorem (see section **1**), which tells us that the average value of any stress component in a homogeneous self-strained elastic body vanishes, giving $\bar{\sigma}_I = 0$. It is easily seen that the result agrees with eqn. (2.1). If we wish to know the local dilatation in the same approximation, we have to solve the differential equations for σ_I in second order. As mentioned above, this has been done for straight dislocation lines. As we would expect, the expression for the *local* dilatation contains not only the pressure derivatives of the elastic constants, but (in the case of an isotropic medium) also the third third-, order elastic constant. According to the theory of the electron gas in a metal, the scattering potential for the electrons is proportional to the local dilatation. Detailed calculations show that in a calculation of the electrical resistivity or dislocations in metals it is essential to take into account the second-order dilatational strains. Numerical results based on the second-order elasticity, theory have been derived for both edge and screw dislocations [22], [23] [24].

The method of Kröner and Seeger [14] looses some of its straightforwardness when it is applied to anisotropic media. First of all, the symmetry of a particular anisotropic medium exists only in the undeformed but not, in general, in the deformed state. The symmetry relations are therefore only exhibited if the constitutive equations are formulated in the initial state. Furthermore, the strains are not sufficient to describe the state of deformation of an anisotropic medium, since the rotation with respect to the crystallographic axes is also important. As long as we consider only singular dislocations (i.e. dislocation arrangements in which the dislocation density is different from zero only along lines or surfaces), it appears best to use the method of Toupin and Rivlin [11] based on the use of displacement gradients in initial coordinates. In isotropic media this method has been applied to the second-order treatment of a screw dislocation in the axis of an infinitely long tube of circular cross section [25]. As was mentioned above, the same problem has also been solved by the stress function method in final coordinates [12]. The comparison shows that the use of displacement gradients leads to much heavier calculations, so that in isotropic media its use cannot be recommended.

4.   Scattering of elastic waves from internal strains or from other elastic waves.

In sections **2** and **3** we dealt exclusively with static problems. We did not encounter any forces due to inertia and therefore did not have to consider the elastic displacements explicitly, at least not for isotropic media. In the present section we shall briefly discuss second-order problems connected with the propagation of elastic waves, in particular in relation to the scattering problems already introduced in section **1**.

The theory of elasticity is useful in describing elastic waves in crystals if the wave-lengths are much longer than the interatomic distances. In solid state physics we encounter such waves in two fields: physical acoustics, where standing or running waves of rather long wave-length are generated in solids by excitation from outside, and thermal motion in the solid at low temperatures, which according to Debye may be described by a superposition of elastic waves. Both types of waves are scattered by each other and by lattice imperfections, including those describable as states of internal strains. Examples for such scattering processes are: (1) The scattering of thermally excited waves from crystal imperfections. This process contributes to the thermal resistivity in solids in which the heat flux is carried by lattice waves. The same process is important in calculating the dragging force on a uniformly moving dislocation due to the thermal vibrations of the crystal. (2) The scattering of waves from each other. This process also may contribute to the low temperature heat conductivity in crystals. The interaction between an externally excited wave and thermal waves is the basic process of the "phonon viscosity" observed in the transmission of hypersonic waves through crystals at low temperatures. (3) The scattering of externally excited waves from internal strains or other inhomogeneities in crystals. This process contributes to the internal friction in solids.

In the majority of these applications the amplitudes of the waves involved are so small that they can be considered to be infinitesimal. In many cases, although not in all, the second order elastic theory suffices to give the essential features of the scattering processes and allows us to obtain quantitative estimates for the scattering cross sections involved. An extensive program is under way at the Technische Hochschule, Stuttgart, to apply in a systematic way the methods of finite elasticity to the scattering problems just outlined. A number of results have been obtained in the field of low temperature heat conductivity. Since these results will interest solid state physicists more than applied mathematicians, we shall confine ourselves mainly to a brief description of the general methods employed.

For the scattering of waves from waves, it is best to use the formulation of the theory in initial coordinates as expounded, for example, in Murnaghan's book [13]. In the theory of scattering of lattice waves from internal strains in isortopic media (to which the detailed calculations have been confined so far), we wish to retain the advantages of describing the state of internal strain in final coordinates using stress functions, and to avoid the use of a displacement field for the static strains. The necessary extension of the theory outlined in section 3 to the superposition of an infinitesimal time-dependent displacement field has been carried out by Bross [26].

In addition to the self-strained state, in which we have neither external nor inertia forces, Bross introduces the final state in which we have both the strains due to to the incompatibilities and the inertia forces. In addition to the strain tensor ε describing the self-strains in the coordinates of the self-strained state, a strain tensor γ is defined in the self-strained state which leads from that state to the final state. γ is a compatible strain and can therefore be expressed in terms of a displacement field s.

An energy density $\psi(\varepsilon, \gamma)$ can now be defined, which has the property that the components of the total stress follow (essentially) from ψ by differentiation with respect to γ. The internal stress has vanishing divergence. This means that the restoring forces vanish for vanishing values of γ, as they should for the description of wave propagation.

For practical purposes ψ is written as a power series in ε and γ. Higher powers in γ than the second are neglected, since we wish to treat the wave amplitudes as infinitesimal. In the usual way a linear second-order partial differential equation for the displacement field s associated with the wave-motion is obtained. The coefficients of this equation are known functions of ε, provided at least third powers of ε have been retained in ψ. This equation may be considered to describe the wave propagation in an inhomogeneous medium, the inhomogeneity of which is determined by the internal stresses. The usual method of solving this wave equation with variable coefficients is by perturbation theory, starting from unperturbed plane waves as the solution of zero order.

5.   The experimental determination of third-order elastic constants.

In problems of crystal physics, in which the linear theory of elasticity is inadequate, the use of non-linear elasticity has to compete with theories based on the atomistic structure of the crystals and on the force laws between the constituents of the crystals. Frequently a treatment based on the concept of atomic physics is necessary in order to obtain a satisfactory solution. However, it is often very difficult to obtain reliable numerical answers in this way due to our limited knowledge of the force laws between atoms in crystals. A typical example for this situation is the interaction between lattice wave propagating in a crystalline array of atoms coupled together by interatomic forces, characterized by the so-called coupling parameters. In the harmonic approximation the coupling parameters between nearest and next nearest neighbour atoms are known for a number of crystals. For a treatment of the scattering of lattice waves, however, anharmonic force laws are required. Unfortunately, very little is known about the numerical values of the anharmonic coupling parameters. This has forced earlier investigators of this problem to simplify it to the extent of replacing the different anharmonic coupling parameters by an average value which could be expressed in terms of the Grüneisen constant, which is a measure of the thermal expansion of the crystal. The situation is very much improved if we are justified to use the continuum description of the crystal, i.e. if all the wave-lengths involved are much larger than the lattice parameters of the crystal. Provided we confine ourselves to the lowest possible order, i.e. second order elasticity, only a limited number of non-linear elastic constants are involved, namely three in isotropic media, and six in cubic media. Since these constants appear in the coefficients of the third power terms in the expression of the energy density in terms of strains or stresses, they are usually called third-order elastic constants or coefficients.

Experimental methods are now available to obtain numerical values for the third-order elastic constants for most crystals in either the polycrystalline or monocrystalline form. Since an extensive discussion of these methods including the experimental data has been given elsewhere [27], we shall confine ourselves to a rather brief discussion of the principle possibilities. A certain combination of these constants can also be obtained from the thermal expansion.

The experimental determination of those third-order constants which may be expressed in terms of the pressure derivatives G' and K' of the ordinary elastic moduli (2 constants for an isotropic medium, and 3 constants for a cubic medium) is relatively simple. The reason for this is that most solids withstand large hydrostatic pressures without fracture or plastic flow. The elastic constants can therefore be measured under large hydrostatic pressure. The most powerful technique of doing this is the measurement of the velocities of ultrasonic waves.

For the measurement of the other third-order constants different methods have to be used, depending on whether under those stresses that are large enough to yield non-linear effects, the materials flow plastically, or whether they still deform elastically. In the latter case the ultrasonic method can be applied with biasing shear stresses rather than a hydrostatic stress. In this way, Hughes and Kelly [28] measured the third-order elastic constants of polycrystalline iron, although with limited experimental accuracy. With rather good accuracy the method has been applied to single crystals of germanium by Bateman, Mason, and McSkimin [29], who have obtained all 6 third-order elastic constants of this cubic crystal.

For polycrystalline ductile material the Poynting effect [30] of hard-drawn wires can be used in order to obtain two of the three third-order constants, provided the drawn wire can be considered to be elastically isotropic. Numerical values for the polycrystalline third-order elastic constants have in this way been obtained for copper and iron. For substances of which perfect whiskers (small monocrystalline fibers) can be grown, it is possible to determine the third-order elastic constants in a rather direct way from the deviations from Hooke's law under high stresses, even if macroscopic crystals would flow or fracture under these stresses. This method has been applied to iron whiskers, although not enough experimental data were available to allow a determination of a complete set of constants.

In summarizing it may be said that with a large enough experimental effort the third-order elastic constants could be determined for most of the materials of interest to crystal physics. In view of the importance of these constants it appears highly desirable that a systematic effort to measure these constants should be made.

We close with a brief remark on fourth-order elastic constants, about which very little is known. The only experimental information available has been derived from shock-wave measurements. These yield the information that for metals such as copper the fourth-order constant

$$K \frac{d^2K}{dp^2}\bigg|_{p \to 0}$$

is about unity. For purposes of comparison it may be noted that the corresponding third-order constant $\dfrac{dK}{dp}\bigg|_{p \to 0}$ is about 5. It appears therefore that the fourth-order constants are somewhat smaller than the third order constants, which is a partial justification for the use of second-order elasticity even under conditions of not truly infinitesimal strains.

Acknowledgments.

The present paper describes in part work that was sponsored by the Deutsche Forschungsgemeinschaft. For interesting and stimulating discussions the author would like to thank Drs. Bross, Kröner, and Stojanovich.

REFERENCES

[1]   G. WEINGARTEN, *Atti Acad. naz. Lincei, Rend. Cl. Sci. fi. mat. natur.*, V. Ser. **10**/1, (1901), 57.

[2]   V. VOLTERRA, *Ann. sci. Ecol. norm. sup. III.*, Ser. **24**, (1907), 401.

[3]   A. TIMPE, *Z. Math. Phys.*, **52**, (1905), 348.

[4]   R. E. PEIERLS, *Proc. Phys. Soc.*, **52**, (1940), 34.

[5]   A. SEEGER, Theorie der Gitterfehlstellen, Handbuch der Physik VII/1, Springer-Verlag Berlin-Göttingen-Heidelberg, (1955).

[6]   G. ALBENGA, *Atti Accad. Sci.*, Torino, *Cl. sci. fi. mat. natur.*, **54**, (1918/19), 864.

[7]   M. REINER, *Deformation and Flow of Solids*, Springer-Verlag, Berlin-Göttingen-Heidelberg, p. 203, (1956).

[8]   C. ZENER, *Trans. Amer. Inst. Min. Metallurg. Eng.*, **147**, (1942), 361.

[9]   A. SEEGER AND P. HAASEN, Phil. Mag. **3**, (1958), 470.

[10] A. SEEGER, *Suppl. Nuovo Cimento*, **7**, (1958), 632.

[11] R. A. TOUPIN AND R. S. RIVLIN, *Journ. math. Phys.*, **1**, (1960), 8.

[12] H. PFLEIDERER, A. SEEGER AND E. KRÖNER, *Z. Naturforschg.*, **15a**, (1960), 758.

[13] F. D. MURNAGHAN, *Finite Deformation of an Elastic Solid*, J. Wiley and Sons, New York, (1951).

[14] A. E. GREEN AND J. E. ADKINS, *Large Elastic Deformations and Non-linear Continuum Mechanics*, Oxford: At the Clarendon Press, (1960).

[15] R. S. RIVLIN, *Rheology, Theory and Applications*, Vol. 1, Academic Press, New York, p. 351, (1956).

[16] R. S. RIVLIN, *Structural Mechanics*, Pergamon Press, Oxford-London-New York-Paris, p. 169, (1960).

[17] E. KRÖNER AND A. SEEGER, *Arch. Rat. Mech. Anal.*, **3**, (1959), 97.

[18] J. F. NYE, *Acta metallurgica*, **1**, (1953), 153.

[19] K. KONDO, Memoirs of the unifying study of the basic problems in engineering sciences by means of geometry, Vol. I, Tokyo: Gakujutsu Bunken Fukyu-Kai, p. 351, p. 458 (1955).

[20] B. A. BILBY, *Progress in Solid Mechanics*, Vol. 1, Amsterdam: North Holland Publishing Company, p. 329, (1960).

[21] B. A. BILBY, R. BULLOUGH AND A. SMITH, *Proc. Roy. Soc.*, London, (1955), **A231**, 263.

[22] A. SEEGER AND H. BROSS, *Z. Naturforschg.*, **15a**, (1960), 663.

[23] H. STEHLE AND A. SEEGER, *Z. Physik*, **146**, (1956), 217.

[24] A. SEEGER AND H. STEHLE, *Z. Physik*, **146**, (1956), 242.

[25] A. SEEGER AND E. MANN, *Z. Naturforschg.*, **14a**, (1959), 154.

[26] H. BROSS, *Habilitationsschrift*, T. H. Stuttgart, (1961); Physica status solidi **2** (1962) (May issue).

[27] A. SEEGER AND O. BUCK, *Z. Naturforschg.*, **15a**, (1960), 1056.

[28] D. S. HUGHES AND J. L. KELLY, *Phys. Rev.*, **92**, (1953), 1145.

[29] T. BATEMAN, W. P. MASON AND H. J. McSKIMIN, *J. appl. Phys.*, **32**, (1961), 928.

[30] J. H. POYNTING, *Proc. Roy. Soc.*, London, **A86**, (1912), 534.

DISCUSSION

R. STOJANOVITCH, *University of Belgrade*

ON THE CALCULATION OF SECOND ORDER EFFECTS IN CONTINUA WITH DISLOCATIONS

The calculation of second-order elastic effects in continua with dislocations as outlined in section 3 of Professor Seeger's paper is based on an iteration procedure for the determination of internal stresses. This procedure is valid under the condition that the strain tensor ε can be presented in the form of a convergent series

$$\varepsilon = \varepsilon^1 + \varepsilon^2 + \varepsilon^3 + \dots \qquad \text{(indices suppressed)}$$

in which ε^1 corresponds to the linear stress-strain relations

$$\sigma_1 = C_1 \varepsilon^1 \quad (C_1 \text{ is the tensor of the second-order elastic constants)}$$

and $\varepsilon^1 > \varepsilon^2 > \dots$, so that ε^{k+1}, as well as $(\varepsilon^k)^2$, can be neglected in comparison with ε^k.

Under such an asumption it is possible to make a distinction between two kinds of second-order effects. Approximating the stress-strain relations by a quadratic polynomial (C_2 = third order elastic constants)

$$\sigma = C_1 \varepsilon + C_2 (\varepsilon)^2$$

within the quadratic approximation we can put $\varepsilon = \varepsilon^1 + \varepsilon^2$ and

$$\sigma = C_1 \varepsilon^1 + C_1 \varepsilon^2 + C_2 [(\varepsilon^1)^2 + 2\varepsilon^1 \varepsilon^2 + (\varepsilon^1)^2]$$

Here $\varepsilon^1 \varepsilon^2$ and $(\varepsilon^2)^2$ are small quantities of higher order than the second in comparison with ε^1, and can be neglected. The complete second-order contribution to the stress is given by $C_1 \varepsilon^2 + C_2 (\varepsilon^1)^2$. In the present approximation we can therefore write

(1) $$\sigma = C_1 \varepsilon^1 + C_1 \varepsilon^2 + C_2 (\varepsilon^1)^2$$

Hence, when the linearized equations for determination of internal stresses are solved, within the second-order approximation of stresses the terms involving the third-order elastic constants, $C_2 (\varepsilon^1)^2$, can be automatically added.

There remains for determination only ε^2, which presents a corrective term in the linear theory, and can be estimated by means of the linear stress–strain relations.

Let x^k be spatial coordinates in terms of which the final (deformed) state of a body with dislocations is given, a_{kl} the corresponding fundamental tensor. ε_{kl} the elastic strain tensor and α_{kl} the (given) dislocation density tensor. The fundamental equations [1] for determination of internal stresses read

$$(2) \quad -\epsilon^{jnm}\epsilon^{ilk}\overset{a}{\nabla}_n\overset{a}{\nabla}_l\,\varepsilon_{mk} = \eta_0^{ij}(\alpha) + \tfrac{1}{2}g^{pq}[\epsilon^{jnm}\epsilon^{ilk}(-2\varepsilon_{nkq} + h_{nkq})(-2\varepsilon_{mlp} + h_{mlp})]_{(ij)}$$

where ϵ^{jnm} is the antisymmetric Levi-Civita tensor, $\overset{a}{\nabla}_n$ denotes the covariant differentiation with respect to the a_{kl}-metric, $g_{pq} = a_{pq} - 2\varepsilon_{pq}$ and

$$(3) \quad \begin{aligned} 2\varepsilon_{pqr} &= \overset{a}{\nabla}_p\varepsilon_{qr} + \overset{a}{\nabla}_q\varepsilon_{rp} - \overset{a}{\nabla}_r\varepsilon_{pq} \\ 2h_{pqr} &= -(\varepsilon_{pqs}\alpha^s_{.r} + \varepsilon_{rps}\alpha^s_{.q} - \varepsilon_{qrs}\alpha^s_{.p}) \end{aligned}$$

$\eta_0^{ij}(\alpha)$ is the symmetric incompatibility tensor, completely specified when the dislocation density tensor is given*. For the sake of brevity we shall write

$$\epsilon^{jnp}\epsilon^{ilk}\overset{a}{\nabla}_n\overset{a}{\nabla}_l\varepsilon_{mk} \equiv (Ink\ \varepsilon)^{ij}$$

and

$$\tfrac{1}{2}g^{pq}[\epsilon^{jnm}\epsilon^{ilk}(-2\varepsilon_{nkq} + h_{nkq})(-2\varepsilon_{mlp} + h_{mlp})]_{(ij)} \equiv Q^{ij}[(-2\varepsilon ... + h ...)^2]$$

Tensors α and ε^1 are of the same order of magnitude [2].

For determination of internal stresses the equations (2) are to be solved together with the equilibrium conditions for stress in absence of body forces

$$(4) \quad \overset{a}{\nabla}_k\sigma^{kl} = 0$$

In the first linear approximation (2) and (4) reduce to

$$(5) \quad -(Ink\ \varepsilon^1)^{ij} = \eta_0^{ij}(\alpha); \quad \overset{a}{\nabla}_k\sigma_1^{kl} = 0$$

with

$$\sigma_1^{kl} = C_1^{klmn}\varepsilon_{mn}^1.$$

In the second linear approximation, writing $\sigma_2^{kl} = C_1^{klmn}\varepsilon_{mn}^2$ and $\varepsilon = \varepsilon^1 + \varepsilon^2$, and retaining only terms of the order of magnitude of ε^2 and $(\varepsilon^1)^2$, we get

$$Q^{ij}[(-2\varepsilon^1 ... -2\varepsilon^2 ... + h ...)^2] \approx Q^{ij}[(-2\varepsilon^1 ... + h ...)^2].$$

Since in the first approximation we have put $\overset{a}{\nabla}_k\sigma_1^{kl} = 0$, the equilibrium conditions for stress reduce to

[1] E. Kröner und A. Seeger, Arch. Rat. Mech. Anal., 3, 97–119 (1959); H. Pfleiderer, A. Seeger und E. Kröner, Zeitschr. fuer Naturforsch., 15a, 758–772 (1960); E. Kröner, Arch. Rat. Mech. Anal., 4, 273–334 (1960).
* The incompatibility tensor is essentially the curl of the dislocation density tensor, See ref. 2.
[2] E. Kröner, Kontinuumstheorie der Versetzungen und Eigenspannungen, Springer-Verlag, Berlin-Goettingen-Heidelberg (1958).

(6) $$\overset{a}{\nabla}_k\sigma_2^{kl} = 0,$$

and for the determination of the corrective strain ε_{kl} we have, besides (6) the equations

(7) $$-\epsilon^{jnm}\epsilon^{ilk}\overset{a}{\nabla}_n\overset{a}{\nabla}_l\varepsilon_{mk}^2 = a^{pq}[\epsilon^{jnm}\epsilon^{ilk}(-2\varepsilon_{nkp}^1 + h_{nkp})(-2\varepsilon_{mlq}^1 + h_{mlq})]_{(ij)},$$

where we have approximated g^{pq} by a^{pq}. (A better approximation is unnecessary since it would furnish us in eqn. (7) with terms of higher order than required.)

If the first-order problem has been solved, the right hand side of eqn. (7) is known. Eqns. (6) and (7) can be solved by the same methods that have been used to solve the linear problem eqn. (5), e.g. by the stress function method described in ref. 1 and 2.

The present work was done during the tenure of a Richard Merton visiting professorship at the Technische Hochschule Stuttgart. The author would like to thank the Deutsche Forschungsgemeinschaft for the award of the visiting professorship.

E. H. LEE: You have mentioned large strain effects associated with dislocations distributed throughout the material. Has any work been done on second-order effects associated with moving dislocations?

It seems to me that these may be important in studying the basic processes of plastic flow.

A. SEEGER's reply:

Replying to the question of Professor E. Lee:

A number of papers have been published on the motion and the dynamics of dislocations within the framework of the linearized theory. The only paper known to me dealing with the non-linear theory of moving dislocations is one by E. F. Holländer [Czech. J. Phys. B **12** (1962)]. It is a treatment of the kinematics of dislocations by non-Riemannian geometry. The more general problem of non-linear effects in the dynamics of dislocations has not yet been solved.

I agree that a non-linear treatment of dislocation dynamics would be of importance in the theory of plastic deformation. One of the basic problems in this field is that of the scattering of elastic waves from a moving dislocation or from a so-called kink in a moving dislocation. As discussed in my paper this problem is one requiring a non-linear treatment. We hope to study this problem in Stuttgart in the future.

FINITE ELASTIC DEFORMATION OF A PLANE STRAIN WEDGE-SHAPED RADIAL CRACK IN A COMPRESSIBLE CYLINDER

Paul J. Blatz*

Guggenheim Aeronautical Laboratory, California Institute of Technology, Pasadena, California

ABSTRACT

Linear elastic theory applied to the problem of calculating the stress-strain distribution at the base of a stationary crack involves itself in a contradiction by predicting a singular stress-strain field. For an assumed strain energy function, the exact nonlinear elastic theory has been applied to the problem of a radial crack spread by tangential forces. The phase plane of the nonlinear equilibrium equation evinces a saddle point and a separatrix. Asymptotic solutions are obtained. The actual deformation at the base of the crack is described under the term "keyhole effect."

1. Introduction.

The problem of the elastic stress-strain distribution around the base of a stationary crack has received much attention [1, 2, 3]. Inherent in all these analyses is the assumption of linearity which implies that the product of Hookean strains or the product of Hookean strain and rotation or the product of rotations can be neglected with respect to the Hookean strain itself. On the other hand, it is generally recognized that a singularity [4] of some sort exists at the base of a crack or indeed, in the neighbourhood of any geometrical discontinuity [5]. Thus the use of linear theory to predict large or singular stress-strain fields immediately restricts the analyst at best to an approximation, if not an inconsistency. The purpose of this report is to show how the actual elastic stress distribution in a simple geometry is modified by accounting for the terms which are ordinarily dropped in linear theory. It will be assumed that the material under discussion is perfectly elastic and compressible, so that no consideration is given to plastic deformation [6].

Because facile application of finite elastic theory is at present restricted to problems in which the displacement field can be specified in some sense, it is necessary to specify first a simple geometry with simple boundary conditions,

---

* Senior Research Fellow, California Institute of Technology, Pasadena, California.

and secondly, a simple strain-energy function. We choose the perfectly elastic lubricated wedge for which linear solutions have already been presented [7]. Since no shear stresses are involved, the complexity of the finite elastic formulation is minimized. In the following, it is assumed that all stress and deformation components are directed along a set of principal coordinate axes.

Secondly, it is necessary to choose a strain energy function which is at once representative of a typically compressible elastomer and at the same time is simple enough to allow for convenient analytical results. In general, the energy stored per unit volume of the deformed isotropic material is at best a function of the invariants [8] which are proper to the deformation tensor, isotropy assumed.

$$W = W\{I_1 \, I_2 \, I_3\} \tag{1}$$

where

$$I_1 = \sum \lambda_i^2 \tag{2}$$

$$I_2 = \sum_{i \neq j} \lambda_i^2 \lambda_j^2 \tag{3}$$

$$I_3 = \Pi \lambda_i^2 \tag{4}$$

$$\lambda_i = 1 + \tilde{e}_i \tag{5}$$

$$\tilde{e}_i = u_{i,i} \, ; \quad i \text{ not summed} \tag{6}$$

Among the supply of available rubbery materials, there are those [9] whose strain energy function is independent of I_2 and for which $\partial W/\partial I_1$ is a constant. For such materials, it follows that $\partial^2 W/\partial I_1 \partial I_3$ is zero, and therefore $\partial W/\partial I_3$ is independent of I_1. Thus we write:

$$W = C(I_1 - 3) + f(I_3) \tag{7}$$

By comparison with linear theory, it is readily shown that (7) can be expressed in a power series of the form

$$W = \frac{\mu_E}{2}(I_1 - 3) - \left(K_E + \frac{\mu_E}{3}\right)\ln J_3 + \left(K_E - \frac{2}{3}\mu_E\right)(J_3 - 1) + \frac{C}{2}(J_3 - 1)^2 + \ldots \tag{8}$$

where $J_3 = \sqrt{I_3}$ (9)

and where μ_E, K_E are respectively the shear and bulk moduli associated with the diagonalized deformation tensor:

$$E_i = \tilde{e}_i + \frac{1}{2}\tilde{e}_i^2 = \frac{\lambda_i^2 - 1}{2} \tag{10}$$

In the Hooke-Cauchy linear theory, E_i is ordinarily approximated by $\tilde{e}_i$, so that μ_E and K_E are also the ordinary coefficients of the linear theory. In what follows, it is assumed that the compressible elastomer is characterized by a strain energy of the form (8) terminated at the linear term in $(J_3 - 1)$. The constitutive law associated with (8) is then given by

$$T_i \lambda_i = t_i J_3 = \mu_E(\lambda_i^2 - 1) + (K_E - \tfrac{2}{3}\mu_E)(J_3 - 1) \tag{11}$$

Here T_i is engineering stress (per unit undeformed cross section), and t_i is the true stress.

Linear solution.

Figure 1 shows a schematic diagram of the problem at hand. An infinitely long rubbery cylinder of radius a is split lengthwise by a radial crack of depth a. Into this crack is inserted a lubricated wedge of flank angle 2ϕ, also of in-

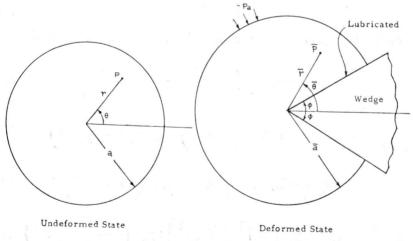

Undeformed State   Deformed State

Figure 1

finite length, the tip of which is assumed to meet the base of the crack (this statement will be subsequently modified). In order to prevent the rubbery log from slipping off the wedge, a compressive radial stress component P_a is applied to the circumferential periphery of the log. Under these specifications the displacement field is given as follows:

$$\bar{r} = \bar{r}(r) \tag{12}$$

$$\bar{\theta} = \phi + (\pi - \phi)\frac{\theta}{\pi} = \phi + (1 - \delta)\theta \tag{13}$$

$$\bar{z} = z \tag{14}$$

where superscript bars denote the coordinate variables of the deformed body. In linear notation, we have:

$$u \quad = \bar{r} - r \tag{15}$$

$$v \quad = r(\bar{\theta} - \theta) = r(\phi - \delta\theta) \tag{16}$$

$$w \quad = \bar{z} - z = 0 \tag{17}$$

$$\varepsilon_r \quad = \frac{du}{dr} \tag{18}$$

$$\varepsilon_\theta \quad = \frac{u}{r} - \delta \tag{19}$$

$$\varepsilon_z \quad = \varepsilon_{r\theta} = 0 \tag{20}$$

After satisfying equilibrium and setting $t_r = -P_a$ at $r = a$, we have:

$$t_r = -p_a - B\left(\frac{1}{r^2} - \frac{1}{a^2}\right) + \frac{\mu_E \delta}{1 - \nu}\ln\frac{a}{r} \tag{21}$$

$$t_\theta = -p_a + B\left(\frac{1}{r^2} + \frac{1}{a^2}\right) + \frac{\mu_E \delta}{1 - \nu}\left(\ln\frac{a}{r} - 1\right) \tag{22}$$

$$t_z = -2\nu p_a + 2\nu\frac{B}{a^2} + \frac{\nu}{1 - \nu}\mu_E \delta\left(2\ln\frac{a}{r} - 1\right) \tag{23}$$

$$2\mu_E\frac{u}{r} = -(1 - 2\nu)p_a + B\left(\frac{1 - 2\nu}{a^2} + \frac{1}{r^2}\right) + \mu_E \delta\left(\frac{1 - 2\nu}{1 - \nu}\ln\frac{a}{r} + 1\right) \tag{24}$$

At this point, it is tempting to specify that $u = 0$ at $r = 0$, and thereby set $B = 0$. However, this step will be deferred until the significance of what happens. at $r = 0$ is clearly understood in the light of the large deformation theory. Following this, equations (21) through (24) will be cast into a form suitable for comparison with the results of the subsequent section.

3. Finite elastic solution.

Following Rivlin [10], the components of the diagonalized deformation tensor associated with (12), (13), (14) are given by:

$$\lambda_r = \frac{d\bar{r}}{dr} \tag{25}$$

$$\lambda_\theta = \frac{\bar{r}}{r}(1 - \delta) \tag{26}$$

$$\lambda_z = 1 \tag{27}$$

Differentiation of (26) with respect to "r" leads to the relation

$$r\frac{d\lambda_\theta}{dr} = -[\lambda_\theta - (1 - \delta)\lambda_r] \tag{28}$$

with which the equilibrium equation can be rewritten:

$$t_\theta - t_r = \bar{r}\frac{dt_r}{d\bar{r}} = -\frac{\lambda_\theta}{\lambda_r(1 - \delta)}[\lambda_\theta - (1 - \delta)\lambda_r]\frac{dt_r}{d\lambda_\theta} \tag{29}$$

In terms of its radial and tangential components, (11) becomes

$$t_r = \mu_E\frac{\lambda_r}{\lambda_\theta} + (K_E - \tfrac{2}{3}\mu_E) - \frac{K_E + \dfrac{\mu_E}{3}}{\lambda_r\lambda_\theta} \tag{30}$$

$$t_\theta = \mu_E\frac{\lambda_E}{\lambda_r} + (K_E - \tfrac{2}{3}\mu_E) - \frac{K_E + \dfrac{\mu_E}{3}}{\lambda_r\lambda_\theta} \tag{31}$$

Substituting into (29) yields

$$\frac{d\lambda_r}{d\lambda_\theta} = -\frac{\lambda_r}{\lambda_\theta} \frac{1 + (1 - 2v)\lambda_r\lambda_\theta \left[\dfrac{(1 - \delta)\lambda_\theta - \lambda_r}{\lambda_\theta - (1 - \delta)\lambda_r}\right]}{1 + (1 - 2v)\lambda^2{}_r} \tag{32}$$

where

$$1 - 2v = \frac{\mu_E}{K_E + \dfrac{\mu_E}{3}} \tag{33}$$

Along with (32), we need (28) rewritten as:

$$\frac{d \ln r}{d\lambda_\theta} = -\frac{1}{\lambda_\theta - (1 - \delta)\lambda_r} \tag{34}$$

It is convenient to define:

$$\lambda'_\theta = \lambda_\theta \sqrt{1 - 2v} \tag{35}$$

$$\lambda'_r = \lambda_r \sqrt{1 - 2v} \tag{36}$$

with which (26), (30), (31), (32), and (34) become:

$$\bar{r} = \frac{r\lambda'_\theta}{(1 - \delta)\sqrt{1 - 2v}} \tag{37}$$

$$\frac{2v}{1 - 2v} - \frac{t_r}{\mu_E} = \frac{1}{\lambda'_r\lambda'_\theta} - \frac{\lambda'_r}{\lambda'_\theta} \tag{38}$$

$$\frac{2v}{1 - 2v} - \frac{t_\theta}{\mu_E} = \frac{1}{\lambda'_r\lambda'_\theta} - \frac{\lambda'_\theta}{\lambda'_r} \tag{39}$$

$$\frac{d\lambda'_r}{d\lambda'_\theta} = -\frac{\lambda'_r}{\lambda'_\theta} \frac{1 + \lambda'_r\lambda'_\theta \left[\dfrac{\lambda'_\theta(1 - \delta) - \lambda'_r}{\lambda'_\theta - (1 - \delta)\lambda'_r}\right]}{1 + \lambda'^2_r} \tag{40}$$

$$\frac{d \ln r}{d\lambda'_\theta} = -\frac{1}{\lambda'_\theta - (1 - \delta)\lambda'_r} \tag{41}$$

At the boundary $(r = a)$, (38) becomes:

$$\frac{2v}{1 - 2v} + \frac{p_a}{\mu_E} \equiv 2k = \frac{1}{\lambda'_{ra} \lambda'_{\theta a}} - \frac{\lambda_{ra}}{\lambda'_{\theta_1}}$$

4. Topology of the phase plane.

In order to investigate the behavior of (40), we look first at the phase plane $(\lambda', \lambda'_\theta)$ and then seek an asymptotic solution. By definition, λ_θ is positive; and, λ_r must also be positive to guarantee continuity of the material. Therefore, Figure 2 describes only the upper right (NE) quadrant of the phase plane. All integration paths in this quadrant will follow the direction $dr < 0$, i.e. from $r = a$ to $r \to 0$. It follows from (41) that the NE quadrant is split by the separatrix

$$\lambda'_r = \frac{\lambda'_\theta}{1 - \delta} \tag{43}$$

into two segements designated as

$$\{\text{I} \quad \text{II} \quad \text{III}\} \quad \text{when} \quad \lambda'_r < \frac{\lambda'_\theta}{1 - \delta} \tag{44}$$

$$\text{IV} \qquad \text{when} \qquad \lambda'_r > \frac{\lambda'_\theta}{1 - \delta} \tag{45}$$

There is also a saddle point at $\lambda'_r = \lambda'_\theta = 0$, so that trajectories in $\{\text{I II III}\}$ are directed toward and along the λ'_θ axis, which in turn acts as a separatrix from the SE quadrant. Similarly, trajectories in IV are directed toward and along the λ'_r axis, which in turns act as a separatrix from the NW quadrant.

In segment IV, it follows, using (40), that:

for $\qquad\qquad dr < 0, \quad d\lambda'_\theta < 0, \text{ and } d\lambda'_r > 0 \tag{46}$

The inequalities (46) suggest that an asymptotic solution obtains as $\lambda'_\theta \to 0$, $\lambda'_r \to \infty$, for which (40) becomes:

$$\frac{d\lambda'_r}{d\lambda'_\theta} = -\frac{1}{\lambda'_r \lambda'_\theta} - \frac{1}{1 - \delta} \tag{47}$$

Integration on the assumption that $(\lambda'_r \lambda'_\theta \ll 1 - \delta)$ yields:

$$\lambda'_r = \sqrt{-2 \ln c \, \lambda'_\theta} \tag{48}$$

which is consistent with this assumption, and with (46).

Substitution into (41) with integration yields:

$$\ln \frac{r}{a} = \frac{\lambda'_\theta}{(1 - \delta) \sqrt{-2 \ln c \, \lambda'_\theta}} \tag{49}$$

Obviously (49) applies only to the case $r > a$, and thus solutions in segment IV are extraneous to the problem at hand.

Returning to segment {I II III}, we note (Figure 2) that the subsegments are designated by:

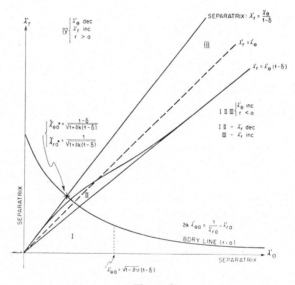

Figure 2
Phase Plane of the Equilibrium Equation

I,   when $\lambda'_r < \lambda'_\theta(1 - \delta)$, in which case, when $dr < 0$, then $d\lambda'_\theta > 0$, and $d\lambda'_r < 0$

$$\tag{50}$$

II, when $\lambda_\theta'(1 - \delta) < \lambda_r' < \dfrac{\lambda_\theta'}{1 - \delta}$, $1 + \lambda_r'\lambda_\theta'\left[\dfrac{\lambda_\theta'(1 - \delta) - \lambda_r'}{\lambda_\theta' - (1 - \delta)\,\lambda_r'}\right] < 0$, in which

case, when $dr < 0$, then $d\lambda_\theta' > 0$ and $d\lambda_r' < 0$ $\qquad$ (51)

III, when $\lambda_\theta'(1 - \delta) < \lambda_r' < \dfrac{\lambda_\theta'}{1 - \delta}$, and $1 + \lambda_r'\lambda_\theta'\left[\dfrac{\lambda_\theta'(1 - \delta) - \lambda_r'}{\lambda_\theta' - \lambda_r'(1 - \delta)}\right] < 0$, in

which case, when $dr < 0$, then $d\lambda_\theta' > 0$, $d\lambda_r' > 0$ $\qquad$ (52)

It is already observed that all paths in subsegment III eventually cross over into {I II}, and so the asymptotic behavior of {I II III} is characterized by $\lambda_r' \to 0$, $\lambda_\theta' \to \infty$, for which (40) becomes

$$\frac{d\lambda_r'}{d\lambda_\theta'} = -\frac{\lambda_r'}{\lambda_\theta'} - (1 - \delta)\lambda_r'^2 \qquad (53)$$

Integration yields:

$$\lambda_r' = \frac{1}{(1 - \delta)\lambda_\theta' \ln c\,\lambda_\theta'} \qquad (54)$$

To the same order of approximation, (41) yields:

$$r\lambda_\theta' = \text{constant} \qquad (55)$$

From the definition (37), it follows that the Lagrangian variable must also approach a constant value designated by a_c, a cavity radius, so that (55) becomes

$$r\lambda_\theta' = \sqrt{1 - 2\nu}\,(1 - \delta)\,a_c \qquad (56)$$

This striking result is one of the unusual phenomena encountered in nonlinear elasticity and will be termed the "keyhole" effect.

Obviously, when the crack is spread tangentially, the appearance of the keyhole at the base of the crack will produce a shear deformation which will tend to prevent the keyhole formation. In order to anticipate and prevent this effect, we assume that the base of the wedge is also shaped as a keyhole, where the keyhole radius is a predetermined function of the quantities

$$a_c = a_c \left\{\frac{p_a}{\mu_E},\ \nu,\ \delta,\ \lambda_{\theta a}\right\} \qquad (57)$$

The boundary condition (42) depends only on p_a/μ_E and v, and the curve for it is depicted in Figure 2. This curve intersects the separatrix at

$$\lambda_{\theta a}^{\prime *} = \frac{1 - \delta}{\sqrt{1 + 2k(1 - \delta)}}, \qquad \lambda_{ra}^{\prime *} = \frac{1}{\sqrt{1 + 2k(1 - \delta)}} \qquad (58)$$

Now observe that at this point the cavity radius must be zero, because

$$\frac{d\ln r}{d\lambda_\theta^\prime} \to -\infty \quad \text{as} \quad (\lambda_{\theta a}^\prime - \lambda_{\theta a}^{\prime *}) \to 0 \qquad (59)$$

Equation (59) implies that a slight increase in $\lambda_\theta^\prime$ immediately reduces r to zero, and therefore $\bar{r} = a_c$ to zero.

Suppose now in addition to applying a compressive stress at $r = a$, the outer boundary is also prevented from displacement after the keyhole-wedge is inserted. This implies that

$$\lambda_{\theta a}^\prime = (1 - \delta)\sqrt{1 - 2v} \qquad (60)$$

In general, for given $\{v, p_a/\mu_E$ and $\delta\}$ there will be some finite a_c. As δ is increased for fixed v and p_a/μ_E, and maintaining condition (56), a_c will decrease until the separatrix is reached, i.e. when

$$\sqrt{1 - 2v}(1 - \delta^+) = \frac{1 - \delta^+}{\sqrt{1 + 2k(1 - \delta^+)}} \qquad (61)$$

This implies that

$$\delta^+ = \frac{1}{1 + \dfrac{2v}{(1 - 2v)\, p_a/\mu_E}} \qquad (62)$$

If now, δ is increased further, either p_a/μ_E must be increased; or, if p_a/μ_E is maintained constant, then the outer boundary will displace outwards, with

$$\lambda_{\theta a}^\prime > \sqrt{1 - 2v}(1 - \delta) \qquad (63)$$

Suppose, on the other hand, that $\delta = \delta^+$, and p_a/μ_E is increased, then the outer boundary will displace inwards, with

$$\lambda_{\theta a}^\prime < \sqrt{1 - 2v}\,(1 - \delta) \qquad (64)$$

From (62), (63) and (64), it follows that the keyhole effect only operates for

$$\frac{p_a}{\mu_E} > \frac{\delta}{1-\delta} \frac{2v}{1-2v} \tag{65}$$

The preceding statements are summarized in Figure 3.

Behaviour of cavity radius a_c

Fix	Vary	Result
$v_1 \dfrac{P_a}{N}$, $\lambda_{\theta a} = 1 - s$	inc $\delta^* \to \dfrac{1}{1 + \dfrac{2v}{1-2v}\left(\dfrac{P_a}{N}\right)}$	$a_c \to 0$
$v_1 \delta, \lambda_{\theta a} = 1 - \delta$	dec $\dfrac{P_a}{N} \to \dfrac{\delta}{1-\delta} \dfrac{2v}{1-2v}$	$a_c \to 0$
$v, \dfrac{P_a}{N}, \delta$	dec $\lambda_{\theta a}^* \to \dfrac{1-\delta}{\left\vert(1-2v)[1+2k(1-\delta)]\right.}$	$a_c \to 0$
$\dfrac{P_a}{N}, \delta, \lambda_{\theta a} = 1 - \delta$	inc v	$a_c \to 0$

Figure 3

5. Nature of the singularity.

At the base of crack, we have, using (50) and (51)

$$\lambda_\theta \to \frac{(1-\delta)a_c}{r} \tag{66}$$

$$\lambda_r \to \frac{r}{(1-2v)(1-\delta)^2 a_c \ln\left[\dfrac{C\sqrt{1-2v}\,(1-\delta)\,a_c}{r}\right]} \tag{67}$$

$$\frac{t_\theta}{\mu_E} \to \frac{(1-2v)(1-\delta)^3 a^2{}_c}{r^2} \ln\left[\frac{C\sqrt{1-2v}(-\delta)a_c}{\gamma}\right] \tag{68}$$

$$\frac{t_r}{\mu_E} \to -(1-\delta)\ln\left[\frac{C\sqrt{1-2v}(1-\delta)\,a_c}{r}\right] \tag{69}$$

In the infinitesimal case, setting $u = 0$, at $r = a$, we have, from (21), (22), (24):

$$\lambda_\theta \to \frac{1-\delta}{4(1-v)}\left[\frac{p_a}{\mu_E}(1-2v)-\delta\right]\frac{a^2}{r^2} \tag{70}$$

$$\lambda_r \to \frac{-1}{4(1-v)}\left[\frac{p_a}{\mu_E}(1-2v)-\delta\right]\frac{a^2}{r^2} \tag{71}$$

$$\frac{t_\theta}{\mu_E} \to \frac{1}{2(1-v)}\left[\frac{p_a}{\mu_E}(1-2v)-\delta\right]\frac{a^2}{r^2} \tag{72}$$

$$\frac{t_r}{\mu_E} \to \frac{-1}{2(1-v)}\left[\frac{p_a}{\mu_E}(1-2v)-\delta\right]\frac{a^2}{r^2} \tag{73}$$

The only similarity in the two theories arises in the case of the tangential stress which approaches infinity with an inverse square dependence on r. This infinite tangential stress arises because what was originally a point becomes deformed into a sector of a circle. The radial stress in the non-linear theory is nonsingular as opposed to another inverse square singularity of opposite sign in the linear theory.

Turning now to the deformation components, we first note that the linear theory predicts an infinite $1/r$-type displacement at the crack base. This is a striking example of the bound inconsistencies of linear theory. Normally, one avoids this by setting $u = 0$, at $r = 0$, rather than $u = 0$ at $r = a$. We chose the latter in order to effect a direct comparison with the nonlinear theory. The linear theory also predicts a $1/r^2$-type singularity for the radial-strain, whereas the nonlinear theory is again nonsingular. Thus a true singularity around the base of a perfectly elastic crack occurs only in the stresses.

Note that, in the linear theory, the sign of all singularities is determined by the coefficient, $[p_a/\mu_E(1-2v) - \delta]$, If we apply (65), we find that this factor is positive if $2v > 1 - \delta$, and vice versa.

6. Numerical results.

Equations (37), (38), (39) were integrated on an IBM 704. Figures 4, 5, 6, 7, 8, respectively describe the behavior of t_θ, t_r, λ_θ and λ_r as a function of

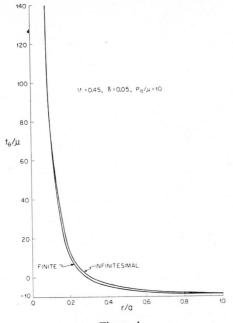

Figure 4
Tangential Stress vs Radius

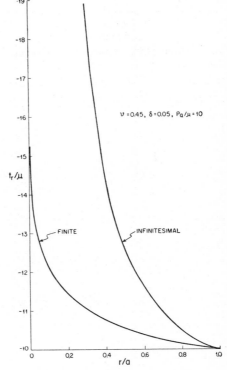

Figure 5
Radial Stress vs Radius

PAUL J. BLATZ

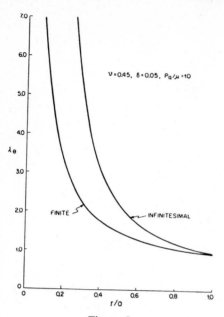

Figure 6
Tangential Deformation Ratio vs Radius

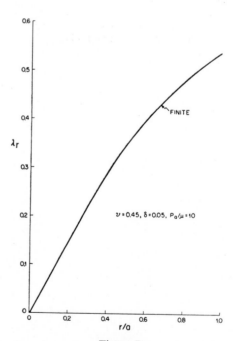

Figure 7
Radial Deformation Ratio vs Radius
(Nonlinear Theory)

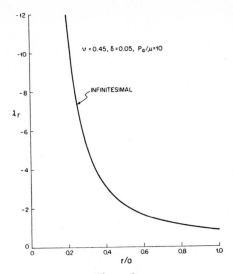

Figure 8
Radial Deformation Ratio vs Radius (Linear Theory)

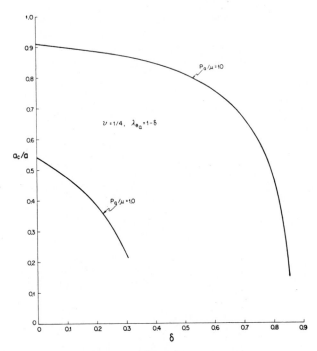

Figure 9
Cavity Radius vs Half-Angle of Wedge

PAUL J. BLATZ

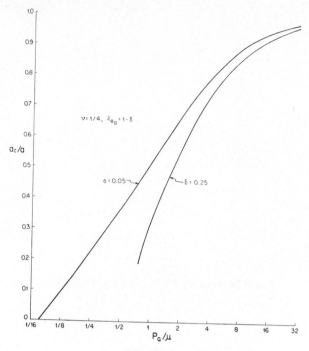

Figure 10
Cavity Radius vs Boundary Pressure

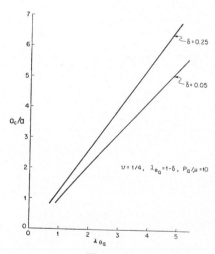

Figure 11
Cavity Radius vs Boundary Displacement

r/a for both linear and nonlinear theories, for the boundary condition $\lambda_{\theta a} = = 1 - \delta$. Figures 9, 10, 11 describe the behavior of the cavity radius summarized in Figure 3.

The writer wishes to thank Professor M. L. Williams* for stimulating discussions on this problem.

REFERENCES

[1] C. E. INGLIS, Stresses in a plate due to the presence of cracks and sharp corners, *Trans. Instn. Naval Archit.*, **55**, (1913), 219.

[2] H. NEUBER, Ein neuer Ansatz zur Lösung räumliche Probleme der Elastizitätstheorie, *Z. Ang. Math. Meck*, **14**, (1934), 203.

[3] I. N. SNEDDON, The distribution of stress in the neighbourhood of a crack in an elastic solid, *Proc. Roy. Soc. A.*, **187**, (1946), 229.

[4] M. L. WILLIAMS, Stress singularities resulting from various boundary conditions in angular corners of plates in extension, *Journal Applied Mechanics*, **19**, (1952), 526.

[5] E. STERNBERG AND R. A. EUBANKS, On concept of concentrated loads, *Journal Rational Mechanics and Analysis*, **10**, (1955), 135.

[6] MURCH S. A. AND P. M. NAGDHI, On infinite elastic perfectly plastic wedge, *Proc. Third U.S. National Congress Applied Mechanics*, June 1958.

[7] E. STERNBERG AND W. T. LOITER, The wedge under a concentrated couple, *Journal Applied Mechanics*, **25**, (1958) 575.

[8] C. TRUESDELL, Mechanical foundations of elasticity, *Journal Rational Mechanics and Analysis*, **1**, (1952), 132.

[9] A. CIFERRI AND P. J. FLORY, Stress-strain isotherm for polymer networks, *Journal Applied Physics*, **30**, (1959), 1498.

[10] R. S. RIVLIN, Large elastic deformations of isotropic materials VI. *Phil Trans. Roy. Soc. London (A)*, **242**, (1949), 173.

* Professor, Californa Institute of Technology, Pasadena, California.

GENERALIZED STRAIN MEASURE WITH APPLICATIONS TO PHYSICAL PROBLEMS

B. R. SETH

*Indian Institute of Technology, Kharag-pur, India, and Mathematics Research Center, United States Army, University of Wisconsin, Madison**

ABSTRACT

All the known strain measures can be represented by the generalized strain measure $(1 - ne)^{-1/n}$ where n may be called the coefficient of strain measure. Any stress-strain tensor relation cannot give a complete quantitative picture. The result obtained by using any one of them will have to be generalized to conform to experimental data. The generalization may be justified by assuming the coefficients of the medium to be functions of the strain invariants. The introduction of new coefficients of the medium may therefore not be found necessary in many cases.

1. Introduction.

The concept of stress is well defined through the primitive concepts of force and area-vector. Such is not the case with strain for which displacement-gradients have to be used, with the result that we find various measures of it used in literature. In particular we have measures due to Cauchy, Green, Hencky, Almansi, Swainger and Wall [1]. The classical theory of elasticity employs the Cauchy measure when the strain is small and only linear terms in displacement gradients referred to the unstrained state are retained. The theory of finite deformation uses the Almansi or Green measure. Hencky's measure is useful in plasticity. Swainger uses linear displacement gradients, but referred to the strained state. Wall combines some of these measures to get new ones. It may therefore be some interst to suggest a generalized strain measure which includes all of them as particular cases.

In general it is difficult to find stress-strain tensor relations suitable for giving good quantitative results. The generalized strain measure can indicate how a particular result may be extended for obtaining better agreement with experimental data. It may be possible to derive these improved results by taking the elastic constants as functions of strain invariants and not as absolute constants. Thus a reasonable justification may be obtained for a number of

* Sponsored by the Mathematics Research Center, United States Army, Madison, Wisconsin, under Contract No. DA-11-022-ORD-2059.

ad hoc empirical formulae used in literature. We may also find that the recent tendency to use new coefficients of the medium may not be pursued in all cases.

2. Generalized strain measure.

As the strain tensor e_{ij} is symmetric we may associate it with a quadric surface, known as Cauchy's strain quadric, at any point P, such that

$$e_{ij}x^i x^j = \text{a constant}. \tag{2.1}$$

If Λ_i be its principal axes and a_i and x_i are the coordinates before and after strain we may write

$$\sum da_i^2 = \sum dx_i^2 / \Lambda_i^2. \tag{2.2}$$

Any suitable function of Λ_i which vanishes for $\Lambda_i = 1$ when there is no deformation may constitute a measure of strain. If we put

$$\Lambda = (1 - ne)^{-1/n}, \tag{2.3}$$

we notice that it includes all the known measures. In fact we have the following results:

$$n = -1, \quad \Lambda = 1 + e, \quad \text{Cauchy } (C)$$
$$n = -2, \quad \Lambda = (1 + 2e)^{\frac{1}{2}}, \quad \text{Green } (G)$$
$$n = 0, \quad \Lambda = \exp(e), \quad \text{Hencky} (H)$$
$$n = 2, \quad \Lambda = (1 - 2e)^{-\frac{1}{2}}, \quad \text{Almansi} (A) \tag{2.4}$$
$$n = 1, \quad \Lambda = (1 - e)^{-1}, \quad \text{Swainger} (S)$$
$$n = \infty, \quad \Lambda = 1, \quad \text{No strain} (N)$$

We can therefore call n the coefficient of strain measure and Λ as a generalized strain measure. The strain components of the measures in (2.4) have been calculated by Cauchy, Green [1], Murnaghan [2], Reiner and Hanin [3] and others. Seth [4] has stressed the use of the A-measure in a number of applications.

We shall now illustrate the use of the generalized strain measure by a few examples. In the case of simple shear it will be shown that Rivlin's [5] result that no two of the normal stresses may be equal can be obtained without using any additional elastic constant.

3. Homogeneous pure strain.

In this case the displacement is given by

$$\mathbf{u} = \mathbf{cx}, \quad \mathbf{c} = \begin{bmatrix} c_1 & 0 & 0 \\ 0 & c_2 & 0 \\ 0 & 0 & c_3 \end{bmatrix} \tag{3.1}$$

The principal pure strains are:

$$e_{11} = \frac{1}{n}(1 - c_1^{-n}), \ e_{22} = \frac{1}{n}(1 - c_2^{-n}), \ e_{33} = \frac{1}{n}(1 - c_3^{-n}). \tag{3.2}$$

The strain invariants are:

$$I = \frac{1}{n}(3 - \sum c_i^{-n}),$$

$$II = \frac{1}{2n^2} \sum (1 - c_i^{-n})(1 - c_j^{-n}), \quad i \neq j, \quad i, j = 1, 2, 3, \tag{3.3}$$

$$III = \frac{1}{n^3}(1 - c_1^{-n})(1 - c_2^{-n})(1 - c_3^{-n}).$$

The cubical dilatation $e_v = (v/v_0 - 1)$, is

$$(1 - nI + n^2 II - n^3 III)^{-1/n} - 1. \tag{3.4}$$

For $n = 0$, which is H-measure, it takes the simpler form $\exp(I) - 1$. For N-measure it is obviously zero, as it should be.

We now treat the cases of simple tension, hydrostatic pressure, simple shear and yield condition. In each case the results given by using generalized strain and a linear stress-strain tensor relation involving two elastic constants are extended and then justified by taking the elastic constants as functions of the strain invariants.

4. Generalized tension-stretch law.

In this case $c_1 = c_2$ and from (3.1) and (3.2) we get

$$I = \frac{1}{n}(3 - 2c_1^{-n} - c_3^{-n})$$

$$II = \frac{1}{n^2}(1 - c_1^{-n})(3 - c_1^{-n} - 2c_3^{-n}), \qquad (4.1)$$

$$1 - c_3^{-n} = \frac{1}{3}n[I \pm 2(I^2 - 3II)^{\frac{1}{2}}].$$

The tension-stretch law is found to be governed by the equation [4]

$$T = \frac{1}{n}E[1 - (1 + s)^{-n}], \qquad (4.2)$$

where E is Young's modulus and s is the ordinary stretch of the classical theory.

For A-measure $n = 2$ and we get the result due to Seth [4]. From (4.2) we derive the following conclusions, not given by the classical theory $n >$ or < 0 according as the reference framwork is strained or unstrained.

(i) A yield point is indicated at $T = E/n$.

(ii) Tension and compression results are not similar.

(iii) For infinite compression, of $T \to -\infty$, thus showing that no amount of stress can reduce the length to zero.

(iv) $\dfrac{dT}{ds} = \dfrac{E}{(1 + s)^{n+1}}$

This is equal to E only at $s = 0$; otherwise the strain increases much faster than stress in tension.

From (4.1) we see that the yield point occurs at $T = E/n$ which is a very high value if the classical value of E is used. It should therefore be generalized. An obvious extension of it is

$$T = = A\left[1 - \frac{1}{(1 + s)^{\alpha}}\right], \qquad (4.3)$$

where A and α are constants to be adjusted. A can now represent the yield stress θ and α can be taken as E/θ.

Comparing (4.2) with (4.3) we see that we can obtain this later form if we take E as given by

$$E = nA \frac{1 - c_3^{-\alpha}}{1 - c_3^{-n}}$$

$$= \alpha A \left[1 - \frac{1}{6}(\alpha - n)\{I \pm 2(I^2 - 3II)^{\frac{1}{2}}\} + \dots \right].$$

(4.4)

As a first approximation $E = \alpha A$; in general it can be taken as a function of the strain invariants I and II.

5. Hydrostatic pressure.

In this case all the c's are equal and the pressure-volume relation is found to be

$$p = \frac{3k}{n} \left[\left(\frac{v_0}{v} \right)^{\frac{1}{3}n} - 1 \right].$$

(5.1)

For A-measures it reduces to Murnaghan's [2] result, which gives very good agreement with Bridgeman's [6] result on the compression of sodium at high pressures. Here k is the ordinary coefficient of cubical expansion. To get better agreement with results at very high pressures, which may be of the order of 20,000 atmospheres, Murnaghan, without giving any justification, generalized (5.1) into

$$p = A \left[\left(\frac{v_0}{v} \right)^{\alpha} - 1 \right],$$

(5.2)

and determined A and α from Bridgeman's experimental data. We can readily see that (5.2) can be derived from (5.1) if k is taken as a suitable function of the invariant. I. From (3.2) we have

$$I = \frac{3}{n}(1 - c^{-n}), \quad c_1^3 = v/v_0.$$

Hence

$$k = \frac{1}{3}nA\frac{(v_0/v)^\alpha - 1}{(v_0/v)^{\frac{1}{3}n} - 1}$$

$$= \frac{A}{I}\left[1 - \left(1 - \frac{1}{3}n\,I\right)^{3\alpha/n}\right] \tag{5.3}$$

$$= A\alpha\left[1 - \frac{1}{6}(3a - n)I + \cdots\right],$$

which is a type of expansion sometimes used for k and which is similar to (4.4). In general this expansion is not valid, but k remains a function of I.

6. Simple shear.

In this case **c** is given by

$$\mathbf{c} = \begin{bmatrix} 1 & c & 0 \\ 0 & 1 & 0 \\ 0 & 0 & 1 \end{bmatrix}$$

Following Love [7] and Reiner [3] we find the following values of the principal strains:

$$e_{11}, e_{22} = \frac{1}{n}[1 - 2^n\{(4 + c)^{\frac{1}{2}} \pm c\}^{-n}], \tag{6.1}$$

$$e_{33} = 0.$$

The generalized strain components are then given by

$$e_{xx}, e_{yy} = \frac{1}{2}(e_{11} + e_{22}) \pm \frac{1}{2}c(4 + c^2)^{-\frac{1}{2}}(e_{11} - e_{22}),$$

$$\tag{6.2}$$

$$e_{xy} = (4 + c^2)^{-\frac{1}{2}}(e_{11} - e_{22}); e_{zz}, e_{zx}, e_{yz} = 0.$$

For A-measure these reduce to $e_{xx} = 0$, $e_{yy} = -\frac{1}{2}c^2$, $e_{xy} = \frac{1}{2}c$; for G-measure they become $e_{xx} = 0$, $e_{yy} = \frac{1}{2}c^2$, $e_{xy} = -\frac{1}{2}c$. In all other measures $e_{xx} \neq 0$.

The stress components are given by

$$\tau_{xx} = \Lambda(e_{xx} + e_{yy}) + 2\mu e_{xx},$$

$$\tau_{yy} = \Lambda(e_{xx} + e_{yy}) + 2\mu e_{yy},$$

$$\tau_{zz} = \Lambda(e_{xx} + e_{yy}) + 2\mu e_{zz}, \qquad (6.3)$$

$$\tau_{xy} = 2\mu e_{xy}, \quad \tau_{yz}, \quad \tau_{zx} = 0.$$

Thus we get normal stresses which give rise to Kelvin and Poynting effects [1]. In both cases such stresses have to be applied to keep the body in equilibrium As e_{xx} is zero only in A- and G-measures, the normal stresses τ_{xx} and τ_{zz} are generally unequal, as pointed out by Rivlin [5]. We obtain this result without using any additional elastic coefficient. From (6.3) we see that the normal stresses can be taken in the form

$$\tau_{ii} = A_{11}e_{11} + B_{11}e_{22}$$

$$= \frac{A_{11}}{n}[1 - 2^n\{(4 + c^2)^{\frac{1}{2}} + c\}^{-n}] + \qquad (6.3)$$

$$+ \frac{B_{11}}{n}[1 - 2^n\{(4 + c^2)^{\frac{1}{2}} - c\}^{-n}]$$

For A- and G-measures we get τ_{ii} proportional to c^2 as has been found by Rivlin [5], Truesdell [1], Green [8] and others.

The shearing stress τ_{xy} is given by

$$\tau_{xy} = \frac{2^n}{n} \frac{[(4 + c^2)^{\frac{1}{2}} - c]^{-n} - [(4 + c^2)^{\frac{1}{2}} + c]^{-n}}{(4 + c^2)^{\frac{1}{2}}} \qquad (6.4)$$

For A-measure it takes the simple form $\frac{1}{2}c$.

The results in (6.3) and (6.4) may be generalized by replacing $-n$ with α and a justification on the lines given in Sections 5 and 6 may be given.

7. Generalized strain in hollow spheres and cylinders.

For the symmetrical deformation of a thick spherical shell subjected to uniform internal and external pressures, the radial displacement, strain components and the stress components are given by [4]

$$u_r = r(1 - P)$$

$$e_{rr} = \frac{1}{n}[1 - P^n\{1 + v(v + 2)\}^{\frac{1}{2}n}], \tag{7.1}$$

$$e_{\theta\theta} = e_{\phi\phi} = \frac{1}{n}(1 - P^n), \tag{7.2}$$

$$e_{r\theta}, e_{\theta\phi}, e_{\phi r} = 0,$$

$$\tau_{rr} = \frac{1}{n}\Lambda[3 - 2P^n - P^n f(v)] + \frac{2\mu}{n}[1 - P^n f(v)]$$

$$\tau_{\theta\theta} = \tau_{\phi\phi} = \frac{1}{n}\Lambda[3 - 2P^n - P^n f(v)] + \frac{2\mu}{n}[1 - P^n]$$

$$\tau_{r\theta}, \tau_{\theta\phi}, \tau_{r\phi} = 0, \tag{7,3}$$

where $V = rdP/Pdr$, $f(v) = [1 + v(v + 2)]^{\frac{1}{2}n}$. P may be determined from a non-linear differential equation resulting from the body-stress equations. At present we shall obtain a yield condition from (7.3) and show that it holds good in all strain measures.

From (7.3) we have, on eliminating P^n

$$\frac{n\tau_{rr} - \tau_{\theta\theta}}{3\Lambda + 2\mu - n\tau_{rr}} = \frac{2\mu[1 - f(v)]}{2\Lambda + 2f(v) + 2\mu f(v)} \tag{7.4}$$

If r' is the radius vector before strain, we have

$$r' = rP,$$

and
$$\frac{dr'}{dr} = P(1 + v). \tag{7.5}$$

These show that $v \to -1$ for infinite extension and $v \to \infty$ for infinite compression. From (7.4) we thus get the inequality

$$-\frac{1 - 2\sigma}{1 - \sigma} < \frac{n(\tau_{rr} - \tau_{\theta\theta})}{3\Lambda + 2\mu - n\tau_{rr}} < \frac{1 - 2\sigma}{2\sigma}. \tag{7.6}$$

Thus, whatever the generalized strain may be and whatever values Λ and μ (constant or variable) may have the yield condition in extension or compression may be written as

$$(\tau_{rr} - \tau_{\theta\theta}) + A_1(\tau_{rr} - \tau_{\phi\phi}) + A_2(\tau_{rr} + \tau_{\theta\theta} + \tau_{\phi\phi}) = k_1 \qquad (7.7)$$

when A_1 $A$and A_2 are independent of n.

Assuming that

$$(\tau_{rr} - \tau_{\theta\theta}) > \tau_{rr} - \tau_{\phi\phi},$$

we may write the generalized yield condition in the form

$$\tau_{11} - \tau_{33} + F_1(\text{I, II III})(\tau_{11,} + \tau_{22} + \tau_{33}) = F_2(\text{I, II, III}), \qquad (7.8)$$

F_1 and F_2 being functions of the invariants I, II, and III, and $\tau_{11}, \tau_{22}, \tau_{33}$ the principal stresses in descending order of magnitude.

The yield condition in (7.8) is true for isotropic and aelotropic materials and for all measures of strain.

If the mean stress is negligible we get

$$\tau_{11} - \tau_{33} = F_2, \qquad (7.9)$$

which is a generalized form of Tresca's yield condition.
Similar results may be obtained from the case of hollow cylinders.

8.   List of symbols.

τ_{ij}	= stress
V_0	= initial volume
s	= infinitesimal strain
e_v	= cubical dilatation
Λ	= Lamé's modulus
$\Lambda_i\ (i=1,2,3)$	= principal stretches
T	= tension
p	= pressure
n, c_1, c_2, c_3	= constants

REFERENCES

[1] Exhaustive references to the works of Cauchy, Green, Almansi and others will be found in C. TRUESDELL, The mechanical foundations of elasticity and fluid mechanics *J. Rational Mech. Anal.*, **1**, (1952), 125–320; **2**, (1953), 593–616 and subsequent papers.

[2] F. D. MURRAGHAN, Finite deformations of an elastic solid, *Amer. J. Math.*, **59**, (1937) 253–260.

[3] F. D. MURRAGHAN, The compressibility o f solids under extreme pressures, *Karman anniv. Vol.*, (1941), 121–136.

[4] F. D. MURRAGHAN, The compressibility of media under extreme pressures, *Proc. Nat. Acad. Sci. U.S.A.*, **30**, (1944), 244–247.

[5] M. REINER, *Deformation and Flow of Solids*, Springer Verlag, (1956), 203–207.

[6] Z. KARNI AND M. REINER, Measures of deformation in the strained and unstrained state, *Bull. Res. Counc. of Israel*, **6C**, (1958), 113.

[7] B. R. SETH, Finite strain in elastic problems, *Phil. Trans. Roy. Soc. London*, (A), **234**, (1935), 231–264.

[8] B. R. SETH AND W. M. SHEPHERD, Fine strain in elastic problems, II, *Proc. Roy. Soc. London*, (A), **156**, (1936), 171–192.

[9] B. R. SETH, Some recent applications of the theory of finite deformation, *Sym. Amer. Math. Soc.*, **3**, (1950), 67–94.

[10] B. R. SETH, Non-linear continuum mechanics, Presidential address, (Section of Mathemathics). *Proc. 42nd Ind. Sci. Congress*, II, (1955).

[11] B. R. SETH, Finite bending of a plate into a spherical shell, *Zeit. Angew. Math. Mech.*, **37**, (1957), 393–398.

[12] B. R. SETH, Poro-plastic deformation, *Rheo. Acta.*, 2/3, (1958), 316–318.

[13] B. R. SETH, Finite strain in engineering design, *Proc. Inter. Congress on Math. for the Engineer*, Brussells, (1958), 386–390.

[14] B. R. SETH, Non-homogeneous yield condition, *Proc. IUTAM Sym. Non-Homogenity in Elasticity and Plasticity*, Warsaw, (1959).

[15] B. R. SETH, Finite deformation of cylindrical shells, *Proc. IUTAM Sym. on Theory o,ʾ Thin Elastic Shells*, Delft, (1959), 355–363.

[16] B. R. SETH. Finite bending of plates into cylindrical shells, Signorini memorial volume, *Ann. Mat. Bologne*, **50**, (1960), 19–125.

[17] B. R. SETH, Finite deformation of plates into shells, *Proc. Inter. Cont. on Partial Diff. Equ. and Continuum Mechanics*, Madison, (1961), 95–105.

[18] B. R. SETH, Stability of finite deformation, Problems of continuum mechanics, Muskhelishvili memorial volume, *Soc. Indust. Appl. Math.*, (1961), 406–414; USSR Acad. Sci., Moscow, (1961),) 359–365.

[19] R. S. RIVLIN, Large elastic deformations of isotropic materials, I-VIII, *Phil. Trans. Roy. Soc. London* (A), **240**, (1948), 459–490, 491–508, 509–525; **241**, (1948), 379–397 and subsequent papers.

[20] R. S. RIVLIN, Solutions of problems in second order elasticity theory, *Jour. Rat. Mech. Anal*, **2**, (1953), 53–81.

[21] R. S. RIVLIN AND J. L. ERICKSON, Large elastic deformations of homogeneous anistropic materials, *Jour. Rat. Mech. Anal.*, **3**, (1954), 281–301.

[22] P. W., BRIDGEMAN, Electrical resistances and volume changes up to 20,000 Kg/cm^2 *Proc. Nat. Acad. Sci., U. S. A.*, **21**, (1935), 109.

23] A. E. H. LOVE, *Mathematical Theory of Elasticity*, 4th ed., Cambridge (1934).

[24] A. E. GREEN AND W. ZERNA, *Theoretical Elasticity*, Oxford, (1954).

[25] A. E. GREEN AND J. E. ADKIN, *Large Elastic Deformations*, Oxford, (1960).

Discussion

H. Giesekus: I do not understand Prof. Seth's conclusion (i) from Eq. (4.2) concerning a yield point at $T = E/n$.

If $n > 0$ and therefore $T = E/n > 0$, then it follows from $(1 + s)^{-n}$, that $s = \infty$.

Thus E/n is a limiting value of T for infinite stretch.

If however, $n < 0$, and therefore $T = E/n < 0$ (i.e. a pressure), then it follows from $(1 + s)^{-n}$ that $s = -1$. Now E/n is a limiting value of T for infinite compression. Therefore Eq. (4.3) is correct only for $n > 0$.

I would prefer to understand by a yield point such a value of stress, where at a *finite* positive or negative stretch a maximum value would be attained.

B. R. Seth's Reply: Giesekus' comments have not taken into consideration the fact that for negative values of n the unstrained state becomes the reference framework in place of the strained one. For example, $n = -1$ refers to Cauchy's measure and $n = -2$ to Green's measure, both of which refer to the unstrained state. The result is that infinite contraction ($s \rightarrow -1$) now corresponds to infinite extension ($s \rightarrow \infty$), and we again get the yield stress as $(1/n)E$.

The value of E in $T = (1/n)E$ is not be looked upon as the conventional value of the Young's modulus. Yielding is a transition phenomenon and $(1/n)E$ only defines the value of the yield stress qualitatively in the transition from the elastic to the plastic state. No macroscopic theory can give the actual value of the yield stress. In like manner the limiting values of $s = \infty$ or -1 only identify the changeover from the elastic to the plastic state.

EXPERIMENTS ON LARGE AMPLITUDE WAVES IN FINITE ELASTIC STRAIN

JAMES F. BELL

The Johns Hopkins University, Baltimore, Maryland, U.S.A.

ABSTRACT

In this paper it is shown that large amplitude plastic waves, experimentally studied by means of the author's diffraction grating technique, may be empirically interpreted in terms of a general theory of waves in finite elastic strain recently developed by C. Truesdell. The theoretical relations are also applicable to the very high stress, high speed shock front which the present author has experimentally identified near the impact face. Since the Truesdell theory is for small amplitude waves propagating in an elastic solid initially subject to a state of stress and finite strain, while the present writer's experiments are for large amplitude wave fronts propagating in an initially stress-free polycrystalline aluminum, the correlations are purely empirical. In the absence of a general theory of large amplitude waves in finite elasticity, these experimental results would seem to imply a greater degree of generality for some aspects of the Truesdell theory than was assumed in its development.

1. Introduction.

When cylindrical metal rods are subjected to a symmetrical free flight axial collision, a constant velocity impact is obtained and the resulting large amplitude plastic waves may be experimentally studied with detailed accuracy by the diffraction grating technique developed by the present writer [1], [2] for this purpose. From over 500 free flight measurements in several metals it was shown [3] that for face-centered cubic metals, plastic waves develop from initial shock waves in the first diameter of the rods. Following the initial development, these plastic waves [3], [4] propagate in a manner agreeing with the strain rate independent finite amplitude wave theory of Karman[5], Taylor [6], Rakhmatulin [7], and White and Griffis [8].

The details of the unloading phenomenon also are given [9], [10] by an extension of the strain rate independent momentum considerations of E. H. Lee [11]. From diffraction grating and other optical measurements I have shown. that the governing stress-strain relation for several f.c.c. crystalline solids is given from the introduction of single crystal measurements into the Taylor [12] and Bishop and Hill [13] theory of the ploycrystalline aggregate. These stress–

strain relations are parabolas, as had been predicted earlier by Taylor [12] in his theory of dislocations.

In addition to the dynamic overstress which had been observed by several investigators, I have found [3] that there also exists an initial very high level short-lived peak stress in the first few microseconds following impact. The dynamic overstress has been examined experimentally from several points of view. By an examination of specimen surface angle behavior as given from diffraction grating measurements, as the wave propagates past a point on the rod it has been shown [3] [14], that there exists a partition of energy between the dilatation and deviatoric components of the initial shock front from which the dynamic overstress itself is determined from stress and energy considerations of the governing parabolic stress-strain law. This energy partition is produced by side wall reflection near the impact face. The determination of the dynamic overstress is made without introducing any strain rate effects. The initial wave front in the first 1/2 diameter was found not only to have the very high peak stress levels referred to above, but also to propagate at a velocity considerably higher than the dilatational velocity for aluminum from linear elasticity.

In the present paper it is shown that nearly all of the detail of wave initiation, propagation, and unloading are given by relations recently obtained by C. Truesdell [15] in his theory of waves in finite elasticity. The Truesdell theory considers the propagation of small amplitude waves in a material under initial stress and finite elastic strain, rather than the present author's experimental situation of large amplitude waves. The experimental results obtained suggest a much larger degree of generality for the Truesdell theory.

2.   Wave speed in finite elastic strain.

C. Truesdell's theoretical study of waves in finite elastic strain is of particular interest to the experimentalist in continuum mechanics since his results are given in terms of wave speeds along the principal axes under varied initial conditions of stress and strain, in a manner permitting of a direct use of the experimental data. The relations of particular interest in the present instance are those for an isotropic material subject to a more general initial state of stress. In each situation the quantities of experimental interest are the longitudinal and transverse wave speeds along a principal axis. For an isotropic material subject to an initial hydrostatic state of stress, Truesdell has given:

$$U_{\parallel}^2 = \frac{4}{3} U_{\perp}^2 + \frac{dp}{d\rho} \tag{1}$$

where $U_{\parallel}$ is the longitudinal wave speed, and $U_{\perp}$ is the transverse wave speed; ρ is the instantaneous mass density, and p is the hydrostatic pressure. These wave speeds correspond to those of small amplitude waves introduced into the material after the initial hydrostatic state has been obtained. For the more general initial state of stress and finite elastic strain, Truesdell gives:

$$\rho U_{11}^2 = \frac{\partial \sigma_1}{\partial \log v_1} \tag{2}$$

for the longitudinal wave speed along a principal axis, and

$$\frac{\rho}{v_1^2} U_{12}^2 = \frac{\sigma_1 - \sigma_2}{v_1^2 - v_2^2} \tag{3}$$

for the transverse wave speed along a principal axis. σ_1 and σ_2 are the principal stresses; v_1 and v_2, the principal stretches; ρ the instantaneous mass density and U_{11} and U_{12} are the longitudinal and transverse wave speed, respectively.

In what follows it is shown that equations (1), (2), and (3) are found experimentally when large amplitude wave fronts produce the initial state which then governs their speed of propagation.

3. The experimental data.

Much of the experimental data upon which the present paper is based has been presented by the author in an earlier series of papers. What is of new interest here is the fact that the data may be interpreted in terms of finite elastic strain as well as from the earlier point of view of dynamic plasticity.

The experimental measurements utilized in this paper, as well as those given in a series of the present author's earlier papers, have been obtained from the observation of the behaviour under dynamic strain of two first-order lines of monochromatic light falling normally on 30,720 lines per inch diffraction gratings. The gauge length in the 3/32 in. measurements shown here in Figure 1 was .001 in., and for the measurements at 1/4 and 1/2 diameters, the gauge length was .005 in. The results shown in the present paper are a further evidence of the high degree of accuracy which may be obtained from the proper use of this experimental technique. The material is dead annealed aluminium, annealed at 1100°F for two hours and furnace cooled.

Behind the high-speed wave front, large amplitude plastic waves develop in two stages, the first involving the stress level of the dynamic overstress, and the second that of the theoretical maximum stress of the finite amplitude plastic wave theory. The latter situation is obtained from one diameter from the impact face, onward.

As has been shown earlier, however [14], a study of surface angle behaviour reveals an equipartition of energy. This equipartition of energy is produced by the reflection of the initial front from the side walls of the cylinders.

By one diameter from the impact face the high stress, high speed initial front has been eliminated, presumably due to a combination of instability and of reflection from the free surfaces of the cylinder. The experimental data indicate that the disappearance of the high speed front occurs in the vicinity of 3/4 diameters. Diffraction grating strain-time measurements at this position show a lack of reproducibility which is not characteristic of any other position along the rod.

Strain-time data from one diameter to a distance of somewhat less than 1/2 the length of the rod is given by the one dimensional, strain rate independent theory of plastic wave propagation independently developed by Karman [5], Taylor [6], Rakhmatulin [7], and White and Griffis [8]. The theory predicts that each level of strain propagates with a constant velocity given by the slopes of a single governing stress-strain curve [equation (4)], and that a relation exists between particle velocity $\dot{u}$ and the corresponding strain [equation (5)].

$$c_p^2 = \frac{1}{\rho_0} \frac{\partial \sigma}{\partial \varepsilon} \tag{4}$$

$$\dot{u} = \int_0^\varepsilon c_p d\varepsilon \tag{5}$$

where c_p is the propagation velocity for a given strain.

The present writer has shown [3], [4] that the velocities of propagation are constant, and that both equations (9) and (5) are satisfied for a parabolic stress-strain law. Furthermore, this parabolic law is given by introducing single crystal data into Taylor's [12] theory of the polycrystalline aggregate, which Bishop and Hill [13] also have considered from a plasticity point of view. Such parabolic laws have been obtained experimentally by the present writer in aluminum, copper, and lead at strains from near the elastic limit to nearly 12%. Impact experiments using the diffraction grating technique have been carried out in aluminum from room temperature to within 100° of the melting point of the metal. Parabolas are obtained at all temperatures. I have found that the coefficient of the parabola for aluminum has a linear dependence upon temperature. For a parabolic stress-strain relation, equations (4) and (5) become (6) and (7), respectively.

$$c_p^2 = \frac{\beta}{2\rho_0 \varepsilon^{\frac{1}{2}}} \tag{6}$$

$$\dot{u}^2 = \frac{8}{9} \frac{\beta}{\rho_0} \varepsilon^{3/2} \tag{7}$$

where the stress-strain relation is equation (8):

$$\sigma = \beta \varepsilon^{\frac{1}{2}} \tag{8}$$

Multiplying the numerator and denominator of equation (6) by $\varepsilon^{\frac{1}{2}}$, we have equation (9):

$$\rho_0 c_p^2 = \frac{\sigma}{2\varepsilon} \tag{9}$$

In an earlier paper [10] it was shown that a secant modulus based upon equation (9) could be used to determine in a simple manner all of the experimental unloading behaviour, including the time of specimen contact, the coefficient of restitution, the largest distance of penetration of maximum strain, the displacement-time behaviour at the free end of the specimens, and the stress-time behaviour at the impact face during unloading. In equation (3), the transverse wave speed also is given by a secant modulus, where it should be noted that the stretch v is $v = 1 + \varepsilon$ and $v^2 \simeq 1 + 2\varepsilon$. Equations (2) and (3) become equations (10) and (11), respectively:

$$\rho \, U_{11}^2 = (1 + \varepsilon_1) \frac{\partial \sigma_1}{\partial \varepsilon_1} \tag{10}$$

$$\frac{\rho \, U_{12}^2}{(1 + \varepsilon_1)^2} = \frac{\sigma_1 - \sigma_2}{2(\varepsilon_1 - \varepsilon_2)} \tag{11}$$

For an impact velocity of 66.5 ft/sec in annealed aluminum, the maximum strain is 2.2% and for 250 ft/sec the maximum strain is 11.6%. Assuming one dimensionality so that σ_2 and ε_2 equal zero, and neglecting $1 + \varepsilon_1$ since strains are relatively small, equation (11) is identical with equation (9), and equation (10) is identical with equation (4). This indicates that for a parabolic stress-strain relation the transverse wave speed, and what might be interpreted as a longitudinal wave speed, are equal. The former is a secant modulus, and the latter is a tangent modulus.

Thus, an empirical agreement is found between Truesdell's [15] theory or small amplitude waves in an initially stressed solid and large amplitude waves propagating in an initially zero-stress state.

Of greater interest than this latter correlation, however, is the fact that there exists a second experimental situation for which the transverse wave speed relation applies. This second condition arises from an examination of wave speeds for the strain-time data above the initial high speed shock front. When this upper plastic front is propagating, the longitudinal stress has dropped from the peak stress to the experimentally determined dynamic overstress. As the present writer has shown [14], this dynamic overstress may itself be computed from surface angle measurements, and it has been shown to be of such a nature that for the situation of uniaxial stress the major portion of the developing strain is that of the deviatoric component.

As was shown [14], the dynamic overstress may be predicted from surface angle behaviour. The surface angle maximum occurs at a strain $\bar{\varepsilon}$ whose corresponding stress from the parabola is $2/3P$, where P is the experimentally determined dynamic overstress. For example, at an impact velocity of 66.5 ft/sec in annealed aluminum with an elastic limit of 1000 psi, the theoretical stress maximum of the plastic wave theory is 8300 psi. This value also has been obtained experimentally [10]. The dynamic overstress varies between 9700 psi and 10,200 psi, depending upon the method of interpreting the data (see [16]). The present author's initial peak stress is approximately 50,000 psi for this impact velocity.

In conducting high temperature tests, I found that occasionally the first diameter behaviour could extend to as far as two or three diameters from the impact face. This behaviour was only observed at higher impact velocities. A test series at room temperature was carried out at impact velocities higher than 80 ft/sec (which had been the upper limit for extensive measurement outside of the first diameter from the impact face.) At approximately 85 ft/sec at room temperature, an occasional test exhibits the high temperature behaviour, in that a lower strain, higher speed wave is present beyond the first diameter. The strain maximum is $\bar{\varepsilon}$ corresponding to the strain at the surface angle maximum of the normal test. The speed $\bar{c}_p$ of $\bar{\varepsilon}$ is $\sqrt{2}$ times that for the maximum strain given by the parabola. Since $\bar{\varepsilon}$ is a strain corresponding to $1/2$ the maximum energy of deformation, and since the wave speed is known, the transverse wave speed relation may be checked. This is given in equation (12) for which P, $\bar{\varepsilon}$, and $\bar{c}_p$ are all known experimentally.

$$\rho_0 \bar{c}_p^2 = \frac{P}{2\bar{\varepsilon}} \tag{12}$$

Since $\bar{\varepsilon}$ is the strain corresponding to a stress, $\bar{\sigma}$, which in turn is $2/3P$, one may conclude that for this situation of uniaxial stress, the deviatoric plastic wave is propagating under a state of stress which includes the hydrostatic component, $P/3$. It has wave speeds given empirically by Truesdell's equation for the transverse wave speed of a small amplitude wave propagating in a material under an equivalent initial state of stress. The experimental details at different impact velocities leading to equation (12) as well as those leading to other results given above, are contained in a manuscript recently submitted for publication [17].

The longitudinal wave speed for the situation involving the dynamic over-stress is not the same as the transverse wave speed of equation (12), as was the case for the finite amplitude wave theory. Of course the wave speeds are also different for the initial high speed fronts. This suggests that the only stable front in the rod is that given by the finite amplitude wave theory. It should be noted that the higher wave speeds and lower strains of the dynamic overstress are *not* related to strain rate.

For the high speed and very high stressed initial front observed in the first 1/2 diameter, neither dynamic plasticity nor linear elasticity are adequate for interpreting the experimental results. In a recent paper [3] it was shown that up to 1/2 diameter from the impact face the initial portion of the strain-time curve contains two high speed initial fronts, following which, the main plastic front develops. Between 1/2 and 3/4 diameters the initial waves disappear and are not present beyond the first diameter, except for a few instances of axial impact at much higher impact velocities.

In that paper [3], too, it was shown that a proper interpretation of the strain-time data required the introduction of three dimensionality in terms of Huygens principle and reflection theory. From this interpretation individual measurements at 1/4 and 1/2 diameters were shown to depend upon axiality. For axial impacts and for known non-axial impacts data were shown which were consistent with such an interpretation. By averaging data from several tests at 1/4 diameter and similarly at 1/2 diameter, and by determining from these data the time for each strain level to traverse the distance between the two positions, axiality variations and the three dimensional effects associated with the close proximity of the impact face were eliminated.

Over 40 diffraction grating measurements of strain and surface angle have been made at distances from 1/16 diameter to 1/2 diameter from the impact face, for impact velocities ranging from 44 ft/sec to 250 ft/sec. Twenty-four of these measurements have been made for an impact velocity of 66.5 ft/sec (hitter velocity, 133 ft/sec), including measurements at 1/16, 3/32, 1/8, 5/32,

1/4, and 1/2 diameters, most of the measurements being at 3/32, 1/4, and 1/2 diameters. In Figure 1, the initial portion of several tests at each of these positions are time-averaged. The strains arriving at each of these positions originate, as was shown earlier (Bell, [3]) in a distributed source at the impact face.

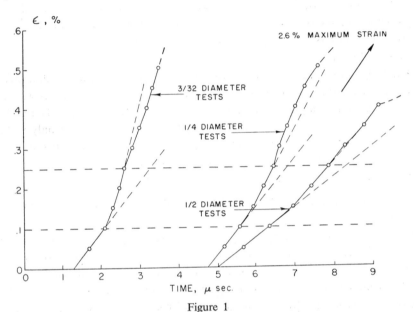

Figure 1

Initial strain-time data obtained from the time-averaging of several tests at each of the indicated distances from the impact face.

In these experiments, two flat-ended identical annealed aluminum rods are in axial collision. A high degree of axiality has been obtained, as has been indicated earlier [4] by an initial optical alignment dynamically checked at the time of impact by means of spark photography of the symmetry of the air shock.

Strain-time measurements made in the immediate vicinity of the impact face are very sensitive to the location of the first point of contact in the impact. A few tests have been identified as axial impacts, but the large majority are known to be slightly non-axial. For each of the wave fronts of Figure 1, one finds that the initial portion of the wave front is sloped because of the distributed source. Furthermore, 3/32 diameter data are relatively much more delayed than data at 1/4 or 1/2 diameters, as would be expected from the variation in the position of first contact.

At a sufficient distance from the impact face, however, a comparison of averaged strain-time curves will minimize both axiality and three dimensional effects. In Figure 2 is shown a strain-time curve obtained from the averaged data at 1/4 and 1/2 diameters. An inspection of the data reveals two initial straight line portions, the first with an amplitude of .001 in/in, and the second with an amplitude of .0025 in/in strain.

From Figure 2, the first front with a strain amplitude of .001 in/in has a velocity of 3.20×10^5 in/sec, and the second at .0025 in/in has a velocity of 1.81×10^5 in/sec. The dilatational velocity from linear elasticity is 2.5×10^5 in/sec, and the equivoluminal or transverse velocity is 1.25×10^5 in sec. These experimental velocities therefore exceed linear elastic values.

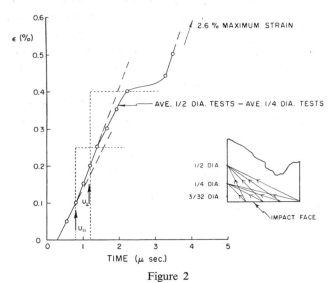

Figure 2

Initial part of the strain-time curve obtained from subtracting averaged 1/4 diameter data from averaged 1/2 diameter data. The lower dashed step is the hypothetical shock front. The upper dashed step is that of the elementary bar theory with a wave speed $c_0 = \sqrt{E/\varrho_0}$

In a slightly non-axial impact, the initiated wave front must involve both dilatational and shear components. This would probably be true for a perfectly axial impact due to the presence of local irregularities and imperfections at the impact face. If a shock front were initiated with a wave speed of the initial front, $\mathbf{U}_{\parallel} = 3.20 \times 10$ in/sec, as in Figure 2, then a substitution of this wave speed and the known particle velocity, $v_0 = 800$ in/sec, into the mass and momentum relations (equations (13) and (14)] across the front gives a stress of 64,000 psi and a strain of .0025 in/in. This strain of .0025 in/in is the value for the combined double front of Figure 2. This hypothetical initial shock front is shown as the fine dotted line in Figure 2.

$$\varepsilon = \frac{v_0}{U_{||} + v_0} \qquad (13)$$

where v_0 is the particle velocity, or in this instance, the impact velocity.

$$\sigma = \rho_0 (U_{||} + v_0) v_0 \qquad (14)$$

Joseph Sperrazza of the Aberdeen Proving Ground, Ballistics Research Laboratories, using piezo crystals cemented to the impact face of one of the specimens, has obtained an experimental value of 55,000 psi for the peak overstress. This is somewhat less than the value of 60,250 psi computed earlier by the present writer from experimental data [3]. The aluminum specimens used by Sperrazza were supplied by the present writer so that the same conditions of annealing, etc., would be met. The peak stresses obtained from these experiments have been found to vary in individual measurements from 43 000 to 55,000 psi for an impact velocity of 66.5 ft/sec. Similar variations are found at other impact velocities.

From the Bridgman [18] relations one may determine the bulk modulus for the second term on the right of equation (1), using equation (15):

$$dp/d\rho = \frac{1}{\rho_0 (a - 2bp)} \qquad (15)$$

where $a = 13.85 \times 10^{13}$ (dynes/cm^2)$^{-1}$

and $b = 4.9 \times 10^{24}$ (dynes/cm^2)$^{-2}$

where $\rho_0 = \rho(1 + \theta) = \rho v_1 v_2 v_3$,

θ being the dilatation, and ρ_0 the initial mass density (.000253 lbs.sec^2/in^4 for aluminum.) For p an average experimental peak stress value is used. The compressibility contribution, $2bp$, in this range of pressures is less than 2%. Thus we have equation (16):

$$dp/d\rho = 4.25 \times 10^{10} \text{ (in/sec)}^2 \qquad (16)$$

A substitution of this value for $dp/d\rho$ and the experimental wave speed $U_{||} = 3.2 \times 10^5$ in/sec into equation (1) results in a transverse wave speed

$U_\perp$ of 2.12×10^5 in/sec. This wave speed is found in Figure 2 at a strain of .2%.

If the stress at $\varepsilon = .0005$ in/in and $\varepsilon = .001$ in/in are determined from the shock equations, and for all other strains one uses the Truesdell [15] equation (3) for the transverse wave in a manner indicated above for an uniaxial stress state, a stress-time history may be determined. Such a computation is shown by the circles of Figure 3.

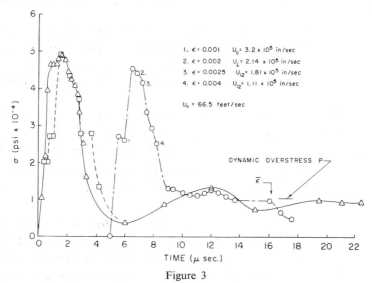

Figure 3

The calculated stress-time behavior at 3/8 diameter (circles) compared with two piezo crystal measurements at the impact face (triangles and squares). $\bar{\varepsilon}$ is the strain of the mean energy from the parabolic stress-strain law, also given experimentally from surface angle data.

From the experimental data of Figure 2, using averaged diffraction grating measurements at 1/2 and 1/4 diameters, the stress is plotted against the mean-time of Figure 1. Thus, the average position at which the stress-time measurements have been made, is 3/8 diameter. In Figure 3 this computed stress-time history is compared with two experimental piezo crystal measurements (designated by □ and Δ) at the impact face for approximately the same impact velocity, 66.5 ft/sec, at which all the data of Figures 2 and 3 were determined. The data of Figure 2 extended only to .5% strain. The calculations of Figure 3 also have included the data for strains higher than those shown.

One of the piezo crystal measurements at the impact face (designated in Figure 3 as □) has, during the initial rise, a step similar to that obtained in the calculated data. Similar stress levels are obtained in comparing the calculated and experimental maxima. The sharp decrease of stress in the calculated data occurs at a strain of .002 in/in, which is that having the wave speed, $U_\perp = 2.12 \times 10^5$ in/sec determined above. At .0025 in/in the stress is approximately 2/3 that of the hypothetical shock front.

What is perhaps of most significance is that by the strain $\bar{\varepsilon}$ the computed stress has fallen to the dynamic overstress, P, as has the piezzo crystal data. The division of the initial rise of the computed front is consistent with the suggestion that both dilatational and shear energies were inaugurated on impact.

The stress rate, $\dot{\sigma}$, of this initial portion of the piezo crystal data has a value of 1×10^{11} psi/sec. The corresponding experimental strain rate, $\dot{\varepsilon}$, is 20,000 in/in/sec. The rising front of the piezo crystal data is essentially the same as that of the calculated stress-time data. The falling portion and the width also are similar.

It would seem reasonable to assume from the comparison of data in Figure 3 that the Truesdell equations (1) and (3) which were used in an empirical fashion predict more detail than one might expect from pure coincidence.

These experimental results have been confined to a single impact velocity. Their range of application must await the carrying out of a fairly extensive experimental program.

In the earlier determination of the initial strain front [3], a very marked change in the wave speed was observed at a strain of .004 in/in. This effect also is shown in the 1/2 in averaged data of Figure 1 and the composite data of Figure 2. One test at 1/2 in separated with a 6μ sec flat at this strain level and was excluded from the calculations given above. The average of the remaining data, however, still shows this variation in wave speeds.

It is interesting to point out that if the linear elastic bar velocity, c_0, is introduced into the mass and momentum relations, equations (13) and (14) for an impact velocity of 66.5 ft/sec, or 800 in/sec, then a strain of .004 in/in is obtained at a stress of 42,000 psi. This latter stress is similar to the peak shown in Figure 3. Presumably, if it were not for the fact that the shear deformation exceeds that at the elastic limit for annealed aluminum ($Y = 1000$ psi), the final state after the first few diameters would be given by the elementary bar theory for a linear elastic rod. The upper dashed step front of Figure 2 shows this equivalent bar front where the wave speed $c_0 = \sqrt{E/\rho_0}$ is 2.06×10^5 in/sec.

The piezo crystal measurement at the impact face (designated as □) also has a step on the decreasing slope at a stress approximately corresponding to that of the computed value at $\varepsilon = .004$ in/in. In two tests a step appears on the

rising front, but only the test shown in Figure 3 had a step on the falling portion. All other piezo crystal data are similar to the test shown as triangles
in Figure 3; i.e., no steps are evident.

In annealed aluminum at an impact velocity of 250 ft/sec. (hitter velocity,
500 ft/sec.), G. L. Filbey [19] has found from diffraction grating and piezo
crystal measurements that the initial peak stress is only 100,000 psi and the
initial wave propagation is strain rate independent, governed by a cubic
stress-strain law. Beyond the first diameter, the parabolic law of lower velocity
impact is again operative. The first diameter high velocity experimental data
indicate the need for an understanding of reflection theory in finite elasticity.

An initial weak shock front propagating into a stress-free material would
appear to be unstable at 66.5 ft/sec. impact velocity, in that the front divides
into a longitudinal and a transverse portion prior to its disappearance. For
this impact velocity, the shock front disappears at approximately 3/4 diameter
from the impact face. The wave speeds are given empirically by Truesdell's
equations.

In earlier papers this writer has shown [14] that a knowledge of strain-time
and surface angle-time as determined from diffraction grating measurements
permits of an experimental determination of a geometric Poisson's ratio. I
found that at 1/4 and 1/2 diameters from the impact face this Poisson's ratio did
not immediately proceed from the elastic value of 1/3 to the incompressible
value of approximately 1/2 at the moment plastic deformation began, but rather
remained at 1/3 to a much higher strain than was characteristic of calculations
from experimental data at distances beyond the first diameter. It is interesting
to point out that a value of 1/3 is consistent with the division of the initial
front shown here in Figure 2, for which the upper transverse portion is presumed to be incompressible.

4.   Summary and Conclusions.

It has been the purpose of this paper to suggest the importance of further
development of shock wave theory in finite elasticity, as well as the development of a theory for finite amplitude wave fronts. The writer has not conducted
the test series proposed by Truesdell [15] for the determination of nine wave
speeds under prescribed conditions so that the question of stored energy may
be considered as well as the relations used above. Such experiments would
have to be properly cognizant of theoretical specifications of independence of
stretches and would have to involve small amplitude waves in a pre-stressed
material. What has been shown here, however, is the interesting empirical
fact that certain portions of the Truesdell theory applying to small amplitude
wave propagation in isotropic materials are in agreement with experimental

data in which the stress state is produced by the large amplitude wave front itself. It seems reasonable to conclude that the experimental results shown in the present paper imply a greater degree of generality to some aspects of the Truesdell theory than was assumed in its development. The large amplitude waves experimentally described in the present paper have heretofore been considered in terms of dynamic plasticity. It is of more than small moment that they also appear to be amenable to being included in the domain of non-linear elasticity.

5. Acknowledgments.

I should like to thank Professors J. L. Ericksen and C. Truesdell for acquainting me with the latter's theoretical work prior to publication, and for their interest in the experimental comparisons which are contained in the present paper. I would like also to thank my able assistant, John Suckling; and Virginia Franzen and Amanda Hollrah, who have carried out many of the calculations. I should like to thank Dr. Joseph Sperrazza and the Ballistics Research Laboratories for the piezo crystal measurements. Some portions of this work were conducted under the sponsorship of the United States Army, Aberdeen Proving Ground, Ballistics Research Laboratories; other portions were under the sponsorship of the United States Air Force Office of Scientific Research.

REFERENCES

[1]   JAMES F. BELL, *J. Appl. Physics*, **27**, (1956), 10.
[2]   JAMES F. BELL, *Proceedings*, 3rd U.S. National Cong. of Appl. Mechanics, (1958).
[3]   JAMES F. BELL, *J. Appl. Physics*, **32**, (1961), 10.
[4]   JAMES F. BELL, *J. Appl. Physics* **31** (1960), 2.
[5]   T. VON KARMAN, N.D.R.C. Report A29, O.S.R.D. 365, (1942).
[6]   G. I. TAYLOR, British Official Report R.C. 329, (1942).
[7]   K. A. RAKHMATULIN, *Prokl. Mat. Mekh.*, **9**, (1945), 19.
[8]   M. P. WHITE AND L. GRIFFIS, N.D.R.C. Report A72, O.S.R.D. 742, (1942).
[9]   JAMES F. BELL, *J. Mech. Physics Solids*, **9**, (1961), 1–15.
[10] JAMES F. BELL, *J. Mech. Physics Solids*, **9**, (1961), 261–278.
[11] E. H. LEE, *Quart. Appl. Mathematics*, **10**, (1953), 4.
[12] G. I. TAYLOR, *The Scientific Papers of Sir Geoffrey Ingram Taylor*, Vol. 1, Nos. 21, 22, 27, 41, Cambridge University Press, (1958).
[13] J. F. W. BISHOP AND R. HILL, *Phil. Mag.*, **42**, (1951), 414, 1298.
[14] JAMES F. BELL, *J. Appl. Physics*, **31**, (1960), 12.
[15] C. TRUESDELL, *Archive for Rational Mechanics & Analysis*, **8**, (1961), 3.
[16] J. E. JOHNSON, D. S. WOOD AND D. S. CLARK, *J. Appl. Mechanics.*, **20**, (1953), 4.
[17] JAMES F. BELL, A single temperature-dependent constitutive equation for the large amplitude dynamic deformation of face-centered cubic metals, (1962).
[18] P. W. BRIDGMAN, *Proceedings Am. Acad. Arts. Sciences*, **77**, (1949), 187.
[19] G. L. FILBEY, Doctoral thesis, The Johns Hopkins University, (1961).

SECOND-ORDER THEORY OF WAVE PROPAGATION
IN ISOTROPIC ELASTIC MATERIALS

C. TRUESDELL

The Johns Hopkins University*, Baltimore, Maryland, U.S.A.

ABSTRACT

If the stress-strain relations for isotropically elastic materials are expanded in series of powers of the principal extensions, the classical linearized theory corresponds to the linear terms, while the theory that results from breaking off the series after the quadratic terms is called the second-order theory. A material which is elastic in the sense of Reiner (1948) is called hyperelastic in the special case when a strain energy exists. In the linearized theory, every isotropic elastic material is hyperelastic, but no such equivalence holds in more accurate theories. In general, there are at most 4 independent second-order elasticities; in the hyperelastic case, they are reduced to 3.

Recent work of Truesdell has shown that in any isotropic elastic material, the acoustical axes for waves travelling down a principal axis of stress and strain coincide with the principal axes; thus, every such wave is either longitudinal or transverse; and exact, general formulae for the speeds of these 9 kinds of waves have been derived. In the present study these results are applied to determination of the second-order elasticities from the wave speeds. Previously Toupin and Bernstein (1961) had shown that certain wave speeds in a state of biaxial tension determine unique values for the 5 first-order and second-order elasticities in the hyperelastic case, generalizing classical results of L. Brillouin (1928) for a state of hydrostatic pressure. In the present study, a simple identity connecting 1 longitudinal-wave speed with 1 transverse-wave speed is shown to be a necessary and sufficient condition for the existence of a strain energy for the second-order theory.

According to the definition of Reiner [1], rendering explicit the proposal of Cauchy, a material is isotropically *elastic* if the stress-strain relations have the form[1]

$$t = \beth_0 \mathbf{1} + \beth_1 c + \beth_2 c^{-1}, \tag{1}$$

where t and c are Cauchy's tensors of stress and deformation, and where the coefficients $\beth_\Gamma$ are scalar functions of the principal invariants of c^{-1}, which we shall denote by I, II, and III. In the more special theory of elasticity pro-

---

[1] We employ the notations used in [2], especially §303 and §26.

* This work was supported in part by a grant from the U. S. National Science Foundation.

posed by Green, there is a stored-energy function, which serves as a potential for the stresses. Materials satisfying the equations of Green's theory we shall call *hyperelastic*.

There are both formal conditions of integrability and work theorems which characterize hyperelastic materials within the more general class of elastic materials. These conditions and theorems, however, are not of a kind such as to allow an easy experimental test. For example, the conditions of integrability assume the forms

$$\frac{\partial}{\partial I}(\sqrt{III}\,\beth_0) - II\frac{\partial}{\partial II}(\sqrt{III}\,\beth_2) - III\frac{\partial}{\partial III}(\sqrt{III}\,\beth_2) = 0,$$

$$II\left[\frac{\partial}{\partial II}(\sqrt{III}\,\beth_0) + \frac{\partial}{\partial III}(\sqrt{III}\,\beth_1)\right] + II\frac{\partial}{\partial II}(\sqrt{III}\,\beth_1) = 0,$$

$$\frac{\partial}{\partial I}(\sqrt{III}\,\beth_1) + III\ \frac{\partial}{\partial II}(\sqrt{III}\,\beth_2) = 0. \qquad (2)$$

There are also a number of exact solutions of the general equations of equilibrium, solutions which yield specific predictions suitable for comparison with measurements on large strain. While the discoverers of these solutions all considered a hyperelastic material, I have examined their results and have found that every one, without exception, is easily extended to the more general theory. Of course the greater freedom of elasticity, in which for isotropic materials there may be three fully independent material functions $\beth_0$, $\beth_1$, and $\beth_2$, not necessarily interconnected by (2), is reflected in these solutions. Unfortunately it is not an easy matter to decide whether this greater generality is superfluous or not. It turns out that all the known universal relations connecting stresses and strains in particular solutions, that is, relations in which the coefficients $\beth r$ do not appear explicitly, are of just the same form in the more general theory. Also, the magnitudes of all the typical gross effects of non-linear elasticity, such as the overall lengthening of a severely twisted cylinder, are insensitive to the presence or absence of a stored energy. The additional freedom of the general theory manifests itself in the details of the stress distribution, not in the typical and accessible phenomena we have grown accustomed to regarding as touchstones of non-linear elasticity.

Against this background I decided a few months ago to study the problem of wave propagation in the hope of finding within it a relation that can serve

as an immediate and simple test for a stored energy. It seemed more economical to construct a fully general theory [3], in the course of which the particular question at issue was decided of itself. Here I shall summarize only
those parts of the theory needed for deriving the test for a stored energy.

By a *wave* I mean either a propagating singular surface of second or higher
order, or a plane infinitesimal oscillation about a state of homogeneous strain,
since all these disturbances obey the same propagation condition. In an isotropic elastic material a wave travelling in a given direction may have an
amplitude pointing only in one of a certain number of uniquely determined
directions; in general, these are three in number, but not orthogonal. It turns
out, however, that in an *isotropic* elastic material much simpler results hold
for a wave travelling down a principal axis of stress and strain. Such a wave
is called a *principal wave*. From physical reasoning we can see what to expect. An isotropic material has no preferred directions of its own, and its
response is independent of the local rotation; the only distinguished directions
a wave travelling in the direction of n will encounter, other than that of n,
are the principal directions of stress and of strain in the deformed body,
and these two orthogonal triads coincide. When n itself is parallel to a principal direction, there remain but three directions altogether that could influence wave propagation, and these are the directions of the principal axes
themselves. Thus, when the principal stretches are distinct, *there are exactly*
9 *kinds of principal waves*; *each of them is either longitudinal or transverse.*
More specifically, for a wave travelling in the direction of a given principal
axis, the amplitude may point either along that axis or along either of the other
two principal axes. Results of this simplicity do not hold for anisotropic
materials, or for non-principal waves in general isotropic materials.

Mathematical analysis confirms the above-stated expectation and yields also
explicit and exact formulae for the speeds of the principal waves. From (1)
we may express the principal stresses t_a as functions of the principal stretches
λ_b:

$$t_a = \beth_0 + \beth_2\lambda_a^2 + \beth_1\lambda_a^{-2}. \tag{3}$$

Then it can be shown that the speed of propagation U_{11} of the longitudinal
waves travelling in the direction of the principal axis corresponding to the
stretch λ_1 is given by

$$\rho U_{11}^2 = \frac{\partial t_1}{\partial \log \lambda_1}, \tag{4}$$

while the speed of propagation U_{12} of the transverse waves travelling in the same direction but having amplitudes parallel to the axis corresponding to the stretch λ_2 is given by

$$\frac{\rho U_{12}^2}{\lambda_1^2} = \frac{t_1 - t_2}{\lambda_1^2 - \lambda_2^2}, \tag{5}$$

where ρ is the density in the deformed material. The truth of these formulae is *independent of the presence or absence of a stored energy*. A proof of them which is somewhat simpler than my original one is given in the appendix.

The next step is to expand these exact formulae in powers of the three principal extensions δ_a, which are defined in terms of the principal stretches λ_a by the formula $\delta_a \equiv \lambda_a - 1$. The results, of course, are going to be the same as if we had started from the second-order theory of elasticity, namely, the theory obtained by expanding (1) in powers of the displacement gradients and retaining only the quadratic terms. A quick way of effecting this latter calculation, which has been carried out at length by many authors over the past seventy years, begins by noting that the classical finite-strain tensor E is exactly quadratic [2, especially §31] in the δ_a; therefore the most general quadratic approximation to (1) is the sum of

    1.   the most general isotropic linear function of E, and

    2.   the most general isotropic quadratic function of the linear approximation to E, which is the classical linearized strain tensor $\tilde{E}$.

Thus we may write down the second-order stress-strain relations by inspection[2]:

$$\frac{t}{\mu} = \frac{\lambda}{\mu} I_E \mathbf{1} + 2E + (\alpha_3 I_{\tilde{E}}^2 + \alpha_4 II_{\tilde{E}})\mathbf{1} + \alpha_5 I_{\tilde{E}} \tilde{E} + \alpha_6 \tilde{E}^2, \tag{6}$$

---

[2] E is defined in the material rather than in space. Its spatial components are obtained by shifting to the points of the deformed material:

$$E_{km} \equiv g_k^\alpha g_m^\beta E_{\alpha\beta} = g_k^\alpha g_m^\beta (g_{pq} x_{,\alpha}^p x_{,\beta}^q - g_{\alpha\beta}),$$

where g_k^α is the shifter. See [2, §16 of the Appendix] for explanation of the method and notation. Thus (6) reads

$$t_m^k = \lambda I_E \delta_m^k + 2\mu E_m^k + \ldots \; .$$

Neither $\tilde{E}$ nor E has the same principal axes as $\mathbf{c}$, and hence (6) would not be a possible exact stress-strain relation for any isotropic elastic material. However, it can be shown that the error is of the order of terms neglected in writing down (6). Perhaps the most straightforward way to see this is to substitute the series (7) into (1) and then expand every quantity systematically in powers of the displacement gradients.

where λ and μ are the classical linear elasticities, and where α_3, α_4, α_5, and α_6 are the dimensionless, constant, second-order elasticities. The same result follows a little more laboriously if we introduce expansions[3] of the response coefficients $\beth_\Gamma$ in (1) in powers of the invariants of E:

$$\frac{\beth_0}{\mu} = \alpha_{00} + \alpha_{01}I_E + \alpha_{02}I_E^2 + \alpha_{03}II_E + \dots,$$

$$\frac{\beth_2}{\mu} = \alpha_{10} + \alpha_{11}I_E + \alpha_{12}I_E^2 + \alpha_{13}II_E + \dots, \tag{7}$$

$$\frac{\beth_1}{\mu} = \alpha_{-10} + \alpha_{-11}I_E + \alpha_{-12}I_E^2 + \alpha_{-13}II_E + \dots,$$

where the $\alpha_{\Gamma\Lambda}$ are dimensionless constants, and where $\alpha_{00} + \alpha_{10} + \alpha_{-10} = 0$. After some labor, we emerge with (6), where the two sets of constants are related as follows:

$$\alpha_1 = \alpha_{01} + \alpha_{11} + \alpha_{-11}, \quad \alpha_2 = \alpha_{10} - \alpha_{-10},$$

$$\alpha_3 = \alpha_{02} + \alpha_{12} + \alpha_{-12}, \quad \alpha_4 = \alpha_{03} + \alpha_{13} + \alpha_{-13},$$

$$\alpha_5 = 2(\alpha_{11} - \alpha_{-11}), \quad \alpha_6 = 4\alpha_{-10}. \tag{8}$$

In neither method is a strain energy employed. If we neglect the non-linear terms in (6), we see that the classical stress-strain relations of hyperelasticity result. That is, *for isotropic materials a test for the presence of a stored energy must rest on effects of the second or higher order in the principal extensions.* That effects of second order, not higher[4], may suffice is seen from the well known fact that isotropic hyperelastic materials have at most 3 independent second-order elasticities, while in the stress-strain relations (6) there may be 4. Indeed, it is easy to show that a stored-energy function exists in the second-order theory if and only if

$$\mu(\alpha_4 + \alpha_5) = 2(\lambda - \mu). \tag{9}$$

I can now make more precise my earlier statement about tests for a strain energy based on the solutions of special problems. While certain stresses in

---

(3) The reordering of indices here is introduced so as to maintain the notation of [2] as far as it goes, but in new material to follow the notation that will be used in the treatise by Noll and Truesdell [4].

(4) We are considering materials subject to no internal constraint. It is fairly well known that for isotropic incompressible materials, a test for the existence of a strain energy must involve effects of the *third* or higher order.

the various solutions depend on both α_4 and α_5, so that sufficiently detailed measurements could check (9) in principle, the magnitudes of all the typical effects in non-linear elasticity turn out to be independent of the value of α_5. Thus, so far as I know, there is no data presently available, despite all the experimental work which has been done, that gives us any reason to believe there is a strain-energy function for the materials tested.

Our problem, now, is to calculate the speeds of principal waves according to the second-order theory. We have before us alternative methods parallel to those used to get (6): Either we can base an independent wave analysis on (6) itself, or we can expand (4) and (5) in powers of the δ_a. The latter method is preferable as being not only more rigorous([5]) but also formally simpler. If we put $\theta \equiv \delta_1 + \delta_2 + \delta_3$ and write $\doteq$ to indicate equality to within an error that is $o(\sum \delta_a^2)$ as $\sum \delta_a^2 \to 0$, then

$$I_E = \theta + \tfrac{1}{2}\sum \delta_a^2, \quad II_E \doteq \delta_1\delta_2 + \delta_2\delta_3 + \delta_3\delta_1,$$

$$\frac{\partial I_E}{\partial \delta_1} = 1 + \delta_1, \qquad \frac{\partial II_E}{\partial \delta_1} \doteq \theta - \delta_1,$$

$$\frac{\beth_0}{\mu} \doteq \alpha_{00} + \alpha_{01}\theta, \; ..., \tag{10}$$

$$\frac{1}{\mu}\frac{\partial \beth_0}{\partial \delta_1} \doteq \alpha_{01} + (2\alpha_{02} + \alpha_{03})\theta + (\alpha_{01} - \alpha_{03})\delta_1, ...,$$

where we are using (7). From (4) and (3), then,

$$\rho U_{11}^2 = (1 + \delta_1)\frac{\partial t_1}{\partial \delta_1}$$

$$\doteq 2(1 + 2\delta_1)\beth_2 - 2(1 - 2\delta_1)\beth_1 + \tag{11}$$

$$+ (1 + \delta_1)\frac{\partial \beth_0}{\partial \delta_1} + (1 + 3\delta_1)\frac{\partial \beth_2}{\partial \delta_1} + (1 - \delta_1)\frac{\partial \beth_1}{\partial \delta_1}.$$

---

[5] Instead of starting from a solution to formally approximate differential equations, we expand an exact consequence of the exact differential equations. By this method, a little more labor would yield an estimate of error. To discover the results, which first appeared in [2], I used this same method but started from more complicated forms of the exact formulae (4) and (5).

By use of $(10)_{5,6}$ and (8) we find from (11) that

$$\frac{\rho U_{11}^2}{\mu} \doteq 2(1 + 2\delta_1)(\alpha_{10} + \alpha_{11}\theta) - 2(1 - 2\delta_1)(\alpha_{-10} + \alpha_{-11}\theta) +$$

$$+ (1 + \delta_1)\left[\alpha_{01} + (2\alpha_{02} + \alpha_{03})\theta + (\alpha_{01} - \alpha_{03})\delta_1\right] +$$

$$+ (1 + 3\delta_1)\left[\alpha_{11} + (2\alpha_{12} + \alpha_{13})\theta + (\alpha_{11} - \alpha_{13})\delta_1\right] +$$

$$+ (1 - \delta_1)\left[\alpha_{-11} + (2\alpha_{-12} + \alpha_{-13})\theta + (\alpha_{-11} - \alpha_{-13})\delta_1\right]$$

$$\doteq 2 + \frac{\lambda}{\mu} + (2\alpha_3 + \alpha_4 + \alpha_5)\theta + (4 + \frac{2\lambda}{\mu} - \alpha_4 + \alpha_5 + 2\alpha_6)\delta_1. \tag{12}$$

Since

$$\rho_0 \doteq \rho(1 + \theta), \tag{13}$$

where ρ_0 is the density in the natural state, (12) yields as the final result the formula

$$\frac{\rho_0 U_{11}^2}{\mu} \doteq 2 + \frac{\lambda}{\mu} + (2 + \frac{\lambda}{\mu} + 2\alpha_3 + \alpha_4 + \alpha_5)\theta +$$

$$+ (4 + \frac{2\lambda}{\mu} - \alpha_4 + \alpha_5 + 2\alpha_6)\delta_1, \tag{14}$$

giving the *second-order speeds of the principal longitudinal waves.* Proceeding in a similar way from (5), we see that

$$\rho U_{12}^2 = \lambda_1^2 \beth_2 - \frac{1}{\lambda_2^2}\beth_1$$

$$\doteq (1 + 2\delta_1)\beth_2 - (1 - 2\delta_2)\beth_1, \tag{15}$$

so that by (10)

$$\frac{\rho U_{12}^2}{\mu} \doteq (1 + 2\delta_1)(\alpha_{10} + \alpha_{11}\theta) - (1 - 2\delta_2)(\alpha_{-10} + \alpha_{11}\theta)$$

$$\doteq 1 + \tfrac{1}{2}\alpha_5\theta + 2\delta_1 + \tfrac{1}{2}\alpha_6(\delta_1 + \delta_2). \tag{16}$$

Thus for the *second-order speeds of principal transverse waves* we obtain the formula

$$\frac{\rho_0 U_{12}^2}{\mu} \doteq 1 + 2\delta_1 + (1 + \tfrac{1}{2}\alpha_5)\theta + \tfrac{1}{2}\alpha_6(\delta_1 + \delta_2). \tag{17}$$

We now have assembled the results necessary for interpreting the criterion for a stored energy as a relation among wave speeds. From (17) we see that

$$\frac{\rho_0}{\mu} \frac{\partial U_{12}^2}{\partial \delta_1} = 3 + \tfrac{1}{2}\alpha_5 + \tfrac{1}{2}\alpha_6, \tag{18}$$

while from (14) it follows that

$$\frac{\rho_0}{\mu} \left(\frac{\partial}{\partial \delta_1} - \frac{\partial}{\partial \delta_2} \right) U_{11}^2 = \frac{2\lambda}{\mu} + 4 - \alpha_4 + \alpha_5 + 2\alpha_6. \tag{19}$$

Writing $U_{\perp}^2$ for $\dfrac{\lambda + \mu}{\rho_0}$, the squared speed of transverse waves according to the linearized theory, we may express (9) in the equivalent form

$$\left(\frac{\partial}{\partial \delta_1} - \frac{\partial}{\partial \delta_2} \right) U_{11}^2 - 4\frac{\partial U_{12}^2}{\partial \delta_1} + 6U_{\perp}^2 = 0. \tag{20}$$

This is the final result, a *universal criterion for a stored energy according to the second-order theory*([6]).

This criterion is expressed directly in terms of wave speeds, all material constants having been eliminated.

Appendix. Derivation of the formulae for the speeds of the principal waves. We replace (1) by the equivalent relation

$$t = \lambda_0 1 + \lambda_1 c^{-1} + \lambda_2 c^{-2}. \tag{21}$$

Hence the equations of motion take on the form

$$T^{km}_{\ \ pq}\, \bar{c}^{1\,pq}_{\ \ \ ,m} + \rho f^k = \rho \ddot{x}^k, \tag{22}$$

([6]) We have presumed throughout this paper that the material obeys the constitutive equation (1), where strain is measured from a natural state, in which the stress vanishes. There are then several other relations similar to (20) which may serve equally well as tests for a stored energy, but all of them are consequences of any one. In [3, §§9 and 11], I have given conditions of compatibility whereby the squared speeds of all 9 kinds of principal waves may be tested for compatibility with (1), either exactly or in the second-order approximation.

where f is the field of extrinsic force, $\ddot{x}$ is the acceleration, and

$$T^{km}{}_{pq} \equiv \frac{\partial t^{km}}{\partial \bar{c}^{-1\,pq}},$$ (23)

$$= \tfrac{1}{2}\lambda_1 \left(\delta^k_m \delta^m_q + \delta^m_p \delta^k_q\right) +$$

$$+ \tfrac{1}{2}\lambda_2 \left(\delta^k_p \bar{c}^{1m}_{\ q} + \delta^k_q \bar{c}^{1m}_{\ p} + \delta^m_p \bar{c}^{1k}_{\ q} + \delta^m_q \bar{c}^{1k}_{\ p}\right) +$$

$$+ g^{km}\left[\frac{\partial \lambda_0}{\partial I}g_{pq} + \frac{\partial \lambda_0}{\partial II}(Ig_{pq} - \bar{c}^1_{pq}) + III\frac{\partial \lambda_0}{\partial III}\bar{c}^1_{pq}\right] +$$

$$+ c^{km}\left[\frac{\partial \lambda_1}{\partial I}g_{pq} + \frac{\partial \lambda_1}{\partial II}(Ig_{pq} - \bar{c}^1_{pq}) + III\frac{\partial \lambda_1}{\partial III}\bar{c}^1_{pq}\right] +$$

$$+ c^k_r\, c^{rm}\left[\frac{\partial \lambda_2}{\partial I}g_{pq} + \frac{\partial \lambda_2}{\partial II}(Ig_{pq} - \bar{c}^1_{pq}) + III\frac{\partial \lambda_2}{\partial III}\bar{c}^1_{pq}\right],$$

as follows by a straightforward calculation. Since

$$\bar{c}^{1\,pq} = g^{\alpha\beta}x^p_{,\alpha}x^q_{,\beta}$$

(24)

$$\bar{c}^{1\,pq}_{,m} = 2X^\alpha_{,m}g^{\beta\gamma}x^{(p}_{,\gamma}x^{q)}_{;\alpha\beta},$$

and since the jump conditions at a singular surface of second order with unit normal n are

$$\left[x^k_{,\alpha\beta}\right] = a^k x^m_{,2}x^p_{,\beta}n_m n_p, \quad \left[\ddot{x}^k\right] = U^2 a^k,$$ (25)

where U is the speed of propagation and a is the amplitude, by substituting (24) into (22) and taking the jump of the resulting equation we obtain the propagation condition

$$Q_{km}(n)a^m = \rho_0 U^2 a_k,$$ (26)

where the acoustical tensor $\mathbf{Q}(n)$ has the form

$$Q^k{}_m = 2\,\frac{\rho_0}{\rho}\,T^{kp}{}_{mq}\,\bar{c}^{\,1qs}\,n_p n_s. \tag{27}$$

In a principal co-ordinate system the form $(23)_2$ of the tensor $T^{km}{}_{pq}$ may be much simplified:

$$T^{11}{}_{11} = \frac{\partial t_1}{\partial \lambda_1^2}, \qquad T^{11}{}_{22} = \frac{\partial t_1}{\partial \lambda_2^2}, \dots$$

$$T^{12}{}_{12} = \frac{t_1 - t_2}{2(\lambda_1^2 - \lambda_2^2)}, \dots, \tag{28}$$

while all components not obtainable from these by permutation of indices or by use of the symmetry relations $T^{km}{}_{pq} = T^{mk}{}_{pq} = T^{km}{}_{qp}$ are identically zero. If n has the components $\cos\theta_1$, $\cos\theta_2$, $\cos\theta_3$, then from (27) we obtain the following explicit form for the acoustical tensor:

$$Q_{11}(n) = \frac{\rho_0}{\rho}\left[\frac{\partial t_1}{\partial\log\lambda_1}\cos^2\theta_1 + \frac{t_1 - t_2}{\lambda_1^2 - \lambda_2^2}\,\lambda_2^2\cos^2\theta_2 + \right.$$

$$\left. + \frac{t_1 - t_3}{\lambda_1^2 - \lambda_3^2}\,\lambda_3^2\cos^2\theta_3\right], \dots, \tag{29}$$

$$Q_{12}(n) = \frac{\rho_0}{\rho}\left[\frac{\lambda_1}{\partial\log\lambda_2} + \frac{t_1 - t_2}{\lambda_1^2 - \lambda_2^2}\,\lambda_1\right]\cos\theta_1\cos\theta_2, \dots.$$

From the second of these formulae we see that $Q_{12}(n) = Q_{21}(n)$ if and only if one or both of the following conditions hold:

$$\frac{\partial t_1}{\partial\log\lambda_2} + \frac{t_1 - t_2}{\lambda_1^2 - \lambda_2^2}\,\lambda_1^2 = \frac{\partial t_2}{\partial\log\lambda_1} + \frac{t_2 - t_1}{\lambda_2^2 - \lambda_1^2}\,\lambda_2^2,$$

$$\cos\theta_1\,\cos\theta_2 = 0. \tag{30}$$

The former condition, supplemented by those obtainable from it by permutation of indices, is necessary and sufficient for the existence of a stored-energy function[7]; the latter, similarly supplemented, that the wave front be normal to a principal axis of stress and strain. Thus we have established the following theorem: *In any isotropic elastic material, for a principal wave the principal directions of stress and strain are also the principal directions of the acoustical tensor, which is symmetric; if, however, the acoustical tensor is symmetric for a single wave travelling in a direction not normal to a principal axis, then the material is hyperelastic.*

For a wave travelling in the principal direction in which the stretch is λ_1, we put $\cos\theta_1 = 1$, $\cos\theta_2 = \cos\theta_3 = 0$ in (29) and obtain

$$Q_{11}(n) = \frac{\rho_0}{\rho} \frac{\partial t_1}{\partial \log \lambda_1},$$

(31)

$$Q_{22}(n) = \frac{\rho_0}{\rho} \frac{t_1 - t_2}{\lambda_1^2 - \lambda_2^2} \lambda_1^2 \ .$$

Taking a as having the components $(1,0,0)$ and $(0,1,0)$ in turn yields obvious solutions of (26), which reduces to (4) and (5), respectively.

REFERENCES

[1] M. REINER, Elasticity beyond the elastic limit, *Am. J. Math.*, **70**, (1948), 433–446.

[2] C. TRUESDELL AND R. A. TOUPIN *The Classical Field Theories*, FLÜGGE'S *Handbuch der Physik*, **3**, Part 1, (1960).

[3] C. TRUESDELL, General and exact theory of waves in finite elastic strain, *Archive for Rational Mechanics and Analysis* **8**, (1961), 263–296. References to earlier work, particularly to the important researches of TOUPIN AND BERNSTEIN, are given in this paper.

[4] W. NOLL AND C. TRUESDELL, *The Non-Linear Field Theories of Mechanics*, FLÜGGE'S *Handbuch der Physik*, to appear in Vol. 8, Part 3.

[5] C. TRUESDELL, The mechanical foundations of elasticity and fluid dynamics, *J. Rat. Mech. Anal.*, **1**, (1952), 125–300.

---

[7] See Eq. (41.11)$_2$ of [5].

Discussion

R. S. RIVLIN: I should like to point out a peculiarity of the materials which Professor Truesdell calls elastic, as distinct from hyperelastic. Suppose we take a body of such material through a closed cycle of deformation quasi-statically. Then, either the work done is zero, or it is positive, or negative. If it is always zero, then the material is hyperelastic,—at any rate for quasi-static deformations. If it is positive for some closed cycle, then it is easily seen that the work done in taking the body through the inverse closed cycle is negative. Thus, unless the material is hyperelastic, we can choose a closed cycle of deformation, such that when the body is taken through this quasi-statically, work is done by the material. By repeatedly taking the body through this closed cycle of deformation, we would continuously extract energy from the body. A material which had this property would be a rather useful source of power and prove the non-validity of the second law of thermodynamics. The extension of this argument to non-quasistatic deformations is evident. The argument presented must surely have been known for many years.

C. TRUESDELL's Reply: The argument has indeed been known for years. In less eloquent and dramatic form, it can be found in §46 of *The Mechanical Foundations*, where it is adduced in criticism of a theory of elasticity proposed by Professor Reiner in 1948. In now withdrawing that criticism, or at least qualifying it strongly, I should like to record a protest against being forced to kneel before a lashing by a pious formula nobody can justify except by reference to some Koran. In the context of finite deformations of continuous media, a meaningful statement of the so-called Second Law of Thermodynamics has still to be given, and, in my humble and perhaps exceptional opinion, a law must be stated before we can justly be asked to obey it. The deformations undergone by elastic materials that are not hyperelastic are always reversible in a definite sense, namely, removal of the stress necessarily results in return of the material to the natural state. Moreover, for isotropic materials the closed cycle to which Professor Rivlin refers must necessarily involve finite deformations, since every isotropic elastic material is hyperelasticic in small strains. Further, contrary to Professor Rivlin's implication, such a cycle could not occur spontaneously, since a peculiar system of stresses sufficient to produce the appropriate, special, finite strains, with possibly incidental phenomena of instability and bifurcation, would have to be applied to the boundary of the specimen.

Thus I do not agree that extension of the argument to non-quasistatic processes is evident. I do feel that this muddy kind of talk does the field much harm. While it is possible that the elastic material without a stored-energy function will not describe any physical material, before such a conclusion can be reached it will be necessary to know, by means of clearly stated and proved mathematical theorems, what undesirable properties such a material has. Some intersting work theorems, not making use of any such nonsense as a quasi-static process, have been proved by Dr. Coleman in No. 2 of Volume 9 of the *Archive* (1962). These give the only rational basis I know for the objection raised by Professor Rivlin. It will be noted that these results compare various equilibrium states, and it is nowhere implied that the parameter t used to pass from one of these states to another is the time in any actual deformation process of any physical material.

It is by the researches of Professor Rivlin himself that the elastic materials without a stored-energy function have been revived. As he first assumed and then proved, under various assumptions, in a sequence of papers, peculiar circumstances may make a material behave like an elastic one when it really is not. Indeed, one can prove quite generally that the stress in any simple material subjected to a strain impulse relaxes as if the material were a perfectly elastic one with time-dependent response. There is no reason at all to expect a stored-energy function to exist in this case, as Professor Rivlin himself remarked.

Finally, if we can prove certain results without use of a stored-energy function, what point is there, as far as those results are concerned, in introducing one?

Nothing I have said should indicate any claim that use of a stored-energy energy function is wrong, or that any particular physical material is or is not hyperelastic. Rather, several different lines of argument suggest that theorists should be permitted to study the more general theory of elasticity and to characterize the special features that distinguish the presence of a stored-energy function.

FINITE DEFORMATIONS OF AN ALMOST INCOMPRESSIBLE ELASTIC SOLID

A. J. M. SPENCER

University of Nottingham, U. K.

ABSTRACT

In the solution of problems in the theory of finite deformations of elastic solids, a great simplification is usually obtained if it is assumed that the elastic solid is incompressible, and the majority of solutions which have been found for materials with a general strain-energy function refer to incompressible solids. To solve problems for compressible materials it is usually necessary to adopt a specific form for the strain-energy function. Real solids are not incompressible, although many rubber-like materials which can undergo large elastic deformations show only small changes in density under ordinary loading conditions. This paper is concerned with isotropic elastic bodies in which, during a finite deformation, the relative change in volume in any element is a small quantity of order ε, but whose deformation is not otherwise constrained. The theory is based in part upon the theory of small deformations superposed on finite elastic deformations, and the theory of finite deformations with a perturbed strain-energy function, although these theories require modification for the present case.

By considering the limiting process of passing from a compressible to an incompressible solid, it is shown that, with little loss of generality, the strain-energy function W of a material of the type considered can be expressed in the form

$$W = W_0(I_1, I_2) + (I_3 - 1) W_1(I_1, I_2) + \varepsilon^{-1}(I_3 - 1)^2 W_2^{(1)}(I_1, I_2),$$

where I_1, I_2, I_3 are the strain invariants, and for possible deformations $I_3 - 1$ is of order ε. Here and henceforth, powers of ε higher than the first power are neglected in comparison to unity. The limiting case of an incompressible solid is obtained when $\varepsilon \to 0$.

A body of elastic material, which in its undeformed state is denoted B_0, is first supposed to have a strain-energy function $W_0(I_1, I_2)$ and to deform as an incompressible body, with displacement vector $\mathbf{v}$, to a body B, the stress components in B being denoted τ^{ij}. It is assumed that the deformation and state of stress of B have been determined. The effect on the above B of replacing the strain-energy function $W_0(I_1, I_2)$ by the function W given above is then considered. If this results in a further small deformation of the body B to a body B', then the displacement vector associated with B' is of the form $\mathbf{v} + \varepsilon\mathbf{v}'$, and the stress components in B' are of the form $\tau^{ij} + \varepsilon\tau'^{ij}$. Stress-strain relations and equilibrium equations for B' are formulated in terms of the strain-energy function W, and quantities which have been determined for the body B. These equations are not sufficient for a solution, and it is also necessary to consider the quantity $p = 2(I_3)^{1/2} \partial W/\partial I_3$, which in the body B is an arbitrary scalar function, but in B' is a definite function of W_1 and $W_2^{(1)}$. By comparing the two cases an additional equation for the components of $\mathbf{v}'$ is obtained, and it is then possible, given suitable boundary conditions, to determine the deformation and state of stress in the body B', to order ε, provided that the related problem for the body B has been solved.

The theory is illustrated by application to the problem of simultaneous extension, inflation and torsion of an almost incompressible circular cyclinder.

1. Introduction.

In the solution of problems in the theory of finite deformations of elastic solids, a great simplification is usually obtained if it is assumed that the elastic solid is incompressible, and the majority of solutions which have been found refer to incompressible materials. Real solids are not incompressible, although many rubber-like materials which can undergo large elastic deformations are subject to only small changes in density under ordinary loading conditions. This paper is concerned with isotropic elastic bodies in which, during a finite deformation, the relative change in volume is a small quantity of order ε, but whose deformation is not otherwise restricted. We describe such a body as an almost incompressible elastic solid.

The strain-energy function of an almost incompressible solid differs from that of a related incompressible solid by terms of order ε. The nature of these additional terms, however, is not immediately obvious, and to find their forms it is necessary to study the limiting process involved in the passage from a compressible to an incompressible body. This is done in Section 3.

In Section 4, equations are formulated for determining stress and displacement, to order ε, in a body of almost incompressible material, when the solution of a corresponding problem for a related incompressible material is known. The theory is based in part on that of a previous paper [1] which considered perturbations of the strain-energy function for elastic materials; this theory is however not directly applicable, since it only covers the cases in which perturbed and unperturbed strain-energy functions both refer to compressible bodies, or both refer to incompressible bodies. The necessary modifications required when the unperturbed and perturbed strain-energy functions refer to incompressible and almost incompressible solids respectively are given in Section 4.

In Section 5, the theory is illustrated by application to the problem of simultaneous extension, inflation and torsion of an almost incompressible circular cylinder.

2. Notation and theory for finite deformations.

The notation adopted is, in the main, that of Green and Zerna [2], who give a full account of the theory of finite deformations. For convenience, the principal notations and formulae of the theory are summarised in this section.

A homogeneous, isotropic elastic body with a strain-energy function W is denoted by B_0 in its undeformed state, and by B in its finitely deformed state. A system of curvilinear coordinates θ_i moves with the body. The θ_i coordinate system has covariant and contravariant base vectors $\boldsymbol{g}_i$, $\boldsymbol{g}^i$ respectively and covariant and contravariant metric tensors g_{ik}, g^{ik} respectively in the body B_0; the corresponding quantities for the θ_i coordinates in B are $\boldsymbol{G}_i$, $\boldsymbol{G}^i$, G_{ik}, G^{ik}. Since the body is isotropic, W is a function of the strain invariants

$$I_1 = g^{rs}G_{rs}, \qquad I_2 = g_{rs}G^{rs}I_3, \qquad I_3 = G/g, \tag{1}$$

where
$$g = |g_{ik}|, \qquad G = |G_{ik}|. \tag{2}$$

The stress-strain relations take the form

$$\tau^{ik} = \Phi g^{ik} + \Psi B^{ik} + pG^{ik}, \tag{3}$$

where $\Phi = 2(I_3)^{-\frac{1}{2}}\partial W/\partial I_1, \quad \Psi = 2(I_3)^{-\frac{1}{2}}\partial W/\partial I_2, \quad p = 2(I_3)^{\frac{1}{2}}\partial W/\partial I_3, \tag{4}$

$$B^{ik} = (g^{ik}g^{rs} - g^{ir}g^{ks})G_{rs}, \tag{5}$$

and τ^{ik} is the contravariant stress tensor referred to coordinates θ_i and measured per unit area of the deformed body. In this paper it is more convenient to use the stress tensor

$$s^{ik} = (I_3)^{\frac{1}{2}}\tau^{ik}, \tag{6}$$

which defines stress measured per unit area of the undeformed body. Equation (3) can readily be expressed in terms of s^{ik}. The equations of equilibrium, in the absence of body forces, are

$$\tau^{ik}\|_i = 0, \tag{7}$$

where the double line denotes covariant differentiation with respect to θ_i coordinates using the metric tensors G_{ik}, G^{ik}. Equations (7) can also be expressed in terms of s^{ik} by using (6).

If the material is incompressible, then $I_3 = 1$, and W is a function of I_1 and I_2 only. In this case

$$\Phi = \partial W/\partial I_1, \quad \Psi = \partial W/\partial I_2, \tag{8}$$

and p is a scalar function of position. Also, the stress tensors τ^{ik}, s^{ik} are then identical.

When the surface force vector $\mathbf{P}$ is prescribed at a surface with unit outward normal vector $\mathbf{n}$, then at that surface

$$\tau^{ik} n_i = P^k, \tag{9}$$

where

$$\mathbf{P} = P^k \mathbf{G}_k, \quad \mathbf{n} = n_i \mathbf{G}^i. \tag{10}$$

3. Stress-strain relations for almost incompressible bodies.

In this section we consider the form taken by the strain-energy function and stress–strain relations when the material is only slightly compressible. Suppose that the strain-energy function $W(I_1, I_2, I_3)$ of the material under consideration can be expressed as a series of powers of $I_3 - 1$, with coefficients which are functions of I_1 and I_2, so that W has the form

$$W(I_1, I_2, I_3) = W_0(I_1, I_2) + (I_3 - 1) W_1(I_1, I_2) + (I_3 - 1)^2 W_2(I_1, I_2) + \ldots \tag{11}$$

Then the scalar functions Φ, Ψ, p are

$$\Phi = 2(I_3)^{-\frac{1}{2}} \{ \partial W_0/\partial I_1 + (I_3 - 1) \partial W_1/\partial I_1 + (I_3 - 1)^2 \partial W_2/\partial I_1 + \ldots \},$$

$$\Psi = 2(I_3)^{-\frac{1}{2}} \{ \partial W_0/\partial I_2 + (I_3 - 1) \partial W_1/\partial I_2 + (I_3 - 1)^2 \partial W_2/\partial I_2 + \ldots \}, \tag{12}$$

$$p = 2(I_3)^{\frac{1}{2}} \{ W_1 + 2(I_3 - 1) W_2 + 3(I_3 - 1)^2 W_3 + \ldots \}.$$

The expressions (12), when introduced into the stress–strain relation, give

$$s^{ik} = \Phi_0 g^{ik} + \Psi_0 B^{ik} + 2I_3 W_1 G^{ik} +$$
$$+ (I_3 - 1)[\Phi_1 g^{ik} + \Psi_1 B^{ik} + 4I_3 W_2 G^{ik}] +$$
$$+ (I_3 - 1)^2 [\Phi_2 g^{ik} + \Psi_2 B^{ik} + 6I_3 W_3 G^{ik}] + \ldots, \tag{13}$$

where

$$\Phi = 2\partial W_0/\partial I_1, \quad \Psi_0 = 2\partial W_0/\partial I_2,$$

$$\Phi_1 = 2\partial W_1/\partial I_1, \quad \Psi_1 = 2\partial W_1/\partial I_2, \tag{14}$$

$$\Phi_2 = 2\partial W_2/\partial I_1, \quad \Psi_2 = 2\partial W_2/\partial I_2,$$

and so on.

Now consider the behaviour of W in the limiting process as the material tends to an incompressible material. This process has been discussed by Rivlin [3]. In the limit of incompressible material, W becomes a function of I_1 and I_2 only, and $\partial W/\partial I_3$ is an arbitrary hydrostatic pressure. In order that (13) may represent the stress-strain relation for an incompressible material when $I_3 \to 1$, it is necessary that $W_2 \to \infty$ in such a way that $(I_3 - 1) W_2$ is finite as $I_3 \to 1$; thus in the limit $I_3 \to 1$, $2I_3W_1 + 4(I_3 - 1)I_3W_2$ becomes the arbitrary hydrostatic pressure p.

Next suppose that the material is not incompressible, but that for the range of finite deformations to be considered $(I_3 - 1)$ is a small quantity of order ε whose square may be neglected compared to unity. Then if $4(I_3 - 1)W_2$ is to be of the same order of magnitude as W_1, then W_1/W_2 must be of the order ε. We therefore write $W_2 = \varepsilon^{-1}W_2^{(1)} + W_2^{(2)}$, where $W_2^{(1)}$ and $W_2^{(2)}$ are of the same order of magnitude as W_1. Also, in the limit of incompressible material, it is possible that $W_3 \to \infty$ while $(I_3 - 1)W_3$ remains finite, so in addition we write $W_3 = \varepsilon^{-1} W_3^{(1)} + W_3^{(2)}$. If now only those terms in the expression for W which give rise to stress components of zero and first orders in ε are retained*, we have

$$W = W_0 + (I_3-1)W_1 + \varepsilon^{-1}(I_3-1)^2 W_2^{(1)} + (I_3-1)^2 W_2^{(2)} + \varepsilon^{-1}(I_3-1)^3 W_3^{(1)}. \tag{15}$$

The stress-strain relation which corresponds to (15) is

$$s^{ik} = \Phi_0 g^{ik} + \Psi_0 B^{ik} + I_3[2W_1 + 4\varepsilon^{-1}(I_3-1)W_2^{(1)}]G^{ik} +$$

$$+ (I_3-1)\{[\Phi_1 + \varepsilon^{-1}(I_3-1)\Phi_2^{(1)}]g^{ik} +$$

$$+ [\Psi_1 + \varepsilon^{-1}(I_3-1)\Psi_2^{(1)}]B^{ik} + I_3[4W_2^{(2)} + 6\varepsilon^{-1}(I_3-1)W_3^{(1)}]G^{ik}\}, \tag{16}$$

---

* There is no evident reason why W should not also contain such terms as $\varepsilon^{-2}(I_3-1)^3 W_2^{(3)}$, $\varepsilon^{-3}(I_3-1)^4 W_4^{(1)}$, and so on. Such terms could readily be incorporated if required, but are not included in the present analysis.

where Φ_0, Ψ_0, Φ_1 and Ψ_1 are given by (14), and

$$\Phi_2^{(1)} = 2\partial W_2^{(1)}/\partial I_1, \qquad \Psi_2^{(1)} = 2\partial W_2^{(1)}/\partial I_2. \qquad (17)$$

4. Perturbation method for almost incompressible bodies.

Consider first a body, denoted B_0 in its undeformed state, of incompressible isotropic elastic material, with strain–energy function W_0. This body deforms into a body B which is in equilibrium. It is supposed that the deformation and state of stress of B are completely known; thus if θ_i is a system of coordinates which has metric tensors g^{ik}, g_{ik} in B_0 and moves with the body, then in B there are known the components of the displacement vector $\mathbf{v}(\theta_i)$, the base vectors $\mathbf{G}_i$, $\mathbf{G}^i$ of the θ_i coordinate system, and the stress tensor s^{ik} (which, since the body is incompressible, is identical to the tensor τ^{ik}) referred to the θ_i coordinates. These quantities are determined by the theory for incompressible materials outlined in Section 2. The stress–strain relation for B is

$$s^{ik} = \Phi_0 g^{ik} + \Psi_0 B^{ik} + p_0 G^{ik}, \qquad (18)$$

where B^{ik} is given by (5), Φ_0 and Ψ_0 by (14), and p_0 is a known scalar function of position.

Now consider that the body B_0 is no longer incompressible, but is of almost incompressible material with strain-energy function W of the form (15). We seek equilibrium configurations* in which the body B_0 is deformed into a body B', the displacement vector describing this deformation being of the form

$$\mathbf{v}(\theta_i) + \varepsilon \mathbf{v}'(\theta_i) + \varepsilon^2 \mathbf{v}''(\theta_i). \qquad (19)$$

It will be found eventually that the term $\varepsilon^2 \mathbf{v}''$ is not required; it is however convenient to retain it at present.

The stress–strain relation for the body B' is given by (16), with all quantities evaluated in B'. Remembering that, in B', $I_3 - 1$ is of order ε, it follows from (16) that in order to find an expression for s^{ik} in B' which is correct to terms of order ε, it is necessary to evaluate, in B', I_3 to order ε^2, Φ_0, Ψ_0, W_1, $W_2^{(1)}$, B^{ik} and G^{ik} to order ε, and Φ_1, Ψ_1, $\Phi_2^{(1)}$, $\Psi_2^{(1)}$, $W_2^{(2)}$ and W_3 to zero order in ε.

---

* The procedure described can only lead to possible solutions; these solutions are not necessarily unique and the equilibrium positions may be unstable.

The treatment of the geometry of the deformation, apart from determining the terms of order ε^2 in the expression for I_3 in B', is identical to the treatment given by Green, Rivlin and Shield [4], and gives the following results, which are all to order ε. The covariant base vectors of the coordinate system θ_i in B' are $\mathbf{G}_i + \varepsilon\,\mathbf{G}_i'$, where

$$\mathbf{G}_i' = \mathbf{v}'_{,i} \;\; = v'_m\|_i \mathbf{G}^m = v'^m\|_i \mathbf{G}_m, \tag{20}$$

and v'_m, v'^m are components of $\mathbf{v}'$ referred to base vectors $\mathbf{G}^i$, $\mathbf{G}_i$ respectively, so that

$$\mathbf{v}' = v'_m \mathbf{G}^m = v'^m \mathbf{G}_m. \tag{21}$$

The metric tensors of θ_i coordinates in B' are $G_{ik} + \varepsilon G'_{ik}$, $G^{ik} + \varepsilon G'^{ik}$, where

$$G'_{ik} = v'_i\|_k + v'_k\|_i, \qquad G'^{ik} = -G^{ir}G^{ks}G'_{rs}. \tag{22}$$

The strain invariants are I_1, I_2, 1 in B and, to the indicated order in ε, are $I_1 + \varepsilon I'_1$, $I_2 + \varepsilon I'_2$, $1 + \varepsilon I'_3 + \varepsilon^2 I''_3$ in B', where,

$$I'_1 = g^{rs}G'_{rs}, \qquad I'_2 = g_{rs}(G'^{rs} + G^{rs} I'_3), \qquad I'_3 = G^{rs}G'_{rs} = 2v'^r\|_r. \tag{23}$$

The expression for I''_3 is obtained by expanding the determinant of the covariant metric tensor in B' to order ε^2, in a manner similar to that employed in a rather different context, by Green and Spratt [5]. This gives

$$I''_3 = 2v'^r\|_r v'^s\|_s - v'^r\|_s v'^s\|_r + 2v''^r\|_r, \tag{24}$$

where v''^i are components of $\mathbf{v}''$ referred to base vectors $\mathbf{G}_i$. The tensor B^{ik} becomes, in the body B', to order ε, a tensor $B^{ik} + \varepsilon B'^{ik}$, where

$$B'^{ik} = (g^{ik}g^{rs} - g^{ir}g^{ks})\,G'_{rs}. \tag{25}$$

In the body B', the scalar functions W_1, $W_2^{(1)}$, Φ_0 and Ψ_0 are functions of $I_1 + \varepsilon I'_1$, $I_2 + \varepsilon I'_2$. By Taylor's expansion to order ε it follows that, for example

$$W_1(I_1 + \varepsilon I'_1, I_2 + \varepsilon I'_2) = W_1(I_1, I_2) +$$

$$+ \varepsilon[I'_1 \partial W_1(I_1, I_2)/\partial I_1 + I'_2 \partial W_1(I_1, I_2)/\partial I_2]$$

$$= W_1(I_1, I_2) + \tfrac{1}{2}\varepsilon[I'_1 \Phi_1(I_1, I_2) + I'_2 \Psi_1(I_1, I_2)]. \qquad (26)$$

Similarly, to order ε

$$W_2^{(1)}(I_1 + \varepsilon I'_1, I_2 + \varepsilon I'_2) = W_2^{(1)}(I_1, I_2) + \tfrac{1}{2}\varepsilon[I'_1 \Phi_2^{(1)}(I_1, I_2) + I'_2 \Psi_2^{(1)}(I_1, I_2)],$$

$$\Phi_0(I_1 + \varepsilon I'_1, I_2 + \varepsilon I'_2) \quad = \Phi_0(I_1, I_2) + \varepsilon[I'_1 A_0(I_1, I_2) + I'_2 F_0(I_1, I_2)], \qquad (27$$

$$\Psi_0(I_1 + \varepsilon I'_1, I_2 + \varepsilon I'_2) \quad = \Psi_0(I_1, I_2) + \varepsilon[I'_1 F_0(I_1, I_2) + I'_2 B_0(I_1, I_2)],$$

where

$$A_0 = 2\partial^2 W_0/\partial I_1^2, \qquad B_0 = 2\partial^2 W_0/\partial I_2^2, \qquad F_0 = 2\partial^2 W_0/\partial I_1 \partial I_2. \qquad (28)$$

The functions Φ_1, Ψ_1, $\Phi_2^{(1)}$, $\Psi_2^{(1)}$, $W_2^{(2)}$ and $W_3^{(1)}$ in B' are only required to zero order in ε, and so may be evaluated as functions of I_1 and I_2, the strain invariants of the body B.

To first order in ε the stress tensor in the body B', referred to curvilinear coordinates θ_i in B' and measured per unit area of the undeformed body, is $s^{ik} + \varepsilon s'^{ik}$. By substituting into (16) the expressions given above for quantities evaluated in B', including all terms up to order ε, we obtain

$$s^{ik} + \varepsilon s'^{ik} = \Phi_0 g^{ik} + \Psi_0 B^{ik} + [2W_1 + 4I'_3 W_2^{(1)}] G^{ik} +$$

$$+ \varepsilon\{\Phi' g^{ik} + \Psi' B^{ik} + \Psi_0 B'^{ik} + p' G^{ik} + \qquad (29)$$

$$+ [2W_1 + 4I'_3 W_2^{(1)}] G'^{ik}\},$$

where

$$\Phi' = I'_1 A_0 + I'_2 F_0 + I'_3 \Phi_1 + (I'_3)^2 \Phi_2^{(1)},$$

$$\Psi' = I'_1 F_0 + I'_2 B_0 + I'_3 \Psi_1 + (I'_3)^2 \Psi_2^{(1)}, \qquad (30)$$

$$p' = I'_1 \Phi_1 + I'_2 \Psi_1 + 2I'_3(W_1 + 2W_2^{(2)}) +$$

$$+ 2I'_1 I'_3 \Phi_2^{(1)} + 2I'_2 I'_3 \Psi_2^{(1)} + 2(I'_3)^2(2W_2^{(1)} + 3W_3^{(1)}) + \qquad (31)$$

$$+ 4I''_3 W_2^{(1)},$$

and $W_0, W_1, W_2^{(1)}, W_2^{(2)}, W_3^{(1)}$ and their derivatives are evaluated with the strain invariants taking the values I_1 and I_2.

If now (29) is to represent the stress-strain relation for incompressible material when $\varepsilon \to 0$, it is necessary that (18) and (29) determine the same values of s^{ik} in this limit. Hence

$$p_0 = 2W_1 + 4I_3'W_2^{(1)}, \tag{32}$$

and since p_0 is a known function, (32) may be regarded as an equation which determines I_3'. From (29) and (32), we have

$$s'^{ik} = \Phi'g^{ik} + \Psi'B^{ik} + \Psi_0 B'^{ik} + p'G^{ik} + p_0 G'^{ik}. \tag{33}$$

The equations of equilibrium for B', in the absence of body forces, can be expressed in the form

$$[s'^{ik} + s^{ir}v'^k \|_r] \|_i = 0. \tag{34}$$

The components of the second-order displacement vector $\mathbf{v}''$ enter into equation (33) only through the term containing I_3'' in the expression (31) for p'. Accordingly (32) and the three equations of equilibrium (34) may be regarded as four equations in which the unknowns are p' and the three components of $\mathbf{v}'$, and a knowledge of these quantities is sufficient to determine, in addition to the first-order displacement vector $\mathbf{v}'$, the first order stress tensor s'^{ik}. Equation (31) then gives an expression for I_3''. Knowledge of I_3'', however, is only of value if it is required to proceed to higher orders of approximation, and for the first-order theory it is preferable to regard p' as an arbitrary function which is required in order to evaluate s'^{ik}, and is to be determined, with the components of $\mathbf{v}'$, from (32), (33) and (34). If this approach is adopted, then the part played by p' in the first-order theory for almost incompressible bodies is similar to that played by p_0 in the theory for incompressible bodies. Also, the components of $\mathbf{v}''$ do not then enter into the expression for s'^{ik}, so it is sufficient to regard the displacement vector in B' as of the form

$$\mathbf{v}(\theta_i) + \varepsilon \mathbf{v}'(\theta_i).$$

The quantities $G'^{ik}, G'_{ik}, I_1', I_2', I_3'$ and B'^{ik} are still given by (22), (23) and (25). Moreover the terms $W_2^{(2)}$ and $W_3^{(1)}$ of the strain-energy function (15) appear finally only in the expression (31) for p', and so, to first order in ε, the values of the displacement and stress components are not affected by the forms of $W_2^{(2)}$ and $W_3^{(1)}$. It is therefore sufficient, for the first-order theory, to specify a strain-energy function of the form

$$W = W_0(I_1, I_2) + (I_3 - 1) W_1(I_1, I_2) + \varepsilon^{-1}(I_3 - 1)^2 W_2^{(1)}(I_1, I_2). \tag{35}$$

With W of this form, s^{ik} is given by (18), and s'^{ik} by (33), with Φ' and Ψ' defined by (30) and p' treated as an arbitrary function. Equations (32) and (34), with boundary conditions, determine p' and the components of $\mathbf{v}'$.

The treatment of surface forces is again identical to that given in [4], except that the conditions are expressed in terms of s^{ik} rather than of τ^{ik}. If $n_i + \varepsilon n_i'$ are the covariant components of the unit normal to the surface of B', referred to base vectors $\mathbf{G}^i + \varepsilon \mathbf{G}'^i$, and $P^k + \varepsilon P'^k$ are the components of the surface force vector, referred to $\mathbf{G}_k + \varepsilon \mathbf{G}_k'$, then

$$P^k + \varepsilon P'^k = [s^{ik} + \varepsilon(s'^{ik} - s^{ik}v'^r \|_{,r})](n_i + \varepsilon n_i'). \tag{36}$$

There are a number of alternative ways of expressing this surface force condition.

5. The simultaneous extension, inflation and torsion of a cylindrical tube.

As an application of the theory the problem of simultaneous extension, inflation and torsion of a circular cylindrical tube of almost incompressible material will be considered. This problem has been solved completely for an incompressible material; the original solution is due to Rivlin [6], but is here used in the form in which it is given by Green and Zerna [2]. Partial solutions have been obtained for compressible material [7], [8], but these do not, for example, determine the radial displacement in explicit form.

We first state the known solution for incompressible material; the results which follow are quoted from [2], with minor changes of notation. A circular cylindrical tube which in its undeformed state has length l, and external and internal radii a_1 and a_2 respectively, undergoes the following successive deformations:

(i) a uniform extension of extension ratio λ parallel to the axis of the tube;

(ii) a uniform inflation of the tube in which its length remains constant and its external and internal radii change to $r_1 = \mu_1 a_1$ and $r_2 = \mu_2 a_2$ respectively;

(iii) a uniform simple torsion in which planes perpendicular to the axis of the tube rotate in their own planes through an angle proportional to the distance of the plane considered from one end, the constant of proportionality being ψ.

The moving coordinates $(\theta_1, \theta_2, \theta_3)$ are chosen to coincide with cylindrical polar coordinates (r, θ, z) in the deformed body. Then the point (r, θ, z) was initially at (ρ, ϕ, ζ), where

$$\rho = \rho(r) = rQ(r), \quad \phi = \theta - \psi z, \quad \zeta = z/\lambda. \tag{37}$$

The metric tensors of the deformed body are

$$G_{ik} = \begin{bmatrix} 1 & 0 & 0 \\ 0 & r^2 & 0 \\ 0 & 0 & 1 \end{bmatrix}, \quad G^{ik} = \begin{bmatrix} 1 & 0 & 0 \\ 0 & r^{-2} & 0 \\ 0 & 0 & 1 \end{bmatrix}. \tag{38}$$

The incompressibility condition gives

$$\rho = rQ = \{\lambda(r^2 + K)\}^{\frac{1}{2}}, \tag{39}$$

where
$$\lambda K = a_1^2(1 - \lambda\mu_1^2) = a_2^2(1 - \lambda\mu_2^2). \tag{40}$$

The metric tensors of the θ_i coordinates in the undeformed body are, after simplification by use of (39)

$$g_{ik} = \begin{bmatrix} \lambda^2 Q^{-2} & 0 & 0 \\ 0 & Q^2 r^2 & -Q^2 \psi r^2 \\ 0 & -Q^2 \psi r^2 & \lambda^{-2} + Q^2 \psi^2 r^2 \end{bmatrix}, \tag{41}$$

$$g^{ik} = \begin{bmatrix} \lambda^{-2} Q^2 & 0 & 0 \\ 0 & \lambda^2 \psi^2 + Q^{-2} r^{-2} & \lambda^2 \psi \\ 0 & \lambda^2 \psi & \lambda^2 \end{bmatrix}. \tag{42}$$

The strain invariants are

$$I_1 = \lambda^{-2} Q^2 + \lambda^2 + Q^{-2} + \lambda^2 \psi^2 r^2, \quad I_2 = \lambda^2 Q^{-2} + \lambda^{-2} + Q^2 + Q^2 \psi^2 r^2, \tag{43}$$

and the tensor B^{ik} is

$$
B^{ik} =
\begin{bmatrix}
\lambda^{-2} + Q^2 + Q^2\psi^2 r^2 & 0 & 0 \\
0 & \lambda^{-2}r^{-2} + \lambda^2 Q^{-2}r^{-2} + Q^2\psi^2 & Q^2\psi \\
0 & Q^2\psi & \lambda^2 Q^{-2} + Q^2
\end{bmatrix}. \quad (44)
$$

The only non-zero Christoffel symbols of the (r,θ,z) system are

$$
\Gamma^1_{22} = -r, \quad \Gamma^2_{12} = \Gamma^2_{21} = r^{-1}. \quad (45)
$$

Solution of the equilibrium equations gives

$$
p_0 = -\lambda^{-2}Q^2\Phi_0 - (\lambda^{-2} + Q^2 + Q^2\psi^2 r^2)\Psi_0 - L(r), \quad (46)
$$

where

$$
L(r) = \int_{r_1}^{r} \{(\lambda^{-2}Q^2 - Q^{-2} - \lambda^2\psi^2 r^2)\Phi_0 + (Q^2 - \lambda^2 Q^{-2})\Psi_0\} r^{-1} dr, \quad (47)
$$

and a constant of integration has been chosen so that there is no traction on the outer surface $r = r_1$. The non-zero components of the stress tensor are

$$
s^{11} = -L(r),
$$

$$
r^2 s^{22} = -L(r) + (Q^{-2} - \lambda^{-2}Q^2 + \lambda^2\psi^2 r^2)\Phi_0 + (\lambda^2 Q^{-2} - Q^2)\Psi_0,
$$

$$
s^{33} = -L(r) + (\lambda^2 - \lambda^{-2}Q^2)\Phi_0 + (\lambda^2 Q^{-2} - \lambda^{-2} - Q^2\psi^2 r^2)\Psi_0, \quad (48)
$$

$$
rs^{23} = \lambda^2\psi r\Phi_0 + Q^2\psi r\Psi_0.
$$

We now consider that the the cylinder is made of slightly compressible material, with strain-energy function of the form (35). The assumed deformation is still of the type defined above, but (39) no longer gives correctly the initial position of a particle whose final radial distance from the axis of the cylinder is r. Instead, we seek a solution in which each particle undergoes, in addition to the radial displacement defined by (39), a small additional radial displacement εu, which depends only on r; thus a point which is initially at (ρ, ϕ, ζ) is finally at $(r + \varepsilon u, \theta, z)$ where ρ, ϕ, ζ are related to r, θ, z by (37) and (39).

With this assumption about the form of the deformation, the incremental displacement vector $\mathbf{v}'$ has, in the notation of Section 4, the following components referred to the base vectors of the polar coordinates (r, θ, z) :

$$v_1' = v'^1 = u(r), \quad v_2' = v_3' = v'^2 = v'^3 = 0. \tag{49}$$

Hence, from (22)

$$G_{ik}' = \begin{bmatrix} 2u_r & 0 & 0 \\ 0 & 2ru & 0 \\ 0 & 0 & 0 \end{bmatrix}, \quad G'^{ik} = \begin{bmatrix} -2u_r & 0 & 0 \\ 0 & -2r^{-3}u & 0 \\ 0 & 0 & 0 \end{bmatrix}, \tag{50}$$

where u_r denotes du/dr. Also, from (23)

$$I_1' = 2\left[\lambda^{-2}Q^2 u_r + (Q^{-2} + \lambda^2 \psi^2 r^2) r^{-1} u\right],$$

$$I_2' = 2\left[(\lambda^{-2} + Q^2 + Q^2 \psi^2 r^2) u_r + (\lambda^{-2} + \lambda^2 Q^{-2} + Q^2 \psi^2 r^2) r^{-1} u\right], \tag{51}$$

$$I_3' = 2(u_r + r^{-1} u).$$

The non-zero components of B'^{ik} are, from (25)

$$B'^{11} = 2(\lambda^{-2} + Q^2 \psi^2 r^2) r^{-1} u, \quad r^2 B'^{22} = 2(\lambda^{-2} + Q^2 \psi^2 r^2) u_r,$$

$$\tag{52}$$

$$B'^{33} = 2(Q^2 u_r + \lambda^2 Q^{-2} r^{-1} u), \quad B'^{23} = 2Q^2 \psi u_r.$$

Next, from (30), the functions Φ' and Ψ' are

$$\Phi' = 2\left\{\left[\lambda^{-2}Q^2 u_r + (Q^{-2} + \lambda^2 \psi^2 r^2) r^{-1} u\right] A_0 + \right.$$

$$+ \left[(\lambda^{-2} + Q^2 + Q^2 \psi^2 r^2) u_r + (\lambda^{-2} + \lambda^2 Q^{-2} + Q^2 \psi^2 r^2) r^{-1} u\right] F_0 +$$

$$\left. + (u_r + r^{-1} u) \Phi_1 + 2(u_r + r^{-1} u)^2 \Phi_2^{(1)}\right\},$$

$$\tag{53}$$

$$\Psi' = 2\left\{\left[\lambda^{-2}Q^2 u_r + (Q^{-2} + \lambda^2 \psi^2 r^2) r^{-1} u\right] F_0 + \right.$$

$$+ \left[(\lambda^{-2} + Q^2 + Q^2 \psi^2 r^2) u_r + (\lambda^{-2} + \lambda^2 Q^{-2} + Q^2 \psi^2 r^2) r^{-1} u\right] B_0 +$$

$$\left. + (u_r + r^{-1} u) \Psi_1 + 2(u_r + r^{-1} u)^2 \Psi_2^{(1)}\right\}.$$

It follows from (33) that the non-zero components of the incremental stress tensor s'^{ik} are

$$
\begin{aligned}
s'^{11} &= \lambda^{-2}Q^2\Phi' + (\lambda^{-2} + Q^2 + Q^2\psi^2 r^2)\Psi' + 2(\lambda^{-2} + Q^2\psi^2 r^2)r^{-1}u\Psi_0 - \\
&\quad - 2u_r p_0 + p', \\
r^2 s'^{22} &= (Q^{-2} + \lambda^2\psi^2 r^2)\Phi' + (\lambda^{-2} + \lambda^2 Q^{-2} + Q^2\psi^2 r^2)\Psi' + \\
&\quad + 2(\lambda^{-2} + Q^2\psi^2 r^2)u_r\Psi_0 - 2r^{-1}u p_0 + p', \\
s'^{33} &= \lambda^2\Phi' + (\lambda^2 Q^{-2} + Q^2)\Psi' + 2(Q^2 u_r + \lambda^2 Q^{-2}r^{-1}u)\Psi_0 + p', \\
rs'^{23} &= \lambda^2\psi r\Phi' + Q^2\psi r\Psi' + 2Q^2\psi r u_r\Psi_0.
\end{aligned}
\tag{54}
$$

From (32) and (51) we have

$$
u_r + r^{-1}u = (p_0 - 2W_1)/(8W_2^{(1)}),
$$

which integrates to give

$$
u = \frac{1}{8r}\left\{ \int_{r_1}^{r} \frac{(p_0 - 2W_1)}{W_2^{(1)}} r\, dr + A \right\},
\tag{55}
$$

where A is a constant which can be chosen to give u any assigned value on any surface $r = $ constant. If, for example, $A = 0$, then there is no additional displacement at the surface $r = r_1$.

The second and third of the equations of equilibrium (34) give, after substitution from (48), (49) and (54)

$$
\partial p'/\partial\theta = 0, \qquad \partial p'/\partial z = 0.
$$

Hence p' depends only on r. The first of (34) is

$$
d[s'^{11} + s^{11}u_r]/dr + r^{-1}[s'^{11} - r^2 s'^{22} + s^{11}u_r - rs^{22}u] = 0,
\tag{56}
$$

which, after substituting from (48) and (54) and integrating, gives

$$
\begin{aligned}
p' &= -2\lambda^{-2}Q^2 u_r\Phi_0 - 2[(\lambda^{-2} + Q^2 + Q^2\psi^2 r^2)u_r + \\
&\quad + (\lambda^{-2} + Q^2\psi^2 r^2)r^{-1}u]\Psi_0 - (u_r + r^{-1}u)L(r) - \lambda^{-2}Q^2\Phi' - \\
&\quad - (\lambda^{-2} + Q^2 + Q^2\psi^2 r^2)\Psi' - L(r) + H',
\end{aligned}
\tag{57}
$$

where

$$L'(r) = \int_{r_1}^{r} \{2Q^2(\lambda^{-2}\Phi_0 + \Psi_0)(u_r - r^{-1}u) +$$
$$+ (\lambda^{-2}Q^2 - Q^{-2} - \lambda^2\psi^2 r^2)\Phi' + (Q^2 - \lambda^2 Q^{-2})\Psi'\}r^{-1}dr, \tag{58}$$

and H' is a constant.

The final expressions for the stress components are obtained by substituting (46) and (57) into (54), with the following results

$$s'^{11} = L(r)(u_r - r^{-1}u) - L'(r) + H',$$

$$r^2 s'^{22} = -[2\lambda^{-2}Q^2\Phi_0 + 2Q^2\Psi_0 + L(r)](u_r - r^{-1}u) -$$
$$- (\lambda^{-2}Q^2 - Q^{-2} - \lambda^2\psi^2 r^2)\Phi' + (\lambda^2 Q^{-2} - Q^2)\Psi' - L'(r) + H', \tag{59}$$

$$s'^{33} = -2\lambda^{-2}Q^2 u_r \Phi_0 - 2[(\lambda^{-2} + Q^2\psi^2 r^2)u_r +$$
$$+ (\lambda^{-2} - \lambda^2 Q^{-2} + Q^2\psi^2 r^2)r^{-1}u]\Psi_0 - L(r)(u_r + r^{-1}u) +$$
$$+ (\lambda^2 - \lambda^{-2}Q^2)\Phi' + (\lambda^2 Q^{-2} - \lambda^{-2} - Q^2\psi^2 r^2)\Psi' - L'(r) + H',$$

$$rs'^{23} = 2Q^2\psi r u_r \Psi_0 + \lambda^2\psi r\Phi' + Q^2\psi r\Psi'.$$

The values of the surface force components are readily deduced from these results.

The moment M of the forces acting on a plane end of the cylinder about the axis of the cylinder, is, to order ε

$$M = 2\pi \int_{r_2}^{r_1} r(r + \varepsilon u)^2 (s^{23} + \varepsilon s'^{23}) \, dr. \tag{60}$$

In the case in which there is no applied traction on the curved surface of the cylinder, and when W has the form (35), it may be verified from the results of this section by means of a rather lengthy algebraic reduction that

$$M = \frac{2\pi}{\lambda\psi} \int_{a_2}^{a_1} \rho^2 \frac{dW}{d\rho} \, d\rho, \tag{61}$$

where ρ is given by (39). This agrees with the general result obtained, for compressible solids, by Green [7].

6. List of symbols.

W	=	strain-energy function
$W_0, W_1, W_2, \ldots$	=	terms of strain-energy function
B_0, B, B'	=	denote undeformed, deformed and second deformed bodies
θ_i	=	convected curvilinear coordinates
$\mathbf{g}_i, \mathbf{g}^i$	=	base vectors of undeformed body

$$\left.\begin{array}{l} \mathbf{G}_i, \mathbf{G}^i \\[1ex] \mathbf{G}_i + \varepsilon\mathbf{G}'_i, \mathbf{G}^i + \varepsilon\mathbf{G}'^i \end{array}\right\} = \text{base vectors of deformed bodies}$$

g_{ik}, g^{ik}	=	metric tensors of undeformed body

$$\left.\begin{array}{l} G_{ik}, G^{ik}, \\[1ex] G_{ik} + \varepsilon G'_{ik}, G^{ik} + \varepsilon G'^{ik} \end{array}\right\} = \text{metric tensors of deformed bodies}$$

$$\left.\begin{array}{l} I_1\ I_2, I_3; \\[1ex] I_1 + \varepsilon I_1, I_2 + \varepsilon I'_2, I_3 + \varepsilon I'_3 + \varepsilon^2 I'' \end{array}\right\} = \text{strain invariants}$$

τ^{ik}	=	stress tensor measured per unit area of deformed body
$s^{ik}; s^{ik} + \varepsilon s'^{ik}$	=	stress tensors measured per unit area of undeformed body
Φ, Ψ, p	=	scalar functions defined by (4)
$B^{ik}; B^{ik} + \varepsilon B'^{ik}$	=	tensors defined by (5) and (25)
$P^k; P^k + \varepsilon P'^k$	=	components of surface force vectors
$n_i; n_i + \varepsilon n'_i$	=	components of unit normals

$$\left.\begin{array}{l} \Phi_0, \Phi_1, \Phi_2, \ldots; \\[1ex] \Psi_0, \Psi_1, \Psi_2 \ldots; A_0, B_0, F_0 \end{array}\right\} = \begin{array}{l}\text{scalar functions defined by (14), (17),}\\ \text{(28)}\end{array}$$

p_0	=	value of p for incompressible body
ε	=	small parameter
$\mathbf{v}; \mathbf{v} + \varepsilon\mathbf{v}' + \varepsilon^2\mathbf{v}''$	=	displacement vectors

$v'_m,\ v'^m,\ v''_m,\ v''^m$	=	components of $\mathbf{v}'$ and $\mathbf{v}''$
$\Phi',\ \Psi',\ p'$	=	scalar functions defined by (30) and (31)
λ	=	extension ratio for cylinder
$a_1,\ a_2$	=	external and internal radii of undeformed cylinder
$r_1,\ r_2$	=	external and internal radii of deformed cylinder
$\mu_1 = r_1/a_1,\ \mu_2 = r_2/a_2$		
ψ	=	constant defining torsion of cylinder
$(r,\theta,z),\ (\rho,\phi,\zeta)$	=	polar coordinates
$Q(r),\ K$	=	defined by (39) and (40)
Γ^i_{jk}	=	Christoffel symbols
$L(r),\ L'(r)$	=	integrals defined by (47) and (58)
$\varepsilon u(r)$	=	superposed radial displacement

REFERENCES

[1]   A. J. M. SPENCER, *Quart. J. Mech. Appl. Math.*, **12**, (1959), 129.
[2]   A. E. GREEN AND W. ZERNA. *Theoretical Elasticity* (Oxford, 1954).
[3]   R. S. RIVLIN, *J. Rat. Mech. Anal.*, **2**, (1953), 53.
[4]   A. E. GREEN, R. S. RIVLIN AND R. T. SHIELD, *Proc. Roy. Soc.*, **A, 211**, (1952), 128.
[5]   A. E. GREEN AND E. B. SPRATT, *Proc. Roy. Soc.* **A, 224**, (1954), 347.
[6]   R. S. RIVLIN, *Phil. Trans. Roy. Soc.*, **A, 242**, (1949), 173.
[7]   A. E. GREEN, *Proc Roy. Soc.*, **A, 227**, (1955), 271.
[8]   A. E. GREEN AND J. E. ADKINS, *Large Elastic Deformations* (Oxford, 1960).

THE GENERAL MEASURE OF DEFORMATION

Z. KARNI AND M. REINER

Technion–Israel Institute of Technology, Haifa, Israel

ABSTRACT

It is found that other second order measures of deformation exist besides the two named after Green and Almansi. These measures have the property of absence of cross terms in simple shear.

NOTATION

A	= of Almansi		k	= scalar functions
C	= of Cauchy		S	= of Swainger
d_{ij}	= deformation tensor		Γ	= shift
G	= of Green		λ_{ij}	= coordinate gradient
H	= of Hencky			

1. When a body is *transferred* from an *initial* position defined by the Cartesian coordinates a_i of all particles to a *final* position defined likewise by x_j, two essentially different cases can be distinguished.

In the one case, none of its dimensions are changed; this constitutes a simple *transport* such as takes place with a *rigid* body. Alternatively, some of its dimensions are changed; this constitutes a *deformation*.

The question then arises after a *measure* of the deformation.

Several special measures have been defined so far either in order to suit some special case or from mathematical convenience. Let the body be a cylindrical rod of length l_0, and let it be extended to length l. We can define two *stretches*, namely

$$\lambda = l/l_0; \quad \bar{\lambda} = l_0/l \tag{1.1}$$

one the reverse of the other. The first relates the stretch to the initial length l_0, the other to the final length l.

The proposed measures named after Cauchy, Green, Hencky, Almansi and Swainger[1] are then in this order:

---

(1) For reference see [1].

$$e^C = \lambda - 1 = e \tag{1.2}$$

$$e^G = \tfrac{1}{2} \cdot (\lambda^2 - 1) = (\lambda - 1) + \tfrac{1}{2} \cdot (\lambda - 1)^2 = e + e^2/2$$

$$e^H = \ln \lambda = (\lambda - 1) - \frac{(\lambda - 1)^2}{2} + \ldots = e - e^2/2 + \ldots$$

$$e^A = \tfrac{1}{2} \cdot (1 - 1/\lambda^2) = (\lambda - 1) - \tfrac{3}{2} \cdot (\lambda - 1)^2 + \ldots = e - \tfrac{3}{2} \cdot e^2 + \ldots \tag{1.3}(²)$$

$$e^S = 1 - 1/\lambda = (\lambda - 1) - (\lambda - 1)^2 + \ldots = e - e^2 + \ldots$$

Alternatively we introduce

$$e^S = 1 - \bar{\lambda} = \bar{e} \tag{1.4}$$

and write

$$e^A = \tfrac{1}{2} \cdot (1 - \bar{\lambda}^2) = (1 - \bar{\lambda}) - \tfrac{1}{2} \cdot (1 - \bar{\lambda})^2 = \bar{e} - \bar{e}^2/2$$

$$e^H = -\ln\bar{\lambda} = (1 - \bar{\lambda}) + (1 - \bar{\lambda})^2/2 - \ldots = \bar{e} + \bar{e}^2/2 - \ldots$$

$$e^G = \tfrac{1}{2} \cdot (1/\bar{\lambda}^2 - 1) = (1 - \bar{\lambda}) + \tfrac{3}{2} \cdot (1 - \bar{\lambda})^2 - \ldots = \bar{e} + \tfrac{3}{2}\bar{e}^2 - \ldots \tag{1.5}$$

$$e^C = 1/\bar{\lambda} - 1 = (1 - \bar{\lambda}) + (1 - \bar{\lambda})^2 - \ldots = \bar{e} + \bar{e}^2 - \ldots$$

We may therefore name λ the Cauchy-stretch and $\bar{\lambda}$ the Swainger-stretch. We see that every measure so far proposed can be expressed in the first order by either the Cauchy measure or the Swainger measure with all other measures adding second order terms, and, except for one measure in each group (namely e^G in the first and e^A in the second group), third and higher order terms.

The differences between these measures can be appreciated by letting the length of the rod be doubled so that $\lambda = 2$; we then find:

$$e^C = 100\%, \quad e^G = 150\%, \quad e^H = 66\%, \quad e^A = 37.5\%, \quad e^S = 50\%$$

while when the length is halved so that $\bar{\lambda} = 2$, they give:

$$e^C = -50\%, \quad e^G = -37.5\%, \quad e^H = -66\%, \quad e^A = -150\%, \quad e^S = -100\%.$$

So far for the case of simple extension.

2. In order to find a general measure, we go back to our description of the process of deformation. The deformation is not a directly observable quantity; what is directly observable is the changes of coordinates.(³)

(²) Two other measures have been proposed by Wall; they are combinations of two of the above.

(³) It is interesting to note that Hooke found his law by employing the latter method.

The x_i will be in general functions of the a_j and conversely i.e.

$$x_i = x_i(a_j); \quad a_i = a_i(x_j) \tag{2.1}$$

and these relations can be observed and described. There cannot be a constant term on the right side of Eqs. (2.1), as this would imply a rigid body translation. What defines a deformation must therefore be measurable in terms of the gradients

$$\lambda_{ij} = \partial x_i / \partial a_j \tag{2.2}$$

or

$$\bar{\lambda}_{ij} = \partial a_i / \partial x_j \tag{2.3}$$

These gradients, which should be distinguished from the *displacement gradients* usually denoted by the letter γ, have been named by Truesdell[2] "deformation gradients" without distinguishing $\bar{\lambda}$ from λ. We cannot adopt this nomenclature because we need *two* terms. We therefore propose to name them *coordinate-gradients* with $\bar{\lambda}$ as *final*-coordinate gradient and λ as initial coordinate gradient.

Note that the tensors λ_{ij} and $\bar{\lambda}_{ij}$ are non-symmetric.

The *displacement* u_i is defined by

$$u_i = x_i - a_i \tag{2.4}$$

From this, the *displacement gradients*

$$\gamma_{ij} = \partial u_i / \partial a_j; \quad \bar{\gamma}_{ij} = \partial u_{i_\gamma} / \partial x_j \tag{2.5}$$

Therefore

$$\gamma_{ij} = \lambda_{ij} - \delta_{ij}; \quad \bar{\gamma}_{ij} = \delta_{ij} - \bar{\lambda}_{ij} \tag{2.6}$$

The deformation, expressed as a tensor of the second rank will naturally be defined as a function of either the coordinate gradients or the displacement gradients with the following provisions:

(i) The function must be isotropic.

(ii) The deformation tensor must be symmetric in order not to include a rigid body rotation.

(iii) When expressed as a function of the displacement gradient, the first order term must be identical with the Cauchy or the Swainger-measure.

(iv) The deformation tensor must vanish identically when the coordinate gradient tensor is a unit tensor.

(v) An extension should be expressed by a deformation component which is positive for an elongation and vice versa.

3. We start from a theorem written by Truesdell[1, p. 131] as follows:

"Two tensors $a^i j$ and $b^i j$ are isotropically related if their matrices **a** and **b** satisfy

$$f(\mathbf{a}, \mathbf{a}', \mathbf{b}, \mathbf{b}') = 0 \qquad (3.1)$$

where primes denote transposition, and where the function f may depend also upon scalar functions of **a** and **b**. In particular **b** is an analytic isotropic function of **a**, if

$$\mathbf{b} = f(\mathbf{a}, \mathbf{a}') = k_0 \mathbf{I} + k_1 \mathbf{a} + k'_1 \mathbf{a}' + k_2 \mathbf{a}^2 + k'_2 \mathbf{aa}' + k''_2 \mathbf{a'a} +$$

$$+ k'''_2 \mathbf{a}'^2 + \ldots \qquad (3.2)(^4)$$

where the k_i, $k'_i \ldots$ are scalar functions of **a**".

We may continue this series by adding next the third order terms

$$k_3 \mathbf{a}^2 \mathbf{a}' + k'_3 \mathbf{aa'a} + k''_3 \mathbf{aa}'^2 + k'''_3 \overset{\text{IV}}{\mathbf{a'a}^2} + \overset{\text{IV}}{k_3} \mathbf{a'aa}' + \overset{\text{V}}{k_3} \mathbf{a}'^2 \mathbf{a} + \qquad (3.2a)$$

The terms $\mathbf{a}^3$ and $\mathbf{a}'^3$ are not included here because, as shown by Reiner[3] through the application of the Cayley-Hamilton equation, $\mathbf{a}^3$ can be expressed by

$$\mathbf{a}^3 = \mathrm{III}_a \mathbf{I} - \mathrm{II}_a \mathbf{a} + \mathrm{I}_a \mathbf{a}^2 \qquad (3.3)$$

where I_a, II_a, III_a, are the principal invariants of the matrix **a** and similarly with regard to $\mathbf{a}'^3$. Fourth order terms like $\mathbf{a}^3 \mathbf{a}'$ are again reducible to second and third order terms already appearing in Eqs. (3.2) and (3.2a), whereas such terms as $\mathbf{a}^2 \mathbf{a}'^2$ should be added to these equations. Our further discussion however is confined to the second order measures of deformation, hence we shall not proceed beyond Eq. (3.2).

If we introduce in Eq. (3.2) for **a** the coordinate gradient λ, we have taken the first step to find an expression for the deformation tensor. However, the tensor **b** thus found is not symmetric. To make it symmetric(^{5}), we replace **a** by **a**' and vice versa in each term of Eq. (3.2) and take the average of both expressions with the result, replacing **a** by λ or $\bar{\lambda}$ and introducing also new coefficients instead of the k's

$$d_{ij} = \aleph \delta_{ij} + \beth (\lambda_{ij} + \lambda_{ji}) + \gimel (\lambda_{i\alpha}\lambda_{\alpha j} + \lambda_{j\alpha}\lambda_{\alpha i}) + \daleth \lambda_{i\alpha}\lambda_{j\alpha} + \daleth \lambda_{\alpha i}\lambda_{\alpha j} \qquad (3.4)$$

(^{4}) Note that k' does not mean the transpose of k, etc.

(^{5}) Note that the following terms are already symmetric — **aa'**, **a'a** — while the following are not symmetric $\mathbf{a}^2$, $(\mathbf{a}')^2 = (\mathbf{a}^2)'$.

Here d_{ij} is the tensor of deformation, while the parameters א to ה are scalar quantities, which in the primitive cases are constants, while in more general cases they are scalar functions of the invariants of the tensor λ_{ij}.

Alternatively, d_{ij} can also be expressed by:

$$d_{ij} = \overline{\aleph}\delta_{ij} + \overline{\beth}(\overline{\lambda}_{ij} + \overline{\lambda}_{ji}) + \overline{\gimel}(\overline{\lambda}_{i\alpha}\overline{\lambda}_{\alpha j} + \overline{\lambda}_{j\alpha}\overline{\lambda}_{\alpha i}) + \overline{\daleth}\overline{\lambda}_{i\alpha}\overline{\lambda}_{j\alpha} + \overline{\he}\overline{\lambda}_{\alpha i}\overline{\lambda}_{\alpha j} \qquad (3.5)$$

4. We now examine special deformation measures.

For first order measures all coefficients beyond א, ב, and $\overline{\aleph}$, $\overline{\beth}$, must vanish. We first set in (3.4) א $= -1$ and ב $= \frac{1}{2}$, and obtain the Cauchy deformation tensor

$$d_{ij}^{C} = \tfrac{1}{2}(\lambda_{ij} + \lambda_{ji}) - \delta_{ij} = \tfrac{1}{2}\left(\frac{\partial x_i}{\partial a_j} + \frac{\partial x_j}{\partial a}\right) - \delta_{ij} \qquad (4.1)$$

Similarly we obtain the Swainger tensor by introducing into (3.5) $\overline{\aleph} = 1$, $\overline{\beth} = -\frac{1}{2}$

$$d_{ij}^{S} = \delta_{ij} - \tfrac{1}{2}(\overline{\lambda}_{ij} + \overline{\lambda}_{ij}) = \delta_{ij} - \tfrac{1}{2}\left(\frac{\partial a_i}{\partial x_j} + \frac{\partial a_j}{\partial x_i}\right) \qquad (4.2)$$

It can be see that for simple extension, Eqs. (4.1) and (4.2) are reduced to Eqs. (1.2, 1) and (1.4) respectively.

Provisions (iv)—(v) do not permit other primitive measures of the first order. We therefore turn to the second order measures with constant coefficients.

Murnaghan [4] first derived the two finite deformations tensors

$$d_{ij}^{G} = \tfrac{1}{2}\left(\frac{\partial x_\alpha}{\partial a_i}\frac{\partial x_\alpha}{\partial a_j} - \delta_{ij}\right) \qquad (4.3)$$

and

$$d_{ij}^{\overline{A}} = \tfrac{1}{2}\left(\delta_{ij} - \frac{\partial a_\alpha}{\partial x_i}\frac{\partial a_\alpha}{\partial x_j}\right) \qquad (4.4)$$

Eq. (4.3) is an expression for the Green-measure in the initial state, Eq. (4.4) an expression for the Almansi-measure in the final state. We have indicated this by putting a bar over the symbol A, thus $\overline{A}$. They are obtained from (3.4) respectively by introducing into the expression for d_{ij} the values א $= -\frac{1}{2}$, ה $= \frac{1}{2}$, ב $= \gimel = \daleth = 0$, and by introducing into (3.5) $\overline{\aleph} = \frac{1}{2}$, $\overline{\he} = -\frac{1}{2}$, $\overline{\beth} = \overline{\gimel} = \overline{\daleth} = 0$. Karni and Reiner [5] derived the two complementary expressions, namely for the Green measure in the final and for the Almansi measure in the initial state as follows:

$$\bar{d}_{ij}^{\bar{G}} = \tfrac{1}{2}\left(\frac{\partial x_i}{\partial a_\alpha}\frac{\partial x_j}{\partial a_\alpha} - \delta_{ij}\right) \tag{4.5}$$

$$d_{ij}^{A} = \tfrac{1}{2}\left(\delta_{ij} - \frac{\partial a_i}{\partial x_\alpha}\frac{\partial a_j}{\partial x_\alpha}\right) \tag{4.6}$$

These again are primitive cases of (3.4) with $\aleph = -\tfrac{1}{2}$, $\daleth = \tfrac{1}{2}$, $\beth = \gimel = \he = 0$ for (4.5) and $\aleph = \tfrac{1}{2}$, $\daleth = -\tfrac{1}{2}$, $\beth = \gimel = \he = 0$ for (4.6) Here also the bar over G, thus $\bar{G}$, in (4.5), indicates that the Green measure as written here refers to the final state.

Equations (4.3)—(4.6) are the primitive second order measures so far proposed. Inspection of the general measure (3.4) and (3.5), however, shows that not all the possibilities for such measures have been exhausted. Nothing has so far been based on the coefficient C. We are able in compliance with provisions (iv)—(v), to introduce into (3.4) $\aleph = -\tfrac{1}{2}$, $\gimel = \tfrac{1}{4}$, $\beth = \daleth = \he = 0$, and into (3.5) $\aleph = \tfrac{1}{2}$, $\gimel = -\tfrac{1}{4}$, $\beth = \daleth = \he = 0$, and obtain the two additional measures,

$$d_{ij}^{\mathrm{I}} = \tfrac{1}{2}\left[\tfrac{1}{2}\left(\frac{\partial x_i}{\partial a_\alpha}\frac{\partial x_\alpha}{\partial a_j} + \frac{\partial x_j}{\partial a_\alpha}\frac{\partial x_\alpha}{\partial a_i}\right) - \delta_{ij}\right] \tag{4.7}$$

$$d_{ij}^{\mathrm{II}} = \tfrac{1}{2}\left[\delta_{ij} - \tfrac{1}{2}\left(\frac{\partial a_i}{\partial x_\alpha}\frac{\partial a_\alpha}{\partial x_j} + \frac{\partial a_j}{\partial x_\alpha}\frac{\partial a_\alpha}{\partial xi}\right)\right] \tag{4.8}$$

This completes the second order measures with constant coefficients which we call primitive. These measures expressed in terms of *displacements gradients* are listed in Table I.

We shall examine the third and fourth order measures in a later research. It should be noted that the Hencky measure comes under the fourth order measures.

5. We now apply the various measures of deformation of the second order to the two basic types of deformation, namely

    (i)   simple extension

    (ii)   simple shear

These applications will illustrate the differences inherent in the various measures.

    (i)   Simple extension is an uni-axial deformation, say in the x_1-direction, expressed by the following relations on the model of Eqs. (2.1). It is defined by

TABLE I

Deformation tensors in terms of displacement gradients

Measure	Symbol	$\varkappa$	$\bar{\varkappa}$	$\sqcap$	$\bar{\sqcap}$	$\lrcorner$	$\bar{\lrcorner}$	$\sqsupset$	$\bar{\sqsupset}$	$\lrcorner\!\lrcorner$	$\overline{\lrcorner\!\lrcorner}$	Deformation tensor
Caucuy	d^C	-1	—	$\tfrac{1}{2}$	—	—	—	—	0	—	$-\tfrac{1}{2}\left(\dfrac{\partial u_i}{\partial a_j}+\dfrac{\partial u_j}{\partial a_i}\right)$
Swainger	d^S	—	1	—	$-\tfrac{1}{2}$	—	0	0	—	0	$\tfrac{1}{2}\left(\dfrac{\partial u_i}{\partial x_j}+\dfrac{\partial u_j}{\partial x_i}\right)$
Green (initial)	d^G	$-\tfrac{1}{2}$	—	0	—	0	—	—	$\tfrac{1}{2}$	—	$-\tfrac{1}{2}\left(\dfrac{\partial u_i}{\partial a_j}+\dfrac{\partial u_j}{\partial a_i}+\dfrac{\partial u_\alpha}{\partial a_i}\dfrac{\partial u_\alpha}{\partial a_j}\right)$
Green (final)	$d^{\bar{G}}$	$-\tfrac{1}{2}$	—	0	—	0	—	0	—	—	$-\tfrac{1}{2}\left(\dfrac{\partial u_i}{\partial a_j}+\dfrac{\partial u_j}{\partial a_i}+\dfrac{\partial u_i}{\partial a_\alpha}\dfrac{\partial u_j}{\partial a_\alpha}\right)$
Almansi (initial)	d^A	—	$\tfrac{1}{2}$	—	—	—	—	—	$-\tfrac{1}{2}$	—	$\tfrac{1}{2}\left(\dfrac{\partial u_i}{\partial x_j}+\dfrac{\partial u_j}{\partial x_i}-\dfrac{\partial u_i}{\partial x_\alpha}\dfrac{\partial u_j}{\partial x_\alpha}\right)$
Almansi (final)	$d^{\bar{A}}$	—	$\tfrac{1}{2}$	—	0	0	0	0	—	$-\tfrac{1}{2}$	$\tfrac{1}{2}\left(\dfrac{\partial u_i}{\partial x_j}+\dfrac{\partial u_j}{\partial x_i}-\dfrac{\partial u_\alpha}{\partial x_i}\dfrac{\partial u_\alpha}{\partial x_j}\right)$
M^I	d^I	$-\tfrac{1}{2}$	—	0	—	$\tfrac{1}{4}$	—	0	0	—	$-\tfrac{1}{2}\left[\dfrac{\partial u_i}{\partial a_j}+\dfrac{\partial u_j}{\partial a_i}+\tfrac{1}{2}\left(\dfrac{\partial u_i}{\partial a_\alpha}\dfrac{\partial u_\alpha}{\partial a_j}+\dfrac{\partial u_j}{\partial a_\alpha}\dfrac{\partial u_\alpha}{\partial a_i}\right)\right]$
M^{II}	d^{II}	—	$\tfrac{1}{2}$	—	0	—	$-\tfrac{1}{4}$	0	—	0	$\tfrac{1}{2}\left[\dfrac{\partial u_i}{\partial x_j}+\dfrac{\partial u_j}{\partial x_i}-\tfrac{1}{2}\left(\dfrac{\partial u_i}{\partial x_\alpha}\dfrac{\partial u_\alpha}{\partial x_j}+\dfrac{\partial u_j}{\partial x_\alpha}\dfrac{\partial u_\alpha}{\partial x_i}\right)\right]$

$$x_1 = \lambda a_1, \qquad x_2 = a_2; \quad x_3 = a_3 \tag{5.1}$$

$$a_1 = x_1/\lambda; \qquad a_2 = x_2; \quad a_3 = x_3 \tag{5.2}$$

The matrices of the coordinate gradients and the displacement gradients are as follows:

$$\lambda_{ij} = \begin{Vmatrix} \lambda & 0 & 0 \\ 0 & 1 & 0 \\ 0 & 0 & 1 \end{Vmatrix} \qquad \bar{\lambda}_{ij} = \begin{Vmatrix} 1/\lambda & 0 & 0 \\ 0 & 1 & 0 \\ 0 & 0 & 1 \end{Vmatrix} \tag{5.3}$$

$$\gamma_{ij} = \begin{Vmatrix} \lambda-1 & 0 & 0 \\ 0 & 0 & 0 \\ 0 & 0 & 0 \end{Vmatrix} \qquad \bar{\gamma}_{ij} = \begin{Vmatrix} 1-1/\lambda & 0 & 0 \\ 0 & 0 & 0 \\ 0 & 0 & 0 \end{Vmatrix} \tag{5.4}$$

The deformation tensors in the various measures are listed in Table II.

(ii) Simple shear in the $x_1 x_2$ plane is defined by

$$x_1 = a_1 + \Gamma a_2; \quad x_2 = a_2; \quad x_3 = a_3 \tag{5.5}$$

$$a_1 = x_1 - \Gamma x_2; \quad a_2 = x_2; \quad a_3 = x_3 \tag{5.6}$$

The matrices of the coordinate gradients and the displacement gradients follow

$$\lambda_{ij} = \begin{Vmatrix} 1 & \Gamma & 0 \\ 0 & 1 & 0 \\ 0 & 0 & 1 \end{Vmatrix} \qquad \bar{\lambda}_{ij} = \begin{Vmatrix} 1 & \Gamma & 0 \\ 0 & 1 & 0 \\ 0 & 0 & 1 \end{Vmatrix} \tag{5.7}$$

$$\gamma_{ij} = \begin{Vmatrix} 0 & \Gamma & 0 \\ 0 & 0 & 0 \\ 0 & 0 & 0 \end{Vmatrix} \qquad \bar{\gamma}_{ij} = \begin{Vmatrix} 0 & \Gamma & 0 \\ 0 & 0 & 0 \\ 0 & 0 & 0 \end{Vmatrix} \tag{5.8}$$

The deformation tensors are listed in Table III.

TABLE II

$$Simple\ extension\ \Delta l = l - l_0,\ e = \frac{\Delta l}{l_0} = \lambda - 1 \quad \bar{e} = \frac{\Delta l}{l} = 1 - \frac{1}{\lambda}$$

Measure	Cauchy	Swainger	Green		Almansi		M^{I}	M^{II}
Symbol	d^C	$d^{\bar{S}}$	d^G	$d^{\bar{G}}$	d^A	$d^{\bar{A}}$	d^{I}	d^{II}
d_{xx}	e	$\bar{e}$	$e(1+\tfrac{1}{2}e)$		$\bar{e}(1-\tfrac{1}{2}\bar{e})$		$e(1+\tfrac{1}{2}e)$	$\bar{e}(1-\tfrac{1}{2}\bar{e})$

All other components of d_{ij} vanish.

6. We have thus found that there exist two second order measures, which we denoted by M^{I} and M^{II}, in addition to the known second order measures named after Green and Almansi. Table III shows that these two measures have a remarkable property, namely *no cross terms appear in simple shear*. This carries with it the conclusion that cross terms are also absent in simple torsion. In other words: let there be a material which in simple extension shows a second order effect. If with such material in torsion, its length is not changed, this would mean that either measure M^{I}, or measure M^{II} are

TABLE III

Simple shear

Measure	Cauchy	Swainger	Green		Almansi		M^{I}	M^{II}
Symbol	d^C	d^S	d^G	$d^{\bar{G}}$	d^A	$d^{\bar{A}}$	d^{I}	d^{II}
d_{xy}	$\dfrac{\Gamma}{2}$	$\dfrac{\Gamma}{2}$	$\dfrac{\Gamma}{2}$		$\dfrac{\Gamma}{2}$		$\dfrac{\Gamma}{2}$	$\dfrac{\Gamma}{2}$
d_{xx}	0	0	0	$\dfrac{\Gamma^2}{2}$	$\dfrac{-\Gamma^2}{2}$	0	0	0
d_{yy}	0	0	$\dfrac{\Gamma^2}{2}$	0	0	$\dfrac{-\Gamma^2}{2}$	0	0

The components d_{xz}, d_{yz}, d_{zz} vanish.

appropriate. It is true that the few specimens which have until now been examined experimentally have all shown an extension of the cylinder or a positive
Poynting effect. However, mathematics must provide the language for dealing
with a case when the Poynting effect is absent. The substantive for a sentence
in this language has now been supplied in M^{I} and M^{II}, i.e. we can say that
the measures M^{I} and / or M^{II} do or do not apply in some hypothetical case.

Acknowledgement.

The research leading to this paper has been sponsored in part by the Air
Research and Development Command, United States Air Force and Contract
AF 61 (052) — 223 through the European office, ARDC.

REFERENCES

[1] C. Truesdell, *J. Rat. Mech. Anal.*, **1**, (1952), 125–300
[2] C. Truesdell and R. O. Toupin, in Fluegge (Editor) Encyclopedia of Physics, **3**,
     (1960) 1, Springer Verlag, 226–793.
[3] M. Reiner, *Amer. J. Math.*, **67**, (1945), 350–362.
[4] F. D. Murnaghan, *Amer J. Math.*, **59**, (1937), 235–260.
[5] Z. Karni and M. Reiner, *Bull. Res. Counc. of Israel*, **8C**, (1960), 89–92.

Discussion

Z. Sobotka: In this extremely valuable paper, the authors have given a general
tensorial formulation of the first-order and second-order strain measures. To
the preceding strain measures of the second and first order, other measures
may be associated, namely Hencky measure and a new measure which the
writer has introduced and which results in relating the deformation to the
arithmetical mean of the deformed and non deformed length as follows:

$$\varepsilon = 2\,\frac{\lambda - 1}{\lambda + 1} = 2\frac{1 - \bar{\lambda}}{1 + \bar{\lambda}} \tag{1}$$

In this case we have $\lambda = 2$ the value of $\varepsilon = 66.7\%$ and for $\lambda = \frac{1}{2}$ that of
$\varepsilon = -66.7\%$, i.e. the same value as for the Hencky measure.

For the three-dimensional state we may write

$$d_{ij} = 2\,\frac{\frac{1}{2}\,(\lambda_{ij} + \lambda_{ij}) - \delta_{ij}}{\frac{1}{2}\,(\lambda_{ij} + \lambda_{ij}) + \delta_{ij}} \tag{2}$$

In order to conserve the tensorial dimensionality, the symmetrical tensor

$$\Lambda_{ij} = \tfrac{1}{2}(\lambda_{ij} + \lambda_{ji}) \tag{3}$$

instead of the non-symmetrical tensor of the coordinate gradient λ_{ij} may be
introduced.

It seems that many new strain measures may be then formulated as follows:

$$d_{ij} = f(\Lambda_{ij}) \tag{4}$$

Expanding the preceding relationship into the absolutely convergent power series and using the rules of tensorial algebra, we may get the following general formula

$$d_{ij} = \aleph_0 \delta_{ij} + \aleph_1 \Lambda_{ij} + \aleph_2 \Lambda_{i\alpha} \Lambda_{\alpha j}$$

yielding a class of other strain measures.

Thus the validity of the authors' general tensorial equation (3, 4) using the symmetrization of the non-symmetrical coordinate gradient λ_{ij} may be extended for the strain-measures being of other forms than have been presented.

Z. KARNI's Reply: It is clear from the text that our Eq. (3.4) is the general expression for the strain tensors of the first and second order only. The more general expression appears in (3.2) and recourse should be made to it while considering measures of higher order such as the Hencky measure (fourth order) and the measure proposed by the discussor. The discussor's Eq. (5), regarded by him as a "general formula yielding a class of other strain measures" is by no means more general than our (3.2). In fact, it is included in the latter, as a substitution of Eq. (3) into the discussor's Eq. (5) readily shows.

AN EXPERIMENTAL INVESTIGATION
OF THE POYNTING EFFECT

I. DETERMINATION OF CHANGES IN LENGTH

AMNON FOUX

Technion–Israel Institute of Technology, Haifa, Israel

ABSTRACT

It is shown that the action of a simple torque on steel wires produce changes in length of the wires in addition to the twist. The relative change in length is positive and proportional to the square of the shear strain.

1. Introduction.

This paper presents an experimental study of changes in length of wires subjected to torsional twists. The investigation was prompted by Poynting's results [1], [2] on the same subject. Half a century ago Poynting observed that the length of four steel wires, two copper wires and one brass wire were increased in torsion. Later Swift [3] found in experiments with large plastic torsion of metal cylinders that all those materials which have the property of work-hardening showed lengthening, while lead showed a shortening. If we consider the plastic deformation of a body as a successive freezing-in of elastic strains, similar results may be expected in the latter case. Timoshenko [4] expected on theoretical grounds that circular rods subjected to torsion should shorten in their length. It was therefore desirable to have more experimental results in order to decide between Poynting and Timoshenko. These are reported upon in the following.

Poynting's experiments which were carried out within the elastic limits have not been repeated. As said before, his experiments were carried out with rather a small number (four) of wires of one kind, and this cannot be considered as sufficient for definite conclusions. The object of the present research was therefore to investigate conditions in a larger number of wires, and to see whether the results can lead to an adequate theory of the effect.

2. Description of apparatus.

The apparatus used for measuring the change in length of a wire while twisted, is shown schematically in Figure 1. For convenience of representation, various parts are shown in the plane of the figure, even though actually they were in different planes.

A steel frame (1) supported on the wall carries a horizontal triangular plate (2), on which a spherical socket (3) is mounted in its centre. A steel rod (4) with a ball on one end passes through a hole in the plate so that the ball rests in the socket, and can be locked in a vertical position by a threaded cap on the socket. On the lower end of the rod (4), there is a chuck (5), into which the upper end of the wire (6) is clamped. At its lower end the wire is being gripped by a similar chuck (5) attached to the centre of a horizontal bar (7) and a vertical rod (8),

Another steel frame (9) supported on the wall two meters below frame (1), carries a large hollow pivot (10) through which the rod (8) passes freely. The pivot can be levelled by three levelling screws (11), and also centered about rod (8) by three centering screws (12). A bearing (13) with a graduated scale (14) is mounted on the pivot (10) free to turn on it. A rectangular turning-plate (15) mounted on the bearing (13) is located right under the horizontal bar (7) attached to the lower chuck.

A nylon thread (16) clamped to two horizontal spacers (17) on each side of the turning-plate is also clamped to the vertical ends of the horizontal bar (7). Thus by turning the turning–plate on its bearing, the lower chuck is turned also through the pull of the nylon thread, and the wire specimen (6) is twisted.

To avoid oscillations of rod (8), two oil dampers (18) and (19) are employed, and thus all possible motions of the rod are damped.

The turning-plate is turned by means of a chain drive and a handle. The angle of twist can be determined by the graduated scale (14).

The measuring device for change in length of the wire is a capacitance gauge, employing a proximity meter. One plate of the capacitor (20) is attached to the lower end of rod (8), and the other is the top surface of a micrometer screw (21) of 0.5 mm pitch mounted vertically through insulators (22) on a triangular plate (23). This plate is suspended on three wires (24) from the top plate (2). The length of wires (24) is adjustable, so that plate (23) can be kept in a horizontal position hanging freely on the upper frame. To avoid oscillations of this plate, three pins extending down are immersed in oil baths (25), acting as dampers. The micrometer screw has a pointer (26) clamped to it, and by means of a graduated scale (27) the turn of the micrometer screw can be determined to a great accuracy.

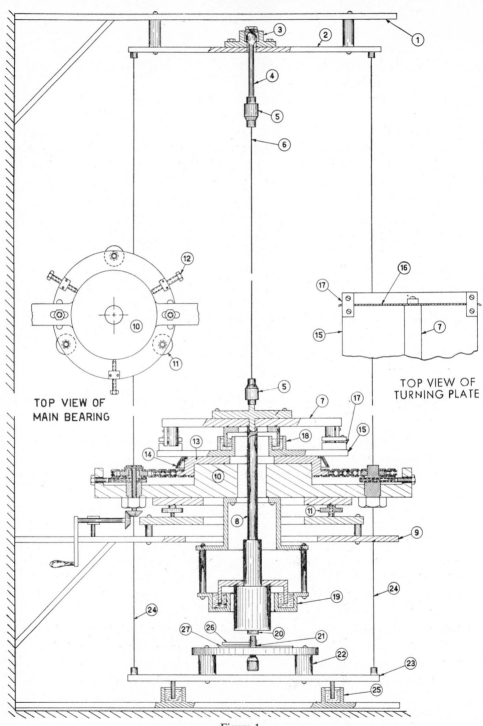

TOP VIEW OF
MAIN BEARING

TOP VIEW OF
TURNING PLATE

Figure 1
Schematic diagram of wire torsion apparatus

A change in length of the specimen wire would result in a change in the width of the gap between plate (20) and micrometer screw (21). The wires (24) provide a means for temperature compensation.

The dial on the proximity meter is calibrated for distance measurements by turning the micrometer screw in and out. Changes in length of the specimen wire due to twisting could now be determined directly from the proximity meter dial. The sensitivity of this device depends on the initial distance between the two capacitor plates.

The whole instrument is enclosed in an insulated cabinet, parts of which are made of double layers of a transparent material to enable observation. The handle by which the wire is twisted, and the electrical connections are the only parts extending out of the insulated cabinet.

3. Wire specimens.

Ten high tensile steel (piano) wires were tested in the apparatus described above. The wires were of different makes and diameters ranging between 0.8 mm and 1.3 mm. They were tested in three states

    a) as drawn,

    b) after application of an axial tension of 95% of the U.T.S.,

    c) after heating to approximately 900°C.

Dimensions and properties of wire specimens are listed in Table I. The letter after the specimen number refers to the state of the wire according to the above category.

4. Procedure of experiments.

(i) Calibration of measuring device:

The proximity meter, used for measuring the relative capacity of the capacitance gauge, was calibrated with the aid of the micrometer screw so that readings on its dial could be converted into distances.

The calibration curve obtained by this method was reproduceable within a very small difference, at any time, as long as the initial distance between the capacitor plates was the same.

After preliminary tests, it was found that two calibration curves were sufficient for the range of specimens tested.

(ii) Measurements of change in length of wires when twisted:

After a wire specimen was inserted in the two chucks and its length determined, the nylon cord was clamped to the cross-bar and the exact zero-twist

AMNON FOUX

TABLE I

Wire specimens

Wire No.	Diameter* in mm	Length in mm	E** in 10^3 kg/mm^2	U.T.S.** in kg/ mm^2	Wire Source
1a	0.800	1576	20.94	260.4	Stahl- u. Draht-
1b	0.800	1585			werk Roeslau
1c	0.800	1585			
2a	0.835	1572	20.11	240.0	A.S.S.A.B.
2b	0.835	1585			Class 300
2c	0.834	1585			
3a	0.900	1576	20.52	266.0	Stahl- u. Draht-
3b	0.900	1585			werk Roeslau
3c	0.900	1585			
4a	0.993	1576	19.60	251.0	Stahl- u. Draht-
4b	0.993	1585			werk Roeslau
4c	0.990	1585			
5a	1.020	1578.5	20.83	257.4	(supplied by
5b	1.020	1585			Prof. Feltham)
5c	1.015	1585			
6a	1.105	1576	20.50	252.4	Stahl- u. Draht-
6b	1.105	1585			werk Roeslau
6c	1.100	1580			
7a	1.200	1576	19.92	236.7	Stahl- u. Draht-
7b	1.200	1585			werk Roeslau
7c	1.190	1580			
8a	1.240	1576	20.71	232.4	A.S.S.A.B.
8b	1.240	1585			class 300
8c	1.240	1580			
9a	1.250	1575	20.57	236.7	Stahl- u. Draht-
9b	1.250	1585			werk Roeslau
9c	1.240	1580			
10a	1.295	1576.5	20.62	240.0	Stahl- u. Draht-
10b	1.295	1585			werk Roeslau
10c	1.290	1580			

* Average of ten measurements, all of which were within 0.005 of the given value. The heat treatment somewhat affected the wire diameter.

** Average of two tests in the as-drawn state giving almost identical results.

position was recorded from the graduated scale on the turning-plate. With the wire in its zero-twist position, the initial gap of the capacitance gauge was set to suit one of the calibration curves.

Turning the handle in one direction caused the wire to twist in the same direction. Dial readings of the proximity meter were taken for every complete revolution of twist. The maximum number of revolution for each wire was depending upon its diameter and its yield strength. Some wires were twisted four revolutions in each direction, while some other wires only three.

Two series of tests were carried out with each wire. In every series a new specimen of the same wire and state was used. Each series consisted of four tests. Each test consisted of two complete cycles of twist of the specimen. A complete cycle was obtained by twisting the wire a little more than four (or three) revolutions in the counter-clockwise direction (assumed as positive), returning to zero-twist, then twisting a little more than four (or three) revolutions in the clockwise direction and returning back to zero-twist position.

Whenever the scale on the turning-plate showed one or several complete revolutions relative to zero-twist position, the gauge reading was recorded. Thus in every cycle two readings for every revolution in each direction were taken. A wire tested in two series of four tests, each of which consisted of two cycles, has thus 32 readings for every revolution in the clockwise direction and 32 readings for every revolution in the counter-clockwise direction for categories (a) and (b). For category (c) one series only was carried out, and the averages are accordingly based on 16 readings. The results listed below are based on the average of these readings.

In carrying out the experiments the wire specimens were subjected to an axial tensile force of 11 kg during the test. This was the weight of part of the apparatus hanging on the wire specimen. In preliminary tests conducted with different axial loads on the wires it was found that these loads had no measurable effect on the elongation of the wires due to twist. The purpose of the axial load was to assist in the uncoiling of the coiled wire specimens.

5. Results.

The axial strain ε can be expressed as:

$$\varepsilon = \frac{\Delta l}{l}$$

where Δl and l are the change in length and the length of the wire specimen respectively.

In general ε will be expressible as a polynomial function of the form:

$$\varepsilon = a\gamma + b\gamma^2 + c\gamma^3 + d\gamma^4 + \ldots$$

where γ is the maximum shear strain expressed as a function of the twist, i.e.

$$\gamma = \frac{r\theta}{l}$$

with r as the wire-specimen radius, l its length and θ its angle of twist.

The part of ε contributed by even powers which we denote by ε_e will be given by

$$\varepsilon_e = \frac{\varepsilon(\gamma) + \varepsilon(-\gamma)}{2} = b\gamma^2 + d\gamma^4 \ldots$$

The part of ε contributed by the odd powers which we denote by ε_0 is

$$\varepsilon_0 = a\gamma + c\gamma^3 + \ldots$$

so that

$$\varepsilon = \varepsilon_0 + \varepsilon_e$$

The experimental data were treated accordingly, and a separation of the even and odd terms of the axial strain was carried out.

It was found that there exist odd order strains ε_0 contributed mainly by the first order term and only in a very small portion by a third order term, in most cases not more than 1 microstrain. Similarly it was found that ε_e is mainly due to the second order term, and only in a very minute portion to a fourth order term well within the experimental error. Higher order terms could not be detected.

A typical graphical representation of the separation of the odd power strains and the even power strains from the experimental observation, is shown in Figure 2(a) for wire No. 8, in the as-drawn state. Figures 2(b) and 2(c) show the observations and separation of results of the same wire after tension and heating respectively. Wire No. 8 was the only one that showed shortening in the as-drawn state.

The total axial strain ε as obtained from observations, the even order axial strain ε_e, and the odd order axial strains ε_0, as calculated, are listed in Tables II, III and IV for each turn in the test.

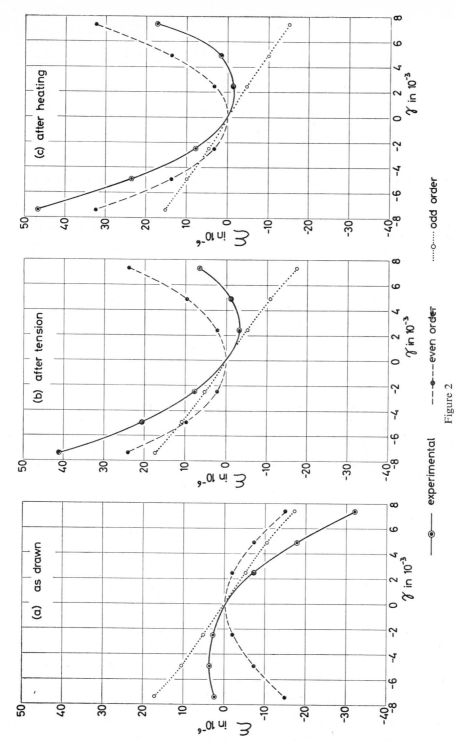

Figure 2

Observed strain, odd and even power strains for wire No. 8

TABLE II

Total axial strains ε

Wire No.	ε in 10^{-6} for number of turns								
	-4	-3	-2	-1	0	1	2	3	4
1a	20.46	11.06	4.68	1.12	0	0.75	4.22	10.69	19.46
1b	22.30	12.60	5.18	0.76	0	0.13	4.10	10.80	20.40
1c	27.40	15.50	6.60	1.95	0	0.69	5.10	12.90	24.90
2a	30.64	18.72	9.04	3.25	0	-0.94	2.00	8.20	16.84
2b	28.30	16.50	7.55	2.34	0	-0.19	2.26	8.38	16.65
2c	33.20	19.60	9.45	3.34	0	-1.07	1.58	7.75	16.30
3a	26.46	15.80	6.67	1.75	0	-0.19	3.49	10.51	19.23
3b	35.65	20.85	9.58	2.71	0	0.10	4.70	13.35	25.45
3c	38.40	22.00	9.71	2.84	0	0.38	5.49	15.50	30.20
4a	0.16	-2.22	-3.84	-2.89	0	4.08	11.05	21.56	33.26
4b	17.80	8.05	-0.89	-2.99	0	6.27	17.55	32.25	50.60
4c	19.60	8.00	0.69	-2.84	0	5.05	14.90	30.10	49.30
5a	—	1.21	0.22	0.03	0	0.45	1.24	1.87	—
5b	43.35	19.70	7.75	1.77	0	1.84	8.08	19.80	35.50
5c	—	21.50	9.02	2.21	0	1.45	8.51	21.40	—
6a	24.29	14.60	7.04	2.26	0	-0.96	0.77	5.50	12.34
6b	49.90	28.60	12.45	3.28	0	1.58	8.74	22.30	41.45
6c	49.50	28.50	12.30	3.74	0	0.95	7.85	21.30	40.60
7a	—	15.41	6.46	1.66	0	0.93	4.67	11.28	—
7b	—	31.45	13.45	3.54	0	2.27	10.80	27.80	—
7c	—	33.00	13.90	3.86	0	1.33	10.10	26.80	—
8a	—	2.30	3.50	3.17	0	-7.23	-17.81	-32.14	—
8b	—	41.25	20.60	7.63	0	-3.31	-1.20	6.57	—
8c	—	47.50	23.60	7.70	0	-1.40	3.90	17.20	—
9a	—	18.95	8.31	2.34	0	0.46	4.48	12.72	—
9b	—	27.55	11.90	2.87	0	1.42	8.54	21.80	—
9c	—	36.80	13.40	3.16	0	2.09	11.90	30.70	—
10a	—	-3.18	-2.44	-1.13	0	2.49	6.58	12.11	—
10b	—	17.10	4.35	-1.61	0	7.66	22.65	44.90	—
10c	—	22.10	6.15	-0.06	0	6.65	22.80	48.90	—

The results listed in Tables III and IV are shown graphically in Figures 3 and 4, where the axial strain is plotted against the maximum shear strain γ. The values of the parameters a, b and c, listed in Tables V, VI and VII, were calculated as follows:

TABLE III

Even order axial strains ε_e

Wire	ε_e in 10^{-6} for number of turns				
No.	0	1	2	3	4
1a	0	0.94	4.45	10.87	19.96
1b	0	0.44	4.64	11.70	21.35
1c	0	1.32	5.85	14.20	26.15
2a	0	1.16	5.52	13.46	23.74
2b	0	1.08	4.91	12.44	22.48
2c	0	1.13	5.51	13.67	24.75
3a	0	0.78	5.08	13.16	22.85
3b	0	1.40	7.14	17.10	30.55
3c	0	1.61	7.60	18.75	34.30
4a	0	0.59	3.60	9.67	16.71
4b	0	1.64	8.33	20.15	34.20
4c	0	1.10	7.80	19.05	34.45
5a	0	0.24	0.73	1.54	—
5b	0	1.80	7.91	19.75	39.43
5c	0	1.83	8.76	21.45	—
6a	0	0.65	3.91	10.05	18.32
6b	0	2.43	10.59	25.45	45.68
6c	0	2.34	10.08	24.90	45.05
7a	0	1.30	5.57	13.35	—
7b	0	2.91	12.13	29.63	—
7c	0	2.60	12.00	29.90	—
8a	0	−2.03	−7.15	−14.92	
8b	0	2.16	9.70	23.91	—
8c	0	3.15	13.75	32.35	—
9a	0	1.40	6.40	15.84	—
9b	0	2.14	10.22	24.67	—
9c	0	2.63	12.65	33.75	—
10a	0	0.68	2.07	4.46	—
10b	0	3.02	13.50	31.00	—
10c	0	3.30	14.48	35.50	—

For a and c values of ε_o, as indicated in Table IV were substituted in the relevant equation. For b, the values as shown in Table III for the third turn were used for the same purpose.

The dependence of parameter b upon the radius of the wires is shown in Figure 5.

TABLE IV

Odd order axial strains ε_0

Wire No.	ε_0 in 10^{-6} for number of turns								
	−4	−3	−2	−1	0	1	2	3	4
1a	0.50	0.19	0.23	0.18	0	−0.19	−0.23	−0.18*	−0.50*
1b	0.95	0.90	0.54	0.32	0	−0.31	−0.54	−0.90*	−0.95*
1c	1.25	1.30	0.75	0.63	0	−0.63	−0.75	−1.30*	−1.25*
2a	6.90	5.26	3.52	2.09	0	−2.10	−3.52	−5.26*	−6.90*
2b	5.82	4.06	2.64	1.26	0	−1.27	−2.65	−4.06*	−5.83*
2c	8.45	5.93	3.94	2.21	0	−2.20	−3.93	−5.92*	−8.45*
3a	3.61	2.64	1.59	0.97	0	−0.97	−1.59	−2.65*	−3.62*
3b	5.10	3.75	2.44	1.31	0	−1.30	−2.44	−3.75*	−5.10*
3c	4.10	3.25	2.11	1.23	0	−1.23	−2.11	−3.25*	−4.10*
4a	−16.55	−11.89	−7.44	−3.48	0	3.49	7.45	11.89*	16.55*
4b	−16.40	−12.10	−9.22	−4.63	0	4.63	9.22	12.10*	16.40*
4c	−14.85	−11.05	−7.11	−3.94	0	3.95	7.10	11.05*	14.85*
5a	—	−0.33	−0.51	−0.21	0	0.21	0.51*	0.33	—
5b	3.92	−0.05	−0.16	−0.03	0	0.04	0.17*	0.05*	3.93
5c	—	0.05	0.26	0.38	0	−0.38	−0.25*	−0.05*	—
6a	5.97	4.55	3.13	1.61	0	−1.61	−3.14	−4.55*	−5.98*
6b	4.22	3.15	1.86	0.85	0	−0.85	−1.85	−3.15*	−4.23*
6c	4.45	3.60	2.22	1.40	0	−1.39	−2.23	−3.60*	−4.45*
7a	—	2.06	0.89	0.36	0	−0.37	−0.90*	−2.07*	—
7b	—	1.82	1.32	0.63	0	−0.64	−1.33*	−1.83*	—
7c	—	3.10	1.90	1.26	0	−1.27	−1.90*	−3.10*	—
8a	—	17.22	10.65	5.20	0	−5.20	−10.66*	−17.22*	—
8b	—	17.34	10.90	5.47	0	−5.47	−10.90*	−17.34*	—
8c	—	15.15	9.85	4.55	0	−4.55	−9.85*	−15.15*	—
9a	—	3.11	1.91	0.94	0	−0.94	−1.92*	−3.12*	—
9b	—	2.88	1.68	0.73	0	−0.72	−1.68*	−2.87*	—
9c	—	3.05	0.75	0.53	0	−0.54	−0.75*	−3.05*	—
10a	—	−7.64	−4.51	−1.81	0	1.81	4.51*	7.65*	—
10b	—	−13.90	−9.15	−4.63	0	4.64	9.15*	13.90*	—
10c	—	−13.40	−8.33	−3.36	0	3.35	8.32*	13.40*	—

* Values used for calculations of a and c.

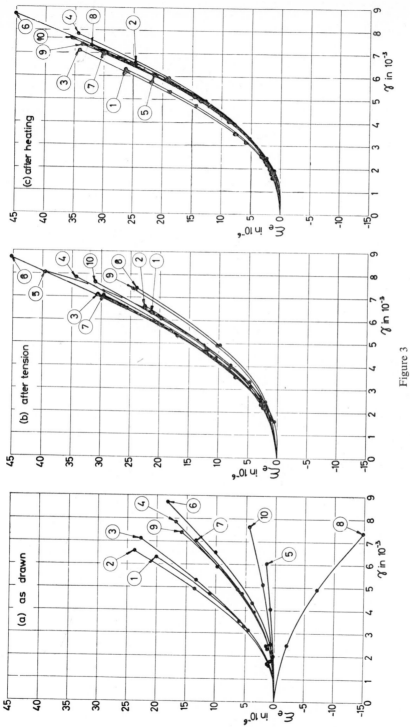

Figure 3

Even order axial strains for all wires $\varepsilon_e = b\gamma^2$

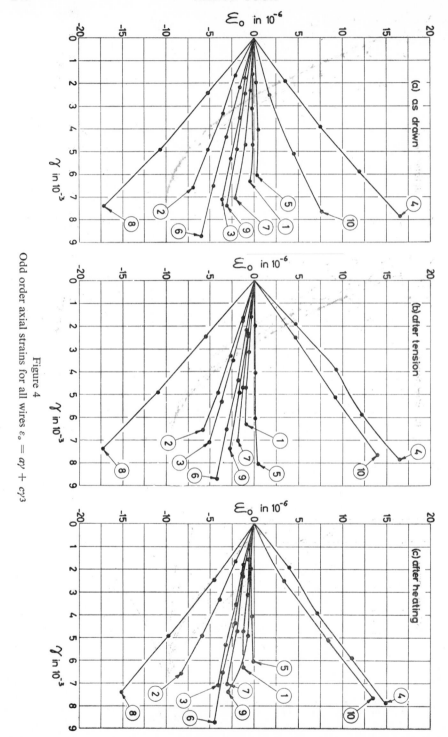

Figure 4
Odd order axial strains for all wires $\varepsilon_o = a\gamma + c\gamma^3$

TABLE V
Coefficients a in 10^{-3}

Wire No.	State a	State b	State c
1	+0.015	−0.24	−0.37
2	−1.07	−0.74	−1.09
3	−0.48	−0.68	−0.65
4	+1.89	+2.00	+1.86
5	+0.18	+0.07	−0.11
6	−0.70	−0.48	−0.56
7	−0.11	−0.30	−0.37
8	−2.03	−2.11	−1.96
9	−0.36	−0.30	+0.06
10	+0.78	+1.76	+1.53

TABLE VI
Coefficients b

Wire No.	State a	State b	State c
1	0.474	0.516	0.627
2	0.536	0.506	0.556
3	0.453	0.597	0.655
4	0.274	0.577	0.549
5	0.042	0.538	0.590
6	0.229	0.590	0.579
7	0.259	0.581	0.593
8	−0.272	0.440	0.591
9	0.283	0.446	0.616
10	0.074	0.523	0.599
Average	0.2352	0.5314	0.5955

TABLE VII
Coefficients c

Wire No.	State a	State b	State c
1	−2.3	+2.2	+4.2
2	+0.9	−3.3	−4.4
3	−0.5	−0.7	+1.5
4	+3.2	+1.3	+0.6
5	−3.5	−1.6	+2.7
6	+0.3	−0.1	+0.2
7	−3.5	+0.9	−1.3
8	−5.4	−4.3	−1.7
9	−1.1	−1.6	−8.5
10	+3.5	+0.8	+3.7

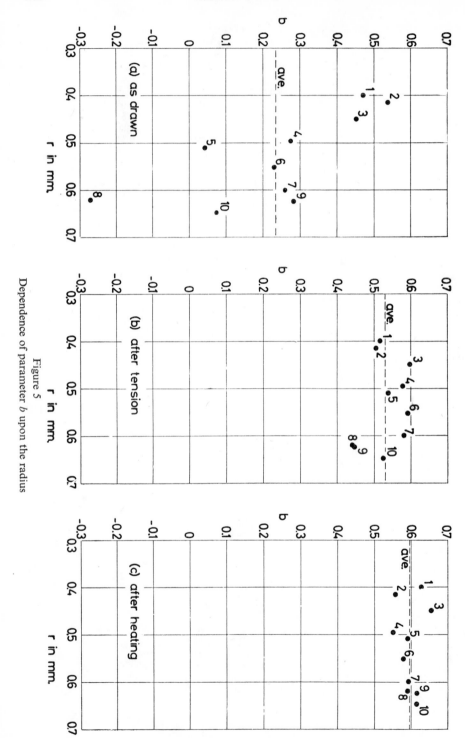

Figure 5
Dependence of parameter *b* upon the radius

6. Remarks on the accuracy of measurements.

(i) Error introduced by the twisting instrument:

The wire specimen is constrained only at the place where the nylon cord, described above, is tightened to the cross bar. This nylon cord is the means by which the wire is twisted. The method of fastening this cord is such that its initial tension has no components in the direction of the wire specimen. This is not the case when the wire is lengthened by Δl, as a result of the twist. The component of the initial tension in the axial direction of the test specimen is now

$$P_z = P \frac{\Delta l}{a} \times 4$$

where P is the initial tension in the cord and $a = 80$ mm is half the length of the nylon cord. The change in length, opposite to the direction of Δl, of the specimen wire due to P_z is

$$\Delta l' = \frac{P_z l}{AE} = \frac{4Pl\Delta l}{a A E}$$

The percentage of the error f, is a constant and equal to

$$f = \frac{\Delta l'}{\Delta l} = 100 \frac{4 P l}{a AE}$$

for a steel specimen of $A = 0.8$ mm^2, $l = 1600$ mm, $P = 500$g, $f = 0.25\%$ of the total elongation of the axial strain.

(ii) Errors introduced by the capacitance gauge:

The calibration curve used with the capacitance gauge, to obtain the change in length of the wire specimens has a range of 180μ.

The reliability of this curve depended on three factors: the determination of the contact point of the micrometer screw and the other capacitor plate, in order to set the initial gap width to suite the calibration curve. The accuracy of the micrometer screw and the accuracy in reading the proximity meter gauge.

The first two factors introduced an error of about $\pm 2\mu$. The third factor, the gauge reading, introduced an error of about $\pm 0.7\mu$. Thus the accuracy of the capacitance gauge is $\pm 2.7\mu$ or ± 1.69 microstrain for a specimen of 1600 mm length. This error is constant and is independent of the number of turns, and affected the accuracy of strain for the first and second turns much more than the strain in the third and fourth turns.

7. Summary.

The experiments described above have been conducted first on the wires in their as-drawn state. The results have shown that the action of a simple torque on steel wires produces not only twists but also changes in length of the wires. The relative changes in length or axial strains depend on the number of turns of one end of the wire with respect to the other end, or what comes to the same upon the strain. On plotting the axial strain against the maximum shear strain at the periphery of the wire, rather uncomprehensible curves result. It is, however, possible to separate the axial strains into two parts: one of odd order $\varepsilon_0 = a\gamma + c\gamma^3$ with c rather small, the other of even order $\varepsilon = b\gamma^2$ parabolic of second order. The distribution of the separated terms of the different wires in the as-drawn state seemed to be quite accidental, and could not be looked upon as the result of an essential property of the steel. On the other hand, it must be remembered that the wires in the as-drawn state are coiled and thus subjected to bending stresses when straightened. Also the cold drawing process used for manufacturing the wires introduces anisotropy in the internal structure of the steel and some deviations from a perfect circle of the cross section of the wires. Treating the wires in tension and heat as described above, eliminated the coiling and the anisotropy. This was effected much more so in heating than in tension. On repeating the experiments with the treated wires, it could be seen, that the distribution of the odd order strains remained accidental, and was more or less the same in all states of the wires (see Figure 4). We shall not be far from a correct guess if we assume that they are due to geometrical properties of the cross section of the wires, and their deviation from perfect circles. The second order strains were changed and became rather uniform in the wires treated in tension, and even more so in the wires treated in heat (see Figure 3).

8. Conclusions.

The parameters a and c in $\varepsilon_0 = a\gamma + c\gamma^3$ seem to be without physical meaning. The parameter b in $\varepsilon_e = b\gamma^2$ depends upon the physical properties of steel.

In the classical theory of elasticity the properties of materials are defined by two parameters λ and μ appearing in the stress-strain relation

$$s_{ij} = \lambda I \delta_{ij} + 2\mu \varepsilon_{ij}$$

Second order effects are absent in this relation, if ε_{ij} is defined as in the classical theory, by

$$\varepsilon_{ij} = \tfrac{1}{2}(u_{i,j} + u_{j,i})$$

It has, however, been shown by Reiner [5], that this definition of strain is the result of an arbitrary linearization of more general expressions, based on considerations of the strain-ellipsoid (see also Karni [6]). Several such general expressions have been proposed. They all imply two properties. Firstly, they result in a lengthening of the wire in torsion. Secondly, the parameter b depends upon the values of λ and μ. The values of the parameters λ and μ will naturally vary from wire to wire. The order of magnitude of this variation will, however, not be very different from that of E. Comparing Table I, we see that this variation is rather small.

It has also been shown by Reiner [7], that the two-parameter equation for the stress-strain relation is a special case of the general four-parameter equation

$$s_{ij} = (\lambda I + \delta II)\delta_{ij} + 2\mu\varepsilon_{ij} + 4\mu_c\varepsilon_{i\alpha}\varepsilon_{\alpha j}$$

The first results when the two additional parameters δ and μ_c vanish.

Both the two parameter equation with a new definition for strain, or the four-parameter equation can offer an explanation to the observed phenomena $\varepsilon_e = b\gamma^2$, which seems to express a material property. A complete understanding of the problem requires additional experimental work as for example measurement of changes in wire diameters, or variation of the axial elongation with the wire radius.

9. Acknowledgement.

The author wishes to thank Professor M. Reiner for suggesting the subject of this work and for his guidance. Thanks are also due to Professor Feltham of Leeds, who supplied some of the wires, and to Mr. P. Schechter, technician in the laboratory, for his help in planning and constructing the apparatus and in carrying out the observations. This research has been sponsored in part by the Air Research and Development Command of the United States Air Force through the European Office, ARDC.

REFERENCES

[1] J. H. POYNTING, On pressure perpendicular to the shear planes, *Proc. Roy. Soc.*, **A82,** (1909), 546.

[2] J. H. POYNTING, On the changes in the dimensions of steel wire when twisted, *Proc. Roy. Soc.*, **A86,** (1912), 534.

[3] H. W. SWIFT, Length changes in metals under torsional overstrain, *Engineering*, **163,** (1947) 253.

[4] S. TIMOSHENKO, *Strength of Materials*, Part II, D. Van Nostrand Co., New York, (1941)

[5] M. REINER, in Grammel (Editor), *Deformation and Flow of Solids*, Springer-Verlag. (1956).

[6] Z. KARNI, Second order terms of deformation in simple shear, *Bull. Res. Counc. of Israel*, **7C.** (1959), 17–32.

[7] M. REINER, Elasticity beyond the elastic limit, *Am. J. Math.*, **70** (1948), 433.

DISCUSSION

A. SEEGER: We have recently also been interested in the Poynting effect, although from a view-point somewhat different from that of the work done here in Haifa [1]. We looked upon the Poynting effect as a means of determining certain combinations of third-order elastic constants (i.e. the coefficients of the third-order terms in the energy expression in terms of the strain components) of isotropic materials, in particular polycrystalline wires.

An isotropic elastic body has in addition to its two second-order constants (modulus of compression K, and shear modulus G) three third-order elastic constants, which in the notation of Murnaghan [2] we denote by l, m, n. For the quantitative application of second-order elasticity in solid state physics problems (a few examples are outlined in my paper) numerical values of l, m, n are needed for a number of materials. These values have to be determined experimentally. Two combinations of the three constants l, m, n can be obtained comparatively easily, namely

$$\frac{dG}{dp}\bigg|_{p=0} = -\left(1 + \frac{G + 3m - \frac{1}{2}n}{3K}\right) \tag{1}$$

and

$$\frac{dK}{dp}\bigg|_{p=0} = -\frac{2}{9}\frac{9l + n}{K} \tag{2}$$

As indicated on the right hand side of Eqs. (1) and (2), these combinations of third-order and second-order elastic constants are equal to the derivatives of shear modulus G and bulk modulus K with respect to hydrostatic pressure p, taken in the limit of small pressure.

Since the materials of interest in solid state physics withstand high hydrostatic pressures without deforming plastically or fracturing, the quantities Eqs. (1) and (2) can be obtained from measurements of elastic constants under large hydrostatic pressures. This has been done by a number of methods, and a considerable body of experimental data is available [1].

In order to get a complete set of the three third-order constants l, m, n, at least one additional experiment is required. In a rough way, the required information may be described as the variation of the shear modulus with shear. Such information may be hard to obtain, since brittle materials tend to fracture under large shearing stresses, whereas ductile materials will deform plastically. If the material can be obtained in the form of a hard-drawn wire without texture, the Poynting effect can be used to supply the necessary data.

In the notation of the paper by Foux, the axial strain due to the Poynting effect may be written as

$$\varepsilon_e = \frac{\Delta l}{l} = b\gamma^2 \tag{3}$$

According to Murnaghan [2], the coefficient b is given by

$$b = -\frac{1}{48GK} \left[4G(K + 4G/3) + 4Gm + (K - 2G/3)n \right] \tag{4}$$

Solving eqns. (1), (2) and (4) for l, m, n gives us

$$-\frac{l}{G} = \frac{1}{2}\frac{K}{G}\frac{dK}{dp} + \frac{4}{9}\frac{dG}{dp} - \frac{4}{9}\frac{G}{K} - \frac{16b}{3} \tag{5}$$

$$-\frac{m}{G} = \frac{dG}{dp}\left(\frac{K}{G} - \frac{2}{3}\right) + \frac{K}{G} + \frac{1}{3} + \frac{2}{3}\frac{G}{K} + 8b \tag{6}$$

$$-\frac{n}{G} = -4\frac{dG}{dp} + 48b + 4\frac{G}{K} \tag{7}$$

In order to evaluate these expressions numerically, we use in addition to Foux's experimental value $b = 0.59$ the following experimental data for iron (for the sources of these data comp. ref. 1):

$$G = 8.26 \cdot 10^3 \text{ kg/mm}^2$$

$$K = 17.0 \cdot 10^3 \text{ kg/mm}^2$$

$$\frac{dG}{dp} = 1.9$$

$$\frac{dK}{dp} = 4.0$$

Inserting these numerical values into Eqs. (5) to (7), we find for iron

$$l/G = -1.6$$

$$m/G = -10.1$$

$$n/G = -22.7.$$

These values are not too different from those derived elsewhere [1] from Poynting's original experiments. Although yielding the same general order of magnitude, the values of Hughes and Kelly [3], obtained from sound velocity measurements in prestrained samples, differ considerably from those found here. It must be kept in mind, however, that the experiments of Hughes and Kelly where the first of their kind, and that the experimental accuracy may have been not very great.

It is interesting to observe that all three third-order elastic constants are negative, and that some of them are one order of magnitude larger than the second-order constants G and K. This had been predicted by Brillouin [4]. The present choice of third-order elastic constants is associated with the so-called Green measure of strain in the initial state. The physical results and their significance are of course independent of the measure of strain. Changing the strain measure will change the numerical values of the third-order elastic constants somewhat. The order of magnitudes and the sign will remain the same, since the various strain measures differ in second-order terms in the displacement gradients that have coefficients of order unity only, i.e. of the same order of magnitude as the coefficients of the linear terms. This means that the main part of the second-order effects in crystals comes from the deviations from Hooke's law, and that not even for a fixed substance is a measure of strain likely to exist that would account for the second-order effects within the frame-work of a linear stress–strain relation.

Poynting also measured the relative change in radius r of a wire under torsion. If we write the radial strain

$$\varepsilon_r \equiv \frac{\Delta r}{r} = b'\gamma^2 \tag{8}$$

we can derive the following relation between the coefficients b and b' (see [1]):

$$b + 2b' = \frac{1}{4}\left(\frac{dG}{dp} - \frac{G}{K}\right). \tag{9}$$

Measurements of ε_e, ε_r, and dG/dp will therefore furnish a check of the experimental accuracy. In the present case we may assume that the experimental accuracy of dK/dp and dG/dp is relatively high, since the calculated pressure variation of Young's modulus E, dE/dp, agrees with the directly measured value [5] (see 1).

Finally I should like to say that it would be highly desirable to have measurements on the Poynting effect on many materials of interest in solid state physics, e.g. such metals as Cu, Ag, Au, Al, Ni, and simple alloys, such as those of the α-brass type. If wires with a well defined texture are used, it might even be possible to draw in this way quantitative conclusions about the third-order constants of anisotropic materials.

[1] A. Seeger and O. Buck, *Z. Naturforschg.* **15a**, 1056 (1960)

[2] F. D. Murnaghan, *Finite Deformation of an Elastic Solid*, John Wiley and Sons, Inc. New York 1951

[3] D. S. Hughes and J. L. Kelly, *Phys. Rev.* **92**, 1145 (1953)

[4] L. Brillouin, Les Tenseurs en Mécanique et en Elasticité, Masson, Paris 1938

[5] A. P. Ekhlakov, V. A. Gladkovskii and K. P. Rodionov, *Phys. Metals Metallogr.* **5**, 169 (1957)

B. R. Seth: In a recent investigation (Seth, B. R., Math. Res. Center Rep. 302) it is shown that the elongation in torsion for both elastic plastic transition and for the fully plastic state are proportional to γ^2. Thus even if the plastic effects tend to appear in the large twisting of wires the relation $\varepsilon_0 = b\gamma^2$ can be expected to hold good.

A. Foux's reply: I am grateful to Dr. Seeger for his thorough discussion and interpretation of my experimental results.

The Statement made by Dr. Seeger on the dependence or rather independence of the third-order parameters on the measure of strain is questionable.

The stress–strain relation is general if it is independent of strain measures, which are mathematical definitions only. Different measures of strain will give different strain tensors. These must be manilipulated by the parameters of the general stress–strain relation, in order not to give a false representation of the physical behaviour under applied forces.

As an illustration I shall take the case of simple shear. The strain tensor in the Almansi measure is given by:

$$\overset{A}{\varepsilon}_{ij} = \frac{1}{2} \begin{Vmatrix} 0 & \gamma & 0 \\ \gamma & -\gamma^2 & 0 \\ 0 & 0 & 0 \end{Vmatrix} \tag{1}$$

and in the Green measure transformed to final coordinates by:

$$\overset{G}{\varepsilon}_{ij} = \frac{1}{2} \begin{Vmatrix} \gamma^2 & \gamma & 0 \\ \gamma & 0 & 0 \\ 0 & 0 & 0 \end{Vmatrix} \tag{2}$$

where γ is the displacement gradient. The simple shear is defined by the deformation of a cubical element and not by the stresses acting on it.

As is suggested by the results of my work, such a state of deformation can be achieved only if normal stresses are present on the faces of the cubical element. We do not know what these stresses are, but they are certainly independent of the measure of strain used to describe their effect on the element. Let us denote these stresses by $\sigma_1^1, \sigma_2^2, \sigma_3^3$ and σ_2^1. The other stresses vanish, as can be seen from the Murnaghan stress–strain relation given by Sokolnikoff in the final coordinates as:

$$\sigma_j^i = [\lambda I + (3l + m - \lambda)I^2 + mII]\delta_j^i$$
$$+ [2\mu - (m + 2\lambda + 4\mu)I]\varepsilon_j^i - 4\mu\varepsilon_\alpha^i\varepsilon_j^\alpha + n\phi_j^i \qquad (3)$$

where $\phi_j^i = \frac{1}{2}\delta_{j\alpha\delta}^{i\beta\gamma}\varepsilon_\beta^\alpha\varepsilon_\gamma^\delta$.

We substitute in this relation the strain invariants, strains and strain products as obtained from both the Almansi strain measure Eq. (1), and the Green measure Eq. (2). We then solve for the third-order parameters in terms of the applied stresses, as listed above, the second-order parameters λ and μ and the displacement gradient γ. For the purpose of estimating the order of magnitude of the parameters, it can be assumed that $\sigma_2^1 = \mu\gamma$.

The results obtained by so doing can be listed in another column added to the table, given by Dr. Seeger, where the values of the parameters based on the Green strain measure are given. These are

	Green	Almansi
l/G	-1.6	$+3.2 \times 10^6$
m/G	-10.1	-10.1
n/G	-22.7	-18.1

This shows that the Murnaghan parameter l is sensitive to the measure of strain used, to an extreme degree. But the stresses obtained, using these parameters, are very nearly the same in both cases

Another and most important remark which I will make is concerned with the change in diameter. At the time of the Symposium I did not have any experimental results on it, but now when this answer is being written, I can add some preliminary results on he change of diameter.

Dr. Seeger predicted that the parameter b' in $(\Delta r/r) = b'\gamma^2$ will be given by

$$b' = \frac{1}{8}\left(\frac{dG}{dp} - \frac{G}{K}\right) - \frac{1}{2}b = -0.114 \tag{4}$$

(see Dr. Seeger Eq. (9)), where the values $(dG/dp) = 1.9, (G/K) = 0.45$ are given by Dr. Seeger, and $b = 0.59$ as reported in the paper. In experimental measurements which are to be published soon, we found the value of b' to be about $+2.3$.

There is a difference between my experimental value and the one predicted on the basis of Murnaghan's theory for torsion of cylindrical rods (Dr. Seeger ref. (2)). This difference may be due to the assumption made in the development of this theory that the change in length of such rod is a function of z alone. In the case of torsion where there is a stress gradient along the radius it is likely that the change in z will be a function of both z and r. This is a much more complicated case, but would certainly lead to a different result.

Finally, I thank Professor Seth for his remark. I want to add that in a material subjected to plastic torsion there is always a core of material which is still in the elastic range.

EXAMINATION OF QUASI-LINEAR ELASTICITY

S. Fersht

Technion–Israel Institute of Technology, Haifa, Israel

ABSTRACT

It is shown that in the quasi-linear stress-strain relation the volume strain ε_V must be introduced in the first term when the displacement gradient is finite.

1. The classical theory of isotropic elasticity is based upon the stress-strain relation

$$s_{ij} = \lambda \varepsilon_{\alpha\alpha} \delta_{ij} + 2\mu \varepsilon_{ij} \tag{1.1}$$

where s_{ij} is the *stress-tensor* and ε_{ij} the "infinitesimal" *strain*-tensor defined by

$$\varepsilon_{ij} = \tfrac{1}{2}(u_{i,j} + u_{j,i}) \tag{1.2}$$

with u_i the *displacement vector*. The parameters λ and μ are assumed as "constants", i.e. as independent of the strain tensor, and the displacement gradients $u_{i,j}$ are assumed as "infinitesimal", so that

$$\varepsilon_{\alpha\alpha} = I = \varepsilon_r = \Delta V/V \tag{1.3}$$

is the *cubical dilatation* with I the first invariant of ε and V the volume of the volume element.

The relation (1.1) is linear in s_{ij} and ε_{ij}. This has been named the Truesdell [1] "tensorial" linearity, in view of the fact that, as shown by Reiner [2], the general stress-strain relation contains a further member of second order in ε_{ij}. For the case when ε_{ij} is not linear in $u_{i,j}$ and λ and μ are not constants but arbitrary power series in the invariants of ε_{ij}, while at the same time the form of Eq. (1.1) is kept unchanged, Truesdell uses the term "quasi-linear".

As "a part of the simplicity of the classical theories arises ... from ... their tensorial linearity", it is obviously of great advantage to use a quasi-linearity. However, in this case Eq. (1.3) is *in general* not valid. It is the aim of the present paper to examine what the consequences of this non-compliance are.

For this purpose we first examine the physical background of Eq. (1.1).

This equation was formulated on the basis of Hooke's "ut tensio sec vis", which presupposes the proportionality of stress and strain. Such proportionality is correct within limits for materials to which it applies, *if we consider separately changes in volume and changes in shape.* Let $-p$ be an *isotropic pressure* and $\mathring{s}_{ij}$ a *stress deviator* so that

$$s_{ij} = -p\delta_{ij} + \mathring{s}_{ij} \tag{1.4}$$

with

$$-p = s_{\alpha\alpha}/3 \tag{1.5}$$

and let $\mathring{\varepsilon}_{ij}$ be the *strain deviator,* so that

$$\mathring{\varepsilon}_{ij} = \varepsilon_{ij} - \frac{\varepsilon_{\alpha\alpha}}{3}\delta_{ij} \tag{1.6}$$

then Hooke's law requires

$$\left.\begin{array}{rl} -p &= \kappa\varepsilon_v \\ \mathring{s}_{ij} &= 2\mu\mathring{\varepsilon}_{ij} \end{array}\right\} \tag{1.7}$$

Introducing the expressions from (1.7) into (1.4), we get

$$s_{ij} = \kappa\varepsilon_v\delta_{ij} + 2\mu\mathring{\varepsilon}_{ij} \tag{1.8}$$

as an alternative to Eq. (1.1) and actually its source, as can be seen from the following:

We introduce the expression for the strain deviator $\mathring{\varepsilon}_{ij}$ from (1.6) into (1.8) and find

$$s_{ij} = \left(\kappa\varepsilon_v - \frac{2}{3\mu}\varepsilon_{\alpha\alpha}\right)\delta_{ij} + 2\mu\varepsilon_{ij} \tag{1.9}$$

If the relation (1.3) is valid, but only then, we can write for the term in brackets on the right side of (1.9)

$$\kappa\,\varepsilon_v \;-\; \frac{2}{3}\mu\varepsilon_{\alpha\alpha} = \left(\kappa - \frac{2}{3}\mu\right)\varepsilon_{\alpha\alpha} \tag{1.10}$$

With such assumption Lamé introduced the parameter named after him

$$\lambda = \kappa - \frac{2}{3}\,\mu \tag{1.11}$$

and thus found Eq. (1.1).

In order to understand the implications of this equation, we derive the inverse relation in which ε is expressed as a function of s. We easily find

$$\varepsilon_{ij} = -\frac{\lambda}{2\mu(2\lambda + 2\mu)}\,s_{\alpha\alpha}\delta_{ij} + s_{ij}/2\mu \tag{1.12}$$

We shall now examine the two quasi-linear relations Eqs. (1.1) and (1.12) in the light of the Green and Almansi measures of strain.

The Green measure of strain* is defined by

$$\overset{G}{e}_{ij} = \frac{1}{2}\left(\frac{\partial x_i}{\partial a_\alpha}\frac{\partial x_j}{\partial a_\alpha} - \delta_{ij}\right) \tag{1.13}$$

with

$$\overset{G}{e}_v = \frac{dV - dV_0}{dV} = (1 + 2I^G + 4II^G + 8III^G)^{\frac{1}{2}} - 1 \tag{1.14}$$

The Almansi measure is defined by

$$\overset{A}{e}_{ij} = \frac{1}{2}\left(\delta_{ij} - \frac{\partial a_\alpha}{\partial x_i}\frac{\partial a_\alpha}{\partial x_j}\right) \tag{1.15}$$

with

$$\overset{A}{e}_v = (1 - 2I^A + 4II^A - 8III^A)^{-\frac{1}{2}} - 1 \tag{1.16}$$

Here a,b,c are the coordinates of the initial state of an elastic body in a Cartesian system, and x,y,z the coordinates of the final state in the same reference system.

---

* This is written here related to the final state, compare Karni and Reiner [3].

2. As the most simple strain, involving as it does one modulus (μ) only, we consider simple shear given by

$$\left.\begin{array}{l} x = a + \Gamma b \\ y = b \\ z = c \end{array}\right\} \tag{2.1}$$

$$\left.\begin{array}{l} a = x - \Gamma y \\ b = y \\ c = z \end{array}\right\} \tag{2.2}$$

We find from (2.1)

$$\frac{\partial x_i}{\partial a_j} = \begin{vmatrix} 1 & \Gamma & 0 \\ 0 & 1 & 0 \\ 0 & 0 & 0 \end{vmatrix} \tag{2.3}$$

and from

$$\frac{\partial a_i}{\partial x_j} = \begin{vmatrix} 1 & -\Gamma & 0 \\ 0 & 1 & 0 \\ 0 & 0 & 1 \end{vmatrix} \tag{2.4}$$

Therefore from (1.12) to (1.15)

$$\overset{G}{e}_{ij} = \tfrac{1}{2}\begin{vmatrix} \Gamma^2 & \Gamma & 0 \\ \Gamma & 0 & 0 \\ 0 & 0 & 0 \end{vmatrix}; \quad \overset{\circ G}{e}_{ij} = \tfrac{1}{2}\begin{vmatrix} \tfrac{2}{3}\Gamma^2 & \Gamma & 0 \\ \Gamma & -\tfrac{1}{3}\Gamma^2 & 0 \\ 0 & 0 & -\tfrac{1}{3}\Gamma^2 \end{vmatrix} \tag{2.5}$$

with $I^G = \tfrac{1}{2}\Gamma^2$, $II^G = -\tfrac{1}{4}\Gamma^2$, $III^G = 0$ (2.6)

and

$$\overset{A}{e}_{ij} = \tfrac{1}{2}\begin{vmatrix} 0 & \Gamma & 0 \\ \Gamma & -\Gamma^2 & 0 \\ 0 & 0 & 0 \end{vmatrix}; \quad \overset{\circ A}{e}_{ij} = \tfrac{1}{2}\begin{vmatrix} \tfrac{1}{3}\Gamma^2 & \Gamma & 0 \\ \Gamma & -\tfrac{2}{3}\Gamma^2 & 0 \\ 0 & 0 & \tfrac{1}{3}\Gamma^2 \end{vmatrix} \tag{2.7}$$

with $I^A = -\tfrac{1}{2}\Gamma^2$, $II^A = -\tfrac{1}{4}\Gamma^2$, $III^A = 0$ (2.8)

Introducing these values into Eq. (1.1) we find

$$
\overset{G}{S}_{ij} = \tfrac{1}{2}\lambda\Gamma^2\,\delta_{ij} + \mu \begin{Vmatrix} \Gamma^2 & \Gamma & 0 \\ \Gamma & 0 & 0 \\ 0 & 0 & 0 \end{Vmatrix} \tag{2.9}
$$

$$
\overset{A}{S}_{ij} = -\tfrac{1}{2}\lambda\Gamma^2\delta_{ij} + \mu \begin{Vmatrix} 0 & \Gamma & 0 \\ \Gamma & -\Gamma^2 & 0 \\ 0 & 0 & 0 \end{Vmatrix} \tag{2.10}
$$

Therefore, should we write the quasi-linear relation in the form of Eq. (1.1), we need to apply, for supporting simple shear, in addition to the shearing stress $\tau = \mu\Gamma$ of the linear relation:

in the G-case, an isotropic tension and a tension in the direction of shear, both of second order

in the A-case, an isotropic pressure and a pressure in the direction of the gradient of shear.

3. The question now arises: let there be a prism on which a shearing stress τ only acts, i.e. without any additional surface forces causing the additional stresses mentioned before—what will be the deformation of the prism? In a general way we can say that there must also be a change of volume, or extensions (or contractions) in the three directions x,y,z, all of second order. That a shearing stress may produce a second order change of volume was foreseen by Kelvin and in a special case this phenomenon was named by Reynolds "dilatancy".

We examine the case

$$
S_{ij} = \begin{Vmatrix} 0 & \tau & 0 \\ \tau & 0 & 0 \\ 0 & 0 & 0 \end{Vmatrix} \tag{3.1}
$$

From Eq. (1.12) we find

$$
\varepsilon_{ij} = \frac{\tau}{2\mu} \begin{Vmatrix} 0 & 1 & 0 \\ 1 & 0 & 0 \\ 0 & 0 & 0 \end{Vmatrix} \tag{3.2}
$$

i.e. only the classical strain of infinitesimal elasticity. This shows that Eq. (1.12) cannot be used in the quasi-linear case, and that Eq. (1.1), of which Eq. (1.12) is a consequence, also must suffer some adjustment.

Let us consider simple shear combined with a pure deformation as described before. This is given by the relations

$$x = a(1 + e_a) + \Gamma b(1 + e_b) \\ y = b(1 + e_b) \\ z = c(1 + e_c) \qquad (3.3)$$

where Γ, e_a, e_b, e_c are constant factors. From (3.3) we find the reverse relations

$$a = \frac{x - \Gamma y}{1 + e_a} \\ b = \frac{y}{1 + e_b} \\ c = \frac{z}{1 + e_c} \qquad (3.4)$$

Introducing the gradients $\partial x_i / \partial a_j$ from (3.4) into (1.12), we find

$$\overset{G}{e}_{ij} = \tfrac{1}{2} \begin{Vmatrix} (1 + e_a)^2 - 1 + \Gamma^2(1 + e_b)^2 & \Gamma(1 + e_b)^2 & 0 \\ \Gamma(1 + e_b)^2 & (1 + e_b)^2 - 1 & 0 \\ 0 & 0 & (1 + e_c)^2 - 1 \end{Vmatrix} \qquad (3.5)$$

$$\overset{G}{e}_v = (1 + \overset{G}{e}_b)^3/(1 - \Gamma^2) - 1; \quad \overset{G}{e}_{\alpha\alpha} = (1 + e_a)^2 + (1 + e_b)^2 + (1 + e_c)^2 + \Gamma^2 - 3 \quad (3.6)$$

and similarly from (1.14)

$$\overset{A}{e}_{ij} = \tfrac{1}{2} \begin{Vmatrix} 1 - 1/(1 + e_a)^2 & \Gamma/(1 + e_a)^2 & 0 \\ \Gamma/(1 + e_a)^2 & 1 - 1/(1 + e_b)^2 - \Gamma^2/(1 + e_a)^2 & 0 \\ 0 & 0 & 1 - 1/(1 + e_c) \end{Vmatrix} \qquad (3.7)$$

$$e_v^A = (1 + e_a)^3/1 - \Gamma^2 - 1 \\ e_{\alpha\alpha}^A = 3 - \frac{1}{(1 + e_a)^2} - \frac{1}{(1 + e_b)^2} - \frac{1}{(1 + e_c)^2} - \frac{\Gamma^2}{(1 + e_a)^2} \qquad (3.8)$$

4. Let us now see under what conditions of stress these strains can be produced, provided Eq. (1.1) is taken as the stress-strain relation.

We first examine the G-case.

The stress-strain-relations (1.1) yield the following equations:

$$\left.\begin{array}{l} \Gamma(1 + e_b)^2 = \tau/\mu \\[4pt] \lambda\overset{G}{e}_{\alpha\alpha} + \mu\left|(1 + e_a)^2 - 1 + \Gamma^2(1 + e_b)^2\right| = 0 \\[4pt] \lambda\overset{G}{e}_{\alpha\alpha} + \mu\left|(1 + e_b)^2 - 1\right| = 0 \\[4pt] \lambda\overset{G}{e}_{\alpha\alpha} + \mu\left|(1 + e_c)^2 - 1\right| = 0 \end{array}\right\} \qquad (4.1)$$

This gives four equations for the determination of the four unknowns Γ, e_a, e_b, e_c in terms of τ.

We find

$$\left.\begin{array}{l} e_a = \sqrt{1 - \left(\dfrac{\tau}{\mu}\right)^2} - 1 \approx -\dfrac{1}{2}\left(\dfrac{\tau}{\mu}\right)^2 \\[10pt] e_b = e_c = 0 \\[4pt] e_v = e_a \\[4pt] \Gamma = \tau/\mu \end{array}\right\} \qquad (4.2)$$

In the A-case we find similarly

$$\left.\begin{array}{l} e_a = e_c = 0 \\[10pt] e_b = \sqrt{\dfrac{1}{1 - \left(\dfrac{\tau}{\mu}\right)^2}} - 1 \approx \dfrac{1}{2}\left(\dfrac{\tau}{\mu}\right)^2 \\[14pt] e_v = e_b \\[4pt] \Gamma = \tau/\mu \end{array}\right\} \qquad (4.3)$$

Conditions for both cases are shown in Figure 1. In both cases we find that the extension (negative or positive) is in one direction only and that the volume strain is equal to the longitudinal strain. This restricts the generality of the situation, and can be correct only in a very special case of material behaviour, namely when Poisson's ratio vanishes. This is so in cork and foam rubber, but not in general. The same conditions prevail for the constitutive equation

$$s_{ij} = \varepsilon_{\alpha\alpha}\delta_{ij} + 2\mu\overset{\circ}{\varepsilon}_{ij} \qquad (4.4)$$

where

$$\overset{\circ}{\varepsilon}_{ij} = \varepsilon_{ij} - \frac{\varepsilon_{\alpha\alpha}}{3}\delta_{ij}$$

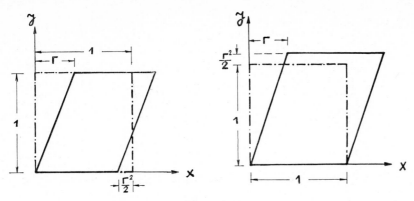

Figure 1

5. We now replace Eq. (1.1) by the following

$$s_{ij} = \lambda \varepsilon_v \delta_{ij} + 2\mu \varepsilon_{ij} \qquad (5.2)$$

We find by the previous method for the Green measure, neglecting $(\tau/\mu)^4$ and higher powers

$$
\left.
\begin{aligned}
e_a &= -\frac{\mu + \lambda}{2\mu + 3\lambda}\left(\frac{\tau}{\mu}\right)^2 \\
e_b &= e_c = \frac{1}{2}\frac{\tau^2\lambda}{\mu^2(2\mu + 3\lambda)} = -\frac{1}{2}\frac{\lambda}{\mu + \lambda}e_a = -v\,e_a \\
e_v &= -\frac{\tau^2}{\mu(2\mu + 3\lambda)} = \frac{\mu}{\mu + \lambda}e_a
\end{aligned}
\right\} \qquad (5.2)
$$

For the Almansi measure we have under the same conditions

$$
\left.
\begin{aligned}
e_a &= e_c = -\frac{1}{2}\frac{\tau^2\lambda}{\mu^2(2\mu + 3\lambda)} = -\frac{1}{2}\frac{\lambda}{\mu + \lambda}e_b = -v\,e_c \\
e_b &= \frac{\mu + \lambda}{2\mu + 3\lambda}\left(\frac{\tau}{\mu}\right)^2 \\
e_v &= \frac{\tau^2}{\mu(2\mu + 3\lambda)} = \frac{\mu}{\mu + \lambda} = e_b
\end{aligned}
\right\} \qquad (5.3)
$$

Here Poisson's ratio appears in its full value.

The same conditions are found for

$$s_{ij} = \kappa \varepsilon_v \delta_{ij} + 2\mu \varepsilon_{ij(0)} \qquad (5.4)$$

where

$$\varepsilon_{ij(0)} = \varepsilon_{ij} - \frac{\varepsilon_v}{3} \delta_{ij}$$

6. Conclusions.

We have therefore found that in the quasi-linear stress-strain relation the equation

$$s_{ij} = \lambda \varepsilon_v \delta_{ij} + 2\mu \varepsilon_{ij}$$

must be used, where $\varepsilon_v \neq \varepsilon_{\alpha\alpha}$.

This is equivalent with

$$s_{ij} = \varepsilon_v \delta_{ij} + 2\mu \varepsilon_{ij(0)}$$

where the *distortion tensor*

$$\varepsilon_{ij(0)} = \varepsilon_{ij} - \frac{\varepsilon_v}{3} \delta_{ij}$$

must be well distinguished from the *deviator*

$$\overset{\circ}{\varepsilon}_{ij} = \varepsilon_{ij} - \frac{\varepsilon_{\alpha\alpha}}{3} \delta_{ij}$$

Only when the displacement gradients are infinitesimal is the distortion tensor identical with the deviator,

I am grateful to Professor M. Reiner for help given.

REFERENCES

[1] C. TRUESDELL, *J. Rat. Mech. Analysis*, **1**, (1952), 125-300.
[2] M. REINER, *Amer. J. Math.*, **70**, (1948), 433.
[3] Z. KARNI AND M. REINER, *Bull. Res. Counc. of Israel*, **8C**, (1960), 89-92.

DISCUSSION

B. R. SETH: For most metals terms in the second and higher degree of the strain components can be neglected though the deformation may be large. In such cases λ, μ of the quasi linear theories are constants and the deviator $e_{\alpha\alpha}$ can still be used.

SURVEY ON SECOND-ORDER ELASTICITY

B. R. SETH

Indian Institute of Technology, Kharagpur, India

The search for secondary effects in elasticity is not a new one. It has been known for long that the relation $T = Es$ should be modified, and experiments have suggested addition of a term of the type $\alpha^2 s^2$. In like manner the elongation of twisted metal wires, with a corresponding decrease in their radius was demonstrated by Poynting. Johnston, Lees and Calthrop observed the same effect when they found that there was a decrease in the heat and electrical conductivities of such wires. Balankin's photo-elastic torsion measurements confirmed it by demonstrating the existence of axial stresses absent in the classical theory [1, 2].

The classical strain is an approximation of the finite strain and is known from the days of Saint-Venant and Cauchy. It was also appreciated that the deformation can be large, as is seen from the expressions for deformation in torsion given by Saint-Venant in his famous memoire, in which he only neglects the radial effect. Voigt pointed out the necessity of using third and higher degree terms of the strain invariants in the strain energy function, though he did not modify the use of classical strains. Thus we see that the two major lines of research in modern finite elasticity, that is, the use of generalised strain measures and improved constitutive equations have engaged the attention of prominent workers in the past.

A piling up of experimental data, not explained by an existing theory, leads to the advancement of research. In 1935 a paper by Seth on finite strain renewed interest in the subject. He gave a second order treatment of tension, pure flexure, torsion and other problems based on quasi-linear stress-strain relation. The displacement components of his flexure and torsion solutions have been widely used. Then followed a series of papers by A. Signorini, F. D. Murnaghan, M. Reiner, C. Truesdell, W. M. Shephard, R. S. Rivlin, K. H. Swainger, A. E. Green, R. Kappus, D. Panov, P.M. Riz, N. V. Zovolinsky, V. V. Novozhilov, J. L. Ericksen, W. Noll and others. The inspiration of Murnaghan was the experiments of Birdgman on the compressibility of sodium under atmospheric pressures as high as 20,000 atmospheres, and that of Reiner was the Poynting and Kelvin effect. Murnaghan found good agreement with experimental results, and Reiner's paper became the starting point of many investigations in elasticity and fluid-mechanics. The inspiration of Rivlin was not unnaturally rubber, as he was for some time associated with the British Rubber Research Association. The Russian workers obtained second-order approximation for problems like torsion of elliptic cylinders. V. V. Novozhilov stressed the need of starting from the fundamental equations of elasticity and applied them to problems of plates and shells. All this lead Truesdell to formulate the mechanical foundations of elasticity to which he and his co-workers have contributed such a lot in recent years [1, 2].

It was stressed by L. N. G. Filon that in actual applications of finite elasticity the strain components, like the boundary conditions and the equations of equilibrium should be referred to the strain framework. The measure of strain thus becomes important and we have some papers presented in this Symposium on the subject.

It is no wonder that the theory of finite elasticity has attracted a number of modern workers. It is responsible for fourteen papers in this Symposium. In its mathematical aspect it has drawn heavily on tensor and matrix algebra and has yielded a number of interesting models which await identification with physical phenomena. Its applications in the elastic domain can be still more fruitful. In ordinary elastic materials like metals the strain remains small even when the yield point is reached, though the deformation and rotation may be large. A quasi-linear theory in which finite strain components and a linear stress-strain tensor relation is used may therefore be found to be satisfactory. A number of applications of this theory have given qualitative explanation of experimental results which could not be dealt with by the classical theory [1, 2]. In general large strains which necessitate the inclusion of second and higher degree terms in the stress-strain relations change the nature, and hence the constitutive equations, of the material. The corresponding results thus remain mostly of theoretical interest.

The retention of second degree terms in the stress-strain relations shows that small amplitude wave propagation can have nine wave speeds for all values of the response coefficients[3]. This is an achievement, and awaits experimental verification. But a dynamic plastic treatment of the large amplitude waves shows experimental agreement with some results of non-linear small amplitude theory [4]. This is not uncommon in elastic-plastic transition. When applied to the spread of a radial crack we again notice a transition described under the term the key-hole effect [5]. These indicate a transition phenomenon, which has hardly been touched. Some theories have been developed but they do not envisage an intermediate transition state like elastic-plastic deformation, depending on deformation parameters of the problem. Recently it has been shown that the quasi-linear theory gives rise to non-linear differential equations arising out of the equations of equilibrium. The turning points of these non-linear equations can be identified with elastic-plastic transition, and the corresponding asymptotic solutions give results of the following type [6]:

(i)   No semi-empirical yield condition like Tresca or Von Mises is required. It comes out of the equations.

(ii) A distinction is made between transition due to extension and that due to contraction.

(iii) It shows work-hardening when it occurs.

(iv) In torsion it shows that the axis of the cylinder never becomes plastic.

(v)   In plastic sheet bending it predicts the form of the plate when it becomes plastic.

These cannot be given by classical elastic-plastic theories.

Unlike the stress tensor there are a number of measures of the strain tensor. The classical linear strain does not explain a number of physical phenomen a. In the normal range of deformation classical strains and constant values of the coefficients of the medium may be found satisfactory. But at the extremes of the range, non-linearity sets in and the coefficients of the medium become functions of the strain invariants. Each known strain measure may give a different result. Thus a generalized strain measure $(1-ne)^{-1/n}$ has been suggested [7]. It contains all the known measures and n can be called the coefficient of strain measure. Another general measure has been suggested [8]. It is

$$d_{ij} = a_1\delta_{ij} + a_2(\lambda_{ij} + \lambda_{ji}) + a_3(\lambda_{i\alpha}\lambda_{\alpha j} + \lambda_{j\alpha}\lambda_{\alpha j}) + a_4\lambda_{i\alpha}\lambda_{j\alpha} + a_5\lambda_{\alpha i}\lambda_{\alpha j}$$

No stress-strain relation can give a complete quantitative picture. The result obtained by using any one of them will have to be generalized to conform to experimental results. Thus generalized measures can suggest the direction in which this should be done. They may also show how complex stress-strain relations may be simplified. They can also give results like torsion without lengthening and shock waves with negative entropy change [9], which are at present considered impractical. But their importance in any further advance may lie in developing non-metric and asymmetric strain forms. These can explain internal polarisation and intertwining of the molecules, thus bridging the gap between macroscopic and microscopic description of matter [10, 11].

The problem of small deformation superimposed on finite deformations can be fascinating. But except in very particular cases of incompressible bodies, it cannot give significant practical results [12, 13].

It has been suggested [14] that second order terms in the stress-strain relations, combined with classical small strains should be used to explain the axial lengthening in torsion. This involves another unknown elastic constant, which is found to be unnecessary. A quasi-linear theory with two elastic constants explains both the axial lengthening and the sectional shortening of metal wires. The result holds good even when the plastic state sets in [6].

Non-linearity in visco-elastic materials due to temperature variations require the preceeding local strain and temperature history, and hence integral representations and memory functions have to be employed. The corresponding numerical computations are found to be heavy [15, 16].

The principle of material indifference is good, but that of spiritual indifference is better.

We have had a lot of discussion on the constitutive equations. It is desirable that generalized abstract frameworks be constructed to cover as many faces of the problem as possible. This can be an end in itself and give inner satisfaction to the worker. But it is equally important in meetings like that of IUTAM that attempts should be made to identify them with physical phenomena, even if some relaxation in them is necessary. Their relative importance is the old difference of opinion between Adam and Eve as to who is responsible for the continuity of the Universe. Any excitement over the relative merit only exhibits a restricted vision.

To sum up, a quasi-linear theory may be found quite sufficient for the explanation of problems involving non-linear elasticity in ordinary materials. In general a distinction should be made between the distortion-tensor and the deviator [17], but if the strains are not large, the difference between the two is negligible. Further advances may be expected in transition problems, generalised strain measures, visco-elasticity, anisotropic materials and interaction fields.

REFERENCES

All references, except 1,2,6, are to papers in this symposium.

[1] B. R. SETH, Non-linear continuum mechanics, Presidential Address, (Section of Mathematics). Proc. 42nd Ind. Sci. Congress, II (1955).

[2] Exhaustive references to the works of Cauchy, Green, Almansi and others will be found in C. TRUESDELL, The mechanical foundations of elasticity and fluid mechanics, J. Rational Mech. Anal., 1, (1952), 125–320; 2, (1953), 593–616 and subsequent papers.

[3] C. TRUESDELL, Second-order theory of wave propagation in isotropic elastic materials.

[4] JAMES BELL, Experiments on large amplitude waves in finite elastic strain.

[5] PAUL J. BLATZ, Finite elastic deformation of a plane strain wedge-shaped radial crack in a compressible cylinder.

[6] B. R. SETH, Mathematics Research Center Reports Nos. 264, 271, 295, and 302, under publication in various journals.

[7] B. R. SETH, Generalized strain measure with applications to physical problems.

[8] Z. KARNI AND M. REINER, The general measure of deformation.

[9] D. R. BLAND, On shock waves in hypersonic media.

[10] ALFRED SEEGER, The application of second-order effects in elasticity to problems of crystal physics.

[11] WATARU SEGAWA, Rheological equations of generalized Maxwell model and Voigt model in three-dimensional non-linear deformation.

[12] HENRYK ZORSKI, On the equations describing small deformations superimposed on finite deformation.

[13] A. J. M. SPENCER, Finite deformations of an almost incompressible elastic solid.

[14] AMNON FOUX, An experimental investigation of the Poynting effect.

[15] E. STERNBERG AND M. E. GURTIN, Further study of thermal stresses in viscoelastic material with temperature-dependent properties.

[16] E. H. LEE, AND T. G. ROGERS, Non-linear effects of temperature variation in stress analysis of insothermally linear visco-elastic materials.

[17] S. FERSHT, Examination of quasi-linear elasticity.

II. PLASTICITY

GEOMETRICAL PROPERTIES OF STRESS FIELDS IN PLASTICALLY NON-HOMOGENEOUS BODIES UNDER CONDITIONS OF PLANE STRAIN

W. Olszak and J. Rychlewski

Polish Academy of Sciences, Warsaw, Poland

ABSTRACT

The plastic non-homogeneity of a body may strongly influence the process of its plasticization. For plane strain of an ideally plastic medium, the well known properties of the slip lines cease to hold. In the present paper the limitations of the geometry of slip lines and trajectories of principal stresses in the general case $K = K(x,y)$ are derived and discussed.

1. Indroduction.

The problems under consideration are those of equilibrium of a plastically non-homogeneous body under conditions of plane strain. By the term of a plastically non-homogeneous body we understand a continuous medium the plastic properties of which depend on the coordinates of the point under consideration. The material is assumed to be rigid-plastic without strain-hardening and incompressible. Under such conditions the (point variable) yield limit which constitutes a characteristic mechanical quantity is expressed thus

$$K = K(P). \tag{1.1}$$

It is a well-known fact that in actual materials the dependency of the yield limit on the coordinates may be caused by various agents, such as a temperature gradient, non-homogeneous strain-hardening, surface working, non-homogeneous composition etc. Less known is the interesting fact that very pronounced plastic non-homogeneity may be produced by a flow of elementary particles, a neutron flow in particular, [8]. Then the variability of K in structures may be of the order of 200 to 300 percent for structural steels. It is interesting to note that the elastic properties of the material are hardly affected[1].

---

[1] According to the proposal in Ref. [1], such a material can, therefore, be classed in the group (2).

It is also a very interesting fact that for many materials the action of a neutron flow leads to a change of the character of the stress-strain curve in the sense of approaching the rigid-plastic model without strain-hardening.

The variability of K complicates considerably the equations of the plane strain problem of a perfectly plastic body. The solutions hitherto obtained are scarce. Let us mention the papers by W. Olszak and W. Urbanowski [1], A. I. Kuznetsov, [2], B. A. Druyanov, [3], W. Olszak and S. Zahorski, [4], A. Sawczuk and A. Stępień, [5], [6], J. Rychlewski, [7]. A detailed survey of the problem of plastic non-homogeneity, with the plane problem inclusive, is contained in the Ref. [8].

The present paper is devoted to a tentative qualitative analysis of the influence of the plastic non-homogeneity on the geometrical properties of the stress tensor field. An equation determining these properties ("geometrical condition of plastic state") is introduced and discussed.

2. Geometry of nets.

By the analysis of the geometrical properties of the stress tensor field we understand the investigation of the orthogonal nets of slip lines and trajectories of principal stresses[2].

Consider an arbitrary orthogonal curvilinear net described in a fixed Cartesian coordinate system thus

$$x = x(\alpha,\beta), \quad y = y(\alpha,\beta). \tag{2.1}$$

Under the term of an α-line we shall understand a line of $\beta = $ const. and vice-versa. The labels refer to the relevant lines. The fundamental fact on which further considerations are based is expressed by the following statement[3]: the Lamé parameters,

$$H_\alpha = \frac{ds_\alpha}{d\alpha} = (x_{,\alpha}^2 + y_{,\alpha}^2)^{\frac{1}{2}}, \quad H_\beta = \frac{ds_\beta}{d\beta} = (x_{,\beta}^2 + y_{,\beta}^2)^{\frac{1}{2}}, \tag{2.2}$$

being functions of α, β and satisfying the relation

$$\left(\frac{H_{\beta,\alpha}}{H_\alpha}\right)_{,\alpha} + \left(\frac{H_{\alpha,\beta}}{H_\beta}\right)_{,\beta} = 0, \tag{2.3}$$

---

[2] The following abbreviations will sometimes be used in what follows: sl — slip lines, tps — trajectories of principal stresses, and ps — plane strain.

[3] A comma before the variable denotes in the entire paper differentiation with respect to the variable indicated. The summation convention is not used here.

determine the curvilinear net except for elementary isometry (translations and reflections), [9]. Hence the conclusion that any fact concerning the internal geometry of the net may be expressed in terms of H_α, H_β. However, the parameters H_α, H_β themselves have not a direct geometrical sense, because they depend on the way of parametrization of the net. In the case of homeomorphism

$$\alpha = \alpha(\alpha^x), \quad \beta = \beta(\beta^x), \tag{2.4}$$

we have

$$H_{\alpha^x} = \alpha' \cdot H_\alpha, \quad H_{\beta^x} = \beta' \cdot H_\beta. \tag{2.5}$$

With a precision of terminology sufficient for the present considerations, we state that by the name of geometrical properties (internal geometry properties) of an orthogonal net we shall understand geometrical facts expressed by the relations between H_α and H_β, and invariant with respect to the transformation (2.4).

For any net we have the following relations: if ϕ is the inclination of the vector tangent to an α-line to the x-axis, then

$$\phi_{,\alpha} = -\frac{H_{\alpha,\beta}}{H_\beta}, \quad \phi_{,\beta} = \frac{H_{\beta,\alpha}}{H_\alpha}, \tag{2.6}$$

whereas the curvatures of the net are

$$\kappa_\alpha = \frac{1}{R_\alpha} = \frac{\phi_{,\alpha}}{H_\alpha} = -\frac{H_{\alpha,\beta}}{H_\alpha H_\beta}, \quad \kappa_\beta = \frac{1}{R_\beta} = \frac{\phi_{,\beta}}{H_\beta} = \frac{H_{\beta,\alpha}}{H_\alpha H_\beta}. \tag{2.7}$$

For the configuration shown in Figure 1 these quantities are positive. It is seen that

$$R_{\alpha,\beta} + H_\beta = -\frac{H_\alpha}{(\phi_{,\alpha})^2}\phi_{,\alpha\beta}, \quad -R_{\beta,\alpha} + H_\alpha = \frac{H_\beta}{(\phi_{,\beta})^2}\phi_{,\alpha\beta}. \tag{2.8}$$

By an isothermal net we understand a net for which, with a certain parametrization (the isothermal parametrization), we have

$$H_{\bar{\alpha}} = H_{\bar{\beta}} = H. \tag{2.9}$$

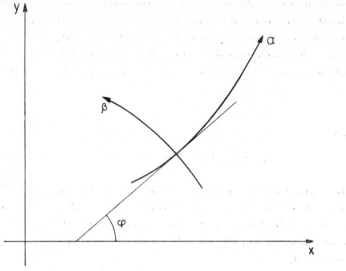

Figure 1

The necessary and sufficient condition for the net given by H_α, H_β to be isothermal, is

$$H_\alpha/H_\beta = A(\alpha) \cdot B(\beta). \tag{2.10}$$

For a homogeneous perfectly plastic body ($K = $ const.), the slip lines have simple geometrical properties constituting a subset in the set of orthogonal nets (Hencky-Prandtl nets). These properties, discovered by H. Hencky, are expressed by the relations(4)

$$\phi_{.\alpha\beta} = 0, \tag{2.11}$$

$$R_{\alpha,\beta} + H_\beta = 0, \qquad -R_{\beta\,\alpha} + H_\alpha = 0. \tag{2.12}$$

Using the symbols

$$\frac{\partial}{\partial s_\alpha} = \frac{1}{H_\alpha}\frac{\partial}{\partial \alpha}, \qquad \frac{\partial}{\partial s_\beta} = \frac{1}{H_\beta}\frac{\partial}{\partial \beta}, \tag{2.13}$$

these equations can be written in the form

$$R_{\alpha,s_\beta} = -1 \qquad R_{\beta,s_\alpha} = 1. \tag{2.14}$$

---

(4) It was erroneously supposed by H. Hencky that the above class contained the polar and Cartesian nets only. This error was corrected by L. Prandtl, whereas the entire class has been indicated explicitely by C. Carathéodory and E. Schmidt; they solved the problem of constructing a Hencky-Prandtl net for two given orthogonal curves cf. [10], [11], [12], [13].

From (2.8) it is seen that, where one of the equations (2.11), (2.12) is satisfied, the two remaining are also satisfied, [10].

The application of the above properties of slip line nets constitutes, as is known, the fundamental way of solving plane strain problems of homogeneous perfectly plastic bodies.

The plastic non-homogeneity influences very strongly the phenomena of plasticization of the body. In particular, the slip lines lose the properties (2.11), which, then, are replaced by certain relations between the geometrical properties of the stress field and the plastic non-homogeneity. To obtain and to analyse these relations, is the aim of the present paper.

3. Basic equations in curvilinear coordinates.

In the sequel it will be convenient to use for the description of the equilibrium of a plastic medium an arbitrary system of orthogonal curvilinear coordinates; this may, in particular, be the net of slip lines or that of trajectories of principal stresses. With this in mind, the following four systems of coordinates will be introduced:

C; x,y – Cartesian coordinates (not related to any physical background);

L; α,β – an arbitrary fixed curvilinear orthogonal system (chosen with no physical reason);

P; γ,δ – orthogonal curvilinear system of trajectories of principal stresses;

S; ξ,η – orthogonal curvilinear system of slip lines.

The angle corresponding to ϕ will, for the system P, be denoted by χ, and for the system S by θ.

Using the L-system, the basic relations for plane strain conditions will be written as follows.

The stress tensor field $\sigma_{ij} = \sigma_{ij}(\alpha,\beta)$ is determined by the relations

$$\sigma_{z\alpha} = \sigma_{z\beta} \equiv 0, \qquad \sigma_{zz} = \tfrac{1}{2}(\sigma_{\alpha\alpha} + \sigma_{\beta\beta}); \tag{3.1}$$

the equilibrium equations are

$$\left. \begin{aligned} H_\beta \sigma_{\alpha\alpha,\alpha} + H_{\beta,\alpha}(\sigma_{\alpha\alpha} - \sigma_{\beta\beta}) + H_\alpha \sigma_{\alpha\beta,\beta} + 2H_{\alpha,\beta}\sigma_{\alpha\beta} = 0, \\ H_\alpha \sigma_{\beta\beta,\beta} + H_{\alpha,\beta}(\sigma_{\beta\beta} - \sigma_{\alpha\alpha}) + H_\beta \sigma_{\alpha\beta,\alpha} + 2H_{\beta,\alpha}\sigma_{\alpha\beta} = 0; \end{aligned} \right\} \tag{3.2}$$

and the yield condition is given by

$$(\sigma_{\alpha\alpha} - \sigma_{\beta\beta})^2 + 4\sigma_{\alpha\beta}^2 = 4K^2(\alpha,\beta). \tag{3.3}$$

The strain rate tensor field $\dot{\varepsilon}_{ij} = \dot{\varepsilon}_{ij}(\alpha,\beta)$ satisfies the relation

$$\dot{\varepsilon}_{z\alpha} = \dot{\varepsilon}_{z\beta} = \dot{\varepsilon}_{zz} \equiv 0 \qquad (3.4)$$

and the incompressibility condition

$$\dot{\varepsilon}_{\alpha\alpha} + \dot{\varepsilon}_{\beta\beta} = 0. \qquad (3.5)$$

The tensors σ_{ij} and $\dot{\varepsilon}_{ij}$ are related by the coaxiality condition

$$\frac{2\dot{\varepsilon}_{\alpha\beta}}{\dot{\varepsilon}_{\beta\beta} - \varepsilon_{\alpha\alpha}} = \frac{2\sigma_{\alpha\beta}}{\sigma_{\beta\beta} - \sigma_{\alpha\alpha}} = \operatorname{ctg} 2\psi, \qquad (3.6)$$

where ψ is the angle between the tangents to the lines α and ξ.

For the needs of the present analysis, the system of static equations (3.2), (3.3) will be sufficient. For the strain field it will only be observed that, for this, the relations derived by H. Geiringer are valid similarly as in the case of $K = \text{const.}$ (cf. [14]). For, in the case $\psi \equiv 0$, the system L coincides with the system S and we have from (3.6) and (3.5)

$$\left.\begin{array}{l} \dot{\varepsilon}_{\xi\xi} = 0 \iff \dot{u}_{\xi,\xi} + \dfrac{H_{\xi,\eta}}{H_\eta}\dot{u}_\eta = 0 \iff \dot{u}_{\xi,s_\xi} - \dot{\theta}_{.s_\xi} u_\eta = 0, \\[3mm] \dot{\varepsilon}_{\eta\eta} = 0 \iff \dot{u}_{\eta,\eta} + \dfrac{H_{\eta,\xi}}{H_\zeta}\dot{u}_\xi = 0 \iff \dot{u}_{\eta,s_\eta} + \dot{\theta}_{,s_\eta}\dot{u}_\xi = 0, \end{array}\right\} \qquad (3.7)$$

where $\dot{u}_\xi$, $\dot{u}_\eta$ denote the components of the velocity vector.

Following now the classical way proposed by M. Lévy, we use the substitutions

$$\sigma_{\alpha\alpha} = \sigma - K\sin 2\psi, \qquad \sigma_{\beta\beta} = \sigma + K\sin 2\psi, \qquad \sigma_{\alpha\beta} = K\cos 2\psi. \qquad (3.8)$$

Now the yield condition is satisfied identically, and the equilibrium equations take the form

$$\left.\begin{aligned}
\sigma_{,\alpha} - 2K\left[\cos 2\psi \cdot \psi_{,\alpha} + \frac{H_\alpha}{H_\beta}\sin 2\psi \cdot \psi_{,\beta} + \frac{H_{\beta,\alpha}}{H_\beta}\sin 2\psi - \frac{H_{\alpha,\beta}}{H_\beta}\cos 2\psi\right] + \\
- K_{,\alpha}\sin 2\psi + \frac{H_\alpha}{H_\beta}K_{,\beta}\cos 2\psi = 0, \\
\sigma_{,\beta} - 2K\left[\frac{H_\beta}{H_\alpha}\sin 2\psi \cdot \psi_{,\alpha} - \cos 2\psi \cdot \psi_{,\beta} - \frac{H_{\alpha,\beta}}{H_\alpha}\sin 2\psi - \frac{H_{\beta,\alpha}}{H_\alpha}\cos 2\psi\right] + \\
+ \frac{H_\beta}{H_\alpha}K_{,\alpha}\cos 2\psi + K_{,\beta}\sin 2\psi = 0,
\end{aligned}\right\} \quad (3.9)$$

This is a quasi-linear set of partial differential equations of the first order, determining the two sought-for functions: the mean stress σ and the angle ψ. It is seen that this equation is always hyperbolic. The net of characteristics is constituted by the slip line net S. In view of the non-linearity, the system of characteristics depends, of course, on the sought-for solution.

If the system L coincides with the system C, we find, of course, the equations given by A. I. Kuznetsov, [2a].

For $\psi \equiv \pi/4$, the system L coincides with the system P, and the equations (3.9), referred to the trajectories of principal stresses, have the form

$$\left.\begin{aligned}
\sigma_{,\gamma} - 2K\,\frac{H_{\delta,\gamma}}{H_\delta} - K_{,\gamma} = 0, \\
\sigma_{,\delta} + 2K\,\frac{H_{\gamma,\delta}}{H_\gamma} + K_{,\delta} = 0.
\end{aligned}\right\} \quad (3.10)$$

For $\psi \equiv 0$, the system L coincides with the system S, and the equations (3.9), referred to the slip lines, have the form

$$\left.\begin{aligned}
\sigma_{,\xi} + 2K\frac{H_{\xi,\eta}}{H_\eta} + \frac{H_\xi}{H_\eta}K_{,\eta} = 0, \\
\sigma_{,\eta} + 2K\frac{H_{\eta,\xi}}{H_\xi} + \frac{H_\eta}{H_\xi}K_{,\xi} = 0.
\end{aligned}\right\} \quad (3.11)$$

Since the slip line net constitutes the net of characteristics and, therefore, a very natural reference frame for plane strain phenomena, some remarks will be devoted to the equations (3.11).

For homogeneous conditions we have at once, making use of (2.6), where $\psi \equiv 0$, the Kötter-Hencky integrals

$$\frac{\sigma}{2K} + \theta = f(\eta), \qquad \frac{\sigma}{2K} - \theta = g(\xi). \tag{3.12}$$

Hence we have immediately the theorems of Hencky on the properties of slip lines, expressed by the Eqs. (2.11), (2.12).

It is seen from (3.11), that for a plastically non-homogeneous body none of the above facts takes place, and what is more, no relations hold that could be considered to constitute a generalization of (3.12). Certain integral relations along the slip lines could only be obtained when postulating additional relations. If there exists, for instance, a function $F(\xi,\eta)$ such that

$$\left.\begin{aligned}
2K\frac{H_{\xi,\eta}}{H_\eta} + \frac{H_\xi}{H_\eta}K_{,\eta} &= F_{,\xi}, \\[2ex]
2K\frac{H_{\eta,\xi}}{H_\xi} + \frac{H_\eta}{H_\xi}K_{,\xi} &= -F_{,\eta},
\end{aligned}\right\} \tag{3.13}$$

then we have

$$p + F = f(\eta), \qquad p - F = g(\xi). \tag{3.14}$$

An analysis shows that this can take place only in a very special case of the geometry of the slip lines and the form of $K = K(\xi,\eta)$. A generalization of the technique of solving plane strain problems based, in the case of $K = \text{const}$, on the relations (3.12) is, for plastically non-homogeneous bodies, not possible([5]).

4. Geometrical condition of plastic state.

The set of equations (3.9) contains two unknown functions: σ and ψ, the latter being a geometrical quantity connected with the slip line net or, in view of $\psi = \chi + \pi/4$, with the net of trajectories of principal stresses. Our aim being to analyse the geometry of these nets, we shall eliminate from the system the mean stress σ. The equations thus obtained is, from the formal point of view, the compatibility condition for the system (3.9) with respect to σ. Differentiating and subtracting the equations we obtain

---

([5]) Let us observe that for anisotropic homogeneous bodies such a generalization can be given (cf. [15], [16]).

$$\frac{1}{2}\frac{H_\beta}{H_\alpha}\cos 2\psi\, K_{,\alpha\alpha} + \sin 2\psi\, K_{,\alpha\beta} - \frac{1}{2}\frac{H_\alpha}{H_\beta}\cos 2\psi\, K_{,\beta\beta} +$$

$$+ [A_1 \cos 2\psi + A_2 \sin 2\psi] K_{,\alpha} + [B_1 \cos 2\psi + B_2 \sin 2\psi] K_{,\beta} +$$

$$+ [(C_1 + C_2)\cos 2\psi + (C_3 + C_4)\sin 2\psi]K = 0, \quad (4.1)$$

where

$$\left.\begin{aligned}
&A_1 = 2\psi_{,\beta} + \frac{1}{2}\left(\frac{H_\beta}{H_\alpha}\right)_{,\alpha} + \frac{H_{\beta,\alpha}}{H_\alpha}, \qquad A_2 = -2\frac{H_\beta}{H_\alpha}\psi_{,\alpha} + \frac{H_{\alpha,\beta}}{H_\alpha}, \\[2mm]
&B_1 = 2\psi_{,\alpha} - \frac{1}{2}\left(\frac{H_\alpha}{H_\beta}\right)_{,\beta} - \frac{H_{\alpha,\beta}}{H_\beta}, \qquad B_2 = 2\frac{H_\alpha}{H_\beta}\psi_{,\beta} + \frac{H_{\beta,\alpha}}{H_\beta}, \\[2mm]
&C_1 = 2\psi_{,\alpha\beta} + \frac{H_\alpha}{H_\beta}(\psi_{,\beta})^2 - \frac{H_\beta}{H_\alpha}(\psi_{,\alpha})^2, \\[2mm]
&C_2 = \left(\frac{H_{\beta,\alpha}}{H_\alpha}\right)_{,\alpha} - \left(\frac{H_{\alpha,\beta}}{H_\beta}\right)_{,\beta} + 2\frac{H_{\alpha,\beta}}{H_\alpha}\psi_{,\alpha} + 2\frac{H_{\beta,\alpha}}{H_\beta}\psi_{,\beta}, \\[2mm]
&C_3 = -4\psi_{,\alpha}\psi_{,\beta} + \frac{H_\alpha}{H_\beta}\psi_{,\beta\beta} - \frac{H_\beta}{H_\alpha}\psi_{,\alpha\alpha}, \\[2mm]
&C_4 = \left(\frac{H_{\beta,\alpha}}{H_\beta}\right)_{,\beta} + \left(\frac{H_{\alpha,\beta}}{H_\alpha}\right)_{,\alpha} + 2\frac{H_{\alpha,\beta}}{H_\beta}\psi_{,\beta} - 2\frac{H_{\beta,\alpha}}{H_\alpha}\psi_{,\alpha} + \\[2mm]
&\qquad\qquad \left(\frac{H_\alpha}{H_\beta}\right)_{,\beta}\psi_{,\beta} - \left(\frac{H_\beta}{H_\alpha}\right)_{,\alpha}\psi_{,\alpha}.
\end{aligned}\right\} \quad (4.2)$$

The equation obtained relates in an arbitrary curvilinear system L the function of plastic non-homogeneity $K(\alpha,\beta)$ to the geometrical quantity ψ (the system L being fixed). It characterizes, therefore, the geometrical properties of the nets of slip lines and trajectories of principal stresses. For a body with a specified non-homogeneity type, when the function $K = K(\alpha,\beta)$ is prescribed, Eq. (4.1) constitutes a quasi-linear partial differential equation of the second order determining the class of admissible nets of slip lines and trajectories of principal stresses. Conversely, if a certain orthogonal net is taken for the slip lines (thus we determine $\psi = \psi(\alpha,\beta)$), Eq. (4.1) constitutes a linear partial differential equation of the second order determining the class of non-homogeneity, for which this net is admissible. The geometry of the stress tensor field $\sigma_{ij} = \sigma_{ij}(\alpha,\beta)$ must be subjected to the limitation (4.1) if it is to satisfy, besides of the equilibrium conditions (3.2), the yield condition (3.3). For these reasons, the relation (4.1) will be called the "geometrical condition of plastic state"[6].

If the system L coincides with C, $\psi \equiv \theta$, the geometrical condition of plastic state is

$$\tfrac{1}{2}\cos 2\theta \cdot K_{,xx} + \sin 2\theta \cdot K_{,xy} - \tfrac{1}{2}\cos 2\theta \cdot K_{,yy} + 2[\theta_{,y} \cdot \cos 2\theta - \theta_{,x}\sin 2\theta]K_{,x} +$$
$$+ 2[\theta_{,x}\cos 2\theta + \theta_{,y}\sin 2\theta]K_{,y} + \{2[\theta_{,xy} + (\theta_{,y})^2 - (\theta_{,x})^2]\cos 2\theta +$$
$$+ [-4\theta_{,x}\theta_{,y} + \theta_{,yy} - \theta_{,xx}]\sin 2\theta\} K = 0. \qquad (4.3)$$

An example.

As an illustration of the above considerations, let us consider an example which is also important for other reasons (cf. [7]). This is the problem of a plastic layer compressed between two rough plates (Figure 2).

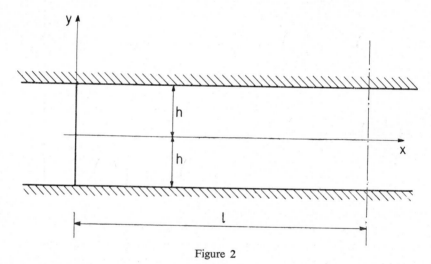

Figure 2

The classical Prandtl solution may easily be generalized to the case of $K = K(y)$, [2c]. However, if $K = K(x)$, difficulties arise. Let us consider the case

$$K = K_0 e^{-\alpha x}, \qquad a = \frac{1}{l}\ln\frac{K_0}{K_l}. \qquad (4.4)$$

---

(6) When using functions of the complex variable for describing plane strain problems of a plastically non-homogeneous body, the Eq.(4.1) constitutes the condition for the Airy function to be real, [7].

A non-homogeneity of a similar type may be generated by a neutron flow falling on the wall $x = 0$, an appropriate temperature field etc.

The geometrical condition of plastic state determines the admissible class of slip line nets in the following manner:

$$\tfrac{1}{2}\operatorname{tg} 2\theta \cdot \theta_{,yy} + \theta_{,xy} - \tfrac{1}{2}\operatorname{tg} 2\theta \cdot \theta_{,xx} + (\theta_{,y})^2 - (\theta_{,x})^2 - a\theta_{,y} + a\operatorname{tg} 2\theta \cdot \theta_{,x} + \frac{a^2}{4} = 0,$$

(4.5)

Let us try to find whether it is possible for $l \gg h$ to assume that the form of slip lines is independent of x. Putting $\theta = \theta(y)$ and $\omega = 2\theta$, we have from (4.5)

$$\operatorname{tg} \omega \cdot \omega'' + (\omega' - a)^2 = 0. \tag{4.6}$$

It is immediately seen that the equation has a particular integral

$$\omega = ay + C. \tag{4.7}$$

The stress field, which corresponds to this solution, is easy to find; this, however, is of no major importance for the following reasons. There are two conditions to be satisfied

$$\tau_{xy}\big|_{y=h} = K(x), \qquad \tau_{xy}\big|_{y=-h} = -K(x), \tag{4.8}$$

and there is one constant only. Therefore, the following relation must hold

$$h = \frac{\pi}{2a} \quad \text{or} \quad \frac{K_0}{K_l} = e^{\pi l/2h} \quad , \tag{4.9}$$

and we have the solution for one thickness only, valid for $K_0 \gg K_l$.

Multiplying the Eq. (4.6) by ω' and integrating, we have

$$\sin \omega = \frac{C_1}{\omega' - a} e^{a/(\omega' - a)} \quad ; \tag{4.10}$$

hence we obtain a formal solution of the Eq. (4.6) in the following parametric form:

$$\left.\begin{aligned}
\omega &= \arcsin \frac{C_1}{t - a} e^{a/(t - a)} \quad , \\[2mm]
y &= C_2 + \int_{t_0}^{t} \frac{1}{\tau} \frac{d}{d\tau} \left[\arcsin \frac{C_1}{\tau - a} e^{a/(\tau - a)} \right] d\tau.
\end{aligned}\right\} \tag{4.11}$$

An analysis of this solution is given in [7]. Here we are concerned only with an illustration of the geometrical condition of plastic state.

Let us observe also that if $K = K(y)$, $\theta = \theta(y)$, then from (4.3), we have immediately

$$K \cos 2\theta = Ay + B \tag{4.12}$$

which corresponds to the solution given in [2c].

Let us return now to the principal line of our considerations. The form (4.1) of the relation between the geometrical properties of the stress field and the plastic non-homogeneity type is not quite satisfactory: it is not sufficiently objective because a certain reference frame L is used. The geometrical condition of plastic state should be expressed in terms of internal geometrical properties of the net S or P, in a manner independent of any reference frame.

With this in view, we substitute $\psi \equiv \pi/4$ in (4.1). Then L coincides with P, and we obtain

$$K_{,\gamma\delta} + \frac{K_{\gamma,\delta}}{H_\delta}K_{,\gamma} + \frac{K_{\delta,\gamma}}{H_\delta}K_{,\delta} + \left[\left(\frac{H_{\delta,\gamma}}{H_\delta}\right)_{,\delta} + \left(\frac{H_{\gamma,\delta}}{H_\gamma}\right)_{,\gamma}\right]K = 0. \tag{4.13}$$

When using the symbols (2.13)(^{7}), this equation may be written thus

$$K_{,s_\gamma s_\delta} - 2\kappa_\gamma K_{,s_\gamma} - \kappa_\delta K_{,s_\delta} - (\kappa_{\gamma,s_\gamma} - 2\kappa_\gamma\kappa_\delta + \kappa_{\delta,s_\delta})K = 0. \tag{4.13}$$

Similarly, if $\psi \equiv 0$, the system L coincides with S and we have

$$\frac{H_\eta}{H_\xi}K_{,\xi\xi} - \frac{H_\xi}{H_\eta} + K_{,\xi}\left[\left(\frac{H_\eta}{H_\xi}\right)_{,\xi} + 2\frac{H_{\eta,\xi}}{H_\xi}\right] -$$

$$- K_{,\eta}\left[\left(\frac{H_\xi}{H_\eta}\right)_{,\eta} + 2\frac{H_{\xi,\eta}}{H_\eta}\right] + 2K\left[\left(\frac{H_{\eta,\xi}}{H_\xi}\right)_{,\xi} - \left(\frac{H_{\xi,\eta}}{H_\eta}\right)_{,\eta}\right] = 0, \tag{4.14}$$

which can also be written in the form

$$K_{,s_\xi s_\xi} - K_{,s_\eta s_\eta} + 3\kappa_\eta K_{,s_\xi} + 3\kappa_\xi K_{,s_\eta} + 2(\kappa_\eta^2 - \kappa_\xi^2 + \kappa_{\eta,s_\xi} + \kappa_{\xi,s_\eta})K = 0. \tag{4.14}$$

(^{7}) The symbols (2.13) are seen not to be differential operations in the usual sense. Thus, for instance,

$$\frac{\partial^2}{\partial s_\alpha \partial s_\beta} = \frac{\partial^2}{\partial s_\beta \partial s_\alpha} + \kappa_\beta \frac{\partial}{\partial s_\beta} + \kappa_\alpha \frac{\partial}{\partial s_\alpha}.$$

On the α-lines /β-lines/ these symbols denote, with normalized parametric representation, derivatives in the usual sense.

The first of our aims (to determine the geometrical properties of the stress field) may be considered to be attained in a sense. The Eqs. (4.13), (4.14) interrelate the Lamé parameters of the nets of slip lines and trajectories of principal stresses and are invariant with respect to their parametrization; therefore (cf. Sec. 2), they determine the internal geometrical properties of these nets. If the type of plastic non-homogeneity, $K = K(\gamma,\delta)$, is specified, the Eq. (4.13) gives a subset of orthogonal nets admissible for trajectories of principal stresses; for specified $K = K(\xi,\eta)$, the Eq. (4.14) gives a subset of orthogonal nets admissible for slip lines.

However, since this fact takes really place, Hencky's theorem (2.11) must constitute a particular case of the geometrical condition of plastic state (4.14). As a matter of fact, if $K = $ const. the last term on the left-hand side of (4.14) is the only remaining one:

$$\left(\frac{H_{\xi,\eta}}{H_\eta}\right)_{,\eta} - \left(\frac{H_{\eta,\xi}}{H_\xi}\right)_{,\xi} = 0. \tag{4.15}$$

Confronting this result with (2.3) and (2.6), we have

$$\left(\frac{H_{\xi,\eta}}{H_\eta}\right)_{,\eta} = \left(\frac{H_{\eta,\xi}}{H_\xi}\right)_{,\xi} = 0 \iff \theta_{,\xi\eta} = 0; \tag{4.16}$$

this is Hencky's theorem concerning the properties of slip line nets. From the form of (4.13) it is seen that the orthogonal nets admissible as trajectories of principal stresses in a homogeneous body are subjected to the limitation

$$[\ln(H_\gamma H_\delta)]_{,\gamma\delta} = 0. \tag{4.17}$$

The sense of the form (2.14) of Hencky's theorem is evident.

However, in the general case, $K \neq$ const., the interpretation of the geometrical condition of plastic state in the form (4.13) or (4.14) does not appeal to our geometrical intuition. Maybe, some natural conclusions and interpretations might be discovered; however, we have not succeeded in finding them. In what follows, we shall discuss various particular cases of geometrical and non-homogeneous properties.

At any rate, it is seen that any orthogonal net may be admitted as a net of slip lines or trajectories of principal stresses for a body of an appropriate non-homogeneity type[8] and, what is still more, for a broad class of them deter-

---

[8] We do not consider the whole of the conditions for which the above facts really take place (boundary-value problems being not discussed).

mined by the Eqs. (4.13) or (4.14). In other words, a set of nets, admissible for slip lines or trajectories of principal stresses, has no common geometrical features to distinguish it in the general set of orthogonal nets. Common is only the character of the relation between the inner geometrical properties and the plastic non-homogeneity type.

5. Trajectories of principal stresses.

Let us now analyze some particular cases of the geometrical condition of plastic state referred to the trajectories of principal stresses. We can express this condition thus

$$K_{,\gamma\delta} + (\ln H_\gamma)_{,\delta} K_{,\gamma} + (\ln H_\delta)_{,\gamma} K_{,\delta} + (\ln H_\gamma H_\delta)_{,\gamma\delta} K = 0. \qquad (5.1)$$

The following research program can be imagined. We take a certain form $K = K(\gamma,\delta)$ (which may depend on the geometry $K = K(\gamma,\delta,H_\gamma,H_\delta)$). Then the non-linear system of the partial differential equations (2.3), (4.13) determines the parameters H_γ, H_δ of the admissible classes of nets. An analysis of this set of equations, or possibly its solution with certain boundary conditions, should furnish information on the geometrical properties of the nets belonging to this class. The realization of such a program is difficult.

There is, however, a simpler approach. This is as follows. The Eq. (4.13) is treated as an equation determining the function $K(\gamma,\delta)$. As such, it is hyperbolic and its form is the canonical one. Let us observe that this is because the set of equations (3.9), treated formally as a set determining σ and K, is hyperbolic and its characteristics are the trajectories of principal stresses (not the slip lines). The best procedure would now be to find the so-called general solution of this problem, that is K expressed in terms of the coefficients of the equation and two arbitrary functions of the variables γ, δ. However, the obtainment of such a general solution (4.13), with no assumption whatever on H_γ, H_δ, encounters difficulties. In what follows we shall try to realize this program for certain nets (or classes of nets).

A. *Nets Containing a Family of Straight Lines.* A Cartesian net ($H_x = H_y = 1$) may consitute a system of trajectories of principal stresses for non-homogeneous bodies of the type

$$K = K(x) + K(y). \qquad (5.2)$$

This consitutes a certain indication for the solution procedure of boundary-value problems for the Eq. (3.9), with rectilinear edges.

The polar net ($H_r = 1$, $H_\phi = r$) may be admitted as a net of trajectories of principal stresses only when

$$K_{,r\phi} + \frac{1}{r} K_{,\phi} = 0, \tag{5.3}$$

or if the non-homogeneity is of the type

$$K = f(r) + \frac{g(\phi)}{r}. \tag{5.4}$$

The dependency of K on the angle may take place only with the factor $1/r$ constituting a damping factor with increasing r. If the point $r = 0$ is to lie in the plastic region, K cannot depend on the angle, because we should have a singularity incompatible with the physical sense.

The result (5.4) is a particular case of a more general relation for the class of nets which have the property that one of the families, the family of the α-lines, for instance, is composed of straight lines. In view of $\kappa_\alpha = 0$, we have from (2.7) $H_\alpha = A(\alpha)$. Choosing the parametrization in such a manner that $H_\alpha = 1$, we have from (2.3) $H_\beta = B_1(\beta)\alpha + B_2(\beta)$. Finally, the parametrization is chosen so that

$$H_\gamma = 1 \quad , \quad H_\delta = \gamma + D(\delta). \tag{5.5}$$

In view of (2.7), we have

$$R_\delta = H_\delta = \gamma + D(\delta). \tag{5.6}$$

It is seen that $D(\delta)$ is the variable radius of curvature of the line $\gamma = 0$, $R_0(\delta)$.

The geometrical condition of plastic state takes the form

$$K_{,\gamma\delta} + \frac{1}{R_\delta} K_{,\delta} + \left(\frac{1}{R_\delta}\right)_{,\delta} K = 0. \tag{5.7}$$

Hence

$$K = \frac{1}{R_\delta} \left[\int_0^\gamma f(\gamma) R_\delta d\gamma + g(\delta) \right]. \tag{5.8}$$

With $R = \text{const}$, we have (5.4).

Let us observe that from the class of nets under consideration only the polar net is a Hencky-Prandtl net, therefore it is the only one in this class that may appear as a P-net for a homogeneous body.

As an illustration of (5.8), we can give the following elementary example, [7]. Let us consider the equilibrium of a thick steel sheet, formed against a smooth die of variable curvature, Figure 3. Let us assume that the trajectories of principal stresses constitute a system of straight lines normal to the die,

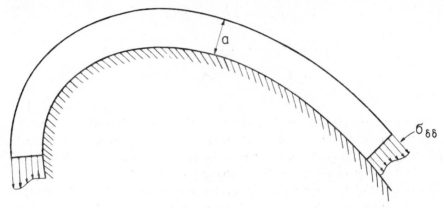

Figure 3

and of the loci of the points having the same distance from it. This is a far-going assumption, but it is certainly natural in some cases. From simple considerations of equilibrium, it follows that

$$g(\delta) = \text{const.},$$

and the assumed form of trajectories of principal stresses may be realized when

$$K = \frac{1}{R(\delta,\gamma)} \left[\int_{\gamma}^{a} \Phi(\gamma)d\gamma + \Phi(\gamma) \right], \qquad \Phi(\gamma) = \sigma_{\delta\delta}, \qquad (5.9)$$

where a denotes the thickness of the sheet.

The pressure distribution over the die is

$$p = -\frac{N}{R_0(\delta)}, \qquad N = \int_{0}^{a} \Phi(\gamma)d\gamma. \qquad (5.10)$$

With an uniform distribution of tractions over the thickness, $\Phi(\gamma) = \text{const} = C$, we have

$$K = C \left[\frac{a-\gamma}{R_0(\delta)} + 1 \right]. \qquad (5.11)$$

The interpretation of the results obtained may, for instance, be such. The equations considered here may also describe static problems of an originally homogeneous body with strain hardening involved by the deformation process. Therefore, with sufficiently small ratios a/R, say

$$\frac{a}{R} < 0.3,$$

we can consider the solution obtained to constitute an image of the state of stress at a certain instant of plastic equilibrium in a strain hardening sheet undergoing the forming process, whereas (5.9) gives the resulting distribution of the yield limit. The description of the process as a result of which the state just discussed takes place requires, of course, additional investigation.

B. *Isothermal nets.*

For these nets, in their isothermal parametrization (which is the only used in what follows), the geometrical plasticity condition may be reduced to a particularly simple form. With the transformation

$$K = T(\gamma,\delta) \cdot h(H), \qquad (5.12)$$

the Eq. (5.1) takes the form

$$hT_{,\gamma\delta} + \left(h \cdot \frac{1}{H} + h' \right) \left(H_\delta T_{,\gamma} + H_{,\gamma} T_\delta \right) +$$

$$+ \left[H_{,\delta} H_{,\gamma} \left(h' \cdot \frac{2}{H} - h \cdot \frac{2}{H^2} + h''H \right) + H_{,\gamma\delta} \left(h' + h \cdot \frac{2}{H} \right) \right] T = 0, \quad (5.13)$$

and we see that, on setting

$$h = \frac{1}{H}, \qquad (5.14)$$

we have finally

$$hT_{,\gamma\delta} - h_{,\gamma\delta} T = 0. \qquad (5.15)$$

This condition, together with (2.3) which has now the form

$$\nabla^2(\ln h) = 0, \qquad (5.16)$$

determines the class of nets admissible for *P*-lines and the non-homogeneity properties. Let us observe that, from (2.6), it follows

$$\frac{h_{,\gamma\delta}}{h} = \theta_{,\gamma\gamma} - \theta_{,\gamma}\theta_{,\delta} = -\theta_{,\delta\delta} - \theta_{,\kappa}\theta_{,\delta} . \qquad (5.17)$$

It is seen immediately that a particular type of the non-homogeneity, admissible for any isothermal net of trajectories of principal stresses, is the following one[9]:

$$T = Ch \quad \text{or} \quad K = \frac{C}{H^2}. \tag{5.18}$$

From the equilibrium conditions (3.10) it is seen that $\sigma = \text{const}$, and our solution corresponds to a very special case of stress distribution

$$\sigma_{\gamma\gamma} = \sigma - \frac{C}{H^2}, \qquad \sigma_{\delta\delta} = \sigma + \frac{C}{H^2}. \tag{5.19}$$

Another evident statement is that

results in
$$h = h_\gamma(\gamma) + h_\delta(\delta) \tag{5.20}$$
$$T = T_\gamma(\gamma) + T_\delta(\delta) \tag{5.21}$$

and vice-versa.

The geometrical properties of the class of nets determined by (5.20) can easilty be stated. From (2.7) we have

$$\kappa_\gamma = h'_\delta(\delta) \quad \text{and is constant on the } \gamma\text{-lines};$$
$$\kappa_\delta = h'_\gamma(\gamma) \quad \text{and is constant on the } \delta\text{-lines}; \tag{5.22}$$

therefore, the net is composed of two orthogonal families of circles. Conversely, if a net of trajectories of principal stresses is of this type, (5.20) follows from (2.7). Therefore, summing up, we can say that if the trajectories of principal stresses constitute two families of circles, then

$$K = \frac{1}{H} \left[f(\gamma) + g(\delta) \right]. \tag{5.23}$$

and vice-versa.

The form of the functions h_γ, h_δ can easily be found for the entire family from the condition of harmonicity (5.16). We have

$$[h_\gamma h''_\gamma - (h'_\gamma)^2] + [h_\delta h''_\delta - (h'_\delta)^2] + [h_\gamma h''_\gamma + h''_\gamma h_\delta] = 0; \tag{5.24}$$

hence
$$\left. \begin{array}{l} h_\gamma = C_1 \sin C\gamma + C_2 \cos C\delta, \\ h_\delta = B_1 \sinh C\gamma + B_2 \cosh C\delta, \end{array} \right\} \tag{5.25}$$

where
$$(C_1 + C_2) + (B_1 - B_2) = 0. \tag{5.26}$$

---

[9] This was, in a different way, previously shown by S. Zahorski.

Thus, for instance, a bipolar net is obtained for $C_1 = B_1 = 0, C = C_2 = B_2 = 1$ and the non homogeneity class admissible for it is

$$K = (\cos \gamma + \cosh \delta)[f(\gamma) + g(\delta)].\qquad(5.27)$$

It is also easy to give the general form of solution of the equations of statics in the nets (5.20) with the non-homogeneity (5.21). The equilibrium equations have the form

$$\left.\begin{array}{l} \sigma_{,\gamma} + (T_\gamma + T_\delta)h'_\gamma - (h_\gamma + h_\delta)T'_\gamma = 0, \\ \sigma_{,\delta} - (T_\gamma + T_\delta)h'_\delta + (h_\gamma + h_\delta)T'_\delta = 0; \end{array}\right\}\qquad(5.28)$$

hence

$$\sigma = h_\delta(T_\gamma + T'_\delta) - h_\gamma(T_\gamma + T'_\delta) - 2[\int T'_\delta h_\delta d\delta - \int T'_\delta h_\gamma d\gamma],\quad(5.29)$$

and the stresses are

$$\left.\begin{array}{l} \sigma_{\gamma\gamma} = -2h_\gamma(T_\gamma + T_\delta) - 2[\int T'_\delta h_\delta d\delta - \int T'_\gamma h_\gamma d\gamma], \\ \sigma_{\delta\delta} = 2h_\delta(T_\gamma + T_\delta) - 2[\int T'_\delta h_\delta d\delta - \int T'_\gamma h_\gamma d\gamma]. \end{array}\right\}\qquad(5.30)$$

The net belonging to the class (5.20) can be obtained by means of the conformal transformation

$$w = \frac{az + b}{cz + d}\ ,\quad w = x + iy,\quad z = \gamma + i\delta\ .\qquad(5.31)$$

Let us consider also the nets obtained by means of the conformal mapping

$$w = z^N.\qquad(5.32)$$

The Lamé parameter is

$$H = \left|\frac{dw}{dz}\right| = N(\gamma^2 + \delta^2)^{(N-1)/2}.\qquad(5.33)$$

and the geometrical condition of plastic state has the form

$$K_{,\gamma\delta} + (N-1)\frac{\delta}{\gamma^2 + \delta^2}K_{,\gamma} + (N-1)\frac{\gamma}{\gamma^2 + \delta^2}K_{,\delta} - 4(N-1)\frac{\gamma\delta}{\gamma^2 + \delta^2}K = 0.\qquad(5.34)$$

This form suggests the idea of applying Laplace's cascade method, [17]. The invariant $l(^{10})$ is

$$l = (N^2 - 1)\frac{\gamma\delta}{(\gamma^2 + \delta^2)^2}.$$

It can be proved by mathematical induction, that the entire sequence or invariants l_n is expressed by the formula

$$l_n = [N^2 - (2n + 1)]\frac{\gamma\delta}{(\gamma^2 + \delta^2)^2}. \tag{5.35}$$

Therefore, for

$$N = \pm(2n + 1)^{1/2} \qquad n = 0, 1, 2, \cdots \tag{5.36}$$

we have

$$l_n = 0, \tag{5.37}$$

and on the n-th step of the cascade procedure, the Eq. (5.34) can be integrated in a general manner. For the "zero" step, we can consider only the cases of $N = \pm 1$, which has already been done [Eq. (5.2), (5.23)]. For the 1-st step, we have $N = \pm\sqrt{3}$, etc. Let us observe also that in none of the above nets, except the Cartesian one, it is possible that $K = K(\gamma)$ or $K = K(\delta)$ or, in particular, $K = $ const.

Finally, let us consider the important case when the trajectories of principal stresses constitute a net of logarithmic spirals:

$$\phi - \ln\frac{r}{a} = \gamma, \qquad \phi + \ln\frac{r}{a} = \delta, \tag{5.38}$$

where r, ϕ denote polar coordinates. The inverse Lamé parameter is

$$h = \frac{a}{\sqrt{2}} \exp\left(\frac{\gamma - \delta}{2}\right), \tag{5.39}$$

and the equation determining the admissible non-homogeneity types reduces to the telegraphic equation

$$T_{,\gamma\delta} + \tfrac{1}{4}T = 0. \tag{5.40}$$

---

(10) Denoted by h in Ref. [17].

Consider two spirals γ and δ and the curve L: $\gamma = \gamma(\delta)$, intersected by these spirals at the points A: (γ,δ_A), B: (γ_B,δ). Consider also two functions $\phi_0(\gamma)$, $\phi_1(\gamma)$. Then, we can give the familiar solution of the Eq. (5.40) (cf. [17])

$$T(\gamma,\delta) = \tfrac{1}{2}[T(\gamma,\delta_A) + T(\gamma_B,\delta)] \; + \tag{5.41}$$

$$+ \tfrac{1}{2} \int_{\cap AB} \{[I_0\phi_1(t) - \phi_0(t)I_{0,t}]dt + [\phi_0(t)I_{0,s} - I_0\phi_2(t)]ds\}$$

which satisfies the conditions

$$T|_L = \phi_0(\gamma), \qquad T_{,\gamma}|_L = \phi_1(\gamma), \qquad T_{,\delta}|_L = \phi_2(\gamma) = \phi_0' - \phi_1\gamma', \quad (5.42)$$

where $I_0 = I_0[\sqrt{(\gamma - t)(\delta - s)}]$ is Bessel's function of the zero order.

6. Slip lines.

It has already been stated that the geometrical properties of slip lines are described by the geometrical condition of plastic state in the form (4.14). As before, we can consider various particular cases of geometry and non-homogeneous properties. Let us observe that all the results obtained in Sec. 5 are valid, in some sense, also for slip line nets, because (4.14) is only another expression of (4.13). This does not mean, of course, that the geometrical properties of the slip lines and the trajectories of principal stresses are the same. As a matter of fact, these differ; and we only mean that by passing to a net inclined at the angle $\pi/4$ to the trajectories of principal stresses, we obtain them for the slip lines. This passage is particularly simple in the case of isothermal nets.

Let us consider the case when the slip lines constitute a Hencky-Prandtl net having the properties (2.11), (2.12). We have

$$\frac{H_\eta}{H_\xi} K_{,\xi\xi} - \frac{H_\xi}{H_\eta} K_{,\eta\eta} + K_{,\xi}\left[\left(\frac{H_\eta}{H_\xi}\right)_{,\xi} + 2\frac{H_{\eta,\xi}}{H_\eta}\right] - K_{,\eta}\left[\left(\frac{H_\xi}{H_\eta}\right)_{,\eta} + 2\frac{H_{\xi,\eta}}{H_\eta}\right] = 0,$$
$$\tag{6.1}$$

and we obtain a broad class of non-homogeneity types for which the Hencky-Prandtl nets may constitute the slip lines. This class includes, of course, the homogeneous case, $K = \text{const}$. With the parametrization of K. Carathéodory and E. Schmidt

$$\theta = \xi + \eta, \tag{6.2}$$

we have

$$R_\xi = - H_\xi, \qquad R_\eta = H_\eta \quad , \tag{6.3}$$

and (6.1) takes the form

$$- \frac{1}{m} K_{,\xi\xi} + m K_{,\eta\eta} + \left[-\left(\frac{1}{m}\right)_{,\xi} + 2 \right] K_{,\xi} + (m_{,\eta} + 2) K_{,\eta} = 0 \tag{6.4}$$

where

$$m = \frac{R_\xi}{R_\eta}. \tag{6.5}$$

The parametrization (6.5) does not include the case when the net contains a family of straight lines. Taking ,in this case, the parametrization as in Sec. 5, we can write (6.1) in the form

$$[\xi + D(\eta)] K_{,\xi\xi} - \frac{1}{\xi + D(\eta)} K_{,\eta\eta} + 3 K_{,\xi} - \left[\frac{1}{\xi + D(\eta)} \right]_{,\eta} K_{,\eta} = 0. \tag{6.6}$$

Let us consider the important particular case when the slip lines constitute a polar net. This corresponds to the case discussed at the end of Sec. 5, when the trajectories of principal stresses constitute a net of logarithmic spirals. Putting $D(\eta) = 0$, $\gamma = r$, $\eta = \phi$, we have from (6.1)

$$r^2 K_{,rr} - K_{,\phi\phi} + 3r K_{,r} = 0. \tag{6.7}$$

Let us discuss the non-homogeneity of the type

$$K = R(r)\Phi(\phi). \tag{6.8}$$

Substituting in (6.7) and separating the variables, we obtain two ordinary differential equations

$$r^2 R'' + 3r R' + \lambda R = 0 \qquad \text{(Euler equation)}, \tag{6.9}$$

$$\Phi'' + \lambda \Phi = 0 , \tag{6.10}$$

where λ stands for an arbitrary parameter. The solutions of these equations are known and there is no need to discuss them. We have obtained a sufficiently broad five-parameter class of admissible non-homogeneities of the type (6.8).

Setting $\lambda = 0$, we obtain the admissible relations between K and the angle or the radius (only):

$$K(\phi) = C_1 \phi + C_2, \tag{6.11}$$

$$K(r) = B_1 \frac{1}{r^2} + B_2.$$
(6.12)

These non-homogeneities correspond to solutions of the Eq. (5.40) which can easily be found.

Let us also observe that the possibility of a certain generalization (mentioned in Sec. 3) of the Kötter-Hencky equations takes only place for

$$\left.\begin{array}{l} \dfrac{H_\eta}{H_\xi} K_{,\xi\xi} + K_{,\xi}\left[\left(\dfrac{H_\eta}{H_\xi}\right)_{,\xi} + 2\dfrac{H_{\eta,\xi}}{H_\xi}\right] + 2K\left(\dfrac{H_{\eta,\xi}}{H_\xi}\right)_{,\xi} = 0, \\[4mm] \dfrac{H_\xi}{H_\eta} K_{,\eta\eta} + K_{,\eta}\left[\left(\dfrac{H_\xi}{H_\eta}\right)_{,\eta} + K\dfrac{H_{\xi,\eta}}{H_\eta}\right] + 2K\left(\dfrac{H_{\xi,\eta}}{H_\eta}\right)_{,\eta} = 0, \end{array}\right\}$$
(6.13)

which means a great limitation as compared with the general case (4.14).

7. Biharmonic states of equilibrium.

By biharmonic states of equilibrium of a plastically non-homogeneous medium we shall understand these tensor fields σ_{ij} which satisfy, in addition to the equilibrium equations and the yield condition, the relation

$$\nabla^2 \sigma = 0.$$
(7.1)

Of course, such states are not characteristic for plastic problems and are quite exceptional (in particular, in the case of $K = \text{const}$). However, there are some reasons to discuss them. Let us observe that they may also constitute solutions of the corresponding problem of equilibrium for a homogeneous elastic body, which is connected, in a obvious mannner, with the problem of uniform reduced stress. Let us recall, in addition, that one of the really elegant solutions of the classical theory—L. A. Galin's solution, [18],—is connected with a biharmonic state in the plastic zone.

Biharmonic states of plastic equilibrium have interesting, very special geometrical properties of the slip lines and the trajectories of principal stresses.

Writing the biharmonicity condition in the system L

$$\left(\frac{H_\beta}{H_\alpha} \sigma_{,\alpha}\right)_{,\alpha} + \left(\frac{H_\alpha}{H_\beta} \sigma_{,\beta}\right)_{,\beta} = 0,$$
(7.2)

and substituting the derivatives of σ from the equilibrium equation (3.9), we have an equation resembling (4.1), except that $\sin 2\psi$ and $\cos 2\psi$ are interchanged. Therefore, the geometrical condition of a biharmonic state of plasticity is expressed by the two relations

$$K_{,\alpha\beta} + A_2 K_{,\alpha} + B_2 K_{,\beta} + (C_3 + C_4)K = 0, \qquad (7.3)$$

$$\frac{H_\beta}{2H_\alpha} K_{,\alpha\alpha} - \frac{H_\alpha}{2H_\beta} K_{,\beta\beta} + A_1 K_{,\alpha} + B_1 K_{,\beta} + (C_1 + C_2)K = 0. \qquad (7.4)$$

For the trajectories of principal stresses and the slip lines (and also for any other net characterized by a constant angle with the principal direction, $\psi = \text{const}$), we obtain *a set of two equations* (7.3) and (7.4). Therefore, for biharmonic states of plastic equilibrium, the form of the equations interrelating $K(\alpha,\beta)$ and H_α, H_β is the same in all the nets constituting constant angles with the net of trajectories of principal stresses.

In particular, for $K = \text{const}$ we find the following necessary condition: all the above nets (therefore, also the nets of slip lines and trajectories of principal stresses) must satisfy the set of equations

$$(\ln H_\alpha H_\beta)_{,\alpha\beta} = 0, \quad \left(\frac{H_{\beta,\alpha}}{H_\alpha}\right)_{,\alpha} = 0, \quad \left(\frac{H_{\alpha,\beta}}{H_\beta}\right)_{,\beta} = 0, \qquad (7.5)$$

that is, they constitute Hencky-Prandtl nets of a special type. This set of equations can be solved in a general manner, [19], and it can be shown that these equations are composed of spirals,

For isothermal nets in the isothermal parametrization, the Eqs. (7.3), (7.4) may be written thus

$$hT_{,\alpha\beta} - h_{,\alpha\beta}T = 0, \qquad (7.6)$$

$$h(T_{,\alpha\alpha} - T_{,\beta\beta}) - (h_{,\alpha\alpha} - h_{,\beta\beta})T = 0. \qquad (7.7)$$

A more detailed analysis of the problems of this Section will be given in [19].

8. Conclusion.

In view of the complicated character of the equations describing the equilibrium in plane strain of a plastically non-homogeneous body, various semi-inverse ways of approach become of particular importance. They enable us to obtain closed-form solutions in a comparatively simple manner. Their importance may be considerable. First, they enable us to examine the qualitative influence of plastic non-homogeneity. Second, they may furnish a measure of efficacy of approximate procedures. Third, in view of the hyperbolic character of the Eqs. (3.9), they may constitute partial solutions in more complicated cases.

This need for semi-inverse methods lies at the origin of the present paper.

It has been observed since very long that, in the course of development, in studies devoted to geometrical problems we find more and more seldom ... figures, whereas in other branches of pure and applied mathematics these become of increasing importance as an explanation method. If in the present paper we do not abandon this deplorable practice, it is certainly because of the deficiencies and incompleteness of our analysis.

REFERENCES

[1] W. OLSZAK AND W. URBANOWSKI a) Non-homogenous thick-walled elastic-plastic cylinder subjected to internal pressure (in Polish; summaries in English and Russian), *Arch. Mech. Stos.*, **7**, (1955), 315–336; b) *Bull. Acad. Pol. Sci.*, Cl. IV, **4**, (1956), 153–163.

[2] A. I. KUZNETSOV, a) Plane deformation of non-homogenoeous plastic bodies (in Russian) *Vestnik Leningrad. Univ.*, *Ser. Mat. Mekh., Astr.*, **3**, (1958), 112–131; b) The problem of torsion and plane strain of non-homogeneous bodies, *Arch. Mech. Stos.*, **10**, (1958), 441–462; c) The problem of a non-homogeneous plastic layer (in Russian; summaries in Polish and English), *Arch. Mech. Stos.*, **12**, (1960), 163–172.

[3] B. A. DRUYANOV, a) Indentation of the thick plastically non homogeneous plate by a rigid punch (in Russian), *Izw. Akad. Nauk SSSR, Mekh. Mashinostr.*, (1959), No 3, 161–166; b) Indentation of a thick plastically non-homogeneous plate by a rough punch (in Russian), *Izw. Akad. Nauk SSSR, Mekh. Mashinostr.* No. 2, (1960), 129–131; c) Indentation of the thin plastically non-homogeneous plate by a rigid punch (in Russian), *Izv. Akad. Nauk. SSSR, Mekh. Mashinostr.* No.4, (1960), 156–1958; d) Indentation of smooth punch into a plastically non-homogeneous semi-plane solved numerically, *Izv. Akad. Nauk SSSR, Mekh. i Mashinostr.* (1961), **3**, 163–166.

[4] W. OLSZAK AND S. ZAHORSKI, a) Some problems of continued platic flow of the eccentric cylinder, *Arch. Mech. Stos.*, **12**, (1960), No 5/6; b) The notion of non-homogeneneity as applied to a problem of continued plastic flow, in *Problems of Continuum Mechanics*, Engl. ed. 311–326. Soc. Industr. Appl. Mech., Philadelphia 1961.

[5] A. SAWCZUK, Limiting equilibrium of a non-homogeneous plastic wedge, in *Non-Homogeneity in Elasticity and Plasticity*, ed. W. Olszak, 1958, Symposium Warsaw, Pergamon Press, London ,New York — Paris — Los Angeles, (1959).

[6] A. SAWCZUK AND A. STEPIEN, Problem of non-homogeneous wedge under plane plastic flow condition (in Polish), *Zesz. Nauk. Politechn. Warsz.*, Bud. (in print).

[7] J. RYCHLEWSKI, Some problems of plastic non-homogeneity, (in prep.)

[8] W. OLSZAK, J. RYCHLEWSKI AND W. URBANOWSKI, Plasticity under Non-Homogeneous Conditions, in *Advances in Applied Mechanics*, vol. VII, Academic Press, (in print).

[9] W. F. KAGAN, Foundations of the Theory of Surfaces (in Russian), Gostekhizdat,(1947).

[10] C. CARATHÉODORY AND E. SCHMIDT, *Zeitschr. f. Angew. Math. u. Mech.*, (1923), 468.

[11] H. HENCKY, Uber einiges statisch bestimmte Fälle des Gleichgewichts in plastischen Körpern, *Zeitschr. f. Angew. Math. u. Mech.*, (1923), 241—251.

[12] L. PRANDTL, Anwendungsbeispiele zu einem Henckyschen Satz über das plastische Gleichgewicht, *Zeitschr. f. Angew. Math. u. Mech.*, (1923), 400—407.

[13] W. PRAGER AND P. H. HODGE *Theory of Perfectly Elastic Solids*, J. Wiley & Sons, (1951).

[14] A. M. FREUDENTHAL AND H. GEIRINGER, The Mathematical Theories of the Inelastic Continuum, *Encycl. of Physics*, VI ed S. Flügge, Springer, (1958), 229—433.

[15] D. D. IVLEV, On the theory of plastic anisotropy, (in Russian), *Prikl. Mat. i Mekh.*, **23**, (1959), No 6.

[16] M. S. SARKISIAN, On the theory of plane deformation of plastic anisotopic bodies (in Russian, *Prikl. Mat. i Mekh.*, 26, (1960), No 6.

[17] F. G. TRICOMI, *Lessioni sulle equazioni a derivate parziali*, Torino, (1954).

[18] L. A. GALIN, Plane elastic-plastic problem (in Russian) *Prikl. Mat. i Mekh.*, **10**, (1946), 365-386.

[19] W. OLSZAK AND J. RYCHLEWSKI, On biharmonic states of ideally plastic bodies, *Arch. Mech. Stos.* (in print).

DISCUSSION

P. GERMAIN:

I was quite interested to learn about the influence of neutrons irradiation on the properties of a plastic material. I want to know if it has been shown experimentally that the yield function is always the same and that only the constant is changed.

AUTHOR'S REPLY:

There exsits a large body of experimental results showing that the bombardment by heavy nuclear particles changes in a very pronounced manner the physical, chemical and, in a particular way, mechanical properties of crystalline and polycrystalline solids. The experimental results prove that the elastic properties of the irradiated material are hardly affected. On the other hand, the yield limit and the stress-strain relations in the plastic range may completely be changed. For certain metals the increase of the yield limit may be two, three, five and even ten-fold. The $\varepsilon - \sigma$ curve, reflecting original strain-hardening, approaches after irradiation the elastic, ideally plastic diagram (cf. our paper, 'Plasticity under Non-Homogeneous Conditions' in *Advances in Applied Mechanics*, Vol. VII. Academic Press, 1962).

The experimental evidence available so far was chiefly obtained with uniaxially strained specimens. I do not know of experiments performed, after irradiation, in combined states of stress. That is why the yield function in our paper was introduced in a possibly sipmle from (change of size, without change of shape). On the other hand, the changes in mechanical properties are, as a rule, non uniformly distributed through the volume which leads directly to the concept of plastically non-homogeneous bodies. Such an approach enables us to develop an adequate theory for bodies exhibiting plastic properties variable through the volume.

ON THEORIES OF CREEP RUPTURE

F. K. G. ODQVIST

The Royal Institute of Technology, Stockholm 70, Sweden

ABSTRACT

The paper is concerned with phenomenological theories of creep rupture of engineering metals such as steel at elevated temperature. A short account of existing
theories of ductile fracture by Hencky (1925), Odqvist (1933) and Hoff (1953) as
well as those of brittle creep fracture by Robinson (1952) and Kachanov (1958)
is given. The identity of the two latter theories is pointed out as emphasized by
Odqvist and Hult (1961).

Kachanov's combined theory of ductile and brittle creep rupture (1958, 1960,
1961) is generalized, taking account of influence of primary creep. The application
of such theory to the problem of creep rupture of thin-walled tubes under internal
pressure is given. In the generalized theory life-time turns out slightly shorter than
in Kachanov's original theory.

1. Introduction.

Creep rupture is the more or less brittle fracture that occurs if a test piece
e.g. of a structural steel is subjected to a constant tensile load at elevated
temperature, say, above 400°C. Recent progress in metal physics has taught
us that this phenomenon is very complex indeed. It occurs in most crystalline
solids and depends upon the pile-up and coalescence of dislocations and
the formation of voids in or between the grains of the crystal structure [1], [2].
These phenomena, however, show individual characteristics, inherent to
each material and there does seem to exist a series of mechanisms involved.
Neverthelesss, if for a creep rupture test, initial stress σ_{10} is plotted against
life time t^* on a log/log basis, curves of very much the same type will be obtained for a number of structural materials. By way of example such typical
curves are shown in Figures 1 through 4, referring to different kinds of structural steels. Most of these curves show two distinct straight parts, the one
corresponding to longer life time definitely steeper than the one corresponding to shorter life time. Usually longer life time means more brittle fracture
than shorter life, where fracture is more ductile. Figures 1 through 3 are
taken from a paper K. Richard [3]. Figures 1 and 2 refer to low-alloy bolt
steels of different tendency to brittleness and Figure 3 to an austenitic stainless
18/8 Cr-Ni steel. All tests were carried out at 500°C (932°F) and were extended
over about 100,000 h. In Figures 1 and 3 individual points show the scatter

295

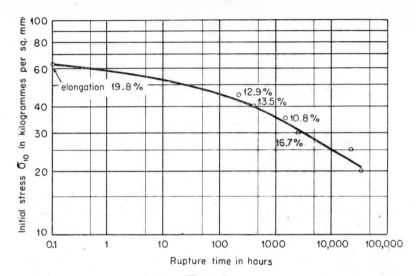

Figure 1
Creep rupture curve for a low alloy CrMoVa bolt steel at 500°C=932°F (K. Richard)

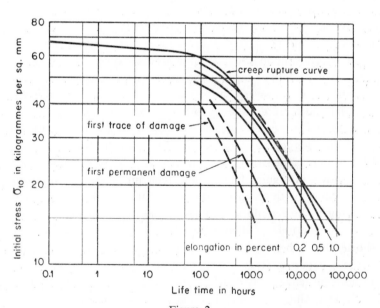

Figure 2
Creep rupture properties of a CrNiMo bolt steel at 500°C=932°F (K. Richard)

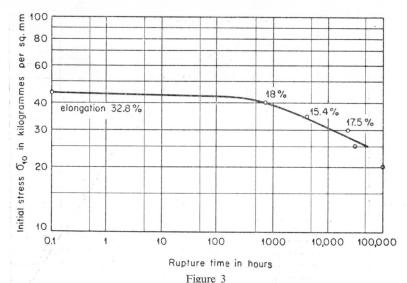

Figure 3

Creep rupture curve for austenitic CrNi steel at 500°C=932°F (K. Richard)

in these tests. Individual variations in ductility is indicated either by values of the elongation or by curves for constant elongation as measured over a length of five diameters of the test pieces.

Figure 4 is taken from a paper by Larson and Miller[4]. Starting from the consideration of creep rupture as a consequence of a so-called rate process, these authors proved that if $\log \sigma_{10}$ be plotted against the variable T $(20 + \log t^*)$, where T is the absolute temperature as measured in the unit $460+°F$, it is possible to include the influence of temperature and construct a unified "master rupture" curve for a given material. Figure 4 corresponds to austenitic stainless steel. The points of K. Richard from Figure 3 have also been introduced and prove to fit in reasonably well.

These facts being established it must be considered an urgent task for engineering mechanics to find their application to such engineering structures as beams, plates, tubes etc. Such applications have been possible so far only by utilization of phenomenological considerations.

The first attempt towards an explanation of a time dependent ductile fracture of a rod in uniform tension under constant load was given by H. Hencky[5] in 1925. His theory refers to visco-plastic bodies having a constant yield limit σ_f independent of total strain according to v. Mises and also an additional flow resistence, so that the total stress becomes

$$\sigma_1 = \sigma_f + 3\mu v \tag{1.1}$$

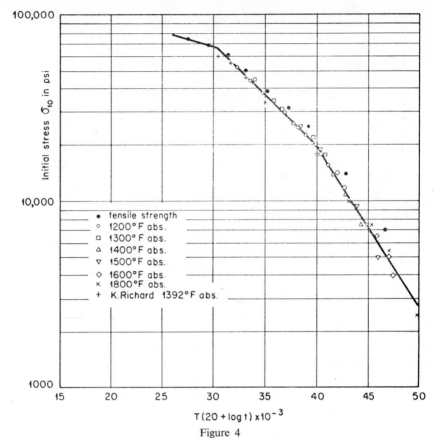

Figure 4

Master rupture curve for 18–8 Mo stainless steel (F. R. Larson and J. Miller)

where v is the natural strain rate and μ is a constant. If A is the cross section and l the length of the rod and A_0, l_0 the initial values of these quantities, the condition of incompressibility yields

$$A_0 l_0 = A l. \tag{1.2}$$

Furthermore we have

$$v = \frac{1}{l}\frac{dl}{dt} = -\frac{1}{A}\frac{dA}{dt}. \tag{1.3}$$

Hencky puts the total load

$$P = \sigma_1 A = \text{constant} \tag{1.4}$$

and makes the assumption that the time t^* for ductile fracture shall correspond to $A = 0$. Then equations (1.1) through (1.4) may be integrated yielding

$$t^* = \frac{3\mu}{\sigma_f} \log \frac{\sigma_{10}}{\sigma_{10} - \sigma_f} \tag{1.5}$$

if $\sigma_1 = \sigma_{10} = P/A_0$ for $t = 0$. Further we have the condition that $\sigma_{10} > \sigma_f$.

This theory was generalized to the case of a strainhardening body by the
present author [6] in 1933. Assuming for the total stress

$$\sigma_1 = \sigma_f + \kappa \frac{A_0 - A}{A} + 3\mu v \tag{1.6}$$

with κ constant and integrating with the same assumptions as Hencky,
one obtains the following generalization of eq. (1.5)

$$t^* = \frac{3\mu}{\sigma_f - \kappa} \log \frac{\sigma_{10} - \kappa}{\sigma_{10} - \sigma_f}. \tag{1.7}$$

The formulae (1.5) and (1.7) were never compared with experiments for the
simple reason that creep rupture was an unknown phenomenon at the time
of their publication. They have been mentioned here only because the fundamental idea of Hencky that ductile fracture corresponds to $A = 0$ has been
taken up by later contributors to the theory. This assumption would correspond to $l = $ infinity according to (1.2), an entirely unrealistic consequence
of the theory. It was clear for Hencky already from the outset however that
contraction of the rod will occur at some point where minor errors of the
geometrical form and hence a minimum in A_0 exists. At such point or points
the flow will be greatly accelerated as compared with other sections and
fracture will finally occur there.

2. N. J. Hoff's theory of ductile fracture.

The first conscious attempt towards a phenomenological theory of ductile
creep rupture is due to N. J. Hoff [7], Considering the creep behaviour of a rod
in tension under constant load P, Hoff assumes the rod to be in the so-called
secondary state of creep throughout the test, cf. Figure 5 where Andrade's
terminology for a creep test under constant load is shown. Unlike Hencky [5]
and Odqvist [6], Hoff then takes account of the strongly non-linear behaviour

of metals in the state of secondary creep, assuming Norton's law for the creep rate

$$v = \left(\frac{\sigma_1}{\sigma_c}\right)^n \tag{2.1}$$

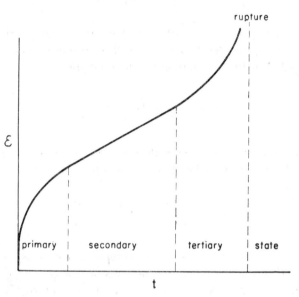

Figure 5

with σ_c and n constant. Equations (1.2), (1.3) and (1.4) remain unchanged and yield the differential equation

$$v = -\frac{1}{A}\frac{dA}{dt} = \left(\frac{P}{A\sigma_c}\right)^n \tag{2.2}$$

Integrating this equation with the initial condition $A = A_0$ for $t = 0$ he obtains

$$n\left(\frac{P}{\sigma_c}\right)^n t = A_0^n - A^n \tag{2.3}$$

The cross section will decrease from its initial value A_0 to $A = 0$ in the finite time t_H^* (subscript H for Hoff), where

$$t_H^* = \frac{A_0^n \sigma_c^n}{nP^n} = \frac{1}{n}\left(\frac{\sigma_c}{\sigma_{10}}\right)^n \tag{2.4}$$

The stress will increase with time t according to

$$\sigma_1 = \frac{A_0 \sigma_{10}}{A} = \sigma_{10} \left[1 - n(\sigma_{10}/\sigma_c)^n t \right]^{-1/n} = \sigma_{10} \left(1 - \frac{t}{t_H^*} \right)^{-1/n} \tag{2.5}$$

Thus σ_1 will become infinite when t approaches the value t_H^*. This entails large strains when approaching failure and would eventually necessitate the use of a definition for finite strain. In such case one should also take account of so-called "cross" terms in the constitutive equation [8]. However, when we are interested in the determination of the rupture time t_H^*, large strains will occur only during the latest small fraction of t_H^* and thus the secondary effects as measured by the cross terms will influence t_H^* only negligibly. This will be true also for other similar cases in the sequel.

3.   L. M. Kachanov's theory of brittle fracture.

As pointed out by L. M. Kachanov [9], the Hoff theory is able to represent only the ductile part of the rupture curve. It does not at all take account of the deterioration of the material, which is the real source of brittleness in creep and may be said to be the real cause of the insidious character of the phenomenon of creep rupture. It is true that Hoff in a later paper [10] has achieved a certain correction to his theory introducing the ultimate rupture stress σ_u into his formula (2.4). This value σ_u is an additional constant of his theory and remains to be determined independently to remove empiricism. I will give here a presentation of Kachanov's theory, which is due to Dr. J. Hult and myself [11].

If A, as before, denotes the cross sectional area of the test bar at the arbitrary moment t there will be only part of it, say $A_r < A$ supporting the load as a consequence of deterioration of the material. Thus we may define the damage D, caused by creep action as

$$D = \frac{A - A_r}{A} \tag{3.1}$$

Instead of (1.4) we now have for the real stress σ_r

$$P = \sigma_1 A = \sigma_r A_r \tag{3.2}$$

Assuming that the rate of damage is a function of the real stress σ_r only and not of the stress history, i.e.

$$\frac{dD}{dt} = f(\sigma_r) \tag{3.3}$$

there results in view of (3.1) and (3.2)

$$\frac{dD}{dt} = f\left(\frac{\sigma_1}{1-D}\right) \tag{3.4}$$

which is a differential equation for the determination of D as a function of time t at given σ_1. The virgin state $D = 0$ holds for $t = 0$ and rupture corresponds to $D = 1$.

If we now add the assumption that the equation (3.4) be separable, we find that under very general conditions the function $f(x)$ must have the form

$$f(x) = Cx^\nu \tag{3.5}$$

where C and ν are constants. If with Kachanov we further introduce the "continuity" $\psi = 1 - D$ as a measure of the carrying capacity of the material (Russian: "sploshnost"), combining (3.4) and (3.5) we arrive at the equation

$$\frac{d\psi}{dt} = -C\left(\frac{\sigma_1}{\psi}\right)^\nu \tag{3.6}$$

which was introduced by Kachanov as his point of departure in 1958. Initial condition is $\psi = 1$ for $t = 0$ and rupture corresponds to $\psi = 0$, which is supposed to occur for $t = t_R$. Integration then yields

$$C\int_0^{t_R} \sigma_1^\nu dt = -\int_1^0 \psi^\nu d\psi_i = \frac{1}{\nu+1} \, . \tag{3.7}$$

In this form the rupture hypothesis has been used by Kachanov.

On the other hand specializing to the case $\sigma_1 = $ constant we have (subscript K for Kachanov)

$$C\sigma_1^\nu t_K = \frac{1}{\nu+1} \tag{3.8}$$

Introducing this into (3.7) we obtain

$$\int_0^{t_R} \frac{dt}{t_K} = 1 \tag{3.9}$$

This equation, which is equivalent to (3.7), states that if an experiment is carried out with a series of consecutive though different constant values of the stress σ_1 with a corresponding value t_K of the rupture time according to (3.8), then the condition (3.9) gives the rupture time t_R for that particular experiment. This is precisely the linear cumulative creep damage equation due to Robinson [12]. He also takes variations in temperature into account and refers each value of t_K to a certain stress and specified temperature.

Equation (3.8) accounts for the right hand, brittle part of the creep rupture curve. From this we may conclude that, generally speaking, we must have

$$v < n. \tag{3.10}$$

Now Kachanov takes a further step combining Hoff's theory with his own. Creep according to equations (2.3) and (2.5) shall operate simultaneously with deterioration according to (3.7). Both processes are supposed to operate independently of each other. That condition which gives the shortest lifetime shall be supposed to prevail.

From (2.5) and (3.7) Kachanov obtains

$$1 = C(1 + v) \int_0^{t_*} \sigma_{10}^v (1 - t/t_H^*)^{-v/n} dt = \frac{n}{n - v} \frac{t^*}{t_K} [1 - (1 - t_K^*/t_H^*)^{(n-v)/n}].$$

This equation may be written

$$t^* = t_H^* \left[1 - \left(1 - \frac{n - v}{n} \cdot \frac{t_K}{t_H^*} \right)^{n/(n-v)} \right] \tag{3.11}$$

and should be used for calculation of the rupture time t_K^* whenever deterioration prevails over ductility, i.e. for

$$t_K^* \leqq t_H^* \tag{3.12}$$

The inequality (3.12) will be fulfilled, according to (3.10) if and only if

$$1 - \frac{n-v}{n} \cdot \frac{t_K}{t_H^*} \geq 0$$

Introducing the notation

$$\bar{\sigma} = \left[\frac{C(1+v)\sigma_c^n}{n-v} \right]^{1/(n-v)} \tag{3.13}$$

we then have, according to (2.3) and (3.8)

$$t_R = t_K^* \quad \text{for} \quad \sigma_{10} < \bar{\sigma}$$

$$t_R = t_H^* \quad \text{for} \quad \sigma_{10} > \bar{\sigma}$$

so that $\bar{\sigma}$ is the stress above which fracture will be ductile and below which fracture will be brittle. For the case of brittle fracture instead of (3.11) we may also write for $\sigma_{10} < \bar{\sigma}$

$$t_K^* = \frac{(\sigma_c/\sigma_{10})^n}{n} \left\{ 1 - \left[1 - \left(\frac{\sigma_{10}}{\bar{\sigma}} \right)^{n-v} \right]^{n/(n-v)} \right\} \tag{3.14}$$

This equation proves that t_K^* will behave asymptotically as $(\sigma_{10}/\bar{\sigma})^{-v}$ for small values of σ_{10}.

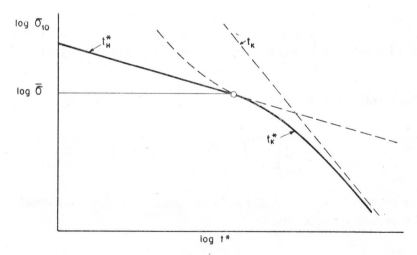

Figure 6

Figure 6 shows the result of Kachanov's theory. It gives at least qualitative agreement with experiments as expressed earlier in the Figures 1 through 4.

In 1960 and 1961 Kachanov [13], [14] has generalized his approach to the creep rupture problem to general states of combined stress substituting for σ_1 in (3.7) the largest principal stress σ_{max}. This assumption seems to be well-founded according to experiments e.g. by A. E. Johnson and N. E. Frost [15] at least for certain structural metals. If in addition to this, the state of stress is inhomogeneous, Kachanov assumes that deterioration of the material shall be locally determined by equation (3.7), inserting σ_{max} for σ_1. Then the deterioration becomes progressive both in space and time. I quote from the English version of his latest paper [14]:

> "If the state of stress of the body is non-homogeneous, one has to differentiate two stages in the analysis of the process of failure of a body. In the first phase (stage of latent failure), $0 \leq t < t_I$, one has at each point of the body $\psi > 0$. At the instant $t = t_I$, at some point (or region) of the body local failure occurs. The spreading of the local failures leads to failure of the entire body at time $t = t_{II}$. We will agree to call the interval $t_I < t \leq t_{II}$ *the stage of the propagation of the failure.*"

End of quotation.

In the quoted papers [13], [14] Kachanov has made a series of interesting applications of this theory, deriving e.g. an integro-differential equation for the propagation of the failure front in a thick-walled tube under internal pressure.

It is worth mentioning that a consequence of this theory is that failure starts from the outer surface of the tubes in good agreement with experimental results. Such experiments are due to Kachanov [13] and also to other research workers, *cf.* E. A. Davis [16]. In fact this is a crucial experiment for the assumptions involved in Kachanov's theory. Any theory for the initiation of brittle fracture in the presence of creep based upon the theory of elasticity would lead to crack initiation at the inner surface of the tube. Still there remains the fact that Kachanov's theory in many cases only gives a qualitative agreement with experiments.

4. Possible improvement of Kachanov's theory.

In the present chapter we shall try to improve Kachanov's theory in one respect. As clearly visible in the Figures 1 through 4, the slope of the ductile part of the rupture curve is much smaller than required by Kachanov's theory (and, of course, also by Hoff's). We shall see that this may be explained by the fact that influence of primary creep has been neglected so far. In his latest paper [10] Hoff has made an attempt towards taking account of primary creep utilizing a formula by A. Nadai [17]. Such theory leads to rather complicated expressions for the rupture time and of course still contains the unknown constant σ_u, the above mentioned ultimate rupture stress.

Primary creep here being supposed to give rise merely to a correction term it is natural to take it into account in an approximate way suggested by the present author [18,] [19].

For ever increasing stress we then have instead of (2.1), introducing new material constants σ_0 and n_0

$$v = -\frac{d}{dt}(\sigma_1/\sigma_0)^{n_0} + (\sigma_1/\sigma_c)^n \qquad (4.1)$$

and here generally we have $n_0 < n$. Perhaps it should be pointed out that the model body represented by (4.1) in general differs from the non-linear Maxwell body as the first term on the right side shall be retained only as long as $d\sigma_1 > 0$. Combining (4.1) with (1.2) through (1.4) we obtain instead of (2.2)

$$-\frac{1}{A}\frac{dA}{dt} = -\frac{1}{\sigma_0^{n_0}}\left(\frac{P}{A}\right)^{n_0-1}\frac{P}{A^2}\frac{dA}{dt} + \frac{1}{\sigma_c^n}\left(\frac{P}{A}\right)^n \qquad (4.2)$$

Integration with the initial condition $A = A_0$ for $t = 0$ yields

$$A_0^n - A^n - \frac{n}{(n-n_0)\sigma_0^{n_0}}(A_0^{n-n_0} - A^{n-n_0}) = n\left(\frac{P}{\sigma_c}\right)^n t \qquad (4.3)$$

Putting as before $P/A = \sigma_1$, $P/A_0 = \sigma_{10}$ and assuming $A = 0$ for the particular value $t = t_K^*$ (subscript P for "primary") we obtain

$$t_P^* = \frac{(\sigma_c/\sigma_{10})^n}{n}\left[1 - \frac{n}{n - n_0}(\sigma_{10}/\sigma_0)^{n_0}\right] \qquad (4.4)$$

for the rupture time to ductile creep rupture. It is easily seen that the curve for t_P^* in a log/log plot falls below that of the straight line for t_H^* according to (2.4). There is also a tendency of the curve for t_P^* to have a smaller slope as required by experience according to Figures 1 through 4.

But it is also possible to modify the Kachanov theory in accordance with eq. (4.1). From (3.7) we have

$$1 = C(1 + v)\sigma_{10}^v A_0^v \int_0^{t_R} \frac{dt}{A^v} = C(1 + v)\sigma_{10}^v A_0^v \int_{A_0}^{\alpha_R A_0} \frac{dt}{dA} \frac{dA}{A^v} \tag{4.5}$$

where $\alpha_R A_0 = A$ is the particular value of A for which brittle rupture will occur. This value will correspond to $t_R = t_{KP}^*$. Introducing dt/dA from (4.2 we obtain

$$1 = \frac{C(1 + v)\sigma_c^n}{\sigma_{10}^{n-v}} \left[\frac{1}{n - v}(1 - \alpha_R^{n-v}) - \frac{(\sigma_{10}/\sigma_0)^{n_0}}{n - n_0 - v}(1 - \alpha_R^{n-n_0-v}) \right] \tag{4.6}$$

At the same time we have

$$t_{KP}^* - \frac{(\sigma_c/\sigma_{10})^n}{n} \left[1 - \alpha_R^n - \frac{n}{n - n_0} \left(\frac{\sigma_{10}}{\sigma_0} \right)^{n_0} \left(1 - \alpha_R^{n-n_0} \right) \right] \tag{4.7}$$

The equations (4.6) and (4.7) give a parametric representation of t_{KP}^* as a function of σ_{10} by means of the parameter α_R. In the special case $\sigma_0 = \infty$ we are reduced to equations (3.11) or (3.14), above.

Transition from ductile fracture according to (4.4) to brittle fracture according to (4.6) and (4.7) occurs whenever

$$t_{KP}^* \leq t_P^* \tag{4.8}$$

i.e. from (4.6) and (4.7) as soon as

$$\alpha_R^n - \frac{n}{n - n_0} \left(\frac{\sigma_{10}}{\sigma_0} \right)^{n_0} \alpha_R^{n-n_0} \geq 0$$

or

$$\sigma_{10} \leq \alpha_R \sigma_0 \left(\frac{n - n_0}{n} \right)^{1/n_0} \tag{4.9}$$

Qn the other hand, from (3.13) and (4.6) we have

$$\sigma_{10} = \bar{\sigma} \left\{ 1 - \alpha_R^{n-v} - \frac{n - v}{n - n_0 - v} \left(\frac{\sigma_{10}}{\sigma_0} \right)^{n_0} \left(1 - \alpha^{n-n_0-v} \right) \right\}^{1/(n-v)} \tag{4.10}$$

and from (4.9) we must have

$$1 > \alpha_r \geq \frac{\sigma_{10}}{\sigma_0} \left(\frac{n}{n - n_0} \right)^{1/n_0} \tag{4.11}$$

Inserting the minimum value of α_R, according to (4.11) into (4.10), we obtain a condition for $\bar{\sigma}$ as a function of $\sigma_{10} = \bar{\sigma}_P$, the boundary between ductile and brittle fracture, viz.

$$
\bar{\sigma} = \bar{\sigma}_P \left\{ 1 - \left(\frac{\bar{\sigma}_P}{\sigma_0} \right)^{n-\nu} \left(\frac{n}{n - n_0} \right)^{(n-\nu)/n_0} - \right.
$$
$$
\left. - \frac{n-\nu}{n - n_0 - \nu} \left(\frac{\bar{\sigma}_P}{\sigma_0} \right)^{n_0} \left[1 - \left(\frac{\bar{\sigma}_P}{\sigma_0} \right)^{n-n_0-\nu} \left(\frac{n}{n - n_0} \right)^{(n-n_0-\nu)/n_0} \right] \right\}^{-[1/(n-\nu)]}
$$
$$
\tag{4.12}
$$

In the special case $\sigma_0 = \infty$ we are reduced to $\bar{\sigma}_P = \bar{\sigma}$ as in Figure 6. For σ_0 finite this boundary will correspond to a slightly smaller value $\bar{\sigma}_P < \bar{\sigma}$. For $\sigma_{10} < \bar{\sigma}_P$ the rupture curve will be given by (4.6) and (4.7) (brittle fracture), otherwise by (4.4) (ductile fracture). The asymptotic behaviour of t_{KP}^* for small values of σ_{10} will be seen from (4.7) and (4.10). Eq. (4.10) yields

$$
\alpha_R = \left[1 - \left(\frac{\sigma_{10}}{\bar{\sigma}} \right)^{n-\nu} + \cdots \right]^{1/(n-\nu)} = 1 - \frac{1}{n-\nu} \left(\frac{\sigma_{10}}{\bar{\sigma}} \right)^{n-\nu} + \cdots
$$

valid for small values of σ_{10}. Inserting this in (4.7) we obtain

$$
t_{KP}^* = \frac{(\sigma_c/\sigma_{10})^n}{n} \left\{ 1 - \left[1 - \frac{1}{n-\nu} \left(\frac{\sigma_{10}}{\bar{\sigma}} \right)^{n-\nu} + \cdots \right]^n + \cdots \right\}
$$
$$
= \frac{\sigma_c^n}{(n-\nu)\sigma_{10}^{\nu}\bar{\sigma}^{n-\nu}} \{ 1 + \cdots \}
\tag{4.13}
$$

this proving that t_{KP}^* will behave asymptotically like $\sigma_{10}^{-\nu}$ as before. The general form of the rupture curve t_{KP}^* will be seen in Figure 7. It offers a better agreement with experiments on creep rupture than Figure 6 as will be seen when comparing with Figures 1 through 4.

5. Creep rupture of thin-walled cylindrical tubes under internal pressure.

Title problem was solved by I. Finnie [20] utilizing the theories of Hoff and of Robinson, reviewed above. It has also been treated by Kachanov [13] using his theory, which as we have seen is essentially equivalent to that of

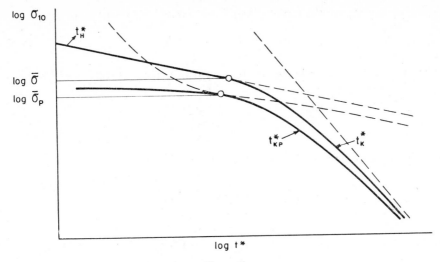

Figure 7

Robinson. We shall here produce a correction to these theories along the lines of the previous chapter.

For a thin-walled cylindrical tube with radius a and thickness h, subjected to internal pressure p we have the principal stresses σ_1, σ_2, σ_3 in circumferential, axial and radial direction

$$\sigma_1 = pa/h, \qquad \sigma_2 = pa/2h = \sigma_1/2, \qquad \sigma_3 = 0, \qquad (5.1)$$

Taking account of primary creep according to a previous paper [18], we then have for the corresponding creep rates

$$v_1 = \frac{3}{2}\left\{F(\sigma_e)\sigma_1/2 + \frac{d}{dt}\left[G(\sigma_e)\sigma_1/2\right]\right\}, \quad v_2 = 0, \quad v_3 = -v_1 \qquad (5.2)$$

where

$$\sigma_e = \sigma_1\sqrt{3}/2, \quad F(\sigma_e) = \left(\frac{\sigma_e}{\sigma_c}\right)^{n-1}\frac{1}{\sigma_c}, \quad G(\sigma_e) = \left(\frac{\sigma_e}{\sigma_0}\right)^{n_0-1}\frac{1}{\sigma_0} \qquad (5.3)$$

The quantities σ_c, σ_0, n and n_0 are material constants and $n > n_0$ as before. The term containing $G(\sigma_e)$ in (5.2) should be retained only as long as we have $d\sigma_e > 0$, i.e. as long as σ_1 increases.

Incompressibility yields

$$ah = a_0 h_0 = \text{constant} \qquad (5.4)$$

F. K. G. ODQVIST

where a_0 and h_0 are the initial values for $t = 0$ of a and h so that

$$\sigma_1 = pa/h = pa^2/a_0 h_0 \tag{5.5}$$

The internal pressure p being constant σ_1 will increase all the time. We introduce the notations

$$\frac{pa_0}{h_0} = \sigma_{10}, \qquad \frac{a}{a_0} = \alpha \tag{5.6}$$

Combining equations (5.2) through (5.6), we obtain

$$\frac{1}{\alpha}\frac{d\alpha}{dt} = \frac{\sqrt{3}}{2}\left[\left(\frac{\sigma_{10}\sqrt{3}}{2\sigma_c}\right)^n \alpha^{2n} + \left(\frac{\sigma_{10}\sqrt{3}}{2\sigma_0}\right)^{no} \cdot 2n_0\alpha^{2no-1}\frac{d\alpha}{dt}\right] \tag{5.7}$$

to be integrated with the initial condition $\alpha = 1$ for $t = 0$. This yields

$$1 - \frac{1}{\alpha^{2n}} - \frac{nn_0\sqrt{3}}{n - n_0}\left(\frac{\sigma_{10}\sqrt{3}}{2\sigma_0}\right)^{no}\left(1 - \frac{1}{\alpha^{2(n-no)}}\right) = n\sqrt{3}\left(\frac{\sigma_{10}\sqrt{3}}{2\sigma_c}\right)^n t \tag{5.8}$$

Ductile fracture will correspond to $\alpha = \infty$, hence the corresponding life time becomes

$$t_P^* = \frac{1}{n\sqrt{3}\left(\frac{\sigma_{10}\sqrt{3}}{2\sigma_c}\right)^n}\left[1 - \frac{n_0 n\sqrt{3}}{n - n_0}\left(\frac{\sigma_{10}\sqrt{3}}{2\sigma_0}\right)^{no}\right] \tag{5.9}$$

In the case of brittle fracture we have, according to (3.7)

$$1 = C(1 + v)\int_0^{t_{KP}^*}(\sigma_{max})^v dt \tag{5.10}$$

We put $\sigma_{max} = \sigma_{10}\alpha^2$, according to (5.5) and obtain from (5.10)

$$1 = C(1 + v)\sigma_{10}^v \int_1^{\alpha_R}\alpha^{2v}\frac{dt}{d\alpha}d\alpha$$

where α_R is that particular value of α which will correspond to fracture. Introducing $dt/d\alpha$ from (5.7) we obtain after integration

$$1 = \frac{C(1+v)(2\sigma_c/\sqrt{3})^v}{(n-v)\sqrt{3}\left(\dfrac{\sigma_{10}\sqrt{3}}{2\sigma_c}\right)^{n-v}}\left\{1 - \frac{1}{\alpha_R^{2(n-v)}} - \frac{n_0(n-v)\sqrt{3}}{n-n_0-v}\left(\frac{\sigma_{10}\sqrt{3}}{2\sigma_0}\right)^{n_0}\left(1-\frac{1}{\alpha_R^{2(n-n_0-v)}}\right)\right\}$$

(5.11)

In addition to this we have the time for brittle fracture, according to (5.8)

$$t^*_{KP} \quad \frac{1}{n\sqrt{3}\left(\dfrac{\sigma_{10}\sqrt{3}}{2\sigma_c}\right)^n}\left\{1 - \frac{1}{\alpha_R^{2n}} - \frac{nn_0\sqrt{3}}{n-n_0}\left(\frac{\sigma_{10}\sqrt{3}}{2\sigma_0}\right)^{n_0}\left(1-\frac{1}{\alpha_R^{2(n-n_0)}}\right)\right\}$$

(5.12)

valid if only

$$t^*_{KP} \leqq t^*_P$$ (5.13)

this condition giving limits for α_R

$$1 < \alpha_R \leqq \left(\frac{n-n_0}{nn_0\sqrt{3}}\right)^{1/2n_0}\sqrt{\frac{2\sigma_0}{\sigma_{10}\sqrt{3}}}$$ (5.14)

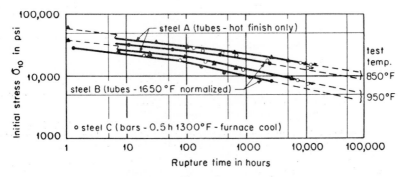

Figure 8

Stress rupture curves for SA-210 tubes and bars (L.F. Kooistra, R.U. Blaser and J.T. Tucker[21])

A similar discussion as that given in connection with formulae (4.8) through (4.13) is possible also in this case. In particular the asymptotic behaviour of the lifetime t^* as a function of initial stress σ_{10} follows similar lines as that in Figure 7. This is in agreement with experience, see e.g. Figure 8, which is taken from a paper by Kooistra, Blaser and Tucker [21]. In the figure initial stress is plotted against lifetime for tubes (σ_{max} in circumferential direction) as well as for bars (σ_{max} in axial direction).

REFERENCES

[1] N. J. GRANT, *Fracture*, Proceedings of an international conference on the atomic mechanism of fracture, held in Swampscott, Massachusetts, April 12–16, 1959, edited by B. L. Averbach, D. K. Felbeck, S. T. Hahn and D. A. Thomas; published jointly by the Technology Press of MIT, John Wiley and Sons, N.Y., and Chapman and Hall, London, (1959), pp. 15–19 and 562–578.

[2] H. CONRAD, *Mechanical Behavior of Materials at Elevated Temperatures*, edited by J. E. Dorn, McGraw-Hill Book Co., (1961), pp. 149–269.

[3] K. RICHARD, "Results of Creep Tests on Steels at 500° up to 100,000 hours" (in German) 4th International Mechanical Engineering Congress, Stockholm 1952. Published only as preprint. See also *Mitt. V. G. B.*, No. 26 1952, p. 606 and No. 39, 1955, p.836.

[4] F. R. LARSON AND J. MILLER, "A time-temperature relationship for rupture and creep stresses", *Trans. ASME*, (1952), 765.

[5] H. HENCKY, "Uber langsame stationäre Strömungen in plastischen Massen mit Rücksicht auf die Vorgänge beim Walzen, Pressen und Ziehen von Metallen, *ZAMM*, 5, (1925), 115.

[6] F. K. G. ODQVIST, Verfestigung von flusseisenähnlichen Körpern, *ZAMM*, 13, (1933), 360.

[7] N. J. HOFF, The necking and rupture of rods subjected to constant tensile loads, *J. Appl. Mech.*, 20, (1953), 105.

[8] M. REINER, The stress-strain-relation of elasticity and the measure of strain, *ZAMM*, 40, (1960), 415.

[9] L. M. KACHANOV, *Izvestia Ak.NAUK, SSSR*, no. 8, (1958), p. 26.

[10] N. J. HOFF, Structures and materials for finite lifetime, Internation Series on Aeronoutical Sciences and Space Flight, *Advances in Aeronautical Sciences*, 2, Pergamon Press (1959), 928.

[11] F. K. G. ODQVIST AND J. HULT, Some aspects of creep rupture, *Arkiv för Fysik*, 19, (1961), 379.

[12] E. L. ROBINSON, Effect of temperature variation on the long-time rupture strength of steels, *Trans.ASME*, 74, (1951), 777.

[13] L. M. KACHANOV, *Theory of Creep* (in Russian), pp. 455, Moscow 1960.

[14] L. M. KACHANOV, Rupture time under creep conditions, in *Problems of Continuum Mechanics*. Contributions in honour of the seventieth birthday of Academician N. I. Muskhelishvili, Philadelphia, (1961), p. 202.

[15] A. E. JOHNSON AND N. E. FROST, *Creep and Fracture of Metals at High Temperature*, Proceedings of a Symposium held at The National Physical Laboratory, 31st May-2nd June 1954, Her Majesty's Stationary Office, (1956), p.363.

[16] E. A. DAVIS. Creep rupture tests for desing of high pressure steam equipment, *ASME Trans.* 82 D, 1960, 453.

[17] A. NADAI, S. Timoshenko 60th Anniversary Volume, New York (1938), p.155.

[18] F. K. G. ODQVIST, "Influence of Primary Creep on Stresses in Structural Parts", VIII Int. Congr. Appl. Mech., Istanbul, 1952, Proc. p.99 (1953); see also *Trans. Roy. Inst. Tech.*, Stockholm, no, 66. (1953), 16 pp.

[19] F. K. G. ODQVIST, *Applicability of the Elastic Analogue in Creep Problems for Plates, Membranes and Beams*, Publ. no. 131, Inst.f.hallfasthetslära, KTH, Stockholm 1960, pp. 39; see also IUTAM Colloquium on Creep in Structures, Stanford University, July 11–15, 1960. Proc. to be published.

[20] I. FINNIE AND W R. HELLER, *Creep of Engineering Materials*, McGraw-Hill, (1959), p.267.

[21] L. F. KOOISTRA, R. U. BLASER AND J. T. TUCKER JR., High-temperature stress rupture testing of tubular specimens, *Trans. ASME*, (1952), p.783.

DISCUSSION

E. H. LEE:

Your theory, supported by experiments, predicts ductile fracture over part of the testing range and brittle fracture otherwise. A plot of the reduction of area at fracture would provide a check on the phenomenon, and I am wondering if you have confirmed your conclusions with such measurements.

AUTHOR'S REPLY:

In reply to Professor Lee and with reference to my Fig. 1 I would like to emphasize that brittleness seems to have a maximum somewhere in the transition region between the Hoff and Kachanov parts of the theoretical curve. The fact that brittleness seems to decrease for larger life time may well be due to the fact that contraction of area then decreases. This quantity, however, was not reported in Richard's work.

In reply to a question by Professor Rosenthal, I would like to say that metal physicists do not seem to agree about the question if ductile creep deformation takes place in grain boundaries or in the interior of the grains. All the more it seems to me remarkable that the simple phenomenological approach of my paper seems to give essential agreement between theory and experiment in creep rupture for a large number of structural metals irrespective of what crystalline mechanism may be behind.

ON THE ANALYTICAL DESCRIPTION OF THE
FLOW OF THIXOTROPIC MATERIALS

A. Slibar

Technische Hochschule Stuttgart, Stuttgart, Germany

AND

P. R. Paslay*

*Rice University and Consultant to Shell Development Co.,
Houston, Texas, U.S.A.*

ABSTRACT

Experience has shown that many materials e.g. grease, drilling mud and various gelatins in continuous or intermittent flow exhibit thixotropic effects of technological importance.

This paper presents a set of constitutive equations which are deduced from physical reasoning in agreement with current understanding of such materials. The particular class of materials under consideration is viewed as a Bingham-type material of constant viscosity and variable critical shear stress. The dependence of the critical shear stress on the deformation rate history is established by use of a memory function.

By adjusting the five physical parameters appearing in the constitutive equations a comparison is obtained with previously published experimental results. This comparison shows that over a variety of deformation rate histories reasonably accurate analytical predictions of the flow of this thixotropic material can be made.

In order to verify the applicability of the proposed analytical formulation two typical flow problems are solved. The predictions of these solutions are shown to be in agreement with physical expectation.

1. Introduction.

The paper is concerned with an aspect of the prediction of the mechanical behaviour of gelatins, greases and slowly coagulating colloidal suspensions that, although well known, has not been fully investigated analytically. This aspect is the dependence of the material rigidity ("stiffness") on time and deformation rate history. This effect may analytically be accounted for by the variation of the critical shear stress necessary to initiate flow. The critical shear stress during deformation will depend on the deformation rate history and in the state of rest will vary with time.

To fix ideas the following experiment is described:

---

* Currently National Science Foundation Fellow at Technische Hochschule Stuttgart, Stuttgart, Germany

Suppose, in a certain rotation viscometer, flow of a sample of this material is initiated after it has not been deformed for a sufficiently long period of time. A certain finite torque T_1 must be applied before flow begins. The torque required to establish and maintain a constant rate of rotation of the viscometer rotor is now observed as a function of time. This torque will decrease with time from its initial value and asymptotically approach another value of torque which depends on the rate of rotation. Continuing the experiment, the driving torque will be removed, and the material will be in a state of rest. As a function of time at rest, the torque required to again initiate flow will be determined. The results will show that this latter value of the torque is less than T_1 if the state of rest has been maintained only for a short time. The starting torque approaches T_1 asymptotically as the resting time increases. This phenomenon is sometimes called "stiffening".

To proceed rationally in postulating a set of constitutive equations for a particular material, it is necessary to have some definite physical process in mind. For example in the case of colloidal suspensions the material is envisioned as a viscous material with additional resistance from a "flocculating" structure that must be overcome to begin and maintain flow. Since the material consi- dered is assumed to be isotropic, the form of the constitutive equations is limited. The requirements for an isotropic material that must be met when stress and deformation rate are related are stated by Truesdell [1]. These requirements are not given explicitly in this paper; however, all equations presented here are suitable for isotropic materials. Finally, any new set of constitutive equations must retain the desired features of the set of equations it replaces. It is shown that the proposed set of equations reduces, by introdu- cing particular values of certain parameters, to all the important sets of consti- tutive equations that have been used to represent this class of materials.

Experiments which seem to give insight into the physical processes governing the behaviour of a typical thixotropic material have been published by Jones and Babson [2]. In their experiments a Couette type viscometer was used to impose upon the material a prescribed deformation rate history. The visco- meter was initially run at a selected uniform speed until a stationary value of the external torque was reached. Then the speed was "instantaneously" changed to produce a different value of the deformation rate and the external torque was observed as a function of time'.

2. Derivation of constitutive equations.

In 1919, E.C. Bingham [3] proposed the one-dimensional stress-deformation- rate equation for a rigid-viscous material. In 1921, E. Buckingham, [4] used Bingham's stress-deformation-rate relation to obtain the solution for axial flow in a circular cylinder. M. Reiner [5], in 1929, used the same equation to solve the problem of Couette flow between concentric cylinders with relative rotation. W. Prager and K. Hohenemser [6], in 1932, formulated three-dimensional stress-deformation-rate relations appropriate for rigid-viscous deformation.

Apparently the most suitable set of equations to describe flow of an incompressible rigid-viscous material is

$$d_{ij} = 0 \quad \text{for } \sqrt{J_2} < \bar{\tau}_0$$

$$2\bar{\mu}d_{ij} = \frac{\sqrt{J_2} - \bar{\tau}_0}{\sqrt{J_2}} \cdot S_{ij} \quad \text{for } \sqrt{J_2} \geqq \bar{\tau}_0 \tag{2.1}$$

where $\bar{\mu}$ is a parameter accounting for the viscous effect, d_{ij} is a component of the deformation rate tensor, J_2 is the quadratic invariant of the reduced stress tensor, $\bar{\tau}_0$ is the critical shear stress of the material for one-dimensional shear, and S_{ij} is a component of the reduced stress tensor.

Equations (2.1) predict that no deformation occurs unless the combination of stresses, measured by J_2 exceeds the critical value $\bar{\tau}_0^2$. The excess of the quadratic invariant over its critical value governs the rate of deformation, the ratio of a deformation-rate component to the corresponding reduced-stress component is constant. That is, in the terminology of Reference 1, the constitutive equations are quasi-linear.

The analytical solutions obtained from the above formulation of the stress deformation rate criterion for steady state conditions predict the motion of an ordinary Bingham material in terms of only two material parameters $\bar{\mu}$ and $\bar{\tau}_0$, independent of the loading history. However, many materials which in the state of deformation can be approximated as Bingham materials possess the property of gelling when in a state of rest for a certain period of time. Flow of a material of this latter type is referred to as retarded Bingham flow. Mathematically, the property of gelling can be analytically accounted for by assuming that the value $\hat{\tau}_1$ of the quadratic invariant of the reduced stress tensor necessary to initiate flow exceeds the value of the material parameter obtained from experiments for sustained flow. The equations proposed in 1959 by Slibar and Paslay [7] for initial monotonic loading of an element of gelled retarded Bingham material are

$$d_{ij} = 0 \quad \text{for } \sqrt{J_2} < \hat{\tau}_1$$

$$2\hat{\mu}.d_{ij} = \frac{\sqrt{J_2} - \hat{\tau}_0}{\sqrt{J_2}} \cdot S_{ij} \quad \text{for } \sqrt{J_2} \geqq \hat{\tau}_1 \tag{2.2}$$

while for post initial loading the set of equations (2.1), with the bars ($^-$) replaced, by tilde ($^\wedge$), is assumed valid until next gelling. In [7] the authors, for simplicity, have assumed the transition from $\hat{\tau}_1$ to $\hat{\tau}_0$ to occur instantaneously when $\hat{\tau}_1$ is initially exceeded.

While experiments on a number of materials show that the "break down" of the critical shear stress occurs almost instantaneously after deformation sets in, there are many other materials in which the "breakdown" takes place too gradually to permit the combined application of deformation laws (2.1) and (2.2). It is the purpose of this paper to arrive at a suitable set of deformation laws for a description of the behaviour of the latter type materials.

In order to account for the time and deformation rate dependence of the critical value of J_2 the set of equations (2.2) can be written as

$$d_{ij} = 0 \qquad \text{for } \sqrt{J_2} < \tau_{\text{crit}}$$

$$2\mu d_{ij} = \frac{\sqrt{J_2} - \tau_{\text{crit}}}{\sqrt{J_2}} \cdot S_{ij} \text{ for } \sqrt{J_2} \geq \tau_{\text{crit}}$$

(2.3)

where now the material parameter τ_{crit} may be viewed as the current value of the critical shear stress necessary to initiate or maintain flow.

First, it seems reasonable to assume that some invariant function of the deformation rate tensor will measure the effect of change of configuration upon the value τ_{crit}. To account for this influence mathematically the simplest function which may be selected seems to be the square root of the second invariant of the deformation rate tensor for the incompressible material, i.e. in rectangular Cartesian co-ordinates,

$$D_2 = \sqrt{\tfrac{1}{2}d_{xx}^2 + \tfrac{1}{2}d_{yy}^2 + \tfrac{1}{2}d_{zz}^2 + d_{xy}^2 + d_{yz}^2 + d_{zx}^2}$$

(2.4)

It is recalled that the square root of the second invariant is proportional to the root mean square of the principal deformation rates and is therefore positive definite.

Secondly, it seems logical to apply a time dependent memory function to the above mentioned deformation rate dependence. The introduction of a memory function which depends on the difference between the current time, t, and the time ξ, when such deformation rate D_2 occurred seems appropriate (see e.g. Lee [8] and Reiner [9]). This makes it possible to weight events so that the effect of a certain D_2 on τ_{crit} is most heavily felt immediately after its occurrence. The simplest mathematical form of such memory function appears to be exponential. Due to the above physical reasoning the combined influence of deformation rate and time can be postulated as

$$D_2 \cdot e^{-\alpha(t-\xi)} \qquad (2.5)$$

in which the parameter α accounts for the recovery after the deformation has taken place. The quantity (2.5) is a weighting function assigning larger multipliers to the more recent past. Since t is the present time, deformation occurring now has a weighting function of unity, whereas any previous deformation has a weighting function less than unity.

The final mathematical expression for the critical shear stress for specific selection of material parameters will have to yield the following two special cases:

    a) the stress deformation rate relations governing the flow of a regular non-gelling Bingham material and

    b) the stress deformation rate relations governing the flow of a retarded Bingham type body.

A mathematical expression for τ_{crit} which is in accordance with physical reasoning and satisfies the above two requirements may be written as

$$\tau_{\text{crit}} = \tau_1 - \frac{\displaystyle\int_{\xi=-\infty}^{t} D_2 \cdot e^{-\alpha(t-\xi)} d\xi}{\beta + \displaystyle\int_{\xi=-\infty}^{t} D_2 \cdot e^{-\alpha(t-\xi)} d\xi} \cdot (\tau_1 - \tau_0) \qquad (2.6)$$

where β is introduced as a new material parameter. Now equations (2.3) and (2.6) form the constitutive equations for the gelling thixotropic material. Combination of equations (2.3) and (2.6) to eliminate τ_{crit} shows that there are the following five material parameters necessary to analytically describe the material: $\mu,\ \tau_0,\ \tau_1,\ \alpha,\ \beta$.

The influence of the complete deformation rate history is expressed through $\int_{\xi=-\infty}^{t} D_2 \cdot e^{-\alpha(t-\xi)} d\xi$, while β represents an additional material parameter accounting for the reduction of τ_{crit} from its maximum value τ_1. From (2.6) there follows that τ_{crit} is limited to values between τ_0 and τ_1.

When $\qquad \displaystyle\int_{\xi=-\infty}^{t} D_2 \cdot e^{-\alpha(t-\xi)} d\xi \ll \beta \quad$ then $\quad \tau_{\text{crit}} \simeq \tau_1$

and when $\quad \displaystyle\int_{\xi=-\infty}^{t} D_2 \cdot e^{-\alpha(t-\xi)} d\xi \gg \beta \quad$ then $\quad \tau_{\text{crit}} \simeq \tau_0$.

The constitutive equations given by equations (2.3) and (2.6) for the following special selections of material parameters yield:

1. With $\tau_1 = \tau_0 = 0$

$$\mu = \mu_N = \text{Newtonian viscosity}$$

the incompressible Newtonian deformation law;

2. With $\mu = \bar{\mu}, \tau_1 = \tau_0 = \bar{\tau}_0$

the incompressible Bingham deformation law, (case a above):

3. With $\alpha \to \infty, \tau_1 = \hat{\tau}_1, \tau_0 = \hat{\tau}_0, \mu = \hat{\mu}, \beta > 0$

the deformation laws for initial monotonic loading of an incompressible retarded Bingham material, (case b above).

3. Shear between parallel plates.

To illustrate the type of predictions which can be obtained with the constitutive equations (2.3) and (2.6) consider two parallel plates with the thixotropic material between them, see Figure 1.

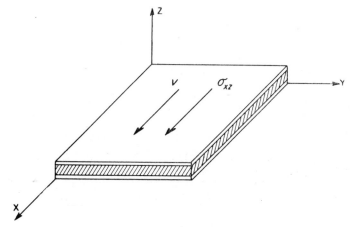

Figure 1
Parallel plates subjected to the shear stress σ_{xz} and
sheared with a relative velocity V

The plates are assumed to be parallel to the x-y-coordinate plane. The distance between the plates, h, is assumed constant and small compared to the dimensions of the plates in the x, y, plane, so that "edge effects" can be neglected.

The first problem to be analyzed is the case where the relative velocity between the plates, initially zero (back to $\xi \to -\infty$), is changed at $\xi = 0$, to V in the x direction and held constant up to the present time t. The only non-trivial stress-deformation rate equation is

$$\sigma_{xz} = \mu \frac{V}{h} + \tau_1 - \frac{\dfrac{V}{2h\alpha\beta} \cdot (1 - e^{-\alpha t})}{1 + \dfrac{V}{2h\alpha\beta}(1 - e^{-\alpha t})} \cdot (\tau_1 - \tau_0) \quad \text{for } t > 0 \quad (3.1)$$

and

$$\tau_{crit} = \tau_1 - \frac{\dfrac{V}{2h\alpha\beta} \cdot (1 - e^{-\alpha t})}{1 + \dfrac{V}{2h\alpha\beta} \cdot (1 - e^{-\alpha t})} \cdot (\tau_1 - \tau_0) \quad \text{for } t > 0 \quad (3.2)$$

The values of σ_{xz} at $t = 0$ and as t approaches ∞ are

$$\sigma_{xz}|_{t=0} = \mu \frac{V}{h} + \tau_1 \qquad (3.3)$$

$$\sigma_{xz}|_{t \to \infty} \to \mu \frac{V}{h} + \frac{\tau_1 + \dfrac{V}{2h\alpha\beta} \cdot \tau_0}{1 + \dfrac{V}{2h\alpha\beta}} \qquad (3.4)$$

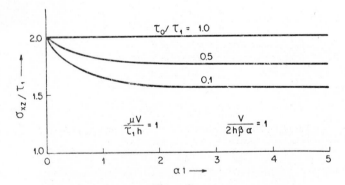

Figure 2

Dimensionless shear stress σ_{xz}/τ_1 versus dimensionless time αt for $\mu V/\tau_1 h = 1$ and $V/2h\alpha\beta = 1$ and indicated values of τ_0/τ_1 for $t < t^*$

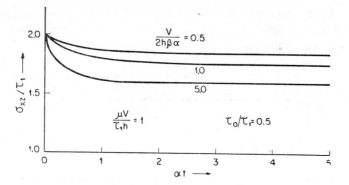

Figure 3

Dimensionless shear stress σ_{xz}/τ_1 versus dimensionless
time at for $\mu V/\tau_1 h = 1$ and $\tau_0/\tau_1 = 0,5$ and indicated
values of $V/2ha\beta$ for $t < t^*$

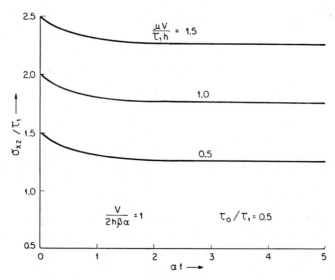

Figure 4

Dimensionless shear stress σ_{xz}/τ_1, versus dimensionless
time at for $\tau_0/\tau_1 = 0.5$ and $V/2ha\beta = 1$ and indicated
values of $\mu V/\tau_1 h$ for $t < t^*$

Figures 2, 3 and 4 show the dependence of the shear stress σ_{xz} on the dimensionless time αt for various combinations of the parameters

$$\frac{\tau_0}{\tau_1}, \quad \frac{\mu V}{\tau_1 h}, \quad \frac{V}{2h\alpha\beta}$$

To illustrate the recovery properties predicted by the proposed equations, assume the relative velocity, V, in the above problem to be zero for $t \geqq t^*$. The value of τ_{crit} as a function of time then becomes

$$\tau_{\text{crit}} = \tau_1 - \frac{\dfrac{V}{2h\alpha\beta}(e^{-\alpha(t-t^*)} - e^{-\alpha t})}{1 + \dfrac{V}{2h\alpha\beta}(e^{-\alpha(t-t^*)} - e^{-\alpha t})} \cdot (\tau_1 - \tau_0) \qquad (3.5)$$

so that as $t \to \infty$, $\tau_{\text{crit}} \to \tau_1$ representing the process of gelling.

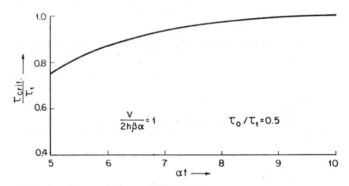

Figure 5

Dimensionless "Gel Strength $\tau_{\text{crit}}/\tau_1$" versus dimensionless time αt for $V/2h\alpha\beta = 1$, $\tau_0/\tau_1 = 0.5$ and $t > t^*$

Figure 5 shows the dependence of $\dfrac{\tau_{\text{crit}}}{\tau_1}$ on αt for the case where $\dfrac{V}{2h\alpha\beta} = 1$ $\dfrac{\tau_0}{\tau_1} = 0.5$, and $\alpha t^* = 5$ for $t \geqq t^*$.

The second problem to be analyzed for shear between parallel plates is the case where the shear stress, σ_{xz}, is initially zero (back to $\xi \to -\infty$) and at $\xi = 0$ is changed to the constant value σ_{xz}^* which is greater than τ_1. The relative shearing velocity $v(t)$, between the plates is to be determined as a function of time for $t > 0$. The only non-trivial constitutive equation is

$$\frac{\mu v(t)}{\tau_1 h} = \frac{\sigma_{xz}^*}{\tau_1} - 1 + \frac{\displaystyle\int_{\xi=0}^{t} \frac{\mu v(\xi)}{\tau_1 h} \cdot e^{-\alpha(t-\xi)} \cdot \alpha d\xi}{\dfrac{2\mu\alpha\beta}{\tau_1} + \displaystyle\int_{\xi=0}^{t} \frac{\mu v(\xi)}{\tau_1 h} \cdot e^{-\alpha(t-\xi)} \, \alpha d\xi} \cdot \left(1 - \frac{\tau_0}{\tau_1}\right) \qquad (3.6)$$

$$\text{for } \sigma_{xz}^* > \tau_1 \text{ and } t > 0$$

and

$$\frac{\tau_{crit}}{\tau_1} = 1 - \frac{\displaystyle\int_{\xi=0}^{t} \frac{\mu v(\xi)}{\tau_1 h} \cdot e^{-\alpha(t-\xi)} \alpha \, d\xi}{\displaystyle\frac{2\mu\alpha\beta}{\tau_1} + \int_{\xi=0}^{t} \frac{\mu v(\xi)}{\tau_1 h} \cdot e^{-\alpha(t-\xi)} \alpha \, d\xi} \left(1 - \frac{\tau_0}{\tau_1}\right) \quad \text{for } t > 0 \text{ (3.7)}$$

Equations (3.6) and (3.7) can be solved for selected material parameters by an elementary numerical integration. For the cases where

$$\frac{\tau_0}{\tau_1} = \frac{1}{2}, \quad \frac{\sigma^*_{xz}}{\tau_1} = 2 \quad \text{and} \quad \frac{2\mu\alpha\beta}{\tau_1} = .1, 1, 10 \; .$$

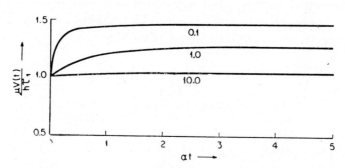

Figure 6

Dimensionless velocity $\mu V/h\tau_1$ versus dimensionless time αt for $\tau_0/\tau_1, = 0.5$ and $\sigma^*_{xz}/\tau_1 = 2$ for $2\mu\alpha\beta/\tau_1 = 0.1, 1,$ and 10

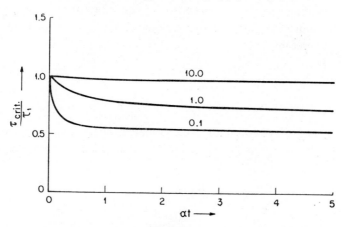

Figure 7

Dimensionless "Gel Strength" τ_{crit}/τ_1 versus dimensionless time αt for $\tau_0/\tau_1 = 0.5$ and $\sigma^*_{xz}/\tau_1 = 2$ for $\mu\alpha\beta/\tau_1 = 0.1, 1,$ and 10

figures 6 and 7 give the dimensionless quantities $\dfrac{\mu v(t)}{h\tau_1}$ and $\dfrac{\tau_{\text{crit}}}{\tau_1}$ as functions of the dimensionless time αt.

4. Comparison with experimental results of Jones and Babson.

To obtain a comparison of the ability of the proposed equations to predict τ_{crit} with sufficient accuracy, experiments are necessary in which the load-deformation rate relation is recorded for laminar flow as a function of time. One such set of experiments has been reported by Jones and Babson [2]. The tests in which results are pertinent to the considerations here were performed with a rotation viscometer. The test consisted of shearing a thin film of a thixotropic material in a rotation viscometer where the material temperature was held constant and the speed was varied while the torque necessary to maintain the prescribed speed was recorded. Each test considered here had the following angular velocity Ω as a function of the time t:

$$\text{for } t < 0 \ \to \ \Omega = \Omega_i$$

and   (4.1)

$$\text{for } t > 0 \ \to \ \Omega = \Omega_f.$$

That is, the material was sheared at the angular velocity Ω_i until the external torque became constant and then, at $t=0$, the angular velocity was changed to Ω_f. The indication on a dial that gave a reading T proportional to torque was recorded as a function of time for $t > 0$. Assuming the sheared film to be sufficiently thin and inertia effects to be negligible, then the torque T is given by the sum of a part due to τ_{crit} and a part proportional to rate of rotation Ω; therefore

$$T = K \frac{\Omega}{\Omega_r} + C \frac{\tau_{\text{crit}}}{\tau_1}, \tag{4.2}$$

where K, Ω_r and C are constants used to match theory and experiment. The function D_2 for these tests is proportional to the angular velocity Ω, so that

$$D_2 = D_0 \frac{\Omega}{\Omega_r} \tag{4.3}$$

where D_0 is another constant available for matching the experimental data with analytical predictions. With the above notation $(\tau_{\text{crit}}/\tau_1)$ becomes

$$\frac{\tau_{crit}}{\tau_1} = 1 - \frac{\dfrac{\Omega_i}{\Omega_r} \cdot D_0 \displaystyle\int_{-\infty}^{0} e^{-\alpha(t-\xi)} d\xi + \dfrac{\Omega_f}{\Omega_r} D_0 \displaystyle\int_{0}^{t} e^{-\alpha(t-\xi)} d\xi}{\beta + \left\{ \dfrac{\Omega_i}{\Omega_r} D_0 \displaystyle\int_{-\infty}^{0} e^{-\alpha(t-\xi)} d\xi - \dfrac{\Omega_f}{\Omega_r} D_0 \displaystyle\int_{0}^{t} e^{-\alpha(t-\xi)} d\xi \right\}} \cdot \left(1 - \frac{\tau_0}{\tau_1} \right)$$

(4.4)

$$= \frac{1 + \dfrac{\tau_0}{\tau_1} \left[\dfrac{D_0}{\alpha\beta} \right] \dfrac{\Omega_i}{\Omega_r} \cdot \left[e^{-\alpha t} (1 - \gamma) + \gamma \right]}{1 + \left[\dfrac{D_0}{\alpha\beta} \right] \dfrac{\Omega_i}{\Omega_r} \left[e^{-\alpha t} (1 - \gamma) + \gamma \right]} \qquad \text{for } t > 0$$

where

$$\gamma = \frac{\Omega_f}{\Omega_i} .$$

To compare Jones and Babson's experimental results with the predictions of the proposed constitutive equations, the equations (4.2) and (4.4) are combined to eliminate τ_{crit}/τ_1 so that

$$T = K \frac{\Omega}{\Omega_r} + C \cdot \frac{1 + \dfrac{\tau_0}{\tau_1} \left[\dfrac{D_0}{\alpha\beta} \right] \dfrac{\Omega_i}{\Omega_r} \left[e^{-\alpha t} (1 - \beta) + \beta \right]}{1 + \left[\dfrac{D_0}{\alpha\beta} \right] \dfrac{\Omega_i}{\Omega_r} \left[e^{-\alpha t} (1 - \beta) + \beta \right]} .$$

(4.5)

The following constants are suitable to match the torque indication T in dial units:

$$\Omega_r \quad = 100 \text{ rpm (a reference value)}$$

$$C \quad = 86.6 \text{ dial units}$$

$$\left[\frac{D_0}{\alpha\beta} \right] = 0.207$$

$$K \quad = 32 \text{ dial units}$$

$$\frac{\tau_0}{\tau_1} \quad = 0.00$$

The predictions of equation (4.5) with the above values as the constants are compared with the experimental results of Jones and Babson in Figure 8. Curve 1 in this figure shows that the maximum deviation between analytical prediction and experiment occurs for the completely gelled material.

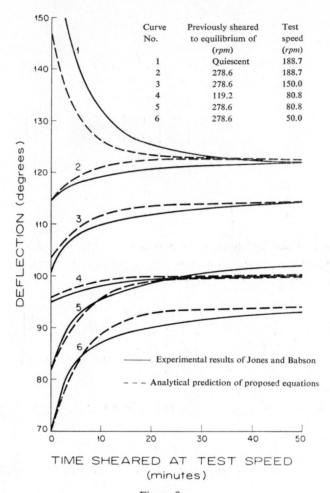

Curve No.	Previously sheared to equilibrium of (rpm)	Test speed (rpm)
1	Quiescent	188.7
2	278.6	188.7
3	278.6	150.0
4	119.2	80.8
5	278.6	80.8
6	278.6	50.0

——— Experimental results of Jones and Babson

– – – Analytical prediction of proposed equations

Figure 8
Comparison of analytical predictions with experimental results of Jones and Babson.

5. Discussion.

The proposed constitutive equations present a means of accounting for the influence of past deformation-rate and its relative time of occurrence upon the instantaneous value of a parameter measuring the state of gelation of a thixotropic material. This influence of past deformation rate on the state of gelation is accomplished mathematically through the current value of an integral over all past deformation. The integrand contains the product of two terms, the first being a function which weighs the event according to the difference of the present time and the time when the deformation occurred.

The second factor in the integrand is an invariant function of the deformation rates.

Clearly the proposed set of constitutive equations is not the most general one to encompass the physical requirements of thixotropic materials. The authors view this study as an attempt to analytically describe the behaviour of thixotropic materials which will have to be compared with additional experimental results.

The analytical predictions of the set of equations presented here have been compared with experimental results given by Jones and Babson [2]. Although the range of deformation rates given in these experiments is not as extensive as desirable, a comparison with analysis is possible and is shown in Figure 8. These analytical predictions are in satisfactory agreement with experimental data for technological use.

It seems interesting to note that for the best agreement between analytical prediction and experiment τ_0 is set to zero. No emphasis was placed on matching the analytical and experimental results in the completely gelled state. The reason being that the authors believe that in this state the measured results very likely will depend upon the different mechanisms introduced in the final stages of gelling.

6. List of symbols.

C, D_0 = constants

D_2 = the positive square root of the quadratic invariant of the deformation-rate tensor. A scalar quantity proportional to the root mean square of the principal deformation rates. In rectangular Cartesian co-ordinates,

$$D_2 = \sqrt{\tfrac{1}{2}d_{xx}^2 + \tfrac{1}{2}d_{yy}^2 + \tfrac{1}{2}d_{zz}^2 + d_{xy}^2 + d_{yz}^2 + d_{zx}^2}.$$

$d_{ij} = \tfrac{1}{2}\left(\dfrac{\partial u_i}{\partial x_j} + \dfrac{\partial u_j}{\partial x_i}\right)$ component of the deformation-rate tensor in Cartesian co-ordinates. This tensor is the instantaneous time rate of change of the strain tensor

h = constant distance between parallel plates

J_2 = quadratic invariant of the reduced stress tensor. In rectangular Cartesian co-ordinates,

$$J_2 = \tfrac{1}{2}S_{xx}^2 + \tfrac{1}{2}S_{yy}^2 + \tfrac{1}{2}S_{zz}^2 + S_{xy}^2 + S_{yz}^2 + S_{zx}^2$$

K = a constant proportional to μ

S_{ij} =   component of reduced stress tensor in Cartesian co-ordinates,

$$S_{ij} = \sigma_{ij} - \delta_{ij} \sum_{k=1}^{3} \sigma_{kk} \quad \text{where} \quad \delta_{ij} \begin{cases} = 1, \text{ for } i = j \\ = 0, \text{ for } i \neq j \end{cases}$$

T =   dial reading proportional to viscometer torque

T_1 =   torque required to initiate flow in a rotation viscometer filled with thixotropic material that is fully jelled

t^* =   value of the time, t, when the relative velocity, V, is set to zero

t =   time

u, v, w =   components of the velocity vector in the x, y, z directions referred to a Cartesian spatial coordinate system.

V =   relative velocity between parallel plates. This velocity is parallel to the plane of either of the plates

γ =   ratio of angular velocities

ξ =   dummy variable in time

μ_N =   Newtonian viscosity, a material constant

$\bar{\mu} \ \bar{\tau}_0$ =   material constants for a Bingham material

$\hat{\mu}, \hat{\tau}_0, \hat{\tau}_1$ =   material constants for a retarded Bingham material

$\mu, \tau_0, \tau_1, \alpha, \beta$ =   material constants for the set of equations proposed for thixotropic materials

τ_{crit} =   instantaneous value for critical shear stress of thixotropic material

σ_{ij} =   component of the stress tensor in Cartesian co-ordinates

Ω =   angular velocity of rotation-viscometer cylinder

REFERENCES

[1] C. TRUESDELL, The Mechanical Foundations of Elasticity and Fluid Dynamics, *J. Rational Mech. and Analysis*, **1** (1952), 125–300.

[2] P.H. JONES AND E.C. BABSON, Evaluation of Rotary-Drilling Muds, *API Drilling and Production Practice*, (1935), 22.

[3] E.C. BINGHAM, An Investigation of the Laws of Plastic Flow, Scientific Paper N. 278, U.S. Bureau of Standards.
    E.C. BINGHAM, *Fluidity and Plasticity and Other Physical and Chemical Properties*, McGraw-Hill Book Company, Inc. New York, N.Y. (1922).

[4] E. BUCKINGHAM, On Plastic Flow Through Capillary Tubes, *Proc. Amer. Soc. for Testing Materials*, **21**(1921), 1154.

[5] M. REINER, The Theory of Plastic Flow in the Rotation Viscometer, *Journal of Rheology*, **1** (1929), 5.

[6] W. Prager and K. Hohenemser, Uber die Ansätze der Mechanik der Kontinua, *Z. für angewandte Math. und Mech.*, **12** (1932), 216.

[7] A. Slibar and Paul R. Paslay, Retarded Flow of Bingham Materials, *J. Appl. Mech.*, **29** (1959), 107–113.

[8] E.H. Lee, Viscoelastic Stress Analysis, *Proc. of the First Symposium on Naval Structural Mechanics*, Pergamon Press, (1960), 456–482.

[9] M. Reiner, Rheology, *Handbuch der Physik*, **6** (1958), 434–550.

Discussion

F. K. G. Odqvist:

I notice that your theory is applicable to bentonite suspensions. As you may know dilute suspensions of such material has been used for the investigations of the transition from laminar to turbulent flow of liquids in tubes. Observation indicates that packages of turbulent motion are formed at some disturbance and may die out or form continuous turbulent motion in the tube. My question is: Does such behaviour have anything to do with your theory of recovery with time?

H. Markovitz:

The bentonite suspensions mentioned by Professor Odquist are quite different from those discussed by the present authors. Those which he mentioned are very delicate and the bentonite is added to make visible the flow lines of a Newtonian fluid. In such experiments it is hoped that the bentonite does not influence the characteristics of the Newtonian behaviour. In this paper, the suspensions are much more concentrated and their constitutive relations are of interest and much more complicated.

J. G. Savins:

A comparison of the analytical predictions, which are based on the ideal model, with experimental results (Fig. 8) shows that the model consistently overestimates the breakdown-buildup rates. Since the original flow data obtained by Jones and Babson suggest their material is more like that of a generalized Bingham plastic, is it possible that the disagreement lies in a direction which suggests that the yield point has been overestimated?

A. B. Metzner:

Several years ago Prof. Eyring has published a comprehensive study of thixotropy in which results obtained in one kind if experiment were used to evaluate the theoretical parameters in his equations: The theory was then used to predict the results of a completely different experiment and good agreement was shown. This appears to be a much more rigorous evaluation of a theory than presented here and I wonder if the authors have further results (perhaps using the same data employed by Eyring) which might shed more critical light on the validity of their theory.

AUTHORS' REPLY:

In answer to Prof. Odquist's comment, we have not yet undertaken a study of the transition from laminar to turbulent flow using the proposed constitutive equations. Perhaps the comments of Dr. Markovitz are of interest in this connection.

In answer to Dr. Savins' question we would like to say that in matching the experimental results a compromise value for C, which is a measure of the yield stress, has to be found. Curve 1 of Fig. 8 represents the torque-time relation from the fully jelled state and shows that the torque is analytically underestimated for this case.

In order to answer Prof. Metzner's comment we have assumed he refers to the paper 'Flow Mechanism of Thixotropic Substances', by Hahn, Ree and Eyring, Ind and Chem. Eng. July 1959. We notice the following differences between their work and ours:

1) Hahn, Ree and Eyring give the shear stress - shear deformation rate relation in a one dimensional non-linear form. The generalization of this relation to three-dimensional constitutive equations for comparison with our relations given by Eq. (2.3) and (2.6) is not obvious.

2) While the constitutive equations proposed by us describe a thixotropic material by use of the five parameters u, τ_0, τ_1, α and β the one-dimensional deformation law of Hahn, Ree and Eyring requires the experimental determination of seven material constants. From the point of view of facilitating the experimental determination of material parameters the equation having fewer parameters appears the more attractive one.

Our original study was primarily directed to describe the flow of Bentonite suspensions and we have not yet performed a comparison with data from other materials. We agree with Prof. Metzner's pinion that such a comparison is desirable.

We would like to express our appreciation to the discussers for their most interesting comments.

STRESS-STRAIN-TIME RELATIONS
AND IRREVERSIBLE THERMODYNAMICS*

D. C. DRUCKER**

Division of Engineering, Brown University, Providence, R.I., U.S.A.

ABSTRACT

Some progress is reported in the continuing search for the essential features of the macroscopic behavior of linear and non-linear material. A comparison is made of the validity, the value, and the interrelation of three approaches to the study of elastic, plastic, and viscous response under isothermal conditions. One approach is through the stability postulate of positive work by the forces of an external agency on the changes it causes; another is the extension of Onsager's reciprocal relations for linear irreversible thermodynamics; and the third is the concept or postulate of path independence. In particular it is shown that the surface of constant rate of entropy production in force or velocity space does not play a significant role in general for non-linear dissipative systems. When instead a limited or full path independence is employed to give a normality condition in force or velocity space, the stability postulate gives convexity. A tentative conclusion is reached that in all probability the desirable synthesis of non-linear macroscopic behavior from the microscopic will involve explicitly or implicitly just as strong a set of postulates as a more direct phenomenological approach.

1. Introduction.

All of the paper is devoted to isothermal mechanical systems without reference to the heat transfer which is a necessary accompaniment to deformation. One reason for this drastic restriction is that the complexities of the isothermal mechanical behavior of non-linear irreversible time-dependent systems provide a sufficient challenge. The other is that temperature effects, chemical action, etc., can be included later by a proper interpretation of "forces" or "stresses" and of "velocities" or "strain rates" [1–4].

A major objective of this continuing study [4–6] is to minimize the set of postulates needed to characterize material behavior. There is always the hope that the minimum number will be the most meaningful in physical terms although there is no possibility of developing a universal explicit stress-strain-time law. Each steel and each aluminum alloy, for example, has its individual stress-strain relation. Tests on one material do not give detailed information

---

* The results in this paper were obtained in the course of research sponsored by the Office of Naval Research under Contract Nonr 562(20) with Brown University.
** Chairman, Physical Sciences Council, Brown University, Providence, R.I., U.S.A.

331

on another. Nevertheless, there is some chance of success. As demonstrated previously [6, 7], the single postulate of stability is sufficient to unify the entire picture of the mechanical behavior of time-independent materials, both elastic and plastic, under isothermal conditions.

In this stability approach, an external agency is imagined to apply a set of forces to an already loaded body and so to cause a set of changes in the displacements of the body. Geometric instability is eliminated by assuming small deformations and satisfying the equations of equilibrium in the undeformed configuration. The stability postulate is that the work done by the forces of the external agency on the *changes* in displacements caused is positive for all permissible added loads. If the permissible loads are of finite magnitude, the material is stable in the large. If infinitesimal forces only are permitted, the material is stable in the small. Neutral stability, or zero work by the external agency on the changes produced, may be included for some material idealizations.

This stability postulate appears to be closely related to the chemical principle of Le Chatelier [1, 2]. When applied to an isothermal or isentropic linear or non-linear elastic (path independent) body undergoing small strains, the postulate of stability leads directly to convexity of the surfaces of constant strain energy and complementary energy in force and displacement space. Applied to an isothermal or isentropic plastic system, the consequences are convexity of the yield and subsequent loading surfaces in force or stress space and the normality of the plastic strain or displacement increment vector to such a surface [6]. These characteristics, plus the fundamental definitions or classifications of material as elastic or as plastic, are the essential features of isothermal or isentropic elasticity and plasticity theory. All general theorems, that is, those valid for all permissible stress-strain relations, are direct consequences of the stability postulate [7].

When the stability postulate is applied to general time-dependent materials [5], it gives much less information all by itself. Before examining the difficulties encountered, consider an alternate approach through the thermodynamics of irreversible processes.

The first and second laws of thermodynamics say little beyond what is now thought obvious in the isothermal mechanical behavior of materials. Work done on the body is stored, or dissipated, or both stored and dissipated. The dissipated energy is non-negative.

Additional useful information is obtained through Onsager's reciprocal relations when the linear dissipative behavior of material is studied. However, Onsager's relations were derived for small disturbances of a linear system from equilibrium or a steady state condition. No clear non-controversial extension of these reciprocal relations to non-linear materials or systems yet exists. Therefore, the applicability of the approach is in doubt because stress-strain-time relations for metals and plastics must be able to describe non-stationary states of strongly non-linear material systems far from equilibrium.

The need for starting from equilibrium or steady state conditions may be circumvented for a while, perhaps indefinitely. The very broad but not un-reasonable common assumption may be adopted of considering the response of extremely complex systems as the result of the combination of the res-ponse of elements exhibiting relatively simple behavior. Familiar idealizations of material properties which may be combined include the linear and non-linear elastic, the linear and non-linear viscous, and the perfectly plastic and work-hardening solid. Physical models can be made or visualized to simulate the measured performance of a real system. For such a model, each component separately must obey the rules appropriate to its class. Each component then can and should be studied by itself. To the extent, therefore, that the model represents the prototype, it is useful to examine in detail the individual classes of behavior separately. Should such a study be successful, information on non-stationary states could be derived directly from the steady state be-havior of the component groups.

From the point of view adopted here, the non-stationary states in the Kelvin or parallel combinations of viscous, elastic, and plastic response simply provide a loading history for each of the elements. Known combinations obviously will offer no conceptual difficulty. However, the appropriate combination for a given material and loading history is not known in general.

2. Onsager's reciprocal relations and linear viscous behavior.

The demonstration that the conventional statements about Onsager's reciprocal relations and the rate of production of entropy are not useful in the general problem requires a brief description of their relevance and value for the linear viscous system. It is the linear viscous or Newtonian body, represented by a linear dashpot in one dimension, which is directly of the type for which irreversible thermodynamics was developed. In this and in all the models or idealized materials to be considered, mass-acceleration terms will be assumed negligible. Velocity $\dot{u}$ is proportional to force P, or in more general form (repeated subscripts in the same term denote summation),

$$\dot{u}_k = L_{ki} P_i \tag{1}$$

where the coefficients L_{ki} are constants.

The rate of dissipation of energy $\dot{D}$ is positive for P_i, or equivalently $\dot{u}_k$, not identically zero;

$$\dot{D} = P_k \dot{u}_k = L_{ki} P_i P_k = \tfrac{1}{2}(L_{ki} + L_{ik}) P_i P_k = \phi(P_i) > 0 \tag{2}$$

In terms of $\dot{u}_k$,

$$\dot{D} = P_k \dot{u}_k = L_{ki}^{-1} \dot{u}_i \dot{u}_k = \tfrac{1}{2}(L_{ki}^{-1} + L_{ik}^{-1}) \dot{u}_i \dot{u} = \psi(\dot{u}_k) > 0 \tag{3}$$

where L_{ik}^{-1} is the matrix of coefficients inverse to L_{ki}

$$P_i = L_{ik}^{-1} \dot{u}_k \tag{4}$$

Linear irreversible thermodynamics is based upon a number of considerations which, for convenience, will be referred to later by the capital letters A through E:

A) Aged systems are studied so that the state is either one of equilibrium or of steady motion and is stable.

B) Systems are supposed fully linear in the range examined. Disturbing "forces" P_i produce "velocities" $\dot{u}_k$ of the form (1).

C) The rate of entropy production for a system disturbed from an equilibrium configuration (maximum entropy, zero rate of entropy production) is proportional to the dissipation rate $\dot{D}$ and is given by (2).

D) The same form (2) applies to the change in the rate of entropy production when a stationary state (minimum entropy production under the given constraints) is perturbed by any P_i which is described as not altering the fixed forces and so not causing any first order changes in entropy production.

E) Microscopic reversibility is assumed (no gyroscopic, Coriolis, or Lorentz type forces) and the average decay of microscopic fluctuations is supposed to follow the macroscopic law.

Onsager's reciprocal relations then follow

$$L_{ki} = L_{ik} \tag{5}$$

Application of (5) to a linear viscous system leads to the result that the surface of constant rate of dissipation in force space

$$\dot{D} = \phi(P_i) = \text{constant} \tag{6}$$

has its normal in the direction given by

$$\frac{\partial \phi}{\partial P_i} = (L_{ki} + L_{ik}) P_k = 2\dot{u}_i \tag{7}$$

As shown in Figure 1, when velocity coordinates are superposed on force coordinates, the velocity vector $\dot{u}_k$ is normal to the surface of constant rate of dissipation in force space.

Similarly, the force vector is normal to the surface of constant rate of dissipation in velocity space

$$\dot{D} = \psi (\dot{u}_k) = \text{constant} \tag{8}$$

because

$$\frac{\partial \psi}{\partial \dot{u}_k} = (L_{ki}^{-1} + L_{ik}^{-1}) \dot{u}_i = 2P_k \tag{9}$$

Both of the surfaces (6) and (8) represent positive definite quadratic forms and are ellipses in two dimensions, as illustrated in Figure 1.

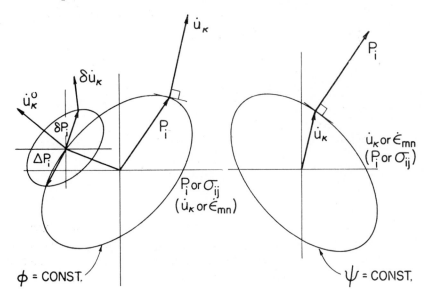

Figure 1

Normality for linear viscous systems

$$\phi = \psi = \dot{D} \equiv P_k \dot{u}_k$$

Relation between $\delta \dot{u}_k$ and δP_i is the same as between $\dot{u}_k$ and P_i

If gyroscopic type forces are present, $L_{ki} \neq L_{ik}$ and the picture is quite different, Figure 2. The addition of a component of $\dot{u}$ in a direction perpendicular to P does not alter the scalar product of P and $\dot{u}$ and so does not affect the rate of dissipation. The velocity vector no longer is normal to the surface of constant ϕ. Correspondingly, the force vector will not be normal to the surface of constant ψ.

When the antisymmetric or gyroscopic type of term $\frac{1}{2}(L_{ki} - L_{ik})$ is absent, Figure 1, $\dot{u}_k$ and ϕ determine P_i. Similarly, P_i and and ψ determine $\dot{u}_k$. When gyroscopic terms are present, $\dot{u}_k$ and ϕ allow two values of P_i in two dimensions. One is denoted by P_i, the other by F, in Figure 2. In more dimensions

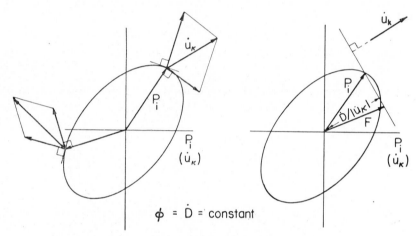

Figure 2

Addition of gyroscopic type terms in a linear system destroys normality

$$L_{ki} \neq L_{ik}$$

there are an infinite number of alternatives. The choice of the proper one requires a knowledge of the antisymmetric coefficients in addition to the rate of dissipation or of entropy production. Pictorially, as illustrated in Figure 3, the ellipse of constant ϕ for a given $\dot{u}_k$ will be larger the greater the values of $L_{ki} - L_{ik}$.

Onsager's reciprocal relations for a linear viscous system thus may be thought of as normality requirements which select the minimum size ellipse or its generalization in more dimensions.

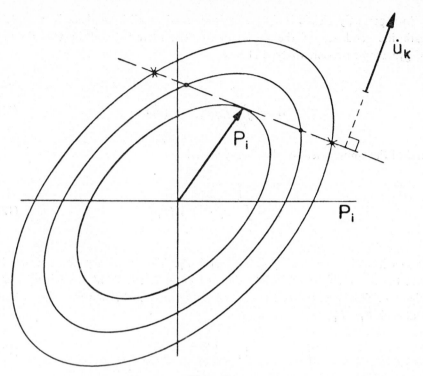

Figure 3
Gyroscopic type terms increase size of ellipse for given $\varphi = \dot{D}$. Onsager's reciprocal relations select the minimum size ellipse

3. Scope of Onsager's reciprocal relations, the stability postulate, and path independence.

ELASTIC BODY.

It is clear that in general the stability postulate and Onsager's reciprocal relations involve basically different concepts. Consider an isothermal perfectly elastic body acted upon by forces P_i^0 which produce displacements u_k^0. Irreversible thermodynamics is not relevant and can give no information on what to expect when δP_i is added and causes δu_k. The stability postulate, however, does provide a non-trivial restriction

$$\delta P_k \delta u_k > 0 \tag{10}$$

for all non-zero additions of force to both linear and non-linear bodies.

In a perfectly elastic body under isothermal conditions, there is complete path independence of the work done or the energy stored in the absence of gyroscopic or Lorentz type effects

$$W = \int_0^{u_k^0} P_k du_k = W(u_k^0) \tag{11}$$

and of the complement of the energy stored

$$V = \int_0^{P_k^0} u_i dP_i = V(P_i^0) \tag{12}$$

for each and every end point u_k^0 and P_i^0. The necessary consequence is that the vector P_i^0 be normal to the surface of constant W at each $u_k = u_k^0$, Figure 4. Similarly, the vector $u_k^{\,0}$ must be normal to the surface of constant V at each $P_i = P_i^0$.

$$P_i = \frac{\partial W}{\partial u_i} \tag{13}$$

$$u_k = \frac{\partial V}{\partial P_k} \tag{14}$$

For homogeneous states of stress and strain, the coordinates of Figure 4 can be taken as ε_{ij} and σ_{ij} instead of u_i and P_i. The functions W and V then are the strain energy density and the complementary energy density respectively.

Path independence provides the normality condition for elastic behaviour as Onsager's relations do for linear viscous behaviour. The stability postulate (10) coupled with normality requires convexity of the surfaces of constant W and of constant V. Neutral stability

$$\delta P_k \delta u_k = 0 \tag{15}$$

permits the limiting case of a flat spot or a straight line.

The differential form of (14)

$$du_k = \frac{\partial^2 V}{\partial P_k \partial P_i} dP_i = M_{ki} dP_i \tag{16}$$

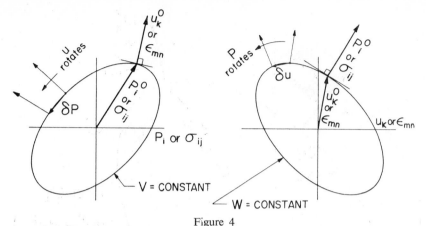

Figure 4

Elastic behavior, linear or non-linear

Complement of energy stored   Energy stored

$$V = \int_0^{P_i} u_i \, dP_i \quad \text{or} \quad \int_0^{\sigma_{ij}} \varepsilon_{ij} \, d\sigma_{ij} \qquad W = \int_0^{u_k} P_k \, du_k \quad \text{or} \quad \int_0^{\varepsilon_{mn}} \sigma_{mn} \, d\varepsilon_{mn}$$

Note that in the general non-linear case, $P_k u_k = $ constant does not coincide with either $W = $ constant or $V = $ constant

where

$$M_{ki} = M_{ik} \qquad (17)$$

bears a strong resemblance to the linear viscous form (1) because of the linearity and the reciprocity. Comparison with the Onsager considerations (A–E) shows that path independence combines at least macroscopic reversibility and the absence of gyroscopic or Lorentz type forces. Reciprocal relations (17) follow much more directly than when the reversibility is microscopic (5).

Plastic Body.

The elastic-plastic body, or its further idealization as rigid-work hardening, is path dependent and irreversible for loading into the plastic range. Non-linearity of response, introduced by the marked distinction between loading and unloading, places plastic behavior outside of the scope of the consideration (B) of Onsager. The yield or loading surface in force or stress space, Figure 5, separates those states of stress which can be reached without plastic deformation from those which necessarily involve further plastic action.

The stability postulate in the form (10), when applied to a rigid — work hardening material, requires the displacement or strain increment to be normal

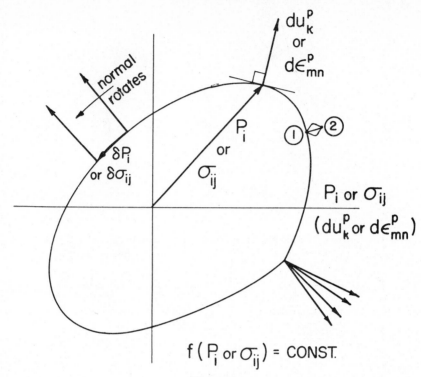

Figure 5
Yield or loading surface for plastic behavior,
$f(P_i)$ or $f(\sigma_{ij})$ = constant.

Normality and convexity follow from the postulate of stability in the large. Path independence of $\int_{1}^{2} P_k du_k^p$ along all neighboring paths of continual loading from ① to ②, which is very close by, also gives normality

to the loading surface and further requires the surface to be convex. A more general statement of the stability postulate is needed for an elastic-plastic body. The external agency is thought of as applying δP_i or $\delta \sigma_{ij}$ and then removing it along an elastic or reversible path. Elastic response over the cycle of addition and removal cancels out for infinitesimal excursions beyond the loading surface even if the elastic modulus should be a function of plastic strain. Thus the net result is the same as for the rigid-plastic body. The plastic displacement or strain increment is normal to the convex loading surface. When the surface $f(P_i \text{ or } \sigma_{ij})$ = constant has a continuously turning tangent, and $df = \dfrac{\partial f}{\partial P_i} dP_i$ or $\dfrac{\partial f}{\partial \sigma_{mn}} d\sigma_{mn} > 0,$ then

$$du_k^p = G(P) \frac{\partial f}{\partial P_k}\left(\frac{\partial f}{\partial P_i}dP_i\right) = N_{ki}dP_i \qquad (18)$$

or

$$d\varepsilon_{ij}^p = G(\sigma)\frac{\partial f}{\partial \sigma_{ij}}\left(\frac{\partial f}{\partial \sigma_{mn}}d\sigma_{mn}\right) = h_{ijmn}d\sigma_{mn} \qquad (19)$$

where

$$N_{ki} = N_{ik}; \quad h_{ijmn} = h_{mnij} \qquad (20)$$

Again, there is linearity and reciprocity in the relation between the differentials of force and displacement. In contrast with the elastic situation, entropy is produced along irreversible paths. The loading surface bounds the region of zero dissipation. The normality of du_k^p or $d\varepsilon_{ij}^p$ to this surface does bear a strong resemblance to Figure 1 for the linear viscous body and to Figure 4 for the elastic body.

Path independence does play a vital role in the normality condition at a smooth point on the loading surface. It enters in the large for the elastic response and in the small for plastic response. Prager's condition of consistency[8], or continuity of behavior from the elastic into the plastic range, is a path independence, but a limited one. Second order fluctuations in force or stress produce no first order fluctuations in displacement or strain. Normality gives this independence in the small, just as in the purely elastic range it gives path independence in the large. The stability postulate need not be employed to show normality if the alternate assumption is made that, for all neighboring paths of continual loading from point (1) on the loading surface to point (2) very slightly outside, the plastic strain is the same and the work done or energy dissipated is the same to the order $\delta P_k \delta u_k$ or $\delta \sigma_{ij}\delta \varepsilon_{ij}$ per unit of volume. This path independence assumption is much stronger than the assumption of linearity in the small. It is a consequence of stability in the large but not in the small. Linearity is required in addition to stability in the small.

At a corner in the loading surface, path independence is limited or entirely absent. The normality condition gives bounds on the direction of the plastic increment of displacement or strain.

Once normality is established for a loading surface with a continuously turning tangent, by making the assumption of path independence in the small, convexity follows from stability in the small alone. An alternate statement is that for plastic systems in equilibrium, changes in force which are tangent to the limiting surface of zero dissipation will produce positive dissipation (of higher than first order).

In summary then for elastic and plastic bodies under isothermal conditions, it appears that the postulate of stability in the large plus path independence of elastic behavior are the macroscopic equivalent of (A,C,E) of the microscopic approach. The stability postulate includes thermodynamic stability but is a stronger requirement.

LINEAR VISCOUS BODY.

Application of the stability postulate to a linear viscous body under isothermal conditions reinforces this conclusion. Consider the initial state to be the equilibrium state of zero applied force. The external agency then adds P_i and produces $\dot{u}_k$. The stability postulate requires

$$P_k \dot{u}_k > 0 \tag{21}$$

for non-zero P_i. This requirement is simply the positive definiteness of entropy production (2) or the second law of thermodynamics.

If the initial state is a steady state $\dot{u}_k^0$ produced by P_i^0, Figure 1, the effect of the addition of force increments δP_i by the external agency is the set of velocity increments $\delta \dot{u}_k$. The stability postulate requires

$$\delta P_k \delta \dot{u}_k > 0 \tag{22}$$

without restriction of the δP_i to changes in force which do not alter the entropy production to first order (D). Conceptually. there is this real difference between the quantities dealt with in the stability postulate and those at the basis (D) of Onsager's relations. Because of linearity, however, (22) and (21) are equivalent. Restricting δP_i to those changes ΔP_i which do not alter entropy production to first order leads to a form of the same appearance as (22)

$$\Delta P_k \Delta \dot{u}_k > 0 \tag{23}$$

As shown in Figure 1, ΔP_i lies in the surface of constant rate of dissipation. Just as δP_i traces out an ellipse in two dimensions, the tip of ΔP_i would trace out an ellipse in a three-dimensional space, $i = 1, 2, 3$, as the tip of δP_i traces out an ellipsoid.

The normality condition, or Onsager's reciprocal relations which are the equivalent, is not derivable from the stability postulate. Antisymmetic terms can be present; $L_{ki} - L_{ik}$ is not necessaily zero, Figure 2. Although gyroscopic, Coriolis, and Lorentz type forces will give rise to the antisymmetry of L_{ki}, it is by no means obvious that the absence of such forces requires symmetry. On the other hand, the condition (E), that the decay of macroscopic and of microscopic fluctuations on the average are the same, may be as sweeping an assumption.

Path independence was seen to be associated with normality for elastic and for plastic bodies. In a purely viscous body, the velocity everywhere is given by the current value of the forces independently of their history. However, the path independence required for normality is greater than the lack of influence of the history of loading. The existence of the mathematical equivalent of the strain energy (11) and the complement of the strain energy (12) for linear elastic response would be sufficient for the viscous body

$$\Omega = \int_0^{\dot{u}_k} P_k d\dot{u}_k = \Omega(\dot{u}_k) \tag{24}$$

and

$$\Lambda = \int_0^{P_i} \dot{u}_i dP_i = \Lambda(P_i) \tag{25}$$

One implies the other but neither seems obvious on gounds other than the validity of the completely equivalent reciprocal relations. Judging from the plastic body example, replacement of P_i, $\dot{u}_k$ by infinitesimal external agency quantities ΔP_i, $\Delta \dot{u}_k$ or δP_i, $\delta \dot{u}_k$ may be more reasonable physically.

$$\omega = \int_0^{\delta \dot{u}_k} \delta P_k d(\delta \dot{u}_k) = \omega(\delta \dot{u}_k) \tag{26}$$

$$\lambda = \int_0^{\delta P_i} \delta \dot{u}_i d(\delta P_i) = \lambda (\delta P_i) \tag{27}$$

but there is no mathematical difference for a linear viscous body.

A possible way out of the difficulty is to avoid microscopic considerations and to start by a definition as for perfectly elastic bodies. A viscous body could be defined as one which obeys (24) and (25) or (26) and (27) in the absence of gyroscopic type forces. For the linear viscous body

$$\Omega = \Lambda = \dot{D}/2 \qquad (28)$$

The normality of $\dot{u}_k$

$$\dot{u}_k = \partial\Lambda/\partial P_k \qquad (29)$$

and of P_i

$$P_i = \partial\Omega/\partial\dot{u}_i \qquad (30)$$

holds as in Figure 1. Convexity of $\dot{D} = $ constant follows from the convexity of Λ and of Ω.

4. Non-linear viscous behavior.

With these rather lengthy preliminary comments, the central problems of the non-linear time-dependent response of material systems become a little clearer. Non-linear viscous behavior

$$\dot{u}_k = \dot{u}_k(P_i) \qquad (31)$$

and its inverse

$$P_i = P_i(\dot{u}_k) \qquad (32)$$

will be examined by itself. This is in accord with the concept that the behavior of real materials can be built up of a combination of the behavior of suitable components treated as real materials in their own right.

Among the questions which arise are those concerning the existence and meaning of normality and convexity conditions, the significant surfaces in force and velocity space, the role of path independence, and the applicability or extension of Onsager's reciprocal relations and the considerations which underlie them.

The rate of dissipation, or the rate of entropy production, appears to occupy a key position in irreversible thermodynamics. From (31) and (32) it may be expressed as a function of P_i or $\dot{u}_k$ alone

$$\dot{D} = P_k\dot{u}_k = \phi(P_i) = \psi(\dot{u}_k) > 0 \qquad (33)$$

Suppose a normality condition holds for surfaces of constant ϕ in force space and, therefore, also in stress space when the state of stress and strain is homogeneous.

$$\dot{u}_k = \beta \frac{\partial \phi}{\partial P_k} = \frac{\phi}{P_m \dfrac{\partial \phi}{\partial P_m}} \frac{\partial \phi}{\partial P_k} \quad . \tag{34}$$

$$\dot{\varepsilon}_{ij} = \beta \frac{\partial \phi}{\partial \sigma_{ij}} = \frac{\phi}{\sigma_{mn} \dfrac{\partial \phi}{\partial \sigma_{mn}}} \frac{\partial \phi}{\partial \sigma_{ij}} \tag{35}$$

The corresponding normality condition in velocity or strain rate space is

$$P_i = \gamma \frac{\partial \psi}{\partial \dot{u}_i} = \frac{\psi}{\dot{u}_m \dfrac{\partial \psi}{\partial \dot{u}_m}} \frac{\partial \psi}{\partial \dot{u}_i} \tag{36}$$

$$\sigma_{ij} = \gamma \frac{\partial \psi}{\partial \dot{\varepsilon}_{ij}} = \frac{\psi}{\dot{\varepsilon}_{mn} \dfrac{\partial \psi}{\partial \dot{\varepsilon}_{mn}}} \frac{\partial \psi}{\partial \dot{\varepsilon}_{ij}} \tag{37}$$

Normality (34–37) based on surfaces of constant rate of entropy production will soon be seen to be ill-founded speculation in general. However, carrying the argument through in logical sequence, despite the non-linearity, Onsager's relations might be supposed to have relevance because considerations (A) and (E) are satisfied. A constant set of forces produces a constant set of velocities or a steady state. The effect of disturbances from this steady state are given by the differential forms of (31) and (32)

$$d\dot{u}_k = \frac{\partial \dot{u}_k}{\partial P_i} dP_i = L_{ki} dP_i \tag{38}$$

and

$$dP_i = \frac{\partial P}{\partial \dot{u}_k} d\dot{u}_k = L_{ik}^{-1} d\dot{u}_k \tag{39}$$

If reciprocal relations hold for all dP_i in these linear forms, then β and γ in (34–37) must be constants. Therefore ϕ must be homogeneous in P_i or σ_{ij}

and ψ must be homogeneous in $\dot{u}_k$ or $\dot{\varepsilon}_{mn}$ under these conditions. In one dimension, this result is the simple power term expression

$$\dot{u} = bP^n \text{ or } \dot{\varepsilon} = b\sigma^n \tag{40}$$

Such forms are permissible but far more restrictive than necessary.

Ziegler [9] emphasizes the restriction of simple reciprocity, of the form $L_{ki} = L_{ik}$, to linear irreversible thermodynamics. In "An Attempt to Generalize Onsager's Principle" he suggests that the fundamental consideration (E) relating microscopic to macroscopic fluctuations may have a simple macroscopic significance. This, he proposes, is that infinitesimal fluctuations $\Delta \dot{u}_k$ can occur, along the surface of constant rate of dissipation in velocity space, while P_i is constant. The immediate result is the normality form (36) without restriction on the relation between force and velocity. Correspondingly, if infinitesimal fluctuations in force, along the surface of constant rate of dissipation in force space, can occur at constant $\dot{u}_k$, the result is the normality form (34) without restriction on (31, 32). Unfortunately, a searching evaluation of these apperently reasonable suppositions on the macroscopic scale is about as difficult as evaluation of the hypotheses on the microscopic scale leading to Onsager's relations. However, a counter-example can be given to show that (34–37) are basically improper forms in general.

5.   Irrelevance of surface of constant rate of entropy production.

An elementary example of a purely viscous system demonstrates that, in general, the velocity vector is not normal to the surface of constant rate of entropy production in force space, and the force vector is not normal to this surface in velocity space. Consider a series combination of two non-linear purely viscous elements of the simplest type, ϕ homogeneous in P_i for each. Suppose ϕ_1 is homogeneous of degree n_1, and ϕ_2 is homogeneous of degree n_2. The series combination is purely viscous but the rate of entropy production

$$\phi = \phi_1 + \phi_2 \tag{41}$$

is not homogeneous in P_i. The resulting velocity is the sum of the contributions from each element

$$\dot{u}_k = \beta_1 \frac{\partial \phi_1}{\partial P_k} + \beta_2 \frac{\partial \phi_2}{\partial P_k} = \frac{1}{n_1} \frac{\partial \phi_1}{\partial P_k} + \frac{1}{n_2} \frac{\partial \phi_2}{\partial P_k} \qquad (42)$$

Therefore

$$\dot{u}_k \neq (\text{constant}) \frac{\partial \phi}{\partial P_k} \qquad (43)$$

unless $n_1 = n_2$, or $\partial \phi_1 / \partial P_k = \partial \phi_2 / \partial P_k$.

The surface for normality will not coincide with the individual surfaces, nor with the composite surface of constant rate of entropy production, except at special points, provided the functional forms ϕ_1 and ϕ_2 are essentially different, as illustrated in Figure 6, and their degree of homogeneity is dif-

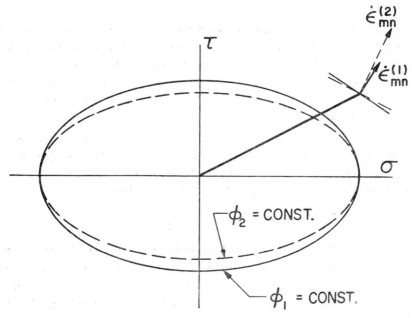

Figure 6

Series combination of two non-linear purely viscous elements, one of Mises form $\varphi_1 = \sigma_1 \dot{\varepsilon}_1 (\sigma^2 + 3\tau^2)/\sigma_1^2$ and the other of Tresca form $\varphi_2 = \sigma_2 \dot{\varepsilon}_2 (\sigma^2 + 4\tau^2)^2/\sigma_2^4$ demonstrates that the surface of constant rate of entropy production $\varphi_1 + \varphi_2$ is irrelevant.

The resultant $\dot{\varepsilon}$ is normal to $\varphi_1/2 + \varphi_1/4$, not to $\varphi_1 + \varphi_2$. Normals coincide along σ axis and τ axis

ferent as well. For definiteness, Figure 6 depicts the familiar stress space of coordinates σ for normal stress and τ for shear stress; ϕ_1 is a Mises type of locus with $n_1 = 2$, and ϕ_2 is a Tresca type of locus with $n_2 = 4$. In this two-dimensional representation,

$$\phi_1 = \sigma_1 \dot{\varepsilon}_1 (\sigma^2 + 3\tau^2)/\sigma_1^2 \tag{44}$$

$$\phi_2 = \sigma_2 \dot{\varepsilon}_2 (\sigma^2 + 4\tau^2)^2/\sigma_2^4 \tag{45}$$

where $\dot{\varepsilon}_1, \sigma_1$ and $\dot{\varepsilon}_2, \sigma_2$ are constants. The surface for which normality holds is a weighted average of ϕ_1 and ϕ_2,

$$\phi_1/n_1 + \phi_2/n_2 = \text{constant} \tag{46}$$

as may be seen from (42).

When σ acts by itself, or τ acts alone, all three sets of surfaces have a common normal. This is a consequence of the assumption of isotropy implicit in (44) and (45). Much of the reasoning in the development of thermodynamic theory is based on scalar quantities or on one component of vector or tensor fields. The preceding discussion shows that, unless care is taken, a blurring of fundamental distinctions may result.

The irrelevance of the surface of constant rate of entropy production in velocity space may be demonstrated with equal ease. The simplest direct illustration is provided by the parallel combination of two elements, ψ_1 homogeneous of degree n_1 in $\dot{u}_k$ and ψ_2 homogeneous of degree n_2 in $\dot{u}_k$.

6. Path independence, normality, and convexity in a non-linear viscous system.

The demonstration of the lack of fundamental connection between normality and the surface of constant rate of entropy production does not indicate a satisfactory alternate approach. Perhaps a postulate or definition of path independence is the proper starting point for non-linear viscosity as it is for non-linear elasticity.

Complete path independence of $\Omega(\dot{u}_k)$ defined by (24) implies complete path independence of $\Lambda(P_i)$ defined by (25), and vice versa, for non-linear as well as linear systems of purely viscous nature (31, 32). The normality relations (29, 30) are a necessary consequence.

Convexity of Ω in velocity space and of Λ in force space then follows from the concept of stability, just as in Figure 1. The very important difference from the linear viscous system is that, in general, neither surface is one of constant rate of dissipation.

Complete path independence in the small, as defined by (26) or (27), leads to exactly the same normality relations (29, 30). A limitation on the local paths in force space, restricting them to lie in the surface $\beta =$ constant in the immediate vicinity of the point representing the applied forces, gives the more general normality form

$$\dot{u}_k = \beta \frac{\partial \Phi}{\partial P_k} \tag{47}$$

which resembles (34). However, β may be any function of P_i and Φ is not $\dot{D}$. Again, convexity of Φ follows from the stability postulate.

Similarly, limited path independence in velocity space leads to

$$P_i = \gamma \frac{\partial \Psi}{\partial \dot{u}_i} . \tag{48}$$

where γ and Ψ may be independent functions of $\dot{u}_k$. One connection between (47) and (48) is through the rate of dissipation

$$\dot{D} = \beta P_k \frac{\partial \Phi}{\partial P_k} = \gamma \dot{u}_i \frac{\partial \Psi}{\partial \dot{u}_i} \tag{49}$$

Local coincidence of the surfaces of constant $\dot{D}$, β, and γ has some physical appeal, because of the use of path independence. However, the independence does not involve the energy dissipation itself. So strong a restriction on β or γ, and consequently on Φ or Ψ as well, therefore is not reasonable.

7. Concluding remarks.

The series or parallel combination of non-linear purely viscous elements in a steady state configuration demonstrates the lack of relevance, in general, of the surface of constant rate of entropy production in force (stress) or velocity (strain-rate) space. Clearly, it is an even less valuable guide-post for combinations of elastic, plastic, and viscous elements in a non-stationary state. Second order statements such as $\delta P_k \delta \dot{u}_k > 0$ or $\delta \sigma_{ij} \delta \dot{\varepsilon}_{ij} > 0$ are needed, not first order $\delta (P_k \dot{u}_k) = 0$ or $\delta (\sigma_{ij} \dot{\varepsilon}_{ij}) = 0$.

A proposal advanced in the paper is to base the development of force-displacement-time or stress-strain-time relations for purely elastic, or purely plastic, or purely viscous systems or materials on the postulate of path independence of an appropriate form and on the stability postulate. Path independence leads to a normality relation; stability gives convexity. In the linear viscous case, they overlap the considerations (A through E) which are at the basis of Onsager's reciprocal relations. Path independence includes reversibility and the absence of gyroscopic, Coriolis, or Lorentz type forces. Stability includes thermodynamic stability and the positive definiteness of entropy production.

Great caution is indicated in any attempt to develop generalizations for complex non-linear systems which reduce to Onsager's reciprocal relations for linear irreversible thermodynamics. Also it must be remembered that Onsager's relations themselves rest upon a number of postulates. They are not necessarily laws of nature even for linear systems.

REFERENCES

[1] I. PRIGOGINE, *Étude Thermodynamique des Phenomenes Irreversible*, Desoer, Liège, 1947.

[2] S. R. DEGROOT, *Thermodynamics of Irreversible Processes*, Interscience Publishers, New York, 1952.

[3] M. A. BIOT, Linear Thermodynamics and the Mechanics of Solids, Proceedings Third U.S. National Congress of Applied Mechanics, *ASME*, 1958, pp. 1–18.

[4] D. C. DRUCKER, *Extension of the Stability Postulate with Emphasis on Temperature Changes*, Plasticity, Proceedings Second Symposium on Naval Structural Mechanics, Pergamon Press, London and New York, 1960, pp. 169–184.

[5] D. C. DRUCKER, A Definition of Stable Inelastic Material, *Journal of Applied Mechanics, ASME*, **26,** (1959), pp. 101–106.

[6] D. C. DRUCKER, *A More Fundamental Approach to Stress-Strain Relations*, Proceedings First U.S. National Congress of Applied Mechanics, *ASME*, 1951, pp. 487–491.

[7] D. C. DRUCKER, *Variational Principles in the Mathematical Theory of Plasticity*, Proceedings Symposia in Applied Mathematics VIII (1956), McGraw-Hill Book Co., New York, 1958, pp.7–22.

D. C. DRUCKER, *Plasticity*, Proceedings First Symposium on Naval Structural Mechanics (1958), Pergamon Press, London and New York, 1960, pp. 407–448.

[8] G. H. HANDELMAN, C. C. LIN AND W. PRAGER, On the Mechanical Behavior of Metals in the Strain-Hardening Range, *Quarterly of Applied Mathematics*, **4,** n. 4, 1947, pp. 397–407.

[9] H. ZIEGLER, An Attempt to Generalize Onsager's Principle *ZAMP*, **9b,** (1958), pp. 748–763.

DISCUSSION

H. ZORSKI:

The 'physical' postulates based on elementary considerations are of utmost importance. However, sooner or later mathematical precise definitions and theory must be developed. It seems that in the case of plasticity the same method as for finitely deformed elastic bodies may be used and the concept of strong ellipticity will play a fundamental role. The procedure is general and consists of introducing the Poincaré equations in variations corresponding to the (in general) non-linear system describing the investigated state of stress and strain. It is necessary to examine the relation between the eigenvalues of the linear and non-linear systems; for the case of a compressed bar with large deflections it may be shown that the linear system contains all eigenvalues of the non-linear one but it may contain more of them.

As concerns Prof. Drucker's stability postulate it certainly implies the positive definiteness of the considered operator but it is not clear whether the strong-ellipticity is also implied. If not, the solution of the boundary value problem may be unstable with respect to a small perturbation in boundary conditions.

Moreover, any definition of stability in terms of integrals over the volume is incomplete, since an instability may occur owing to singularities of the coefficients or external agencies. On the other hand the body may be 'locally unstable' but 'stable in the whole'.

Dr. Coleman's remark concerning replacing the condition $A^{ijpq}\alpha_i\alpha_q\beta_j\beta_p > 0$ by the condition $A^{ijpq}\alpha_{iq}\alpha_{jp}$ (α_{iq} is a symmetric tensor) is interesting but the former condition is in a natural way connected with the considered operator, say, $-Lw = A_i{}^{pq}{}_j w^j{}_{,pq}$; in fact introducing the exponential Fourier transform $\bar{w}^i$ of w^i, in the case of constant $A_i{}^{pq}{}_j$ we obtain the energy integral in the form

$$(Lw, w) = \int\int_{-\infty}^{\infty}\int A_i{}^{pq}{}_j\,\bar{w}_i^i\bar{w}^j\beta_p\beta_q d_\beta$$

PROF. DRUCKER'S REPLY:

Dr. Zorski's contribution is very welcome because it does bring out clearly the difference between stability of a system and stability of the material of which the system is composed. My postulate, expressed in words, is one of stability in general. However it is not permissible to require systems to be stable under all loadings while there is every reason to specify stable material in most practical situations. It would be extremely interesting to see just how Dr. Zorski's condition of strong ellipticity differs, if at all, from the postulate of stability applied to systems as a whole. Caution must be exercised in treating the locally as well as globally non-conservative problems of plasticity in a manner analogous to problems of elasticity. This difficulty is touched upon in my closing survey in this volume at the end of part II, Plasticity and in the reference 'The Role of Experiment in the Development of Theory', Proceedings of the Fourth U. S. National Congress of Applied Mechanics, ASME, June 1962.

ON THE STATIONARITY OF STRESS
AND STRAIN DISTRIBUTIONS IN CREEP

JAN HULT

Chalmers University of Technology, Gothenburg, Sweden

ABSTRACT

A definition of stationarity of a tensor is adopted, which refers to the ratio between its components. The conditions for stationarity of stress and strain in a body subject to creep are then investigated. It is concluded, that a mechanical equation of state will predict stationary stress and strain fields if and only if it possesses a certain simple form.

1. Introduction.

In studies on creep in structures the term stationary is almost invariably used to designate a state of constant rate of creep strain. Occasionally the term refers to the state of stress, which is then said to be stationary, if it does not change during the creep process. In this paper the latter sense of the word will be adopted and also expanded, cf. Prager [1].

The occurrence of stationary states of stress and strain implies a great simplification in the analysis of structures subject to creep, and it should be of interest, therefore, to study the circumstances under which such states are possible. In particular this study deals with the connection between the stationarity and the creep law on which the analysis is based.

2. General considerations.

Consider a body, loaded by surface forces and subject to creep. The location of a point within the body is defined by the coordinates x_1, x_2, and x_3 or, for short, x_k. The states of stress and strain are defined by the respective tensors, the components of which are generally functions of both the location within the body and the time; $\sigma_{ij} = \sigma_{ij}(x_k, t)$, $\varepsilon_{ij} = \varepsilon_{ij}(x_k, t)$.

DEFINITION: A tensor $a_{ij}(x_k, t)$ is *stationary*, if it can be written as

$$a_{ij}(x_k, t) = X_{ij}(x_k) \cdot T(t) . \tag{1}$$

If a tensor possesses this property, the following relations hold for the ratio between any two of its components

$$\frac{\partial}{\partial t} \left[\frac{a_{\alpha\beta}(x'_k, t)}{a_{\alpha\beta}(x''_k, t)} \right] = 0 \ . \tag{2}$$

$$\frac{\partial}{\partial x_l} \left[\frac{a_{\alpha\beta}(x_k, t')}{a_{\alpha\beta}(x_k, t'')} \right] = 0 \ ; \qquad l = 1, 2, 3 \tag{3}$$

Here x'_k and x''_k denote any two points in the body and t' and t'' denote any two instances.

These relations, which follow immediately from eq. (1), may be used as alternative definitions of the stationarity of a tensor.

A stationary stress tensor may be written as

$$\sigma_{ij}(x_k, t) = \sigma^0_{ij}(x_k) \cdot S(t) \tag{4}$$

where $\sigma^0_{ij}(x_k)$ denotes the stress tensor at the instant $t = 0$, and $S(t)$ is a dimensionless scalar time function, normalized in the sense $S(0) = 1$. Let $L_i(\bar{x}_k, t)$ denote the applied load vector in the surface point $\bar{x}_k$. From the boundary condition

$$\sigma_{ij}(\bar{x}_k, t) \cdot n_j(\bar{x}_k) = L_i(\bar{x}_k, t)$$

where $n_j(\bar{x}_k)$ is the surface normal unit vector in the point $\bar{x}_k$, then follows that a stationary stress field may arise only if the load is also stationary in the sense

$$L_i(\bar{x}_k, t) = L^0_i(\bar{x}_k) \cdot S(t) \ . \tag{5}$$

Given a load variation of this nature, we shall speak of *complete stationarity*, if stationary stress and strain fields arise for any time function $S(t)$. If stationary fields result only when $S(t) \equiv \text{constant} = 1$, we shall speak of *incomplete stationarity*.

CORROLARY: The conditions for incomplete stationarity are contained in the conditions for complete stationarity.

3. Basic equations.

The body is assumed to be subject to creep according to the mechanical equation of state

$$\frac{d\varepsilon_c}{dt} = \frac{F(\sigma)}{G(\varepsilon_c)} \ .$$

Here ε_c denotes the creep strain. If, however, the elastic strain is small compared with the creep strain, ε_c may be replaced by the total strain ε

$$\frac{d\varepsilon}{dt} = \frac{F(\sigma)}{G(\varepsilon)} \ . \tag{6}$$

Introducing the function

$$H(\varepsilon) = \int_0^\varepsilon G(s)ds \tag{7}$$

the creep law (6) may alternatively be written as

$$\frac{d}{dt} H(\varepsilon) = F(\sigma) \tag{8}$$

where

$$H(0) = 0 \ . \tag{9}$$

In general this creep law does not predict stationary stress and strain fields in the sense defined above. For certain classes of functions $H(\varepsilon)$ and $F(\sigma)$ however, stationary fields do result. This matter will be discussed below for the cases of a simple truss, a beam subject to bending, and a general three-dimensional body. The analysis will be limited to small strains only, i.e. $\sigma/E \ll \varepsilon \ll 1$.

The following theorems can readily be proven and will be referred to several times below:

THEOREM I: *The identity* $f(x \cdot y) \equiv g(x) \cdot h(y)$ *holds if and only if f is a simple power function* $f(z) = a \cdot z^v$.

THEOREM II: *The identity* $f^{-1}(x \cdot y) \equiv g(x) \cdot h(y)$ *holds if and only if f is a simple power function* $f(z) = a \cdot z^v$.

4. Simple truss.

The plane symmetrical truss shown by Figure 1 is loaded by a force $P(t)$. If the stress in the vertical bar is denoted σ_1 and that in the inclined bars σ_2 there results the one equilibrium equation

$$\sigma_1 + \sqrt{2} \cdot \sigma_2 = \frac{P(t)}{A} \tag{10}$$

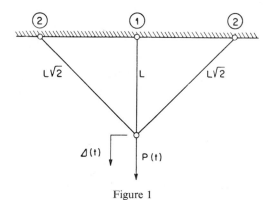

Figure 1

where A is the cross sectional area of the bars. The required additional relation between the stresses is obtained from the creep law. With

$$\varepsilon_1 = \frac{\Delta(t)}{L}, \qquad \varepsilon_2 = \frac{\Delta(t)}{2L} \tag{11), (12}$$

where $\Delta(t)$ is the elongation of the vertical bar, there results in view of eq. (6)

$$R = \frac{F(\sigma_1)}{F(\sigma_2)} = \frac{G(\varepsilon_1) \cdot \dfrac{d\varepsilon_1}{dt}}{G(\varepsilon_2) \cdot \dfrac{d\varepsilon_2}{dt}} = \frac{2 \cdot G \left[\dfrac{\Delta(t)}{L} \right]}{G \left[\dfrac{\Delta(t)}{2L} \right]} \cdot \tag{13}$$

From eqs. (11), (12) follows that the state of strain in the truss is stationary irrespective of the creep law. The state of stress, however, will in general not be stationary, since eq. (13) does not satisfy eq. (2) for an arbitrary form of the function $G(\varepsilon)$.

From Theorem I, however, follows that the ratio R is independent of time if and only if G is a simple power function

$$G(\varepsilon) = B \cdot \varepsilon^m \tag{14}$$

where B and m are constants.

The ratio R then takes the form

$$R = \frac{F(\sigma_1)}{F(\sigma_2)} = 2^{m+1} \ . \tag{15}$$

The stresses now follow from eqs. (10) and (15). If, in particular, $P(t)$ is a constant, the stresses will then also be constant. Hence the state of stress is incompletely stationary if and only if G is a simple power function. From eq. (7) follows that H must then also be a simple power function

$$H(\varepsilon) = \frac{B}{m+1} \varepsilon^{m+1} = C \cdot \varepsilon^\mu \tag{16}$$

where C and μ are constants.

Complete stationarity by eq. (2) implies that the ratio σ_1/σ_2 must be independent of time for any load variation $P(t)$ i.e.,

$$\sigma_1 = \lambda \cdot \sigma_2$$

where λ is a constant. From eq. (15) then follows the condition for complete stationarity

$$\frac{F(\lambda \sigma_2)}{F(\sigma_2)} = 2^{m+1} \ .$$

From Theorem I follows that this holds for any σ_2 if and only if F is a simple power function

$$F(\sigma) = D \cdot \sigma^n \tag{17}$$

where D and n are constants.

Hence for this particular truss incomplete stationarity of stress and strain is obtained if and only if $H(\varepsilon)$ is a simple power function, whereas complete stationarity is obtained if and only if, in addition, $F(\sigma)$ is a simple power function.

It is of interest to note that both the well-known secondary creep law attributed to Norton [2]

$$\frac{d\varepsilon}{dt} = k \cdot \sigma^n \tag{18}$$

and that for primary creep proposed by Nadai [3]

$$\frac{d\varepsilon}{dt} = K \cdot \frac{\sigma^n}{\varepsilon^m}$$

belong to this latter category. The secondary creep laws suggested by Soderberg [4]

$$\frac{d\varepsilon}{dt} = k_1 (e^{\frac{\sigma}{\sigma_1}} - 1)$$

and by Prandtl [5] and Nadai [3]

$$\frac{d\varepsilon}{dt} = k_2 \sinh \frac{\sigma}{\sigma_2}$$

however both imply only incomplete stationarity of the stress distribution.

This indicates a significant difference between the Norton creep law (18) on the one hand and the various other secondary creep laws on the other. This difference, which appears to have been unobserved so far, clearly emphasizes the advantage of using the Norton creep law in problems which concern time dependent loading. It also indicates a possibility to check experimentally which of the two classes of secondary creep laws that gives the best description of creep caused by time dependent loading.

5. Beam subject to bending.

Consider a straight beam with monosymmetrical cross section. If a bending moment $M(t)$ is applied perpendicularly to the symmetry plane, the beam will deform into the shape of a circular arc, cf. Figure 2.

Stationarity of the resulting stress distribution by definition implies that it can be written as

$$\sigma(z, t) = \phi(z) \cdot M(t) . \tag{19}$$

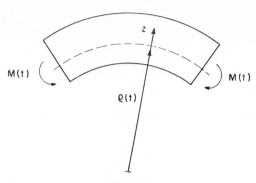

Figure 2

Here z is the transverse coordinate within the beam, referred to some arbitrarily chosen beam fibre. For simplicity the origin of z is chosen such that $\phi(0) = 0$, i.e. the origin falls on the neutral surface.

If the radius of curvature of the neutral surface is denoted $\rho(t)$, the strain at an arbitrary point equals

$$\varepsilon(z, t) = \frac{z}{\rho(t)} = z \cdot \kappa(t) \tag{20}$$

where $\kappa(t)$ denotes the curvature of the neutral surface. Hence in case of pure bending of a beam, the state of strain is stationary independent of the creep law.

Insertion into eq. (8) yields the stress distribution

$$\sigma(z, t) = F^{-1} \left\{ \frac{\partial}{\partial t} H[z \cdot \kappa(t)] \right\}. \tag{21}$$

Incomplete stationarity of the stress field implies that σ is a function of z alone. i.e.

$$\frac{\partial}{\partial t} H[z \cdot \kappa(t)] = \psi(z)$$

whence, considering eq. (9)

$$H[z \cdot \kappa(t)] = \psi(z) \cdot t .$$

By Theorem I this is fulfilled for any z and t if and only if H is a simple power function, cf. eq. (16).

The conditions for complete stationarity may now be investigated. First H must be a simple power function

$$H(\varepsilon) = C \cdot \varepsilon^{\mu} . \tag{16}$$

From eq. (21) then follows the stress distribution

$$\sigma(z, t) = F^{-1} \left[C z^{\mu} \cdot \frac{d}{dt} \kappa^{\mu}(t) \right] .$$

Complete stationarity of the stress field implies that this stress distribution can be written in the form of eq. (19) for any arbitrary curvature variation $\kappa(t)$. By virtue of Theorem II this requires that F be a simple power function, cf. eq. (17).

Hence the conditions for incomplete and complete stationarity are identical with those obtained for the simple truss. This result suggests that the conditions might apply also to an arbitrary structure, which will now be examined.

6. General structure.

In tensorial notation the generalized creep law based on eq. (6) is written as, cf. Odqvist [6]

$$\frac{\partial \varepsilon_{ij}(x_k, t)}{\partial t} = \frac{F[\sigma_e(x_k, t)]}{G[\varepsilon_e(x_k, t)]} \cdot \frac{3}{2} \cdot \frac{s_{ij}(x_k, t)}{\sigma_e(x_k, t)} \tag{22}$$

where the stress deviation tensor s_{ij}, the effective stress σ_e, and the effective strain ε_e are defined by

$$s_{ij} = \sigma_{ij} - \frac{1}{3} \sigma_{kk} \delta_{ij} \tag{23}$$

$$\sigma_e = \left(\frac{3}{2} s_{ij} s_{ij} \right)^{\frac{1}{2}} \tag{24}$$

$$\varepsilon_e = \left(\frac{2}{3} \varepsilon_{ij} \varepsilon_{ij} \right)^{\frac{1}{2}} \tag{25}$$

The stress and strain distributions are now assumed to be stationary:

$$\begin{cases} \sigma_{ij}(x_k, t) = \sigma_{ij}^0(x_k) \cdot S(t) & (4) \\ S(0) = 1 & (26) \end{cases}$$

and

$$\begin{cases} \varepsilon_{ij}(x_k, t) = \varepsilon_{ij}^*(x_k) \cdot E(t) & (27) \\ E(0) = 0 \quad . & (28) \end{cases}$$

Here the stress tensor $\sigma_{ij}^0(x_k)$ must satisfy the general equilibrium equations, and the strain tensor $\varepsilon_{ij}^*(x_k)$ must satisfy the general compatibility equations.

From eq:s (24), (25) then follows

$$\sigma_e(x_k, t) = \sigma_e^0(x_k) \cdot S(t) \tag{29}$$

$$\varepsilon_e(x_k, t) = \varepsilon_e^*(x_k) \cdot E(t) \tag{30}$$

and eq. (22) can be written as

$$\varepsilon_e^*(x_k) \cdot \frac{dE(t)}{dt} = \frac{F[\sigma_e^0(x_k) \cdot S(t)]}{G[\varepsilon_e^*(x_k) \cdot E(t)]} \tag{31}$$

or, considering eq. (7)

$$\frac{\partial}{\partial t} H[\varepsilon_e^*(x_k) \cdot E(t)] = F[\sigma_e^0(x_k) \cdot S(t)] . \tag{32}$$

7. Incomplete stationarity.

With

$$S(t) = 1$$

eq. (32) yields, considering the initial condition (28) and eq. (9)

$$H[\varepsilon_e^*(x_k) \cdot E(t)] = F[\sigma_e^0(x_k)] \cdot t .$$

By virtue of Theorem I this requires H to be a simple power function

$$H(\varepsilon) = C\varepsilon^\mu . \tag{16}$$

Complete stationarity.

Assuming eq. (16) to hold, eq. (32) takes the form

$$C\varepsilon_e^{*\mu}(x_k) \frac{d}{dt} E^\mu(t) = F\left[\sigma_e^0(x_k) \cdot S(t)\right] .$$

By virtue of Theorem I this requires F to be a simple power function

$$F(\sigma) = D\sigma^n . \tag{17}$$

Hence the general character of the results obtained with the truss and the beam has been established.

Finally a remark should be made on the ensuing stationary state. Insertion of the stationarity conditions (16) and (17) into eq. (32) shows that the creep law

$$\frac{d\varepsilon}{dt} = K\frac{\sigma^n}{\varepsilon^m}$$

gives rise to a state of strain governed by the scalar relation

$$\varepsilon_e(x_k, t) = \left[(m+1)K\right]^{\frac{1}{m+1}} \cdot \sigma_e^{0\,\frac{n}{m+1}}(x_k) \cdot \left[\int_0^t S^n(s)\,ds\right]^{\frac{1}{m+1}}$$

in addition to the tensorial relation expressing coaxiality of the stress deviation and strain tensors. This extension of the elastic analog for creep to the case of strain hardening and time dependent loading has previously been noted by Hoff[7].

REFERENCES

[1] W. PRAGER, Total Creep under Varying Loads, *J. Aer. Sci.*, **24**, (1957), 153–155.

[2] F. H. NORTON, *Creep of Steel at High Temperatures*, Mc Graw-Hill Book Co., New York (1929).

[3] A. NADAI, *The influence of Time upon Creep. The Hyperbolic Sine Creep Law.* Timoshenko Anniversary Volume, Macmillan Co., New York, (1938).

[4] C. R. SODERBERG, The interpretation of creep tests for machine design, *Trans. ASME*, **58**, (1936), 733.

[5] L. PRANDTL, Ein Gedankenmodell zu kinetischen Theorie der festen Körper, *Zeits. angew. Math. u. Mech.*, **8**, (1928), 85–106.

[6] F. K. G. ODQVIST, *Engineering Theories of Metallic Creep*, Symposium su la Plasticità nella Scienza delle Costruzioni, Varenna ,(1956).

[7] N. J. HOFF, Ed., Stress Distribution in the Presence of Creep, Chap. 12 of *High Temperature Effects in Aircraft Structures*, Pergamon Press, London, (1958).

SOME PROBLEMS OF NON-LINEAR RHEOLOGY

ZDENĚK SOBOTKA

Czechoslovak Academy of Sciences, Prague, Czechoslovakia

ABSTRACT

The non-linear deformation of various bodies is treated from the rheological point of view. Author derives first the laws of long-time deformation of conctete using the variable rheological parameters. Further, after developing the general rheological relationships by means of tensor analysis, the formulae are established which represent the simple second-order effects as well as the combined higher-order phenomena depending on products of two different rheological variables.

1. Introduction.

The present paper deals with different kinds of the non-linear bodies treated from the rheological point of view. Particular attention will be given to the relationships between the non-linearity and second-order phenomena.

It may be shown that the same case of non-linearity may be represented by different rheological models and by different combinations of the rheological elements.

The rheological analysis of the non-linear bodies may be performed in several different ways.

The first approach applies the usual rheological elements with the variable rheological parameters. The non-linearity arising from the finite deformation may be suitably analyzed using the Hencky measure of strain.

Another approach may be effected by the use of the non-linear rheological elements and by the linear coupling thereof in the same manner as in Reiner's linear rheological system. The non-linear rheological functions may be expressed by means of the power-series development. The absolutely convergent infinite power series representing the general rheological relationships may be replaced by the closed formulae containing the products of the scalar functions of principal invariants and of the principal tensors.

The most general method of the rheological analysis consists in non-linear coupling of the non-linear rheological elements. The rheological relationships for this case are given in terms containing the functions of mixed invariants of two tensors. Besides the interpretation of the usual second-order phenomena, the analysis of combined second-order and third-order effects depend-ng on products of two different rheological variables will be given using that general method.

2. The bodies with variable rheological parameters.

The simplest approach to the rheological analysis of the non-linear bodies may be effected by the use of standard linear rheological models with variable parameters.

As an example of such an approach, the simplified analysis of the long-time deformation of concrete will be derived. The author has proposed for concrete the rheological model shown in Figure 1 with the structural formula

$$C = H - (N/StV) - (H/N/StV) = B - (K/StV) \qquad (2.1)$$

where H = Hooke solid,
N = Newton liquid,
StV = Saint-Venant body,
B = Bingham body and
K = Kelvin solid.

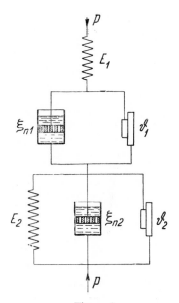

Figure 1
A rheological model for concrete

The different yield stresses of two Saint-Venant elements follow the inequality

$$\vartheta_1 > \vartheta_2. \tag{2.2}$$

If the stress acting on the body is greater then both yield stresses, the C-body becomes the Burgers body with the structural formula

$$Bu = H - N - (H/N) = M - K, \tag{2.3}$$

$M = H - N$ denoting the Maxwell liquid.

If the rheological parameters, i.e. both Young's moduli E_1 and E_2, the coefficients of normal viscosity ξ_{n1} and ξ_{n2}, and the yield stresses ϑ_1 and ϑ_2, are constant, and the stress s does not vary with time, the strain is given by the following equation

$$\varepsilon = \frac{s}{E_1} + \frac{s - \vartheta_1}{\xi_{n1}} t + \frac{s - \vartheta_2}{E_2}(1 - e^{-E_2 t/\xi_{n2}}) + \varepsilon_0 e^{-E_2 t/\xi_{n2}}, \tag{2.4}$$

where ε_0 is the initial strain of the complex $H/N/StV$.

In order to express the non-linear properties of concrete, the author has introduced, according to the generalized Reiner's procedure, the coefficients of viscosity variable with time, which for compression are given by:

$$\xi_{n1} = \xi_{n0} \frac{1 + W}{1 + \bar{W}}(1 + 2.5 m)(1 - m^5) \; \frac{10c(3k - 2m)}{k} \cdot \frac{2\psi + 1}{3(3 - 2\psi)} \cdot$$
$$\cdot (\alpha_0 + \alpha_1 t + \alpha_2 \sqrt{t}), \tag{2.5}$$

$$\xi_{n2} = \kappa \xi_{n0} \frac{1 + W}{1 + \bar{W}}(1 + 2.5m)(1 - m^5)\frac{2k - m}{k} \cdot \frac{2\psi + 1}{3(3 - 2\psi)}(1 - e^{-\alpha t}). \tag{2.6}$$

According to the preceding equations, the viscosity of concrete depends on the viscosity ξ_{n0} of the cement paste, on its volume water-cement ratio W on the volume water-cement ratio $\bar{W}$ of the concrete, further on the relative volume m of the sand in the mortar on the relative volume c of cement and that of gravel k in the concrete, on the relative humidity ψ of the surrounding medium and finally on the time t. α_0, α_1, α and κ are constants which depend on the nature and quality of the cement and the aggregates, and on the compacting and curing of the concrete. In the usual conditions of compacting and curing, we have for limestone aggregates $\alpha_0 = 0.5$, $\alpha_1 = 0.029$, $\alpha_2 = 0.13$, and the coefficient of viscosity ξ_{n1} is obtained in kg day/cm².

The non-linearity with respect to the stress and strain may be introduced by replacing the deformation on the left side of Eq. (2.4) by a function which is linearly related to the right side. Then we, have

$$F(\varepsilon) = \frac{s}{E_1} + \frac{s - \vartheta_1}{\xi_{n1}} t + \frac{s - \vartheta_2}{E_2}(1 - e^{-(E_2 t/\xi_{n2})}) + \varepsilon_0 e^{-(E_2 t/\xi_{n2})} \qquad (2.7)$$

In place of the general function on the left side of Eq. (2.7), the use of the power function may be suitable.

The preceding procedure is not exact. Eq. (2.7) is a modification of the linear Eq. (2.4) taking into account the non-linear rheological properties of the concrete and it cannot be regarded as a true rheological equation but only as a semi-empirical formula.

A more exact procedure takes into account the variability of rheological parameters already in the derivation of the rheological equations. A simple form of variable parameters in the rheological model of concrete (Figure 1) may be given as follows

$$E_1 = a_0 - a_1 s - a_2 s^2,$$

$$E_2 = b_0 - b_1 s - b_2 s^2,$$

$$\xi_{n1} = \alpha_0 + \alpha_1 t + \alpha_2 t^2 - \alpha_3 s - \alpha_4 s^2,$$

$$\xi_{n2} = \beta_0 + \beta_1 t + \beta_2 t^2 - \beta_3 s - \beta_4 s^2,$$

$$(2.8)$$

where $a_0, a_1, a_2, b_0, b_1, b_2, \alpha_0, \alpha_1, \alpha_2, ..., \beta_1, \beta_2, ...$ etc. are constant material parameters.

Taking into consideration that the displacements in the C-body are additive, we find for the stress which does not vary with time, by the usual methods, the following expression for the strain rate

$$f = \frac{s - \vartheta_1}{\alpha_0 + \alpha_1 t + a_2 t^2 - \alpha_3 s - \alpha_4 s^2} + \qquad (2.9)$$

$$+ \frac{d}{dt}\left(\frac{s - \vartheta_2}{b_0 - b_1 s - b_2 s^2}\left\{1 - e^{-\frac{2(b_0 - b_1 s - b_2 s^2)\ [\text{arctg } 2\beta_2 t + \beta_1)/\sqrt{K}) - \text{arctg}(\beta_1/\sqrt{K})]}{\sqrt{K}}}\right\} + \right.$$

$$\left. + \varepsilon_0 e^{-\frac{2(b_0 - b_1 s - b_2 s^2)[\text{arctg } 2\beta_2 t + \beta_1/\sqrt{K}) - \text{arctg } \beta_1/\sqrt{K}]}{\sqrt{K}}}\right),$$

where

$$K = 4\beta_2(\beta_0 - \beta_3 s - \beta_4 s^2) - \beta_1^2. \qquad (2.10)$$

Eq. (2.9) is valid for $K > 0$.

For $K < 0$, we obtain

$$f = \frac{s - \vartheta_1}{\alpha_0 + \alpha_1 t + \alpha_2 t^2 - \alpha_3 s - \alpha_4 s^2} +$$

$$+ \frac{d}{dt}\left(\frac{s - \vartheta_2}{b_0 - b_1 s - b_2 s^2}\left\{1 - \left[\frac{(2\beta_2 t + \beta_1 + \sqrt{-K})(\beta_1 - \sqrt{-K})}{(2\beta_2 t + \beta_1 - \sqrt{-K})(\beta_1 + \sqrt{-K})}\right]^{2(b_0 - b_1 s - b_2 s^2)/\sqrt{-K}}\right\} +$$

$$+ \varepsilon_0\left[\frac{(2\beta_2 t + \beta_1 + \sqrt{-K})(\beta_1 - \sqrt{-K})}{(2\beta_2 t + \beta_1 - \sqrt{-K})(\beta_1 + \sqrt{-K})}\right]^{2(b_0 - b_1 s - b_2 s^2)/\sqrt{-K}}\right). \tag{2.11}$$

The term ε_0 in Eqs. (2.9) and (2.11) denotes the initial value of the deformation in the portion K/StV of the rheological model of the C-body.

Integrating Eq. (2.9) or Eq. (2.11), respectively, leads to the following formulae for the long-time deformation under the stress which does not vary with time

$$\varepsilon = \frac{s}{a_0 - a_1 s - a_2 s^2} + \frac{2(s - \vartheta_1)}{\sqrt{D}}\left(\text{arctg}\,\frac{2\alpha_2 t + \alpha_1}{\sqrt{D}} - \text{arctg}\,\frac{\alpha_1}{\sqrt{D}}\right) + \tag{2.12}$$

$$+ \frac{s - \vartheta_2}{b_0 - b_1 s - b_2 s^2}\left[1 - e^{-2\left((b_0 - b_1 s - b_2 s^2)/\sqrt{K}\right)(\text{arctg}(2\beta_2 t + \beta_1)/\sqrt{K} - \text{arctg}\,\beta_1/\sqrt{K})}\right] +$$

$$+ \varepsilon_0 e^{-\left(2(b_0 - b_1 s - b_2 s^2)/\sqrt{K}\right)(\text{arctg}\,2\beta_2 t + \beta_1)/\sqrt{K} - \text{arctg}\,\beta_1/\sqrt{K})},$$

where

$$D = 4\alpha_2(\alpha_0 - \alpha_3 s - \alpha_4 s^2) - \alpha_1^2 \tag{2.13}$$

for $K > 0$, $D > 0$;

$$\varepsilon = \frac{s}{a_0 - a_1 s - a_2 s^2} + \frac{s - \vartheta_1}{\sqrt{-D}}\ln\frac{(2\alpha_2 t + \alpha_1 - \sqrt{-D})(\alpha_1 + \sqrt{-D})}{(2\alpha_2 t + \alpha_1 + \sqrt{-D})(\alpha_1 - \sqrt{-D})} + \tag{2.14}$$

$$+ \frac{s - \vartheta_2}{b_0 - b_1 s - b_2 s^2}\left[1 - e^{-2\left((b_0 - b_1 s - b_2 s^2)/\sqrt{K}\right)(\text{arctg}(2\beta_2 t + \beta_1)/\sqrt{K} - \text{arctg}\,\beta_1/\sqrt{K})}\right] +$$

$$+ \varepsilon_0 e^{-2\left((b_0 - b_1 s - b_2 s^2)/\sqrt{K}\right)(\text{arctg}(2\beta_2 t + \beta_1)/\sqrt{K} - \text{arctg}\,\beta_1/\sqrt{K})}$$

for $K > 0$, $D < 0$;

$$\varepsilon = \frac{s}{a_0 - a_1 s - a_2 s^2} + \frac{2(s - \vartheta_1)}{\sqrt{D}} \left(\text{arctg} \frac{2\alpha_2 t + \alpha_1}{\sqrt{D}} - \text{arctg} \frac{\alpha_1}{\sqrt{D}} \right) +$$

$$+ \frac{s - \vartheta_2}{b_0 - b_1 s - b_2 s^2} \left\{ 1 - \left[\frac{(2\beta_2 t + \beta_1 + \sqrt{-K})(\beta_1 - \sqrt{-K})}{(2\beta_2 t + \beta_1 - \sqrt{-K})(\beta_1 + \sqrt{-K})} \right]^{2(b_0 - b_1 s - b_2 s^2)/\sqrt{-K}} \right\} +$$

$$+ \varepsilon_0 \left[\frac{(2\beta_2 t + \beta_1 + \sqrt{-K})(\beta_1 - \sqrt{-K})}{(2\beta_2 t + \beta_1 - \sqrt{-K})(\beta_1 + \sqrt{-K})} \right]^{2(b_0 - b_1 s - b_2 s^2)]/\sqrt{-K}}$$

for $K < 0$, $D > 0$;

$$\varepsilon = \frac{s}{a_0 - a_1 s - a_2 s^2} + \frac{s - \vartheta_1}{\sqrt{-D}} \ln \frac{(2\alpha_2 t + \alpha_1 - \sqrt{-D})(\alpha_1 + \sqrt{-D})}{(2\alpha_2 t + \alpha_1 + \sqrt{-D})(\alpha_1 - \sqrt{-D})} +$$

$$+ \frac{s - \vartheta_2}{b_0 - b_1 s - b_2 s^2} \left\{ 1 - \left[\frac{(2\beta_2 t + \beta_1 + \sqrt{-K})(\beta_1 - \sqrt{-K})}{(2\beta_2 t + \beta_1 - \sqrt{-K})(\beta_1 + \sqrt{-K})} \right]^{2(b_0 - b_1 s - b_2 s^2)/\sqrt{-K}} \right\} +$$

$$+ \varepsilon_0 \left[\frac{(2\beta_2 t + \beta_1 + \sqrt{-K})(\beta_1 - \sqrt{-K}}{(2\beta_2 t + \beta_1 - \sqrt{-K}((\beta_1 + \sqrt{-K})} \right]^{2(b_0 - b_1 s - b_2 s^2)/\sqrt{-K}} . \tag{2.16}$$

for $K < 0$, $D < 0$.

Neglecting the quadratic terms in Eqs. (2.8) leads to great simplifications, and if the stress does not vary with time, we get the following simple formula for the long-time deformation

$$\varepsilon = \frac{s}{a_0 - a_1 s} + \frac{s - \vartheta_1}{\alpha_1} \ln \frac{(\alpha_0 + \alpha_1 t - \alpha_3 s)}{\alpha_0 - \alpha_3 s} +$$

$$+ \frac{s - \vartheta_2}{b_0 - b_1 s} \left[1 - \left(\frac{\beta_0 + \beta_1 t - \beta_3 s}{\beta_0 - \beta_3 s} \right)^{-(b_0 - b_1 s)/\beta_1} \right] + \tag{2.17}$$

$$+ \varepsilon_0 \left(\frac{\beta_0 + \beta_1 t - \beta_3 s}{\beta_0 - \beta_3 s} \right)^{-(b_0 - b_1 s)/\beta_1}$$

3. The elastoplastic tensorial non-linearity and the second-order effects.

The general non-linear stress-strain relationship

$$s_{ij} = F_{ij}(\varepsilon_{rs}) \tag{3.1}$$

may be, under certain conditions, developed into absolutely convergent power series as follows

$$s_{ij} = A_0 \delta_{ij} + A_1 \varepsilon_{ij} + A_2 \varepsilon_{i\alpha} \varepsilon_{\alpha j} + A_3 \varepsilon_{i\alpha} \varepsilon_{\alpha\beta} \varepsilon_{\beta j} + \ldots, \tag{3.2}$$

where A_0, A_1, A_2, A_3, etc. are scalar coefficients which may depend upon the temperature, time, etc.

The left-hand side of Eq. (3.2) being a symmetrical tensor of the second rank, it follows from the tensorial dimensionality that the absolutely convergent series of the terms on the right-hand side are also the symmetrical tensors of rank two, which may be expressed by the three principal tensors

$$\delta_{ij}, \ \varepsilon_{ij}, \ \varepsilon_{i\alpha} \varepsilon_{\alpha j}$$

and by the functions of the three principal invariants of the strain tensor

$$I_\varepsilon = \delta_{ij} \varepsilon_{ij},$$

$$II_\varepsilon = \varepsilon_{ij} \varepsilon_{ij}, \tag{3.3}$$

$$III_\varepsilon = \varepsilon_{ij} \varepsilon_{j\alpha} \varepsilon_{\alpha i}.$$

Then, we may write, as shown by M. Reiner [9], [10], [14] and W. Prager [8], the following equation

$$s_{ij} = \aleph_0 \delta_{ij} + \aleph_1 \varepsilon_{ij} + \aleph_2 \varepsilon_{i\alpha} \varepsilon_{\alpha j}, \tag{3.4}$$

where $\aleph_0$, $\aleph_1$ and $\aleph_2$ are invariants being the functions of the principal invariants I_ε, II_ε, III_ε given by Eqs. (3.3).

The third term on the right side represents the influence of the elastoplastic second-order effects.

If in the case of the infinitesimal strain, the value of the scalar function $\aleph_2$ is of the same order as those of the functions $\aleph_0$ and $\aleph_1$, the third term on the right side of Eq. (3.4), depending on the product of two strain components, is very small of the second order and may be neglected. Then, Eq. (3.4) became linear in tensors.

If however, the value of $\aleph_2$ is considerably greater then those of $\aleph_0$ and $\aleph_1$, the third term on the right side of Eq. (3.4) may be of the same order as the first two terms, and we obtain Eq. (3.4) which is non-linear in tensors even in the case of the infinitesimal deformation.

When the strain is finite which may be emphasized by replacing ε by e writing

$$s_{ij} = \aleph_0 \, \delta_{ij} + \aleph_1 \, e_{ij} + \aleph_2 \, e_{i\alpha} \, e_{\alpha j}, \tag{3.4a}$$

the second-order effects represented by the third term on the right side are of considerable value and cannot be neglected.

If the functions $\aleph_0$, $\aleph_1$ and $\aleph_2$ are constant, the Eq. (3.4) describes the elastic linear solid with linear second-order phenomena.

The scalar functions $\aleph_0$, $\aleph_1$ and $\aleph_2$ follow from the functional relationships between the invariants of the stress and strain tensor. Introducing Eq. (3.4) into the formulae of stress invariants leads to the following three non-linear equations for calculating the scalar functions:

$$I_s = 3\aleph_0 + \aleph_1 I_\varepsilon + \aleph_2 II_\varepsilon,$$

$$II_s = 3\aleph_0^2 + \aleph_1^2 II_\varepsilon + \aleph_2^2 IV_\varepsilon +$$

$$+ 2\aleph_0\aleph_1 I_\varepsilon + 2\aleph_0\aleph_2 II_\varepsilon + 2\aleph_1\aleph_2 III_\varepsilon, \tag{3.5}$$

$$III_s = 3\aleph_0^3 + \aleph_1^3 III_\varepsilon + \aleph_2^3 VI_\varepsilon +$$

$$+ 3\aleph_0^2\aleph_1 I_\varepsilon + 3\aleph_0\aleph_1^2 II_\varepsilon + 3\aleph_0^2\aleph_2 II_\varepsilon + 3\aleph_0\aleph_2^2 IV_\varepsilon +$$

$$+ 3\aleph_1^2\aleph_2 IV_\varepsilon + 3\aleph_1\aleph_2^2 V_\varepsilon + 6\aleph_0\aleph_1\aleph_2 III_\varepsilon.$$

The higher-order invariants appearing in the preceding equation may be expressed by means of the three principal invariants according to the formulae

$$IV_\varepsilon = \frac{1}{6}I_\varepsilon^4 + \frac{1}{2}II_\varepsilon^2 - I_\varepsilon^2 II_\varepsilon + \frac{4}{3}I_\varepsilon III_\varepsilon,$$

$$V_\varepsilon = \frac{1}{6}I_\varepsilon^5 + \frac{5}{6}II_\varepsilon III_\varepsilon + \frac{5}{6}I_\varepsilon^2 III_\varepsilon - \frac{5}{6}I_\varepsilon^3 II_\varepsilon, \tag{3.6}$$

etc.

Then, the stress-strain relationship may be fully determined by the three invariant equations of state

$$I_s = I_s(I_\varepsilon, II_\varepsilon, III_\varepsilon),$$

$$II_s = II_s(I_\varepsilon, II_\varepsilon, III_\varepsilon),$$

$$III_s = III_s(I_\varepsilon, II_\varepsilon, III_\varepsilon). \tag{3.7}$$

Using the combined stress-strain invariants $\Pi_{s\varepsilon}$, $\Pi_{s\varepsilon\varepsilon}$ leads to the three linear equations for determining the scalar functions on the right side of Eq. (3.4):

$$
\begin{aligned}
I_s &= 3\aleph_0 + \aleph_1 I_\varepsilon + \aleph_2 II_\varepsilon, \\
\Pi_{s\varepsilon} &= \aleph_0 I_\varepsilon + \aleph_1 II_\varepsilon + \aleph_2 III_\varepsilon, \\
\Pi_{s\varepsilon\varepsilon} &= \aleph_0 II_\varepsilon + \aleph_1 III_\varepsilon + \aleph_2 IV_\varepsilon,
\end{aligned}
\tag{3.8}
$$

where

$$
\begin{aligned}
\Pi_{s\varepsilon} &= s_{ij}\varepsilon_{ij}, \\
\Pi_{s\varepsilon\varepsilon} &= s_{ij}\varepsilon_{j\alpha}\varepsilon_{\alpha i}.
\end{aligned}
\tag{3.9}
$$

Then

$$
\aleph_0 = \frac{\begin{vmatrix} I_s & I_\varepsilon & II_\varepsilon \\ \Pi_{s\varepsilon} & II_\varepsilon & III_\varepsilon \\ \Pi_{s\varepsilon\varepsilon} & III_\varepsilon & IV_\varepsilon \end{vmatrix}}{\begin{vmatrix} 3 & I_\varepsilon & II_\varepsilon \\ I_\varepsilon & II_\varepsilon & III_\varepsilon \\ II_\varepsilon & III_\varepsilon & IV_\varepsilon \end{vmatrix}}, \quad
\aleph_1 = \frac{\begin{vmatrix} 3 & I_s & II_\varepsilon \\ I_\varepsilon & \Pi_{s\varepsilon} & III_\varepsilon \\ II_\varepsilon & \Pi_{s\varepsilon\varepsilon} & IV_\varepsilon \end{vmatrix}}{\begin{vmatrix} 3 & I_\varepsilon & II_\varepsilon \\ I_\varepsilon & II_\varepsilon & III_\varepsilon \\ II_\varepsilon & III_\varepsilon & IV_\varepsilon \end{vmatrix}}, \tag{3.10}
$$

$$
\aleph_2 = \frac{\begin{vmatrix} 3 & I_\varepsilon & I_s \\ I_\varepsilon & II_\varepsilon & \Pi_{s\varepsilon} \\ II_\varepsilon & III_\varepsilon & \Pi_{s\varepsilon\varepsilon} \end{vmatrix}}{\begin{vmatrix} 3 & I_\varepsilon & II_\varepsilon \\ I_\varepsilon & II_\varepsilon & III_\varepsilon \\ II_\varepsilon & III_\varepsilon & IV_\varepsilon \end{vmatrix}}.
$$

Similarly, we can define the three scalar functions ϕ_0, ϕ_1 and ϕ_2 in the following equation which is inverse to Eq. (3.4)

$$
\varepsilon_{ij} = \phi_0 \delta_{ij} + \phi_1 s_{ij} + \phi_2 s_{i\alpha} s_{\alpha j}. \tag{3.11}
$$

By similar reasoning as shown before, the author has derived such a formula from the general equation for the elastoplastic anisotropic media

$$
s_{ij} = F_{ij}(C_{mnrs}\varepsilon_{rs}), \tag{3.12}
$$

where C_{mnrs} are the components of the fourth-rank tensor characterizing the anistropic properties of the material. The function on the right side may be developed into the absolutely convergent McLaurin series as follows

$$s_{ij} = a_0 A_{ikjl}\delta_{kl} + a_1 A_{ijkl}\varepsilon_{kl} + a_2 A_{ijklmn}\varepsilon_{kl}\varepsilon_{mn} + a_3 A_{ijklmnpq}\varepsilon_{kl}\varepsilon_{mn}\varepsilon_{pq} + \dots, \qquad (3.13)$$

where a_n are the scalar coeffiients which may depend on time, temperature, etc. and A_{ijkl}, A_{ijklmn}, $A_{ijklmnpq}$, ... etc. are the components of the tensors of different ranks.

The preceding series may be rewritten following the rules of tensor analysis in the form:

$$s_{ij} = \aleph_0 B_{ijkl}\delta_{kl} + \aleph_1 B_{ijkl}\varepsilon_{kl} + \aleph_2 B_{i\alpha kl}B_{\alpha jmn}\varepsilon_{kl}\varepsilon_{mn}, \qquad (3.14)$$

where $B_{ijkl}\delta_{kl}, B_{ijkl}\varepsilon_{kl}, B_{i\alpha kl}B_{\alpha jmn}\varepsilon_{kl}\varepsilon_{mn}$

are the principal transformed strain tensors of the second rank.

The method using the combined stress–strain invariants leads to the linear equations for determining the scalar functions $\aleph_0, \aleph_1$ and $\aleph_2$:

$$\begin{aligned}
\mathrm{I}_s &= \aleph_0 B_{ijkl}\delta_{ij}\delta_{kl} + \aleph_1 B_{ijkl}\delta_{ij}\varepsilon_{kl} + \aleph_2 B_{i\alpha kl}B_{\alpha jmn}\delta_{ij}\varepsilon_{kl}\varepsilon_{mn}, \qquad (3.15)\\[4pt]
\Pi_{s\varepsilon} &= \aleph_0 B_{ijkl}\varepsilon_{ij}\delta_{kl} + \aleph_1 B_{ijkl}\varepsilon_{ij}\varepsilon_{kl} + \aleph_2 B_{i\alpha kl}B_{\alpha jmn}\varepsilon_{ij}\varepsilon_{kl}\varepsilon_{mn},\\[4pt]
\Pi_{s\varepsilon\varepsilon} &= \aleph_0 B_{ijkl}\varepsilon_{i\alpha}\varepsilon_{\alpha j}\delta_{kl} + \aleph_1 B_{ijkl}\varepsilon_{i\alpha}\varepsilon_{\alpha j}\varepsilon_{kl} + \aleph_2 B_{i\alpha kl}B_{\alpha jmn}\varepsilon_{i\beta}\varepsilon_{\beta j}\varepsilon_{kl}\varepsilon_{mn}.
\end{aligned}$$

Denoting the invariants of the transformed strain tensor $B_{ijkl}\varepsilon_{kl}$ by

$$\begin{aligned}
\mathrm{I}_{BO} &= B_{ijkl}\delta_{ij}\delta_{kl},\\[4pt]
\mathrm{I}_B &= B_{ijkl}\delta_{ij}\varepsilon_{kl} = B_{ijkl}\varepsilon_{ij}\delta_{kl}, \qquad (3.16)\\[4pt]
\mathrm{II}_B &= B_{i\alpha kl}B_{\alpha jmn}\delta_{ij}\varepsilon_{kl}\varepsilon_{mn}
\end{aligned}$$

and the combined invariants of the strain tensor ε_{ij} and of the transformed strain tensor by

$$\begin{aligned}
\Pi_{BO\varepsilon} &= \mathrm{I}_B = B_{ijkl}\varepsilon_{ij}\delta_{kl},\\[4pt]
\Pi_{B\varepsilon} &= B_{ijkl}\varepsilon_{ij}\varepsilon_{kl},\\[4pt]
\Pi_{BB\varepsilon} &= B_{i\alpha kl}B_{\alpha jmn}\varepsilon_{ij}\varepsilon_{kl}\varepsilon_{mn}, \qquad (3.17)\\[4pt]
\Pi_{BO\varepsilon\varepsilon} &= B_{ijkl}\varepsilon_{i\alpha}\varepsilon_{\alpha j}\delta_{kl},\\[4pt]
\Pi_{B\varepsilon\varepsilon} &= B_{ijkl}\varepsilon_{i\alpha}\varepsilon_{\alpha j}\varepsilon_{kl},\\[4pt]
\Pi_{BB\varepsilon\varepsilon} &= B_{i\alpha kl}B_{\alpha jmn}\varepsilon_{i\beta}\varepsilon_{\beta j}\varepsilon_{kl}\varepsilon_{mn},
\end{aligned}$$

we get the linear equations for computing the three unknown scalar functions $\aleph_0$, $\aleph_1$ and $\aleph_2$ in the following abbreviated form:

$$I_s \quad = \aleph_0 I_{B0} + \aleph_1 \ I_B + \aleph_2 \ II_B,$$

$$II_{s\varepsilon} = \aleph_0 II_{B0\varepsilon} + \aleph_1 II_{B\varepsilon} + \aleph_2 II_{BB\varepsilon},$$

$$II_{s\varepsilon\varepsilon} = \aleph_0 II_{B0\varepsilon\varepsilon} + \aleph_1 II_{B\varepsilon\varepsilon} + \aleph_2 \ II_{BB\varepsilon\varepsilon}.$$

(3.18)

The solution of the preceding linear set gives the scalar functions $\aleph_K$ in the form of functions of the simple and combined invariants

$$\aleph_k = \aleph_k(I_s, II_{s\varepsilon}, II_{s\varepsilon\varepsilon}, I_{B0}, I_B, II_B, II_{B0\varepsilon}, II_{B\varepsilon}, II_{BB\varepsilon}, II_{B0\varepsilon\varepsilon}, II_{B\varepsilon\varepsilon}, II_{BB\varepsilon\varepsilon}). \qquad (3.19)$$

The rheological model of the elastoplastic body with second-order-effects is shown in Figure 2a. It consists of a number of different Hooke and Saint-Venant elements connected in series. As deformation proceeds, more Hookean strings are tightened and more Saint-Venant elements are called into the action. In this way, the strain hardening is represented. When the principal vertical chain of Hooke and Saint-Venant is extended, the point O on Figure 2a is

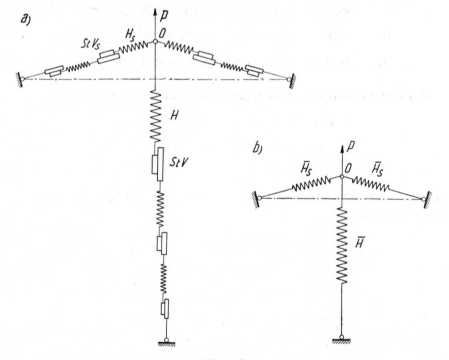

Figure 2

The rheological model of the elastoplastic body with the elastoplastic second-order phenomena

moved upwards and this will cause a second-order extension in both the lateral chains of the rheological elements.

The rheological model in Figure 2a may be replaced by a simple model in Figure 2b consisting of three non-linear springs H with variable moduli of deformation which are capable of interpreting the general non-linear deformation with the non-linear second-order phenomena.

4. The non-linear Kelvin solid.

The linear parallel coupling of the non-linear rheological elements $\bar{H}$ and $\bar{N}$ results in the non-linear Kelvin solid, which, according to Reiner's notation has the following structural formula.

$$\bar{K} = \bar{H}/\bar{N} \tag{4.1}$$

Proceeding as before, we may express the general rheological equation of this solid

$$s_{ij} = H_{ij}(\varepsilon_{rs}) + N_{ij}(f_{rs}) \tag{4.2}$$

in the following manner

$$s_{ij} = \aleph_0 \delta_{ij} + \aleph_1 \varepsilon_{ij} + \aleph_2 \varepsilon_{i\alpha}\varepsilon_{\alpha j} + \aleph_3 f_{ij} + \aleph_4 f_{i\alpha}f_{\alpha j}, \tag{4.3}$$

where $\aleph_0, \aleph_1, \aleph_2, \aleph_3$ and $\aleph_4$ are functions of the simple and combined invariants of the stress, strain and flow tensors.

These five scalar functions $\aleph_0$, $\aleph_1$, $\aleph_2$, $\aleph_3$ and $\aleph_4$ may be determined from the following five linear equations

$$
\begin{aligned}
I_s &= 3\aleph_0 + \aleph_1 I_\varepsilon + \aleph_2 II_\varepsilon + \aleph_3 I_f + \aleph_4 II_f, \\
II_{s\varepsilon} &= \aleph_0 I_\varepsilon + \aleph_1 II_\varepsilon + \aleph_2 III_\varepsilon + \aleph_3 \Pi_{\varepsilon f} + \aleph_4 \Pi_{\varepsilon f f}, \\
II_{s\varepsilon\varepsilon} &= \aleph_0 II_\varepsilon + \aleph_1 III_\varepsilon + \aleph_2 IV_\varepsilon + \aleph_3 \Pi_{\varepsilon\varepsilon f} + \aleph_4 \Pi_{\varepsilon\varepsilon f f}, \quad (4.4) \\
II_{sf} &= \aleph_0 I_f + \aleph_1 \Pi_{\varepsilon f} + \aleph_2 \Pi_{\varepsilon\varepsilon f} + \aleph_3 II_f + \aleph_4 III_f, \\
II_{sff} &= \aleph_0 II_f + \aleph_1 \Pi_{\varepsilon f f} + \aleph_2 \Pi_{\varepsilon\varepsilon f f} + \aleph_3 III_f + \aleph_4 IV_f,
\end{aligned}
$$

where $\Pi_{s\varepsilon}$, $\Pi_{s\varepsilon\varepsilon}$ are the combined invariants of the stress and strain tensor, Π_{sf}, Π_{sff}, those of the stress and flow tensor; $\Pi_{\varepsilon f}$, $\Pi_{\varepsilon\varepsilon f}$, $\Pi_{\varepsilon f f}$, $\Pi_{\varepsilon\varepsilon f f}$, the combined invariants of the strain and flow tensor (strain–rate tensor).

The scalar functions $\aleph_k$ depend on stress invariants, strain invariants, strain-rate (flow) invariants and on the combined invariants of stress, strain and flow tensor. Taking into account the relationships between the combined invariants, which will be explicated in detail in section 6, we may write

$$\aleph_k = \aleph_k(I_s, II_s, III_s, I_\varepsilon, II_\varepsilon, III_\varepsilon, I_f, II_f, III_f, \Pi_{s\varepsilon}, \Pi_{s\varepsilon\varepsilon}, \Pi_{ss\varepsilon}, \Pi_{\varepsilon f}, \Pi_{\varepsilon\varepsilon f}, \Pi_{\varepsilon f f}). \quad (4.5)$$

The stress is completely defined as a function of strain, strain rate and the invariants thereof when the dependence of the five invariants I_s, $\Pi_{s\varepsilon}$, $\Pi_{s\varepsilon\varepsilon}$, Π_{sf}, Π_{sff} on the 9 principal invariants of the tensors ε_{ij} and f_{ij} is given.

Then, Eq. (4.5) may be rewritten in the form

$$\aleph_k = \aleph_k(I_\varepsilon, II_\varepsilon, III_\varepsilon, I_f, II_f, III_f, \Pi_{\varepsilon f}, \Pi_{\varepsilon\varepsilon f}, \Pi_{\varepsilon f f}). \quad (4.5a)$$

The third term on the right side of Eq. (4.3) expresses the elastoplastic second-order phenomena if the function $\aleph_3$ is variable. If this function becomes a constant, the third term defines the elastic second-order effects.

Similarly, the second-order viscous effects are given by the fifth term on the right side of Eq. (4.3).

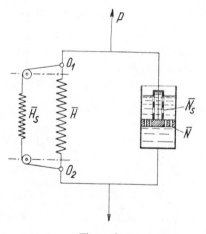

Figure 3
A rheological model for a Kelvin solid with simple second-order effects

The rheological model for a Kelvin solid with simple second-order phenomena is shown in Figure 3. Denoting by $\bar{H}$, $\bar{H}_s$, $\bar{N}$ a $\bar{N}_s$ the ideal non-linear elements, we have a symbolic model for the Kelvin solid with simple second-order effects. The elastoplastic second-order effect is represented by the ideal non-linear spring $\bar{H}_s$. When, in the case of pull, the point O_1 is moved upwards and the point O_2 downwards, in the spring $\bar{H}_s$ arises a second-order tension.

To the end, to represent the viscous second order phenomena, the usual viscous element is completed by an inner cylinder with holes. When the piston is moved with a relatively great velocity, the liquid cannot pass through the holes of the inner cylinder rapidly enough in order not to raise any difference between the levels outside and inside this cylinder, which causes the second-order viscous resistance to the motion.

It should be emphasized that the second-order elements $\bar{H}_s$ and $\bar{N}$ may be in some cases linear even when the principal elements are non-linear. This represents the anisotropy of deformation which in cross direction remains elastic whereas in the principal direction it begins to be elastoplastic

In order to describe the second-order effects more in detail, the author has proposed the rheological model for Kelvin solid containing the symbolic positive and negative non-linear springs $\bar{H}_{1s}$ and $\bar{H}_{2s}$ representing the cross tension and cross compression as shown in Figure 4. The positive and negative cross viscosity however can be represented by the same rheological element $\bar{N}_s$ which was described above.

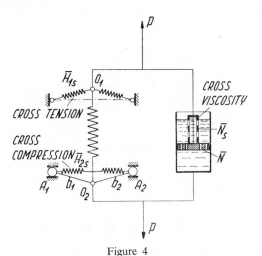

Figure 4
A rheological model of a Kelvin solid with orientated second-order effects

The element $\bar{H}_{2s}$ for the cross compression consists of two springs and of two bars b_1 and b_2 which are attached by means of a hinge to the principal branch in the point O_2. The other ends A_1 and A_2 lie in two sliding bearings, and these can move in the horizontal direction. If the point O_2 is moved downwards or upwards, respectively, the points A_1 and A_2 approach together, which causes a second-order compression in the element $\bar{H}_{2s}$.

5.   The non-linear Maxwell liquid.

The non-linear Maxwell liquid is given by linear coupling in series the non-linear rheological elements $\bar{H}$ and $\bar{N}$ according to the structural formula

$$\bar{M} = \bar{H} - \bar{N}. \tag{5.1}$$

The general rheological equation of the non-linear Maxwell liquid

$$f_{ij} = H_{ij}(\dot{s}_{kl}) + N_{ij}(s_{kl}) \tag{5.2}$$

may be expressed as follows

$$f_{ij} = \aleph_0 \delta_{ij} + \aleph_1 \dot{s}_{ij} + \aleph_2 \dot{s}_{i\alpha} \dot{s}_{\alpha j} + \aleph_3 s_{ij} + \aleph_4 s_{i\alpha} s_{\alpha j}, \tag{5.3}$$

where $\aleph_0$, $\aleph_1$, $\aleph_2$, $\aleph_3$ and $\aleph_4$ are the scalar functions of the invariants.

The third term on the right side represents the elastoplastic second-order effects whereas the fifth term expresses the effect of viscous second-order phenomena.

The scalar functions $\aleph_0$, $\aleph_1$, $\aleph_2$, $\aleph_3$ and $\aleph_4$ follow from five linear equations which are quite analogous to Eqs. (4.4) valid for non-linear Kelvin solid:

$$
\begin{aligned}
I_f &= 3\aleph_0 + \aleph_1 I_{\dot{s}} + \aleph_2 II_{\dot{s}} + \aleph_3 I_s + \aleph_4 II_s, \\
II_{f\dot{s}} &= \aleph_0 I_{\dot{s}} + \aleph_1 II_{\dot{s}} + \aleph_2 III_{\dot{s}} + \aleph_3 II_{s\dot{s}} + \aleph_4 II_{sss}, \\
II_{f\ddot{s}} &= \aleph_0 II_{\dot{s}} + \aleph_1 III_{\dot{s}} + \aleph_2 IV_{\dot{s}} + \aleph_3 II_{s\dot{s}\dot{s}} + \aleph_4 II_{ss\dot{s}\dot{s}}, \\
II_{fs} &= \aleph_0 I_s + \aleph_1 II_{s\dot{s}} + \aleph_2 II_{s\dot{s}\dot{s}} + \aleph_3 II_s + \aleph_4 III_s, \\
II_{fss} &= \aleph_0 II_s + \aleph_1 II_{sss} + \aleph_2 II_{sss\dot{s}} + \aleph_3 III_s + \aleph_4 IV_s.
\end{aligned}
\tag{5.4}
$$

The problem is completely defined when the 5 invariants on the left side of Eq. (5.4) are given in the form of functions of the 9 principal invariants of the tensors $\dot{s}_{ij}$ and s_{ij}.

The rheological model of the general non-linear Maxwell liquid with second order effects is shown on Figure 5. The elements representing the second-order phenomena are constructed in quite an analogous manner as those in the model for a Kelvin solid in Figure 4.

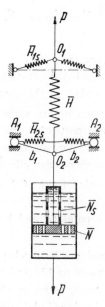

Figure 5
A rheological model for the non-linear Maxwell liquid with second-order effects

6. The isotropic general non-linear body with combined higher-order effects.

The most general method of expressing the rheological behaviour of various bodies consists in non-linear coupling of the non-linear rheological elements which may be written briefly by the structural formula $(\bar{H}, \bar{N})$. In such a case the components of the stress tensor may be given by the general rheological equation

$$s_{ij} = F_{ij}(\dot{s}_{kl}, \varepsilon_{mn}, f_{pq}), \tag{6.1}$$

where $\dot{s}_{kl}$ are the components of the stress-rate tensor.

Developing the function F_{ij} by means of tensor analysis, the author has obtained the following general formula which is valid for the general elasto-plasticoviscous bodies

$$
\begin{aligned}
s_{ij} = & \; \aleph_0 \delta_{ij} + \aleph_1 \dot{s}_{ij} + \aleph_2 \dot{s}_{i\alpha} \dot{s}_{\alpha j} + \aleph_3 \varepsilon_{ij} + \aleph_4 \varepsilon_{i\alpha} \varepsilon_{\alpha j} + \\
& + \aleph_5 f_{ij} + \aleph_6 f_{i\alpha} f_{\alpha j} + \\
& + \aleph_7 (\dot{s}_{i\alpha} \varepsilon_{\alpha j} + \varepsilon_{i\alpha} \dot{s}_{\alpha j}) + \aleph_8 (\dot{s}_{i\alpha} f_{\alpha j} + f_{i\alpha} \dot{s}_{\alpha j}) + \\
& + \aleph_9 \dot{s}_{i\alpha} \varepsilon_{\alpha\beta} \dot{s}_{\beta j} + \aleph_{10} \varepsilon_{i\alpha} \dot{s}_{\alpha\beta} \varepsilon_{\beta j} + \aleph_{11} \dot{s}_{i\alpha} f_{\alpha} \; \dot{s}_{\beta j} + \aleph_{12} f_{i\alpha} \dot{s}_{\alpha\beta} f_{\beta j}.
\end{aligned}
\tag{6.2}
$$

The 13 scalar functions $\aleph_k$ are invariants which may be expressed also as functions of the 15 principal combined invariants of tensors $\dot{s}_{ij}$, ε_{io} and f_{ij}, They may depend on various scalars as the temperature, time, etc.

In the general case, these functions are variable with the components of the three tensors $\dot{s}_{ij}$, ε_{ij}, f_{ij}. In a particular case, they may be also constants, and then Eq. (6.2) describes the state of finite deformation of the general linear viscoelastic body with higher-order effects.

The first term on the right side of Eq. (6.2) represents the volume effects containing the volumetric components of the tensors $\dot{s}_{ij}$, ε_{ij} and f_{ij}. The volume effects may be also expressed separately, and Eq. (6.2) has thus 15 terms on the right side.

Using the above notation and the Kronecker's delta we have reduced the number of the 15 principal tensors to 13, replacing with scalar functions the infinite absolutely convergent power series in which the function F_{ij} of three variables in Eq. (6.1) may be developed. All components of the three tensors $\dot{s}_{ij}$, ε_{ij} and f_{ij} related to the principal axes of tensor $\dot{s}_{ij}$ namely may be expressed in terms of the 9 principal values of those tensors and by the 6 Euler angles between the principal axes of the tensor $\dot{s}_{ij}$ and those of tensors ε_{ij} and f_{ij}.

Relating the components of the three above tensors to the principal axes of the tensor ε_{ij}, we may rewrite Eq. (6.2) in the following manner

$$
\begin{aligned}
s_{ij} = & \; \aleph_0 \delta_{ij} + \aleph_1 \dot{s}_{ij} + \aleph_2 \dot{s}_{i\alpha} \dot{s}_{\alpha j} + \aleph_3 \varepsilon_{ij} + \aleph_4 \varepsilon_{i\alpha} \varepsilon_{\alpha j} + \\
& + \aleph_5 f_{ij} + \aleph_6 f_{i\alpha} f_{\alpha j} + \\
& + \aleph_7 (\dot{s}_{i\alpha} \varepsilon_{\alpha j} + \varepsilon_{i\alpha} \dot{s}_{\alpha j}) + \aleph_8 (\varepsilon_{i\alpha} f_{\alpha j} + f_{i\alpha} \varepsilon_{\alpha j}) + \\
& + \aleph_9 \dot{s}_{i\alpha} \varepsilon_{\alpha\beta} \dot{s}_{\beta j} + \aleph_{10} \varepsilon_{i\alpha} \dot{s}_{\alpha\beta} \varepsilon_{\beta j} + \aleph_{11} \varepsilon_{i\alpha} f_{\alpha\beta} \varepsilon_{\beta j} + \aleph_{12} f_{i\alpha} \varepsilon_{\alpha\beta} f_{\beta j}.
\end{aligned}
\tag{6.3}
$$

Similarly, relating all tensor components to the principal axes of the flow tensor f_i, we get

$$
\begin{aligned}
s_{ij} = {}& \aleph_0 \delta_{ij} + \aleph_1 \dot{s}_{ij} + \aleph_2 \dot{s}_{i\alpha} \dot{s}_{\alpha j} + \aleph_3 \varepsilon_{ij} + \aleph_4 \varepsilon_{i\alpha} \varepsilon_{\alpha j} + \\
& + \aleph_5 f_{ij} + \aleph_6 f_{i\alpha} f_{\alpha j} + \\
& + \aleph_7 (\dot{s}_{i\alpha} f_{\alpha j} + f_{i\alpha} \dot{s}_{\alpha j}) + \aleph_8 (\varepsilon_{i\alpha} f_{\alpha j} + f_{i\alpha} \varepsilon_{\alpha j}) + \\
& + \aleph_9 \dot{s}_{i\alpha} f_{\alpha\beta} \dot{s}_{\beta j} + \aleph_{10} f_{i\alpha} \dot{s}_{\alpha\beta} f_{\beta j} + \aleph_{11} \varepsilon_{i\alpha} f_{\alpha\beta} \varepsilon_{\beta j} + \aleph_{12} f_{i\alpha} \varepsilon_{\alpha\beta} f_{\beta j}.
\end{aligned}
\tag{6.4}
$$

In quite an analogous way, we may express the components of the stress-rate tensor $\dot{s}_{ij}$ and those of the tensors ε_{ij} or f_{ij}, respectively by means of the other tensor components. Thus, we have the 12 various equivalent tensorial equations for determining the state of finite deformation of the general non-linear elastoviscoplastic body.

Besides the terms expressing the volume effects and the first-order effects, Eqs. (6.2), (6.3) and (6.4) contain also the terms representing the second-order and third-order effects.

The terms $\aleph_2 \dot{s}_{i\alpha} \dot{s}_{\alpha j}$, $\aleph_4 \varepsilon_{i\alpha} \varepsilon_{\alpha j}$, $\aleph_6 f_{i\alpha} f_{\alpha j}$ in Eq. (6.2) represent the simple second order effects depending on the squares or on the products of the variables of the same kind.

The terms $\aleph_7 (\dot{s}_{i\alpha} \varepsilon_{\alpha j} + \varepsilon_{i\alpha} \dot{s}_{\alpha j})$ and $\aleph_8 (\dot{s}_{i\alpha} f_{\alpha j} + f_{i\alpha} \dot{s}_{\alpha j})$ in Eq. (6.2) express the combined second-order effects which depend on the products of two different variables. Comparing these terms with the corresponding members in Eqs. (6.3) or (6.4), respectively, we draw the conclusion that the combined second-order effects may be defined in the three different but equivalent manners.

The four last terms in Eq. (6.2), namely $\aleph_9 \dot{s}_{i\alpha} \varepsilon_{\alpha\beta} \dot{s}_{\beta j}$, $\aleph_{10} \varepsilon_{i\alpha} \dot{s}_{\alpha\beta} \varepsilon_{\beta j}$, $\aleph_{11} \dot{s}_{i\alpha} f_{\alpha\beta} \dot{s}_{\beta j}$, $\aleph_{12} f_{i\alpha} \dot{s}_{\alpha\beta} f_{\beta j}$ determines the third-order effects depending on products of two different variables. Similarly, the third-order effects are expressed by the four last terms of Eqs. (6.3) and (6.4) respectively.

Multiplying Eq. (6.2) successively by δ_{ij}, $\dot{s}_{ij}$, $\dot{s}_{i\alpha} \dot{s}_{\alpha j}$, ε_{ij}, $\varepsilon_{i\alpha} \varepsilon_{\alpha j}$, f_{ij}, $f_{i\alpha} f_{\alpha j}$, $\dot{s}_{i\alpha} \varepsilon_{\alpha j} + \varepsilon_{i\alpha} \dot{s}_{\alpha j}$, $\dot{s}_{i\alpha} f_{\alpha j} + f_{i\alpha} \dot{s}_{\alpha j}$, $\dot{s}_{i\alpha} \varepsilon_{\alpha\beta} \dot{s}_{\beta j}$, $\varepsilon_{i\alpha} \dot{s}_{\alpha\beta} \varepsilon_{\beta j}$, $\dot{s}_{i\alpha} f_{\alpha\beta} \dot{s}_{\beta j}$, $f_{i\alpha} \dot{s}_{\alpha\beta} f_{\beta j}$, and performing the summation with respect to i and j, we get the set of 13 linear equations for the scalar functions $\aleph_k$. Expressing all combined invariants of tensors s_{ij}, $\dot{s}_{ij}$, ε_{ij} and f_{ij} in terms of the 21 principal invariants of the set of these tensors, the solution of those equations gives the scalar functions $\aleph_k$ in terms of these invariants as follows

$$\aleph_k = \aleph_k \, (s_{ij}\delta_{ij}, \; s_{ij}s_{ij}, \; s_{ij}s_{j\alpha}s_{\alpha i}, \; \dot{s}_{ij}\delta_{ij}, \; \dot{s}_{ij}\dot{s}_{ij}, \; \dot{s}_{ij}\dot{s}_{j\alpha}\dot{s}_{\alpha i},$$

$$\varepsilon_{ij}\delta_{ij}, \; \varepsilon_{ij}\varepsilon_{ij}, \; \varepsilon_{ij}\varepsilon_{j\alpha}\varepsilon_{\alpha i}, \; f_{ij}\delta_{ij}, \; f_{ij}f_{ij}, \; f_{ij}f_{j\alpha}f_{\alpha i},$$

$$s_{ij}\varepsilon_{ij}, \; s_{ij}s_{j\alpha}\varepsilon_{\alpha i}, \; s_{ij}\varepsilon_{j\alpha}\varepsilon_{\alpha i}, \; s_{ij}\dot{s}_{ij}, \; s_{ij}s_{j\alpha}\dot{s}_{\alpha i}, \; s_{ij}\dot{s}_{j\alpha}\dot{s}_{\alpha i}, \tag{6.5}$$

$$\dot{s}_{ij}\varepsilon_{ij}, \; \dot{s}_{ij}\dot{s}_{j\alpha}\varepsilon_{\alpha i}, \; \dot{s}_{ij}\varepsilon_{j\alpha}\varepsilon_{\alpha i}).$$

Then, the components of the stress tensor given by Eq. (6.2) may be expressed in terms of the components of the three tensors $\dot{s}_{ij}, \varepsilon_{ij}$ and f_{ij} and of the 21 principal invariants.

For the nonlinear body with the general rheological equation

$$s_{ij} = F_{ij}(\varepsilon_{kl}, f_{mn}), \tag{6.6}$$

the tensorial Eq. (6.2) is simplified to

$$s_{ij} = \aleph_0 \delta_{ij} + \aleph_1 \varepsilon_{ij} + \aleph_2 \varepsilon_{i\alpha}\varepsilon_{\alpha j} + \aleph_3 f_{ij} + \aleph_4 f_{i\alpha}f_{\alpha j} +$$

$$+ \aleph_5 (\varepsilon_{i\alpha}f_{\alpha j} + f_{i\alpha}\varepsilon_{\alpha j}) + \aleph_6 \varepsilon_{i\alpha}f_{\alpha\beta}\varepsilon_{\beta j} + \aleph_7 f_{i\alpha}\varepsilon_{\alpha\beta}f_{\beta j}, \tag{6.7}$$

where the 8 scalar functions $\aleph_k$ may be expressed in terms of the 9 principal invariants of the tensors ε_{ij} and f_{ij} as follows

$$\aleph_k = \aleph_k \, (\varepsilon_{ij}\delta_{ij}, \varepsilon_{ij}\varepsilon_{ij}, \varepsilon_{ij}\varepsilon_{j\alpha}\varepsilon_{\alpha i}, f_{ij}\delta_{ij}, f_{ij}f_{ij}, f_{ij}f_{j\alpha}f_{\alpha i}, \varepsilon_{ij}f_{ij}, \varepsilon_{ij}\varepsilon_{j\alpha}f_{\alpha i}, \varepsilon_{ij}f_{j\alpha}f_{\alpha i}) \tag{6.8}$$

when the dependence of the invariants $I_s, \Pi_{s\varepsilon}, \Pi_{s\varepsilon\varepsilon}, \Pi_{sf}, \Pi_{sff}, \Pi_{s\varepsilon f}, \Pi_{s\varepsilon\varepsilon f}, \Pi_{s\varepsilon ff}$ on those 9 invariants is given.

The simplest rheological model of the body determined by Eq. (6.7) is shown in Figure 6. The rheological meaning of different elements is defined by the terms of Eq. (6.7) written on that figure whereas the first term $\aleph_0 \delta_{ij}$ belongs simultaneously to the principal spring and dashpot.

The physical meaning of the combined second-order and third-order effects depending on the products of two different variables is analogous to that of the simple second-order effects. In the present case, the material possesses the viscoelastic or viscoelastoplastic properties in the cross directions.

As an example of the application of Eq. (6.7), let us consider the case of finite simple shear calculated by M. Reiner [9], [14] without viscous effects.

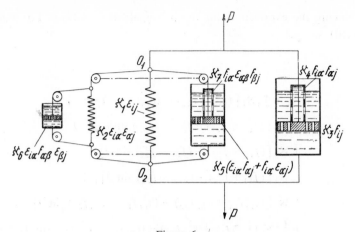

Figure 6

The simplest rheological model of the viscoelastic solid with different second-order and third-order effects.

Let a sheet consisting of a material which can suffer large deformation be fixed between two parallel runners as shown in Figure 7. After the displacement of the upper runner, the circle drawn on the undeformed sheet in Figure 7 a is deformed into an ellipse as shown on Figure 7b. Two radii of the circle normal to each other in the directions 1 and 2 are rotated by the angle $\theta = \operatorname{arctg}\left(\frac{\varepsilon_{xy}}{2}\right)$ into the positions **1** and **2** and extended or contracted respectively, into half-axes of the ellipse in the principal directions of strain **1** and **2**.

From Eq. (6.7) we get the principal stresses in the directions of of principal axes **1** and **2** as follows

$$s_{ii} = \aleph_0 + \aleph_1 \varepsilon_{ii} + \aleph_2 \varepsilon_{ii}^2 + \aleph_3 f_{ii} + \aleph_4 f_{ii}^2 + \tag{6.9}$$

$$+ 2\aleph_5 \varepsilon_{ii} f_{ii} + \aleph_6 \varepsilon_{ii}^2 f_{ii} + \aleph_7 \varepsilon_{ii} f_{ii}^2.$$

The values of normal shearing stress components according to the Mohr's diagram in Figure 7c are given by (see M. Reiner [9])

$$s_{xx} = \tfrac{1}{2}(s_{11} + s_{22}) - \tfrac{1}{2}(s_{11} - s_{22}) \sin \theta,$$

$$s_{yy} = \tfrac{1}{2}(s_{11} + s_{22}) + \tfrac{1}{2}(s_{11} - s_{22}) \sin \theta,$$

$$s_{zz} = s_{33}, \tag{6.10}$$

$$s_{xy} = -\tfrac{1}{2}(s_{11} - s_{22}) \cos \theta, \quad s_{xz} = s_{zy} = 0.$$

Introducing the expressions for the principal stresses from Eq. (6.9) into Eqs. (6.10) we get

$$
\begin{aligned}
s_{xx} = {}& \aleph_0 + \tfrac{1}{2}\{\aleph_1 [(\varepsilon_{11} + \varepsilon_{22}) - (\varepsilon_{11} - \varepsilon_{22}) \sin \theta] + \\
& + \aleph_2 [(\varepsilon_{11}^2 + \varepsilon_{22}^2) - (\varepsilon_{11}^2 - \varepsilon_{22}^2) \sin \theta] + \\
& + \aleph_3 [(f_{11} + f_{22}) - (f_{11} - f_{22}) \sin \theta] + \\
& + \aleph_4 [(f_{11}^2 + f_{22}^2) - (f_{11}^2 - f_{22}^2) \sin \theta]\} + \\
& + \aleph_5 [(\varepsilon_{11} f_{11} + \varepsilon_{22} f_{22}) - (\varepsilon_{11} f_{11} - \varepsilon_{22} f_{22}) \sin \theta] + \\
& + \tfrac{1}{2}\{\aleph_6 [(\varepsilon_{11}^2 f_{11} + \varepsilon_{22}^2 f_{22}) - (\varepsilon_{11}^2 f_{11} - \varepsilon_{22}^2 f_{22}) \sin \theta] + \\
& + \aleph_7 [(\varepsilon_{11} f_{11}^2 + \varepsilon_{22} f_{22}^2) - (\varepsilon_{11} f_{11}^2 - \varepsilon_{22} f_{22}^2) \sin \theta]\},
\end{aligned}
\tag{6.11}
$$

$$
\begin{aligned}
s_{yy} = {}& \aleph_0 + \tfrac{1}{2}\{\aleph_1 [(\varepsilon_{11} + \varepsilon_{22}) + (\varepsilon_{11} - \varepsilon_{22}) \sin \theta] + \\
& + \aleph_2 [(\varepsilon_{11}^2 + \varepsilon_{22}^2) + (\varepsilon_{11}^2 - \varepsilon_{22}^2) \sin \theta] + \\
& + \aleph_3 [(f_{11} + f_{22}) + (f_{11} - f_{22}) \sin \theta] + \\
& + \aleph_4 [(f_{11}^2 + f_{22}^2) + (f_{11}^2 - f_{22}^2) \sin \theta]\} + \\
& + \aleph_5 [(\varepsilon_{11} f_{11} + \varepsilon_{22} f_{22}) + (\varepsilon_{11} f_{11} - \varepsilon_{22} f_{22}) \sin \theta] + \\
& + \tfrac{1}{2}\{\aleph_6 [(\varepsilon_{11}^2 f_{11} + \varepsilon_{22}^2 f_{22}) + (\varepsilon_{11}^2 f_{11} - \varepsilon_{22}^2 f_{22}) \sin \theta] + \\
& + \aleph_7 [(\varepsilon_{11} f_{11}^2 + \varepsilon_{22} f_{22}^2) + (\varepsilon_{11} f_{11}^2 - \varepsilon_{22} f_{22}^2) \sin \theta]\},
\end{aligned}
\tag{6.12}
$$

$$
s_{zz} = \aleph_0,
\tag{6.13}
$$

$$
\begin{aligned}
s_{xy} = {}& -\tfrac{1}{2}[\aleph_1 (\varepsilon_{11} - \varepsilon_{22}) + \aleph_2 (\varepsilon_{11}^2 - \varepsilon_{22}^2) + \\
& + \aleph_3 (f_{11} - f_{22}) + \aleph_4 (f_{11}^2 - f_{22}^2) + \\
& + 2\aleph_5 (\varepsilon_{11} f_{11} - \varepsilon_{22} f_{22}) + \\
& + \aleph_6 (\varepsilon_{11}^2 f_{11} - \varepsilon_{22}^2 f_{22}) + \aleph_7 (\varepsilon_{11} f_{11}^2 - \varepsilon_{22} f_{22}^2)] \cos \theta.
\end{aligned}
\tag{6.14}
$$

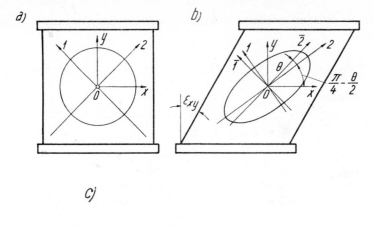

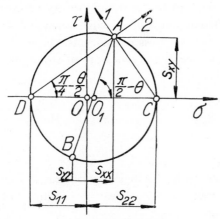

Figure 7
Reiner's representation of finite simple shear

The principal strains depend on the principal stretches, which according to M. Reiner [9] are given by

$$\lambda_{11} = \frac{1 - \sin \theta}{\cos \theta} = \operatorname{tg}\left(\frac{\pi}{4} - \frac{\theta}{2}\right), \ \lambda_{22} = \frac{1 + \sin \theta}{\cos \theta} =$$

$$= \operatorname{tg}\left(\frac{\pi}{4} + \frac{\theta}{2}\right), \ \lambda_{33} = 1 \tag{6.15}$$

and the principal stretch rates have the following values

$$\dot{\lambda}_{11} = -\frac{1 - \sin \theta}{\cos^2 \theta} \dot{\theta}, \quad \dot{\lambda}_{22} = \frac{1 + \sin \theta}{\cos^2 \theta} \dot{\theta}, \quad \dot{\lambda}_{33} = 0. \tag{6.16}$$

Assuming different measures of strain and strain rate, for example Cauchy-measure

$$\varepsilon_{ii}^C = \lambda_{ii} - 1, f_{ii}^C = \dot{\varepsilon}_{ii}^C = \dot{\lambda}_{ii}, \tag{6.17}$$

Hencky-measure

$$\varepsilon_{ii}^H = \ln \lambda_{ii}, \quad f_{ii}^H = \dot{\varepsilon}_{ii}^H = \frac{\dot{\lambda}_{ii}}{\lambda_{ii}}, \tag{6.18}$$

or Green-measure

$$\varepsilon_{ii}^G = \tfrac{1}{2}(\lambda_{ii}^2 - 1), \quad f_{ii}^G = \dot{\varepsilon}_{ii}^G = \lambda_{ii}\dot{\lambda}_{ii}, \text{ etc.}, \tag{6.19}$$

and introducing into Eqs. (6.17), (6.18) and (6.19) the expressions (6.15) and (6.16), we get the different values of principal strain and strain-rates and then from Eqs. (6.11)−(6.14) the stress components.

Taking, for example, the Hencky-measure of strain and of strain rate, we obtain from Eq. (6.14)

$$s_{xy} = \left(\aleph_1 \cos\theta + \aleph_6 \dot{\theta} \ln \frac{\cos\theta}{1-\sin\theta} + \aleph_7 \frac{\dot{\theta}^2}{\cos\theta} \right) \ln \frac{\cos\theta}{1-\sin\theta} + \aleph_3 \dot{\theta}. \tag{6.20}$$

7. Conclusions.

The non-linear problems in rheology may be treated assuming the parametrical, tensorial or deformational non-linearity according to the different strain and strain-rate measures.

The parametrical non-linearity is less general and less exact than the tensorial non-linearity which makes possible the exact interpretation of all simple and combined higher-order phenomena as has been shown in the preceding section.

Some equations of the parametrical non-linearity has been given in section 2 for simple one-dimensional states of stress and strain. However, those equations may be extended to the two-dimensional and three-dimensional deformation.

Using the shear modulus $\mu_{ij} - \mu_{ijkl}s_{kl}$, depending on the stress components we may obtain the following non-linear stress-strain relationship

$$\varepsilon_{ij} - \varepsilon_m\delta_{ij} = \frac{s_{ij} - s_m\delta_{ij}}{2(\mu_0 - \mu_1 s_{\alpha\beta})}, \tag{7.1}$$

i.e. approximately

$$\varepsilon_{ij} - \varepsilon_m \delta_{ij} = \frac{1}{2\mu_0}(s_{ij} - s_m \delta_{ij})\left(1 + \frac{\mu_1}{\mu_0} s_{\alpha\beta} + \dots\right), \qquad (7.2)$$

where ε_m is the mean strain and
s_m the mean stress.

The preceding equations describe also approximately the simple second-order effects.

In order to interpret the higher-order phenomena, the usual rheological models should be completed by the particular elements which are called into action not until the deformation is sufficiently large.

It has been shown that besides the simple second-order effects depending on the products of the same variable, the combined higher-order phenomena may arise depending on the products of two different variables. The author has observed such phenomena at the large time-dependent deformation in the soils having water between the grains, which may be taken for two-phase systems.

8. List of symbols.

A_{ijkl} = scalar coefficients
a = material constant
B = Bingham body
B_{ijkl} = tensorial coefficient of anisotropy
Bu = Burgers body
b = material constant
C = rheological body representing the behavior of concrete
C_{mnrs} = tensor of anisotropy
c = relative volume of cement in concrete
D = constant
F_{ij} = deformational function
H = Hooke solid
$\bar{H}$ = non-linear Hooke solid
H_{ij} = deformational function
K = Kelvin solid, also constant

$\bar{K}$ = non-linear Kelvin solid

k = relative volume of gravel in concrete

$\bar{M}$ = non-linear Maxwell liquid

m = relative volume of sand in the mortar

N = Newton-liquid

$\bar{N}$ = non-linear viscous liquid

StV = Saint-Venant body

s_m = mean stress

$\bar{W}$ = water-cement ratio of the cement

W = water cement ratio of the concrete

α = constant, also dummy index

β = constant, also dummy index

ε_m = mean strain

ξ_n = coefficient of normal viscosity

κ = constant

ψ = relative humidity

$\Pi_{s\varepsilon}, \Pi_{s\varepsilon\varepsilon}$ = combined invariants of stress and strain tensor

REFERENCES

[1] T. ALFREY, *Mechanical behaviour of high Polymers*, Interscience Publishers, Inc. New York — London (1948).

[2] M. A. ARNAN, M. REINER AND M. TEINOWITZ, *Research on Loading Tests of Reinforced Concrete Floor Structures*, The Research Council of Israel, Jerusalem (1950).

[3] ST. BECHYNE, *Concrete Structures I. Technology of Concrete*. Vol. 4. Deformational Properties of Concrete (in Czech). Prague (1959).

[4] A. M. FREUDENTHAL, *The Inelastic Behavior of Engineering Materials and Structures*, J. Wiley and Sons, Inc., New York, Chapman and Hall, Ltd., London, (1950).

[5] I. I. GOLDENBLAT, *Some Problems of the Mechanics of Deformable Media* (in Russian), Moscow, (1955).

[6] J. MANDEL, Application du calcul opérationnel a l'étude des corps viscoélastiques. *Cahiers du Groupe Francais d'Etudes de Rhéologie*. Tome III. Paris, (1958).

[7] W. OLSZAK AND J. LITWINISZYN, The non-linear phenomenon of certain liquid flow representing a rheological model (in Polish). *Archiwum Mechaniki Stosowanej*, **5**, Warszawa, (1953).

[8] W. PRAGER, *Journal of Applied Physics*, **16**, (1945), 837–840.

[9] M. REINER, *American Journal of Mathematics*, **67**, (1945), 35.

[10] M. REINER, Elasticity Beyond the Elastic Limit. *Am. J. Math.*, **70**, (1948), 433–446.

[11] M. REINER, *Twelve Lectures on Theoretical Rheology*. North-Holland Publishing Co., Amsterdam, Interscience Publishers, Inc., New York (1949).

[12] M. REINER, *Deformation and Flow*. H. K. Lewis and Co., Ltd., London (1949).

[13] M. REINER, *Theoretical Rheology. Building Materials* (ed. by M. Reiner). North-Holland Publishing Co., Amsterdam (1954).

[14] M. REINER, *Phenomenological Macrorheology. Rheology, Theory and Application,* vol. 1 (ed. by F. R. Eirich). Academic Press Inc., Publishers, New York (1956).

[15] M. REINER, *Deformation, Strain and Flow.* H. K. Lewis and Co., Ltd., London (1960)

[16] Z. SOBOTKA, *Theory of Plasticity and Limiting States of Engineering Structures,* vol. 1 (in Czech). Czechoslovak Academy of Sciences, Prague (1954).

[17] Z. SOBOTKA, Rheological Laws of the Long-Time Deformation of Concrete, *Silicates,* 2, 117–138, Prague (1958).

[18] Z. SOBOTKA AND V. SATAVA, Rheology in Silicates, *Silicates,* **2,** 79–105, Prague (1958).

DISCUSSION

L. PUST:

Dr. Sobotka has shown here some theoretical problems of nonlinear rheology. I will mention now one material of mechanical engineering which has similar properties. Such a material consists of fibres oriented parallel in one direction and stresses mainly in tension. There are for example steel cable consisting of wires compressed together by prestressing during the manufacture or by the cable tension. During the deformation of such an element microdisplacement occurring among the individual fibres causes internal friction of the material and even a change in the equivalent shear modulus of elasticity.

The relation between force and axial displacement of the two fibres (or cylinders) depends also on the history of the deformation of the material, i. e. on its previous state of stress and strain and on the manner in which the system has obtained the condition of the instant being studied. If we limit our consideration only to the periodic events, we can write the shear deformation γ in this form

$$\gamma = \frac{\pi}{\pi\mu}\left(1 - 2\ln 0.64\sigma_y\cdot\frac{\gamma^2 - 1}{E}\right) + \text{sign}\,\frac{d\tau}{dt}\left\{\frac{1}{2}\left(1 + \frac{\tau_{max}}{k\sigma_y}\right)\right.$$

$$\cdot\ln\left(1 + \frac{\tau_{max}}{k\sigma_y}\right) - \left(1 + \frac{\tau_{max}}{2k\sigma_y} + \frac{\tau\,\text{sign}\,d\tau/dt}{2k\sigma_y}\right)\ln\left(1 + \frac{\tau_{max}}{2k\sigma_y} +\right.$$

$$\left.+ \frac{\tau\,\text{sign}\,d\tau/dt}{2k\sigma_y}\right)\left.\right\}\frac{2k\sigma_y}{\mu\pi}, \qquad |\tau| \leqq \tau_{max} \leqq (k\sigma_y),\ \sigma_y < 0$$

where τ_{max} is the maximum shearing stress at harmonic motion, k is the coefficient of friction on the contact surface, σ_y is the prestressing.

This deformation γ, which in limit cases does not depend on the radius R of fibres, can be divided into two parts. The first part

$$\frac{\tau}{\pi\mu}\left[-2\ln 0.64\,\sigma_y\frac{v^2 - 1}{E} - \ln\left(1 + \frac{\tau_{max}}{2k\sigma_y}\right)\right] = \frac{\tau}{\mu^*}$$

determines the elastic part of deformation γ, the equivalent shear modulus of elasticity μ^* being given by

$$\mu^* = \frac{\pi\mu}{\ln\left\{\left[0.64\,\sigma_y\frac{v^2-1}{E}\right]^2\left(1+\frac{\tau_{max}}{2k\sigma_y}\right)\right\}}$$

is a function of σ_y and τ_{max}.

The second part given by the expression

$$\left(\operatorname{sign}\frac{d\tau}{dt}\right)\frac{2k\sigma_y}{\pi\mu}\left\{\frac{1}{2}\left(1+\frac{\tau_{max}}{k\sigma_y}\right)\ln\left(1+\frac{\tau_{max}}{k\sigma_y}\right)-\left(1+\frac{\tau_{max}}{2k\sigma_y}\right)\cdot\right.$$

$$\left.\cdot\ln\left(1+\frac{\tau_{max}}{2k\sigma_y}\right)-\frac{\left(\frac{\tau}{2k\sigma_y}\right)^2}{1+\left(\frac{\tau_{max}}{2k\sigma_y}\right)}\right\}$$

is again a nonlinear function of stresses τ, σ_y and τ_{max} and determines the irreversible part of deformation γ, causing internal damping by vibrations

These expressions are valid for the case when in contact surfaces only partial slip occurs. At large deformation full slip occurs and the change of equivalent modulus and internal friction is much larger.

DISCUSSION

E. BEN-ZVI:

Basing himself on exepriment, the author proposed a sharp Rheological equation of state for concrete.

According to the author's statement the experiments were carried out in a uniaxial state of stress, and partly in a biaxial state of stress, e. g. the simple shear.

Although, the uniaxial state of stress serves as a base for any Rheological equation of state, including Hooke's Solid, it can be shown that equations so derived, are good for the calculations of deformation, but they do not serve as a proof for the stresses. On the other hand, even in the case of simple compression, the fracture occurs in a direction parallel to the compressive forces, although neither by the classical theory of elasticity nor by the Rheological equation proposed by the author, tensile stresses could occur in the direction of the fracture [1]. Owing to the brittle nature of concrete, the 'H' elements in the Rheological Model may exist up to the fracture, when the internal forces out of simple compression may produce tensile components, e. g. as shown in the following sketch.

Cross Tension due to Simple Compression

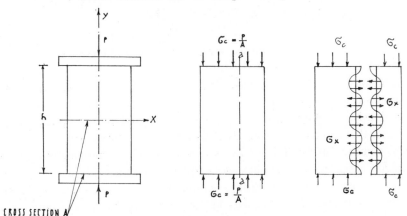

Pulse tension stress $= \sigma = C_1 \cos 2\pi n\, y/h + C_2 \sin 2\pi n\, y/h$
C_1 and C_2 are functions of X and σ_c

The correct stress-strain relation, especially in problems of so called 'Combined Stresses' seems to be still an unsolved problem. This is worth-while to mention when such a Rheological equation of state is proposed.

AUTHOR'S REPLY:

The author wishes to thank Mr. E. Ben-Zvi and Dr. L. Půst for their valuable discussions.

Mr. E. Ben-Zvi elucidates some problems concerning the interventions of internal tensile stresses at the fracture of a concrete specimen in simple compression.

Obviously, author's equations with variable rheological parameters, contained in section two, were derived for long-time deformation only whereas they are not concerned with the problem mentioned by the discussor.

The point of departure for such problems may be tridimensional relationships such as the general parametrically non-linear equation for C-body (Fig. 1)

---

(1) Ben-Zvi, E., "Fracture of Solids under Combined Stresses," *Bulletin of the Research Council of Israel* June 1961.

$$\frac{d}{dt}\left[\frac{^2\lambda^{ijkl}}{^2E^{ijkl}}\frac{d}{dt}\left(\frac{\sigma^{ij}}{^1E^{ijkl}}\right)\right] + \frac{d}{dt}\left\{\left[\frac{^2\lambda^{ijkl}}{^2E^{ijkl}}\left(\frac{1}{^1\lambda^{ijkl}} + \frac{1}{^2\lambda^{ijkl}}\right) + \frac{1}{^1E^{ijkl}}\right]\sigma^{ij}\right\} +$$

$$+ \frac{\sigma^{ij}}{^6\lambda_{ijkl}} =$$

$$= \frac{^1\delta^{ij}}{^1\lambda^{ijkl}} + \frac{d}{dt}\left[\frac{^2\lambda^{ijkl}}{^2E^{ijkl}}\left(\frac{^1\delta^{ij}}{^1\lambda^{ijkl}} + \frac{^2\delta^{ij}}{^2\lambda^{ijkl}}\right)\right] + \frac{d\varepsilon_{kl}}{dt} + \frac{d}{dt}\left(\frac{^2\lambda^{ijkl}}{^2E^{ijkl}}\frac{d\varepsilon_{kl}}{dt}\right),$$

$^1E^{ijkl}$, $^2E^{ijkl}$ being the first and second variable tensorial modulus of elasticity, $^1\lambda^{ijkl}$, $^2\lambda^{ijkl}$ the coefficients of viscosity, etc. A better approach should consist in applying a more general tensorial equation describing also the higher-order effects such as Eq. (6.4).

Obviously, the problem is a very complex one and author agrees with the discussor that still there does not exist an appropriate solution to it.

The comment of Mr. E. Ben-Zvi is very valuable, emphasizing the complex character of the fracture of solids under combined stresses.

The contribution of Dr. L. Půst presenting the formula for shear deformation of periodically stressed cables may be considered as that appertaining to the range of parametrical non-linearity, assuming the variable equivalent stress-depending shear modulus μ^* given by the discussor and completing the considerations by an equivalent coefficient of viscosity

$$\eta^* = \frac{2k\sigma y}{\pi\mu}\left\{\frac{1}{2}\left(1 + \frac{\tau_{max}}{k\sigma_y}\right)\ln\left(1 + \frac{\tau_{max}}{k\sigma_y}\right) - \right.$$

$$\left. - \left(1 + \frac{\tau_{max}}{2k\sigma_y}\right)\ln\left(1 + \frac{\tau_{max}}{2k\sigma_y}\right) - \frac{\left(\frac{\tau}{2k\sigma_y}\right)^2}{1 + \frac{\tau_{max}}{2k\sigma_y}}\right\}$$

resulting from the last discussor's equation.

This contribution is extremely valuable and of great importance for investigation, analysis and technology of cables.

SECOND ORDER EFFECT IN
CRYSTAL PLASTICITY:
DEFORMATION OF SURFACE LAYERS IN
FACE-CENTERED CUBIC AGGREGATES

D. Rosenthal and W. B. Grupen

Department of Engineering, University of California, Los Angeles, U.S.A.

ABSTRACT

Deviations from proportionality in the (lattice) strain-stress relationships obtained by means of X-ray diffraction from surface layers of plastically-deformed aggregates cannot be reconciled with Taylor's theory of a homogeneous multislip mechanism[1]. It is found that as a rule the initial plastic deformation, at least up to 3%, proceeds in these layers with a much lower computed stress than that required by the multislip mechanism. The existence of a soft surface layer was further demonstrated experimentally by means of a flat polycrystalline specimen one grain thick. It is also known that a single slip mechanism can proceed with little or no strain-hardening. Based on this accumulated experimental evidence a model of heterogeneous plastic deformation is proposed for the soft surface layer. A two-fold mechanism of slip is visualized: a) a predominant single mechanism for the (unconstrained) region of the layer adjacent to the free surface and b) a multislip mechanism for the region adjacent to the grain boundary and to the deeper seated layers of the same grain.

The feasibility of a single slip is discussed from the point of view of the escape mechanism of dislocations through the free surface, and the feasibility of a heterogeneous plastic deformation is considered from the point of view of compatibility of deformation.

The model is shown to account satisfactorily for the observed experimental data. It is also apt to throw a light on the role of surface layers in fatigue.

1. Introduction.

The plastic behavior of surface layers in polycrystalline aggregates recently has attracted much attention because of its possible implication in fatigue [1]. From the point of view of crystal plasticity this behavior is but a part of a more general problem which consists of predicting the plastic behavior of polycrystalline aggregates from that of a single crystal. In 1928 G. Sachs attempted such a prediction for the axial tension of face-centered cubic (FCC) metals [2]. He assumed that each grain in the aggregate deforms by a single

---

(1) G. I. Taylor, *Journal Institute of Metals*, **62**, (1938), also *Deformation and Flow of Solids*, (I.U.T.A.M.) Springer, Berlin, (1956).

slip independently of its neighbors. As pointed out by G. I. Taylor [3] this assumption amounted to disregarding the geometrical continuity of the aggregate, but it led to establishing a lower bound on the average stress applied to the aggregate. To account for the fit between the grains Taylor previously advanced his own theory of a five slip mechanism [4]. An important feature of this theory is the assumption that each grain is subjected to the same homogeneous deformation as that which is measured macroscopically. This assumption was disproved by subsequent experimental evidence [5], [6]. However, Bishop and Hill [7] were able to show that under plausible conditions, discussed in Appendix C, it was permissible to compute the average axial stress acting on the aggregate as if the grains deformed in the manner assumed by Taylor. The satisfactory agreement between computed and measured stress-strain curves of polycrystalline aluminum in axial tension [4], appeared to provide convincing experimental support for Bishop and Hill's argument.

Taylor's theory did not concern itself with surface aggregates. However, Greenough [8] sought to find in this theory an explanation for the occurrence of residual stresses in surface aggregates of plastically extended polycrystalline thin wires of iron, copper, magnesium and aluminum. The stresses were determined by the X-ray diffraction techniques described in Part I. They were found to be of both signs: compressive in one type of aggregate, tensile in another type of aggregate. The occurrence as well as sign of the residual stresses were accounted for on Taylor's theory by the fact that while all grains deformed the same amount, the axial stresses to which they were subjected varied according to their orientation with respect to the axis of the specimen.

Subsequent work on larger specimens [9] revealed striking discrepancies with Taylor's theory. For one thing, the magnitude of the residual stresses differed by a factor varying from five to ten from that predicted by this theory. For another, the compressive residual stress appeared to predominate as if the whole surface layer were "softer" than the bulk of the material. In addition M. Kaufman showed in an unpublished thesis [10] that the magnitude of the residual stress tended to a constant value as the plastic strain began to exceed the first few %. The inference from this work was that the interactions responsible for the residual stress were of a transient nature: they appeared at the initiation of plastic deformation but tended to disappear at a later stage. Consequently they could not be based on Taylor's original multislip mechanism, because this mechanism was assumed to continue undisturbed throughout the whole range of plastic deformation.

Before a suitable modification of Taylor's theory could be attempted, it was necessary to clear up two points about which conflicting statements have been made in the literature [9]. One concerned the existence and behavior of the surface layer, the second pertained to the influence which the orientation of the surface aggregates had on the observed behavior. Accordingly two sets of experiments were performed: one of a more exploratory nature regarding the existence of the surface layer, the other of a more systematic nature regarding the role of orientation. Both are described in Part I of the present paper.

PART I. EXPERIMENTS

2. Experimental procedure.

As in most of the previous work the stresses acting on the surface aggregates were determined by the X-ray diffraction technique, because this technique explores only a thin surface layer, a few microns thick. The underlying procedure is based on Bragg's law which relates the angle of diffraction to the magnitude of the interplanar distance d_{hkl} of a given family of planes in an aggregate of grains suitably oriented for diffraction. When use is made of a spectrogoniometer, it is convenient to select aggregates in which the *interplanar distance d_{hkl} is normal to the surface*. For brevity such an aggregate will be called the [hkl] aggregate[2].

Suppose now the specimen is subjected to a uniaxial stress, tension or compression. The ensuing deformation causes a change Δd_{hkl} in the interplanar distance d_{hkl} and a corresponding shift $\Delta\theta$ in the diffraction angle θ. It follows from Bragg's law that

$$\varepsilon_{hkl} = \frac{\Delta d_{hkl}}{d_{hkl}} = -\cot\theta_m \Delta\theta_m \tag{1}$$

where θ_m refers to the so-called peak intensity measured in the diffraction record. The quantity ε_{hkl} is called *lattice strain*. The error from all sources affecting the measurement of ε_{hkl} has been estimated to be $\pm 20 \times 10^{-6}$, or $\pm 20\,\mu$ in/in in a more convenient notation. These sources are briefly reviewed in Appendix A.

Below the yield stress the lattice strain ε_{hkl} varies proportionally to the applied stress, σ_a as shown in Figures 3 and 4. In the case of elastic isotropy the same relationship exists between ε_{hkl} and the actual stress σ_{hkl} acting on the aggregate, and on Taylor's theory of homogeneous deformation this relationship between ε_{hkl} and σ_{hkl} extends into the plastic range as well. In particular the above relationship can be utilized to compute the amount of residual stress left in the aggregate on unloading as also shown in Figure 3 and 4.

---

(2) The notation [hkl] here refers to the so-called X-ray diffraction rather than crystallographic indices, see e.g. C.S. Barret, *Structure of Metals*, McGraw-Hill, N.Y., (1952).

A.   Exploratory tests. These tests consisted of measuring residual lattice strains in two types of polycrystalline aluminum alloy foil(3) specimens:

1) specimens of constant thickness, one grain thick and

2) specimens of different thicknesses containing many grains through the thickness.

The choice of the material was dictated by the following three considerations:

1) the face-centered cubic (FCC) type of crystal structure;

2) the near isotropy of the elastic constants;
and

3) the ease of producing grains of controlled size and thickness.

A1.   The object of the first series of tests was to decide between three alternatives regarding the origin of the residual stress:

1) interaction between surface and bulk aggregates, in which case no residual stress should be revealed;

2) interaction between soft and hard surface aggregates, in which case some of the residual stresses should be tensile and some should be compressive;
and

3) interaction between soft surface layer and hard interior of the same grain, in which case the residual stress should be largely compressive. The specimens had a uniform thickness of 0.005 inch and an average grain diameter of 0.015 inch. This choice of dimensions insured that each grain effectively occupied the whole thickness of the specimen, yet was small enough to form an aggregate of at least 10 grains for the selected interplanar distances d_{hkl}.(4)

The residual lattice strains were measured on duplicate specimens, after these specimens had been subjected to plastic strains — and corresponding axial stresses—reported in Table I. The lattice strains measured in the four aggregates [420], [511–333], [331], and [422] were compared to those computed from Taylor's theory. It is manifest from Table I that there is general disagreement in order of magnitude and partial disagreement in sign.

The presence of residual strains excludes the first alternative, the interaction between surface and bulk aggregates. The predominantly positive sign and disagreement with Taylor's theory makes the hypothesis of interaction between hard and soft surface aggregates highly unlikely. We are thus led to the conclu-

---

(3) Foil is defined as a sheet of metal .005 inch or less in thickness. The alloy was of the 1100 type in the annealed, stress-free, or 0 condition, with an average % composition: Si + Fe = 1.0; Cu = 0.2; Mn = 0.05; Zn = 0.10 others = 0.15; *Y.S.* (0.2% offset) = 4,000 psi and *T.S.* = 11,000 to 15,000 psi.

(4) For more details see reference [11].

TABLE I

Residual lattice strains in specimens one grain thick

Unloaded from		Residual lattice strains, $\times 10^6$ aggregates							
Stress	Strain	[420]		[511–333]		[331]		[422]	
psi	%	Meas- ured	Com- puted*	Meas- ured	Com- puted*	Meas- ured	Com- puted*	Meas- ured	Com- puted*
6200	0.75	33±35	12	30±20	6	—		—	
10400	3.25	97±20	20	100±10	10	—		—	
13000	9.00	139±20	25	135±20	13	127±20	—13	116±30	—14

* According to Taylor's Theory.

sion that the observed residual strains are due to an interaction between soft surface layer and hard interior of the same grain.[5]

*A*2. The object of this series of tests was to check further the hypothesis of soft surface layer by measuring residual strains in specimens of various thicknesses. The idea was that as the thickness of the specimen approached the thickness of the layer, less and less constraint would be imposed on the layer and consequently less and less residual strain should be observed. Since it was technically difficult to achieve uniform strain by extension of foils less than 0.005 inch thick, the residual strains were produced by rolling. The equivalence of this procedure with tension was checked on specimens 0.005 inch thick. The influence of extraneous factors such as surface friction also has been taken into account. [11]

TABLE II

Residual lattice strains in specimens of various thicknesses and average grain size 0.0015 inch

Specimen thickness inch	Strain %	Residual lattice strain, $\times 10^6$ aggregate		Remark
		[420]	[511–333]	
0.005	9	145±15	125±10	Tension
0.005	8	150±15	125±10	Rolling
0.002	8	110±10	70±10	Rolling
0.001	8	70±20	25±15	Rolling

Table II summarizes the data for the most sensitive aggregates [420] and [511–333]. It is seen that the residual lattice strains are drastically reduced as the thickness has decreased from 0.005 to 0.001 inch. Extrapolation of data,

---

[5] Since the strains are measured at right angle to the applied stress, positive strains correspond to compressive axial stresses.

Figure 1 suggests that they fall to zero as the thickness is reduced to a small fraction of 0.001 inch. This finding not only lends support to the existence of soft surface layer in the observed aggregates, but it also gives a rough estimate of its thickness, which appears to be of the order of a few microns.

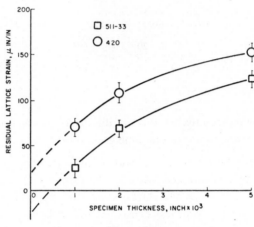

Figure 1

Influence of thickness of specimen on the amount of lattice strain in surface layer of [420] and [511–333] aggregates

B. Systematic tests. The exploratory tests which have been described gave substantial evidence for the existence of a soft surface layer in aggregates adjacent to the free surface of the specimen. Yet, they did not give enough indication as to how the residual stresses varied with the orientation of these aggregates. In order to make the variation more conspicuous it was desirable to increase the magnitude of the observed lattice strains, especially since according to Kaufman [10], most of the discrepancy was to be expected at low values of the applied plastic strain. By the same token it seemed also more expedient to multiply the readings by taking them under stepwise increasing loads rather than by loading and unloading the specimen each time.

To fulfill the first objective the low yield stress aluminum alloy 1100 was replaced by a high stress aluminum alloy 6061([6]). The second objective was realized simply by mounting the loading device directly on the goniometer table. However, in view of the limited size of the table it was necessary to load the specimens in compression rather than in tension. Comparison of the lattice strains of the [420] aggregate obtained in compression with the lattice strains

([6]) Nominal % composition: Cu = 0.25; Si = 0.6, Mg = 1.0, Cr = 0.25, Yield Strength (0.2% offset) = 7,700 psi, *T.S.* = 18,000 psi in the stress free or 0 condition.

obtained previously by M. Kaufman in tension [10] disclosed no significant differences due to change of sign of the applied load. The details of the loading assembly are further discussed in Appendix B.

3. Experimental results.

The experimental data have been summarized in the form of diagrams as follows.

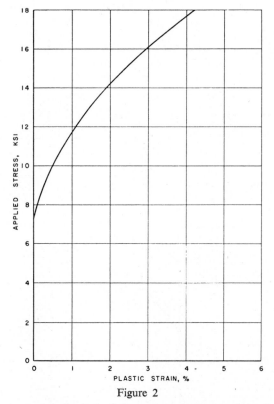

Figure 2

Applied stress versus plastic strain in compression for 6061 aluminum alloy

Figure 2 represents the applied, true, stress versus plastic strain in compression on duplicate specimens up to about 5% strain and 19,000 psi, which corresponded to the maximum capacity of the load cell. Extrapolation of the curve to zero plastic strain gives a value of about 7500 psi in reasonable aggreement with the 0.2% Yield Strength in tension. Since it was necessary to maintain a constant load during the X-ray exposure, the plot of Figure 2 does not correspond to a constant rate of loading. Rather, the plastic strain at a given stress level was the amount measured after the transient creep had practically subsided. The additional strain due to creep was of the order of 0.5% at each level.

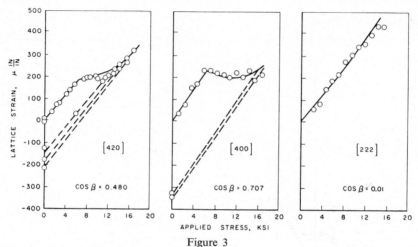

Figure 3

Lattice strains versus applied stress for aggregates [400] [420] and [222]

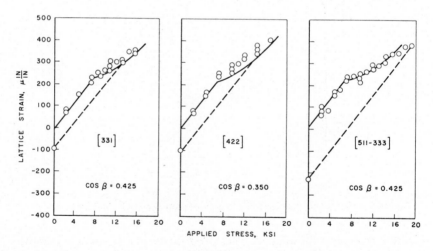

Figure 4

Lattice strains versus applied stress for aggregates [331] [422] and [511–333]

The lattice strains for the various aggregates [*hkl*] are plotted in Figures 3 and 4 as a function of the applied stress. Some general features can be noted at once.

a. There is the expected proportionality between lattice strain and applied stress in the elastic range. The slope of the line varies slightly with direction. It is the smallest for the [222] aggregate and the largest for the [400] aggregate —in accord with the directional properties of the Young's modulus of elasticity. However, the variation is not great[7] and it is consistent with the small elastic anisotropy of aluminum.

b. With the exception of the [222] aggregate all plots depart from proportionality at about the value of the applied stress corresponding to 0.2% Yield Strength; the curve becomes less steep, but it resumes a steeped (upward) trend at some higher stress. This stress is different for different orientations. It is the highest for the [400] aggregate, with the result that the stress interval covering the low grade portion of the curve is here the widest. The interval reduces to zero for the [222] aggregate which preserves the proportional trend throughout the whole range of stress.

Commensurate with these intervals are also the amounts of residual strain left after unloading. The strains before and after unloading corresponding to the same applied stress are connected by straight lines which follow rather closely the original slope in the elastic range.

Compared to the exploratory tests reported previously the systematic tests confirm the fact that the surface layer as a whole is "softer" than the bulk of the material. In addition they show that the softness is due to the tendency on the part of the layer to strain harden less than the bulk of the material, rather than to its having a lower yield stress. This tendency which is manifest at lower plastic strains tends to taper off at higher plastic strains. However, the most conspicuous feature of the observed strain hardening is its strong dependence on the nature of the aggregate [hkl] to which the surface layer belongs.

PART II. THEORY

The experimental data on aluminum alloys reported in Part I clearly indicate that Taylor's multislip mechanism cannot explain satisfactorily the trends observed in the lattice strain-stress diagrams of surface layers of FCC aggregates in the plastic range. The main shortcoming of this mechanism appears to be its inability to account for the strong dependence on orientation which the strain hardening of these layers exhibits during the first few percent of plastic flow. The almost total lack of strain hardening in the surface layer of the [400] aggregate suggests that a single slip may play a major role in the mechanism of plastic deformation near the surface. For it is known that only single slip can initiate plastic deformation without strain hardening. Of course, a single

---

(7) Considering the experimental error of 4%.

slip mechanism cannot operate in the bulk of the material, but it might conceivably operate in the surface layer because of its thinness and proximity to the free surface. On the atomic scale the phenomenon is reduced to the motion of dislocations. We must therefore examine under what circumstances dislocations escaping through the free surface can be made to conform to the mechanism of single slip in the layer of crystal adjacent to this surface.

Consider first what happens in the bulk of the crystal, Here the multislip mechanism is assumed to operate in accordance with Taylor's theory. Let ρ be the density of dislocations, i.e., the number of dislocation lines per unit area of the crystal, corresponding to the imposed axial strain ε_0 in uniaxial tension. The density ρ is known to increase with ε_0 from an order of magnitude of 10^8 to 10^{12} per sq. cm. as ε_0 increases from a fraction to a tenfold of one percent.

When the axial strain changes from ε_0 to $\varepsilon_0 + \Delta\varepsilon_0$, there is a corresponding shear strain increment $\Delta\gamma_i$ on each of the operative slip systems. In turn, to each increment $\Delta\gamma_i$ there corresponds an average displacement Δl_i of the dislocations belonging to the slip system i such that [8]

$$b\rho\Delta l_i = \Delta\gamma_i \tag{1}$$

Here b is the Burgers vector, i.e. the unit distance the atoms above the slip plane move with respect to the atoms below the slip plane, when one dislocation line has passed from one end of the crystal to the other. Alternatively consider a portion of crystal one unit thick. Then the product $\rho\Delta l_i$ represents the number of dislocation lines that have passed through this portion to produce the imposed shear strain increment $\Delta\gamma_i$.

Summing the contributions from all actual slip systems to the imposed axial strain increment $\Delta\varepsilon_0$, we have for a randomly oriented aggregate in accordance with Taylor's theory

$$b\rho\Delta l_a = T_a\Delta\varepsilon_0 \tag{2}$$

where T_a is a numerical factor, equal approximately to 3.1, and $\Delta l_a = \Sigma\Delta l_i$. Both are averaged over the whole randomly oriented polycrystalline aggregate.

In the case of surface grains we are interested not in the whole aggregate but in aggregates $[hkl]$ having a common interplanary distance d_{hkl} normal to the free surface. For such aggregates a formula similar to Eq. (2) can be derived, viz.

$$b\rho\Delta l_{hkl} = T_{hkl}\Delta\varepsilon_0 \tag{3}$$

---

[8] see e.g. A. Cottrell, *Dilocations and Plastic Flow in Crystals*, Clarendon Press, Oxford (1953).

in which T_{hkl} has the values listed in Table III for the crystallographic directions considered in the present work.

TABLE III

Averaged resolved shear — axial strain ratios for Taylor's five slip system, T_{hkl} and single slip system, S_{hkl} as well as direction cosines of the single slip direction in [hkl] aggregates

Aggregate [hkl]	T_{hkl}	S_{hkl}	$\cos \beta$
400	2.9	2.1	0.707
420	3.0	2.2	0.480
511–333	3.05	2.2	0.425
331	3.2	2.4	0.425
422	3.15	2.3	0.350
222	3.40	2.3	0.01
Averaged over all aggregates	T_a 3.1	S_a 2.2	

The above relationships apply when plastic flow has already set in. Prior to the initiation of plastic flow single slip can already begin to operate on the most favorably oriented slip system in the interior of the grain as well as in its layer adjacent to the free surface. However, in the interior of the grain it cannot continue operating alone because of the constraints imposed on the displacements at the grain boundaries. At variance with this restriction single slip can conceivably not only begin but also continue operating in the regions of the surface layers sufficiently removed from the grain boundaries, because here the presence of a free surface imposes less constraints on displacements. This should be particularly true of shear displacements normal to the surface. We postulate accordingly that *single slip is feasible only when it contributes to these displacements*. The geometrical and physical feasibility of single slip in the surface layer is further discussed in Appendix C.

Assuming the validity of the proposed model we now proceed to the evaluation of the fraction of dislocations which are responsible for the shear displacement normal to the free surface. We consider a wafer of the surface layer one unit thick, comprised between two planes of the assumed single slip system. Let $N_1 = \rho_1 \Delta l_1$ be the number of dislocations leaving the wafer through the free surface. The relative shear displacement caused by their motion is then

$$\Delta \gamma_1 = N_1 b \tag{4}$$

and the relative displacement in the direction z normal to the free surface is

$$\Delta \gamma_1 \cos \beta = b N_1 \cos \beta \tag{5}$$

where β is the angle between the direction of the Burgers vector and the normal to the free surface.

Alternately we can call the product

$$N_t = N_1 \cos \beta \qquad (6)$$

the number of dislocations per unit thickness of the wafer contributing to the shear displacement normal to the surface.

The dislocations N_t are made up of two streams: a) the dislocations which have passed through the interface separating the surface layer from the remainder of the crystal, b) the dislocations which have been activated within the surface layer. Not all of these dislocations will escape through the free surface. Some of them will get stuck due to interactions with other dislocations, point defects, etc. We shall assume that on passing through a layer of thickness dz in the direction normal to the free surface, the fraction dN_z of the arriving dislocations N_z that gets stuck is proportional to N_z and dz, thus

$$dN'_z = -\alpha N_z dz \qquad (7)$$

At the same time new dislocations have been provided from the layer dz. Let $\rho_0 \Delta l_0$ be the average number of the contributing dislocations per unit thickness for the whole surface layer and let t be the thickness of this layer.

Then the contribution from the layer dz will be

$$dN''_z = \rho_0 \Delta l_0 \, dz/t \qquad (8)$$

and the total contribution will be

$$dN_z = -\alpha N_z \, dz + \rho_0 \Delta l_0 \, dz/t \qquad (9)$$

Solving for N_z we have

$$N_z = C e^{-\alpha z} + \rho_0 \Delta l_0/\alpha t \qquad (10)$$

where C is a constant of integration.

For $z = 0, N_z$ is the number of dislocations contributed from the interior of the grain. The total number of dislocations arriving from all slip systems is $\rho \Delta l_{hkl}$ according to Eq. (3). Let δ be the contributing fraction. Then

$$C = \delta \rho \Delta l_{hkl} - \rho_0 \Delta l_0/\alpha t \qquad (11)$$

and

$$N_z = \delta \rho \Delta l_{hkl} \, e^{-\alpha z} + \rho_0 \Delta l_0 (1 - e^{-\alpha z})/\alpha t \qquad (12)$$

For $z = t =$ thickness of the surface layer

$$N_t = \delta\rho\Delta l_{hkl}\,e^{-\alpha t} + \rho_0\Delta l_0\,(1 - e^{-\alpha t})/\alpha t \tag{13}$$

When $t \to \infty$, $N_t \to \rho_0\Delta l_0/\alpha t$ (14)
and according to Eq. (6)

$$N_1 \to \rho_0\Delta l_0/\alpha t \cos\beta \tag{15}$$

i.e. N_1 tends to a constant value independent of the conditions prevailing in the grain interior. On this view relation (15) also characterizes the plastic deformation of a thick single crystal in single slip. There are, however, indications in the literature [12] that such a grain would strain-harden as readily as if it were subjected to a multislip mechanism in a polycrystalline aggregate. That is, the shear strain increment $N_1 b$ is equivalent to the shear strain increment $\rho\Delta l_{hkl} b$, insofar as the behaviour of an aggregate of thick single crystals is concerned, having all a common interplanar distance d_{hkl} normal to the surface. We can therefore write

$$\rho\Delta l_{hkl} b = N_1 b = b\rho_0\Delta l_0/\alpha t \cos\beta \tag{16}$$

whence

$$\rho_0\Delta l_0/\alpha t = \rho\Delta l_{hkl} \cos\beta \tag{17}$$

and formula (13) becomes

$$N_t = \rho\Delta l_{hkl}\left[\delta e^{-\lambda/\cos\beta} + \cos\beta\,(1 - e^{-\lambda/\cos\beta})\right] \tag{18}$$

where for convenience we have put

$$\rho_0\Delta l_0/\rho\Delta l_{hkl} = \lambda \tag{19}$$

The corresponding amount of shear strain increment is

$$\Delta\gamma_t = bN_t \tag{20}$$

This increment, we recall, is due to a single slip mechanism. Hence the average contribution from the $[hkl]$ aggregate to the axial strain increment $\Delta\varepsilon_0$ is not $\Delta\gamma_t/T_{hkl}$, as in the case of a multislip mechanism, but $\Delta\gamma_t/S_{hkl}$, where the coefficients S_{hkl} have been computed and are listed in column 3, Table III for the aggregates of interest in the present work. Calling $\alpha_{hkl}\Delta\varepsilon_0$ the corresponding contribution to the axial strain increment, we have

$$\Delta\gamma_t/S_{hkl} = \alpha_{hkl}\Delta\varepsilon_0 \tag{21}$$

or using relations (20) and (18)

$$b\rho l_{hkl}/S_{hkl} \left[\delta e^{-\lambda/\cos\beta} + \cos\beta \left(1 - e^{-\lambda/\cos\beta} \right) \right] = \alpha_{hkl}\Delta\varepsilon_0 \tag{22}$$

Replacing the product $b\rho\Delta l_{khl}$ by its expression (3) we have finally

$$\frac{T_{hkl}}{S_{hkl}} \left[\delta e^{-\lambda/\cos\beta} + \cos\beta \left(1 - e^{-\lambda/\cos\beta} \right) \right] = \alpha_{hkl} \tag{23}$$

According to Equations (20) and (21) $\alpha_{hkl}\Delta\varepsilon_0$ is due to dislocations contributing to the component of shear displacement normal to the surface, Since there are no constraints imposed on this component, it appears feasible to postulate that the *resulting fraction of axial strain causes little or no strain hardening at the strain level* ε_0. Under this assumption the increase $\Delta\sigma_{hkl}$ of the stress applied to the surface layer beyond the yield stress $\sigma_{Y.S.}$ depends mainly on $(1 - \alpha_{hkl})\varepsilon_0$. For simplicity we shall assume that it depends only on this fraction, Putting

$$1 - \alpha_{hkl} = \omega_{hkl} \tag{24}$$

we have

$$\Delta\sigma_{hkl}(\omega_{hkl}\varepsilon_0) = \frac{T_{hkl}}{T_a}\Delta\sigma_a(\omega_{hkl}\varepsilon_0) \tag{25}$$

where T_a and $\Delta\sigma_a$ refer to the whole randomly oriental polycrystalline aggregate.

The functional relation between $\Delta\sigma_a$ and ε_0 is provided by the ordinary stress strain diagram, Figure 2. The increase $\Delta\sigma_{hkl}$ can therefore be read from the same diagram by substituting $\omega_{hkl}\varepsilon_0$ for ε_0.

To obtain the numerical value of ω_{hkl} we still must determine the values oï δ, λ and $\cos\beta$. Of these cosine β for various $[hkl]$ aggregates can be obtained by the same averaging procedure as S_{hkl} and T_{hkl}. They are listed in column 4, Table III for the aggregates of our current interest.

The quantities λ and δ cannot be determined from the proposed model and they must be obtained experimentally. The coefficient λ, we recall, is the ratio of the number of dislocations per unit length generated in the surface layer by single slip to the number of dislocations per unit length generated in the interior of the same grain by multislip for the same axial strain. This ratio can therefore be expected to depend mainly on S_{hkl}/T_{hkl}. However, according to Table III the ratio S_{hkl}/T_{hkl} is almost the same for all the aggregates under review. We have therefore assumed λ to be a constant.

The fraction δ conceivably can likewse depend on S_{hkl}/T_{hkl} and on that account it can be taken to be the same for all aggregates. However, it cannot be assumed to be independent of ε_0. Indeed, an increase of axial strain is apt to produce a greater entanglement of dislocations at the multislip—single slip interface thereby decreasing the value of δ. In view of the small amount of plastic strain imposed on the specimens in the present work, a linear dependence of δ on axial strain appeared sufficient. That is

$$\delta = a + b\varepsilon_0 \tag{26}$$

where a and b are two more constants to be added to λ. We are thus saddled with three unknowns for the determination of which three experimental data must be provided. Considering however the wealth and variety of data presented in Figures 3 and 4 this restriction does not seem to be particularly serious insofar as the experimental check of the proposed model is concerned.

To minimize the error we have selected the three experimental data from those obtained on aggregates [400] and [420] for which the deviations from proportionality were the greatest. Thus we have picked out

a) the value of lattice strain at the applied stress of 16 ksi in the [400] aggregate,

b) the value of lattice strain at the same applied stress of 16 ksi in the [420] aggregate, and

c) we have subjected ω to the condition $(d\sigma_{420}/d\sigma_a) \to 0$ as plastic strain $\varepsilon_0 \to 0$. This amounts, as easily seen, to putting $\omega = 0$ for $\varepsilon_0 = 0$.[9]

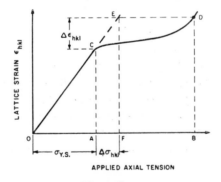

Figure 5

Conversion of lattice strain increment $\Delta\varepsilon_{hkl}$ to stress increment $\Delta\tau_{hkl}$ (schematic)

---

(9) This follows from Equation (25) and the fact that the slope $d\sigma_a(\omega\varepsilon_o) \,/\, d(\omega\varepsilon_o)$ becomes equal to the slope $d\sigma_a(\varepsilon_o)/d\varepsilon_o$ when the plastic strain tends to zero. We have accordingly

$$\frac{d\sigma_{hkl}(\omega\varepsilon_0)}{d\sigma_a(\varepsilon_0)} = \frac{T_{hkl}}{T_a}\frac{d\sigma_a(\omega\varepsilon_0)}{d\varepsilon_0} \bigg/ \frac{d\sigma_a(\varepsilon_0)}{d\varepsilon_0} = \frac{T_{hkl}}{T_a}\frac{d\sigma_a(\omega\varepsilon_0)}{d(\omega\varepsilon_0)}\left[\frac{d\omega}{d\varepsilon_0}\varepsilon_0 + \omega\right] \bigg/ \frac{d\sigma_a(\varepsilon_0)}{d\varepsilon_0}$$

For ε_o tending to zero this expression tends to $T_{hkl}\omega/T_a$.

With the data provided under a) and b) the values of the corresponding stress increments $\Delta\sigma_{hkl}$ can be read directly from the lattice strain-stress diagrams using a graphical procedure. This is illustrated in Figure 5. The line OC embodies the relationship, the Hooke's law, existing between lattice strain and axial stress acting on the surface layer of the hkl aggregate below the yield stress. We postulate the same relationship above the yield stress, as indicated by the dashed line CE. Below the yield stress the axial stress, σ_{hkl} acting on the aggregate is also very nearly the same as the applied stress, σ_a, because of the near isotropy of the elastic constants in aluminum and its alloys. However, above the yield stress σ_{hkl} is different from σ_a which accounts for the departure from proportionality manifest in the diagram OCD. To obtain the stress increment $\Delta\sigma_{hkl}$ corresponding to the applied stress OB it suffices to relocate the lattice strain DB on the extension of the line OC. The stress increment $\Delta\sigma_{hkl}$ can then be read directly as the intercept AF on the abscissa. Using the same procedure in reverse it is of course possible to compute the whole portion CD from known values of $\Delta\sigma_{hkl}$, i.e. according to Eq. (25) from known values of ω_{hkl}.

Results.

The procedure illustrated in Figure 5 has been used first to obtain the values of the constants, a, b, and λ. We found it was sufficient to round off the results to one significant figure. These were as follows

$$a = 1, \quad b = -10, \quad \lambda = 0.4$$

Knowing the values of the constants we could then compute systematically the values of $\Delta\sigma_{hkl}$ as a function of ε_0 for all aggregates under review. The corresponding values of lattice strains were obtained using the procedure of Figure 5 in reverse. They were plotted as solid lines past the yield stress in Figure 3 and 4. Considering the probable error of $\pm 30\ \mu$ in/in the agreement between computation and experiment is judged to be satisfactory.

4. Discussion.

According to our second postulate as long as ω is less than one, the stress in the surface layer will be smaller than the applied uniaxial stress. True, the factor T_{hkl}/T_a exceeds unity for several aggregates, but according to Table III the increment is small, less than 10%, and for small strains it is more than offset by the overriding influence of $\cos\beta$. The aggregate [222] is a notable exception. Here the slip direction happens to make a right angle with the surface normal in most of the grains belonging to the aggregate. The contribution to $\cos \beta$ from the remainder of the grains is not sufficient to influence the average $\cos \beta$ substantially. As a result this average is close to zero and ω is close to unity. That is, the surface layer of the [222] aggregate is subjected to about the same stress as the bulk of the material, in agreement with experimental findings.

While more extensive data are necessary to reach a final conclusion, it seems reasonable to expect that behavior similar to that of the [222] aggregate is an exception rather than a rule, and that the surface layer as a whole should strain harden less than the grain interior for small plastic strains. This expectation is borne out by the results of work by Andrade and Kennedy [16] on "A Surface Effect in the Creep Behavior of Polycrystalline Lead". Commenting on these results Andrade [14] stated "that the surface layer, of thickness of the order of grain diameter, opposed an abnormally low resistance to the longitudinal stress" That the observed low resistance may be due to a greater ease of slip is strongly suggested by later work of Rachinger [15]. According to this investigation slip contributed much more to the high temperature creep of aluminum at the surface of the specimen than in its interior, where grain boundary movement was the predominant contribution. However, the most convincing proof regarding the existence of the surface layer and its low strain hardening ability is provided by the work of Wood [16]. Wood showed that in the course of fatigue under low applied stress a sliding movement occured on a family of parallel planes confined to a surface layer of a few microns thick. This movement led ultimately to a crack formation at the interface between the surface layer and the grain interior. The lack of strain hardening was inferred from the persistence of sharp X-ray diffraction records throughout the test.

5. Conclusion.

The data presented in this paper and the theoretical model devised for their interpretation all lend support to the conclusion that the surface layer of polycrystalline face-centered cubic aggregates strain hardens less in the early stages of plastic deformation than the bulk of the material.

1. The experimental evidence is based on the values of lattice strain measured in various aggregates of a polycrystalline aluminum and aluminum alloy. There is further evidence that the obtained result is confined to a thin surface layer a few microns thick of the grain, and that it varies with the orientation of the grain with respect to the surface. There is a final indication that the observed "softness" of the surface layer tends to disappear with increasing amounts of plastic deformation.

2. The proposed theoretical model accounts satisfactorily for the observed behavior by considering the motion and interactions of dislocations near the free surface. For lack of a quantitative knowledge regarding the nature and extent of interactions occuring on the atomic level two appropriate postulates are made concerning the nature and extent of a single slip in the surface layer. They are based on the known fact that only single slip can produce plastic deformation without causing immediate strain hardening. They also imply that the proposed model is physically feasible – a point which, however, deserves further scrutiny.

3. The fact that the "softness" of the surface layer tends to disappear with increasing plastic strain is an indication that the plastic behavior of the layer ultimately may be governed by the same multislip mechanism as the underlying grain interior. This is also implied by the behavior of the theoretical model. For that reason it appears justified to classify the observed phenomenon as a second order effect of crystal plasticity.

6. Acknowledgements.

The authors wish to express their indebtness to the Air Office of Scientific Research for the support of the experimental work, labelled "Systematic Tests" in the paper. They also wish to acknowledge the contributions of Dr. N. E. Friedman and Dr. D. Hazony to the phase of research concerned with these tests.

APPENDIX A

ESTIMATED ERRORS IN COMPUTATION OF LATTICE STRAIN

Two sorts of errors affect this computation. One has to do with the use of the angular shift $\Delta\theta_m$, the other concerns the location of the peak intensity.

a. The use of the angular shift of the peak intensity introduces an error which depends on the degree of line broadening [17]. The error is small so long as the diffraction line remains narrow. However, the onset of plastic deformation is generally accompanied by line broadening, and as a result the error is no longer negligible. For the experimental conditions listed in Table IV it has been estimated to reach a value of 60×10^{-6}, when the κ alpha one two doublet becomes unresolved. Incidentally, the same error appears to result from use of the angular shift of the centroid of the combined lines K alpha one and two [17].

In the present work the line broadening even at the final stage of deformation, which was 5%, was still far below the amount causing disappearance of the

TABLE IV

Data on X-ray diffraction

Slit system: Colimating slit 4°; blocked off laterally to irradiate an area 6 mm wide.
Receiving slit: front 1°, back 2°. Scanning speed: 1/8° per minute. Time constant: 48 seconds

Target	Crystal direction	Diffraction angle ($K\alpha$)	% Intensity diffracted by surface grains
Cr	111 (222)	78.28	96
Co	100 (400)	62.00	86
Co	331	74.32	83
Co	210 (420)	80.99	82
Cu	211 (422)	68.70	66
Cu	511– 111	81.19	62

doublet. In terms of the half-width of the K alpha line it was estimated as having caused at the most a threefold increase of the initial half width value. The estimated error in strain would then be less than 20×10^{-6}. The experimental error was much larger.

b. Most, if not all, of the experimental error resulted from the difficulties attending the location of the peak intensity in a continuous run. Since the change of the count rate with angle is zero at the maximum intensity, spurious effects cannot be smoothed out. This is readily seen in the typical intensity records, Figure 6. The direct determination of the position of the peak intensity was therefore abandoned. Instead two indirect methods were used. One of the methods—the slope intersection method—consisted of extending the practically straight portions of the curve at the inflexion points to their intersection at point K, Figure 6. The location of this "virtual" peak could be established to within $\pm 0.01°$. The other method — the peak separation method — consisted of the determination of the true peak by a graphical procedure based on the separation of the K alpha one two doublet, [18] Figure 7.

The latter procedure utilizes more information from the record than the former. However, it is also affected by a larger experimental error, since it is confined to the lower portions of the curves, and it is inapplicable for a large overlap of these curves.

As an additional check the angular shift of the centroid of the combined K alpha one and two curves was also determined. Here, all the information contained in the record is being utilized. However, the result is greatly affected

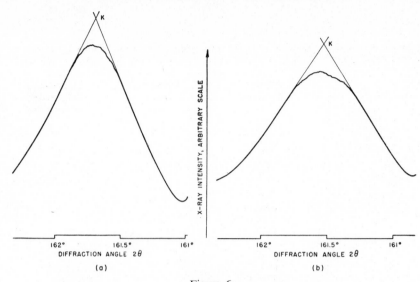

Figure 6

The slope intercept method of determining the diffraction peak position
(a) Elastic range (b) Plastic range

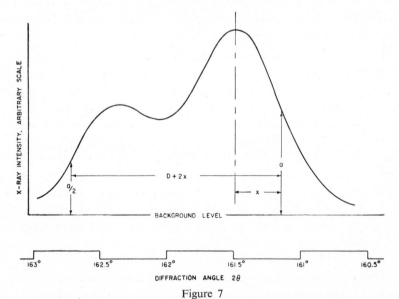

Figure 7

The peak separation method of determining the diffraction peak positions

by the somewhat arbitrary location of the background cut-off. In the final
analysis, none of the three methods wherever used appeared to be superior in
reproducibility to the two others.

Most of the experimental data in the systematic tests could be plotted on a smooth curve to within $\pm 30 \times 10^{-6}$ or $\pm 30\mu$ in/in in a more convenient notation. Points outside these limits also revealed larger discrepancies between the three methods. As they occured mostly at the final stage of deformation, the distortion of the intensity profiles due to excessive line broadening could not be ruled out. These points were not included in the final plots.

APPENDIX B

DETAILS OF SPECIMENS AND LOADING ASSEMBLY FOR COMPRESSION TESTS

The specimens were machined in the form of hollow cylinders 1/2 in. O.D., 5/16 in. I.D., and 1.2 in. long. They were strung, along with a hollow cylindrical load cell, on a hardened steel bolt. The pressure on both, the specimen and the load cell, was applied by tightening one of the retaining nuts which were threaded on the bolt. A special ring sliding over a flattened portion of the bolt was inserted between the nut and the specimen to eliminate torsional effects which might be produced by tightening. The bolt also served as a rotating shaft. The necessary driving force was provided by a stream of compressed air impinging on a small impeller soldered to one of the nuts. The total assembly and the details are shown in Figures 8 and 9, respectively.

The rotation of the loading assembly about its axis was used to average out variations of stress due to eccentric loading, to insure a more representative sampling, and to attenuate spurious effects of grain size on the profile of the diffracted X-ray intensity.

The load cell was calibrated up to 4000 lbs. with a probable error of ± 30 lbs. or ± 250 psi in terms of the stress applied to the specimen.

Because of the short length of the specimen, the mechanical strain was determined from the variation of the external diameter under load. The measurements were taken only in the plastic range. They were converted to axial strain by assuming constant volume. Since the diameter was measured only to $\pm 5 \times 10^{-4}$, the strains had a probable error of $\pm 0.2\%$.

APPENDIX C

GEOMETRICAL AND PHYSICAL FEASIBILITY OF SINGLE SLIP IN SURFACE LAYER

Assume for simplicity the surface layer has the form of a wafer with a square base, and let one side of the square be aligned with the axial or x direction. The geometrical feasibility of single slip in the central portion of this layer can be insured in the simplest way by assigning a relative width $= \alpha_{hkl}$ to this portion, where α_{hkl} is given by Eq. (23) of the main body of the paper, and by subjecting the displacements to a continuous transition from the value

Figure 8

The Compression loading assembly mounted on the goniometer table (A) Frame supporting the loading assembly. (B) Bearing allowing free rotation of the loading assembly. (C) Bearing. (I) Compressed air outlet for rotating the specimen. (O) Vertical circle with a Vernier for varying the inclination of the specimen axis with respect to the incident beam. (T) Goniometer table. (L) Leveling and adjusting screw. (K) Knife edge for setting the irradiated surface in the path of the beam.

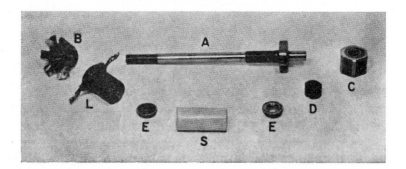

Figure 9

Exploded view of the compression loading assembly. (A) Central threaded shaft for supporting the specimen and the load cell. (B) Left end nut provided with an impeller to drive the shaft. (C) Retaining nut. (D) Sliding anti-torsion ring. (E, E) Fittings. (L) Load cell consisting of a hollow steel cylinder with strain gages. (S) Specimen in the form of a hollow cylinder

imposed by the single slip to the value imposed by uniaxial tension at the grain boundary. To comply with these two boundary conditions the transition region must be subjected to a heterogeneous multislip mechanism.

In Figure 10 the transition from single slip to uniaxial tension has been depicted schematically for the displacement u_x in the axial direction by neglecting the changes in the thickness of z direction. If ε_0 is the average macroscopic strain in the x direction, $\alpha_{hkl}\varepsilon_0$ is the contribution to this strain from the single

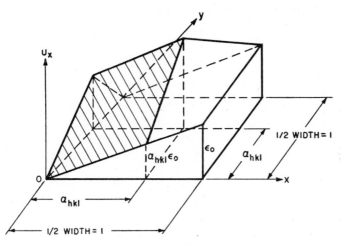

Figure 10

Schematic representation of the transition of axial displacement u_x in the single slip region to the uniaxial displacement u_x at the grain boundary

slip and $(1-\alpha_{hkl})\varepsilon_0$ is the contribution from the multiple slip displacements. Similar diagrams can be drawn for the displacements in the y and z directions. The average macroscopic strains ε_{yy} and ε_{zz} computed from the displacements u_y and u_z at the grain boundary can still be made equal to $-\varepsilon_0/2$ as in uniaxial tension, and likewise the average macroscopic shear strains can be made equal to zero, but the local strains in the single slip region and in the transition region will be quite different from either $-\varepsilon_0/2$ or zero. Under these circumstances the establishment of physical feasibility of the proposed model becomes a formidable problem, unless some simplifying assumptions can be made.

Bishop and Hill [7] were able to specify a condition under which it is permissible to compute the average macroscopic stress acting on an aggregate from the work of deformation by assuming that all grains deform homogeneously under the imposed macroscopic strain. The condition is that the statistical distribution of the aggregate is such that no correlation exists between local stress and displacement over any plane section through the specimen. This condition becomes obviously too restrictive when applied to the surface layer of a selective aggregate of crystals of the [hkl] variety. Nevertheless, we adopt it as a working hypothesis for want of a better approach. Accordingly, we compute the average macroscopic stress acting on the surface layer of an [hkl] aggregate from the work of deformation by assuming that all contributing layers deform homogeneously under imposed macroscopic strain. This assumption has been used implicity in deriving Eq. (25) of the main body of the paper.

REFERENCES

[1] N. THOMPSON, Some Observations on the Early stages of Fatigue Fracture, in Monograph on *Fracture*, Edit. B.L. Averbach et al. The Technology Press of M.I.T. and John Wiley & Sons. N. Y., (1959).

[2] G. SACHS, *Z. VDI*, **72**, (1928), 734.

[3] G. I. TAYLOR, 1955 *I. U. T. A. M. Colloquium in Madrid*, Julius Springer, Berlin, 1956.

[4] G. I. TAYLOR, *Journal Institute of Metals*, **62**, (1938), 307.

[5] S. C. BARRET AND L. H. LEVENSON, *Trans. A. I. M. E.* **137**, (1940), 112.

[6] W. BOAS AND G. J. OGILVIE, *Acta Metallurgica*, **2**, (1954), 655.

[7] J. F. W. BISHOP AND R. HILL, *Phil. Mag.*, **42**, (1951), 414 and **42**, (1951), 1298.

[8] G. B. GREENOUGH, *Proc. Roy. Soc.*, **A197**, (1944), 556.

[9] G. B. GREENOUGH, *Progress in Metal Physics*, **3**, (1952), 176, Interscience, New York.

[10] M. KAUFMAN, *X-ray Lattice Strains in Plastically Deformed Metals*, Ph. D. Thesis University of California, Los Angeles, (1954).

[11] W. B. Grupen, *Residual Lattice Strains in Aluminum*, M. S. Thesis, University of California, Los Angeles, (1959).

[12] M. S. PATERSON, *Acta Metallurgica*, **3**, (1955), 491.

[13] E. N. DA C. ANDRADE AND A. J. KENNEDY, *Proceedings Phys. Soc.*, **64**, (1951), 363.

[14] E. N. DA C. ANDRADE, The Concept of Creep, in Monograph *Creep and Recovery*, A. S. M., 1957, Cleveland, Ohio.

[15] A. W. RACHINGER, *Journal Inst. of Metals*, **81**, (1952), 33.

[16] W. A. WOOD, Some Basic Studies of Fatigue in Metals, in Monogtaph on *Fracture* (see ref. 1).

[17] A. R. LANG, *Journal of Applied Physics*, **27**, (1956), 485.

[18] W. A. RACHINGER, *Journal of Scientific Instruments*, **25**, (1948), 254.

DISCUSSION

D. C. DRUCKER:

The specimens employed were just one grain thick. Does this affect the discrepancy between the prediction of Taylor's theory and data?

F. K. G. ODQVIST:

Would not the beautiful researches given by Professor Rosenthal revive the X-ray measurements of stresses in structural parts under load which were popular in the 1930-ies? This might be possible due to the fact that we may now obtain a sound basis for calculating a correction taking account for the compression stresses usually observed in such measurements.

CH. H. LERCHENTHAL:

Prof. Rosenthal mentioned two techniques for measuring strains in micro-crystallites. There is a third method which might prove useful viz, the photoelastic surface layer technique. It has been shown, at least qualitatively, that this technique is capable of differentiating between the strains in individual metal crystallites [1]. It would be interesting to know whether it has been tried to employ this method for quantitative determination of the kind of strains with which Prof. Rosenthal's paper dealt.

PROF. D. ROSENTHAL'S REPLY:

1. In reply to Dr. Drucker's question, the interaction between adjacent surface grains would lead to the same result as the interaction between grains in the bulk, and it would not account for the observed discrepancy between Taylor's multislip theory and the experimental data. Neither would it explain the decrease of the residual lattice strain with the thickness of the specimen. On the other hand, the existence in each grain of a surface layer adjacent to the free surface is confirmed by the work of Wood cited in the paper and it provides a satisfactory and, so far as we can see, the only explanation of the observed phenomena.

2. Dr. Odqvist's remark about the origin of this work is quite correct. We did start with the hope of being able to devise a non destructive method of residual stress measurements. At present, we believe our work is more important in connection with the elucidation of the role of the surface layer in fatigue. Our future program is aimed principally in this direction and we hopefully expect some significant results.

3. In reply to the question raised by Dr. H. Lerchenthal, we do not believe that the photoelastic stress coat method will provide the same information as the X-Ray diffraction method, even though it might reveal stresses in individual grains. The point is that the stress coat follows changes of strain rather than stress in the substratum. While residual strains could thus be measured, e. g. on unloading, it is not sure that these strains will be the same as the lattice strains referred to in the present paper.

---

[1] F. Zandmann, "Stress Analysis by Photo-elastic Varnishes", Steel (Acier). **21**. 9 (Sept. 1956), 356/64, Fig. 12.

SURVEY ON SECOND-ORDER PLASTICITY

D. C. DRUCKER

Brown University, Providence, Rhode Island, U.S.A.

At first thought, the set of papers presented under the label of PLASTICITY seemed too diverse to permit a unified survey. Fortunately, some of the opening statements by Professor Truesdell crystallized for me the essential unity of so much of the work. In his usual elegant, concise, and provocative style he said that he found it difficult to understand why plasticity and the rest of mechanics had gone separate ways. One of his points in elaboration was his feeling that a yield criterion should be an outcome of theory and not a postulate.

Surely I speak for all of us who have been labelled as plasticians for the purpose of this meeting, when I say that we believe that most of mechanics adopts our philosophy. No branch of mechanics, or rheology, should turn its back on physical reality. We can but hope that all branches will join our forward stream which absorbs physical information as it is developed and translates it into useful mathematical terms.

The converse approach often is of great value. Professor Truesdell and his disciples have contributed enormously to the clarification of physical thought by their cautions against mathematically inappropriate developments. However, we shudder at the idea that a flattening of the stress-strain curve predicted to occur at very large strains in a homogeneous non-linear elastic body should be translated as the yielding of an elastic-plastic metal, a phenomenon which occurs at strains of the order of 0.001 after nearly perfectly linear behavior, Figure 1 and Figure 2.

Essential physical concepts must be incorporated in theory at the beginning. They are not produced by the mathematical formalisms. The best theory is the simplest self-consistent one containing the basic ideas necessary for the problem at hand. Completeness is impossible; physical reality is so complex that it must be idealized if it is to be formalized. Truly elastic or truly plastic materials do not exist. These are names given to those aspects of material

Received May 29, 1962.

behavior which are time-independent within our chosen time scale, and within the environmental conditions imposed.

Elasticity (hyperelasticity seems an unnecessarily elaborate term) implies that full description is possible by state variables and reversible paths. The departures from elastic behavior of a nominally elastic material are of interest and sometimes of great practical importance. However, they are of second-

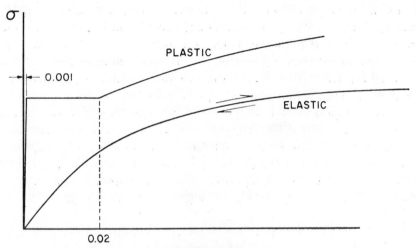

Figure 1
There is a fundamental distinction between plasticity and non-linear elasticity

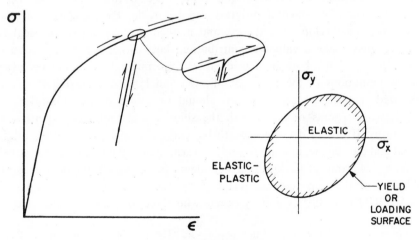

Figure 2
Yielding is idealized as abrupt

order value in comparison with the theory of elasticity for small strains and rotations, or the theory of elasticity for large displacements when the latter is required by the material or the problem.

Plasticity describes the physical fact that beyond a limited set of states of stress in metals there is a profound difference between loading and unloading. Essentially, elastic behavior occurs within a limited domain of stress, elastic-plastic behavior is found outside, Figure 2. The boundary of this domain is a little blurred in actuality. It is idealized as sharp and called the yield or loading surface. A theory of tremendous power can then be developed, which agrees with the real world remarkably well. It is naive to insist on the need to understand in full detail the blurring of the yield values by time effects, or by small departures from linear elastic behavior of metals, before making the idealization. The physical world never is fully understood, nor is it necessarily appropriate to include all known behavior in a mathematical model. A simple picture, treated with elementary but correct mathematics, containing the essence of the physical behavior relevant to the problem, is far superior to a complex treatment of the greatest generality for a deficient physical content. For example, when temperature effects are important, the first order temperature terms are a necessity, the higher order terms of other types often are a luxury.

What has been said in general terms about elasticity and plasticity applies equally well to creep and to other time-dependent rheological behavior. This is the basic unifying thread for the summary of the PLASTICITY papers. It is through a comparison of theory and experiment, with theory building upon new experimental information, and experiment in turn examining theory critically, that fundamental progress can be made. Experiments which do not lead to or develop basic theory, and mathematics devoid of physical relevance, may make a valuable contribution, but neither are in the realm of rheology or of any branch of mechanics. Experimentalists should be aware of the limitations of the most complicated and learned-appearing theory of idealized materials. Mathematicians should be aware of the limitations of experimental results obtained with the shiniest and the most expensive of apparatus. If proper decisions are to be made, rheologists had better understand and participate, in a limited way at least, in *both* theory and experiment*.

With this group of background statements, perhaps a clearer picture can be obtained of the important steps taken by the many contributors to the PLASTICITY SESSION and by others who spoke on plasticity and creep in

---

* For an extended discussion of this question see "The Role of Experiment in the Development of Theory" Proceedings of the Fourth U. S. National Congress of Applied Mechanics, ASME, June 1962, to appear.

the generalized sense. There was little obvious coherence because so many fascinating aspects of the physical world lie open to exploration, and modern engineering practice requires their immediate utilization or understanding Several papers, not officially part of the SESSION presented results of direct interest. A few of these are:

a) the finding by Bell that, in dead-annealed aluminum, the prediction of Truesdell's theory of wave propagation through an *elastic* medium under large strain was valid at prior *plastic* strains of 3% produced by the same impact. This result for a wave of unloading is especially significant.

b) the unpredictable and uncorrelatable first order, and the well-correlated second order Poynting effects, found by Foux in those of his steel wires which were without appreciable residual stress.

c) the discussion by Seeger of *plasticity* in terms of imperfections (mainly dislocations) and second through fourth order *elasticity*. A possible, although not obvious, tie may exist with the experimental results of Bell. Plastic deformation creates extensive regions of large elastic strain on a sub-microscopic level.

In the official PLASTICITY SESSION, Rosenthal in a joint paper with Grupen discussed the difference between the physical behavior of surface layers of the order of a few microns thick, and the main body of the material. This difference appeared even when the entire specimen was just one grain thick. The softness of the surface layer in the plastic region for strains up to a few percent was demonstrated by back-reflection X-ray diffraction technique. Etching of the metal surface was avoided because it would produce a marked disturbance of the surface layers under study. The metal was examined both during the loading and after unloading when a marked residual stress remained. This softness disappeared with higher strains, confirming the concept of single slip or the escape of dislocations in a very thin surface layer only, prior to the cross-slip induced by the geometric constraint of the bulk of the material. Although much remains before these findings and the earlier ones of Wood can be related quantitatively to the fatigue of metals, their relevance is clear.

The other papers of the SESSION also looked first at the physical situation and the demands of engineering practice, but gave a little more emphasis to a mathematical or a theoretical treatment than to a description of the physical phenomenon itself.

Olszak began the presentation of his joint paper with Rychlewski with a reference to the interesting effects of radiation on the properties of steel. Data was presented to show both a raised yield strength and a flat yield portion of the stress-strain curve for some steels not normally possessing a sharp yield point. Radiation thus was seen to produce a material which could be treated as perfectly plastic but inhomogeneous because the intensity of the radiation would differ from point to point. The authors discussed semi-inverse methods of solving for the slip line field. Their point of view is that a convenient solution to a physically neighboring problem is a great help in practice.

Odqvist too adopted the practical point of view in his approach to creep rupture. Rupture is far less understood than flow. However, much was done with a clever combination of the ductile rupture theory of Hoff and the brittle rupture theory of Robinson. Odqvist generalized Kachanov's theory by taking primary creep into account and so was able to correlate with the shorter lifetimes found experimentally. Establishing the importance of primary creep went far beyond curve fitting, because it clarified the observed physical behavior.

Hult examined the creep problem from a quite different direction. He concluded that a creep law which generalizes the one dimensional strain-hardening form $d\varepsilon/dt = K\sigma^n/\varepsilon^m$ is necessary and sufficient to produce stationary stress and strain fields in the extended sense when the applied loads vary but are kept in ratio at all times. There is a clear advantage, therefore, in using such a form of stress-strain relation or the simpler non-hardening form $d\varepsilon/dt = K\sigma^n$ when the data permits. The special position of the simpler form in the general theory was observed recently[*], and extension of the results to a hardening form might well be worth investigation.

The paper of Slibar and Paslay discussed a Bingham material exhibiting a gradual breakdown of the critical shear stress with deformation. Again somewhat crude approximations are found instead of elegance because a physical picture was sought for an observed phenomenon. Agreement between prediction and the rotation viscometer results of Jones and Babson was fairly good. Improvement awaits additional data giving the influence of the past deformation rate and its time of occurence on the state of gellation. More subtle points, such as the stability and uniqueness of solutions to boundary value problems, then will be open for study.

Unfortunately, neither Finzi nor Yoshimura and Takenaka were present to discuss their work. The motivation and the place of their results in the framework of plasticity theory, therefore, could not be ascertained beyond the description given in their papers. It does appear on first glance that the uniqueness criterion of Finzi is related closely to my stability postulate, and that the dependence of the yield surface on the existing state of strain pos-

---

[*] C. R. Calladine and D. C. Drucker, "Nesting Surfaces of Constant Rate of Energy Dissipation in Creep", Quarterly of Applied Mathematics, v. 20 (1962) pp. 79–84. See also Journal of Mechanical Engineering Sciences, IME, v. 4 (1962) pp. 1–11.

tulated by Yoshimura and Takenaka is but one of the many possible special cases.* However, the mathematical development in both papers is more sophisticated than in earlier work.

Sobotka began his oral presentation with the description of the rheological behavior of concrete. Once again, the practical motivation for theoretical development was emphasized both at the start and the end when mention was made of application to systems of soil and water. However, the need for the very elaborate treatment of first, second, and third order effects with a vast array of constants or functions of invariants did not seem to arise from the physical situation.

In conclusion, it seems desirable to try to clarify the different aspects of the general attack on inelastic behavior by a return to the necessity for and the philosophical implications of theoretical and analytical development. One of the major objectives is the solution of engineering problems of immediate importance. The thin-walled pressure vessel sketched in Figure 3 provides a typical example. Brittle fractures occurred in the knuckle region of large storage vessels under interior pressure (hydrostatic test) at temperatures a little above the freezing point. Calculation of the *plastic* limit pressure for torispherical and toriconical heads** did provide a practical answer for the

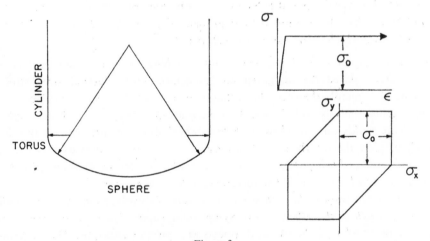

Figure 3

Fairly crude approximation are highly satisfactory for solutions to engineering problems

---

* F. Edelman and D. C. Drucker, "Some Extensions of Elementary Plasticity Theory", Journal of the Franklin Institute, vol. 251 (1951) pp. 581–605.

** R. T. Shield and D. C. Drucker, "Design of Thin-Walled Torispherical and Toriconical Pressure-Vessel Heads", Journal of Applied Mechanics, v. 28 (1961) pp. 292–296.

fracture problem because when the limit pressure was reached, large plastic deformations occurred locally and brittle fracture resulted if the temperature was below the relevant transition temperature.

As sketched in Figure 3, the computations were based upon the drastic assumption of perfect plasticity (flat yield). In addition, the simple Tresca or maximum shearing stress yield criterion was chosen although it is but a crude approximation to some aspects of the real behavior of the steel. Furthermore, the resulting criterion of yielding for the shell in terms of the moment and force resultants was approximated for ease of computation. The combination of all these rough and refined approximations need not shock either the engineer or the mathematician. Limit pressures computed remain within about 10% of the exact answer for a perfectly plastic material. Greater accuracy is hardly warranted for a material like steel which not only work-hardens appreciably prior to fracture but which is variable in yield strength by a much greater margin than 10%.

The question which comes to mind immediately is the sensitivity of the answers obtained to the assumptions which are made. Suppose work-hardening and inhomogeneity were taken into account and the yield criterion chosen was closer to physical reality. Our knowledge of the general theory and the laws which govern material behavior is scanty, but still sufficient to state with confidence, that the computed limit pressure is a very good meaningful approximation which is insensitive to such details.

Far more precision of statement and searching analysis of physical concepts are required for an adequate description of the actual stress-strain behavior of metals than for the solution of most of the current problems of engineering analysis and design. Two alternate procedures have been employed. One builds on a mathematical base which describes idealized properties and expands the mathematical description in a series form as first order, second order, third order, etc. Another looks for broad unifying physical concepts which are translated to appropriate mathematical form as needed. It is this latter approach, with some of its partially explored aspects for small strains, which is described in my Symposium paper. There is an enormous advantage in placing the physical aspects in a primary position. The explanation of observed effects then will not be sought within a framework of elaborate mathematics which cannot contain them. Furthermore, the importance of new experimental information can be judged and, when warranted, place made for it in the theory. Higher order effects have a more direct, although perhaps less precise, meaning. In the alternate approach employing series expansion, the meaning of order is defined fully, but the essence of the physical behavior of a material may be hidden in the infinite sequence of terms of highest order which are dropped.

If the physical approach is successful, as it is in elasticity and time-independent plasticity, theory is truly predictive in a qualitative and occasionally in a general quantitative sense. The hope is that for time-dependent materials, the basic concepts expressed in suitable mathematical form will provide the key to both the phenomenological behavior studied by the materials scientist, and the solution to problems of technological importance sought by the engineer.

III. FLUID DYNAMICS

NON-NEWTONIAN FLOW AND COILING OF
MACROMOLECULES

J. Schurz

Institut für Physikalische Chemie der Universität Graz, Austria

ABSTRACT

The non-Newtonian flow of dissolved macromolecules is, at very high and very low shear rates, confined by two Newtonian regions characterized by two viscosity coefficients η_0 and η_∞. From measurements of flow curves at different temperatures, for both η_0 and η_∞ an activation energy can be determined, which is lower for η_∞ than for η_0. The difference of the activation energies can be regarded as that energy which is reversibly transferred to and stored in the solute molecules, thereby modifying them. If these molecules are coiled chains, the modification will be connected with a change in the molecular shape and therefore also in the coiling mode. Thus it is to be expected, that the difference of the activation energies is related to the coiling mode of the solute molecules, which can be expressed e.g. by the "statistical chain element" A_m. Flow curve measurements on a series of macromolecules in solution demonstrate that this expectation is fulfilled and a relation exists between these two figures.

The rheological performance of high polymeric chain molecules in solution is intimately connected with the properties of the molecular chains. As they undergo rotation, orientation and deformation in the laminar flow field, their deformability, together with size and shape, controls the observed deviations from Newtonian flow (Peterlin has stressed the change which the hydrodynamic interaction suffers as the shear gradient varies). In particular, the decrease of the "apparent" shear viscosity coefficient, as well known and much studied for such solutions, is closely connected with molecular properties, namely molecular weight, shape, coiling, and, although not in a straighforward fashion, molecular weight distribution. These relationships emerge from a picture, in which the molecules themselves are the governing units for flow, a condition which will exist only in very dilute solutions. One may assume that in more concentrated solutions too the molecular properties are reflected in the flow behaviour, although here flow units and molecules may no more be identical, or even the state of solution must be depicted in another way on the whole: as a so-called "infinite network" (Bueche), which additionally may contain temporary entanglements; or as a system in which aggregation

427

and de-aggregation take place as a consequence of concentration, temperature and hydrodynamic forces.

The flow behaviour of a solution is generally expressed in the so-called "flow curve", in which a parameter describing the flow is plotted against a parameter describing the force initiating flow. We have been using the flow curves as introduced by Philippoff, in which the logarithm of the "mean shear gradient" D (which should better be named a reduced flow velocity, as proposed by Peterlin) is plotted against the logarithm of the maximum shear stress σ[1]. Details of the measuring procedure and the evaluation have been published [1]. It may be mentioned, that in such measurements—they are performed in the capillary high pressure viscometer—only the shear viscosity function is taken into consideration, and no attempt is made to estimate the contributions of other viscosity functions (cf. Meskat [2]), this must wait until appropriate instruments are constructed (under way at our institute) or available.

We have tried to detect empirical relations between flow curves and molecule properties. Our starting point was the observation by Umstätter, that a relation exists between the inflection point in the log-log flow curve and the molecular weight of the solute. We were able to coin this relation into the form

$$\hat{D} = a \,.\, M^{-b} \tag{1}$$

where $\hat{D}$ = ordinate of the inflection point, and a and b are constants which must be determined empirically [1]. This relation is bound to the condition that the value of $\hat{D}$ is independent of concentration; in cases where this is not fulfilled, eq. (1) holds only for one concentration. We have regarded the condition, that $\hat{D}$ is independent of concentration, as an indication that the flow units do not change in size. As a whole, eq. (1) holds astonishingly well and accurately for a great number of systems, as shown in Table I, which gives a compilation of a and b values as determined by various authors.

Relations were also found between the slope of the flow curves and solute concentration, and also a way was pointed out to estimate the polymolecularity from the flow curves [1].

Recently, our attention was directed to the question, whether the degree of coiling, i. e. the "coiling ability" (cf. p. 4) which chain molecules display, would be contained in the flow curve [3]. We started from the well-known fact, that the flow curve begins with a range of constant viscosity at very low shear gradient, the η_0-range, and after having passed through the s-shaped, variable viscosity region, it ends again with a constant viscosity, the η_∞-range, which is

---

(1) $D = (4Q)/(\pi R^3)$, $\sigma = (Rp)/(2L)$

TABLE 1

Constants of the equation $\hat{D} = a.M^{-b}$ for various systems

System	°C	c	a	$-b$
Cellulosetrinitrate/butylacetate	25		$3.3 \cdot 10^{16}$	2.4
Na-celluloseglycolate/6%NaOH	,,		$1.0 \cdot 10^{22}$	3.5
Viscose/8%NaOH	,,		$9.7 \cdot 10^{36}$	4.5
Viscose/15%NaOH	,,		$6.9 \cdot 10^{35}$	4.23
Cellulosetriacetate/ethylenchlorhydrine	,,	1%	$2.94 \cdot 10^{14}$	1.88
Cellulose/EWNN	,,	0.1%	$2.06 \cdot 10^{9}$	0.9
Cellulose/Cuen	,,	~1%	$1.49 \cdot 10^{19}$	2.8
Rubber/toluene	,,		$1.76 \cdot 10^{20}$	2.72
Polyacrylonitrile/dimethylformamide	,,		$3.4 \cdot 10^{12}$	1.75
Polystyrene/toluene	,,	1%	$9.2 \cdot 10^{10}$	1.1
Polyisobutylene/toluene	,,	0.5%	$2.8 \cdot 10^{10}$	2.4
Polyvinylpyrrolidon/water	,,	3%	$2.55 \cdot 10^{15}$	2.67
Polyethylene(1.p.)/tetraline	130	1–1.5%	$3.66 \cdot 10^{8}$	0.68
Polyvinylalcohol/water*	40	15%	$4.0 \cdot 10^{6}$	0.87
Polyisobutylene/lubrication oil	25	2–20%	$2.82 \cdot 10^{10}$	1.65

* Measurements from a vibration type viscometer, $\hat{f}$ (frequency) instead of $\hat{D}$.

attained only at rather high values of the shear gradient. The measurement of η_∞ is not easy, sometimes impossible, and a number of sources of error must be accounted for; η_∞ is considerably lower than η_0. This may be interpreted by assuming that the hydrodynamic forces have exerted upon the solute some modification, which reversibly reduces their viscosity from η_0 to η_∞—reversibly, since after removal of the high shearing forces, η_0 is readily restored. Thermodynamically it may be stated, that a portion of the energy exerted upon the solution has been stored reversibly in the molecule enhancing its free energy, but decreasing its viscosity contribution. Now this amount of free energy may be obtained, if we compare the activation energies of flow for both the η_0 and the η_∞ regions. An eventual difference should account for the free energy stored in the molecule. The difference in activation energy is easily obtained by measuring the temperature dependence of both η_0 and η_∞, calculating the activation energy for each case in the usual way from a $\ln \eta$ vs. $1/T$ plot, and taking the difference. This difference in the activation energy should bear a relationship to the coiling of the solute molecules.

Chain molecules in solution are of an indeterminate shape and can therefore only be described by statistics. This is done, e.g. by the method put forward by W. Kuhn, in which the molecular chain is thought of as a succession of links of length A_m, connected in a random flight fashion. If in addition the condition is met, that both the length of the stretched chain L, and the mean-square end-to-end distance are the same for both the real molecule and the A_m chain, then one and only one value of A_m is possible. It is obvious, that A_m must be a measure for the degree of coiling of the molecular chain, the smaller it is, the more coiled the molecule.

In general the coiling of a molecule in a solution is a consequence of several effects. Basically, each molecular chain displays a certain inherent degree of coiling, this "coiling ability" being a function of its chemical composition, as it goes back to valence angle, hindrance of free rotation and its modification by the solvent-solute forces. It can be described by the figure A_m, which has been called the "statistical chain element" by Kuhn. Another figure would be the "persistence length" a as introduced by Porod; for the cases discussed here it is approximately connected with A_m by $A_m = 2a$. If the molecule is stretched, its entropy is lowered and therefore a force must be overcome (restoring force), which has been calculated by Kuhn and Mark, and which is essentially the same as in the case of ideal rubber elasticity. In the steady state in solution, this force sets up an equilibrium with the forces existing between solvent and solute molecules, and this equilibrium—together with the excluded volume effect—determines the degree of coiling in this solution. On the other hand, if the hydrodynamic forces stretch the molecules, there is also observed a resistance, which is proportional to the stretching rate, dh/dt (if h is the end-to-end distance). This "shape resistance" will, therefore, be large for fast deformations and vanish for the case of rest. It is governed by a "change of constellation time" (Kuhn), and determines the stiffness of the molecule.

Unfortunately, no fully satisfactory theory exists for the flow of high polymeric solutions. Many attempt have been published (Kuhn, Eyring, Peterlin, Bueche, etc.), and on the whole we may say that this interesting topic is in rapid development. So far agreement exists on the model in which chain molecules are rotated in the velocity field, whereby this rotation is of varying rate, so that an orientation results by the fact that the molecules retain certain positions for longer, others for shorter periods. It is also agreed, that in the course of this rotation the molecules undergo deformation, they are stretched in one direction and compressed in a right angle to it. Bueche is talking about a "compression-dilation cycle", which is sinusoidally inforced by the shear gradient, but has a phase difference to it, which gives rise to a viscous loss. In any event we may expect a deformation. It would be desirable to know something about the variation of the mean square end-to-end distance $\bar{h}^2$ as a function of the shear gradient, but such knowledge is not yet available.

Anyway, several considerations scattered in the literature suggest that the variation is not too large, and by no means complete stretching of the molecule takes place (so that $\sqrt{\bar{h}^2}$ would approach L). We may assume, that on the whole a mean deformation takes place (which must be thought of as a dynamical one!), which changes $\sqrt{\bar{h}^2}$ to $x \cdot \sqrt{\bar{h}^2}$. The energy necessary for this is taken from the force promoting flow, and is stored in the molecule. In the case of perfect steady state this deformation should give rise merely to a restoring force; in the case of changing deformation, as by rotation, there must be added the contribution of the shape resistance, as characterized by the "change of constellation time".

As a consequence of this discussion the expectation emerges that a relation should exist between the activation energy difference and the coiling of the

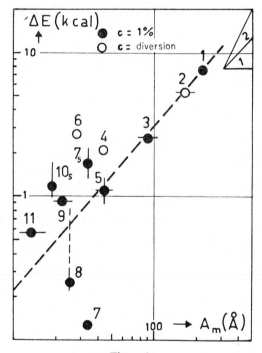

Figure 1

$\triangle E$ as a function of A_m for several macromolecular systems

1. Cellulose trinitrate—butylacetate;   2. Na-cellulose glycolate—6%NaOH;   3. Cellulose triacetate—ethylenchlorohydrine; 4. Polystyrene—toluene; 5. Polycrylonitrile—dimethylformamide; 6. Polyvinylpyrrolidone—water; 7. Polyisobutylene—toluene; 7s. Polyisobutylene—cetane; 8. Polymethylmethacrylate—toluene; 9. Vinyon N-dimethylformamide; 10. Polyvinylalcohol—water(s); 11. Rubber—toluene

chain molecules, as measured e.g. by the figure A_m. To test this, we have performed a great number of measurements. Many difficulties had to be overcome, and in some cases the accuracy is not very high due to the troubles which are provided by measuring η_∞. Furthermore, we ought to investigate the dependence of the activation energy difference on molecular weight and on solute concentration. Such measurements are under way, but rather lengthy, so here we have selected data on samples of possibly highest molecular weight, and confined them on a solute concentration of 1%. This should at least give comparable data, although for absolute considerations at least the extrapolation of the data to zero concentration is indispensable. We have performed it for some cases only and will therefore dispense with it in this paper.

In Table II and Figure 1 we have compiled our data. In Figure 1, the activation energy difference ΔE is plotted against A_m in a double log plot. We observe, that doubtlessly a relation exists; in consideration of the difficulties

TABLE II

Activation energy difference $\triangle E$ and coiling of several systems

		M.10^{-5}	P'	c	$\triangle E$ kcal	$A_m(\overset{\circ}{A})$
1.	Cellulose trinitrate -butylacetate	1.78	600	1%m	7.55	220
2.	Na-cellulose glycolate -6%NaOH	1.1	510	3%m	5.35	150–180
3.	Cellulose triacetate -ethylenchlorohydrine	1.04	360	1%m	2.58	80–100
4.	Polystyrene -toluene	5.0	4800	2%m	2.14	44
5.	Polyacrylonitrile -dimethylformamide	0.25	470	1%m	0.83–1.38	40–50
6.	Polyvinylpyrrolidone -water	5.62	5070	6%m	2.7	28
7.	Polyisobutylene -toluene	1.0	1785	1%m	0.125	34
7s.	Polyisobutylene -cetane	0.4	715	1%e	1.4–2.3	30–40
8.	Polymethylmethacrylate -toluene	16.0	16000	1%e	0.23–0.9	25
9.	Vinyon N -dimethylformamide	0.74	1290	3%m	0.94	20–25
10.	Polyvinylalcohol -water (s)	0.75	1700	1%e	1–2	19
11.	Rubber -toluene	17.8	52400	1%m	0.58	10–18

In the c-column means m: measured, e: extrapolated. (s) means: measurement by a vibration type viscometer. P' is the number of C–C links. The system 7s was measured in a couette-type viscometer.

encountered during the measurements, the scattering of the points is not too high—in particular if we consider that the independent determination of A_m too is at present not yet very precise (the values are taken from the literature, cf. [4]). So, a relation exists which we may put in this way:

$$\Delta E = k \cdot A_m^n \tag{2}$$

According to our measurements as presented here the exponent n appears between 1 and 2. Also, the impression is stipulated that the relation holds better for molecules known as stiff. The differences in number of chain links (P') too are to be noted. More data must be compiled until a detailed discussion is possible, so we also postpone an attempt for a theoretical interpretation to that time. We are currently performing measurements to complete our data (above all concerning the extrapolation of ΔE to zero concentration). This will lead to a precision and enhanced support of eq. (2), and allow the testing of ideas and hypothesis, which aim at its theoretical interpretation. It would also be of great interest to look for a relation between the ΔE values and a stiffness parameter, e.g. the "change of constellation time" by Kuhn. But data for the last figure are so scarce, that for the time being such a comparison is not possible.

REFERENCES

[1] J. SCHURZ, Koll. Z., **154**, (1957), 97; **155**, (1957), 45, 55.
   M. HERMANN UND J. SCHURZ, Chem. Ing. Techn., **33**, (1961), 356.
[2] W. MESKAT, in: Messen und Regeln in der chemischen Technik, Hrsg. J. Hengstenberg, B. Sturm und O. Winkler, Springer Verlag (1957), 698.
[3] J. SCHURZ, Rheolog. Acta, **1**, (1958), 261.
[4] Die Physik der Hochpolymeren, Bd. II, Hrsg. H. A. Stuart, Springer Verlag, (1953).

DISCUSSION

H. MARKOVITZ: How big was the temperature difference which you measured by means of the device which you mentioned that you had in your apparatus?

SCHURZ'S REPLY: This is, of course, only a minimum for the value of this effect since it is known that the maximum temperature is not on the wall but rather in the interior of the tube.

BOUNDS FOR VISCOSITY COEFFICIENTS
OF FLUID MIXTURES
BY VARIATIONAL METHODS*

Zvi Hashin**

University of Pennsylvania, Philadelphia, Pa, U.S.A.

ABSTRACT

A variational principle for steady Stokes flow (neglect of inertia terms) of isotropic non-homogeneous fluids is established. This is applied to the derivation of lower and upper bounds for the effective viscosity coefficients of mixtures of different fluids for the initial Newtonian and the ultimate non-Newtonian stages of flow.

1. Introduction.

The present work is concerned with the establishment of some variational principles for linear viscous flow theory (Stokes flow) and their application to the prediction of the effective viscosity coefficient of mechanical fluid mixtures in the Newtonian and non-Newtonian stages of flow.

Heterogeneous fluids, which consist of different phases, may be divided into two classes: in the first, one of the phases may be taken as rigid; these are generally known as suspensions. In the second, all phases deform; these will be here referred to as mixtures. A suspension may be regarded as a special case of a mixture in which one of the phases has infinitely large viscosity.

The problem of the determination of the effective coefficient of viscosity of heterogeneous fluids is one of long standing. Most of the work has been done for suspensions which are easier to treat than mixtures. The pioneering research in this field is that of Einstein [1] who derived the viscosity coefficient of the simplest suspension, consisting of a viscous fluid containing a very small amount of rigid speres. This was later generalized by Taylor [2] to the case where the spheres are fluid droplets of finite viscosity.

---

* The results given in this paper have been obtained in the course of research sponsored by the Office of Naval Research under Contract Nonr 551 (42), NR 064–458 with the University of Pennsylvania, Philadelphia, Pa.

** On leave of absence from the Technion-Israel Institute of Technology, Haifa, Israel.

Numerous attempts have been made to generalize Einstein's result to the case of finite volume concentration of suspended material. A review of the extensive literature on this subject is beyond the scope of this paper and may be found in [3, 4, 5]. The results found up to now are far from being conclusive. Different authors have used different assumptions or empirical parameters which resulted in a large number or formulae which are at times in direct contradiction.

The analogous mixture problem is much more difficult and has received much less attention.

The present paper deals with the mixture problem and instead of attempting to derive an expression for the effective viscosity coefficient, upper and lower bounds for this quantity are established. The practical value of such bounds is of course determined by their closeness. As it turns out, these bounds are quite close when the ratio between the viscosity coefficients of the constituting phases is not too large, however for the case of a suspension they become only of academic interest.

These bounds are derived by application of some variational principles for linear viscous flow which will be established below. The developments and applications are completely analogous to previous treatment of a related elasticity problem [6].

2. Variational principles.

The viscous flow considered here is incompressible, Newtonian, steady and of linear type. Thus the flow is described by the Navier-Stokes equations in which inertia terms are neglected. Since measurements of viscosity can be performed at very slow velocities this aproximation does not seem to lead to appreciable errors in the case of the problem treated here.

Let $\sigma_{ij}^{(0)}$ and $\varepsilon_{ij}^{(0)}$ be known stress and strain rate fields in a homogeneous and isotropic viscous fluid of volume V and boundary surface S. The stress-strain rate relation is then given by

$$\sigma_{ij}^{(0)} = \sigma^{(0)}\delta_{ij} + 2\mu_0\varepsilon_{ij}^{(0)} \qquad (2.1)$$

where μ_0 is the viscosity coefficient, $\sigma^{(0)}$ is the pressure (with reversed sign), the range of subscripts is 1, 2, 3 and the δ_{ij} are the Kronecker delta.

Eq. (2.1) can be rewritten in the equivalent form

$$s_{ij}^{(0)} = 2\mu_0 \varepsilon_{ij}^{(0)} \tag{2.2}$$

where $s_{ij}^{(0)}$ is the stress deviator, the $\varepsilon_{ij}^{(0)}$ being deviatoric because of the incompressibility of the fluid.

The strain rates are given in terms of the known velocity field $u^{(0)}_i$ by

$$\varepsilon_{ij}^{(0)} = \tfrac{1}{2}(u_{i,j}^{(0)} + u_{j,i}^{(0)}) \tag{2.3}$$

where a comma denotes differentiation.

Let part of whole of the fluid be changed to a fluid of different viscosity coefficient μ which may vary in space and let the same boundary values of velocities $u_i^{(0)}(S)$ be prescribed for the homogeneous fluid and the new fluid. The stress, pressure, velocity and strain rate fields in the new fluid are unknown and are denoted by σ_{ij}, σ, u_i and ε_{ij} respectively.

The deviatoric stress polarization tensor p_{ij} defined by

$$s_{ij} = 2\mu_0 \varepsilon_{ij} + p_{ij} \tag{2.4}$$

is now introduced. Here the s_{ij} are the deviatoric components of the σ_{ij}.

Define also

$$u_i' = u_i - u^{(0)} \tag{2.5}$$

and consequently

$$\varepsilon_{ij}' = \varepsilon_{ij} - \varepsilon_{ij}^{(0)} \tag{2.6}$$

and also

$$\sigma' = \sigma - \sigma^{(0)} \tag{2.7}$$

Once the ε_{ij}' and p_{ij} are known the ε_{ij} and σ_{ij} can be found from (2.6) and (2.4). The ε_{ij}' and p_{ij} will here be chosen as the unknowns and in the following variational principles in terms of these will be formulated.

The volume integral

$$F_p = F_0 - \int_{(V)} \left(\frac{p_{ij}p_{ij}}{2(\mu - \mu_0)} - p_{ij}\varepsilon'_{ij} - 2p_{ij}\varepsilon^{(0)}_{ij} \right) dV \qquad (2.8)$$

where

$$F_0 = \int_{(V)} s^{(0)}_{ij}\varepsilon^{(0)}_{ij}\, dV \qquad (2.9)$$

subject to the subsidiary conditions

$$\sigma'_{,i} + \mu_0\nabla^2 u'_i + p_{ij,j} = 0 \qquad (2.10)$$

$$u'_{j,j} = 0 \qquad (2.11)$$

and the boundary condition

$$u'_i(S) = 0 \qquad (2.12)$$

is stationary for

$$p_{ij} = 2(\mu - \mu_0)\varepsilon_{ij} \qquad (2.13)$$

The stationary value of F_p is an absolute maximum when

$$\mu > \mu_0 \qquad (2.14)$$

and an absolute minimum when

$$\mu < \mu_0 \qquad (2.15)$$

Furthermore the stationary value of F_p is equal to the energy dissipation in the new fluid.

The proof of these variational principles is entirely analogous to that of corresponding principles for the linear theory of elasticity which have been established and proved in detail in [6]. The present variational principles may be obtained from these for infinitely large bulk modulus, replacement of strains by strain rates, shear modulus by viscosity coefficient and strain energy by dissipation of energy.

3. Bounds for effective viscosity coefficient of mixtures in the Newtonian stage of flow.

Consider a mixture which consists of a number of different fluid phases. It will be assumed that in the initial stage of flow the mixture is quasi-isotropic and quasi-homogeneous and that its stress-strain rate relation can be adequately described by an effective coefficient of viscosity which is independent of the strain rate. This is the Newtonian stage of flow. The ultimate non-Newtonian stage will be considered in section **4**.

For the sake of simplicity a two phase fluid will be treated. The case of a fluid consisting of an arbitrary number of phases is completely analogous and only the final results will be stated for that case. For details see [6].

Consider a fluid region of volume V and surface S. The boundary values of the velocities are taken as

$$u_i^{(0}(S) = \varepsilon_{ij}^{(0} x_j \tag{3.1}$$

where the $\varepsilon_{ij}^{(0}$ are constant deviatoric strain rates and the x_j Cartesian coordinates with respect to a fixed system of axes. When the fluid consists of only one homogeneous phase, it follows from linear viscous flow theory that the strain rate field throughout the fluid is constant and given by $\varepsilon_{ij}^{(0)}$.

When the same fluid region consists of a two phase or multiphase fluid and (3.1) is again prescribed on the boundary, the strain rate field changes. However it is easily shown by conversion of volume integrals to surface integrals that the mean strain rates are equal to $\varepsilon_{ij}^{(0)}$.

The assumed quasi-homogeneity of the heterogeneous fluid will here be interpreted in the following way: consider any fixed reference cube in the fluid which is small compared to the entire fluid region, yet large in comparison to the size of phase regions in it. The mean values of quantities such as velocity, strain rate or phase volume fraction are the same for the whole fluid region and the reference cube.

The variational formulation of Section **2** is now applied to a reference cube of unit volume. The $\varepsilon_{ij}^{(0)}$ there defined are then identified with the present mean strains and the ε_{ij}' with the deviations from the mean. Accordingly in the reference cube

$$\varepsilon_{ij} = \varepsilon_{ij}^{(0)} + \varepsilon_{ij}' \tag{3.2}$$

$$\bar{\varepsilon}_{ij}' = 0 \tag{3.3}$$

where the bar denotes mean value.

To define the effective viscosity coefficient μ^* it is assumed that the dissipation of energy within the reference cube can be represented in the form

$$F = 2\mu^* \varepsilon_{ij}^{(0)} \varepsilon_{ij}^{(0)} \tag{3.4}$$

Let V_1 and V_2 be the volumes of the two constituting fluid phases and v_1 and v_2 their volume fractions so that

$$v_1 + v_2 = 1 \tag{3.5}$$

Then v_1 and v_2 are the phase volumes contained in the unit volume reference cube. In order to evaluate (2.8) for the reference cube the following polarization field is chosen[1]

$$p_{ij} = p_{ij}^{(1)} \quad \text{in} \quad V_1$$
$$p_{ij} = p_{ij}^{(2)} \quad \text{in} \quad V_2 \tag{3.6}$$

where the $p_{ij}^{(1)}$ and $p_{ij}^{(2)}$ are constant.

Introducing (3.6) into (2.8) the following result is obtained

$$F_p = F_0 + F' - \left(\frac{p_{ij}^{(1)} p_{ij}^{(2)}}{2(\mu_1 - \mu_0)} + \frac{p_{ij}^{(2)} p_{ij}^{(2)}}{2(\mu_2 - \mu_0)} - 2\bar{p}_{ij} \varepsilon_{ij}^{(0)} \right) \tag{3.7}$$

where

$$F_0 = 2\eta_0 \varepsilon_{ij}^{(0} \varepsilon_{ij}^{(0)}$$

Here $\bar{p}_{ij}$ is the mean value of (3.6) given by

$$p_{ij} = p_{ij}^{(1)} v_1 + p_{ij}^{(2)} v_2 \tag{3.8}$$

F' is given by

$$F' = \int_{(V)} p_{ij} \varepsilon'_{ij} dV \tag{3.9}$$

and μ_1 and μ_2 are the viscosity coefficients of the two fluid phases respectively.

---

[1] Note that the variational formulation admits an arbitrary choice of polarization. The present choice is one that permits treatment for arbitrary phase region geometry.

In order to evaluate F in terms of the polarization components, these are developed into a Fourier series within the reference cube

$$p_{ij} = \bar{p}_{ij} + \sum_{-\infty}^{\infty}{}' p_{ij}^{klm} \exp\left[\frac{2\pi\iota}{L} \left(kx_1 + lx_2 + mx_3 \right) \right] \tag{3.10}$$

Here the p_{ij} are given by (3.8), the k, l, m are integers whose range is $-\infty$ to $+\infty$, the prime after the summation sign denotes that zero values of the k, l, m are excluded, the p_{ij}^{klm} are complex constants, L is the side of the reference cube and ι is the square root of -1.

The velocity components in the reference cube can be written in the form

$$u_i = u_i^{(0)} + u_i' \tag{3.11}$$

where the strain rates ε_{ij}' are derived from the u_i' and $u_i^{(0)}$ is of the form (3.1). The u_i' are now developed into the Fourier series

$$u_i' = \sum_{-\infty}^{\infty}{}' u_i^{klm} \exp\left[\frac{2\pi\iota}{L} (kx_1 + lx_2 + mx_3) \right] \tag{3.12}$$

Introducing (3.10) and (3.12) into (2.10) and (2.11) the u_i^{klm} can be uniquely expressed in terms of the p_{ij}. The ε_{ij}' are then found from differentiation of (3.12). Inserting these into (3.9) the following result is found[2]

$$F' = -\frac{1}{5\mu_0} \sum_{-\infty}^{\infty}{}' p_{ij}^{klm} p_{ij}^{*klm} \tag{3.13}$$

where the asterisk denotes a complex conjugate.

It should be noted that in order to comply with (21.2) the u_i' should vanish on the surface of the reference cube whereas in this case only their average vanishes. The replacement of the rigorous condition (2.12) by the weaker average condition is the same kind of approximation as that involved in the presentation of the energy dissipation in a heterogeneous fluid by (3.4). Also the perturbation due to the non-vanishing of the surface of the u_i' will become

---

[2] For details see analogous derivation in [6].

smaller with decreasing size of the non-homogeneities, compared to the reference cube, and can be decreased at will by increasing the size of the cube.

Squaring both sides of (3.10) and integrating over the reference cube, using (3.8), yields the result

$$p_{ij}^{(1)} p_{ij}^{(1)} v_1 + p_{ij}^{(2)} p_{ij}^{(2)} v_2 = \bar{p}_{ij} \bar{p}_{ij} + \sum_{-\infty}^{\infty}{}' \, p_{ij}^{klm} p_{ij}^{*klm} \qquad (3.14)$$

It follows from (3.13) and (3.14), using (3.6) and (3.8), that

$$F' = - \frac{1}{5\mu_0} \, (p_{ij}^{(1)} - p_{ij}^{(2)}) \, (p_{ij}^{(1)} - p_{ij}^{(2)}) \qquad (3.15)$$

Thus (3.7) can now be expressed in terms of the polarization (3.6) and known quantities,

It follows from the maximum condition (2.14) that whenever

$$\mu_1 > \mu_0 \qquad \mu_2 > \mu_0 \qquad\qquad (3.16)$$

then F_p satisfies the inequality

$$F_p < F \qquad\qquad (3.17)$$

Conversely, from the minimum condition (2.15), whenever

$$\mu_1 < \mu_0 \qquad \mu_2 < \mu_0 \qquad\qquad (3.18)$$

$$F_p > F \qquad\qquad (3.19)$$

Taking F in the form (3.4) and F_p in the form (3.7), using (3.15)—the inequalities (3.17) and (3.19) become bounds for the effective viscosity coefficient μ^*. In order to find the best bounds for a polarization field of type (3.6)—(3.7) has to be maximized for condition (3.16) and minimized for condition (3.18). Differentiating (3.7), where F is given be (3.15), with respect to $p_{ij}^{(1)}$ and $p_{ij}^{(2)}$ the following extremum conditions are found

$$\frac{p_{ij}^{(1)}}{2\,(\mu_1 - \mu_0)} + \frac{1}{5\mu_0}(p_{ij}^{(1)} - p_{ij}^{(2)})v_2 - \varepsilon_{ij}^{(0)} = 0 \qquad (3.20)$$

$$\frac{p_{ij}^{(2)}}{2\,(\mu_2 - \mu_0)} + \frac{1}{5\mu_0}(p_{ij}^{(2)} - p_{ij}^{(1)})v_1 - \varepsilon_{ij}^{(0)} = 0 \tag{3.21}$$

It can be proved that (3.20) and (3.21) are maximum conditions when (3.16) holds and minimum conditions when (3.18) holds.

Solving for the $p_{ij}^{(1)}$ and $p_{ij}^{(2)}$, introducing the results in (3.7) and using (3.17) and (3.19) the following bounds for μ^* are obtained

$$\mu^* \gtrless \mu_0 + \frac{1}{2}\frac{B}{1 - \dfrac{B}{5\mu_0}} \tag{3.22}$$

where

$$B = \frac{v_1}{\dfrac{1}{2\,(\mu_1 - \mu_0)} + \dfrac{1}{5\mu_0}} + \frac{v_2}{\dfrac{1}{2\,(\mu_2 - \mu_0)} + \dfrac{1}{5\mu_0}} \tag{3.23}$$

and the upper inequality sign in (3.22) applies for (3.16) and the lower for (3.18).

It remains to specify the value of μ_0 which will yield the best upper and lower bounds, given by (3.22). It can be proved by differentiation that the expression in the R. H. S. of (3.22) is a monotonically increasing function of μ_0. Hence the highest lower bound is obtained by taking the largest value of μ_0 that complies with (3.16). This is clearly μ_1. Analogously the lowest upper bound is obtained when taking the lowest value of μ_0 that complies with (3.18). This is μ_2. The best bounds are accordingly obtained when introducing in turn μ_1 and μ_2 into (3.22) and (3.23). The results are

$$\mu_1^* = \mu_1 + \frac{v_2}{\dfrac{1}{\mu_2 - \mu_1} + \dfrac{2v_1}{5\mu_1}} \tag{3.24}$$

$$\mu_2^* = \mu_2 + \frac{v_1}{\dfrac{1}{\mu_1 - \mu_2} + \dfrac{2v_2}{5\mu_2}} \tag{3.25}$$

$$\mu_1^* < \mu^* < \mu_2^* \tag{3.26}$$

In the case of a mixture consisting of n different fluid phases the bounds are

$$\mu_1^* = \mu_1 + \frac{1}{2}\, \frac{B_1}{1 - \dfrac{B_1}{5\mu_1}} \tag{3.27}$$

$$\mu_2^* = \mu_2 + \frac{1}{2}\, \frac{B_2}{1 - \dfrac{B_2}{5\mu_2}} \tag{3.28}$$

where

$$B_1 = \sum_{r=2}^{r=n} \frac{2v_r}{\dfrac{1}{\mu_r - \mu_1} + \dfrac{2}{5\mu_1}} \tag{3.29}$$

$$B_2 = \sum_{r=1}^{r=n-1} \frac{2v_r}{\dfrac{1}{\mu_r - \mu_n} + \dfrac{2}{5\mu_n}} \tag{3.30}$$

and μ_1 and μ_n are the smallest and largest viscosity coefficients, respectively, of the different fluid phases.

An interesting result is obtained when the bounds defined by (3.22) and (3.23) are worked out for the choice $\mu_0 = 0$ and $\mu_0 \to \infty$. A limiting process yields the following results

$$\frac{1}{\mu_1^{*(0)}} = \frac{v_1}{\mu_1} + \frac{v_2}{\mu_2} \tag{3.31}$$

$$\mu_2^{*(\infty)} = \mu_1 v_1 + \mu_2 v_2 \tag{3.32}$$

These expressions have been used as "rule of thumb" formulae for the effective viscosity coefficient of two phase fluids. The present derivation shows that these are the worst bounds that can be derived by the method here used. Analogous expressions are found for an arbitrary number of fluid phases.

When the ratio between μ_2 and μ_1 is not too large the bounds (3.24) and (3.25) yield a good estimate for μ^*. The bounds calculated for several ratios of $\dfrac{\mu_2}{\mu_1}$ are shown in the figure. For $\dfrac{\mu_2}{\mu_1} = 2$, the difference between the bound is too small for the scale of the figure.

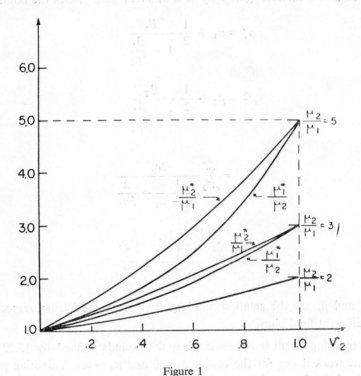

Figure 1

Bounds for effective Newtonian viscosity coefficients of mixtures

In the extreme case of a suspension of rigid particles in a fluid, one of the viscosity coefficients, μ_2 say, has to be taken as infinite. Then the upper bound (3.25) also becomes infinitely large whereas the lower bound (3.24) reduces to

$$\mu_1^* = \mu_1 \left(1 + 2.5\frac{v_2}{v_1}\right) \qquad (3.33)$$

It is interesting to note that for very small v_2, (3.23) reduces to Einstein's well known result. However when (3.24) is worked out for very small v_2 this expression does not reduce to Taylor's result. This should be expected since in Taylor's work it has been assumed that the fluid droplets are held in spherical shape by surface tension whereas the present treatment excludes surface tension.

4. Bounds for effective viscosity coefficient of mixtures in the non-Newtonian stage of flow.

It is known from experiments that the viscosity coefficient of fluid mixtures is a function of the applied strain rate. It is generally found that the slope of the shear stress-strain rate curve decreases with increasing strain rate and after some time the slope becomes constant (see for example [5]). The initial slope of the curve may be taken as the Newtonian viscosity coefficient whereas the ultimate slope, which is here denoted by $\mu_{(\infty)}^*$, may be called the ultimate non-Newtonian viscosity coefficient.

This phenomenon may be attributed in part to the change of shape of fluid phase regions with continuing flow. It should be remembered that although the actual shape of regions did not enter into the preceding analysis a basic assumption used was isotropy of the fluid as a whole. It is physically clear that in shear flow, for example, the fluid regions will elongate in the direction of flow, thus changing initial isotropy to anisotropy as flow continues. It is of course very difficult to draw conclusions about the actual change of geometry and nothing of the kind will be attempted here. Instead an idealized model of the ultimate stage of flow will be used. It will be assumed that after sufficient time has passed all phase regions have become cylindrical with generators in the direction of flow, the actual shape of cross section of these cylinders being arbitrary. It is furthermore assumed that plane isotropy remains in planes which are normal to the direction of flow.

The previous method for derivation of bounds for the effective viscosity coefficient can be applied in an analogous way in this case. Let it be assumed that the fluid is in macroscopic shear flow in 1 direction. Thus

$$\mu_1^{(0)} = \varepsilon_{12}^{(0)} x_2$$

$$(4.1)$$

$$u_2^{(0)} = u_3^{(0)} = 0$$

It follows that the only non-vanishing $\varepsilon_{ij}^{(0)}$ are $\varepsilon_{12}^{(0)} = \varepsilon_{21}^{(0)}$.

Carrying through the analysis as before, taking into account isotropy in the 23 plane only, the following bounds for the effective viscosity coefficient $\mu_{(\infty)}^*$ are found in the case of a two phase fluid,

$$\mu_{(\infty)1}^* = \mu_1 + \cfrac{v_2}{\cfrac{1}{\mu_2 - \mu_1} + \cfrac{v_1}{2\mu_1}}$$

$$(4.2)$$

$$\mu_{(\infty)2}^* = \mu_2 + \cfrac{v_1}{\cfrac{1}{\mu_1 - \mu_2} + \cfrac{v_2}{2\mu_2}} \tag{4.3}$$

$$\mu_{(\infty)1}^* < \mu_{(\infty)}^* < \mu_{(\infty)2}^* \tag{4.4}$$

The analysis can, of course, be generalized to the case of an arbitrary number of phases.

Comparison of (4.2) and (4.3) with (3.24) and (3.25) shows that the only difference is the coefficient of the second term in the denominator which is increased from $\frac{2}{5}$ to $\frac{1}{2}$. Accordingly the present bounds give lower values than those for the isotropic fluid in agreement with the experimental fact that the ultimate coefficient of viscosity is lower than the initial Newtonian one. However, an unfortunate feature of the bounds is that the differences $\mu_1^* - \mu_{(\infty)1}^*$, and $\mu_2^* - \mu_{(\infty)2}^*$ are of the order of the differences $\mu_2^* - \mu_1^*$ and $\mu_{(\infty)2}^* - \mu_{(\infty)1}^*$. It follows that while the bounds may give a useful estimate of the effective viscosity coefficient for Newtonian flow, they are not of practical value for an estimate of the reduction in the coefficient of viscosity in the ultimate stage of non-Newtonian flow.

It is of interest to note that when μ_2 is taken as infinitely large and v_2 very small, (4.2) reduces to

$$\mu_{(\infty)1}^* = \mu_1 (1 + 2v_2) \tag{4.5}$$

which coincides with Jeffery's [7] expression for the viscosity coefficient of a fluid containing a small volume fraction of very elongated rigid ellipsoids which are oriented in flow direction.

5. Conclusion.

Variational theorems for linear viscous flow have been established and applied to the derivation of bounds for the effective viscosity coefficients of mixtures of Newtonian fluids. Bounds have been given for the initial Newtonian stage of flow and for the ultimate stage of non-Newtonian flow.

When the ratios between viscosity coefficients of the constituting fluids are not too large the bounds may be close enough to give a good estimate for the effective viscosity coefficient. However no useful quantititative estimate is obtained for the difference between the initial Newtonian viscosity coefficient and the ultimate non-Newtonian one.

An important feature of the method is the arbitrariness in fluid phase region geometry in contradistinction to usual assumptions of spherical or ellipsoidal shapes.

The bounds which have been given are expressed in terms of fluid phase viscosity coefficients and volume fractions only. An important question which arises is whether such information is sufficient to uniquely define the viscosity coefficient of mixtures. While this question remains at present unanswered it is of interest to mention a related problem where it has been answered. Brown [8] has shown that the effective electric conductivity of a two phase material is not defined by such information and that the statistical details of phase distribution are of influence. Hashin and Shtrikman [9] have derived bounds for the electric conductivity of such materials by methods similar to ones here used and have shown that these are the most restrictive bounds that can be given in terms of phase properties and volume fractions. In view of Brown's work it can be concluded that improvement of those bounds would necessitate consideration of statistical details.

It is not known at present whether better bounds than the present ones can can be derived in terms of phase viscosity coefficients and volume fractions. It seems likely that if they can be improved this cannot be carried up to coincidence and that as in the case described above statistical details are pertinent.

These considerations should also be of importance for the case of suspensions of rigid particles in a viscous fluid where generally it has been attempted to derive an expression for the effective viscosity coefficient without considering the possibility that this quantity might not be determinate in terms of the volume fraction of suspended particles and the fluid viscosity coefficient.

Acknowledgement.

The author is grateful to Dr. H. Yeh for his interest in this work and for helpful discussions.

REFERENCES

[1] A. EINSTEIN, Eine neue Bestimmung der Moleküldimensionen, *Ann. Phys.* ,**19**, (1906). 289–306, **34**, (1911), 591–592.

[2] G. I. TAYLOR, The viscosity of a fluid containing small drops of another fluid, *Proc. Roy. Soc.*, **A138**, (1932), 41–48.

[3] J. J. HERMANS, *Flow Properties of Disperse Systems*, (Hermans, Ed.) North Holland Publ., Amsterdam (1953).

[4] H. L. FRISCH AND R. SIMHA, The viscosity of colloidal suspensions and macro-molecular solutions, *Rheology*, F. R. Eirich, Ed., Vol. 1, Academic Press, New York (1956).

[5] M. REINER, Rheology, *Encycl. Phys.*, S. Flügge, Ed. Vol. 6, Springer Verl. Berlin (1958).

[6] Z. HASHIN AND S. SHTRIKMAN, On some variational principles in elasticity and their application to the theory of two phase materials, Un. of Penna. Contr. Nonr 551 (42) TR 1, July (1961).

[7] G. B. JEFFERY, The motion of ellipsoidal particles immersed in a viscous fluid, *Proc. Roy. Soc.*, **A102**, (1923), 161–169.

[8] W. F. BROWN, JR., Solid mixture permittivities, *J. Chem. Phys.*, **23**, (1955), 1514–17.

[9] Z. HASHIN AND S. SHTRIKMAN, Note on the effective physical constants of composite materials, *J. Franklin Inst.*, **271**, (1961), 423–426.

DISCUSSION

J.G. OLDROYD: It would seem that the theory does not apply to miscible liquids, because distinct phases are assumed. On the other hand, it is well known that, when immiscible liquids form an emulsion, one liquid or the other is likely to be in the form of droplets whose identity is preserved because of interfacial tension. Here all surface tension effects are ignored and I wonder if the author will say more about the type of mixture the theory can be applied to.

Z. HASHIN's reply: The surface tension effect would cause a difference in normal pressure at the fluid phase interfaces. It seems likely that the error due to the neglect of this is small when the viscous stresses produced at the niterface are large compared to this pressure difference.

A criterion for the importance of surface tension might perhaps be given by the magnitude of a characteristic non-dimensional number. A suitable choice might be the number $\sigma/\mu V$, where σ, μ and V are surface tension, viscosity coefficient and velocity respectively. This number is the ratio of the Reynolds number to the Weber number. In view of what has been said above it could be expected that whenever this number is small, surface tension would be a secondary effect.

An important feature of the present theory is arbitrariness of phase region geometry. Since the interfacial pressure difference due to surface tension depends on the curvature of the interface it seems very unlikely that this effect can be taken into account without introduction of assumptions concerning phase geometry (such as spherical droplets). Such geometrical assumptions will of course introduce errors. Whether these are more serious than those due to the neglect of surface tension or vice versa remains at present an open question.

CROSS-STRESSES IN THE FLOW OF AIR
AT REDUCED PRESSURES

A. Foux and M. Reiner
Technion–Israel Institute of Technology, Haifa

ABSTRACT

The cross stresses effect as discovered by Reiner in the laminar flow of air at atmospheric pressure was investigated at an ambient pressure 2/3 and 1/3 atmosphere. It was found that the effect decreases with decreasing ambient pressure. At high rates of flow an instability sets in and a Taylor-Saffman effect is developed which increases with decreasing ambient pressure.

1. Introductory.

In accordance with the Navier-Stokes equations, which embody the classical theory of fluid dynamics, laminar flow is accompanied by tangential tractions (τ) acting in area-elements the normals of which are in the direction of flow (x), and in the directions of the velocity gradient (y), in addition to the isotropic pressure (p), which must comply with the boundary conditions. Reiner [1] has defined *cross-stresses* which are normal tractions (σ) in the three mutually normal directions x,y,z [1], and has shown theoretically that, in general, such cross-stresses will not vanish but constitute second (and higher) order effects. In such cases the Navier-Stokes equations do not adequately describe the mechanism of flow. Reiner [1, 2] and Popper and Reiner [3] have shown experimentally that in the laminar flow of air, forces come into play which can be interpreted as due to cross-stresses, but Taylor and Saffman [4] have shown that such forces can be predicted from the Navier-Stokes equations provided the apparatus has certain imperfections. Applying Occam's razor [2] one might be satisfied with Taylor and Saffman's theory as long as its results would not contradict experience. There is one result about which more will be said in the following Section, which can be compared with experience. It refers to the dependence of the magnitude of the effect upon the ambient airpressure (p_0). In accordance with Taylor and Saffman the effect is supposed to *increase* with *decreasing* ambient pressure. The present research was planned to check this result. However, apart from this purpose, the results of a research

---

[1] Weissenberg and his school speak of directions 1, 2, 3
[2] "Theories are not to be multiplied without necessity"

examining in what manner cross-forces depend upon the ambient pressure should be of interest in their own right.

2. Taylor and Saffman's theory.

Taylor and Saffman have examined how two imperfections in the apparatus may affect the fluid dynamics of torsional air flow. These are

(A)   a slight error in the perpendicularity of the plane of either the stator or rotor to the axis of rotation, constituting a wedge,

(B)   a vibration of the rotor in the directions of its axis.

Let

$$p' = (p-p_0)/p_0 \tag{2.1}$$

be the dimensionless excess pressure. Then the total pressure

$$P = \int (p - p_0)\, dA \tag{2.2}$$

behaves like

(A)

$$P \propto e^2\, \frac{\omega^2}{d^4}\, \frac{1}{p_0} \tag{2.3}$$

(B)

$$P \propto \frac{\alpha^2 \omega^2}{d^4}\, \frac{1}{p_0} \tag{2.4}$$

Here d is the gap at the centre, ω is the angular velocity, and e and α are quantities subject to chance, dependent on the geometrical and constructional details of the apparatus, but independent of p_0. In both cases the effect should *increase* with *decreasing* ambient pressure p_0.

It will be shown that in the experiments reported upon in the present paper, the observed effect decreases in its stable range with decreasing p_0. This rules out the Taylor-Saffman theory as an adequate explanation of the observed effect, in this range. However, our observations also show that a Taylor-Saffman effect is superimposed at high velocities when instabilities become active.

3. Description of apparatus.

The apparatus used in the present investigation was the vacuum pump described in the papers by Popper and Reiner [3] and Reiner [1]. It is shown here in Figure 1, in a section. S is the stator, R the rotor. The latter is driven

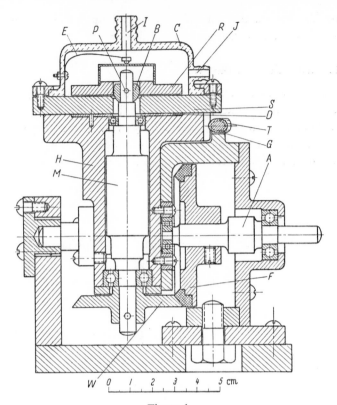

Figure 1
Section of centripetal vacuum pump

by the main shaft M. However, R is not fixed to M; it can rotate freely around the ball B, and it can also be displaced along the axis of rotation. It rotates together with the shaft about the axis of M. This is achieved by means of the pins P, which protrude from B, and enter into two short radial slots in R. During rotation, the cross-force in the direction of the velocity gradient, which is a pressure, maintains a gap d between the plates, thus supporting the rotor. The axis of the rotor can be changed by means of a hand-wheel from the vertical to a horizontal position. The weight component of the rotor which tends to bring the plates together is then gradually changed from its full weight (W) to zero. The total pressure (P) includes in addition the pressure (P_s) from the spring E. The rotor is insulated electrically from the stator. The plates thus form a capacitor. This property is used to find the mean width D of the gap, by measuring the capacity with the use of an impedance bridge. The dielectric constant of air was taken as unity and edge effects were neglected. The distance D in cm is then found from the relation:

$$D = A/(0.9 \times 4\pi \times C) \tag{3.1}$$

where A is the net area of the plate in cm², and C is the capacity in $\mu\mu F$, which is the measured capacity minus the capacity of the wires. In our case $A = 18.5$ cm², and therefore

$$D(\mu) = \frac{16\ 350}{C(\mu\mu F)} \tag{3.2}$$

For vacuum pumping the instrument is provided with a cup C as shown in Figure 1. For our observations the nipples I and J were open to the ambient atmosphere.

In order to determine the effects in a rarefied atmosphere, a chamber was designed and built, in which the instrument could be made to work under different ambient pressures.

The stator and rotor were made of hardened tool-steel. The working surfaces were grounded and polished by hand. They can be regarded as constituting surfaces of revolution with a deviation from axial symmetry which in the worst case did not exceed 1μ, and approached flatness to the same degree.

4. Experiments at atmospheric pressure with varying loads.

In a series of experiments at atmospheric pressure, which were reported upon previously [1] it was found that the distance D increases with increasing angular velocity ω. The ratio $(\omega/D)^2$ may therefore be considered as a measure of the effect. However, it was found that $(\omega/D)^2$ is not a constant. This can be understood in two ways. Firstly, the gap distance D, as found from capacity measurements which is a mean distance, will not be identical with the thickness d of the laminar layer in which the flow takes place. In general

$$D = d + d_0 \tag{4.1}$$

Secondly, centrifugal forces act upon the air layer in the gap, which oppose the centripetal forces supporting the load P. These centrifugal forces have been investigated by Stewartson [5]. They were found to be proportional to ω^2, independent of d. We can therefore write

$$P_f = c_f\omega^2 \tag{4.2}$$

Were P_f is a centrifugal tension force acting in the direction of the axis of rotation, and c_f is a constant coefficient depending upon the radius R of the rotor and the density ρ of the air.

Let P_p be the pressure force exerted through the centripetal action and assume

$$P_p = c_p \left(\frac{\omega}{d}\right)^2 \tag{4.3}$$

where c_p is a coefficient depending likewise upon R, ρ and some other factors for which an appropriate theory will have to account.

Whether this coefficient c_p is a constant will presently be examined.

In any case we can write for equilibrium conditions

$$P_p = P + P_f \tag{4.4}$$

or

$$P = c_p \left(\frac{\omega}{d}\right)^2 - c_f\omega^2 \tag{4.5}$$

from which

$$d^2 = -\frac{c_p}{c_f + 1/\dfrac{\omega^2}{P}} \tag{4.6}$$

In the experiments mentioned before the bearing load was varied by changing the position of the axis of rotation. The weight of the rotor was $W = 69\ g$. By tilting the axis to the angles 19.5° and 42°, the normal forces became $W/3 = 23g$ and $2W/3 = 46g$. The spring pressure was $P_s = 16g$. The total pressure forces were therefore 85g, 62g, and 39g respectively.

It was found that if D was plotted against ω^2/P the curves for different values of P come very near to each other. This suggests that Eq. (4.6) can be considered as a good approximation.

This equation shows that the curve should approach a horizontal assymptote with ordinate c_p/c_f. Furthermore the derivative of d^2 with respect to ω^2/P at $\omega^2/P = 0$ is equal to c_p. These relations make it possible to check whether the two parameters c_p and c_f, calculated as will be described below, agree with the form of the graphs in which the d^2 are plotted against ω^2/P.

5. Experiments at atmospheric pressure with a single load.

In the first stage experiments were carried out at atmospheric pressure with the axis of the rotor in vertical position. The full weight $W = 69g$ of the rotor was therefore active, and P was equal to 85g. Four series of observations were carried out, each one comprising six complete tests ranging from $\Omega = 1000$ to 15 600 rev.p.m. They were denoted in chronological order by E, O, F. In addition, the observations reported upon before 1958, denoted by O, were included in the analysis. The results are listed in Tables I and II.

Table I lists the average distance D versus ω^2/P for series 0.

TABLE I

Data for tests of series 0

Ω in 10^3 r.p.m.	2.4	3.0	3.6	4.2	4.8	5.4	6.0	6.6	7.2	7.8	8.4
$\omega^2/P*$		0.755	1.187	1.691	2.314	3.022	3.813	4.713	5.708	6.787	7.962	9.246
D ave in μ		4.098	4.434	4.675	4.876	5.121	5.266	5.446	5.595	5.711	5.814	5.950

Ω in 10^3 r.p.m.	9.0	9.6	10.2	10.8	11.4	12.0	12.6	13.2	13.8
ω^2/P	10.613	12.064	13.623	15.289	17.004	18.863	20.794	22.808	24.931
D ave in μ	6.033	6.142	6.293	6.392	6.488	6.535	6.619	6.709	6.804

Ω in 10^3 r.p.m.	14.4	15.0	15.6
ω^2/P	27.161	29.488	31.862
D ave in μ	6.876	6.952	7.011

* ω^2/P in dynes^{-1} sec$^{\mp 2} \times 1000/981$

Table II lists the average distance D versus ω^2/P for series E, D, F.

TABLE II

Data for series E, D, F

Ω in 10^3 r.p.m.	$\omega^2/P*$	E	D	F
1	0.129	3.36	—	—
1.5	0.291	—	3.509	3.904
2	0.518	4.24	3.957	4.320
3	1.165	4.88	4.564	4.873
4	2.059	5.38	5.065	5.366
5	3.224	5.74	5.387	5.751
6	4.635	6.10	5.721	6.029
7	6.318	6.34	5.950	6.301
8	8.271	6.62	6.200	6.619
9	10.447	6.85	6.429	6.864
10	12.905	7.08	6.682	6.966
11	15.623		6.728	7.184
12	18.564		6.776	7.338
13	21.840		6.943	7.398
14	25.350		6.876	

* ω^2/P in dynes^{-1}sec$^{-2} \times 1000/981$

6. Determination of parameters for atmospheric pressure.

In order to determine the values for d_0 separately for the different series, and the parameters c_p and c_f in best agreement with all of them, the following procedure was adopted:

The values of D were plotted as functions of ω^2/P for the series O, E, D and F. The aim was to express theoretically "the first part of each curve", assuming that at higher velocities the disturbing dynamical effects foreseen by Taylor and Saffman may come into play.

Using Eqs. (4.6) and (4.1), we write

$$(D - d_0')^2 = c_p / \left[c_f + 1 / \frac{\omega^2}{P} \right] \tag{6.1}$$

There are three unknowns d_0', c_p and c_f for the calculation of which we selected three points on each curve as follows:

(a) D in μ for the observation with smallest ω^2/P in dynes^{-1}sec^{-2}
(b) D for $\omega^2/P = 2$ dynes^{-1}sec^{-2}
(c) similar for $\omega^2/P = 8$ dynes^{-1}sec^{-2}

The data are listed in Table III, together with the calculated values of c_p, c_f and d_0'. We write d_0' for d_0 when calculated separately for each one of the series O, E, D, F.

TABLE III

Calculated parameters for four observation series

Series	Coordinates of selected three points			Calculated parameters		
	a	b	c	$c_p^{(1)}$	$c_f^{(2)}$	$d_0'^{(3)}$
O	(0.756 , 4.10)	(2 , 4.78)	(8 , 5.84)	2.766	0.162	2.74
E	(0.132 , 3.36)	(2 , 5.35)	(8 , 6.58)	5.983	0.229	2.48
D	(0.600 , 4.02)	(2 , 5.03)	(8 , 6.17)	5.277	0.238	2.36
F	(0.295 , 3.91)	(2 , 5.33)	(8 , 6.58)	5.393	0.226	2.75

(1) c_f in 10^{-8} dynes sec^2 cm^2
(2) c_p in dynes sec^2
(3) d_0' in μ

In order to find the best common values for c_p and c_f, which we denote by $\bar{c}_p$ and $\bar{c}_f$, a parabolic weight function was assumed in which the greater weight was given to those observations which started nearest to $\omega^2/P \to 0$. We find then the following values of the parameters:

$\bar{c}_p = 5.5756 \times 10^{-8}$ in dyne cm^{2}sec^2
$\bar{c}_f = 0.2261$ in dyne sec^2

The best values for d, denoted by $\bar{d}$, were then calculated from Eq. (4.6) introducing $\bar{c}_p$ and $\bar{c}_f$ as above, for a chosen spectrum of ω^2/P. In Table IV the calculated $\bar{d}$ and $\bar{d}^2$ are listed against chosen ω^2/P.

TABLE IV

Mean thickness of laminar layer $\bar{d}$ for various ω^2/P

ω^2/P in dynes^{-1}sec^{-2}	$\bar{d}$ in μ	$\bar{d}^2$ in μ^2
0.132	0.8454	0.7146
0.295	1.2417	1.5420
0.528	1.6217	2.6300
0.755	1.8968	3.5979
1	2.1325	4.5474
2	2.7711	7.6788
3	3.1571	9.9671
4	3.4221	11.7110
6	3.7675	14.1945
8	3.9850	15.8804
10	4.1349	17.0978
12	4.2451	18.0207
16	4.3954	19.3195
20	4.4938	20.1941
25	4.5774	20.9530
30	4.6362	21.4942
∞	4.9659	24.6599

In Graph I the values of d^2 thus arrived at, are plotted against ω^2/P, and denoted as "theoretical curve". In order to compare this theoretical curve with the experimental observations, the following procedure was adopted:

For every series, the value D was taken from the individual curves of series O, E, D, F for a range of ω^2/P up to $\omega^2/P = 10$ dynes^{-1} sec^{-2} (the "first part of the curve" in the meaning explained above). By subtracting the values of $\bar{d}$ from each of these D, we find different values of d_0. From these, the average $\bar{d}_0$ for each series was calculated with the results shown here:

Series	O	E	D	F
$\bar{d}_0$ in μ	1.9807	2.5820	2.2354	2.5674

It was found that the $\bar{d}_0$ were within 0.25 μ of the different d_0.
Applying Eq. (4.1), we calculated the values for

$$d = D - \bar{d}_0 \qquad (6.2)$$

taking the values for D from Tables I and II. We then plotted d^2 against ω^2/P on the same Graph I and show thus the deviations of the observational points from the theoretical curve.

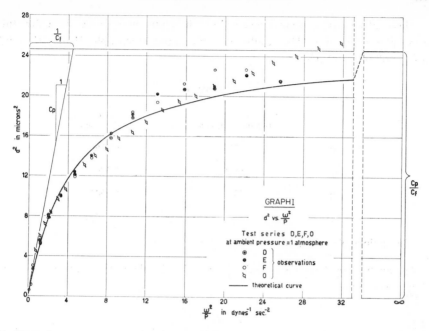

GRAPH I

d^2 vs. $\frac{\omega^2}{P}$

Test series D,E,F,0
at ambient pressure = 1 atmosphere

⊛   D
●   E   } observations
○   F
♮   0

———— theoretical curve

7. Experiments in air at reduced pressures.

Experiments of the same kind as reported before for ambient pressure of one atmosphere, were carried out for air at reduced pressures. Four series, each one consisting of six tests and denoted by VA, VB, VC, VD, were carried out for 2/3 atmosphere. Similarly another four series denoted by VE, VF, VG, VH, were carried out for 1/3 atmosphere. The results are listed in Table V.

TABLE V

Data for tests of series VA-VD, VE-VH

Ω in 10^3 r.p.m	$\omega^2/P*$	VA	VB	VC	VD	VE	VF	VG	VH
1.5	0.296	4.294	3.946	4.013	—	3.844	—	—	—
2	0.526	5.113	4.329	4.305	4.272	4.184	—	3.983	4.165
3	1.184	5.574	4.885	4.846	4.791	4.593	4.795	4.513	4.547
4	2.104	5.877	5.347	5.271	5.129	4.869	5.103	4.833	4.870
5	3.288	6.147	5.663	5.605	5.501	5.105	5.308	5.023	5.111
6	4.734	6.424	5.941	5.894	5.781	5.296	5.546	5.295	5.303
7	6.444	6.756	6.165	6.203	5.907	5.441	5.743	5.465	5.439
8	8.417	7.084	6.394	6.473	6.124	5.574	6.033	5.634	5.559
9	10.652	7.381	6.574	6.663	6.276	5.733	6.301	5.850	5.709
10	13.151	7.545	6.784	6.779	6.468	5.839	6.723	6.105	5.839
11	15.913	7.760	6.978	6.960	6.558	6.040	6.890	6.332	5.996
12	18.937	8.208	7.187	7.084	6.693	6.245	7.093	6.928	6.161
13	22.225	—	7.439	7.203	6.864	6.457	7.616	7.267	—
14	—	—	—	—	—	—	9.478	—	—

* ω^2/P in dynes^{-1} sec^{-2}

These observations were processed in the same manner as those for full atmospheric pressure. The results are represented in Graphs II and III, and in the following Table:

TABLE VI

	$\bar{c}_p$ in 10^{-8} dyne cm²sec²	$\bar{c}_f$ in dyne sec²
Full atm.	5.5756	0.2261
2/3 atm	3.6808	0.1805
1/3 atm	2.4361	0.2542

8. Discussions of results.

As can be seen from Graphs I, II, and III, the theoretical curves in accordance with equation

$$d^2 = \bar{c}_p \bigg/ \left[\bar{c}_f + 1 \bigg/ \frac{\omega^2}{P} \right] \tag{8.1}$$

represent fairly well the observations within the range $0 < \omega^2/P < 6$ dynes^{-1} sec^{-2} for all three pressures. However, a systematic deviation can be observed as the observations for $4 < \omega^2/P < 8$ lie always slightly below the theoretical curve. Around $\omega^2/P = 10$, the observations begin to scatter, and are always *above* the theoretical curve. We accordingly can distinguish three regions, namely, one very stable $0 < \omega^2/P < 6$, one fairly stable $6 < \omega^2/P < 10$, and finally the last unstable region.

The results are embodied graphically in Graph IV. The square of the thickness of the laminar layer between the plates (d^2) is shown as a function of the square of the angular velocity (ω^2) in relation to the bearing force (P). The three regions mentioned before are evident. There is the first well defined region with a tangent at the origin, the slope of which is a measure for $\bar{c}_p$

In Graph V, the relative magnitudes of $\bar{c}_p$ and $\bar{c}_f$ in relation to those of ambient pressure of one atmosphere are shown. These are denoted by c_p' and c_f'. The ratio c_p'/c_f' is also shown. As can be seen from Eq. (8.1), there is an asymptotic approach of the theoretical curve for $\omega^2/P \to \infty$ with $d^2 = \bar{c}_p/\bar{c}_f$. The ratio c_p'/c_f' is therefore an indication of the relative position of the asymptote. The Graph shows within observational error a linear relation between

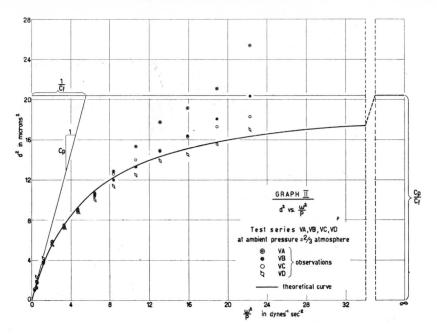

GRAPH II

d² vs. ω²/P

Test series VA,VB,VC,VD
at ambient pressure = ²/₃ atmosphere

⊛ VA
● VB } observations
○ VC
↯ VD

—— theoretical curve

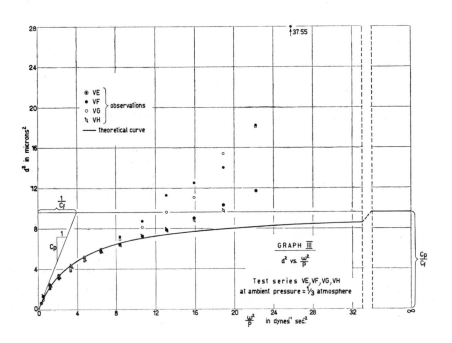

⊛ VE
● VF } observations
○ VG
↯ VH

—— theoretical curve

GRAPH III

d² vs. ω²/P

Test series VE,VF,VG,VH
at ambient pressure = ¹/₃ atmosphere

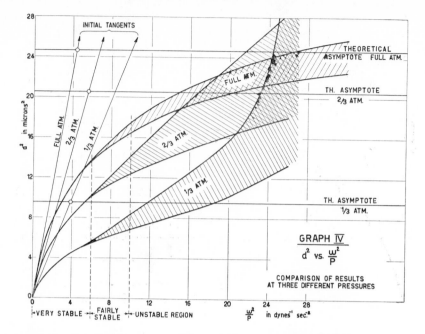

GRAPH IV

d^2 vs. $\dfrac{\omega^2}{P}$

COMPARISON OF RESULTS
AT THREE DIFFERENT PRESSURES

the centripetal parameter $\bar{c}_p$ and the ambient pressure, tending to zero with the pressure. In contradistinction, the centrifugal parameter $\bar{c}_f$ first falls with the reduced p, and then tends to increase, with $\bar{c}_f$ for $p_0 = {}^1/_3$ larger than $\bar{c}_f$ for $p_0 = 1$.

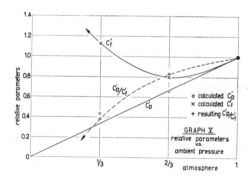

GRAPH V
relative parameters
vs.
ambient pressure

9. Conclusions.

The present research has shown that when air is put in torsional flow between two circular discs, of which one is stationary and the other is turning around its axis with an angular velocity ω, there develops a thrust bearing pressure supporting an external load P equal to the weight of the rotor. This action is opposed by the centrifugal action of classical mechanics. Equilibrium of both together with load P is reached at a certain gap d between the discs. When the velocity of rotation of the rotor disc is reduced, the distance d between both discs is automatically reduced, and the thrust bearing action is the same as before. However, the centrifugal force which is proportional to ω^2 becomes smaller while the ratio d^2/ω^2 increases. With $\omega \to 0$, $(d/\omega)^2$ is the measure of the centripetal action, represented by the tangent to the curve at the origin. The vertical distance between this tangent and the curve at any speed is a measure of centrifugal action. The net pressure supports the weight of the rotating disc.

The combined effect seems to follow the equation $d^2 = c_p \bigg/ \left(c_f + \dfrac{1}{\omega^2/P} \right)$

where c_p and c_f are constants depending on the geometrical dimensions of the discs and the ambient pressure within a certain range of stability at comparatively low velocities. When this range is passed, another effect, first described by Taylor and Saffman as resulting from the Navier-Stokes equations, is added. In this range the effect tends to increase with decreasing ambient pressure. Conditions are represented graphically in Graph VI. The theory of the inertial centrifugal forces in the torsional flow has been developed by Stewartson[5]. His result is much lower then that which we found.

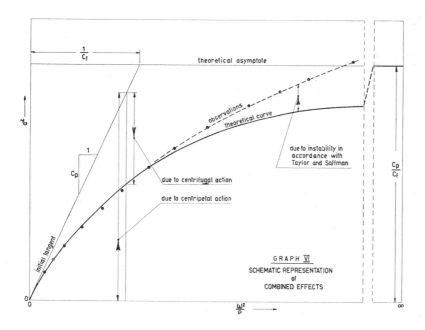

The kinetic theory of Chapman and Cowling [6] predicts an additional centrifugal action which should increase with decreasing ambient pressure. This seems to be in accordance with our results, provided the centrifugal and centripetal actions can be superposed.

To sum up: Our experiments show that there exist cross-stresses in the laminar flow of air which neither the kinetic theory of monatomic gases nor the theory of viscid fluids as embodied in the Navier-Stokes equations can explain. This leaves open as providing a possible explanation: either a kinetic theory of di-atomic gases or an elastico-viscosity of air as tentatively proposed by Reiner [1,2] before.

10.   Acknowledgements.

The research reported in this paper has been sponsored in part by the Air Research and Development Command, United States Air Force through the European Office ARDC.

We have much profited from discussions, both oral and in letters, with Professors J. G. Cowling, K. Stewartson and P. G. Saffman. Dr. B. Popper and Mr. P. Schechter of the staff of the Technion have participated in the execution of the experiments and preparation of the Report.

List of symbols.

A	=	area
C	=	capacity
c_f	=	coefficient of centrifugal force
c_p	=	coefficient of centripetal force
D	=	clear distance of plates, measured electrically
d	=	differential
d	=	hydrodynamical thickness of gap
d_0	=	$D - d$
e	=	chance quantity
g	=	acceleration of gravity
P	=	total axial pressure force
P_f	=	centrifugal force
P_p	=	centripetal force
P_s	=	pressure force from spring
p	=	isotropic pressure
p_0	=	ambient pressure

p' = dimensionless excess pressure
R = radius of plate
W = weight of rotor
x, y, z = coordinates
α = chance quantity
λ = non-dimensional quantity
ρ = density of air
σ = normal traction
τ = tangential traction
η = coefficient of viscosity
ω = angular velocity in $\sec^{-1}$
Ω = angular velocity in rev. per minute

REFERENCES

[1] M. REINER, The centripetal-pump effect in a vacuum pump, *Proc. Roy. Soc.,* **A247,** (1958) 152.
[2] M. REINER, A centripetal pump effect in air, *Proc. Roy. Soc.,* **A240,** (1957), 173.
[3] B. POPPER AND M. REINER, *Cross-stresses in Air. Boundary Layer Research,* Springer Verlag, (1958).
[4] G. TAYLOR, AND P. G. SAFFMAN, *J. Aeronaut. Sciences,* **24,** (1957), 553.
[5] K. STEWARTSON, *Proc. Cambr. Phil. Soc.,* **49,** (1952), 333–341.
[6] S. CHAPMAN AND T. G. COWLING, *The Mathematical Theory of Non-uniform Gases,* Cambridge, University Press, (1952).

DISCUSSION

H. MEDWIN: Since the Reiner apparatus has surface imperfections of the order of 0.1 microns, one may expect that when the discs are operated at a separation of, say, 3 microns, large pressure swings will be generated in the "valleys" as one plate moves past the other. Very crudely, the alternating pressures caused by this piston action can be expected to be of magnitude $p_1 = (0.1/3) p_0$ where p_0 is the ambient pressure. One of the "second order" consequences of such large pressure swings is the generation of large static radiation pressures. For a plane wave this radiation pressure is given by $p_2 \simeq p_1^2/p_0 c^2 = \rho_0 u_2^1$, where ρ_0 is the ambient density, c the speed of sound and u_1 is the particle velocity. For the data and assumptions, above, $p_2 \simeq 10^3/\text{dyne/cm}^2$. It will be observed that this postulated explanation of the forces observed in Reiner's experiments in air, has the following characteristics in common with Reiner's data: 1) the radiation pressure decreases with decreasing ambient pressure; 2) the radiation pressure increases with increasing

R.P.M. (through the particle velocity term); 3) the radiation pressure increases as the plate separation is reduced; 4) the order of magnitude of the radiation pressure is about the same as observed in Reiner's experiments.

FOUX AND REINER'S reply: The mechanism which Mr. Medwin assumes to be operative is similar to the one assumed by Taylor and Saffman. There are not only "valleys" but also "hills", and to a first approximation the influence of one cancels the influence of the other. In a second approximation a pressure remains, which however would have to increase with decreasing ambient pressure. In our experiments different discs were used with naturally different imperfections. The effect, however, was of the same order of magnitude.

FLOW OF NON-NEWTONIAN FLUIDS AT SMALL REYNOLDS NUMBER BETWEEN TWO DISCS: ONE ROTATING AND THE OTHER AT REST

L. Rintel

*Technion–Israel Institute of Technology, Haifa, Israel**

1. The present note may be regarded as an amplification of a paper by Srivastava [1] with (nearly) the same title. The qualification refers to the adjective "infinite" which the discs have in Srivastava's paper; in the present paper an attempt is made to apply the theory on finite discs of radius a. In this way stress-boundary conditions are taken care of, which Srivastava has neglected.

Srivastava calls a fluid non-Newtonian when the stress tensor τ_j^i is related to the rate of strain or rather flow tensor e_j^i by

$$\tau_j^i = - p\delta_j^i + \mu_{_n} e_j^i + \mu_c e_\alpha^i e_j^\alpha \qquad (1.1)**$$

More specifically such a fluid is called a Reiner-fluid, and when it is incompressible, a Reiner-Rivlin fluid. Srivastava assumes such incompressibility, and we shall follow him.

Srivastava uses his theory in order to explain what was called by G. I. Taylor [2] the Reiner-effect. We quote from Srivastava's paper as follows: "Reiner [3] performed an experiment in which a gap of air (d) was maintained between two discs, one $(z = 0)$ rotating (Ω) and the other $(z = d)$ at rest, and found that the manometer placed at the centre of the non-rotating disc indicates a thrust". We may add that not only is there a thrust at the centre, but that the whole apparatus acts as an automatically maintained air thrust bearing. In these experiments the gap thickness d was in the average $5\mu = 5 \times 10^{-4}$cm with a corresponding velocity Ω of about 500 sec^{-1}. This makes the Reynolds number $R = \rho\Omega d^2/u_{_n} \approx 10^{-1}$. Srivastava accordingly neglects terms with powers of higher order of R.

---

* On leave from the Negev Research Institute, Beersheva, Israel.
** Using Srivastava's notation.

Writing

$$u = - r\Omega Rh'/2, \quad v = r\Omega g, \quad w = d\Omega Rh \tag{1.2}$$

he finds for the mean pressure p

$$p = - \mu_v \Omega \left(0.5\, R^3 h^2 - Rh' - 0.15\, \frac{r^2}{d^2} R + P_0 \right) +$$

$$+ \mu_c \Omega^2 \left[3.5\, R^2 h'^2 + \frac{r^2}{d^2}\, (0.25\, R^2 h''^2 - 0.5) \right] \tag{1.3}$$

where

$$h = - \frac{1}{10}\eta^2 + \frac{7}{30}\eta^3 - \frac{1}{6}\eta^4 + \frac{1}{30}\eta^5 \tag{1.4}$$

$$g = 1 - \eta$$

with

$$\eta = z/d \tag{1.5}$$

and P_0 is an integration constant.

He also finds for the stress component τ_z^z

$$\tau_z^z = \mu_v \Omega \left(0.5\, R^3 h^2 + Rh' - 0.15\, R\frac{r^2}{d^2} + P_0 \right) +$$

$$+ \mu_c \Omega^2 \left(0.5\, R^2 h'^2 + 1.5\, \frac{r^2}{d^2} \right) \tag{1.6}.$$

This yields

$$\tau_z^z|_{\eta=0} = \mu_v \Omega P_0 - 0.15\, \rho r^2 \Omega^2 + 1.5\, \mu_c \Omega^2 \frac{r^2}{d^2} = \tau_z^z|_{\eta=1} \tag{1.7}.$$

So far Srivastava.

2. We now proceed to make use of the stress-boundary conditions. The boundaries of the body of air are $z = 0$ or $\eta = 0$, $z = d$ or $\eta = 1$ and $r = a$; the normal stresses acting on them being τ_z^z for $z = 0$ and $z = d$ and τ_r^r for $r = a$.

We consider τ_r^r on the boundary $r = a$. Somewhere beyond the edge of the discs, say at $r = a + \varepsilon$, the ambient air will be at rest with $\tau_r^r = -\tilde{p}$, where $\tilde{p}$ is the atmospheric pressure. We cannot expect $\tau_r|_{r=a}$ to be equal to

$-\tilde{p}$. But ε will be a very small length, comparable with d, and we may apply an analogy to St. Venant's principle in the theory of elasticity by assuming that

$$\frac{1}{d}\int_0^d \tau_r^r\big|_a \, dz = -\tilde{p} \tag{2.1}$$

We need an expression for τ_r^r, which Srivastava has not calculated.

From (1.1)

$$\tau_r^r = -p + \mu_v \, e_r^r + \mu_c \, e_\alpha^r e_r^\alpha \tag{2.2}$$

But

$$e_j^i = \Omega \left\| \begin{matrix} -Rh' & 0 & -\dfrac{r}{2d}Rh'' \\[2mm] \cdot & -Rh' & \dfrac{r}{d}g' \\[2mm] \cdot & \cdot & 2Rh' \end{matrix} \right\| \tag{2.3}$$

from which

$$e_\alpha^r e_r^\alpha = \Omega^2 \left(R^2 h'^2 + \frac{r^2}{4d^2} R^2 h''^2 \right) \tag{2.4}$$

so that

$$\tau_r^r = \mu_v \Omega \left(0.5 R^3 h^2 - 0.15 \frac{r^2}{d^2} R - 2 Rh' + P_0 \right) - $$
$$- \mu_c \Omega^2 \left(2.5 R^2 h'^2 - 0.5 \frac{r^2}{d^2} \right) \tag{2.5}$$

Neglecting terms in R^2 and R^3 and considering that h_0 and h_1, vanish, Eq. (2.5) now gives

$$\int_{\eta=0}^{\eta=1} \tau_r^r d\eta = \Omega \left[\mu_v \left(P_0 - 0.15 \frac{r^2}{d^2} R \right) + 0.5 \frac{r^2}{d^2} \Omega \mu_c \right] \tag{2.6}$$

and therefore from (2.1)

$$\mu_v \Omega P_0 = a^2 \Omega^2 \left(0.15 \rho - 0.5 \frac{\mu_c}{d^2} \right) - \tilde{p} \tag{2.7}$$

With this, the mean pressure is from (1.3)

$$p = \tilde{p} - 0.15\,a^2\Omega^2\rho - \mu_v.\,R\Omega\left(0.5\,R^2h^2 - h' - 0.15\frac{r^2}{d^2}\right) +$$

$$+ \mu_c\Omega^2\left[3.5\,R^2h'^2 + \frac{r^2}{d^2}(0.25\,R^2h''^2 - 0.5) + 0.5\frac{a^2}{d^2}\right] \qquad (2.8)$$

and from (1.6)

$$\tau_z^z = -\tilde{p} + 0.15\,a^2\Omega^2\rho + \mu_v\,\Omega R\left(0.5\,R^2h^2 + h' - 0.15\frac{r^2}{d^2}\right) +$$

$$+ \mu_c\Omega^2\left(0.5\,R^2h'^2 + 1.5\frac{r^2}{d^2} - 0.5\frac{a^2}{d^2}\right) \qquad (2.9)$$

and

$$\tau_z^z\big|_{\eta=1} = -\tilde{p} + 0.15\,\Omega^2\rho(a^2 - r^2) + 0.5\frac{\mu_c\Omega^2}{d^2}(3r^2 - a^2) \qquad (2.10)$$

The traction $\tau_z^z\big|_{\eta=1}$ accordingly varies from $-\tilde{p} + 0.15a^2\Omega^2\rho - 0.5\ \mu_c\Omega^2\frac{a^2}{d^2}$ at the centre $r = 0$ and $-\tilde{p} + \mu_c\Omega^2\,\frac{a^2}{d^2}$ at the edge $r = a$. If we consider *cross-stresses only*, there is a point $r = a/\sqrt{3}$, at which $\tau_z^z\big|_{\eta=1}$ vanishes, or changes occur from a pressure to a tension.* The tractions τ_z have a resultant force

$$P_z = 2\pi \int_0^a \tau_z^z\big|_{\eta=1} r\,dr = -\tilde{p}a^2\pi + \pi\left(0.3\Omega^2\rho + \frac{\mu_c\Omega^2}{d^2}\right)\frac{a^4}{4} \qquad (2.11)$$

Note that this resultant force is the one acting *upon the fluid*. The force acting upon the disc at rest is, taking into account $-\tilde{p}\,a^2\pi$ on the free surface,

$$\bar{P}_z = -\pi\frac{a^2}{4}\Omega^2\left(0.3\rho + \frac{\mu_c}{d^2}\right) \qquad (2.12)$$

It consists of two parts: one, resulting from the centrifugal forces, is independent of d, the other, resulting from cross-forces, is inversely proportional to d^2. Both are proportional to Ω^2.

----

* This result is in agreement with that found by Braun and Reiner [4].

3. Discussion and conclusions.

Taking atmospheric pressure $\tilde{p}$ as our zero point, the pressure at the centre of the disc has been found as

$$p_0 = \left(-0.15\,\rho + 0.5\,\mu_c\,\frac{1}{d^2}\right) a^2\Omega^2 \tag{3.1}$$

while the force acting upon the disc at rest $(z = d)$ in a vertical direction (z) is

$$\bar{P}_z = -\pi\,\frac{a^2}{4}\,\Omega^2(0.3\,\rho + \mu_c/d^2) \tag{3.2}$$

It is remarkable that μ_v does not appear in any one of these expressions. This can be understood from the fact that viscous tractions act *tangentially* only. The mass force *does* appear, as it causes an isotropic stress in all directions. In accordance with (3.1) it causes a reduction of the pressure at the centre of the disc from $\tilde{p}$ ro $\tilde{p} - 0.15\,\rho\,a^2\Omega^2$. (This is in accordance with Stewartson's result [7]). It also causes a force $-0.075\,\pi\ a^2\Omega^2\rho$ acting on the disc, with the tendency of reducing the distance d between the discs. If μ_c is positive, the cross viscous forces act in the same direction, assisting the mass forces. In order to explain the automatic air thrust bearing action, we must therefore assume that μ_c is negative. However, we then come by (3.1) into conflict with the observation of a thrust in the centre of the non-rotating disc. Reiner has observed both in the case of air [5] and of a simple liquid such as toluene [6], that *there is an automatic thrust bearing action accompanied by a pressure at the centre.*

We therefore must conclude, in opposition to Srivastava, that the equation of the Reiner-Rivlin fluid does not adequately describe facts as observed until now. This result has been announced before by Reiner.

I thank Professor Reiner for his interest and help.

This research has been sponsored in part by the Air Research and Development Command, U. S. Airforce, through its European Office.

REFERENCES

[1] A. C. SRIVASTAVA, *Quart. J. Mech. Appl. Math.*, **14**, (1961), 353.
[2] G. I. TAYLOR AND P. G. SAFFMAN, *J. Aero. Sc.*, **24**, (1957), 73.
[3] M. REINER, *Proc. Roy. Soc.*, A, **240**, (1957), 553.
[4] L. BRAUN AND M. REINER, *Quart. J. Mech. Appl. Math.*, **5**, (1952), 42.
[5] M. REINER, *Proc. Roy. Soc.*, A, **247**, (1958), 152–167.
[6] M. REINER, Physics of Fluids, **3**, (1960), 427–432.
7] K. STEWARTSON, *Proc. Cambr. Phil. Soc.*, **49** (1953), 333.

Discussion

L.T.F. Broer: There appears not to be any direct information on the pressure at the rim. The reason for taking it equal to ambient pressure boils down to the fact that the entrance region is small compared with the diameter, and the plausible assumption that there will be no excessive pressure gradients in this region. It seems reasonable therefore to neglect the pressure difference over this region.

SECOND-ORDER EFFECTS IN THE TORSIONAL FLOW OF A GAS IN ACCORDANCE WITH THE KINETIC THEORY

M. BENTWICH AND M. REINER

Technion–Israel Institute of Technology, Haifa, Israel

ABSTRACT

It is shown that the kinetic theory of mon-atomic gases is unlikely to account for the Reiner effect in a torsional flow.

When air is sheared in torsional flow between two discs, one stationary, the other rotating with constant velocity ω, and the distance d between both discs is very small (some microns) so that the velocity gradient ω/d is large, then Reiner [1] has shown that the air is drawn inside between the discs in a *centripetal* manner, and that at the same time a *thrust bearing pressure* is developed between both plates. No theory has yet been established for this effect. It is the purpose of the present note to investigate whether an appropriate theory can be based on a kinetic theory of gases which takes account of second-order effects.

The most general stress-deformation relationship for a gas treated as a continuum can be arrived at by considering the mechanics of an aggregate of particles. This method was used by Maxwell [2], who deduced the Boyle-Mariotte law for a uniform gas at rest. For a gas not in a thermostatic state, the relationship between pertinent quantities can be arrived at by solving the non-linear integral Maxwell-Boltzmann equation. No close-form accurate solutions (except for the trivial thermostatic state) of the latter are available. Chapman and Enskog [3] and Truesdell [4] present a method of solution of the Maxwell-Boltzmann equation, using repeated iterations. Though these authors differ in their approach, they both take the thermostatic state as their zero'th iteration. Both, as did Maxwell before, find a viscous stress-rate-of-strain relationship as the result of the first iteration. As a result of their second iteration, both arrive at the same expression for the pressure tensor as a function of the gas's mean velocity and velocity-gradients, when a steady state[1] and uniform temperature is assumed.

---

(1) The difference in the approaches of [4] and [3] leads to variations in the expressions representing time derivatives. See reference [4, sec. 2, footnote 6].

We shall use the results obtained by Chapman and Enskog, and Ikenberry and Truesdell up to and including the second iteration in order to predict the gas behaviour in a torsional laminar flow. With v_i denoting the flow field, η as coefficient of viscosity, p hydrostatic pressure, E_{ij} non-divergent strain tensor, the second order approximation to the pressure tensor p_{ij} is given in both references [3] and [4] by

$$p_{ij} = p\delta_{ij} - 2\eta\, E_{ij} + \frac{2\eta^2}{p}(E_{\alpha i} v_{j,\alpha} + E_{\alpha j} v_{i,\alpha}) + \frac{2\eta^2}{p} v_\alpha \frac{\partial}{\partial x_\alpha}(E_{ij}) -$$

$$- \frac{4\eta^2}{3p} E_{\alpha\beta} E_{\alpha\beta} \delta_{ij} + \frac{2\eta^2}{p}\frac{\partial v_\alpha}{\partial x_\alpha} E_{ij} \qquad (1)(^2)$$

where

$$E_{ij} = \tfrac{1}{2}(v_{i,j} + v_{j,i}) - \tfrac{1}{3} v_{\alpha,\alpha}\delta_{ij} \qquad (2)$$

The stress equations are in the case of rotational symmetry with vertical axis z, neglecting gravity, reduced to the following two equations

$$\frac{\partial p_{rr}}{\partial r} + \frac{\partial p_{rz}}{\partial z} + \frac{p_{rr} - p_{\theta\theta}}{r} = -\rho a_r \qquad (3)$$

and

$$\frac{\partial p_{rz}}{\partial r} + \frac{\partial p_{zz}}{\partial z} + \frac{p_{rz}}{r} = -\rho a_z \qquad (4)$$

where ρ is the gas density and a the acceleration. Note that the stress tensor p_{ij} is positive when a pressure, and therefore has the opposite sign when introduced in the stress-equations in the usual writing. This makes the right side of Eqs. (3) and (4) negative.

We proceed in an inverse method, considering a flow field with respect to circular cylindrical coordinates (r,θ,z) given by

$$v_1 = 0, \quad v_2 = \frac{\omega}{d} rz, \quad v_3 = 0 \qquad (5)$$

with

$$a_r = -\left(\frac{\omega}{d}\right)^2 z^2 r; \quad a_z = 0 \qquad (6)$$

(^{2}) From Eq. (6), Section 15, 3 Chapman and Cowling, p. 265, with $\bar{\omega}_2 = 2$, $\bar{\omega}_6 = 8$.

Substituting these expressions into Eqs. (1) and (2) we get

$$p_{ij} = p\delta_{ij} - \frac{\eta\omega}{d} \begin{Vmatrix} 0 & 0 & 0 \\ 0 & 0 & r \\ 0 & r & 0 \end{Vmatrix} - \left(\frac{\eta\omega}{d}\right)^2 \cdot \frac{2}{3}\frac{1}{p} \begin{Vmatrix} r^2 & 0 & 3rz \\ 0 & -2r^2 & 0 \\ 3rz & 0 & r^2 \end{Vmatrix} \quad (7)$$

Note that from Eq. (5)

$$v_{\alpha,\alpha} = 0. \quad (8)$$

Such flow is not associated with a change of volume, and therefore even a compressible material is in this case not further compressed in the course of flow. We therefore need not take into consideration the equation of continuity nor the last term on the right side of Eq. (1). However, we must take account of the equation of state. If the two plates are of metal, as is the case in Reiner's experiments, we may assume that the process is isothermal, and therefore in accordance with Boyle-Mariotte's law

$$\rho = \frac{\rho_0}{p_0}p = p/C \quad (9)$$

where the atmospheric pressure

$$p_0 = 1.013 \times 10^6 \text{ dyne cm}^{-2}$$

the density of air at atmospheric pressure

$$\rho_0 = 1.3 \times 10^{-3} \text{g cm}^{-3}$$

and therefore the constant

$$C = 7.79 \times 10^8 \text{cm}^2\text{sec}^{-2}.$$

With Eqs. (7), (6) and (9), the stress-equations (3) and (4) now become

$$\left[1 + \frac{2}{3}\left(\frac{\eta\omega}{d}\right)^2 \frac{r^2}{p^2}\right]\frac{\partial p}{\partial r} + 2\left(\frac{\eta\omega}{d}\right)^2 \frac{rz}{p^2}\frac{\partial p}{\partial z} - \frac{16}{3}\left(\frac{\eta\omega}{d}\right)^2 \frac{r}{p} = \left(\frac{\omega}{d}\right)^2 \frac{p}{C} z^2 r \quad (10)$$

$$2 \left(\frac{\eta \omega}{d} \right)^2 \frac{rz}{p^2} \frac{\partial p}{\partial r} + \left[1 + \frac{2}{3} \left(\frac{\eta \omega}{d} \right)^2 \frac{r^2}{p^2} \right] \frac{\partial p}{\partial z} - 4 \left(\frac{\eta \omega}{d} \right)^2 \frac{z}{p} = 0 \qquad (11)$$

Solving these equations for $\dfrac{\partial p}{\partial r}$ and $\dfrac{\partial p}{\partial z}$ yields

$$A \frac{\partial p}{\partial r} = r \left\{ \left(\frac{16}{3p} + \frac{pz^2}{\eta^2 C} \right) \left[\left(\frac{d}{\eta \omega} \right)^2 + \frac{2r^2}{3p^2} \right] - 8 \frac{z^2}{p^3} \right\} \qquad (12)$$

$$A \frac{\partial p}{\partial z} = \frac{4z}{p} \left\{ \left(\frac{d}{\eta \omega} \right)^2 + \frac{2r^2}{3p^2} - \frac{r^2}{2p} \left(\frac{16}{3p} + \frac{pz^2}{\eta^2 C} \right) \right\} \qquad (13)$$

where the denominator A is given by

$$A = \left[\left(\frac{d}{\eta \omega} \right)^2 + \frac{2r^2}{3p^2} \right]^2 - \left(\frac{2rz}{p^2} \right)^2 \qquad (14)$$

We shall not attempt to integrate these equations. If we had done so, and expressed p as a function of r and z, we would have had to use the boundary conditions for determining the integration constants appearing in the general solution. These refer to the stresses

$$P_{rr}|_{r=R}, \quad P_{rz}|_{r=R},$$

where R is the radius of the plates. Let P be the bearing force acting on stator and rotor in the vertical direction and positive if a pressure. We should then have,

$$P = 2\pi \int_{r=0}^{r=R} P_{zz}|_{z=d} \, r dr = 2\pi \left\{ \int_0^R P_{zz}|_{z=0} \, r dr + R \int_0^d P_{rz}|_{r=R} \, dz \right\} \qquad (15)$$

Furthermore, at the free edge of the apparatus where the body of the air between the plates borders at the ambient air, we must have,

$$P_{rr}|_{r=R} = p_0 \qquad (16)$$

and

$$P_{rz}|_{r=R} = 0 \qquad (17)$$

if the ambient air outside the discs is at rest.

Now from Eq. (7)

$$p_{rr} = p_{zz} = p - \frac{2r^2}{3p}\left(\frac{\eta\omega}{d}\right)^2$$

$$p_{rz} = -\frac{2rz}{p}\left(\frac{\eta\omega}{d}\right)^2 \qquad\qquad (18)$$

Conditions (16) and (17) evidently cannot be complied with. Indeed, the air cannot be expected to be at rest at $r = R + \varepsilon$, where ε is small. This means that (5) is not a solution complying with the boundary conditions. Here an analogy to St. Venants' principle in the theory of elasticity can help. Considering that in our case $d \ll R$, we may assume that, if we modify condition (16) to

$$\frac{1}{d}\int_0^d p_{rr}|_{r=R}\,dz = p_0 \qquad\qquad (19)$$

there will be some deviations from the velocity field, Eq. (5). These will, however, be confined to a very small region at the edge to a depth in the direction $-r$ comparable with the magnitude of d, which is negligible. With regard to condition (17), this can be complied with for $z = 0$, but at $r = R$, $p_{zr}|_{r=R,z=d}$ $= -\frac{2Rd}{p}\left(\frac{\eta\omega}{d}\right)^2$, and cannot be got rid of. However, consider conditions at the surface of the rotor, in contact with the streaming air. There the rotor suffers a tangential traction which at the rim $r = R$ is $p_{z\theta} = -R\frac{\eta\omega}{d}$. This and the traction τ_{zr} give a resultant $p_{zt} = -R\frac{\eta\omega}{d}\left[1 + \frac{4\eta^2\omega^2}{p^2}\right]^{1/2}$.

The deviation from the direction of θ, along a true circle, is $p_{zr}/p_{z\theta} = 3.4\times 10^{-10}\omega$.

The highest velocity attained in Reiner's experiment is of the order 1300 sec^{-1}. In this case $p_{rz}/p_{z\theta} = 5\times 10^{-7}$rad $= 10^{-2}$ seconds of angle. This is smaller than any precision which can be obtained in the machining of the plate, and the tractions $p_{zr} = p_{rz}$ can therefore be neglected.

For our problem we now only have to know the sign of $\frac{\partial p_{rr}}{\partial r}$. If this should be positive, the radial pressure would decrease in the direction from the edge towards the centre in a centrifugal manner. The kinetic theory can therefore explain the centripetal pumping effect only if $\partial p_{rr}/\partial r$ is negative. Furthermore, since $p_{zz} = p_{rr}$, the same criterion applies with regard to the thrust bearing effect.

From Eq. (18) we have

$$\frac{\partial p_{rr}}{\partial r} = \frac{\partial p}{\partial r}\left[1 + \frac{2}{3}\left(\frac{\eta\omega}{d}\right)^2 \frac{r^2}{p^2}\right] - \frac{4}{3}\left(\frac{\eta\omega}{d}\right)^2 \frac{r}{p} \tag{20}$$

Introducing $\partial p/\partial r$ from Eq. (12) we find

$$A\frac{\partial p_{rr}}{\partial r} = r\left(\frac{\eta\omega}{d}\right)^2 \left\{\left[\left(\frac{d}{\eta\omega}\right)^2 + \frac{2}{3}\frac{r^2}{p^2}\right]^2 \left(\frac{4}{p} + \frac{p}{\eta^2 C}z^2\right) - 8\frac{z^2}{p^3}\left(\frac{d}{\eta\omega}\right)^2\right\} \tag{21}$$

We see that $\dfrac{\partial p_{rr}}{\partial r}\Big|_{r=0}$ vanishes, as is to be expected, considering the axial sym-

metry of flow. Furthermore $\dfrac{\partial p_{rr}}{\partial r}\Big|_{z=0} = \dfrac{4r}{p}\left(\dfrac{\eta\omega}{d}\right)^2$ and this is positive

throughout $0 \leq r \leq R$ with positive p. In general, the denominator A can be

written as $\left(\dfrac{d}{\eta\omega}\right)^4 + \dfrac{4r^4}{9p^4} + \dfrac{4r^2}{p^4}\left[\dfrac{p^2}{3}\left(\dfrac{d}{\eta\omega}\right)^2 - z^2\right]$ and this is positive for

all $z < \dfrac{p}{1.7}\left(\dfrac{d}{\eta\omega}\right)$. But $0 \leq z \leq d$, and the condition for a positive value of

quantity within brackets is therefore $\omega < \dfrac{p}{1.7\eta} = 0.3 \times 10^{10} \sec^{-1}$. This co-

vers all possible cases. With regard to the nominator, this will be positive if

$\dfrac{4}{p}\left(\dfrac{d}{\eta\omega}\right)^2 - \dfrac{8z^2}{p^3}$ is positive. This is the case for all $z < \dfrac{dp}{1.4\eta\omega}$. As before, we,

now find $\omega < \dfrac{p}{1.4\eta} = 0.4 \times 10^{10} \sec^{-1}$.

In acordance with the kinetic theory under consideration, the hydrostatic
pressure between the discs therefore tends to increase everywhere with the
radius, reaching ambient atmospheric pressure at the edge. This implies a
centrifugal action in contradistinction to the action shown in the experiments mentioned above. The phenomenon revealed in these experiments
therefore cannot be explained, *even qualitatively*. However, certain points
must be considered before one can definitely state that the kinetic theorey
fails to explain the phenomena under consideration, namely:

(i) Only two iterations for the solution of the Maxwell-Boltzman equation have been taken into account. It might be possible that further iterations
will *change the sign* of the second order terms.

(ii) The solution developed here does not comply exactly with the boundary
conditions at the vertical edge of the space between both discs. It is concei-
vable that a better approximation to this boundary condition might *change
the sign* of the second order terms.

(iii)   Experiments were performed with air or di-atomic gases, while the theory refers to a mon-atomic gas. It might be possible that experiments with a mon-atomic gas would indeed not show the cross-stresses effect.

We are inclined to believe that points (i) and (ii) would not substantially change the situation as presented here. In order to be able to reply to the third question, experiments with inert gases will be carried out.

We are grateful to Professors Cowling and Truesdell for their generous advice given orally and in many letters.

This research has been sponsored in part by the Air Research and Development Command, U.S. Airforce, through its European Office.

REFERENCES

[1]   M. REINER, *Proc. Roy. Spc.* **A 241**, (1958), 152.

[2]   J. C. MAXWELL, *Phil. Trans. Roy. Soc.*, **157**, (1866), 49.

[3]   S. CHAPMAN AND T. G. COWLING, *The Mathematical Theory of Non-uniform Gases* Cambridge, University Press (1952).

[4]   E. IKENBERRY AND A. C. TRUESDELL, *J. Rat. Mech. Anal.*, **5**, (1956), 1.

[5]   S. GOLDSTEIN, Modern Developments in Fluid Dynamics, Oxford Univ. Press, 1938.

DISCUSSION

C. TRUESDELL: The statement in the abstract is not in the least substantiated by the analysis. In the kinetic theory, one must take the equations as they stand; nothing is left at disposal to be adjusted. In (9), the "constant" $C = k\theta/m$, where θ is the temperature. In isothermal flow at uniform density, which is assumed, p also is constant. This is contradicted by (12) and (13) which show that p depends on r and z. If θ is allowed to vary, then η varies also, since η is proportional to θ; substitution of (1) into (3) and (4) now leads to something more complicated than (12) and (13), but in any case (1) is no longer correct, since the thermal stresses found by Maxwell are now not zero. Finally, this flow is dissipative and hence from the equation of energy, not mentioned in the present paper, it follows that p and θ increase without limit. The time dependence of the phenomenon is essential in my analysis of the much simpler problem of rectilinear shearing. In the present case, there is no proof at all that assumed velocity field (5) is compatible with the kinetic theory. The analysis is wrong from first to last as far as the kinetic theory is concerned and has no bearing on the problem suggested by the title.

H.S. GREEN: I would like to suggest the possibility of interpreting the Reiner effect as a thermo-mechanical effect. This possibility arises because, I understand, the experiments demonstrate a second-order effect, and the rate of heat production per unit volume is also of the second-order, being proportional to the square of the velocity gradient. Of course we do not know without detailed calculation whether a thermo-mechanical effect of the right order of magnitude should be present in these experiments. But it would be of considerable interest in any case to measure the temperature distribution over the disc. I assume this could be done. That would help to decide whether thermal effects are of any importance.

L.J.F. BROER: Even at constant wall temperature thermo-mechanical effects cannot be ruled out a priori as there is considerable dissipation. The heat generated must flow to the wall, therefore the temperature at the median plane will be higher than at the wall. As the dissipation is proportional to the square of the rate of shear there will be a positive radial temperature gradient in this median plane.

M. REINER's reply: Professor Truesdell may be correct in all his criticism on the manner in which we generalized his solution of the problem of rectilinear shearing to the case of torsional flow. However, if we make all the corrections required to meet his criticisms — will this change the *centrifugal* effect which we found in our paper into the centripetal effect of Reiner, found experimentally? In other words, will a correct analysis change the sign of $\partial p_{rr}/\partial r$ from positive to negative?

M. BENTWICH's reply: As Prof. Truesdell points out, had both the temperature and the density of the medium been uniform throughout the space $d > z > o$ $o < r < R$, it would have been senseless to find pressure variations there. However, unlike Prof. Truesdell, I believe that the density need not, *necessarily*, be uniform in the space considered. Hence it has yet to be shown that the uniformity of the temperature (Eq.(9), is incompatible with the derived pressure variations (Eqs. (12) and (13)). Indeed in the following equation of continuity

$$\rho_{,\alpha}(v_\alpha) + \rho(v_{\alpha,\alpha}) = 0$$

the second summation vanishes because the velocity field given by Eq. (5) satisfies Eq. (8). With this velocity field a sufficient condition for the vanishing of the first summation is that the density distribution should be rotationally symmetric. Consequently though it is assumed that "the material is not further compressed in the course of flow" (see text below Eq.(8)) it is not necessary that either $\partial p/\partial z$ or $\partial p/\partial r$ should vanish.

J.L.F. Broer, H.S. Green as well as Truesdell state that the mechanical dissipation associated with the torsional flow may give rise to a non-uniformity in the temperature distribution; this would be incompatible with one of the initial assumptions. In order to estimate this thermo-mechanical effect the temperature distribution $T(r,z)$ will be obtained here as the solution of the classical diffusion equation (Goldstein [5], p.606, Eq. (13)), when the rate of dissipation per unit volume is $\eta(\omega/d)^2 r^2$ and when the boundiary conditions are:

$$T = T_0 \text{ at } z = 0, \ z = d \text{ and } r = R$$

These conditions imply that the fast rotation of the upper disc, with the resulting effective convection at the inlet to the gap, and the high conductivity of the metal discs cause all boundaries to be at the ambient temperature T_0. The solution sought is given by

$$\frac{T_0 - T}{T_0} = \left[P_r \frac{(\omega R)^2}{C_v J T_0} \right] \left(\frac{R}{d} \right)^2 \frac{1}{16} \left\{ \sum_{n=1}^{\infty} K_n J_0 \left(\alpha_n \frac{r}{R} \right) \frac{\cosh\left[\alpha_n (2z - d)(2R \right.}{\cosh\left(\alpha_n d/2R \right)} + \right.$$

$$\left. + \left[\left(\frac{r}{R} \right)^4 - 1 \right] \right\}$$

where

$$K_n = \int_0^1 \xi J_0(\alpha_n \xi)(1 - \xi^4) d\xi / \int_0^1 \xi J_0^2(\alpha_n \xi) d\xi$$

J, P_r and C_v are Joule's constant, Prandtl Number and the specific heat at constant volume respectively. Here J_0 is Bessel Function of order zero and α_n $(n = 1, 2 \cdots)$ are the roots of

$$J_0(\alpha_n) = 0$$

Evidently $(T - T_0)$ has a maximum at $r = 0$, $z = (d/2)$, which is given by:

$$\left(\frac{T_0 - T}{T_0} \right)_{max} = \left[P_r \frac{(\omega R)^2}{C_0 J T_0} \right] \left(\frac{R}{d} \right)^2 \frac{1}{16} \left\{ \sum_{n=1}^{\infty} K_n \operatorname{sech}(\alpha_n d/2R) - 1 \right\}$$

Thus, in view of the rapid convergence of the summation ΣK_n towards unity, the expression in the curly brackets is $0(d/R)^2$ and $|(T-T_0)/T_0|$ is at the most $0(P_r\omega^2 R^2 c_b^{-1} J^{-1} T_0^{-1} 10^{-1})$ or $0(10^{-3})$ when $R \sim 1\mathrm{cm}$ $\omega \sim 10^3 \sec^{-1}$ and $T_0 \sim 300°K$. It is then noted that $2\eta E_{ij}$ is the predominant term on the r.h.s. of Eq. (1) and that the term $\lambda T_{,i}$, with λ constant, can be shown to be the predominant in the analogous generalized expression for q; (see Ref. 3. pp. 122 and 265). Consequently though the classical diffusion equation was derived by assuming the following relationships

$$q_i = \lambda T_{,i} \qquad p_{ij} = <\delta_{ij}p - 2\eta E_{ij}$$

hold, it is not unreasonable to expect that when the higher order effects are accounted for, the termo-mechanical effect is rather small.

OBSERVATIONS ON THE SELF-ACTING THRUST AIRBEARING EFFECT

EDWIN BOUSSO

Technion–Israel Institute of Technology, Haifa, Israel

ABSTRACT

In a number of instruments Popper and Reiner have demonstrated such an effect, coupled with centripetal pumping. In a new instrument it is shown that there are two conditions under which the effect can be observed, namely

1) when the discs are parallel as nearly as possible, and a Reiner second-order-effect is present, and

2) when the discs are inclined to each other, and a Taylor-Saffman effect implicit in the Navier-Stokes equation prevails.

Systematic observations of these two effects are reported upon.

1. Introduction.

When a cylindrical disc revolves parallel to a flat plate at a moderate distance from it, air naturally tends to leave the gap between them, due to centrifugal action, and the pressure of the medium between them is reduced. If this revolving plate or rotor is free to move axially it will approach the fixed plate because of the pressure difference acting on both of its sides. However, when the gap is thus reduced to a few microns, the rotor will not come any nearer and a state of equilibrium will be attained. This is due to the centripetal pumping action discovered by Reiner [1], which operates increasingly with reduction of the gap between the plates.

If an axial force is applied in order to reduce the gap, a new state of equilibrium will be reached. Because of the narrow gaps involved, very high velocity gradients are attained, even at comparatively low speeds.

This arrangement constitutes a self-acting thrust airbearing.

Taylor and Saffman [2] have shown by a theoretical analysis on the basis of the Navier-Stokes equations that when the discs are not exactly parallel such a thrust bearing effect should be present.

This prediction was checked in the investigation which is reported upon in the present paper.

2. Description of the instrument.

The instrument has two rotating discs with a stator suspended between them (see Figure 1).

The rotors (18) and the stator (17) are made of high quality carbon steel, hardened and tempered. The diameter of the rotors is 60.00 ± 0.01 mm, that of the stator and the disc on which it is suspended 64.00 ± 0.01 mm. The working surfaces were ground and polished similary to optical surfaces. The surface roughness is 0.1μ peak to valley. The plates were flattened to within 0.15μ. Surface roughness was measured in a "Talysurf" machine. Flatness was measured by observing the number of fringes between an optical flat and the given surfaces.

One rotor is mounted on a spherical seat, on an axle (21) running in fixed ball bearings. These bearings produce the reaction to the axial force applied to vary the gap. The other rotor, also mounted on a spherical seat is mounted on a second axle (11) runing in roller bearings. These bearings allow axial play of the axle mounted in them, thus permitting the gap between rotors and stator to adjust itself to axial load.

In order to insure colinearity of the axles, their housings were bored in one operation. The housing of the instrument is also of steel. The rotors are not mounted rigidly on their axle, but are mounted on spherical seats (20), which allow them to align themselves dynamically perpendicular to the axis of rotation. They are driven by means of pins (19), protruding from the seats into grooves in the rotors.

The stator has a slightly larger diameter than the rotors in order to insure complete coverage of their area in case the stator swings during measurements. The stator is suspended by an extra fine recording tape (16), 24 microns thick and 6.27 mm wide, onto a disc (14) of the same diameter.

The rotors are belt-driven (6) by means of two wheels mounted on an intermediate axle. The driving wheels are grooved. The driven wheels are smooth in order to prevent the belt tension from producing a force in an axial direction.

The common axle is connected to a driving motor by means of a flexible rubber coupling. The motor speed is regulated by means of a variable voltage transformer. The motor itself is connected to the base of the instrument through flexible mountings in order to minimize the vibrations transmitted to the instrument which is also mounted on 4 flexible mounts. Through these mounts the instrument can be brought to a horizontal position.

The gap between the stator and rotor is regulated by varying the axial force applied to the axis (11) by means of lever system (10), on which weights (9) act.

The gap between rotors and stator is calculated from the electrical capacity of the rotors-stator, the insulated stator forming one plate of a condenser

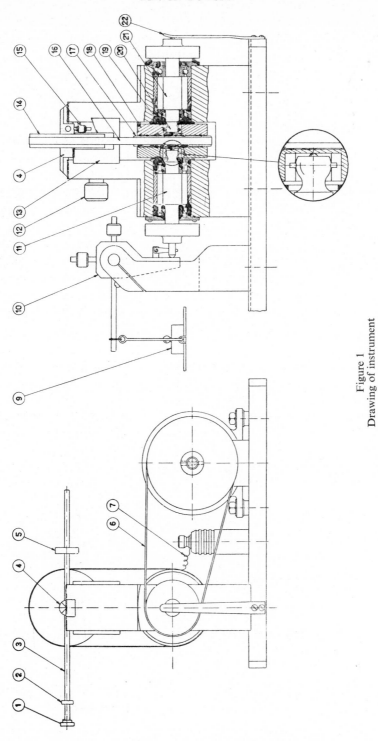

Figure 1
Drawing of instrument

and the two rotors the other. The connection to the stator is by means of a fine wire (7) inserted between the tape and stator. Contact to the rotors is maintained through brushes (22). Electrical contact is improved by smearing graphite on the rotor seats and between the axles and brushes (22).

The rotors have a simple cylindrical shape. The object was to create a shape which could be finished with the maximum precision. The rotors and stator are ground on a surface grinder to a parallelness of 1.5 microns. The moment of inertia of the rotors about the axis of revolution is almost twice that about an axis through the centre of gravity perpendicular to the axis of revolution. When revolving, the principal axis of inertia of the rotors aligns itself along the axis of revolution. Because of the wedge-shape of the rotors the flat areas will not be perpendicular to the axis. They will subtend an angle equal to half the wedge angle to the perpendicular to the axis of revolution. This angle is much smaller than that which would have been obtained if the rotors had been rigidly attached to the axis, because of inaccuracy of the ball bearings. The main advantage of these rotors is that they align themselves parallel to the stator surface due to the fact that the higher velocity gradients on the side closer to the stator create greater pressure perpendicular to the surface than on the opposite side. Thus an aligning force is brought into play and the rotors being free, submit to it.

On the other hand, the rotors can be made to be purposely inclined against the stator by displacing the stator radially. Part of the rotors is thus uncovered, and the pressure acts only on part of them. The pressure distribution is now asymmetrical. Since the moment of the pressure forces about the centre of the rotors must be zero, the average pressure on the exposed side must be higher than that on the other side. The normal pressure being proportional to the gradient, the gradient on the exposed side must be greater. Therefore the rotor must align itself with its axis at an angle to the axis of rotation (see Figure 2).

According to Taylor and Saffman a hydrodynamic type of bearing is thus formed.

3. Experiment in symmetrical loading.

A number of experiments were carried out in order to determine the relationship between the load P, the gap size δ and the speed of rotation Ω, in the case when rotors were completely covered by the stator, and rotors and stator were therefore parallel.

The load was applied by means of dead weights (9), acting through a lever system (10). The only source of error was the bearing friction. The axis of the

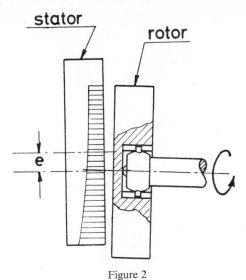

Figure 2
Schematic pressure distribution for inclined rotor

instrument was kept in the horizontal position in order to eliminate the weight of the rotor and stator from affecting the load. If was found nevertheless that the roller bearings had a tendency to drive their axle inwards the stator when rotating, due to the roller axis not being parallel to the main axis. The driving force of 20 grams was independent of running speed, and was added to the load applied by means of the weights.

Two procedures were adopted, namely,

    (i)   speed kept constant and load varied,

    (ii) load kept constant and speed varied.

The results obtained by the two methods were identical.

Figure 3 shows the gap size δ plotted as a function of the speed of rotation Ω on a log-log scale for various loads. Approximately straight lines were obtained for different loads. At high speeds and low loads the gap tends to reach a limiting value.

Figure 4 shows the reverse dependence, i.e. $\delta = f(P)$. The slope is quite constant for each speed, but varies for different speeds.

The permissible bearing loads were relatively small. For loads greater than about 400 grams intermittent contact between the plates was observed. In the arrangement under which these results were obtained, we may assume

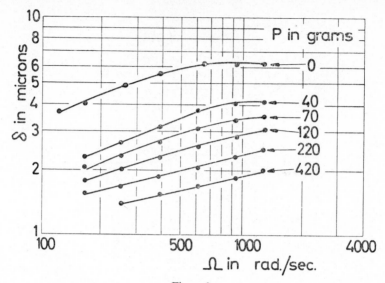

Figure 3

Gap size δ as a function of speed Ω for various loads and symmetrical arrangement

that rotors and stator were working on the same axis, and were parallel. This is due to the self-aligning properties of both rotors and the stator, as described in **2.** A definite (if small) bearing pressure was automatically maintained. This result may be said as due to a Reiner-effect.

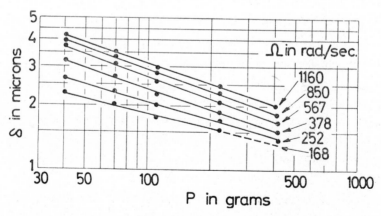

Figure 4

Gap size δ as a function of load P for various speeds and symmetrical arrangement

4. Experiments with asymmetrical positioning.

In the second series of experiments the stator was radially displaced, and the rotors thus made to be inclined against the stator. It was observed that with such non-parallelity, the size of the gap *increased* considerably.

Measurements were made on lines similar to those previously described, in order to determine the influence of stator eccentricity on load capacity and gap size.

(a) In the first stage the centre of the stator was displaced by by $e = 15$ mm with respect to the axis of rotation. Readings were taken for the ranges $\Omega = 140$ to 1000 sec^{-1} and $P = 40$ to 820 gram. In calculating the gap size, the covered area only was taken into account. The distance was calculated as though rotor and stator were parallel, giving only approximative results.

Figures 5 and 6 show the dependence of gap size on the speed of rotation Ω, and the load P, for an eccentricity of $e = 15$ mm. It is seen that for a given speed and load, the gap is approximately double that obtained in symmetrical loading. The slopes of $\delta = f(\Omega)$ for a given load P on a log-log scale vary between 0.35 to 0.44. The slopes of $\delta = f(P)$ for a given speed decreases from -0.3 for low loads to -0.5 for the higher ones.

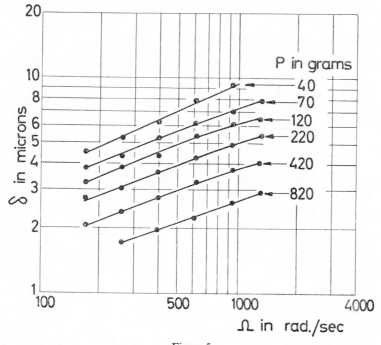

Figure 5

Gap size δ as a function of speed Ω for various loads and asymmetrical arrangement

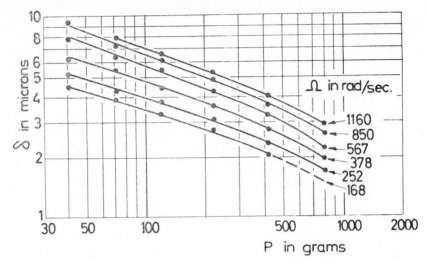

Figure 6
Gap size δ as a function of load P for various speeds and asymetrical arrangements

(b) The dependence of gap size δ on the radial displacement of the stator was measured. The observations were carried out for a constant bearing load (220 g) in the same speed range as above (Figure 7).

In the second series it was found that the average gap increases with eccentricity to a certain point after which it begins to decrease. The superposition of the centripetal effect together with the Taylor and Saffman effect produces the comparative increase in gap size.

Obviously this increase has a limit since the greater the increase in e the smaller the bearing surface will be, this resulting in reduced load capacity.

Experimentally it was found that the maximum average gap size was obtained for $e = 12$ mm. A further increase in e reduced the average gap.

5. Discussions and conclusions.

The present paper reports upon experiments in which air is made to flow torsionally between a circular rotating disc and a flat plate. When the gap between both is very small a self-acting thrust bearing pressure is developed. This pressure is at a minimum, but larger than zero, when the planes of disc and plate are parallel and increases when the disc is made to be inclined against the plate. The first effect was described by Reiner, and may be named Reiner-effect. The second was theoretically evinced by Taylor and

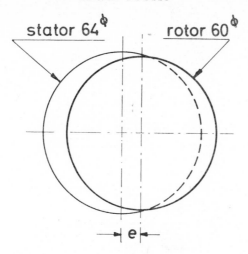

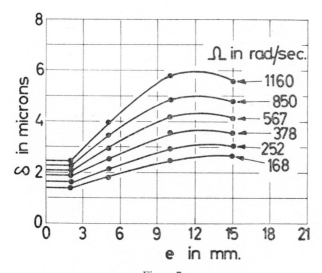

Figure 7

Gap size δ as a function of radial displacement e of the stator for various speeds and a load of 220 grams

Saffman, and may be named after them. No theory has yet been definitely established for the Reiner-effect. For this further experiments are needed in which rotors of different diameters are used, and the local pressure at the centre of the disc is measured. Such experiments are planned by the author.

SYMBOLS

δ =   gap size

e =   eccentricity

Acknowledgment.

I wish to express my thanks to Prof. M. Reiner and Dr. B. Popper for their help and guidance in carrying out this work.

REFERENCES

[1]   M. Reiner, *Proc. Roy. Soc.*, A, **240,** (1957), 173.

[2]   G. I. Taylor and P. G. Saffman, *J. Aeronaut. Sciences*, **24,** (1957), 553.

KINETIC THEORY OF SECOND ORDER EFFECTS IN FLUIDS

R. G. Storer and H. S. Green

University of Adelaide, South Australia

ABSTRACT

General expressions are derived for the calculation of the second order coefficients for transport in fluids on the basis of the kinetic theory. For the particular case of an incompressible isothermal fluid, approximate expressions are obtained for the second order coefficients in terms of a microscopic relaxation time and hence in terms of the first order coefficient of viscosity. It is shown how this theory can be extended to fluids with "memory" and to obtain expressions for the effects of arbitarily high order.

1. Introduction.

Many attempts have been made to formulate a statistical mechanical theory of transport in fluids which relates the first order transport coefficients to the detailed molecular dynamics [1 − 5]. Some calculations have also been made of the second order effects i. e., those effects which are linear in the second derivatives, or quadratic in the gradients of the macroscopic parameters [1], [6].

We present an extension of the method of Green [5], which, in principle, enables one to obtain terms to any desired order. This theory also represents an advance on the previous second order results in-as-much as the expressions obtained do not depend on any assumption of a particular molecular model nor do they restrict one to the use of the Maxwell-Boltzmann equation.

The second order coefficients are expressed explicitly as statistical averages involving time integrals over the whole past history of the system. For "normal" fluids with a short relaxation time, it is possible to simplify these expressions considerably, and obtain approximate formulae for the second-order coefficients in terms of the first order coefficient of viscosity. It is also possible to obtain formal stress-strain relations for plastics and other fluids with a "memory", these relations involve effects of arbitrarily high order. In the absence of external forces these results can be evaluated approximately, in terms of a characteristic relaxation time.

2. Notation and fundamentals.

We consider a fluid of N identical molecules, each of mass m, in a non-equilibrium state described by the phase-space distribution function

$$F_N = F_N(\mathbf{x}_1, ..., \mathbf{x}_N; \xi_1, ... \xi_N; t). \tag{1}$$

Here $\mathbf{x}_i$, ξ_i represent the position and velocity of the ith particle. The time evolution of F_N is described by Liouville's equation,

$$\frac{dF_N}{dt_N} = \frac{\partial F_N}{\partial t} + \sum_i \xi_i \cdot \frac{\partial F_N}{\partial \mathbf{x}_i} - \sum_i \frac{1}{m} \frac{\partial \Phi_N}{\partial \mathbf{x}_i} \cdot \frac{\partial F_N}{\partial \xi_i} = 0 \tag{2}$$

where $\Phi_N = \frac{1}{2}\Sigma_{ij} \phi(\mathbf{x}_i, \mathbf{x}_j) = \frac{1}{2}\Sigma_{ij} \phi_{ij}$ \tag{3}

is the potential energy of the molecules. By a slight extension one can take account of external forces and many components.

The mean of any function of the $\mathbf{x}_i$ and ξ_i, $A(\mathbf{x}, \xi)$, is given by

$$\langle A(\mathbf{x},\xi) \rangle_i = \int \int F_N A \prod_j d\xi_j \prod_{j \neq i} d\mathbf{x}_i. \tag{4}$$

Then

$$\langle m \rangle_i = \rho(\mathbf{x}_i) \text{ is the density at } \mathbf{x}_i,$$

$$\langle \xi_i \rangle_i = \mathbf{u}(\mathbf{x}_i) \text{ is the local mass velocity,}$$

and the local temperature $T(\mathbf{x}_i)$ is given by

$$\langle m\mathbf{v}_i^2 \rangle_i = 3k\, T(\mathbf{x}_i)$$

where

$$\mathbf{v}_i = \xi_i - \mathbf{u}(\mathbf{x}_i).$$

Define $\beta(\mathbf{x}_i) = 1/kT(\mathbf{x}_i)$ and let $\mu(\mathbf{x}_i)$ be the local chemical potential per unit mass.

If $Ei = \frac{1}{2}\mathbf{v}^2 + \frac{1}{2}\sum_j \phi_{ij}/m$, \tag{5}

$$P_i = \mathbf{v}_i\mathbf{v}_i + \frac{1}{2}\sum_j \mathbf{r}_{ij} F_{ij}/m \tag{6}$$

and

$$Q_i = (E_i - \mu)\mathbf{v}_i + \frac{1}{2}\sum_j \mathbf{r}_{ij}\mathbf{v}_i \cdot E_{ij}/m, \tag{7}$$

(here $F_{ij} = -\nabla\phi_{ij}$ and $\mathbf{r}_{ij} = \mathbf{x}_i - \mathbf{x}_j$),

then the local internal energy per unit mass is

$$U = \langle E_i \rangle_i, \tag{8}$$

the local pressure tensor is

$$\mathbf{p} = \rho \langle P_i \rangle_i, \tag{9}$$

and the local thermal flux is

$$\mathbf{q} = \rho \langle Q_i \rangle_i. \tag{10}$$

If

$$D = \frac{\partial}{\partial t} + \mathbf{u} \cdot \frac{\partial}{\partial x_i} \tag{11}$$

the macroscopic equations, describing the conservation of mass, momentum and energy are

$$D\rho + \rho \nabla \cdot \mathbf{u} \qquad = 0 \tag{12}$$

$$\rho D\mathbf{u} + \nabla \cdot \mathbf{p} \qquad = 0 \tag{13}$$

$$\rho DU + (\mathbf{p} \cdot \nabla) \cdot \mathbf{u} + \nabla \cdot \mathbf{q} = 0$$

To the first order

$$\mathbf{p} = p\mathbf{1} - \xi \nabla \cdot \mathbf{u} \mathbf{1} - 2\eta \nabla_s \mathbf{u} \tag{15}$$

$$\nabla_s \mathbf{u} = \tfrac{1}{2}(\nabla \mathbf{u} + \mathbf{u} \nabla) - \tfrac{1}{3} \nabla \cdot \mathbf{u} \mathbf{1} \tag{16}$$

$$\mathbf{1} \equiv \text{unit tensor}$$

and

$$\mathbf{q} = - K \nabla T / T \tag{17}$$

define the hydrostatic pressure p and the coefficients of volume viscosity ξ shearing viscosity η, and thermal conduction K.

3. Theory.

F is expanded in the form

$$F_N = F_N^{(0)} + F_N^{(1)} + F_N^{(2)} + \dots \tag{18}$$

where

$F_N^{(1)}$ is of the first order,

$F_N^{(2)}$ is of the second order, etc.

As the zero'th order approximation to F_N, we take

$$F_N^{(0)}(\mathbf{x}, \xi; \lambda(\mathbf{x}, t) = \exp\left[- \int \beta(\mathbf{x}) p(\mathbf{x}) d\mathbf{x} + \Sigma_i m\beta(\mathbf{x}_i)(\mu(\mathbf{x}_i) - E_i) \right] \tag{19}$$

where $\beta(\mathbf{x}_i)$, $\mu(\mathbf{x}_i)$ and $\mathbf{u}(\mathbf{x}_i)$ (in E_i) depend on the local values of temperature, chemical potential per unit mass and velocity respectively. We use $\lambda(\mathbf{x}_i, t)$ to represent this collection of macroscopic parameters.

Because of the form of $F_N^{(0)}$ it is more convenient to define the function

$$L_N = \log F_N, \tag{20}$$

and to look for a similar expansion of L_N in terms of the derivatives of the macroscopic parameters. Thus

$$L_N = L_N^{(0)} + L_N^{(1)} + L_N^{(2)} + \ldots \tag{21}$$

Since L_N satisfies the same differential equation as F_N, for this expansion to be self-consistent we must have

$$\frac{dL_N}{dt_N} = \frac{dL_N^{(0)}}{dt_N} + \frac{dL_N^{(1)}}{dt_N} + \ldots = 0 \tag{22}$$

As will be shown, $dL_N^{(0)}/dt_N$ can be written as a series with terms of the first order, second order, etc.; thus

$$\frac{dL_N^{(0)}}{dt_N} = \left(\frac{dL_N^{(0)}}{dt_N} \right)^{(1)} + \left(\frac{dL_N^{(0)}}{dt_N} \right)^{(2)} + \ldots$$

$$= R_N^{(1)}(\mathbf{x}, \xi;\ \lambda(\mathbf{x}, t)) + R_N^{(2)}(\mathbf{x}, \xi;\ \lambda(\mathbf{x}, t)) + \ldots \tag{23}$$

The procedure to obtain expressions for $L_N^{(1)}$, $L_N^{(2)}$ etc., is as follows: we separate the operator d/dt_N into two parts

$$\frac{d}{dt_N} = \frac{d}{dt_N^{\circ}} + \frac{d}{dt_{N'}} \tag{24}$$

where

d/dt_N° operates on the $\mathbf{x}_i$, ξ_i which appear explicitly, and $d/dt_{N'}$ operates on $\mathbf{x}_i$, t appearing in the $\lambda(\mathbf{x}_i, t)$, i.e. in β, $\mathbf{u}$ and μ. This separation is necessary because the operator $d/dt_{N'}$ always produces a higher order term, whereas d/dt_N° in general does not do so. Fundamentally this arises from the difference between the microscopic relaxation process described by d/dt_N° and the macroscopic relaxation process described by $d/dt_{N'}$. We now write

$$\frac{dL_N^{(0)}}{dt_N} = R_N^{(1)} + R_N^{(2)} + \ \dots \tag{25}$$

$$\frac{dL_N^{(1)}}{dt_N} = \frac{dL_N^{(1)}}{dt_N^\circ} + \frac{dL_N^{(1)}}{dt_{N'}} + \ \dots \tag{26}$$

$$\frac{dL_N^{(2)}}{dt_N} = \frac{dL_N^{(2)}}{dt_{N'}^\circ} + \ \dots \atop \text{etc.} \tag{27}$$

To satisfy equation (22) we make the identification

$$\frac{dL_N^{(1)}}{dt_N^\circ} + R_N^{(1)} \ (\mathbf{x}, \xi; \ \lambda(\mathbf{x}, t)) \ = \ 0 \tag{28}$$

$$\frac{dL_N^{(2)}}{dt_N^\circ} + \frac{dL_N^{(1)}}{dt_{N'}} + R^{(2)} \ (\mathbf{x}, \xi; \ \lambda(\mathbf{x}, t)) \ = \ 0 \atop \text{etc.} \tag{29}$$

Now, equation (28) can be solved in the form

$$L_N^{(1)} \ = \ -\int_{-\infty}^{t} R_N^{(1)} \ (\mathbf{x}', \xi' : \ \lambda(\mathbf{x}, t)) \, dt' \tag{30}$$

where $\mathbf{x}_i'$, ξ_i' are the positions and velocities of a set of particles at time t', which by their natural motions reach $\mathbf{x}_i$, ξ_i at time t. We use this result to obtain the equation for $L_N^{(2)}$ i.e.

$$\frac{dL_N^{(2)}}{dt_N^\circ} = -R_N^{(2)} + \frac{d}{dt_{N'}} \int_{-\infty}^{t} R_N^{(1)} \ (\mathbf{x}', \xi'; \ \lambda(\mathbf{x}, t)) \ dt'. \tag{31}$$

As well as being an operator, d/dt_N is also a function of $\mathbf{x}_i$ and ξ_i, so we must write the solution of (31) as

$$L_N^{(2)} \ = \ -\int_{-\infty}^{t} R_N^{(2)} \ (\mathbf{x}', \xi'; \ \lambda(\mathbf{x}, t)) dt' \ +$$

$$+ \ \int_{-\infty}^{t} dt' \frac{d}{dt_{N'}} (\mathbf{x}', \xi') \int_{-\infty}^{t'} dt'' \ R_N \ (\mathbf{x}'', \xi''; \ \lambda(\mathbf{x}, t)) \tag{32}$$

In principle, we can continue this procedure to find L_N to any desired order. Having calculated L_N, it is then a straightforward process to find F_N e.g.

$$F \ = \exp\left[L^{(0)} + L_N^{(1)} + L_N^{(2)} + \ldots \right]$$

$$= F_N^{(0)} \left[1 + L_N^{(1)} + \frac{1}{2!} L_N^{(1)} \cdot L_N^{(1)} + L_N^{(2)} \right] \tag{33}$$

to the second order.

The ensemble average of $\mathbf{P}_i$ and $\mathbf{Q}_i$ calculated with F_N then gives us expressions for the pressure tensor and the heat flux to the same order as F_N.

4. Example.

To illustrate the above method, we consider an incompressible fluid with no gradient of temperature or chemical potential. For this case, we write

$$L_N^{(0)} \ (\mathbf{x}, \xi; \ \lambda(\mathbf{x}, t)) \ = \ -\beta p V + m\beta\mu N - m\beta\sum_i E_i \tag{34}$$

where V is the volume of the fluid under consideration. Now

$$\frac{dL_N^{(0)}}{dt_N} = m\beta\sum_i (D\mathbf{u} + \mathbf{v}_i \cdot \nabla\mathbf{u}) \cdot \mathbf{v}_i + \frac{\beta}{2}\sum_{ij} F_{ij}(\mathbf{u}(\mathbf{x}_i) - \mathbf{u}(\mathbf{x}_j)) \tag{35}$$

so that, since $D\mathbf{u} = 2\eta\,\nabla \cdot (\nabla_s \mathbf{u})/\rho$ to the second order (from Eqs. (12), (13), (15)),

$$R_N^{(1)} \ = \ \sum_i m\beta\mathbf{P}_i \,:\, \nabla\mathbf{u} \tag{36}$$

and

$$R_N^{(2)} \ = \ \tfrac{1}{4}\beta\sum_{ij} \mathbf{r}_{ij}\mathbf{r}_{ij}F_{ij} \,:\, \nabla\nabla\mathbf{u} \ + \ m\beta\eta/\rho \ \sum_i \mathbf{v}_i \cdot \nabla^2\mathbf{u} \tag{37}$$

Also

$$\frac{d}{dt_N'} \ (\mathbf{x}', \xi') \ R_N^{(1)}(\mathbf{x} \ , \xi \ ; \ \lambda(\mathbf{x}, t))$$

$$= \left(D + \sum_i \mathbf{v}_i' \cdot \frac{\partial}{\partial\mathbf{x}_1} \right) R_N^{(1)}$$

$$= m\beta \ \sum \ \mathbf{P}''\mathbf{v}_i' \,:\, \nabla\nabla\mathbf{u}$$

$$- \ m\beta \sum_i \mathbf{v}_i''\mathbf{v}_i' \,:\, (\nabla\mathbf{u}) \cdot (\nabla\mathbf{u} + \mathbf{u}\nabla) \tag{38}$$

where

$$\mathbf{v}_i' \ = \ \xi_i' \ - \ \mathbf{u}(\mathbf{x}_i)$$

$$\mathbf{P}_i' \ = \ \mathbf{v}_i'\mathbf{v}_i' + \tfrac{1}{2}\sum_j \mathbf{r}_{ij}' F_{ij}'.$$

Thus from (30), (32) and (33)

$$F_N = F_N^o \left[1 - m\beta \sum_i \int_{-\infty}^{t} \mathbf{P}^i dt' : \nabla_s \mathbf{u} \; + \right.$$

$$+ \tfrac{1}{2} m^2 \beta^2 \left(\sum_i \int_{-\infty}^{t} \mathbf{P}^i dt' : \nabla_s \mathbf{u} \; \right)^2 -$$

$$- \tfrac{1}{4}\beta \sum_{ij} \int_{-\infty}^{t} \mathbf{r}'_{ij} \, \mathbf{r}'_{ij} \, \mathbf{F}'_{ij} \, dt' \; \vdots \; \nabla\nabla\mathbf{u} \; -$$

$$- m\beta \, \eta/\rho \; \sum_i \int_{-\infty}^{t} \mathbf{v}'_i \, dt' \; \cdot \; \nabla^2 \mathbf{u} \; +$$

$$+ m\beta \sum_i \int_{-\infty}^{t} dt' \int_{-\infty}^{t'} dt'' \; \mathbf{P}''_i \, \mathbf{v}'_i \; \vdots \; \nabla\nabla\mathbf{u} \; -$$

$$\left. - 2m\beta \sum_i \int_{-\infty}^{t} dt' \int_{-\infty}^{t'} dt'' \; \mathbf{v}''_i \, \mathbf{v}'_i \; : \; (\nabla\mathbf{u}) \cdot (\nabla_s \mathbf{u}) \right] \qquad (39)$$

$$\text{to the second order.}$$

Now if $\langle .. \rangle_i^0$ denotes the mean formed with $F_N^{(0)}$, we have

$$\mathbf{p} = \rho \langle \mathbf{P}_i \rangle_i^0 \; - m\beta\rho \; \langle \mathbf{P}_i \sum_j \int_{-\infty}^{t} \mathbf{P}'_j \, dt' \; : \nabla_s \mathbf{u} \rangle_i^0 \; +$$

$$+ \tfrac{1}{2} m^2 \beta^2 \; \langle \mathbf{P}_i \sum_{jk} \int_{-\infty}^{t} dt' \int_{-\infty}^{t} dt'' \, \mathbf{P}'_j \; : \nabla_s \mathbf{u} \, \mathbf{P}''_k \; : \nabla_s \mathbf{u} \rangle^0 \; -$$

$$- m\beta \; \langle \mathbf{P}_i \sum_j \int_{-\infty}^{t} dt' \int_{-\infty}^{t} dt'' \, \mathbf{v}''_j \, \mathbf{v}'_j \; : \; (\nabla\mathbf{u}) \cdot (\nabla_s \mathbf{u}) \rangle_i^0 \qquad (40)$$

So that, using the symmetry properties of $F_N^{(0)}$, we find

$$\mathbf{p} = p\mathbf{1} - 2\eta \, \nabla_s \mathbf{u} \; + a\nabla_s \mathbf{u} \; \cdot \; \nabla_s \mathbf{u} \; +$$

$$+ b\nabla_s \mathbf{u} \; : \; \nabla_s \mathbf{u}\mathbf{1} + c(\nabla\mathbf{u} \cdot \mathbf{u}\nabla \; - \; \mathbf{u}\nabla \cdot \nabla\mathbf{u}) \qquad (41)$$

with

$$\eta = \frac{m\beta\rho}{15} \; \langle \mathbf{P}_i \; : \; \sum_j \int_{-\infty}^{t} \mathbf{P}'_j \, dt' \rangle^0 \qquad (42)$$

$$a = \frac{4m^2\beta^2}{105} \langle \mathbf{P}_i : \int_{-\infty}^{t} dt' \int_{-\infty}^{t} dt'' \, \mathbf{P}_i \cdot \mathbf{P}_i \rangle_i^0 \; -$$

$$- \frac{2m\beta\rho}{15} \langle \mathbf{P}_i : \int_{-\infty}^{t} dt' \int_{-\infty}^{t} dt'' \, \mathbf{v}_i'' \, \mathbf{v}_i' \rangle_i^0 \tag{43}$$

$$b = \frac{m^2\beta^2\rho}{105} \langle \mathbf{P}_i : \int_{-\infty}^{t} dt' \int_{-\infty}^{t} dt'' \, \mathbf{P}_i' \, \mathbf{P}_i'' \rangle_i^0 \; +$$

$$+ \frac{m^2\beta^2\rho}{45} \langle \mathrm{Tr}\mathbf{P}_i \sum_{j \neq i} \int_{-\infty}^{t} dt' \int_{-\infty}^{t} dt'' \, \mathbf{P}_j' \cdot \mathbf{P}_j'' \rangle_i^0 \; -$$

$$- \frac{m\beta\rho}{15} \langle \mathbf{P}_i : \int_{\infty}^{t} dt' \int_{-\infty}^{t} dt'' \, \mathbf{v}_i'' \, \mathbf{v}_i' \rangle_i^0 \; -$$

$$- \frac{m\beta\rho}{9} \langle \mathrm{Tr} \, \mathbf{P}_i \sum_{j \neq i} \int_{-\infty}^{t} dt' \int_{-\infty}^{t} dt'' \, \mathbf{v}_j' \mathbf{v}_j'' \rangle_i^0$$

$$c = -\frac{m\beta\rho}{30} \langle \mathbf{P}_i : \sum_{j} \int_{-\infty}^{t} dt' \int_{-\infty}^{t} dt'' \, \mathbf{v}_j' \, \mathbf{v}_j'' \rangle_i^0 \tag{44}$$

To obtain some idea of the magnitude of these expressions we define a microscopic relaxation time, τ, such that

$$\int_{-\infty}^{t} A(\mathbf{x}', \xi') \, dt' \approx \tau A(\mathbf{x}, \xi) \tag{45}$$

where A is any function of the microscopic coordinates. For a dilute gas we can also neglect the explicit dependence of the parameters on the interparticle potential and take

$$F_N^{(0)} = V^{-1} (\tfrac{1}{2}\beta m/\pi)^{3N/2} \exp(-\tfrac{1}{2}\beta m \sum_i \mathbf{v}_i^2). \tag{46}$$

With these approximations we find

$$\eta = \tau\rho/m\beta = \tau p \tag{47}$$

$$a = 2\tau^2\rho/m\beta = 2\eta^2/p \tag{48}$$

$$b = 0$$

$$c = -\tau^2\rho/2m\beta = -\eta^2/2p \tag{50}$$

so that

$$\mathbf{p} = p\mathbf{1} - 2\eta\,\nabla_s\mathbf{u} + 2\eta^2/p\,\nabla_s\mathbf{u}\cdot\nabla_s\mathbf{u} - \eta^2/2p(\nabla\mathbf{u}\cdot\mathbf{u}\nabla - \mathbf{u}\nabla\cdot\nabla\mathbf{u}) \quad (51)$$

5. Theory of fluids with memory.

The form of the results (42) – (44), involving time integrals over the whole past history of the fluid, suggests that one might be able to account qualitatively for the behaviour of fluid systems which is not completely determined by present conditions.

The fact that the present molecular state of a fluid does depend on its past history can be demonstrated very clearly by using another integral of the differential equation (22). If we write $L_N = L_N^\circ + L_N^\delta$, so that the equation assumes the form

$$\frac{dL_N^\delta}{dt_N} = -\frac{dL_N^\circ}{dt_N} = -R_N(\mathbf{x}, \xi;\ \lambda(\mathbf{x}, t)) \quad (52)$$

we can write down an exact solution:

$$L_N^\delta = -\int_{-\infty}^{t} R_N(\mathbf{x}', \xi', \lambda(\mathbf{x}'\,t'))\,dt' \quad (53)$$

with successive terms of the development of R_N given by (36) and (37). This result is not very useful for practical computational purposes, because the variation of the fluid velocity and other macroscopic variables with time is usually rather complicated, and these appear explicitly in the result of (53) as functions of time. The above formula does however bring out the fact that the molecular distribution may be affected by the macroscopic state of the system at earlier times. If the characteristic relaxation time is short, only the values of $\lambda(\mathbf{x}', t')$ near to $t' = t$ will contribute to the value of the integral; but of course there are other interesting possibilities.

In speaking of a short relaxation time, it is necessary to consider that the standard of comparison is the reciprocal of the velocity gradient. Thus even very viscid fluids do not retain a memory of past behaviour, provided the rate of strain to which they are subjected is sufficiently small, Conversely. when the rate of strain is sufficiently large even inviscid fluids acquire memory. Mathematically this means that, soon after second order effects become important, effects of arbitrarily high order come into play. We can show that this is so quite rigorously, under certain conditions where $\nabla\mathbf{u}$ may be quite large while $\nabla\nabla\mathbf{u}$ and higher derivatives are negligible. Under such conditions, the stress tensor depends very sensitively on the geometry of the situation. Neglecting the explicit effect of the intermolecular forces we take

$$L_N^{(0)} = -\tfrac{1}{2} m\beta \sum_i \mathbf{v}_i^2 \tag{54}$$

to within a normalization constant.

Hence

$$L_N^{(1)} = - m\beta \sum_i \int_{-\infty}^{t} \mathbf{v}_i' \mathbf{v}_i' \, dt' : \nabla\mathbf{u}, \tag{55}$$

$$L_N^{(2)} = - m\beta \sum_i \int_{-\infty}^{t} dt' \int_{-\infty}^{t} dt'' \, \mathbf{v}_i'' \mathbf{v}_i' : \nabla\mathbf{u} \cdot (\nabla\mathbf{u} + \mathbf{u}\nabla) \tag{56}$$

$$L_N^{(3)} = - m\beta \sum \int_{-\infty}^{t} dt' \int_{-\infty}^{t'} dt'' \int_{-\infty}^{t''} dt''' \, \mathbf{v}_i''' \mathbf{v}_i' : [\nabla\mathbf{u} \cdot \nabla\mathbf{u} \cdot (\nabla\mathbf{u} + \mathbf{u}\nabla) +$$
$$+ \, \nabla\mathbf{u} \cdot (\nabla\mathbf{u} + \mathbf{u}\nabla) \cdot \mathbf{u}\nabla] \tag{57}$$

To evaluate these expressions we use the approximation of Eq. (45). Then

$$L_N^{(0)} = -\tfrac{1}{2} m\beta \sum_i \mathbf{v}_i \mathbf{v}_i : \mathbf{1}$$

$$L_N^{(1)} = -\tfrac{1}{2} m\beta \sum_i \mathbf{v}_i \mathbf{v}_i : 2\nabla\mathbf{u}\,\tau \tag{58}$$

$$L_N^{(2)} = -\tfrac{1}{2} m\beta \sum_i \mathbf{v}_i \mathbf{v}_i : 2\nabla\mathbf{u} \cdot (\nabla\mathbf{u} + \mathbf{u}\nabla) \frac{1}{2!} \tau^2$$
$$\text{etc.}$$

We can sum this sequence in the form

$$L_N = -\tfrac{1}{2} m\beta \sum_i \mathbf{v}_i \mathbf{v}_i : [\exp(\tau\nabla\mathbf{u}) \cdot \exp(\tau\mathbf{u}\nabla)], \tag{59}$$

so that

$$F_N \propto \exp\{-\tfrac{1}{2} m\beta \sum_i \mathbf{v}_i \mathbf{v}_i : [\exp(\tau\nabla\mathbf{u}) \cdot \exp(\tau\mathbf{u}\nabla)]\}. \tag{60}$$

Now

$$\int \mathbf{v}\mathbf{v} \exp(-\mathbf{v} \cdot \mathbf{A}\mathbf{v}) \, d\mathbf{v} = \tfrac{1}{2}\mathbf{A}^{-1} \int \exp(-\mathbf{v} \cdot \mathbf{A} \cdot \mathbf{v}) \, d\mathbf{v} \tag{61}$$

where $\mathbf{A}$ is any symmetric tensor, so that, after the normalization of F_N, we obtain for the pressure tensor

$$\mathbf{p} = \rho\langle \mathbf{v}_i \mathbf{v}_i \rangle_i = p \exp(-\tau\mathbf{u}\nabla) \cdot \exp(-\tau\nabla\mathbf{u}). \tag{62}$$

We can illustrate this with two simple examples. First, consider two plates, one stationary in the XOY- lane, the other in the plane defined by $z = d$ moving with a velocity w in the OX-direction. We take the velocity distribution of the fluid between the plates to be

$$\mathbf{u} = [wf(z), 0, 0] \tag{63}$$

so that

$$\nabla\mathbf{u} = \begin{bmatrix} 0 & 0 & 0 \\ 0 & 0 & 0 \\ wf' & 0 & 0 \end{bmatrix} \tag{64}$$

Since $(\nabla\mathbf{u})^2 = 0$,

$$\mathbf{p} = p\exp(-\tau\mathbf{u}\nabla)\cdot\exp(-\tau\nabla\mathbf{u})$$

$$= p\begin{bmatrix} 1 & 0 & -\tau wf' \\ 0 & 1 & 0 \\ 0 & 0 & 1 \end{bmatrix}\begin{bmatrix} 1 & 0 & 0 \\ 0 & 1 & 0 \\ -\tau wf' & 0 & 1 \end{bmatrix}$$

$$= p\mathbf{1} + \begin{bmatrix} f'^2\eta^2 w^2/p & 0 & -f'\eta w \\ 0 & 0 & 0 \\ -f'\eta w & 0 & 0 \end{bmatrix},$$

$$(\tau p = \eta \text{ from Eq. } (47))$$

The hydrodynamical equation (13), is in this case

$$\nabla\cdot\mathbf{p} = 0, \tag{66}$$

which gives

$$f(z) = z/d, \quad \text{i.e.}$$

$$\mathbf{p} = p\mathbf{1} + \begin{bmatrix} \eta^2 w^2/pd^2 & 0 & -\eta w/d \\ 0 & 0 & 0 \\ -\eta w/d & 0 & 0 \end{bmatrix}, \tag{67}$$

For this situation the second order expression gives the exact result.

Secondly, suppose that the plates are circular, of radius R, and that they are rotating with angular velocity w about the z-axis. If

$$\mathbf{u} = \mathbf{w}\mathbf{x}\mathbf{r}f(z) = [-yfw, xfw, 0], \tag{68}$$

then

$$\nabla\mathbf{u} = \begin{bmatrix} 0 & wf & 0 \\ -wf & 0 & 0 \\ -yf'w & xf'w & 0 \end{bmatrix}, \tag{69}$$

and

$$\exp\left(-\tau \nabla \mathbf{u}\right) =$$

$$= \begin{bmatrix} \cos\lambda & -\sin\lambda & 0 \\ \sin\lambda & \cos\lambda & 0 \\ f'/f\ \{y\sin\lambda - x(1-\cos\lambda)\} & f'/f\ \{-x\sin\lambda - y(1-\cos\lambda)\} & 1 \end{bmatrix} \quad (70)$$

$$\text{where } \lambda = \tau\,wf(z).$$

Thus, in cylindrical polar coordinates,

$$p_{rr} = p\{1 + (f'/f)^2 r^2 (1-\cos\lambda)^2\}$$

$$p_{\phi\phi} = p\{1 + (f'/f)^2 r^2 \sin^2\lambda\}$$

$$p_{zz} = p \qquad\qquad\qquad\qquad\qquad\qquad (71)$$

$$p_{r\phi} = p(f'/f)^2 r^2 \sin^2\lambda\,(1-\cos\lambda)$$

$$p_{rz} = -\,p(f'/f)^2 r^2 (-\cos\lambda)$$

$$p_{\phi z} = -\,(f'/f)\,r\sin\lambda$$

It can be seen that for large values of λ (of the order of unity), this pressure tensor involves τ to arbitrarily high orders.

One of us (R. G. S.) wishes to thank General Motors – Holden's Limited for a fellowship.

REFERENCES

[1] S. CHAPMAN AND T. G. COWLING, *Mathematical Theory of Non-Uniform Gases*, (C.U.P. 1939).

[2] M. BORN AND H. S. GREEN, *A General Kinetic Theory of Liquids*, (C.U.P. 1949).

[3] M. S. GREEN, *J. Chem. Phys.*, **22**, (1954), 398.

[4] H. MORI, *Phys. Rev.*, **112**, (1958), 1829.

[5] H. S. GREEN, *J. Math. Phys.*, **2**, (1961), 344.

[6] E. IKENBERRY AND A. C. TRUESDELL, *J. Rat. Mech. Anal.*, **5**, (1956), 1.

DISCUSSION

H. GIESEKUS: The equation of state (62), from which follow, as consequences, all further results, has a very interesting form. This can be shown perhaps somewhat clearer, if one introduces the operator $\delta_c/\delta t$ by the following definition, where $\mathbf{A}$ denotes a symmetric tensor:

$$\frac{\delta_c \mathbf{A}}{\delta t} = -\,(\mathbf{A}\cdot\nabla\mathbf{u} + \mathbf{u}\nabla\cdot\mathbf{A}).$$

With this operator Eq. (62) can be written in the form

$$\mathbf{p} = p \left[\exp \left(\tau \frac{\delta c}{\delta t} \right) \right] \mathbf{1}$$

Our operator $\delta_c/\delta t$ denotes the difference between contravariant convective and material time derivatives (see Eq. (8) of my paper in this volume), and it becomes identical with the first for quantities, which are constant with respect to time in a spatial reference system. Therefore the operator $\exp[\tau(\delta_c/\delta t)]$ describes in a very simple manner the transformation of the isotropic tensor p **1,** which corresponds to the state of rest, to the tensor **p,** no more isotropical because of the flow gradient $\nabla \mathbf{u}$. Two points here seem remarkable: Firstly $\delta_c/\delta t$ is connected with the contravariant and not with covariant convective derivative. Therefrom follows that in shear flow normal stress effects occur in flow direction only, but not in gradient direction. Secondly, the normal stress effect in flow direction is a pressure, whereas, for elastico-viscous fluids, it is a traction. This would be incompatible with a positive relaxation time claimed by the second law of thermodynamics, if invariance with reference to the group of totations could be postulated. But as is obvious from the premises, this is not the case, because inertia is the fundamental property for this effect. It seems to me very interesting, that—as is shown in this paper—a material, whose inertia is responsible for normal stress effects gives just the opposite sign of the effect as a material in which elastic relaxation causes the respective effect.

In the above example only transport of momentum is responsible for first and higher order effects. But if potential forces due to intermolecular interaction come into action, I think, for the stress or pressure part, resulting from these forces, the principle of invariance with respect to rotations must hold, and then one must expect that the respective normal stresses in flow direction are not pressures but tractions.

H.S. GREEN's REPLY: Perhaps I should add, in reply to Dr. Giesekus, that it is not difficult to determine the effect of the intermolecular forces on the pressure tensor. That was one of the reasons for our investigation, since the result we have given could also be obtained in principle from Boltzmann's equation, by a development of the calculations of Chapman and Erskog. The result of including terms involving the intermolecular forces is to complicate the formula we have given somewhat, but would not, I think, change it radically.

May I also say, in connection with Dr. Giesekus' very interesting observation on the invariance properties of the pressure tensor, I have myself
noticed that it follows from our formula that

$$\frac{\partial \mathbf{p}}{\partial \tau} = -(\mathbf{u} \nabla \cdot \mathbf{p} + \mathbf{p} \cdot \nabla \mathbf{u})$$

which, is like the result Dr. Giesekus has written on the board, with $\mathbf{p}$ instead
of A and the derivative with respect to the relaxation time τ instead of with
respect to t.

NON-NEWTONIAN EFFECTS IN SOME GENERAL ELASTICO-VISCOUS LIQUIDS

K. Walters

Department of Applied Mathematics, University College of Wales, Aberystwyth, U. K.

ABSTRACT

Consideration is given to elastico-viscous liquids whose behaviour at small rates of shear is characterized by a general linear equation of state. Suitable equations of state for use under all conditions of motion and stress are formulated and a number of steady flow problems are solved for two special cases (liquids A′ and B′) in each of which the liquid is completely specified by its relaxation spectrum $N(\tau)$. It is shown that liquid B′ exhibits all the essential features of observed steady non-Newtonian behaviour, with the exception of the observed variation in apparent viscosity with rate of shear.

1. Introduction.

Oldroyd [1], [2], [3] has discussed in a general way the formulation of rheo-logical equations of state for general validity, and has developed the theory in detail for the particular class of idealized liquids whose behaviour at small rates of shear is characterized by equations of state of the form

$$p_{ik} = p'_{ik} - p\, g_{ik}, \tag{1}$$

$$\left(1 + \lambda_1 \frac{\partial}{\partial t}\right) p'_{ik} = 2\eta_0 \left(1 + \lambda_2 \frac{\partial}{\partial t}\right) e_{ik}^{(1)}, \tag{2}$$

p_{ik} being the stress tensor, p an arbitrary isotropic pressure, $g_{ik}(x)$ the metric tensor of a fixed coordinate system x^i, and $e_{ik}^{(1)}$ the rate of strain tensor, which in terms of the velocity vector v_i is given by

$$e_{ik}^{(1)} = \tfrac{1}{2}[v_{i,k} + v_{k,i}]. \tag{3}$$

By considering generalizations of equation (2) that would be suitable as uni-versally valid equations of state, Oldroyd [1],[2],[3] has shown that it is possible to predict (qualitatively) many of the observed features of non-Newtonian behaviour in real elastico-viscous liquids. This is clearly of significance in the

---

(1) Covariant suffixes are written below, contravariant suffixes above and the usual sum-mation convention for repeated suffixes is assumed. A suffix following a comma indicates a covariant derivative.

process of formulating general rheological equations of state for real liquids, but it must be borne in mind that the theory can only be potentially useful for a real liquid for which equation (2) is a reasonable approximation at small rates of shear. There are many elastico-viscous liquids that cannot be characterized by such a simple equation as (2), and this places a limitation on the usefulness of Olroyd's analysis. What is clearly needed is a comparable analysis for a liquid with a more general linear equation of state at small rates of shear.

It has been shown elsewhere [4] that the general linearized equations of state for an incompressible liquid can be written in the form of (1) and

$$p'_{ik}(x, t) = 2 \int_{-\infty}^{t} \Psi(t - t') \, e_{ik}^{(1)}(x, t') \, dt', \tag{4}$$

where

$$\Psi(t - t') = \int_{0}^{\infty} \frac{N(\tau)}{\tau} e^{-\frac{(t-t')}{\tau}} d\tau, \tag{5}$$

$N(\tau)$ being the distribution function of relaxation times (or the 'relaxation spectrum'). We note at this point that the equations of state (4) must be associated, not with the particular point x^i in space over a period of time, but with the same material element over a period of time: the element which is instantaneously at the point x^i at time t. In consequence, the integral occurring in equation (4) must be regarded as a convected integral following the moving material [cf. 1]. Only under the restrictive conditions of small rates of shear in a stationary material element can the convected integral be written as in equation (4).

The problem is now one of generalizing equation (4) into a form that can be applied to materials in general motion, in which the rate of strain is not necessarily small. This of course involves replacing the integral occurring in equation (4) by a convected integral following the moving material. Oldroyd has included convected integration in his general analysis [1], and we shall do no more than write down the required equation, which is (cf. [1], equation (57))

$$p'_{ik}(x, t) = 2 \int_{-\infty}^{t} \Psi(t - t') \frac{\partial x'^m}{\partial x^i} \frac{\partial x'^r}{\partial x^k} \, e_{mr}^{(1)} \, (x', t') \, dt', \tag{6}$$

where $x'^i = x'^i (x, t, t')$ is the position at time t' of the element which is instantaneously at the point x^i at time t. In general, the displacement functions x'^i cannot be expressed as simple functions of the usual kinematic variables and it is necessary to determine them separately in each individual flow problem.

Equation (6) is not the only possible simple generalization of equation (4), since we could equally well write[2]

$$p'^{ik}(x,t) = 2 \int_{-\infty}^{t} \Psi(t-t') \frac{\partial x^i}{\partial x'^m} \frac{\partial x^k}{\partial x'^r} e^{(1)mr}(x',t')dt, \qquad (7)$$

which also satisfies all the conditions for general validity, since suffixes may be raised in (4) under the restrictive conditions in which the equation is supposed true.

The equations of state (6) and (7) may be regarded as the simplest possible invariant generalizations of the general linearized equations of state (4). For convenience, we shall refer to the liquid with equations of state (1) and (6) as liquid A', and to the liquid with equations of state (1) and (7) as liquid B'. The liquids designated A and B by Oldroyd [1] are then special cases of A' and B', respectively, obtained by substituting

$$N(\tau) = \eta_0 \frac{\lambda_2}{\lambda_1} \delta(\tau) + \eta_0 \frac{(\lambda_1 - \lambda_2)}{\lambda_1} \delta(\tau - \lambda_1), \qquad (8)(^3)$$

in equations (5), (6) and (7). The Newtonian liquid is also a special case, obtained by writing

$$N(\tau) = \eta_0 \delta(\tau). \qquad (9)$$

In the following sections, a number of simple flow problems are solved by considering suitable velocity distributions compatible with the equations of state (1) and (6) or (7), the equations of motion.

$$p_{,k}^{ik} + \rho F^i = \rho f^i, \qquad (10)(^4)$$

and the equation of continuity

$$e^{(1)i}_{\ \ i} = 0. \qquad (11)$$

---

(2) The reader is referred to reference [1] for the details.
(3) δ denotes a Dirac delta function, defined in such a way that

$$\delta(x) = 0, \ (x \neq 0); \quad \int_{-\infty}^{\infty} \delta(x)dx = \int_{0}^{\infty} \delta(x)dx = 1.$$

(4) F^i and f^i are the body force and acceleration vectors, respectively, and ρ denotes the density of the fluid.

In this way it is possible to explore the extent to which liquids A′ and B′ can be used as suitable prototypes to explain the behaviour of some real liquids.

2. Simple shearing flow.

We consider first the problem of steady simple shearing. Cartesian axes Ox^i are chosen such that the velocity distribution is given by

$$v^1 = 0, \quad v^2 = 0, \quad v^3 = \gamma x^2, \tag{12}$$

where γ is a constant, and the only non-vanishing rate-of-strain components are than $e_{23}^{(1)} = e_{32}^{(1)} = \tfrac{1}{2}\gamma$. No difficulty is encountered in obtaining the displacement functions $x''(x, t, t')$ in this simple problem: we have

$$x'^1 = x^1, \ x'^2 = x^2, \ x'^3 = x^3 - \gamma x^2 (t - t'). \tag{13}$$

In the case of liquid A′, the equations of state reduce to

$$p'_{ik} = \gamma \int_{-\infty}^{t} \Psi(t - t') \left[\frac{\partial x'^2}{\partial x^i} \frac{\partial x'^3}{\partial x^k} + \frac{\partial x'^3}{\partial x^i} \frac{\partial x'^2}{\partial x^k} \right] dt', \tag{14}$$

and from equations (5), (13) and (14), we obtain the following explicit expressions for the stress components in terms of $N(\tau)$:

$$P_{11} = -p, \ P_{22} = -2\gamma^2 \int_{0}^{\infty} \tau N(\tau)\, d\tau - p, \ P_{33} = -p, \tag{15}$$

$$P_{12} = P_{13} = 0, \ P_{23} = \gamma \int_{0}^{\infty} N(\tau)\, d\tau = \gamma\eta_0,$$

where η_0 is the limiting viscosity at small rates of shear [4].

In the case of liquid B′, we have, instead,

$$p'_{ik} = \gamma \int_{-\infty}^{t} \Psi(t - t') \left[\frac{\partial x^i}{\partial x'^2} \frac{\partial x^k}{\partial x'^3} + \frac{\partial x^i}{\partial x'^3} \frac{\partial x^k}{\partial x'^2} \right] dt', \tag{16}$$

and the corresponding stress distribution is

$$P_{11} = -p, \ P_{22} = -p, \ P_{33} = 2\gamma^2 \int_{0}^{\infty} \tau N(\tau)\, d\tau - p, \tag{17}$$

$$P_{12} = P_{13} = 0, \ P_{23} = \gamma\eta_0.$$

In this simple flow problem, the equation of continuity is automatically satisfied by the velocity distribution (12), and the equations of motion serve simply to determine p as a function of position.

We note first that normal stress-differences are present in both liquids, since in the general case of liquid A', we have (since $N(\tau)$ is essentially positive)

$$p_{11} = p_{33} > p_{22}, \tag{18}$$

and in the general case of liquid B',

$$p_{11} = p_{22} < p_{33}.$$

The exceptional case when the normal stresses are all equal corresponds to liquids for which $N(\tau)$ satisfies

$$\int_0^\infty \tau N(\tau)\, d\tau = 0 \tag{19}$$

and

$$\int_0^\infty N(\tau)\, d\tau = \eta_0. \tag{20}$$

There is a unique solution of these equations,

$$N(\tau) = \eta_0 \delta(\tau), \tag{21}$$

which corresponds to the Newtonian liquid of constant viscosity η_0. This means that all elastico-viscous liquids of the type considered will exhibit normal stress differences when the rate of shear is not restricted to be small.

Further inspection of equations (15) and (17) reveals that the relation between the shearing stress p_{23} and the velocity gradient γ in both cases is the same as that for a Newtonian liquid of constant viscosity η_0, so that these liquids will not exhibit the usually observed decrease in apparent viscosity with increasing rate of shear [see, for example, (5), (6)].

3. Steady flow between rotating coaxial cylinders.

We now investigate the motion when the liquid A' (and later B') is contained between vertical coaxial cylinders and subjected to a simple type of shearing motion. This motion is supposed brought about by causing the cylinders to rotate about their common axis with different angular velocities. Cylindrical polar coordinates (r, θ, z) are chosen with $0z$ measured vertically upwards along the axis of the cylinders, and two-dimensional axially symmetric flow is assumed in which the physical components of velocity are $(0, r\omega(r), 0)$. In this case, the only non-vanishing physical components of the rate-of-strain tensor are

$$e^{(1)}_{(r\theta)} = e^{(1)}_{(\theta r)} = \tfrac{1}{2} r \frac{d\omega}{dr}. \tag{22}$$

We write $x^1 = r$, $x^2 = \theta$, $x^3 = z$, and the displacement functions can then be written in the form

$$r' = r, \; \theta' = \theta - \omega(r) \; (t - t'), \; z' = z. \tag{23}$$

From equations (6), (22) and (23), the physical components of the stress tensor in the case of liquid A' are given by[5]

$$\theta\theta' = zz' = rz' = \theta z' = 0,$$

$$rr' = -2\left[r \frac{d\omega}{dr} \right]^2 \int_0^\infty \tau N(\tau) d\tau, \tag{24}$$

$$r\theta' = \eta_0 \left[r \frac{d\omega}{dr} \right].$$

Expressed in terms of the same variables, the equations of motion (10) require

$$\frac{d}{dr} rr' + \frac{rr'}{r} = \frac{\partial p}{\partial r} - \rho r \omega^2, \tag{25}$$

$$\frac{d}{dr} r\theta' + 2\frac{r\theta'}{r} = 0, \tag{26}$$

$$0 = \frac{\partial p}{\partial z} + \rho g, \tag{27}$$

where g is the acceleration due to gravity. From equations (24) and (26), we have

$$r \frac{d^2\omega}{dr^2} + 3 \frac{d\omega}{dr} = 0, \tag{28}$$

which has a solution of the form

$$\omega = a - \frac{b}{r^2}, \tag{29}$$

where $a = \left(\dfrac{r_1^2 \omega_1 - r_2^2 \omega_2}{r_1^2 - r_2^2} \right)$ and $b = \dfrac{r_1^2 r_2^2 (\omega_2 - \omega_1)}{(r_2^2 - r_1^2)}$,

---

[5] Obtained by working in terms of the covariant components of the stress and rate of strain tensors, and later transforming to physical components in cylindrical polar directions.

ω_1 and ω_2 being the angular velocities of the cylinders with radii r_1 and r_2 ($> r_1$) respectively. The velocity distribution is in fact indistinguishable from that in a Newtonian liquid of constant viscosity η_0.

From equations (24), (25), (27) and (29), we obtain the following expression for p:

$$p = \rho \left[\frac{a^2 r^2}{2} - 2ab \log r - \frac{b^2}{2r^2} \right] - \frac{6b^2}{r^4} \int_0^\infty \tau N(\tau) \, d\tau - \rho g z + \text{constant}. \quad (30)$$

It is of interest to determine the vertical normal pressure $(-zz)$ required to keep the upper surface of the liquid horizontal. From (30), (since zz' is zero), we have

$$- zz = \rho \left[\frac{a^2 r^2}{2} - 2ab \log r - \frac{b^2}{2r^2} \right] + p^x - \rho g z + \text{constant}, \quad (31)$$

where

$$p^x = \text{constant} - \frac{6b^2}{r^4} \int_0^\infty \tau N(\tau) \, d\tau. \quad (32)$$

The contribution $p^x(r)$ represents an additional radial variation of vertical normal pressure, over and above that arising from the centripetal acceleration of the liquid. If the liquid is sufficiently viscous, (i.e. if $N(\tau)$ is sufficiently large), this contribution will be the dominant part of the radial variation of vertical normal pressure. From equation (32) we see that this constraining pressure increases with r, since $\int_0^\infty \tau N(\tau) d\tau$ is essentially positive. Hence, if the liquid were suddenly given a free horizontal surface. the tendency would be for the liquid to fall near the inner cylinder and rise near the outer, (corresponding to the negative Weissenberg effect).

In a similar way, it can be shown that in the case of liquid B'

$$p^x = \text{constant} + \frac{2b^2}{r^4} \int_0^\infty \tau N(\tau) d\tau. \quad (33)$$

This equation implies that the constraining pressure decreases with r, so that if the liquid were suddenly given a free horizontal surface, the tendency would be for the liquid to rise near the inner cylinder and fall near the outer. This corresponds to the positive Weissenberg effect, which has been observed in many liquids (see, for example, [6], [7], [8]).

4. Flow through straight pipes of arbitrary section.

It is of interest to determine whether liquids A' and B' can flow steadily in straight lines through cylindrical pipes of arbitrary cross-section under a constant pressure gradient. Such a motion is not always possible for idealized elastico-viscous liquids, as Oldroyd [3] has shown.

We take a velocity distribution, referred to Cartesian axes $0x^i$, of the form

$$v^1 = 0, \quad v^2 = 0, \quad v^3 = v^3(x^1, x^2), \tag{34}$$

which satisfies the equation of continuity (11) without any restriction on v^3. Solving equations (3), (6), (7) and (34) for the stress components, we have in the case of liquid A',

$$p'_{11} = -2\gamma_1^2 \int_0^\infty \tau N(\tau)\, d\tau, \quad p'_{22} = -2\gamma_2^2 \int_0^\infty \tau N(\tau)\ d\tau, \quad p'_{33} = 0,$$

$$\tag{35}$$

$$p'_{23} = \eta_0 \gamma_2, \quad p'_{13} = \eta_0 \gamma_1, \quad p'_{12} = -2\gamma_1 \gamma_2 \int_0^\infty \tau N(\tau)\, d\tau,$$

and in the case of liquid B',

$$p'_{11} = 0, \quad p'_{22} = 0, \quad p'_{33} = 2[\gamma_1^2 + \gamma_2^2] \int_0^\infty \tau N(\tau)\, d\tau,$$

$$\tag{36}$$

$$p'_{23} = \eta_0 \gamma_2, \quad p'_{13} = \eta_0 \gamma_1, \quad p'_{12} = 0,$$

where $\gamma_1 = \partial v^3/\partial x^1$ and $\gamma_2 = \partial v^3/\partial x^2$. In the absence of body forces, the equations of motion (10) become

$$\frac{\partial p'_{11}}{\partial x^1} + \frac{\partial p'_{12}}{\partial x^2} = \frac{\partial p}{\partial x^1}, \quad \frac{\partial p'_{12}}{\partial x^1} + \frac{\partial p'_{22}}{\partial x^2} = \frac{\partial p}{\partial x^2}, \quad \frac{\partial p'_{13}}{\partial x^1} + \frac{\partial p'_{23}}{\partial x^2} = \frac{\partial p}{\partial x^3}. \tag{37}$$

The third equation of motion requires (in the case of both liquid A' and B')

$$\eta_0 \left[\frac{\partial^2 v^3}{\partial(x^1)^2} + \frac{\partial^2 v^3}{\partial(x^2)^2} \right] = -P, \tag{38}$$

where P is a constant, independent of position.

Substituting the stress distributions (35) and (36) into the first two equations of motion, we find that these equations impose no further restriction on v^3 in either case and serve simply to determine p. This means that liquids A' and B′ can flow in straight lines through cylindrical pipes of arbitrary cross-section under a constant pressure gradient. The problem resolves itself into finding a solution of equation (38) subject to prescribed boundary conditions. The form of v^3 will be the same as that for a Newtonian liquid of constant viscosity η_0.

5. Flow between rotating coaxial cones.

We now investigate the motion of liquids A′ and B′ when contained between two cones with a common vertex and vertical axis, rotating about their axis with different angular velocities. An arrangement of this sort has been set up experimentally by Roberts [6], [9], [10], and has been used by him to measure normal stress differences in some real elastico-viscous liquids.

The motion of the fluid particles is assumed to be steady and in horizontal circles, so that, referred to spherical polar coordinates (r, θ, ϕ), we are led to consider a velocity distribution with physical components

$$v_{(r)} = 0, \quad v_{(\theta)} = 0, \quad v_{(\phi)} = r \sin \theta \omega(\theta). \tag{39}$$

In this case, the only non-vanishing physical components of the rate of strain tensor are

$$e^{(1)}_{(\theta\phi)} = e^{(1)}_{(\phi\theta)} = \tfrac{1}{2} \sin \theta \frac{d\omega}{d\theta}. \tag{40}$$

We write $x^1 = r$, $x^2 = \theta$, $x^3 = \phi$, and the displacement functions can then be written in the form

$$r' = r, \quad \theta' = \theta, \quad \phi' = \phi - \omega(\theta)(t - t'). \tag{41}$$

From equations (6), (40) and (41), the physical components of the stress tensor in the case of liquid A′ are given by

$$rr' = 0, \quad \phi\phi' = 0, \quad r\theta' = 0, \quad r\phi' = 0,$$

$$\theta\theta' = -2 \left[\sin \theta \frac{d\omega}{d\theta} \right]^2 \int_0^\infty \tau N(\tau) d\tau, \quad \theta\phi' = \eta_0 \left[\sin \theta \frac{d\omega}{d\theta} \right]. \right\} \tag{42}$$

The equation of continuity is automatically satisfied by the velocity distribution (39), and the problem is now one of determining under what conditions equations (39) and (42) satisfy the equations of motion (10), which in this case reduce to

$$-\frac{\theta\theta'}{r} = \frac{\partial p}{\partial r} - \rho g \cos\theta - \rho r \sin^2\theta \, \omega^2, \tag{43}$$

$$\frac{1}{r}\frac{d\theta\theta'}{d\theta} + \frac{\theta\theta'\cot\theta}{r} = \frac{\partial p}{r\partial\theta} + \rho g \sin\theta - \rho r \sin\theta \cos\theta \, \omega^2, \tag{44}$$

$$\frac{1}{r}\frac{d\theta\phi'}{d\theta} + \frac{2\theta\phi'}{r}\cot\theta = 0. \tag{45}$$

Equation (45) requires

$$\frac{d}{d\theta}\left[\sin\theta\,\frac{d\omega}{d\theta}\right] + 2\cos\theta\,\frac{d\omega}{d\theta} = 0, \tag{46}$$

which determines ω as a function of θ uniquely if the boundary conditions are prescribed. Any further restriction on ω from the first two equations of motion must mean that it will not be possible to maintain a velocity distribution of the form (39) when the liquid A' is contained between rotating co-axial cones.

Substituting the stress components (42) into equations (43) and (44) and eliminating p, we obtain

$$\rho r^2 \sin^2\theta\omega\,\frac{d\omega}{d\theta} + \frac{d}{d\theta}\left[\sin\theta\,\frac{d\omega}{d\theta}\right]^2 \int_0^\infty \tau N(\tau)d\tau = 0, \tag{47}$$

which is a restriction on ω that is not in general compatible with (46). From (46) and (47), we deduce that a velocity distribution of the form (39) is possible only when the inertia terms in the equations of motion can be neglected and when the semi-angles of the two cones are sufficiently near to $\frac{1}{2}\pi$ to allow the neglect of the second-term in equation (46). In this case, approximately,

$$\sin\theta\,\frac{d\omega}{d\theta} = \gamma_0, \tag{48}$$

a constant, i.e. the rate of shear is uniform throughout the liquid, and the state of stress is, from (42), also uniform.

The same conclusions are reached when consideration is given to liquid B', except that in this case the uniform stress distribution is given by

$$\left.\begin{array}{l} rr' = 0, \quad \theta\theta' = 0, \quad \phi\phi' = 2\gamma_0^2 \int_0^\infty \tau N(\tau)\,d\tau, \\[2mm] r\theta' = 0, \quad r\phi' = 0, \quad \phi\theta' = \eta_0\gamma_0. \end{array}\right\} \tag{49}$$

The above theory is suitable for comparison with the experimental results of Roberts [6], [9], [10] since these were obtained by shearing different liquids between a horizontal flat plate and a cone of semi-angle very near to $\frac{1}{2}\pi$. Working with a number of polymer and colloidal solutions over a wide range of γ_0, Roberts found consistently that the distribution of normal stresses was equivalent to an extra tension along the streamlines, the normal stresses in any plane perpendicular to the streamlines being equal. In terms of the variables defined above, this implies

$$rr' \,=\, \theta\theta' \,<\phi\phi' \tag{50}$$

From equations (42) and (49), we deduce that liquid B′ would exhibit the observed stress distribution, but that liquid A′ would not.

6. Conclusion.

We may summarise the results of the preceding sections as follows. In the case of a liquid of type A′, no variation in apparent viscosity would be observed in simple shearing; the liquid would exhibit the *negative* Weissenberg effect when sheared between coaxial cylinders; steady rectilinear flow through straight pipes of arbitrary cross-section under a constant pressure gradient would be possible; the normal stress distribution in the case of flow between a horizontal flat plate and a cone of semi-angle very near to $\frac{1}{2}\pi$ would *not* be of a type that has so far been measured experimentally.

In the case of a liquid of type B′, no variation in apparent viscosity would be observed in simple shearing; the liquid would exhibit the *positve* Weissenberg effect when sheared between coaxial cylinders; steady rectilinear flow through straight pipes of arbitrary section under a constant pressure gradient would be possible; the normal stress distribution in the case of flow between a horizontal flat plate and a cone of semi-angle very near to $\frac{1}{2}\pi$ would be in qualitative agreement with Roberts' experimental results on certain elastico-viscous liquids.

We may conclude that, as far as available experimental results are concerned, liquid A′ is not a suitable prototype to explain the more common types of real elastico-viscous behaviour, but that the idealized liquid B′ shows all the main features of commonly observed steady non-Newtonian behaviour, with the exception of the usually observed decrease in apparent viscosity with increasing rate of shear. This suggests that a suitable slight modification of liquid B′ might well be a useful prototype on which to base a qualitative treatment when sufficient experimental results are available for a given material. This is considered elsewhere [11].

7. List of Symbols.

p_{ik}	= stress tensor
p'_{ik}	= that part of the stress tensor related to the distortion
$e^{(1)}_{ik}$	= rate of strain tensor
$N(\tau)$	= distribution function of relaxation times
x^i	= general curvilinear coordinates
x'^i	= displacement functions
η_0	= limiting viscosity at small rates of shear
F^i	= body force vector
f^i	= acceleration vector
$v_{(r)}, v_{(\theta)}, v_{(z)}$	= physical components of the velocity vector in cylindrical polar directions
$e^{(1)}_{(rr)}$ etc.	= physical components of the rate of strain tensor in cylindrical polar directions
rr, etc.	= physical components of the stress tensor in cylindrical polar directions
rr', etc.	= physical components of p'_{ik} in cylindrical polar directions
γ	= velocity gradient

REFERENCES

[1] J.G. OLDROYD, *Proc. Roy. Soc.*, A **200**, (1950), 523.

[2] J.G. OLDROYD, *Quart. J. Mech. Applied Math.*, **4**, (1951), 271.

[3] J.G. OLDROYD, *Proc, Roy. Soc.*, A **245**, (1958), 278.

[4] K. WALTERS, *Quart. J. Mech. Applied Math.*, **13**, (1960), 444.

[5] J.G. OLDROYD, D.J. STRAWBRIDGE AND B.A. TOMS, *Proc. Phys. Soc.*, **64B**, (1951), 44.

[6] A. JOBLING AND J.E. ROBERTS, *Rheology*, Vol.2 (ed. F.R. Eirich) (New York, 1958), Ch. 13.

[7] K. WEISSENBERG, *Proc. 1st. Int. Congr. Rheology*, Holland, (1948), 29.

[8] K. WEISSENBERG, *Proc. Roy. Soc.*, A **200**, (1950), 183.

[9] J.E. ROBERTS, Unpublished Ministry of Supply Report (1952).

[10] J.E. ROBERTS, *Proc. 2nd. Int. Congr. Rheology*, Oxford, (1953), 99.

[11] K. WALTERS, *Quart. J. Mech. Applied Math.*, **15**, (1962), 63.

DISCUSSION

C. TRUESDELL: Are not your fluids A' and B' simple fluids in the sence of Noll? If so, could not the work be shortened by using the general solutions for viscometric flows obtained by Coleman and Noll?

J.G. SAVINS: It would be helpful, particularly to the experimentalist, if the author would supplement this analysis with a description of the predicted pressure differences distribution which would arise on shearing liquids A' and B' between coaxial rotating cones. This would seem to be a critical test of any model which predicts the Weissenberg effect. For example both the Weissenberg conjecture and the Reiner-Rivlin liquid predict the pressure will be a maximum at the axis of rotation; but the former predicts the pressure will vanish at a distance equal to one-third of the radius of the cones.

K. WALTER's reply: The work contained here may well be included in the general solutions for viscometric flows obtained by Coleman and Noll. However, there is still a need for a search for *simple* equations of state that give rise to the kind of non-Newtonian behaviour that is often observed in real liquids, and at the same time are simple enough for the mathematician to explore their implications in situations other than those involving simple shearing. The work contained here is therefore to be thought of as a basis for a more detailed mathematical analysis.

I am indebted to Dr. Savins for pointing out the need for greater detail in the analysis of section 5. This will be carried out in the near future.

NON-LINEAR STRESS, RATE OF STRAIN RELATIONS AT FINITE RATES OF SHEAR IN SO-CALLED "LINEAR" ELASTICO-VISCOUS LIQUIDS

J. G. OLDROYD

University of Wales (Swansea), U.K.

ABSTRACT

At sufficiently small variable rates of shear the rheological behaviour of many liquids can be represented by linear differential equations connecting the stresses and the rates of strain in a material element, each being a function of the time; such liquids are often called "linear" elastico-viscous liquids. It can be proved that a dilute emulsion of one linear elastico-viscous liquid dispersed in another, or a dilute suspension of particles of a linear visco-elastic solid in a linear elastico-viscous liquid, is also a linear elastico-viscous liquid in the above sense, though sometimes with an essentially more complicated linear response to stress than either of its component materials separately. The case when the differential equations of state are of finite order N is considered.

Passing from small rates of strain to finite rates, the precise description of rheological behaviour requires the recasting of the rheological equations of state of linear elastico-viscous liquids into a more general form, so that they may be valid for a material element in a general state of flow, while keeping them consistent with the known linear behaviour at small variable strain rates. It is found that, in the process of generalization of the equations of state, it is impossible to avoid the occurrence of product terms in the stresses and velocity gradients if the equations are to have the right mathematical form to express properties independent of the frame of reference and also independent of the translation and rotation of the material element as a whole in space. As a consequence the (so-called) linear elastico-viscous liquids must in general show the following non-linear effects when they are sheared at finite rates: the variation of apparent viscosity with the rate of shear, e.g. in a Couette viscometer or in simple shearing; the Weissenberg climbing effects, in either a positive or a negative sense; and the occurrence of differences in the normal stresses in different directions, during shearing, which may be in the sense of an extra tension along the streamlines, as observed in some real liquids by Roberts, or may be a more complicated distribution of stress differences.

1. "Linear" elastico-viscous liquids.

The rheological behaviour of many liquids, when subjected to small variable rates of shear, is described approximately by a linear differential equation relating the shear stress τ and rate of shear γ, each being a function of the time t. Such liquids are sometimes referred to as "linear" elastico-viscous liquids. When the liquid may be regarded as incompressible and the shear stress, rate-of-shear relationship takes the form

$$\left(1 + \alpha_1 \frac{d}{dt} + \alpha_2 \frac{d^2}{dt^2} + \ldots + \alpha_N \frac{d^N}{dt^N}\right)\tau$$

$$= \eta_0 \left(1 + \beta_1 \frac{d}{dt} + \beta_2 \frac{d^2}{dt^2} + \ldots + \beta_N \frac{d^N}{dt^N}\right)\gamma, \tag{1}$$

where the constant η_0 is the limiting viscosity at small rates of shear and $\alpha_1, \beta_1, \alpha_2, \beta_2, \ldots, \alpha_N, \beta_N$ are constants of which α_N and β_N do not both vanish, we shall refer to the liquid as an elastico-viscous liquid of type N.

It follows from previous work [1], [2] that a dilute suspension of Hookean elastic solid spheres in a liquid or an emulsion of an ordinary Newtonian liquid dispersed in another Newtonian liquid is an elastico-viscous liquid of type 1; and that a dilute emulsion of a liquid of type M dispersed in a liquid of type N, with constant interfacial tension between the two components, is a liquid of type (at most) $1 + 2M + 3N$.

It is a simple matter to combine the different equations (1) corresponding to shearing in different planes and write down equations of state for an elastico-viscous liquid of type N (subjected to small rates of strain) in a form independent of the coordinate system. Since the liquid is assumed to be incompressible we may suppose that an arbitrary isotropic pressure p may be superposed on any system of stresses, without having any effect on the deformation. So the stress tensor p_{ik} may be written as

$$p_{ik} = p'_{ik} - p\delta_{ik}, \tag{2}$$

where p is arbitrary, δ_{ik} is the Kronecker delta, and p'_{ik} is related to the rate-of-strain tensor

$$e_{ik} \equiv \frac{1}{2}\left(\frac{\partial v_k}{\partial x_i} + \frac{\partial v_i}{\partial x_k}\right); \tag{3}$$

here $x_i (i = 1, 2, 3)$ denotes an orthogonal Cartesian coordinate and v_i denotes a component of velocity. To be consistent with (1) the latter relationship is taken to be

$$\left(1 + \alpha_1 \frac{d}{dt} + \ldots + \alpha_N \frac{d^N}{dt^N}\right)p'_{ik}$$

$$= 2\eta_0 \left(1 + \beta_1 \frac{d}{dt} + \ldots + \beta_N \frac{d^N}{dt^N}\right)e_{ik}. \tag{4}$$

This is a set of six equations which is invariant under a transformation from one Cartesian coordinate system to another. Incompressibility implies a restriction on the rate-of-strain tensor, namely

$$e_{ii} = \frac{\partial v_i}{\partial x_i} = 0, \tag{5}$$

where the usual convention of summation over the values $1, 2, 3$ is adopted for repeated small latin suffixes.

Equations (2) and (4) define unambiguously the rheological behaviour of a stationary element of liquid subjected to small variable rates of shear, because under these conditions there is no ambiguity in what is meant by the rate of change d/dt of any quantity involved. In the present paper we consider further the class of idealized liquids whose behaviour at small rates of shear is completely described by the equations (2) and (4).

2. Equations of state suitable for general flow.

In order to study the behaviour of an elastico-viscous liquid of type N in a general state of flow, it will be necessary to construct a set of rheological equations of state defining a type of behaviour that is both consistent with equations (2) and (4) when the rate of strain is sufficiently small and also independent of the motion of the material as a whole in space. For this purpose equations (2) and (4) may be taken over as they stand, provided a suitable interpretation is given to the symbol d/dt.

The simplest possible rate of change that takes into account the rate of translation of the material element in space, measured by the velocity vector v_i, and the rate of rotation of the element, measured by the vorticity tensor

$$\omega_{ik} \equiv \tfrac{1}{2}\left(\frac{\partial v_k}{\partial x_i} - \frac{\partial v_i}{\partial x_k}\right), \tag{6}$$

is the material derivative $\mathscr{D}/\mathscr{D}t$ [3] defined by:

(i) for a scalar quantity S (a function of position x_i and time t),

$$\frac{\mathscr{D}S}{\mathscr{D}t} \equiv \frac{\partial S}{\partial t} + v_j \frac{\partial S}{\partial x_j}; \tag{7}$$

(ii) for a vector quantity V_i,

$$\frac{\mathscr{D}V_i}{\mathscr{D}t} \equiv \frac{\partial V_i}{\partial t} + v_j \frac{\partial V_i}{\partial x_j} + \omega_{ij} V_j; \tag{8}$$

(*iii*) for a second-order tensor quantity T_{ik},

$$\frac{\mathscr{D}T_{ik}}{\mathscr{D}t} \equiv \frac{\partial T_{ik}}{\partial t} + v_j \frac{\partial T_{ik}}{\partial x_j} + \omega_{ij}T_{jk} + \omega_{kj}T_{ij}. \tag{9}$$

If d/dt is interpreted as $\mathscr{D}/\mathscr{D}t$ wherever it occurs in equation (4), it can be proved that the equations of state are then of the right form for universal validity, i.e. they specify rheological behaviour that is independent of the coordinate system and independent of the motion in space of the material, and they are also consistent with what is known of the behaviour when the rate of strain is small.

It is immediately obvious from (9) that this interpretation of d/dt in (4) destroys the linear nature of the equation: whereas at small rates of strain the equations were linear differential relationships between partial stress components p'_{ik} and velocity gradients $\partial v_i/\partial x_k$, we now have products of these quantities present. The first material time derivative of the stress involves simple products of velocity gradients and stresses, and higher material time derivatives involve products of higher degree. The equations of state (2) and (4), interpreted so as to be applicable with consistency to a material element in a general state of motion, are linear in the stresses but of degree $N + 1$ in stresses and velocity gradients together. The term "linear" liquids is therefore appropriate only if we restrict attention to rates of shear so small that simple products of rates of shear with themselves and with stresses are negligibly small.

The material derivative $\mathscr{D}/\mathscr{D}t$ is not the only possible time derivative that has the ordinary significance of the time derivative d/dt at small rates of shear and that introduces into the equations no dependance of rheological behaviour on translation and rotation in space. For example, the convected derivatives of stress and rate of strain as defined by Oldroyd [4], which are to be regarded as time derivatives following the material element and correcting for translation, rotation *and deformation* of the element, could be used in place of $\mathscr{D}/\mathscr{D}t$ in interpreting the rate-of-change terms of equation (4). The possible alternative generalized forms of the equations of state all involve additional product terms in the stress and velocity gradients (which would all be negligibly small at low rates of strain), but the equations remain linear in the stresses alone and of degree $N + 1$ in stresses and velocity gradients taken together.

We are therefore led to consider the set of equations (2) and

$$\left(1 + \alpha_1 \frac{\mathscr{D}}{\mathscr{D}t} + \alpha_2 \frac{\mathscr{D}^2}{\mathscr{D}t^2} + \ldots + \alpha_N \frac{\mathscr{D}^N}{\mathscr{D}t^N}\right) p'_{ik}$$

$$= 2\eta_0 \left(1 + \beta_1 \frac{\mathscr{D}}{\mathscr{D}t} + \beta_2 \frac{\mathscr{D}^2}{\mathscr{D}t^2} + \ldots + \beta_N \frac{\mathscr{D}^N}{\mathscr{D}t^N}\right) e_{ik} \quad (10)$$

as the simplest possible (but not the only possible) equations of state for an idealized elastico-viscous liquid of type N subjected to finite rates of strain.

3. Simple shearing at a finite rate.

The significance of the inevitable non-linear terms in the full equations of state of a so-called "linear" elastico-viscous liquid can be seen most clearly by examining in detail a very simple type of flow in which the rate of strain is finite. When a liquid of type N is sheared steadily between two parallel flat plates, one fixed and one moving in its own plane, we can take the velocity distribution as

$$v_1 = 0, \quad v_2 = 0, \quad v_3 = \gamma x_2, \tag{11}$$

where γ is a constant. The acceleration of the fluid is zero at every point and the equations of motion are therefore satisfied if the components of partial stress p'_{ik} are all constant and the isotropic pressure p is equal to the hydrostatic pressure (i.e. the pressure distribution that would be present, determined by the body-force field alone, if the fluid were everywhere at rest).

The only non-vanishing components of vorticity and rate-of-strain corresponding to the velocity distribution (11) are

$$\omega_{23} = -\omega_{32} = \tfrac{1}{2}\gamma. \quad e_{23} = e_{32} = \tfrac{1}{2}\gamma, \tag{12}$$

and these values are now substituted in the six equations (10) in order to determine the constant partial stresses p'_{ik} in terms of γ. (Equation (9) must be used repeatedly to determine the components of the N successive material derivatives of the stress and rate-of-strain tensors.) Anticipating that the solution of (10) for the partial stress tensor has

$$- p'_{22} = p'_{33} = P(\gamma), \quad p'_{23} = p'_{32} = Q(\gamma), \tag{13}$$

as the only non-vanishing components, i.e.

$$p'_{ik} = \begin{bmatrix} 0 & 0 & 0 \\ 0 & -P & Q \\ 0 & Q & P \end{bmatrix},$$

we determine P and Q in terms of γ as follows. From (9),

$$\frac{\mathscr{D}p'_{ik}}{\mathscr{D}t} = \gamma \begin{bmatrix} 0 & 0 & 0 \\ 0 & Q & P \\ 0 & P & -Q \end{bmatrix}, \quad \frac{\mathscr{D}^2 p'_{ik}}{\mathscr{D}t^2} = \gamma^2 \begin{bmatrix} 0 & 0 & 0 \\ 0 & P & -Q \\ 0 & -Q & -P \end{bmatrix},$$

$$\frac{\mathscr{D}^3 p'_{ik}}{\mathscr{D}t^3} = \gamma^3 \begin{bmatrix} 0 & 0 & 0 \\ 0 & -Q & -P \\ 0 & -P & Q \end{bmatrix}, \quad \frac{\mathscr{D}^4 p'_{ik}}{\mathscr{D}t^4} = \gamma^4 \begin{bmatrix} 0 & 0 & 0 \\ 0 & -P & Q \\ 0 & Q & P \end{bmatrix},$$

and so on. Tbe corresponding derivatives of e_{ik} are given by the same formulae, but with $\frac{1}{2}\gamma$ substituted for Q and zero for P. Substitution in (10) leads to the following two equations for P and Q

$$\begin{aligned} (1 - \alpha_2\gamma^2 + \alpha_4\gamma^4 &- \alpha_6\gamma^6 + \ldots)P \\ &- (\alpha_1\gamma - \alpha_3\gamma^3 + \alpha_5\gamma^5 - \ldots)Q \\ &= -\eta_0\gamma(\beta_1\gamma - \beta_3\gamma^3 + \beta_5\gamma^5 - \ldots), \end{aligned} \tag{14}$$

$$\begin{aligned} (\alpha_1\gamma - \alpha_3\gamma^3 + \alpha_5\gamma^5 &- \ldots)P \\ &+ (1 - \alpha_2\gamma^2 + \alpha_4\gamma^4 - \alpha_6\gamma^6 + \ldots)Q \\ &= \eta_0\gamma(1 - \beta_2\gamma^2 + \beta_4\gamma^4 - \beta_6\gamma^6 + \ldots). \end{aligned} \tag{15}$$

The solution of (14) and (15) is elementary, and is obtained most simply in the following way. Equations (14) and (15) are equivalent to the complex equation

$$\begin{aligned} (P + iQ)[1 + \alpha_1(i\gamma) &+ \alpha_2(i\gamma)^2 + \alpha_3(i\gamma)^3 + \ldots] \\ &= i\eta_0\gamma[1 + \beta_1(i\gamma) + \beta_2(i\gamma)^2 + \beta_3(i\gamma)^3 + \ldots], \end{aligned} \tag{16}$$

since the two sides of (14) are the real parts, and those of (15) are the imaginary parts, of the two sides of (16). Hence

$$P + iQ = \frac{i\eta_0\gamma(1 + i\beta_1\gamma - \beta_2\gamma^2 - i\beta_3\gamma^3 + \beta_4\gamma^4 + \ldots)}{1 + i\alpha_1\gamma - \alpha_2\gamma^2 - i\alpha_3\gamma^3 + \alpha_4\gamma^4 + \ldots}. \tag{17}$$

Equating the real and imaginary parts of the two sides of (17), we have explicit expressions for P and Q as functions of γ.

The physical significance of the solution (17) is, first, that the shear stress corresponding to the constant velocity gradient γ is

$$p_{23} = p'_{23} = Q = \eta\gamma, \tag{18}$$

where the apparent viscosity η is not a constant but a function of the rate of shear defined by

$$\frac{\eta(\gamma)}{\eta_0} = \frac{\begin{aligned}&[(1 - \alpha_2\gamma^2 + \alpha_4\gamma^4 - \ldots)(1 - \beta_2\gamma^2 + \beta_4\gamma^4 - \ldots) \\ &+ (\alpha_1\gamma - \alpha_3\gamma^3 + \alpha_5\gamma^5 - \ldots)(\beta_1\gamma - \beta_3\gamma^3 + \beta_5\gamma^5 - \ldots)]\end{aligned}}{(1 - \alpha_2\gamma^2 + \alpha_4\gamma^4 - \ldots)^2 + (\alpha_1\gamma - \alpha_3\gamma^3 + \alpha_5\gamma^5 - \ldots)^2}. \tag{19}$$

The numerator and the denominator in this expression are each polynomials of degree N in γ^2, and it is clear that η tends to η_0 as γ tends to zero. Secondly, the normal stresses p_{11}, p_{22}, p_{33} are all different and the greatest difference between them is

$$p_{33} - p_{22} = 2P(\gamma) = \frac{\begin{aligned}&2\eta_0\gamma^2\,[(\alpha_1 - \alpha_3\gamma^2 + \alpha_5\gamma^4 - \ldots)(1 - \beta_2\gamma^2 + \beta_4\gamma^4 - \ldots) \\ &- (\beta_1 - \beta_3\gamma^2 + \beta_5\gamma^4 - \ldots)(1 - \alpha_2\gamma^2 + \alpha_4\gamma^4 - \ldots)]\end{aligned}}{(1 - \alpha_2\gamma^2 + \alpha_4\gamma^4 - \ldots)^2 + (\alpha_1\gamma - \alpha_3\gamma^3 + \alpha_5\gamma^5 - \ldots)^2}, \tag{20}$$

with p_{11} mid-way in value between p_{22} and p_{33}. The numerator and denominator in (20) are polynomials of degree N in γ^2, and for small γ it is seen that the stress differences are in general of the order of magnitude of γ^2.

4. Conclusion.

We are led to the conclusion that the simplest possible equations of state that correspond to "linear" elastic-viscous behaviour at small rates of strain imply behaviour which is very far from a linear relationship between stresses and rates of strain at finite rates. In steady simple shearing flow with a finite velocity gradient, for example, the elastico-viscous liquid of type N will exhibit a variable apparent viscosity, depending on the rate of shear in a complicated way defined by an equation of the type (19). It will also exhibit differences in the normal stresses along and perpendicular to the streamlines, which are known to give rise to such phenomena as the Weissenberg climbing effect.

In the present paper, it must be emphasized, only the simplest possible generalizations of the linear stress, rate-of-strain relations observable at small rates have been considered in detail. Real liquids that are "linear" at small rates will often have, in their equations of state for general flow, additional product terms in the stresses and rates of strain that are not present in equation

(10); such product terms are, of course, negligible, and their presence is not experimentally detectable, at small rates of shear. Any extra terms inserted in (10) will in general lead to complication, rather than to any simplification, of the forms of $\eta(\gamma)$ and $P(\gamma)$, and it follows that real liquids that are elastico-viscous of type N at small rates must certainly be expected to show variable-viscosity and normal-stress effects at larger rates of shear. The magnitudes and signs of the normal stress differences and hence the magnitude and sense of the Weissenberg effect are critically dependent on any extra product terms that require to be inserted in equation (10).

5. List of symbols.

d/dt	=	rate of change.
$\mathcal{D}/\mathcal{D}t$	=	rate of change following the material (equations (7)–(9)).
e_{ik}	=	rate-of-strain tensor component (equation (3)).
i	=	$\sqrt{(-1)}$.
N	=	order of the linearized differential equation of state.
p	=	isotropic pressure (arbitrary).
p_{ik}	=	stress tensor component.
p'_{ik}	=	partial stress tensor component.
P	=	normal stress difference (equations (13)).
Q	=	shear stress (equations (13)).
t	=	the time.
$v_i (i = 1, 2, 3)$	=	velocity vector components.
$x_i (i = 1, 2, 3)$	=	rectangular Cartesian coordinates.
$\alpha_1, ..., \alpha_N$	=	constant coefficients.
$\beta_1, ..., \beta_N$	=	constant coefficients.
γ	=	rate of shear (velocity gradient) in shearing flow.
δ_{ik}	=	Kronecker delta ($= 1$ if $i = k$; $= 0$ if $i \neq k$).
η	=	variable apparent viscosity in simple shearing flow.
η_0	=	limiting viscosity at small rates of shear.
τ	=	shear stress.
ω_{ik}	=	vorticity tensor component (equation (6)).

REFERENCES

[1]   J. G. OLDROYD, *Proc. Roy. Soc.*, **A218,** (1953), 122–132.
[2]   J. G. OLDROYD, *Proc. Roy. Soc.*, **A232,** (1955), 567–577.
[3]   J. G. OLDROYD, *Proc. Roy. Soc.*, **A245,** (1958), 278–297.
[4]   J. G. OLDROYD, *Proc. Roy. Soc.*, **A200,** (1950), 523–541.

DISCUSSION

D. R. Bland: The conoitions on the constans in equations [1] can be expressed more precisely. If

$$P(D) = 1 + \alpha_1 D + \alpha_2 D^2 + \cdots + \alpha_N D^N$$

and
$$Q^*(D) = \eta_0(1 + \beta_1 D + \beta_2 D^2 + \cdots + \beta_M D^M)$$

so that $P(D)\, T = Q^*\,(D)\, \gamma$, then the zeros of $P(D)$ and $Q^*\,(D)$ are all real, negative and distinct, the zeros of $P(D)$ interlace those of $Q^*\,(D)$ and the least zero (in absolute magnitude) is a zero of $P(D)$. If N and M are defined as the highest powers of D in $P(D)$ and $Q(D)$ with non-zero coefficients, then $M = N - 1$ or $M = N$. In the former case the liquid exhibits instantaneous elasticity, in the latter it does not.

H. Giesekus: Prof. Oldroyd mentions a simple example of an elastico-viscous liquid of type N. In connection with this there may be remembered a second very simple example too: If there is a Newtonian liquid obeying the equation of state

$$\overset{0}{p_{ik}}{}' = 2\eta_0 e_{ik},$$

in which N different kinds of particles are suspended or dissolved, so that the extra-stresses of the nth kind obey an equation of the Maxwell type:

$$\left(1 + \tau_n \frac{\mathscr{D}}{\mathscr{D}t}\right) p_{ik}^{n;} = 2\eta_0 c_n e_{ik}$$

with relaxation time τ_n and effective concentration c_n then this system represents an elastico-viscous liquid of type N.

In an earlier paper (cf.ref. [18] at the end of my paper in this volume). I have shown, that a suspension of so called soft-elastic dumbbells represents an elastico-viscous liquid of type $N = 1$, if one substitutes the contravariant convected derivative $\delta/\delta t$ (cf. Eq.(8) of my paper in this volume instead of $\mathscr{D}/\mathscr{D}t$. Therefore a suspension with N different kinds of soft-elastic dumbbells represents a generalized Oldroyd liquid B of type N. In such a case the stress-strain relation of the dumbbell springs is more complicated, the character of the suspension changes in direction to a liquid of the type treated above by Prof. Oldroyd: Shear viscosity will depend on γ^2 and if one takes into account hydrodyvamic interaction of the dumbbell spheres, normal stress in the direction of flow gradient takes also a finite value. This is dealt in my own paper in this volume.

A.B. METZNER: We have determined (and published) the normal stresses as well as the shearing stresses of molten polymers and have fitted the results to one of Oldroyd's equations. While the fit was good, extrapolation of the equation to new deformation rates yielded unrealistic predictions. Would Prof. Oldroyd comment on the probability of this being due to limitations of the theoretical equations as opposed to inadequate data?

J.G. OLDROYD'S REPLY: In reply to Dr. Metzner's question, it is quite likely that the theoretical equations used were sufficient to explain behaviour at fairly small rates of deformation, but not at larger rates. A *simple* set of rheological equations of state will usually be only approximate for any real liquid and must be expected to have limitations of this sort.

SIMPLE FLUIDS WITH FADING MEMORY

Berl\d

BERNARD D. COLEMAN

Mellon Institute, Pittsburgh, Pennsylvania, U.S.A.

AND

WALTER NOLL

Mathematics Department, Carnegie Institute of Technology,

Pittsburgh, Pennsylvania, U.S.A.

ABSTRACT

The definition of a simple fluid was introduced by one of the authors in 1958. It expresses a concept of fluidity more general than that expressed by most definitions of "non-Newtonian" fluids proposed previously. The theory of simple fluids is believed to cover almost all mechanical phenomena in real fluids including memory effects such as stress-relaxation.

This report summarizes the theory of simple fluids. The notion of fading memory is made precise with the use of function space concepts. A mathematical description of stress-relaxation is presented. It is indicated how the theory of Newtonian fluids and the memory theory of linear viscoelasticity result as appropriate first-order approximations to the theory of simple fluids with fading memory. More general approximations give rise to second and higher order analogues of Newtonian fluid theory and linear viscoelasticity.

Introduction.

In this paper we summarize some aspects of the mathematical theory of fluid behaviour we have developed during the last four years [1−3]. We first explain what we call a simple fluid with fading memory and then show how various classical linear theories of fluid and viscoelastic behaviour arise naturally as first-order approximations to our theory. In doing this we are able to describe the circumstances in which the classical theories can be expected to loose their physical applicability and are able to exhibit complete second-order extensions of the classical theories within the framework of our theory.

The intuitive notion of fluidity is vague enough to motivate different mathematical theories of hydrodynamics. The theory we outline here is sufficiently general to cover a wide range of mechanical phenomena, yet it is specific enough to have content. Our goal, however, has not been to just write down some kind of general constitutive equation and hope that its consequences agree with experiment, but rather to find that constitutive assumption which expresses, in mathematical language, the essence of certain intuitive prejudices about fluidity. It turns out that most of the nonclassical theories of fluids studied in the past may be reinterpreted to fall as special cases within the framework of our theory. Exceptions are Ericksen's theory of anisotropic fluids [4–7] and Truesdell's theory of Maxwellian fluids [8].

Our concept of a fluid furnishes a language in which one can describe, among others, the phenomena of "shear-dependent viscosity," "normal stress effects" and "gradual stress relaxation." Of course, no theory with content has total generality; every theory describes only certain aspects of nature. Our theory of fluids is purely mechanical, and among the mechanical phenomena not covered are surface tension and phase transitions.

In rough terms, the basic ideas behind our definition of a simple fluid with fading memory are these —

(a) *The concept of a simple material*: A simple material is a substance for which the present stress is determined by the history of the strain.

(b) The *concept of a fluid*: A fluid is a substance with the property that all local states with the same mass density are intrinsically equivalent in response, with all observable differences in response being due to definite differences in history.

(c) *The principle of fading memory*: Deformations which occurred in the distant past should have less effect on the present value of the stress than deformations which occurred in the recent past.

We call a material obeying (a) and (b) a *simple fluid*(¹); a material which also obeys (c) we call a *simple fluid with fading memory*.

In Part I we outline the mathematical formulation which makes the ideas (a), (b) and (c) precise. We point out that it is an immediate consequence of (a) and (b) that all simple fluids obey the

Basic constitutive assumption of classical hydrostatics: The stress on a fluid which has remained at rest at all times is a hydrostatic pressure depending only on the density.

(¹) The mathematical theory of general *incompressible* simple fluids is a manageable theory in which several hydrodynamical problems with physical applications can be solved; cf. references [9–12]. We do not discuss this work here.

When we add the fading memory principle (c), we can strengthen this observation and obtain

Gradual stress relaxation: Consider a fluid which until time 0 has been subjected to various deformations (which we need not specify) and suppose that for all times t greater than 0 the fluid is in a fixed configuration. Then, as $t \to \infty$ the stress in the fluid gradually decays to a hydrostatic pressure which depends only on the density.

In Part II we discuss the behaviour of simple fluids with fading memory in the limits of slow flow and small deformations. We present theorems showing the following —

Newtonian behaviour in slow motions: In the limit of very slow flows the stress in a fluid is approximately given by the constitutive equation of a linearly viscous fluid.

Linear viscoelastic behaviour in infinitesimal deformations: If the history of a fluid happens to be such that all the configurations the fluid experiences are infinitesimally close to each other, then the stress in the fluid is approximately given by Boltzmann's [13] classical theory of infinitesimal viscoelasticity (with the equilibrium shear modulus set equal to zero).

In Part II we also discuss second-order behaviour for slow motions and small deformations.

It should be emphasized that this article gives only an outline of our theory of constitutive equations of fluids. In order to enable the physicist to see the basic ideas and structure of the theory without becoming lost in a forest of symbolism, we have omitted proofs of nearly all our assertions.

On notation: Light-face latin majuscules, with the exception of *P*, denote tensors. The term *tensor* is used here as a synonym for linear transformation of a three-dimensional vector space. When a fixed Cartesian coordinate system in space is used, our tensors may be identified with matrices of Cartesian components.

PART I. BASIC CONCEPTS

1. Kinematical preliminaries.

Consider a material point *P* which occupies the position **x** in Euclidian space $\mathscr{E}$ when the body under consideration is in its reference configuration $\mathscr{C}$. Let $\xi(P,\tau)$ be the position of *P* in $\mathscr{E}$ at time τ; $\xi(P,\tau)$ can be regarded as a function of **x** and τ:

$$\xi(P,\tau) = \chi_{\mathscr{C}}(\mathbf{x},\tau). \tag{1.1}$$

The gradient of this function $\chi_\mathscr{C}$ with respect to $\mathbf{x}$,

$$F_\mathscr{C}(\tau) = \operatorname{grad}_\mathbf{x}\chi_\mathscr{C}(\mathbf{x},\tau), \tag{1.2}$$

is a tensor called the *deformation gradient* (for P) at time τ computed taking the configuration $\mathscr{C}$ as a reference. Of course, $F_\mathscr{C}(\tau)$ depends not only on the local configuration at P at time τ but also on the choice of the reference configuration $\mathscr{C}$.

It is sometimes convenient to use for the reference configuration the configuration at some particular time t. To do this we express $\xi(P,\tau)$ as a function of $\mathbf{x}$ and τ,

$$\xi(P,\tau) = \chi_t(\mathbf{x},\tau), \tag{1.3}$$

where $\mathbf{x}$ is now the position of P in $\mathscr{E}$ at time t:

$$\mathbf{x} = \xi(P,t). \tag{1.4}$$

The gradient of $\chi_t(\mathbf{x},\tau)$ with respect to $\mathbf{x}$,

$$F_t(\tau) = \operatorname{grad}_\mathbf{x}\chi_t(\mathbf{x},\tau), \tag{1.5}$$

is called the *relative deformation gradient* (for P) at time τ. It is a measure of the "strain" required to go from the configuration at time t to the configuration at time τ. In applications of the concept of a relative deformation gradient, t is usually interpreted as the present time and τ as a past time ($\tau \leqq t$).

Let $F_t^T(\tau)$ denote the transpose of $F_t(\tau)$. The tensor $C_t(\tau)$ defined as

$$C_t(\tau) = F_t^T(\tau)F_t(\tau) \tag{1.6}$$

is called the *relative right Cauchy-Green tensor* (for P) at time τ. By definition, $C_t(\tau)$ is a symmetric tensor,

Let us put $\tau = t - s$, $0 \leqq s < \infty$, and consider the function $G(\ )$ defined as follows:

$$G(s) = C_t(t - s) - I, \tag{1.7}$$

where I is the unit tensor. This function $G(\ )$, which is most important to the theory of simple fluids, may be called the *reduced history*. (Of course,

$G(\ )$ depends on P and t, but to simplify notation we do not make this dependence explicit.)

It follows from (1.5)–(1.7) that

$$C_t(t) = F_t(t) = I \tag{1.8a}$$

and hence that

$$G(0) = 0. \tag{1.8b}$$

If at all past times the configuration at a material point has been the same as the configuration at the present time, then

$$G(\ ) = 0(\ ), \tag{1.9a}$$

where $0(\ )$ is a function whose value for each s is the zero tensor

$$0(s) = 0, \qquad 0 \leq s < \infty. \tag{1.9b}$$

We call $0(\ )$ the *zero function*.

The n'th order derivative of $G(s)$ at $s = 0$ determines the n'th Rivlin-Ericksen tensor [14] A_n as follows:

$$A_n = (-1)^n \left. \frac{d^n\, G(s)}{ds^n} \right|_{s=0}. \tag{1.10}$$

The tensor

$$D = \tfrac{1}{2}A_1 \tag{1.11}$$

is called the *stretching tensor*; it can be shown to be equal to the symmetric part of the velocity gradient tensor.

2. Simple fluids.

We say that the material at P is *simple* if the present stress $S(t)$ on P is determined when $F_{\mathscr{C}}(\tau)$ at P is prescribed for all times τ earlier that t. In symbols,

$$S(t) = \mathop{\mathscr{S}_{\mathscr{C}}}\limits_{\tau = -\infty}^{t} (F_{\mathscr{C}}(\tau)). \tag{2.1}$$

This operator $\mathscr{S}_{\mathscr{C}}$, which maps the functions $F_{\mathscr{C}}(\ )$ into the tensors $S(t)$, is called a functional. Of course, $\mathscr{S}_{\mathscr{C}}$ need not be a linear operator. Since for a given motion $F_{\mathscr{C}}(\ )$ depends on the choice of the reference configuration $\mathscr{C}$, it is clear that the form of $\mathscr{S}_{\mathscr{C}}$ must also depend on the choice of $\mathscr{C}$. (We shall not here go into a detailed discussion of the dependence of $\mathscr{S}_{\mathscr{C}}$ on $\mathscr{C}$, nor shall we discuss the identities which $\mathscr{S}_{\mathscr{C}}$ must obey to be compatible with our intuitive ideas that the behaviour of a body should be independent of the observer.)

We say that the material at P is a *simple fluid* if the form of $\mathscr{S}_{\mathscr{C}}$ in (2.1) remains invariant under all changes of the reference configuration $\mathscr{C}$ which preserve the mass density of $\mathscr{C}$ at P.

In other words, a simple fluid, as defined here, has no intrinsic preference for a particular configuration out of a class of configurations of equal volume. Furthermore, since the group of all those changes of the reference configuration which preserve density includes the group of all rotations of the reference configuration, it follows that a simple fluid has no intrinsically preferred directions.

The following basic theorem is proved in reference [1].

Theorem characterizing simple fluids: The material at P is a simple fluid if and only if the present stress S on P is determined by the history of the motion through an equation of the form

$$S = \overset{\infty}{\underset{s=0}{\mathscr{H}}} (G(s);\rho). \tag{2.2}$$

Here, the operator $\mathscr{H}$ is a functional which has for its argument the reduced history $G(\ )$ [see (1.5)—(1.7)] and which is labelled by a real number ρ to be interpreted as the present value of the density; $\mathscr{H}$ obeys the following relation for each function $G(\ )$ and for all constant orthogonal tensors Q:

$$Q\overset{\infty}{\underset{s=0}{\mathscr{H}}} (G(s);\rho)Q^{T} = \overset{\infty}{\underset{s=0}{\mathscr{H}}} (QG(s)Q^{T};\rho). \tag{2.3}$$

In reading equation (2.2) it should be borne in mind that the function $G(\ )$, the number ρ, and the tensor S will depend, in general, on the time t and the point P under consideration. The form of the functional $\mathscr{H}$ depends only on P.

A corollary to the above theorem is the following observation [1,11] which justifies the basic constitutive assumption of hydrostatics.

Theorem on simple fluids always at rest: If $G(\ )$ happens to be the zero function of (1.9), then S is a hydrostatic pressure $-pI$, where p depends only on ρ.

In symbols, this theorem states

$$\mathop{\mathscr{H}}_{s=0}^{\infty}(0(s);\rho) = -p(\rho)I. \qquad (2.4)$$

3. Fading memory.

Let us use the functional $\mathscr{H}$ of (2.2) to define a new functional $\mathscr{F}$ as follows

$$\mathop{\mathscr{F}}_{s=0}^{\infty}(G(s);\rho) = \mathop{\mathscr{H}}_{s=0}^{\infty}(G(s);\rho) - \mathop{\mathscr{H}}_{s=0}^{\infty}(0(s);\rho). \qquad (3.1)$$

It follows from (2.3) that $\mathscr{F}$ must obey the identity

$$Q\mathop{\mathscr{F}}_{s=0}^{\infty}(G(s);\rho)Q^T = \mathop{\mathscr{F}}_{s=0}^{\infty}(QG(s)Q^T;\rho), \qquad (3.2)$$

for each function $G(\ )$ and for all constant orthogonal tensors Q. It follows directly from the definition (3.1) that

$$\mathop{\mathscr{F}}_{s=0}^{\infty}(0(s);\rho) = 0; \qquad (3.3)$$

i.e., for each ρ the value of $\mathscr{F}$ at the zero function $0(\ )$ is the zero tensor 0.

Using (3.1), (2.2) and (2.4) we see that

$$S = -p(\rho)I + \mathop{\mathscr{F}}_{s=0}^{\infty}(G(s);\rho), \qquad (3.4a)$$

where

$$-p(\rho)I = \mathop{\mathscr{H}}_{s=0}^{\infty}(0(s);\rho). \qquad (3.4b)$$

In other words, the value of the functional $\mathscr{F}$ is the extra stress, i.e. the difference between the present stress on a point and the stress which the point would be supporting had the point been in its present configuration at all times in the past.

The mathematical embodiment of the intuitive notion of fading memory appears to us to rest on the following two ideas:

(1) That into the function space of all reduced histories $G(\ )$ there should be introduced a *norm* (or magnitude) $\| G(\ ) \|$ which should be interpretable as the "distance" of a given reduced history $G(\ )$ from the zero function $0(\ )$. This norm should have the property that in the calculation of $\| G(\ ) \|$ greater emphasis be placed on the values $G(s)$ for small s (recent past) than on the values for very large s (distant past).

(2) That with respect to this norm $\| G(\ ) \|$ the functional $\mathscr{F}$ should be smooth in some sense. For example, one could assume that as the norm of $G(\ )$ approaches zero, the values $\overset{\infty}{\underset{s=0}{\mathscr{F}}}(G(s);\rho)$ approach the zero tensor uniformly in ρ and with an error term that is approximately linear in $G(\ )$.

We can achieve the requirements laid down in (1), above, by defining the norm $\| G(\ ) \|$ as follows([2])

$$\| G(\ ) \| = \left[\int_0^\infty tr\{G^2(s)\}h^2(s)ds \right]^{1/2}. \tag{3.5}$$

Here, $tr\,G^2(s)$ indicates the trace of $G(s)G(s)$, and h, called an *influence function*, is a positive, continuous, real-valued function which goes to zero rapidly as $s \to \infty$. For the validity of most of the propositions to be quoted here, it is not necessary to specify the form of $h(s)$. It suffices to assume that, for large s, $h(s)$ approaches zero monotonically and faster than $s^{-3/2}$. We shall suppose that some such function h has been selected and inserted into (3.5). The set $\mathfrak{H}$ of functions $G(\ )$ for which the norm (3.5) is finite forms a Hilbert space. Henceforth, whenever we consider reduced histories $G(\ )$, we shall assume that they are in $\mathfrak{H}$. We note that in this Hilbert space the norm of $0(\ )$ is zero, and the statement that a relative history $G(\ )$ is "small in norm" can be interpreted as meaning that $G(\ )$ is "close to" $0(\ )$.

Let $\mathscr{G}$ be a tensor-valued functional defined over our Hilbert space $\mathfrak{H}$. We say that $\mathscr{G}$ possesses a *Fréchet derivative* at the function $B(\ )$ if there exists

---

([2]) This definition, coinciding with that used in reference [3], corresponds to the choice $p=2$ in the notation of reference [2]. The L_2 (i.e. Hilbert space) norm is now preferred by us over the one which we discussed in detail in reference [11]. We remark that it follows from the results proved in reference [2] that all the theorems of reference [11] are also valid in our present Hilbert space.

a functional $\delta\mathscr{G}$ such that the following equation holds for all functions $G(\ )$ in $\mathfrak{H}$:

$$\overset{\infty}{\underset{s=0}{\mathscr{G}}} (B(s) + G(s)) = \overset{\infty}{\underset{s=0}{\mathscr{G}}} (B(s)) + \delta\overset{\infty}{\underset{s=0}{\mathscr{G}}} (B(s); G(s)) + o(\|G(\ )\|), \quad (3.6a)$$

where $\delta\overset{\infty}{\underset{s=0}{\mathscr{G}}} (B(s); G(s))$ is both *linear* and *continuous* (i.e. bounded) in $G(\ )$, and where $o(\|G(\ )\|)$ goes to zero faster than the norm of $G(\ )$, i.e.

$$\lim_{\|G(\ )\| \to 0} \frac{o(\|G(\ )\|)}{\|G(\ )\|} = 0. \quad (3.6b)$$

In words, $\mathscr{G}$ has a Fréchet derivative at $B(\ )$ if the difference between the values of $\mathscr{G}$ at $B(\ )$ and $B(\ ) + G(\ )$ is given to a good approximation by a continuous, linear functional of $G(\ )$ whenever $G(\ )$ is small in norm.

We can, of course, go on and ask whether $\delta\mathscr{G}$, regarded as a functional of its first variable, has a Fréchet derivative $\delta^2\mathscr{G}$ at $B(\ )$, for each choice of $G(\ )$. If the answer is yes, and if $\delta^2\mathscr{G}$ meets certain technical requirements of joint continuity, then we say that $\mathscr{G}$ has a *Fréchet derivative of order two* at $B(\ )$. One can similarly define Fréchet derivatives of any finite order.

We say that a functional, such as our $\mathscr{F}$ defined in (3.1), is a *memory functional of order n* if $\mathscr{F}$ vanishes at the zero history $0(\ )$, i.e. obeys (3.3), and if $\mathscr{F}$ has a Fréchet derivative of order n at $0(\ )$. Formally, $\mathscr{F}$ is a memory functional of order n if $\mathscr{F}$ obeys the following relation for all $G(\ )$

$$\overset{\infty}{\underset{s=0}{\mathscr{F}}} (G(s); \rho) = \sum_{k=1}^{n} \frac{1}{k!} \delta^k \overset{\infty}{\underset{s=0}{\mathscr{F}}} (G(s); \rho) + o(\|G(\ )\|^n; \rho) \quad (3.7a)(^3)$$

where

$$\lim_{\|G(\ )\| \to 0} \frac{o(\|G(\ )\|^n; \rho)}{\|G(\ )\|^n} = 0, \quad (3.7b)$$

_____

(^{3}) This definition still is meaningful for $n = 0$, in which case it says that $\mathscr{F}$ is a memory functional of order zero if $\mathscr{F}$ obeys (3.3) and is continuous at $0(\ )$.

and $\delta^k \mathscr{F}$, the k'th order Fréchet differential of $\mathscr{F}$ at $0(\ )$, is a bounded homogeneous polynomial functional of degree k.[4]

We believe that the appropriate way to incorporate the idea (2) into the mathematization of the notion of fading memory is to assume that the functional $\mathscr{F}$ is a memory functional of some finite order n. For all the propositions to be stated here it is sufficient that $n = 2$.[5]

Therefore, we say that a simple fluid is a *simple fluid with fading memory* if, with respect to our Hilbert space norm (3.5), the functional $\mathscr{F}$ defined in (3.1) is a memory functional of order n, where $n \geq 2$.

Given any reduced history $G(\ )$ in $\mathfrak{H}$ and a positive number γ, we can define a function $G_{(\gamma)}(\ )$ as follows:

$$G_{(\gamma)}(s) = \begin{cases} 0, & 0 \leq s < \gamma \\ G(s - \gamma), & s > \gamma. \end{cases} \tag{3.8}$$

We call $G_{(\gamma)}(\ )$ the *statical extension* of $G(\ )$ by the amount γ. It has the following physical meaning. If $G(\ )$ is the reduced history of a material point P up to the time t, $G_{(\gamma)}(\ )$ is the reduced history of P up to time $t + \gamma$ assuming that for all times between t and $t + \gamma$ P is held at rest, i.e. held fixed in the configuration it had at time t. Now, if $\mathrm{tr}G^2(s)$ remains bounded, it follows from (3.5) that

$$\lim_{\gamma \to \infty} \| G_{(\gamma)}(\ ) \| = \lim_{\gamma \to \infty} \| G_{(\gamma)}(\ ) - 0(\ ) \| = 0; \tag{3.9}$$

that is, for every bounded $G(\ )$, $G_{(\gamma)}(\ )$ approaches $0(\ )$ in $\mathfrak{H}$ as γ increases. Since

---

[4] By this we mean that there must exist a completely symmetric, jointly continuous, multilinear, functional $\delta^k \underset{s=0}{\overset{\infty}{\mathscr{F}}} (G_1(s)\ldots G_k(s);\sigma)$ of k function variables $G_1(\ )\ldots G_k(\ )$ such that $\delta^k \underset{s=0}{\overset{\infty}{\mathscr{F}}} (G(s);\rho)$ has the same value as $\delta^k \underset{s=0}{\overset{\infty}{\mathscr{F}}} (G_1(s) \ldots G_k(s);\rho)$ whenever the $G_i(\ )$ are all equal to $G(\ )$.

[5] As the reader might expect, the presence of ρ in the definition (3.1) requires that certain natural, but uninteresting, assumptions concerning smoothness and uniformity in ρ must be added to the definition of a memory functional in order to prove limit theorems for infinitesimal deformations such as our Theorem on Infinitesimal Viscoelastic Behavior of Section 5. (Our other theorems do not require such assumptions.) We shall not go into details on these matters except to mention that for the theorem just mentioned it suffices to grant that $p(\rho)$ of (3.4b) be continuously differentiable in ρ and that the convergence shown in (3.7b) be uniform in ρ. Of course, these particular mathematical technicalities do not arise in the case of an incompressible fluid.

a memory functional of any order n, $n \geq 0$, is continuous at the zero function, we have, by (3.3), the following result

$$\lim_{\gamma \to \infty} \underset{s=0}{\overset{\infty}{\mathscr{F}}} (G_{(\gamma)}(s);\rho) = \underset{s=0}{\overset{\infty}{\mathscr{F}}} (0(s);\rho) = 0, \qquad (3.10)$$

and on combining this with (3.4a) we get a

Theorem on stress relaxation: Let $G(\ )$ be a bounded history; let $G_{(\gamma)}(\ )$ be the statical continuation of $G(\ )$ by an amount γ; and let $S_{(\gamma)}$ be the stress corresponding to $G_{(\gamma)}(\ )$. Then

$$\lim_{\gamma \to \infty} S_{(\gamma)} = - p(\rho)I \qquad (3.11)$$

where $- p(\rho)I$ is given by (3.4b). We note that (3.11) holds also for unbounded histories $G(\ )$ in $\mathfrak{H}$ if the influence function decays exponentially.

This proposition tells us that for a simple fluid with fading memory, no matter what the previous history of a material point has been, if we hold the point in a fixed configuration the stress on it will eventually decay to a hydrostatic pressure which depends on only the density. In other words, the stress on a fluid which has been at rest a long time is approximately the same as the stress on a fluid which has been at rest forever.

PART II. APPLICATIONS

4. Slow motions.

We have just seen that the stress in a fluid which has been at rest a long time is approximately given by the constitutive equation of a perfect fluid:

$$S = - p(\rho)I. \qquad (4.1)$$

The theory of Newtonian fluids is based on the following constitutive equation for the stress:

$$S = - pI + (\lambda \operatorname{tr} D)I + 2\eta D; \qquad (4.2)$$

here D is the stretching tensor; p, η and λ are functions of ρ alone; η and λ are called *coefficients of viscosity*. When a fluid is at rest we have $D = 0$

and (4.2) reduces to (4.1). Thus, the significance of p in (4.2) is clear; p is the hydrostatic pressure the fluid would be supporting if it were at rest at its present density.

It is clear that all materials obeying (4.2) are simple fluids. Furthermore it can be shown, using the isotropy condition (2.3), that (4.2) holds for any simple fluid for which the stress depends only on ρ and the velocity gradient, with a linear dependence on the latter.[6]

For some substances, such as water, the theory of Newtonian fluids accounts remarkably well for experimental measurements over a very wide range of conditions. Other substances, such as molten polymers and polymer solutions, definitely do not obey (4.2) exactly. However, our intuition and many rheological measurements suggest that the theory of Newtonian fluids should approximate the behavior of nearly all real fluids in the limit of slow motions. To show how this observation is in accord with the general theory of simple fluids with fading memory we must make precise what we mean by a "slow motion." We do this in the following way.

Let a reduced history $G(\ )$ be given. We say that $G^{(\alpha)}(\ )$ is a *retardation of* $G(\ )$ if

$$G^{(\alpha)}(s) = G(\alpha s), \quad 0 \leq s < \infty, \tag{4.3a}$$

where the *retardation factor* α is a number in the range.

$$0 < \alpha < 1. \tag{4.3b}$$

In rough language $G^{(\alpha)}(\ )$ corresponds to a kinematical history "essentially the same" as that which gives rise to $G(\ )$, with the exception that the new history "has been carried out at a slower rate."

Let D be the stretching tensor and A_n the n'th Rivlin-Ericksen tensor associated with $G(\ )$, and let $D^{(\alpha)}$ and $A_n^{(\alpha)}$ be the corresponding tensors for $G^{(\alpha)}(\ )$. By (1.10), (1.11) and (4.3), we have

$$D^{(\alpha)} = \alpha D, \quad A_n^{(\alpha)} = \alpha^n A_n. \tag{4.4}$$

The following theorem, holding for all simple fluids with fading memory, shows that the theory of Newtonian fluids does indeed furnish a complete

---

[6] In essence this was first shown by Stokes; it is in fact an immediate consequence of the now famous representation theorem for isotropic tensor functions of one tensor variable. For a recent direct proof see reference [15], Sec. 59.

first-order correction to the theory of perfect fluids in the limit of slow motions (i.e. small α).[7]

Theorem on Newtonian behavior: Let $G(\ )$ be an arbitrary reduced history, differentiable at $s = 0$; let $G^{(\alpha)}(\ )$ be a retardation of $G(\ )$ and let $S^{(\alpha)}$ be the stress corresponding to $G^{(\alpha)}(\ )$. Then

$$S^{(\alpha)} = -pI + (\lambda \operatorname{tr} D^{(\alpha)})I + 2\eta D^{(\alpha)} + o(\alpha), \tag{4.5a}$$

where p, λ, η depend only on the present value of the density, ρ, [p being given of course, by (2.4)] and $o(\alpha)$ is such that

$$\lim_{\alpha \to 0} \frac{o(\alpha)}{\alpha} = 0. \tag{4.5b}$$

Essentially the same argument as is used to prove this theorem can be used to find complete approximations of order n in α to $S^{(\alpha)}$. The approximations increase in complexity and therefore diminish in usefulness as n gets large, but yet the approximation of order two is not without interest for it shows us the nature of the first corrections to be made upon the breakdown of Newtonian behavior. The complete second-order approximation is

$$S^{(\alpha)} = -pI + \left[\frac{\lambda}{2} \operatorname{tr} A_1^{(\alpha)}\right] I + \eta A_1^{(\alpha)} +$$
$$+ \left[\mu_1 \operatorname{tr} (A_1^{(\alpha)})^2 + \mu_2 (\operatorname{tr} A_1^{(\alpha)})^2 + \mu_3 \operatorname{tr} A_2^{(\alpha)}\right] I + \tag{4.6a}$$
$$+ \left[\mu_4 \operatorname{tr} A_1^{(\alpha)}\right] A_1^{(\alpha)} + \mu_5 (A_1^{(\alpha)})^2 + \mu_6 A_2^{(\alpha)} + o(\alpha^2),$$

where $o(\alpha^2)$ goes to zero faster than α^2, i.e.

$$\lim_{\alpha \to 0} \frac{o(\alpha^2)}{\alpha^2} = 0. \tag{4.6b}$$

Here, p and the μ_i are functions of ρ alone. The first term, $-pI$, is of order zero in α; the terms in λ and η are of order one in α; the terms in the μ_i are of order two in α. Noting that $A_1^{(\alpha)} = 2D^{(\alpha)}$, we see that the first three terms of (4.5a) and (4.6a) are the same.

---

[7] For the proof, which is not trivial, we refer to reference [2].

It follows from (4.6) that in the case of a steady simple shearing flow, to within terms of order two in α, there is still proportionality between the shearing stress and rate of shear although nonlinear normal stress effects do already appear. For such a flow terms reflecting a nonlinear dependerce of shearing stress on rate of shear first appear when one examines terms of order three in α.

It is to be emphasized that the approximations (4.5) and (4.6) both hold for the retardation of an *arbitrary* reduced history $G(\ )$ in our Hilbert space $\mathfrak{H}$, provided, of course, that $dG(s)/ds$ and $d^2G(s)/d^2s$ exist at $s = 0$, so that A_1 and A_2 have meaning. (Actually, even this differentiability at $s = 0$ can be relaxed by working with generalized derivatives.) For $s \neq 0$, $G(s)$ need not even be continuous.

5. Finite linear viscoelasticity.

If we specialize the fading memory assumption (3.7a) to the case $n = 1$ and insert it in (3.4a) we have

$$S = - p(\rho)I + \delta\mathscr{F} \underset{s=0}{\overset{\infty}{}}(G(s);\rho) + o(\| G(\ )\| ;\rho), \tag{5.1}$$

Now, $\delta\mathscr{F}$ is a continuous linear functional and $o(\| G(\ )\| ;\rho)$ approaches the zero tensor *faster* than $\| G(\ )\|$. It therefore follows that $o(\| G(\ )\|;\rho)$ is small in comparison to $\delta\mathscr{F} \underset{s=0}{\overset{\infty}{}}(G(s);\rho)$ whenever $G(\ )$ has a small Hilbert space norm. Thus, in the limit

$$\| G(s) \| \to 0, \tag{5.2}$$

the equation

$$S = - p(\rho)I + \delta\mathscr{F} \underset{s=0}{\overset{\infty}{}}(G(s);\rho) \tag{5.3}$$

approximates the general constitutive equation of a simple fluid with fading memory and with an error that approaches zero faster than $\| G(\ )\|$.

We call the theory based on constitutive equations of the form (5.3) *finite linear viscoelasticity of fluids*. We shall later discuss kinematical situations in which such a theory can be expected to approximate the theory of simple fluids with fading memory, but first let us use equation (3.2) and the continuity of $\delta\mathscr{F}$ to simplify (5.3).

There is a theorem to the effect that any bounded linear functional over a Hilbert space of functions may be written as an inner product, i.e. an integral transform. Applying this theorem to $\delta\mathscr{F}$ we get

$$\delta\,\mathscr{F}\,(G(s);\rho) \;=\; \int_{0}^{\infty} \Gamma\,(s,\rho)\,\{G(s)\}\,ds\,, \tag{5.4}$$

where $\Gamma(s,\rho)\{\ \}$, for each s and each ρ, is a linear transformation of the space of symmetric tensors into itself. ($\Gamma(s,\rho)\{\ \}$ may be regarded as a fourth-order tensor.) It is a consequence of (3.2) that, for each s and ρ, $\Gamma(s,\rho)\{\ \}$ must be an isotropic transformation; i.e. the identity

$$Q[\Gamma(s,\rho)\{G\}]Q^{T} = \Gamma(s,\rho)\{QGQ^{T}\} \tag{5.5}$$

must hold for all orthogonal tensors Q and all symmetric tensors G. The representation theorem for such isotropic transformations states that $\Gamma(s,\rho)\{G(s)\}$ must be of the form

$$\Gamma(s,\rho)\{G(s)\} = m(s,\rho)G(s) + l(s,\rho)[\text{tr } G(s)]I \tag{5.6}$$

where $m(s,\rho)$ and $l(s,\rho)$ are scalar functions of the time lapse s and the present density ρ.

It turns out that once we know that (5.6) holds it follows from the assumed continuity of $\delta\mathscr{F}$ that

$$\int_{0}^{\infty} m^{2}(s,\rho)h^{-2}(s)ds,$$

and

$$\int_{0}^{\infty} l^{2}(s,\rho)h^{-2}(s)ds$$

are finite.

On combining (5.6), (5.4) and (5.3) we find that the constitutive equation of finite linear viscoelasticity for fluids has the form [3]

$$S = -\,p(\rho)I + \int_{0}^{\infty} m(s,\rho)G(s)ds + \left[\int_{0}^{\infty} l(s,\rho)\ \text{tr } G(s)ds\right]I. \tag{5.7}$$

Now let us consider cases in which (5.7) should be useful; i.e. cases in which $\| G(\ ) \|$ is small.

Our intuition suggests that one such case should arise when the motion is such that all the "strains" experienced by the material point are "infinitesimal." One way to define what we mean by "infinitesimal strains" is to pick a reference configuration $\mathscr{C}$ and to put

$$H_{\mathscr{C}}(\tau) = F_{\mathscr{C}}(\tau) - I, \qquad (5.8a)$$

$$\varepsilon = \sup_{-\infty < \tau < \infty} \sqrt{\text{tr} \left[H_{\mathscr{C}}(\tau) H_{\mathscr{C}}^T(\tau) \right]}, \qquad (5.8b)$$

and to say that the *strain relative to* $\mathscr{C}$ *is always infinitesimal if*

$$\varepsilon \ll 1. \qquad (5.9)$$

We note that the *displacement gradient* tensor $H_{\mathscr{C}}$ which we introduced in (5.8a) has the property that its symmetric part is the familiar *infinitesimal strain tensor* $E_{\mathscr{C}}$:

$$E_{\mathscr{C}} = \frac{1}{2} \left[H_{\mathscr{C}} + H_{\mathscr{C}}^T \right]. \qquad (5.10)$$

Now it can be proved that once $\mathscr{C}$ is fixed it is true for each t that $G(s)$ (depending implicitly on t) is given by

$$G(s) = E_{\mathscr{C}}(t - s) - E_{\mathscr{C}}(t) + O(\varepsilon^2, s) \qquad (5.11a)$$

$$= O(\varepsilon, s) \qquad (5.11b)$$

where $O(\varepsilon^n, s)$ here indicates an unspecified tensor-valued function of ε and s with the property that $O(\varepsilon^n, s)/\varepsilon^n$ is uniformly bounded. It follows from (5.11b) that, when ε approaches zero, $\| G(\ ) \|$ approaches zero at least as fast as ε. Thus, when (5.9) holds, (5.7) should give a good approximation for the stress. It is interesting to note, however, that it follows from (5.11a) that when (5.6) holds, the equation (5.7) is approximated, to within terms of order one in ε, by the equation[8]

$$S(t) = -p(\rho_{\mathscr{C}})I + \mathop{\mathscr{I}}_{s=0}^{\infty} (E_{\mathscr{C}}(t - s); \ \mathscr{C}). \qquad (5.12a)$$

---

[8] This is a consequence of the analysis outlined in reference [3].

Here $\rho_{\mathscr{C}}$ is the density of the reference configuration $\mathscr{C}$, $-p(\rho_{\mathscr{C}})$ is the equilibrium hydrostatic pressure corresponding to $\mathscr{C}$; and $\mathscr{I}_{\mathscr{C}}$ is the following linear functional of the history of $E_{\mathscr{C}}$:

$$\mathop{\mathscr{I}}_{s=0}^{\infty}(E_{\mathscr{C}}(t-s);\rho_{\mathscr{C}}) = 2\mu(0,\rho_{\mathscr{C}})\,E_{\mathscr{C}}(t) + 2\int_0^\infty E_{\mathscr{C}}(t-s)\,\frac{\partial\mu(s,\rho_{\mathscr{C}})}{\partial s}ds +$$

$$+ \operatorname{tr}\left\{\lambda(0,\rho_{\mathscr{C}})\,E_{\mathscr{C}}(t) + \int_0^\infty E_{\mathscr{C}}(t-s)\,\frac{\partial\lambda(s,\rho_{\mathscr{C}})}{\partial s}ds\right\}I; \qquad (5.12b)$$

$\mu(s,\rho)$ and $\lambda(s,\rho)$ are related to $m(s,\rho)$, $l(s,\rho)$ and $p(\rho)$ of (5.7) by the equations

$$\mu(s,\rho) = -\int_s^\infty m(\sigma,\rho)d\sigma \quad \lambda(s,\rho) = -2\int_s^\infty l(\sigma,\rho)d\sigma + \rho\,\frac{dp(\rho)}{d\rho}. \qquad (5.12c)$$

The functions λ and μ may be regarded as time-dependent Lamé coefficients for the response to a step-function history.[9] It can be shown that for each ρ

$$\lim_{s\to\infty}\mu(s,\rho) = 0, \quad \lim_{s\to\infty}\lambda(s,\rho) = \lim_{s\to\infty}\left(\lambda(s,\rho) + \frac{2}{3}\mu(s,\rho)\right) = \rho\,\frac{dp(\rho)}{dp}; \qquad (5.12d)$$

$\rho\,dp(\rho)/d\rho$ is just the equilibrium modulus of compression.

The equations (5.12) give the same expression for the stress as Boltzmann's original theory of infinitesimal viscoelasticity [15] when that theory is specialized to the case of zero equilibrium shear modulus.

We have the following

Theorem on infinitesimal viscoelastic behavior: The stress in a simple fluid with fading memory is given by an equation of the form

$$S(t) = -p(\rho_{\mathscr{C}})I + \mathop{\mathscr{I}}_{s=0}^{\infty}(E_{\mathscr{C}}(t-s);\rho_{\mathscr{C}}) + o(\varepsilon) \qquad (5.13a)$$

where $\mathscr{C}$ is an arbitrary fixed reference configuration; $\rho_{\mathscr{C}}$ is the density corresponding to $\mathscr{C}$; $E_{\mathscr{C}}$ and ε are defined by (5.8) and (5.10); $\mathscr{I}$ is the

---

[9] In other words, in a stress relaxation experiment in which a previously resting fluid is suddenly deformed at $t = 0$ and then held in a fixed configuration, $\mu(t,\rho)$ is the apparent shear modulus and $\lambda(t,\rho) + 2/3\mu(t,\rho)$ is the apparent modulus of compression at time t; $\mu(0,\rho)$ and $(\lambda(0,\rho) + 2/3\,\mu(0,\rho)$ give these moduli for the instantaneous response.

linear functional defined in (5.12b) and having the property (5.12d); and $o(\varepsilon)$ is such that

$$\lim_{\varepsilon \to 0} \frac{o(\varepsilon)}{\varepsilon} = 0. \tag{5.13b}$$

It should be emphasized that this theorem not only justifies certain applications of the theory of infinitesimal viscoelasticity but also suggests when that theory should break down: from the point of view of the general theory of simple fluids with fading memory, (5.12b) should be expected to give a useful constitutive equation for the stress only when (5.9) holds.

Fortunately, however, when we consider the definition (3.5) we see that we can make $\| G(\ ) \|$ small without confining ourselves to kinematical situations in which (5.9) holds. Thus, we expect the theory of *finite linear viscoelasticity* [equation (5.7)] to be useful in many circumstances in which the theory of *infinitesimal viscoelasticity* [equation (5.12b)] fails to be applicable.

To elaborate on this point, we note that it follows from (3.5) that in order for $\| G(\ ) \|$ to be small it is not necessary that the magnitude of $G(s)$ be small for all s but only that $G(s)$ be small in magnitude for small s (recent past). Now, since $G(0) = 0$, $\| G(\ ) \|$ will be small, for example, in a slow motion. More precisely, if $G(\ )$ is any function in the space $\mathfrak{H}$ which is continuous at $s = 0$; i.e. if

$$\lim_{s \to 0} G(s) = 0 \tag{5.14}$$

and if $G^{(\alpha)}(\ )$ denotes a retardation of $G(\ )$, then[10]

$$\lim_{\alpha \to 0} \| G^{(\alpha)}(\ ) \| = 0. \tag{5.15}$$

It follows from (5.15) that (5.7) will give a good approximation for $S^{(\alpha)}$ when α is small. In this case of slow motion, however, it follows from our theorem on Newtonian behavior that (5.7) will itself be well approximated by the equation of a Newtonian fluid, (4.2).

Another circumstance in which the theory of finite linear viscoelasticity holds is found by considering (3.8) and (3.9). It follows from those equations,

---

[10] Equation (5.15) is a consequence of Theorem 1 of reference [2].

and our present discussion, that if we consider a material point P which has a bounded past history up to time $t = 0$ and if we hold P in a fixed configuration for all $t > 0$, then for t sufficiently large (5.7) should give a good approximation for the stress on P. In other words, if we restrict our attention to times after the deformation has ceased for a while, then (5.7) can be applied to any stress relaxation experiment to predict the rate of decay of stress. This is true even in the case of large deformations or the sudden stopping of a fast steady flow. (If the motion is never fast, then, of course, (5.7) will be applicable also while the fluid is being deformed).

It is most interesting to note that although the theory of finite linear viscoelasticity has a greater range of physical applicability than the theory of infinitesimal linear viscoelasticity, the behavior of a fluid in the finite theory involves only those three material functions which occur in the infinitesimal theory, namely, $p(\rho)$, $\mu(s,\rho)$ and $\lambda(s,\rho)$. Experimenters can use this fact to predict certain finite strain and steady flow behavior from infinitesimal behavior, as, for example, in the stress relaxation experiments mentioned above.

If one applies (5.7) to a steady simple shearing flow and calculates the ratio of the shearing stress S_{xy} to the rate of shear K, it is found that this ratio η is independent of κ and is given by

$$\frac{S_{xy}}{\kappa} = \eta = \int_0^\infty sm(s,\rho)ds = - \int_0^\infty s\frac{\partial\mu(s,\rho)}{\partial s}ds. \qquad (5.16)$$

Of course, if the motion becomes too fast (5.7) and hence (5.16) no longer apply, and S_{xy}/κ ceases to be a constant. For a given fluid the η of (5.16) is the same as the η of (4.5a).

Remarks on measures of strain: The reduced history $G(\ )$ occuring in (5.7) was defined [see (1.7)] to be essentially the history of the relative right Cauchy-Green tensor C_t:

$$G(s) = C_t(s) - I \qquad (5.17)$$

Instead of using (5.17), we could have defined $G(\ )$ by

$$G(s) = C_t^{\frac{1}{2}}(s) - I, \qquad (5.18)$$

where $C_t^{\frac{1}{2}}$, the positive definite square root of C_t, is a tensor called the *relative right stretch tensor* and is just as "natural" a measure of strain as C_t. We could also have used the definition

$$G(s) = C_t^{-1}(s) - I; \tag{5.19}$$

in fact, any tensor function $A(\ )$ related to $C_t(\ )$ by a smooth one-to-one transformation and having the property $A(0) = I$ could be used to replace $C_t(\ )$ in (5.17). The different choices of the measure of strain yield the same theory of infinitesimal linear viscoelasticity but yield different theories of finite linear viscoelasticity. The difference of the stresses computed using two different finite linear theories is, however, of order greater than one in $\| G(\ ) \|$. Hence, since any finite linear theory can be expected to be accurate only when terms of order greater than one in $\| G(\ ) \|$ can be neglected, we can say that the various theories corresponding to the various measures of strain are equivalent.

On the basis of a molecular model for certain incompressible fluids, Lodge[16] has derived a constitutive equation corresponding to (5.7)([11]) when $G(s)$ is defined in accordance with (5.19). Our analysis shows that any other molecular model for a fluid compatible with our concept of fading memory must give the same result to within terms of order one in $\| G(\ ) \|$.

Normal stress differences for steady simple shearing flow are of order two in $\| G(\ ) \|$. Hence, though the theories of finite linear viscoelasticity predict normal stress effects, the predictions of these theories should not be taken seriously. For reliable results on normal stress differences in steady shearing flows, one must turn to an expression such as (4.6) which shows complete terms to within terms of order two in α, or to the theory to be discussed below which is complete to within terms of order two in $\| G(\ ) \|$.

6. On finite second-order viscoelasticity.

If we write out our fading memory assumption (3.7) for the case $n = 2$ making use of the results of the previous section we obtain

$$S = -p(\rho)I + \int_0^\infty m(s,\rho)G(s)ds + \left[\int_0^\infty l(s,\rho) \text{ tr } G(s)ds \right] I +$$

$$+ \underset{s=0}{\overset{\infty}{\mathscr{Q}}} (G(s);\rho) + o(\| G(\ ) \|^2). \tag{6.1}$$

([11]) Specialized, of course, in accordance with the assumption of incompressibility.

Here $\mathscr{Q}$ is a continuous quadratic functional of $G(\ )$. Since

$$\lim_{\|G(\ )\| \to 0} \frac{o(\|G(\ )\|^2)}{\|G(\ )\|^2} = 0,$$

if we strike out the term $o(\|G(\ )\|^2)$ in (6.1) we obtain an expression which approximates the constitutive equation of a simple fluid with fading memory to within terms of order two in $\|G(\ )\|$. We call the theory based on that expression *finite second-order viscoelasticity for fluids*.

The continuous quadratic functional $\mathscr{Q}$ of (6.1) may be expressed in terms of a bounded symmetric operator on our Hilbert space $\mathfrak{H}$. It is not possible, in general, to represent $\mathscr{Q}$ by integrals. An integral representation does exist, however, if the operator corresponding to $\mathscr{Q}$ is completely continuous in the technical sense of Hilbert space theory. We consider only this special case.

If one combines this assumption of complete continuity with the isotropy condition (3.2), one can show that $\mathscr{Q}$ has the representation

$$\mathscr{Q}(G(s);\rho) = \int\limits_0^\infty \int\limits_0^\infty \left\{ q(s_1,s_2,\rho) \left[\mathrm{tr}\ G(s_1) \right] G(s_2) + r_1(s_1,s_2,\rho) G(s_1) G(s_2) \right\} ds_1 ds_2 +$$

$$+ \left[\int\limits_0^\infty \int\limits_0^\infty \left\{ r_2(s_1,s_2,\rho) \left[\mathrm{tr}\ G(s_1) \right] \left[\mathrm{tr}\ G(s_2) \right] + r_3(s_1,s_2,\rho)\ \mathrm{tr}\ \{G(s_1) G(s_2)\} \right\} \right. \cdot$$

$$\left. \cdot\ ds_1 ds_2 \right] I. \tag{6.2a}$$

The functions r_i can be chosen to be symmetric in the sense that

$$r_i(s_1,s_2,\rho) = r_i(s_2,s_1,\rho), \quad i = 1,2,3; \tag{6.2b}$$

in which case the four functions q, r_1, r_2, r_3 are uniquely determined by $\mathscr{Q}$. In deriving this result we have used representation theorems for tensor polynomials of the type proved by Spencer and Rivlin [17, 18].

Hence for simple fluids the complete constitutive equation of finite second-order viscoelasticity has the form

$$S = - p(\rho)I + \int\limits_0^\infty m(s,\rho)G(s)ds + \int\limits_0^\infty \int\limits_0^\infty \Big\{ q(s_1,s_2,\rho)[\mathrm{tr}\ G(s_1)]G(s_2) +$$

$$+ r_1(s_1,s_2,\rho)G(s_1)G(s_2) \Big\} ds_1 ds_2 +$$

$$+ \Big[\int\limits_0^\infty l(s,\rho)\ \mathrm{tr}\ G(s)ds + \int\limits_0^\infty \int\limits_0^\infty \Big\{ r_2(s_1,s_2,\rho)[\mathrm{tr}\ G(s_1)][\mathrm{tr}\ G(s_2)] +$$

$$+ r_3(s_1,s_2,\rho)\ \mathrm{tr}\ [G(s_1)G(s_2)] \Big\} ds_1 ds_2 \Big]I , \qquad (6.3)$$

and if the r_i are chosen in accordance with (6.2b) then the seven material functions $p, m, q, l, r_1, r_2, r_3$ occurring in the theory are uniquely determined by the fluid under consideration.

Of course, to different choices of the measure of strain in equations (5.17)–(5.19) correspond different theories of second-order viscoelasticity. These different theories are equivalent in the sense that the corresponding stresses differ only by terms of order greater than two in $\| G( ) \|$.

ACKNOWLEDGEMENT

The research leading to this paper was supported by the Air Force Office of Scientific Research under Contract AF 49(638)541 with Mellon Institute and by the National Science Foundation under Grant NSF–G6745 to Carnegie Institute of Technology.

REFERENCES

[1]   W. NOLL, *Arch. Rational Mech. Anal.*, **2**, (1958), 197–226.
[2]   B. D. COLEMAN AND W. NOLL, *Arch. Rational Mech. Anal.*, **6**, (1960), 355–370.
[3]   B. D. COLEMAN AND W. NOLL, *Revs. Modern Phys.*, **33**, (1961), 239–249.
[4]   J. L. ERICKSEN, *Kolloid-Zeits.*, **173**, (1960), 117–122.
[5]   J. L. ERICKSEN, *Arch. Rational Mech. Anal.*, **4**, (1960), 231–237.
[6]   J. L. ERICKSEN, *Trans. Soc. Rheology*, **4**, (1960), 29–39.
[7]   J. L. ERICKSEN, *Arch. Rational Mech. Anal.*, **8**, (1961), 1–8.
[8]   C. TRUESDELL, *J. Math. pures appl.*, **30**, (1951), 111–158.
[9]   B. D. COLEMAN AND W. NOLL, *Arch. Rational Mech. Anal.*, **3**, (1959), 289–303.
[10] B. D. COLEMAN AND W. NOLL, *J. Appl. Phys.*, **30**, (1959), 1508–1512.
[11] B. D. COLEMAN AND W. NOLL, *Ann. New York Acad. Sciences*, **89**, (1961), 672–714.
[12] B. D. COLEMAN, *Arch. Rational Mech. Anal.* , **9**, (1962), 213–300.
[13] L. BOLTZMANN, *Sitzber. Akad. Wiss. Wien, Math. naturw. Kl.* 70 (II), (1874), 275–306.
[14] R. S. RIVLIN AND J. L. ERICKSEN, *J. Rational Mech. Anal.*, **4**, (1955), 323–425.
[15] J. SERRIN, Mathematical principles of classical fluid mechanics, In *Encyclopedia of Physics*. S. Flügge, Ed., VIII/I (Fluid Mechanics I), 125–263. Springer, Berlin (1959).
[16] A. S. LODGE, *Trans. Faraday Soc.*, **52**, (1956), 120–130.
[17] A. J. M. SPENCER AND R. S. RIVLIN, *Arch. Rational Mech. Anal.*, **2**, (1959), 309–336, 435–446.
[18] A. J. M. SPENCER AND R. S. RIVLIN, *Arch. Rational Mech. Anal.*, **4**, (1960), 214–230.

DISCUSSION

E.H. LEE: Since the energy dissipated in viscous flow may appear as heat energy, presumably an all inclusive theory of simple fluids should include the influence of temperature. In particular, viscoelastic response of materials is known to be highly temperature sensitive, and I wonder whether you have attempted to include this possibly important physical variable in the theory.

B.D. COLEMAN'S REPLY: Yes, we have.

STATISTICAL RHEOLOGY OF SUSPENSIONS AND SOLUTIONS WITH SPECIAL REFERENCE TO NORMAL STRESS EFFECTS

Hanswalter Giesekus

Farbenfabriken Bayer A. G., Leverkusen, Germany

ABSTRACT

After formulating the rheological equation of state for that class of fluids in which normal stresses in steady shear flow occur in flow direction only (Weissenberg fluids), two examples of suspensions are presented to show that, in the general case, normal stresses in the direction of flow gradient do not vanish. In suspensions of particles with permanent anisotropy of shape, in which the Brownian movement is negligible, normal stress effects appear as first-order effects. As is the case with shear stress, these are a pronounced function of the type of flow.

A very general formulation of the theory of dilute suspensions and solutions is possible. This is done specifically in the case of rigid particles. A deduction of an integral equation is offered for which solutions are stated and discussed.

1. Introduction.

Although over 15 years have now passed since Reiner (1945) predicted normal stress effects in sheared fluids, and Weissenberg (1947) observed such effects for the first time, it is today hardly possible to claim that those effects are meanwhile completely understood. With regard to the experimental side a number of questions still remain unanswered, for clearly evident as normal stress effects often are their quantitative determination in most cases continues to be just as ever delicate. An even greater number of questions, however, concern their theoretical understanding, i.e. an insight into the conditions and nature of the occurence of the effects in connection with the structure of fluids.

Thus, for years the problem has been studied and discussed in steady shear flow, (which is probably the only class of flow types for which measuring arrangements are known so far), whether normal stress effects occur in flow direction only or in gradient direction also, and, at least until recently, opinions in this respect differed widely[1]. The author, therefore, has tried to clear up this problem with the methods of statistical rheology, at least for the case of dilute suspensions and solutions. This will be the subject of the following remarks.

---

[1] *Cf.* on the one hand, e.g. Roberts [8] and Philippoff [15] and, on the other hand, e.g. Markovitz and Williamson [9].

First of all, a brief reference is submitted with respect to the phenomenological theory of fluids as this constitutes the framework for the subsequent considerations. This is followed by formulating the rheological equation of state for that class of fluids (Weissenberg fluids) where, in the case of flow type outlined above, normal stresses occur in the direction of flow only, and conditions are shown under which the suspensions satisfy such an equation of state. Next suspensions of spheroid dumbbells and spheroids are examined and discussed with respect to their normal stress effects, assuming a case of predominant Brownian movement. In addition, the boundary case of negligible Brownian movement is analyzed by means of an example of a two-dimensional suspension of cross dumbbells. Finally, some comments are offered with respect to the formulation of a general theory of dilute suspensions of rigid particles. After briefly discussing the statistical problem there follows an analysis of the hydrodynamic problem, centering on the statement and solution of an integral equation of the second kind.

2. Phenomenological rheology of fluids.

A fluid is understood to be a body for which the rheological equation of state can be represented by an isotropic tensor function of a sequence of kinematic tensors, in which the deformation tensor, however, is not present[2]. In a certain range around zero, as is well-known, such a function can be expanded into a series of the kinematic tensors; in this respect because of isotropy only dot products of tensors occur with coefficients that are scalar functions of the tensor invariants. When selecting for representation the sequence of rotational invariant kinematic tensors $\mathbf{f}^{(n)}$, viz.

$$\mathbf{f}^{(1)} = \tfrac{1}{2}(\nabla\mathbf{v} + \mathbf{v}\nabla) \qquad \boldsymbol{\omega} = \tfrac{1}{2}(\nabla\mathbf{v} - \mathbf{v}\nabla)$$

$$\mathbf{f}^{(n+1)} = \frac{\mathscr{D}\mathbf{f}^{(n)}}{\mathscr{D}t} = \frac{D\mathbf{f}^{(n)}}{Dt} + \left[\boldsymbol{\omega}\cdot\mathbf{f}^{(n)} - \mathbf{f}^{(n)}\cdot\boldsymbol{\omega}\right] , \qquad (1)$$

the first terms of the series for an incompressible fluid[3] are:

$$\begin{aligned}
\mathbf{s} = {}& -p\mathbf{1} + \aleph^{(1)}\mathbf{f}^{(1)} \quad + \\
&+ \aleph^{(2)}\mathbf{f}^{(2)} + \aleph^{(11)}\mathbf{f}^{(1)2} \quad + \\
&+ \aleph^{(3)}\mathbf{f}^{(3)} + \aleph^{(21)}\left[\mathbf{f}^{(2)}\cdot\mathbf{f}^{(1)} + \mathbf{f}^{(1)}\cdot\mathbf{f}^{(2)}\right] + \cdots , \quad (2)
\end{aligned}$$

---

[2] We restrict ourselves to "simple fluids" according to Noll [11].

[3] The dot characterizes the dot product or, when after a tensor, the latter's trace. Powers of tensors are to be understood as dot products.

wherein $\aleph^{(\alpha...\delta)}$ are material functions. Assuming the state of rest to be a regular point of the equation of state within the sense of the theory of functions —in this case we speak of *elastico-viscous fluids*[4]—then these functions can be expanded into a series in the invariants, for incompressible fluids say in the form:

$$\aleph^{(\alpha...\delta)} = \aleph_0^{(\alpha...\delta)} +$$
$$+ \aleph_{11}^{(\alpha...\delta)}(\mathfrak{f}^{(1)2}_{\cdot}) +$$
$$+ \aleph_{21}^{(\alpha...\delta)}(\mathfrak{f}^{(2)}.\mathfrak{f}^{(1)}_{\cdot}) + \aleph_{111}^{(\alpha...\delta)}(\mathfrak{f}^{(1)3}_{\cdot}) + ... \qquad (3)$$

In this case an order is assigned to each term of the series (i.e. the sum of the upper and lower indices of the coefficients $\aleph_{m...n}^{(\alpha...\delta)}$) so that the expansion can be arranged in a unique manner. The number of terms increases greatly with the order[5].

The equation of state is highly simplified when restricting the scope of the study to special flow types. For steady shear flow, as is well-known, it is reduced to

$$s_{11} = -p - \gamma^2 G(\gamma^2) \qquad s_{12} = s_{21} = \gamma H(\gamma^2)$$
$$s_{22} = -p + \gamma^2 F(\gamma^2) \qquad s_{23} = s_{32} = 0$$
$$s_{33} = -p \qquad\qquad s_{31} = s_{13} = 0. \qquad (4)$$

The indices characterize here, in their natural sequence, the direction of the velocity gradient, the direction of flow and the indifferent direction, γ is the shear rate. This means that we have a total of three material functions of which $H(\gamma^2)$ is the effective shear viscosity, whereas $F(\gamma^2)$ and $G(\gamma^2)$ in various combinations cause the different normal stress effects, cf. e.g. [20]. For incompressible elastico-viscous fluids these functions, of course, can be expanded in powers of the invariant γ^2, and the following applies to the absolute terms:

$$F_0 = -\tfrac{1}{2}\aleph_0^{(2)} + \tfrac{1}{4}\aleph_0^{(11)} \qquad \aleph_0^{(2)} = -(F_0 + G_0)$$
$$G_0 = -\tfrac{1}{2}\aleph_0^{(2)} - \tfrac{1}{4}\aleph_0^{(11)} \qquad \aleph_0^{(11)} = 2(F_0 - G_0)$$
$$H_0 = \tfrac{1}{2}\aleph_0^{(1)} \qquad\qquad \aleph_0^{(1)} = 2H_0. \qquad (5)$$

---

[4] Contrary to this fluids with a singular flow behaviour when at rest are called by us *quasi-plastic fluids*, cf. [25].

[5] The phenomenological theory of fluids is presented in [22] especially based on studies by Spencer and Rivlin [12].

In lowest approximation, therefore, the normal-stress behaviour is described by the two coefficients $\aleph_0^{(2)}$ and $\aleph_0^{(11)}$ or by the quantities F_0 and G_0 which are equivalent to these. The second law of thermodynamics, furthermore, entails that

$$- \aleph_0^{(2)} = F_0 + G_0 \geqq 0. \tag{6}$$

Any information beyond that, however, does not appear to be obtainable by means of phenomenological principles.

3. Weissenberg fluids.

In search of a general equation of state Weissenberg [6] stated a principle according to which $G \equiv 0$ for fluids in steady shear flow. Recently, Grossman [14] elaborated a new formulation of this principle by which the basic concepts and consequences are marked even more clearly. Weissenberg's postulate leads to an equation of state for the elastic body which can be represented as a quasi-linear relation(6), when using Finger's measure of deformation or Green's measure of strain which is closely connected with the former(7). This principle, however, is not directly applicable to elastico-viscous fluids. The above deduction by Weissenberg is to be regarded as an analogical conclusion rather than as a strict consequence resulting therefrom.

In the study of suspensions of dumbbells we have now, following a calculation of S. Prager [10], met with an equation of state in the following form:

$$\mathbf{s} = \mathbf{s}_0 - \rho \frac{\mathfrak{D} \mathbf{S}}{\mathfrak{D} t}, \tag{7}$$

In this $\mathbf{s}_0$ is a Newtonian stress term originating from the suspending agent and ρ the density, whereas

$$\frac{\mathfrak{D} \mathbf{S}}{\mathfrak{D} t} = \frac{D \mathbf{S}}{D t} - [\mathbf{v} \nabla . \mathbf{S} + \mathbf{S} . \nabla \mathbf{v}] \tag{8}$$

means the contravariant convected derivative of a symmetrical tensor with non-negative eigenvalues which, just like the stress in the general case, is an isotropic function of the kinematic tensors and which can be expanded

---

(6) "Quasi-linear" means that the coefficients may be functions of the invariants.

(7) Grossman works with the tensor density $\mathbf{c}^{-1}/\mathrm{III}_{\mathbf{c}^{-1}}^{1/2}$ associated with Finger's measure of deformation and calls this "separation tensor". The spatial Green's measure is given by $\hat{\mathbf{e}} = \frac{1}{2}(\mathbf{c}^{-1}-\mathbf{1})$, cf. e.g. [19].

according to Eq. (2). For elastico-viscous fluids it is possible to represent the associated material functions in analogy to Eq. (3). Now the most salient feature of this equation of state is that it always follows that $G \equiv 0$ for steady shear flow. We have, therefore, called the fluids obeying this equation *Weissenberg fluids*[8].

Such an equation of state is found not only for rigid and elastic dumbbells but also for any networks of spherical drag bodies suspended in Newtonian fluids as long as all the forces of interaction are completely transferred to the fluid[9], and the flow of the suspending agent is not systematically perturbep by the movement of the particles. For such a system, in which N different types of particles may be present, the tensor of state $\mathbf{S}$ adopts the following form:

$$\mathbf{S} = \sum_{i=1}^{N} \frac{n_i}{2 B_i} \langle \mathbf{r}_i \, \mathbf{r}_i \rangle, \tag{9}$$

wherein $i = 1 \ldots N$ denotes the type of particle, n_i their number in the unit of mass, B_i their mobility constant and $\mathbf{r}_i$ their position vector (originating from an arbitrary reference point moving with the fluid), the arrow-shaped brackets indicating the average of all particles. $\mathbf{S}$ therefore is an average of the tensor product of the particle position vectors with themselves, weighted in proportion to concentration and mobility[10].

An even clearer interpretation of this quantity is possible by assigning to the state of rest — as is always possible with an elastico-viscous fluid — an isotropical tensor of state

$$\overset{\circ}{\mathbf{S}} = \sum_{i=1}^{N} \frac{n_i}{2 B_i} \langle \overset{\circ}{\mathbf{r}}_i \, \overset{\circ}{\mathbf{r}}_i \rangle = \sum_{i=1}^{N} \overset{\circ}{\eta}_i \, \mathbf{1} \tag{10}$$

and considering the deformation of network because of the flow process a deformation of N different nested continua[11]. When mapping from $\overset{\circ}{\mathbf{r}}_i$ to $\mathbf{r}_i$ by the tensor $\mathbf{a}_i$:

$$\mathbf{r}_i = \mathbf{a}_i \cdot \overset{\circ}{\mathbf{r}}_i = \overset{\circ}{\mathbf{r}}_i \cdot \tilde{\mathbf{a}}_i, \tag{11}$$

there follows directly

(8) The specializations following from Eq. (7) have been discussed in detail for general and stationary flow processes in [22].

(9) That is, no solid-like continuous bonds must exist.

(10) The derivation of these expressions is given in [21].

(11) A more detailed description of the relations described below is found in [26].

$$\mathbf{S} = \sum_{i=1}^{N} \overset{\circ}{\eta}_i \frac{\mathbf{a}_i \cdot \tilde{\mathbf{a}}_i}{|\mathbf{a}_i|} = \sum_{i=1}^{N} \overset{\circ}{\eta}_i \frac{\mathbf{c}_i^{-1}}{\mathrm{III}_{\mathbf{c}_i^{-1}}^{1/2}} = \overset{\circ}{\eta} \overline{\left[\frac{\mathbf{c}^{-1}}{\mathrm{III}_{\mathbf{c}^{-1}}^{1/2}} \right]}. \tag{12}$$

This quantity is the tensor density associated with Finger's measure of deformation (i.e. Grossman's separation tensor, cf. ([7])) averaged by the intrinsic viscosities $\overset{\circ}{\eta}_i$ as weight factors over all continua. The tensor of state $\mathbf{S}$ thus essentially describes the deformation of the network structure because of the flow process.

On the basis of this result it is now possible to apply also Weissenberg's principle (in the sense of Grossman's formulation) to the elastico-viscous fluids. When substituting in Eq. (12) for the deformation tensors a quasi-linear expression of the partial stresses, thus entering Eq. (9), there results after a simple calculation for the equation of state an expression in the form

$$\mathbf{s} = \beth^{(0)}\mathbf{1} + \beth^{(1)}\hat{\mathbf{f}}^{(1)} + \beth^{(2)}\hat{\mathbf{f}}^{(2)} + \beth^{(3)}\hat{\mathbf{f}}^{(3)} + \ldots \tag{13}$$

wherein

$$\hat{\mathbf{f}}^{(n)} = -\frac{1}{2} \frac{\mathfrak{D}^n \mathbf{1}}{\mathfrak{D}t^n} \tag{14}$$

designates the sequence of the contravariant kinematic tensors. In this case the $\beth^{(n)}$ represent functions of the invariants of the kinematic tensors. While Weissenberg's principle for the elastic solid resulted in a quasi-linear relation in Finger's deformation measure or Green's strain measure (i.e. in the spatial *contravariant deformation* or *strain tensor*), in the case of the elastico-viscous fluid there results instead a quasi-linear equation of state in the *contravariant kinematic tensors*.

4. Suspensions of spheroid dumbbells and spheroids.

In the preceding section we had already exceeded the range of the purely phenomenological considerations and found the equation of state of the Weissenberg fluid by means of model concepts. Two essential assumptions were necessary for the deduction: first, the drag bodies had to have spherical shape at least in the mean, i.e. it had to be possible to express their drag resistance by a scalar constant; second, the grouping of these particles had to be such that the flow would not be systematically pertrubed by their motion.

From these assumptions it would have to be expected that any deviations from the behaviour of a Weissenberg fluid always occur where at least one of the conditions outlined above is no longer complied with. In line with this consideration we have analyzed some model suspensions and found that our assumptions were confirmed.

As a simple example of a situation where the first condition is no longer complied with, we selected a suspension of rigid dumbbells in which the spheres, however, have been replaced by spheroids (ellipsoids of revolution). cf. Figure 1. With this model (and also, of course, with the sphere-type dumbbell) the second condition is violated too when the distance of the dumbbell bodies is not very large as compared with their diameters. The quantitative calculation was carried out following an earlier calculation [17] using known formulae for the drag resistance in the translational motion of spheroids[12], i.e. the quantities F_0, G_0 and H_0 as well as the more expressive ratios of these quantities:

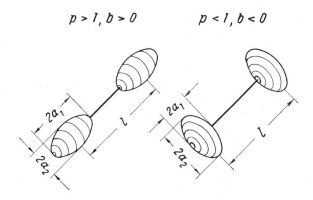

$$p > 1, b > 0 \qquad p < 1, b < 0$$

Figure 1
Spheroid dumbbells

$$n_F = F_0/\tau H_0, \quad n_G = G_0/\tau H_0, \quad m = G_0/F_0 \tag{15}$$

were calculated as a function of the axis ratio of the spheroids $a_1/a_2 = p$, respectively of the parameter of slenderness equivalent to this

$$b = (p^2 - 1)/(p^2 + 1) \tag{16}$$

wherein $\tau = (6\,D_{rot})^{-1}$ signifies the relaxation time.

---

(12) Cf. e.g. Lamb [1].

This calculation was carried out firstly neglecting flow perturbation and secondly including this perturbation for the ratio between effective radius and distance[13] $r_{eff}/l = 1/10$. It was found that n_F varies only within relatively narrow limits, that is in the unperturbed case between 8/7 for $p = 0$ and 9/7 for $p = \infty$. These data are slightly reduced by the flow perturbation, and this is the more pronounced the smaller the value of p. But even for $p = 0$ the deviation is only about 1.6% in the case mentioned.

Considerably more interesting is the shape of the function m which is a measure of the deviation from the behaviour of a Weissenberg fluid[14]. For $p = \infty$ this function has the maximum value 1/6 which is independent from r_{eff}/l and decreases monotonously with decreasing p. In the unperturbed case when $p = 1$ then of course $m = 0$, whereas negative values are received for $p < 1$ with the minimum value $-1/8$ for $p = 0$. When considering the flow perturbation, however, m becomes zero even with $p > 1$, in our case for $p \approx 1.4$, whereas the boundary value for $p = 0$ is then about -0.1660. Although this value, contrary to the upper boundary value, depends on r_{eff}/l and, therefore, may drop even lower with a higher value of this ratio, as a consequence of the terms of higher order in r_{eff}/l neglected in this case, it must however reach a minimum, and even become positive again, with a further increase of r_{eff}/l, for the boundary value $r_{eff}/l \to \infty$ corresponds to a circular disc which will be discussed in the next example as a boundary case of a spheroid. Including the result obtained there we shall have ample reason, although we are unable to determine here exactly the absolute minimum of m, to justify the assumption that this quantity will not be greatly below the above value and will certainly be small in magnitude as compared to 1.

In view of the fact that the model discussed here is after all quite artificial, i.e. at least with respect to the finer details, it would be difficult to verify it by a real suspension, we have also carried out calculations in respect of a second model: a dilute suspension of spheroids. This model, as is well-known, has first been studied by Jeffery [2] and has later on been further discussed by Peterlin [4] as well as by Kuhn and Kuhn [5]. Despite the preparatory work by these authors, who were only interested in shear viscosity but not in the normal stress effects, the calculations are quite laborious in detail. We have, therefore, calculated the above three ratios (15) as a function of the axis ratio p and the parameter b respectively by means of an electronic computer (Zuse Z 22). The results are shown in Figure 3. The ratio n_F tends for $p = 0$ (circular

---

(13) The effective radius r_{eff} is defined in such a way that a spheroid dumbbell with this radius has the same H_0 - value as a sphere-type dumbbell with the radius $r = r_{eff}$.

(14) Because of the slight variation of n_F the shape of n_G differs only immaterially from that of m.

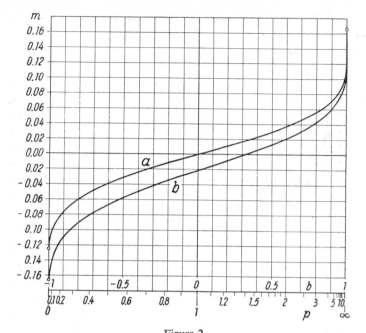

Figure 2

Suspensions of spheroid dumbbells: the ratio of both normal stress components
(a) without hydrodynamic interaction ($r_{eff}/l=0$)
(b) with hydrodynamic interaction ($r_{eff}/l=1/10$)

disc) towards the boundary value 15/28 and drops monotonously to $p=1$ (sphere) where it becomes zero. It increases again for $p>1$ and tends for $p=\infty$ (slender rod) towards 9/7. Unlike the former model this quantity, therefore, undergoes pronounced variations. The ratio n_G has quantitatively a similar shape. It is interesting to note that here the boundary value, however, has at both sides the same value 3/14, although it is approximated much more quickly at the left side than at the right side. With n_F and n_G m is, of course, also everywhere positive definite. This quantity has an absolute maximum of 2/5 in the boundary of round discs and drops to a minimum value about 2/25 at $p \approx 6$ to rise then very slowly[15] towards the boundary value 1/6. With the spheroid suspension the deviation from the Weissenberg behaviour is thus the greatest for round discs and the smallest for moderately prolate spheroids ($p \approx 6$). Here too, however, the

---

(15) "Very slowly" refers to the p-scale: for $p=100$ m still is about 29%, for $p=1000$ still about 19% smaller than the boundary value.

maximum value of m is still small as compared to 1, i.e. the normal stress component in flow direction is in any case considerably greater than that in flow gradient direction.

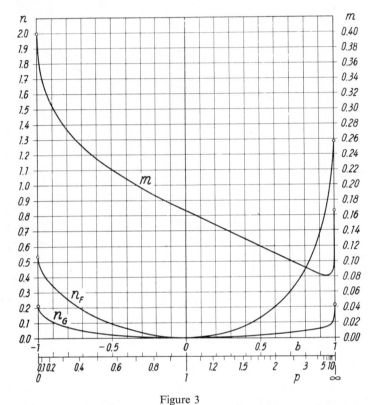

Figure 3

Suspensions of spheroids: the ratios of normal stress components and shear stress and of both normal stress components

The first fact to be noted when comparing the two model suspensions with each other is that both coincide completely in the normal stress behaviour as far as $p = \infty$ is concerned[16]. A second point, however, is even more significant: while m takes on exclusively positive values for spheroids, it also has negative values for spheroid dumbbells if p drops below a critical value. The normal stress component in direction of the flow gradient, therefore, is a traction in this case whereas it is a pressure if m is positive. The deviating behaviour of the spheroid dumbbells with sufficiently flat dumbbell bodies

---

[16] This holds true, as shown by Kotaka [13] also for Kuhn's rods.

will be attributed to the shape of these particles: their cross section (normal to the axis of revolution) rises starting with the centre from zero to a maximum and drops only after this maximum has been reached, whereas it decreases monotonously from the start in the case of the spheroids.

Our calculations, in addition, yield some indications on models of suspensions and solutions of a more general nature. First of all we may deduct that suspensions of elongate particles exhibit appreciably less deviation from the Weissenberg behaviour than those with oblate particles. Our analysis, furthermore, shows that in the case of the sphere-type dumbbells the deviations from the Weissenberg behaviour finally stem from the fact that the flow perturbation induced by the relative motion of the spheres in the surrounding fluid is, at equal distance from the centre, in the direction of the movement twice as great as vertically to this. This results in various values of the drag constant (a) for the radial flow-off (flow part of the equation of state) and (b) for the rotation (diffusion part of the equation of state). When regarding, instead of a dumbbell or a rod, an elongate structure composed of spherical elements such as a coiled macromolecule (necklace model), rather than the two drag constants referred to above, two values, whose relative difference is bound to considerably smaller than the former two values enter the calculation as a mean for the radial flow-off and for the rotational motion. As a result of this the quotient m is also bound to be considerably smaller than would correspond to the boundary value 1/6 for slender rods: while for these the condition of the scalar mobility constant no longer applies because of the preferred direction of axis, it almost prevails medially in the case of a free-draining coil (which may be quite elliptical), which means that it largely approaches the Weissenberg behaviour.

Just as the anisotropy of mobility is reduced when changing over from rod-like to coiled molecules, this will also apply to the case when a suspension or solution is more concentrated. The interaction of the neighbouring particles, which at least combine to form transient aggregates, reduces the influence of the anisotropy of shape assigned to the individual particles, thus also causing a reduction of the values m.

As much as the considerations outlined above still call for a more precise and deeper study, they nevertheless permit, even in their present form, an obvious interpretation of those observations on high-polymer solutions and similar systems which behave as Weissenberg fluids within the range of accuracy of observation. Appreciable deviations from the Weissenberg behaviour will be expected, in accordance with the above considerations, especially in those cases where dilute suspensions of either very slender or, even better, disc-shaped or lamellar particles are concerned.

In this connection it may be mentioned that recently Philippoff [16] showed by means of stress-optical methods on 6 dilute suspensions of rigid particles the deviations from the Weissenberg behaviour, while being able to reproduce under the same conditions of observation the earlier results that high-polymer solutions are Weissenberg fluids([17]).

5. Suspensions without Brownian Movement.

The results reported and discussed in the preceding section have been obtained under the condition that the Brownian movement dominates and that the influence of the flow can be treated as a "perturbation". A complete survey, however, would also call for a study of the other boundary case. This, on the other hand, is considerably more complicated, because of the following reason: the Brownian movement alone causes an equipartition of directions of orientation or in the case of elastic particles a distribution of parameters corresponding to a minimum of the free energy. This is a boundary behaviour which is easy to survey and, consequently, very suitable as a starting position for a perturbation calculation. The influence of the flow on the particles in the absence of Brownian movement, on the other hand, is not as simply described. It is, therefore, intended to discuss this briefly in this section. Although the Brownian movement is entirely neglected in this, it is nevertheless simple to understand, at least qualitatively, of which nature the modifications caused by it will be.

For the sake of brevity we shall limit this discussion to the motion of rigid particles in two-dimensional steady types of flow([18]). Without restricting the generality it is possible in this case to specialize on cross dumbbells, cf. Figure 4, whose shape is characterized by the parameter([19]).

$$b = (l_1^2 - l_2^2) \: / \: (l_1^2 + l_2^2) \: . \tag{17}$$

([17]) Philippoff concludes from these results that deviations from the Weissenberg behaviour can only be observed with suspensions of *rigid* particles. According to the analyses mentioned above, however, rigidity is likely to be less significant than shape. The Weissenberg behaviour is induced by the flexibility of the chain molecules rather than by their deformation properties, i.e. the largely random-like short-range order of the nearest neighbour particles. Suspensions of elastic dumbbells or elastic rods, on the other hand, should qualitatively show the same deviations as those of corresponding rigid particles.

([18]) The state of motion of rigid particles in three-dimensional flow is discussed in [23] and the state in two-dimensional flow in [24].

([19]) This quantity has the same meaning as the quantity defined by equation (16) for spheroids: cross dumbbells and spheroids with equal b are completely equivalent with respect to the state of motion.

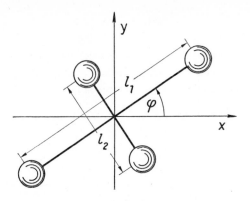

Figure 4
Cross dumbbell

Two-dimensional steady flow fields of incompressible fluids can be represented, when adjusting the reference system in a suitable manner, by a gradient tensor of the form

$$\nabla v = \begin{Vmatrix} 0 & \varepsilon+\omega \\ \varepsilon-\omega & 0 \end{Vmatrix}. \tag{18}$$

Here, the scalar quantities ε and ω characterize the deformation and rotation part of the flow velocity, whereas the type of flow can be described by the quotient

$$\rho = \omega/\varepsilon. \tag{19}$$

The type of flow assigned to the tensor ∇v, given spatial constancy, is easily found by integrating Eq. (18). For $\rho < 1$ the flow pattern is represented by two families of hyperbolas with joint asymptotes and for $\rho > 1$ by a family of ellipses with joint axis ratio. In the case of pure deformation flow ($\rho = 0$) the asymptotes are perpendicular to each other; in the case of simple shear flow ($\rho = 1$) they coincide and the one family of hyperbolas degenerates accordingly to form a family of straight lines; in the case of the pure rotation flow ($\rho = \infty$) finally, the ellipses degenerate, of course, into circles.

The motion of the cross dumbbells in these types of flow is given by the equation

$$\dot{\rho} = b\varepsilon \cos 2\rho + \omega. \tag{20}$$

Two types of motion are contained in this: if $\rho < b$, the particles adjust themselves steadily under a fixed angle, if $\rho > b$ they gyrate with a non-uniform speed; in the boundary case the particles also adjust themselves, although this adjustment is unilaterally unstable[20].

Now the study of the type of motion enables us to calculate the additional stresses which are caused by such particles in a fluid in which they are suspended[21]. If n cross dumbbells[22] with the rotation mobility B_{rot} are present in the unit volume, this is expressed by

$$\mathbf{s} = \frac{n}{2B_{rot}} \varepsilon \begin{Vmatrix} s_{11}^* & s_{12}^* \\ s_{12}^* & s_{22}^* \end{Vmatrix} \tag{21}$$

wherein s_{ik}^* only depends on ρ. This then has the following consequences: All stress components are directly proportional to the rate of deformation with a given type of flow. Accordingly, there is, first, no structural viscosity and, second, the normal stress effects occur here as first order rather than as second order effects, more precisely expressed, as first order effects with respect to the magnitude of ε since, when changing the sign of ε, s_{11}^* and s_{22}^* also change their signs.

The additional stresses are plotted as a function of the type of flow in Figure 5, where for a clearer representation ρ has been replaced by the equivalent quantity

$$R = (1 - \rho)/(1 + \rho) = (\varepsilon - \omega)/(\varepsilon + \omega) \tag{22}$$

as abscissa. As shown by the graph, the tensor component s_{12}^* which is proportional to the shear viscosity, has a maximum for the pure deformation flow $(R = 1)$ and decreases with increasing rotation until reaching $\rho = b$, where the steady adjustment of the particles changes into the non-uniform rotational motion. With a further increase in rotation s_{12}^* increases again, and in the point $\rho = b$ even with a vertical tangent on the left side. For a heavily predominant rotation a boundary value is reached which is between $1/2$ and 1 depending on the slenderness of the particle.

---

[20] An essentially equal behaviour exists in three-dimensional types of flow. Here, too, the particles adjust themselves either in a stationary position or move periodically at a non-uniform speed.

[21] For details see [25].

[22] Although, contrary to the state of motion, there exists no equivalence with respect to additional stresses, the cross dumbbells reproduce, at least in first approximation, the behaviour of rigid particles.

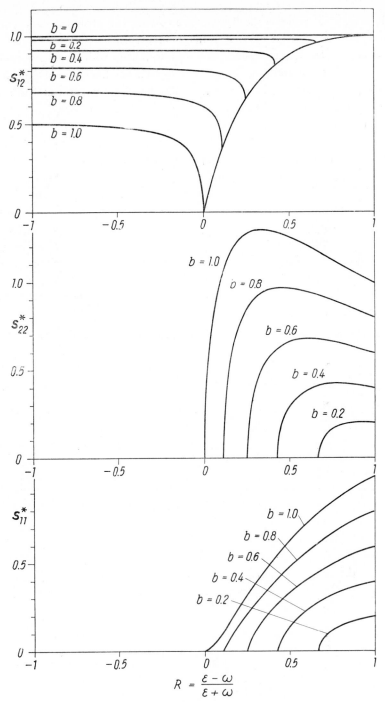

Figure 5
Stress components vs. type of flow

No less pronounced is the dependence of the normal-stress coefficients s_{11}^* and s_{22}^* on the type of flow. For the pure deformation flow they take the common value b. While s_{11}^* decreases monotonously with increasing rotation, s_{22}^* increases at first and then decreases only after passing through a maximum. Both components reach at the position $\rho = b$ the value zero, and this value is then retained for all types of flow with $\rho > b$ (i.e. in which the particles gyrate.)

The most important result yielded by our study thus turns out to be that both types of motion, i.e. stationary adjustment and non-uniform rotational movement, have a decisive influence on the equation of state. For those types of flow with which the particles change from the stationary adjustment to gyration, i.e. for $\rho = b$, the equation of state becomes singular[23]. As this condition is independent of ε, a singular point of the equation of state also corresponds to the state of rest ($\varepsilon = 0$): our suspensions, therefore, represent *quasi-plastic* rather than elastico-viscous fluids, i.e. while their equation of state can be expanded in accordance with Eq. (2) in the kinematic tensors, it is impossible to express their coefficient functions as power series of the invariants of these tensors.

When generalizing the model in question in such a way as to replace the rigid bonds by elastic ones, a behaviour resembling structural viscosity is obtained. For types of flow with stable adjustment of the particles the viscosity always *increases* with rate of deformation in this case.

EXCURSUS

Illustration of the two-dimensional types of flow and the motion of suspended particles

The variety of two-dimensional types of flow can be illustrated by means of a simple setup[24]. This is a four-roller apparatus similar to the one first described by Taylor [3]. Contrary to this apparatus, however, in our case the two diagonally opposite rather than the two neighbouring rollers are mechanically coupled, cf. Figure 6, and these pairs of rollers are provided with separate drives, permitting an infinitely variable adjustment of their speeds u_1 and u_2 between the extremes U and $- U$. When adjusting, for example, $u_1 = U$ and varying u_2 from $- U$ to U, the entire variety of two-dimensional

---

[23] In three-dimensional flow there is also a second class of singular types of flow in the case of which even the stresses (and not only the stress derivatives) change discontinuously, i.e. those where a stable adjustment or type of motion becomes unstable in favour of an other one.

[24] Described in detail in [24].

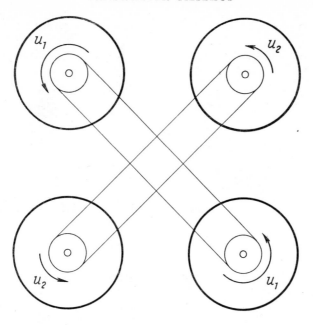

Figure 6
Four-roller apparatus

flow patterns from pure deformation ($\rho = 0$) to pure rotation flow ($\rho = \infty$) is produced in close approximation in the flow trough. To render the motion of particles in such flow fields visible, these are pivoted practically without friction on a needle provided in the centre of the trough, thus preventing any migration. Figure 7 gives four examples therein. A better way to illustrate these processes, especially the changeover from the fixed adjustment to the non-uniform gyration, is to film them[25].

6. Outlines of a general statistical theory of dilute suspensions, especially of rigid particles.

While the rheological behaviour of some special suspensions has been discussed in the preceding sections without going, however, in detail into the foundations, it is finally intended to deal, at least, with the fundamentals of the statistical rheology of dilute suspensions. Although this is restricted to rigid particles, a major share of the considerations can be transferred to elastic particles.

---

[25] Such a film was shown during the lecture.

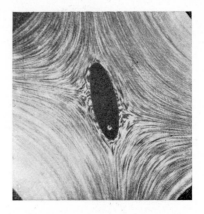

(a) Elliptic field of flow $(\rho \approx 1.5)$

(b) Elliptic particle, adjusted in a hyperbolic field of flow $(\rho \approx 0.37)$

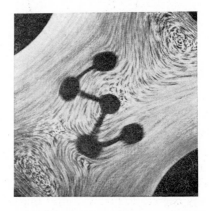

(c) Elastic W-particle, adjusted in a field of pure deformation flow $(\rho \approx 0)$

(d) Elastic W-particle, gyrating and undergoing deformation in a hyperbolic field of flow $(\rho \approx 0.75)$

Figure 7

Some examples of two-dimensional flow and the motion of suspended particles

The so far most general formulation of the statistical rheology has been given by Kirkwood and co-workers [7]. These authors, however, have primarily applied their theory to models of macromolecules describing these by systems of isolated singularities of the flow field. The main difference of our following considerations lies in the fact that for the description of conditions with rigid particles we have to cover closed surfaces with singularities. This leads not only to a substitution of the sums by integrals but also to another form of basic equations.

As reported in an earlier study [18] it is advisable to distinguish between two part problems in building up statistical rheology: the hydrodynamic problem and the statistical problem. In the case of the hydrodynamic problem an individual suspended particle is studied, and the question concerns the behaviour in the flow field of such particle, to which a number of free parameters have been assigned, and which, in addition, may possibly be subjected to a torque; in other words the nature of its motion, the extent to which it contributes to the additional stresses and to which it perturbs the flow process. With the statistical problem, however, a manifold of particles is studied and the frequency distribution of the parameters resulting from flow and Brownian movement is determined. This distribution makes it possible to obtain first the so-called diffusion part of the additional stresses and to take then the average of all quantities depending on these parameters. In this way one finds the total amount of the stresses of all particles, i.e. the rheological equation of state.

(a) The statistical problem
In view of the fact that it is intended to deal here primarily with the hydrodynamic problem, only a brief outline of the statistical problem is offered in advance. The basic equation of the statistical problem has the form of a conservation law and means that no particles are generated or annihilated in the flow process but that the variation of particle density with time is exclusively caused by "fluxes". When summarily characterizing the particle parameters by the symbol $\mathbf{P}$ and their time derivative by $d\mathbf{P}/dt = \mathbf{V}$ and when $\rho(\mathbf{P})$ denotes the density of probability, this basic equation reads:

$$\frac{a\rho(\mathbf{P})}{dt} + \operatorname{div}(\rho\mathbf{V}) = 0. \tag{23}$$

The operator div is to be understood in this equation as operator in the configurational space of the parameters $\mathbf{P}$.
In the case of rigid particles the only degrees of freedom important for the problem are those of orientation. It is, therefore, possible to represent $\mathbf{P}$, e.g., by the three Eulerian angles ϑ,ψ,φ[26]. The expression for the line element of this configurational space (that is an infinitesimal rotation) is

---

[26] When characterizing the coordinate system fixed in space by the x-, y- and z-axes and the system fixed in the particles by the x'-, y'- and z'-axes, then ϑ denotes the angle between the z- and the z'-axes, ψ the angle between the nodal line and the x-axis, φ the angle between the nodal line and the x'-axis.

$$dw^2 = d\vartheta^2 + d\psi^2 + d\varphi^2 + 2\cos\vartheta\, d\psi d\varphi, \tag{24}$$

and, in accordance with the metric tensor thus established, the divergence gets the form:

$$\mathrm{div}(\rho V) = \frac{1}{\sin\vartheta}\frac{\partial}{\partial\vartheta}(\rho\dot\vartheta\sin\vartheta) + \frac{\partial}{\partial\psi}(\rho\dot\psi) + \frac{\partial}{\partial\varphi}(\rho\dot\varphi). \tag{25}$$

Now then the speed of rotation $V = \{\dot\vartheta,\dot\psi,\dot\varphi\}$ is split into two parts, the diffusion part $V^{(D)}$ and the flow part $V^{(S)}$. The first part can be expressed by

$$\rho V^{(D)} = -D_{rot} \cdot \mathrm{grad}\ \rho, \tag{26}$$

wherein the contravariant components of the gradient in our configurational space are given by

$$\mathrm{grad}\ \rho = \left\{\frac{\partial\rho}{\partial\vartheta}\ ,\ \frac{1}{\sin^2\vartheta}\left(\frac{\partial\rho}{\partial\psi} - \cos\vartheta\frac{\partial\rho}{\partial\varphi}\right)\ ,\ \frac{1}{\sin^2\vartheta}\left(-\cos\vartheta\ \frac{\partial\rho}{\partial\psi} + \frac{\partial\rho}{\partial\varphi}\right)\right\} \tag{27}$$

and

$$D_{rot} = kT\ B_{rot} \tag{28}$$

represent the rotation-diffusion tensor, B_{rot} the rotation-mobility tensor which is closely connected with the former.

To the flow part, however, applies a term in form of

$$V^{(S)} = \vec\omega + b..f\ , \tag{29}$$

wherein $\vec\omega$ is the vector of the rotation velocity which is dual to the tensor ω, $f = f^{(1)}$ denotes the deformation velocity tensor and b a tensor of third order fixed in the particle[27].

The next step is to express D_{rot} and b by means of the known transformation formulae by components of a system fixed with respect to the particle, $\vec\omega$ and f, on the other hand, by those of a system fixed in space, selecting as a

---

[27] The two-dimensional analogue to this relation is given by Eq. (20).

system with respect to the particle preferably such which is a system of principal axes for the tensors $\mathbf{D}_{rot}$ and $\mathbf{b}$([28]), whereas the system fixed in space is preferably orientated in such a way that $\mathbf{f}$ is diagonal.

The statistical basic equation arrived at in this way shall not be written down here because of its length. For rotation-symmetrical particles the diffusion part is reduced to the so-called angular part of the Laplace differential equation([29]), whose eigenfunctions are known to be the spherical surface harmonics, while $\mathbf{V}^{(S)}$ can be expressed by the motion of a unit vector on the surface of the unit sphere. Since the probability distribution will then no longer depend on the angle ρ, the problem is greatly simplified. This makes it understandable that exclusively suspensions with rotation-symmetrical particles have so far been analyzed.

Although it is more complicated, it should be possible to solve the statistical basic equation also in the general case in a similar way as in the special case of rotation-symmetrical particles. It is, however, not intended to discuss this in detail within the scope of this paper.

(b)   The hydrodynamic problem

The hydrodynamic problem primarily concerns the finding of suitable solutions of the Navier-Stokes differential equation where inertia terms are neglected

$$\mu\nabla^2\mathbf{v} = \nabla p, \quad \nabla \cdot \mathbf{v} = 0, \tag{30}$$

wherein μ denotes the viscosity of the incompressible Newtonian suspending agent. When characterizing the set of all position vectors by $\mathbf{r}$ and the subset of all position vectors ending on the surface of any particle by $\mathbf{R}$, then the boundary conditions for points of sufficiently large distances from any particles are:

$$\mathbf{v}(\mathbf{r}) = \overset{\circ}{\mathbf{v}} + \mathbf{r} \cdot (\overset{\circ}{\mathbf{f}} + \overset{\circ}{\boldsymbol{\omega}}), \quad p(\mathbf{r}) = \overset{\circ}{p} \ . \tag{31}$$

To the particle surfaces, on the other hand, applies:

$$\mathbf{v}(\mathbf{R}) = \mathbf{u} + \mathbf{R} \cdot \mathbf{w} = \mathbf{u} + \vec{w} \times \mathbf{R}, \tag{32}$$

([28]) An essential condition for this, of course, is that it is possible to bring both tensors on principal axes by the same transformation. This is by no means trivial, although proof is readily obtained for any rigid systems of spherical drag-bodies without hydrodynamic interaction. The presence of special symmetry properties, therefore, is not a necessary condition for the above requirement.

([29]) It is assumed that rather than exact rotation symmetry the existence of an axis of symmetry of an order higher than second order is sufficient for the above consequences.

wherein **u** is a translational motion, **w** an anti-symmetrical tensor and $\vec{\mathbf{w}}$ a vector dual to this. These quantities characterize an individual particle and, consequently, may take on different values for various particles.

The Lorentz-Oseen basic solution[30]

$$\mathbf{v(r)} = \frac{1}{8\pi\mu}\left(\frac{1}{r} + \frac{\mathbf{r}\,\mathbf{r}}{r^3}\right).\,\mathbf{k}, \quad p(\mathbf{r}) = \frac{1}{4\pi}\frac{\mathbf{r}}{r^3}.\,\mathbf{k}, \tag{33}$$

now enables us to construct solutions of our problem by covering the surfaces of all particles with such singularities:

$$\mathbf{v(r)} = \overset{\circ}{\mathbf{v}} + \mathbf{r}.\,(\overset{\circ}{\mathbf{f}} + \overset{\circ}{\omega}) + \frac{1}{8\pi\mu}\oint_R\left[\frac{1}{|\mathbf{r}-\mathbf{R}|} + \frac{(\mathbf{r}-\mathbf{R})(\mathbf{r}-\mathbf{R})}{|\mathbf{r}-\mathbf{R}|^3}\right].\,d\mathbf{k(R)},$$

$$p(\mathbf{r}) = \overset{\circ}{p} + \frac{1}{4\pi}\oint_R\frac{(\mathbf{r}-\mathbf{R})}{|\mathbf{r}-\mathbf{R}|^3}.\,d\mathbf{k(R)}. \tag{34}$$

The only task now left is to find the distributions of forces $d\mathbf{k(R)}$ compatible with the boundary conditions[31].

Let us assume that this problem has been solved and thus we are asking for the averages of the field tensors. For this purpose we set

$$\mathbf{R} = \mathbf{R}_v + \overset{\circ}{\mathbf{R}}, \tag{35}$$

i.e. we split the vector **R** into a part characterizing any reference point in the interior of the v-th particle and a part describing the position of the surface points of this particle in relation to its reference point. Assuming that no resultant force acts on an individual particle, i.e. that

$$\oint d\mathbf{k(\overset{\circ}{R})} = 0 \tag{36}$$

applies, there follows by simple calculation:

[30] This is an analogue to the dipole solution of the Laplace equation and describes the flow perturbance produced by an infinitesimal sphere located in the origin of the coordinates when pulling this sphere with the force **k**.

[31] In the case of concentrated suspensions this distribution, of course, also depends on the relative position of the neighbouring particles, while in the case of dilute suspensions it depends only on shape and orientation of the particular particle itself.

$$\bar{p} = \overset{\circ}{p} - \frac{n}{3} \; \langle \, \oint \overset{\circ}{\mathbf{R}} \cdot d\mathbf{k} \, \rangle, \tag{37}$$

$$\bar{\mathbf{f}} = \overset{\circ}{\mathbf{f}} - \frac{n}{10\mu} \; \langle \frac{2}{3} \oint \overset{\circ}{\mathbf{R}} \cdot d\mathbf{k} \, \mathbf{1} - \oint d\mathbf{k} \, \overset{\circ}{\mathbf{R}} - \oint \overset{\circ}{\mathbf{R}} d\mathbf{k} \rangle, \tag{38}$$

$$\bar{\boldsymbol{\omega}} = \overset{\circ}{\boldsymbol{\omega}} - \frac{n}{6\mu} \; \langle \, \oint d\mathbf{k} \, \overset{\circ}{\mathbf{R}} - \oint \overset{\circ}{\mathbf{R}} d\mathbf{k} \, \rangle. \tag{39}$$

The barred quantities represent the spatial averages of the respective field quantities while the arrow-shaped brackets designate mean values with respect to orientation and n denotes the number of particles in the unit volume.

From Eqs. (37) and (38) there results for the hydrodynamic part of the stress tensor:

$$\bar{\mathbf{s}}' = -\bar{p}\mathbf{1} + 2\mu\bar{\mathbf{f}} = -\overset{\circ}{p}\mathbf{1} + 2\mu\overset{\circ}{\mathbf{f}} - \frac{n}{5} \langle \oint \overset{\circ}{\mathbf{R}} \cdot d\mathbf{k}\mathbf{1} - \oint d\mathbf{k}\overset{\circ}{\mathbf{R}} - \oint \overset{\circ}{\mathbf{R}} d\mathbf{k} \rangle. \tag{40}$$

In addition, however, there is yet a second part originating from the singularities (i.e. from the mechanical stresses in the actual particles). This part is easiest obtained by placing a control area into the suspension and regarding the forces acting on this area. Because of Eq. (36) only those parts contribute to the stress which are intersected by the control area. This gives after simple conversion by partial integration the part of stress originating from the particles:

$$\bar{\mathbf{s}}'' = -n \langle \oint \overset{\circ}{\mathbf{R}} d\mathbf{k} \rangle, \tag{41}$$

so that the complete equation of state gets the form

$$\bar{\mathbf{s}} = -\bar{p}\mathbf{1} + 2\mu\bar{\mathbf{f}} - n \langle \oint \overset{\circ}{\mathbf{R}} d\mathbf{k} \rangle. \tag{42}$$

The averages $\bar{\mathbf{s}}, \bar{p}, \bar{\mathbf{f}}$ and $\bar{\boldsymbol{\omega}}$ are phenomenological field quantities, whereas $\overset{\circ}{p}, \overset{\circ}{\mathbf{f}}$ and $\overset{\circ}{\boldsymbol{\omega}}$ represent auxiliary quantities which are only required to calculate the distribution of forces on the particle surface. Our above formulae, however, show that we make a mistake of higher order only with respect to particle concentration when replacing $\overset{\circ}{\mathbf{f}}$ by $\bar{\mathbf{f}}$ in the calculation of the additional stresses according to Eq. (41).

Finally, it may be pointed out that in all phenomenological quantities a distribution of forces occurs only in the form of the mean value of the tensor

$$\boldsymbol{\sigma} = - \oint \overset{\circ}{\mathbf{R}} d\mathbf{k}. \tag{43}$$

When anticipating that, in the absence of external torques, $\boldsymbol{\sigma}$ itself generally is not but $\langle \boldsymbol{\sigma} \rangle$ is always a symmetrical tensor, it is possible to write Eqs. (37), (38), (39) and (42) in the form:

$$\bar{p} = \overset{\circ}{p} + \frac{n}{3} \langle \boldsymbol{\sigma}. \rangle , \tag{37a}$$

$$\bar{\mathbf{f}} = \overset{\circ}{\mathbf{f}} - \frac{n}{5\mu} \langle \boldsymbol{\sigma} - \frac{1}{3}(\boldsymbol{\sigma}.) \rangle, \tag{38a}$$

$$\bar{\omega} = \overset{\circ}{\omega}, \tag{39a}$$

$$\bar{\mathbf{s}} = - \bar{p}\mathbf{1} + 2\mu\bar{\mathbf{f}} + n\langle \boldsymbol{\sigma} \rangle. \tag{42a}$$

From these formulae it is directly evident that with $\overset{\circ}{\mathbf{f}}$ also $\bar{\mathbf{f}}$ has zero trace but not necessarily $\bar{\mathbf{s}}$ too.

As a last but also most difficult part problem, there remains now to be discussed the determination of the distribution of forces, and the tensors $\boldsymbol{\sigma}$, $\mathbf{B}_{rot}$ and $\mathbf{b}$ to be derived therefrom. For this, we revert to Eq. (34) relating it this time, however, to an individual particle rather than to a totality; the index zero over $\overset{\circ}{\mathbf{R}}$ is omitted however in the following. By means of simple operations we obtain from this equation:

$$\mathbf{s(r)} = - p\mathbf{1} + \mu(\nabla\mathbf{v} + \mathbf{v}\nabla)$$

$$= - \overset{\circ}{p}\mathbf{1} + 2\mu\overset{\circ}{\mathbf{f}} - \frac{3}{4\pi} \oint_{\mathbf{R}} \frac{(\mathbf{r} - \mathbf{R})(\mathbf{r} - \mathbf{R})(\mathbf{r} - \mathbf{R}).d\mathbf{k(R)}}{|\mathbf{r} - \mathbf{R}|^5} . \tag{44}$$

For every surface element, however, the sum of the forces acting on it must vanish (because the inertia is neglected). The imaginary fluid located in the interior of the particle moves like a rigid body so that only by a hydrostatic pressure P, which must not necessarily coincide with $\overset{\circ}{p}$, it may contribute to the forces on the surface area, whereas the stress $\mathbf{s(R)}$ acts on the outside, this quantity being regarded as a boundary value of the stress in the fluid approaching from an external point to the surface. This gives the relation

$$d\mathbf{k(R)} = - [\mathbf{s(R)} + P\,\mathbf{1}] \cdot d\mathbf{A(R)} \tag{45}$$

wherein $d\mathbf{A}(\mathbf{R})$ means the directed surface element assigned to the vector $\mathbf{R}$. When this is inserted in Eq. (44), there results after simple conversion the formula

$$s(\mathbf{r}) = 2\mu\overset{\circ}{\mathbf{f}} + \frac{3}{4\pi}\oint_{\mathbf{R}}\frac{(\mathbf{r}-\mathbf{R}(\mathbf{r}-\mathbf{R})(\mathbf{s}-\mathbf{R}).\mathbf{r}(\mathbf{R}).d\mathbf{A}(\mathbf{R})}{|\mathbf{r}-\mathbf{R}|^5}$$

In this, use has been made of the fact that the integral on the right, when substituting $\mathbf{s}(\mathbf{R})$ by the unit tensor, vanishes for an external point. In addition, the undetermined quantity $\overset{\circ}{p}$ has been omitted ([32]). Eq. (46) applies to every external point, but not directly, when replacing $\mathbf{r}$ by a surface point $\mathbf{R}'$. In this case an additional term enters which describes the influence of the infinitesimal surroundings of $\mathbf{R}'$:

$$s(\mathbf{R}') = 2\mu\overset{\circ}{\mathbf{f}} + \frac{3}{4\pi}\oint_{\mathbf{R}}\frac{(\mathbf{R}'-\mathbf{R})(\mathbf{R}'-\mathbf{R})(\mathbf{R}'-\mathbf{R}).\mathbf{s}(\mathbf{R}).d\mathbf{A}(\mathbf{R})}{|\mathbf{R}'-\mathbf{R}|^5}$$

$$+ \tfrac{1}{2}[\mathbf{nn}.\mathbf{s}(\mathbf{R}') + \mathbf{s}(\mathbf{R}').\mathbf{nn} + (\mathbf{n}.\mathbf{s}(\mathbf{R}').\mathbf{n})(1 - 2\mathbf{nn})]. \tag{47}$$

Here $\mathbf{n}$ denotes the normal unit vector of the surface element at the position $\mathbf{R}'$.

This equation can be substantially simplified by scalar multiplication by $\mathbf{n}$: Except for $1/2\,\mathbf{n}.\mathbf{s}$, all terms inclosed in square brackets cancel each other out so that there remains:

$$\mathbf{n}.\left\{\frac{1}{2}\mathbf{s}(\mathbf{R}') - 2\mu\overset{\circ}{\mathbf{f}} - \frac{3}{4\pi}\oint_{\mathbf{R}}\frac{(\mathbf{R}'-\mathbf{R})(\mathbf{R}'-\mathbf{R})(\mathbf{R}'-\mathbf{R}).\mathbf{s}(\mathbf{R}).d\mathbf{A})}{|\mathbf{R}'-\mathbf{R}|^5}\right\} = 0. \tag{48}$$

While the vanishing of the bracket itself does not follow from this relation, a quantity $\mathbf{s}^*(\mathbf{R}')$ which satisfies the equation

$$s^*(\mathbf{R}') = 4\mu\overset{\circ}{\mathbf{f}} + \frac{3}{2\pi}\oint_{\mathbf{R}}\frac{(\mathbf{R}'-\mathbf{R})(\mathbf{R}'-\mathbf{R})(\mathbf{R}'-\mathbf{R}).\mathbf{s}^*(\mathbf{R}).d\mathbf{A}(\mathbf{R})}{|\mathbf{R}'-\mathbf{R}|^5} \tag{49}$$

supplies the true distribution of forces for the surface since

$$\mathbf{n}.\mathbf{s}^* = \mathbf{n}.\mathbf{s} \tag{50}$$

([32]) This is no restriction of the generality. Otherwise, we would only have to formulate the above integral relation for the quantity $s(\mathbf{r}) + \overset{\circ}{p}\,\mathbf{1}$ instead of for $s(\mathbf{r})$.

applies([33]). Eq. (49) thus is an integral equation for the distribution of forces the solution of which supplies a complete answer to the hydrodynamic problem([34]).

This equation is of the type of an integral equation of the second kind, and accordingly, it is possible to state for it directly a solution in form of a Neumann series. When writing symbolically—the asterisk is now omitted for the sake of simplicity:

$$\mathbf{s} - \mathcal{K}\mathbf{s} = 4\mu\overset{\circ}{\mathbf{f}} \tag{49a}$$

$$\mathcal{K}\mathbf{s} = \frac{3}{2\pi}\oint_R \frac{(\mathbf{R}'-\mathbf{R})(\mathbf{R}'-\mathbf{R})(\mathbf{R}'-\mathbf{R}).\mathbf{s}(\mathbf{R}).dA(\mathbf{R})}{|\mathbf{R}'-\mathbf{R}|^5}, \tag{49b}$$

this series, as is well-known, reads:

$$\mathbf{s} = 2\{\mathcal{I} + \mathcal{K} + \mathcal{K}^2 + \mathcal{K}^3 + ...\}\,2\mu\overset{\circ}{\mathbf{f}}, \tag{50}$$

wherein $\mathcal{I}$ denotes the unit operator. The convergence of this series, of course, has to be examined.

From this solution it is easily shown that it complies with the condition (36), i.e. it corresponds to a particle which is not subjected to any external forces. Likewise, the tensor assigned in accordance with Eq, (43)

$$\sigma = \oint \mathbf{R}\mathbf{s} . d\mathbf{A} \tag{51}$$

is symmetrical, which means that no torque is exerted either on such particles. They thus move exclusively under the influence of the flow field. The solution given by Eq. (50), therefore, corresponds to the *flow part* of the equation of state.

As is readily seen, the operator of Eq. (50), i.e. the series in curved brackets, is a tensor of fourth order forming a double dot product with $\overset{\circ}{\mathbf{f}}$. In accord-

---

(33) Once $\mathbf{s}^*$ has been calculated, it is possible to obtain $\mathbf{s}$ from this by means of the formula derived from Eq. (47):

$$\mathbf{s} = \tfrac{1}{2}\,[\mathbf{s}^* + \mathbf{n}\mathbf{n}.\mathbf{s}^* + \mathbf{s}^*.\mathbf{n}\mathbf{n} + (\mathbf{n}.\mathbf{s}^*.\mathbf{n})\,(1-2\mathbf{n}\mathbf{n})]. \tag{47a}$$

This quantity, however, is of no interest for our considerations.

(34) When substituting $\mathbf{s}(\mathbf{R}) = -P\mathbf{1}$ for any arbitrary internal point into Eq. (46), followed by $\mathbf{r}$ tending towards a surface point, Eq. (48) is obtained again after simple conversion. This gives the first part of the proof that our solutions satisfy the boundary conditions since they show that the symmetrical part of the zero-trace tensor $\nabla\mathbf{v}$ in the interior vanishes. What remains then still to be proved is that the antisymmetrical part in the interior is constant.

ance with this, σ is a linear function of $\overset{\circ}{\mathbf{f}}$. When expressing this equation in the form

$$\sigma = 2\{\mathscr{G}^{(0)} + \mathscr{G}^{(1)} + \mathscr{G}^{(2)} + ...\} 2\mu\overset{\circ}{\mathbf{f}}, \tag{52}$$

the first term is the unit tensor multiplied by the particle volume V, whereas the following terms can be obtained recursively. Their Cartesian components are:

$$\mathscr{G}^{(0)}_{ikv\mu} \overset{\circ}{f}_{v\mu} = V\delta_{iv}\delta_{k\mu}\overset{\circ}{f}_{v\mu} = V\overset{\circ}{f}_{ik}$$

$$\mathscr{G}^{(n)}_{ikv\mu}\overset{\circ}{f}_{v\mu} = \sum_{m=0}^{n} \oint_{R} \mathscr{R}^{(m)}_{ikv} dA_\mu(\mathbf{R})\overset{\circ}{f}_{v\mu} \tag{53}$$

with

$$\mathscr{R}^{(0)}_{ikl} = R_i\delta_{kl}$$

$$\mathscr{R}^{(1)}_{ikl} = \frac{3}{2\pi}\oint_{R'}\frac{(R'_i - R_i)(R'_k - R_k)(R'_l - R_l)(R'_\mu - R_\mu)\, dA_\mu(\mathbf{R}')}{|\mathbf{R}' - \mathbf{R}|^5}$$

$$\mathscr{R}^{(m)}_{ikl} = \frac{3}{2\pi}\oint_{R'}\mathscr{R}^{(m-1)}_{ikv}\frac{(R'_v - R_v)(R'_l - R_l)(R'_\mu - R_\mu)\, dA_\mu(\mathbf{R}')}{|\mathbf{R}' - \mathbf{R}|^5}. \tag{54}$$

From these formulae the symmetry of σ, as claimed above, is immediately seen.

In addition, it may be pointed out that for spherical particles, of course, the $\mathscr{G}^{(n)}_{iklm}$ with $n > 0$ are also isotropical tensors. For $n = 1$, e.g., we have

$$\mathscr{G}^{(1)}_{iklm} = \frac{1}{5}V\delta_{il}\delta_{km}. \tag{55}$$

Zeroth and first approximation together thus amount to as much as 96% of the Einstein value of the exact solution.

Since the tensor $\mathbf{b}$, discussed in connection with the statistical problem, is governed by the flow part, we are able to calculate this quantity. In this case too, we depart from Eq. (34) and calculate from this the rotation velocity

$$\omega(r) = \frac{1}{2}(\nabla v - v\nabla) = \overset{\circ}{\omega} - \frac{1}{8\pi\mu}\oint_{R}\frac{(r-R)dk - dk(r-R)}{|r-R|^3}$$

$$= \overset{\circ}{\omega} + \frac{1}{8\pi\mu}\oint_{R}\frac{(r-R)s.dA - dA.s(r-R)}{|r-R|^3} \qquad (56)$$

Equivalent to this is the vectorial formulation:

$$\vec{\omega}(r) = \overset{\circ}{\vec{\omega}} + \frac{1}{8\pi\mu}\oint_{R}\frac{(r-R)\times s.dA}{|r-R|^3}, \qquad (56a)$$

wherein $\vec{\omega}$ and $\overset{\circ}{\vec{\omega}}$ denote the vectors dual to the antisymmetrical tensors ω and $\overset{\circ}{\omega}$. For an internal point, however, $\omega(r)$ represents tensor w, independent of r, and $\vec{\omega}(r)$ the vector $\vec{w}$ according to Eq. (32) respectively which in the case of rigid particles, in turn, corresponds to the quantity $V^{(S)}$ of Eq. (29). This means that

$$b..\overset{\circ}{f} = \frac{1}{8\pi\mu}\oint_{R}\frac{(r-R)\times s.dA}{|r-R|^3}, \qquad (57)$$

wherein r must be an internal point—e.g. $r = 0$—and s must be substituted in accordance with Eq. (50). The Cartesian components of b then read:

$$b_{ijk} = \frac{\varepsilon_{iv\mu}}{2\pi}\oint_{R}\frac{(r_v - R_v)\{\delta_{\mu j}\delta_{\lambda k} + \mathscr{K}_{\mu\lambda jk} + ...\}dA_{\lambda}(R)}{|r-R|^3}. \qquad (57a)$$

Herein $\varepsilon_{iv\mu}$ denotes the well-known permutation symbol.

Eq. (50), however, is not the general solution of the integral equation (49) but only a particular integral. In general, a solution of the homogeneous equation

$$s - \mathscr{K}s = 0 \qquad (58)$$

must be added. The solutions of this equation can be subdivided into two classes. To the first belongs a non-vanishing resultant force

$$K = \oint dk = -\oint s.dA, \qquad (59)$$

but a vanishing torque

$$M = \oint\{Rdk - dkR\} = -\oint\{Rs.dA - dA.sR\} = \tilde{\sigma} - \sigma, \qquad (60)$$

to the second, inversely, a vanishing resultant force but a non-vanishing torque. Only the second class is of importance for our problem, as the *diffusion part* of the equation of state and the rotation-diffusion constant are determined from it.

If Eq. (58) is to possess a non-trivial solution, then $\mathscr{K}^n$s must not converge against zero. Such solution is obtained when it is possible to state any function $\overset{\circ}{s}$ for which $\mathscr{K}^n\overset{\circ}{s}$ converges in the limit $n \to \infty$ against a function s, and this limiting function

$$s = \lim_{n \to \infty} \mathscr{K}^n \overset{\circ}{s} \tag{61}$$

is the desired solution.

It is easy now to state such $\overset{\circ}{s}$-functions for the two cases mentioned above, i.e. those functions which correspond to the translational or the rotational motion of an infinitesimal sphere, in which case the singularity of these functions must necessarily coincide with an interior point of the particle. When equating, e.g., **r** to zero, these functions are for translational motion:

$$\overset{\circ}{s}(\mathbf{r}') = -\frac{3}{4\pi}\frac{\mathbf{r}'\mathbf{r}'\mathbf{r}'}{r'^5} \cdot \mathbf{K} \tag{62}$$

and for rotational motion:

$$\overset{\circ}{s}(\mathbf{r}') = -\frac{3}{4\pi}\frac{\mathbf{r}'\mathbf{r}' \cdot \mathbf{M} - \mathbf{M} \cdot \mathbf{r}'\mathbf{r}'}{r'^5}. \tag{63}$$

It can be easily proved that the quantities **K** and **M** occurring in these expressions coincide with the corresponding quantities defined in Eqs. (59) and (60) and that for Eq. (62) $\mathbf{M} = 0$, for Eq. (63), inversely, $\mathbf{K} = 0$.

When inserting into Eq. (56) the solution of the homogeneous equation obtained by introducing Eq. (63) into Eq. (61), where however $\overset{\circ}{\omega}$ must now be equated to zero, a linear tensor relation between ω and **M** is obtained, whose coefficient after definition is the rotation mobility. When introducing now instead of the tensors ω and **M** the vectors $\vec{\omega}$ and $\vec{\mathbf{M}}$, which are dual to them, the components of the tensor $\mathbf{B}_{rot}$, defined by the equation

$$\vec{\omega} = \mathbf{B}_{rot} \cdot \vec{\mathbf{M}}$$

are

$$\{\mathbf{B}_{rot}\}_{ik} = \frac{3}{32\pi^2\mu}\varepsilon_{iv\mu} \lim_{n \to \infty} \oint_{\mathbf{R}'} \frac{R'_\nu}{R'^3}\left\{\mathscr{K}^n_{\mu\lambda\rho\sigma}\frac{R_\rho R_\tau \varepsilon_{\tau\sigma k} + R_\sigma R_\tau \varepsilon_{\tau\rho k}}{R^5}\right\} dA_\lambda(\mathbf{R}'). \tag{65}$$

At this stage the study has to be interrupted for the time being. Although the methods presented in this paper do not yet constitute an explicit approach to the problems dealt with by the examples of the preceding sections, it may be seen at the present stage of theory that they offer some substantial advantages as compared with the earlier methods, and these advantages are bound to become manifest when it is desired to gain a survey on the order of magnitude of effects, e.g. for determining the extreme values of the quantities n_F, n_G and m discussed in section 4 or for obtaining an answer to the question which parameters of particle shape influence the rheological properties and which do not.

List of symbols.

The numbers in parentheses indicate the formulae, where the symbols appear for the first time.

$\mathbf{a}_i$	$=$	mapping tensor with respect to the deformation of the i-th network structure	(12)
$d\mathbf{A}$	$=$	vector of surface element	(45)
b	$=$	parameter of slenderness of a spheroid or a cross dumbbell	(16;17)
$\mathbf{b}$	$=$	third order tensor connected with a particle	(29)
B, B_i	$=$	scalar mobility constant (of the i-th kind of particle)	(9)
B_{rot}	$=$	scalar rotation-mobility constant	(21)
$\mathbf{B}_{rot}$	$=$	tensor of rotation-mobility	(28)
$\mathbf{c}^{-1}, \mathbf{c}^{-1}_i$	$=$	Finger's measure of deformation(of the i-th network structure)	(12)
D/Dt	$=$	material time derivative	(1)
$\mathscr{D}/\mathscr{D}t$	$=$	rotational invariant time derivative	(1)
$\mathfrak{D}/\mathfrak{D}t$	$=$	contravariant convective time derivative	(7)
$\mathbf{D}_{rot}$	$=$	rotation-diffusion tensor	(26)
$\mathbf{f}$	$=$	flow tensor	(29)
$\mathbf{f}^{(n)}, \hat{\mathbf{f}}^{(n)}$	$=$	rotational invariant (contravariant) kinematic tensors	(1;13)
F	$=$	shear-flow normal-stress function with respect to the direction of flow	(4)
G	$=$	shear-flow normal-stress function with respect to the direction of flow gradient	(4)
$\mathscr{G}$	$=$	generalised moment of operator $\mathscr{K}$	(52)
H	$=$	shear-viscosity function in shear flow	(4)
$\mathscr{I}$	$=$	unit operator	(50)
$d\mathbf{k}$	$=$	force on a surface element	(34)

$\mathbf{K}$	=	resultant force on a particle	(59)
$\mathscr{K}$	=	integral operator	(49b)
m	=	ratio of both shear-flow normal-stress functions	(15)
$\mathbf{M}, \vec{\mathbf{M}}$	=	tensor (vector) of torque	(60; 64)
n, n_i	=	number of particles (of the i-th kind) in the unit volume	(9; 21)
n_F, n_G	=	ratios of shear-flow normal-stress and shear-stress functions	(15)
$\mathbf{n}$	=	unit vector of normal direction	(47)
p	=	hydrostatic pressure; ratio of spheroid diameters	(2; 16)
P	=	hydrostatic pressure in the interior of a particle	(45)
$\mathbf{P}$	=	aggregate of particle parameters	(23)
$\mathbf{r}, \mathbf{r}_i$	=	position vector of a particle (of the i-th kind) or of a point of the flow field	(9; 31)
R	=	parameter of flow type in two-dimensional flow	(22)
$\mathbf{R}$	=	position vector of surface points	(32)
$\mathbf{s}, s_{ik}$	=	stress tensor (Cartesian components)	(2; 4)
s_{ik}^*	=	components proportional to s_{ik} (viscosity coefficients)	(21)
$\mathbf{S}$	=	tensor of state of a Weissenberg-fluid	(7)
$\mathbf{u}$	=	translation-velocity of a particle	(32)
$\mathbf{v}$	=	velocity of the flow field	(1)
V	=	volume of a particle	(53)
$\mathbf{V}$	=	time derivative of particle parameters	(23)
$\mathbf{w}, \vec{\mathbf{w}}$	=	tensor (vector) of particle rotation-velocity	(32)
γ	=	shear	(4)
ε	=	deformation part of two-dimensional flow	(18)
$\overset{\circ}{\eta}, \overset{\circ}{\eta}_i$	=	intrinsic viscosity of a Weissenberg fluid (connected with the i-th network structure)	(10; 12)
ϑ	=	Eulerian angle	(24)
μ	=	viscosity of Newtonian suspending agent	(30)
ρ	=	mass density; parameter of the flow type in two-dimensional flow; distribution of parameters	(7;19;23)
$\boldsymbol{\sigma}$	=	generalised moment of a particle	(43)
τ	=	relaxation time	(15)
φ	=	orientation angle of a cross dumbbell; Eulerian angle	(20;24)
ψ	=	Eulerian angle	(24)
ω	=	rotation part of two-dimensional flow	(18)
$\boldsymbol{\omega}, \vec{\boldsymbol{\omega}}$	=	tensor (vector) of rotation velocity	(1;29)
$\aleph^{(\alpha \ldots \delta)}$	=	material functions connected with the equation of state	(2)
$\aleph_{m \ldots n}^{(\alpha \ldots \delta)}$	=	material constants connected with the equation of state	(3)

$\beth^{(n)}$ = material functions connected with the equation of state
of a Weissenberg fluid (13)

∇ = nabla operator (del) (1)

∇^2 = Laplace's operator (30)

1 = unit tensor (idem factor) (2)

III = third invariant of a second order tensor (12)

REFERENCES

[1] H. Lamb, *Hydrodynamics*, 6th ed. Cambridge (1952), pp. 604–5.

[2] G. B. Jeffery, *Proc. Roy. Soc.*, **A102**, (1922), 161.

[3] G. I. Taylor, *Proc. Roy. Soc.*, **A146**, (1934), 501.

[4] A. Peterlin, *Z. Phys.*, **111**, (1938), 232.

[5] W. Kuhn and H. Kuhn, *Helv. Chim. Acta*, **28**, (1945), 97.

[6] K. Weissenberg, Proc. 1st Intern. Congr. Rheology, Amsterdam 1948, Vol. I, 29 (1949).

[7] J. G. Kirkwood, *Rec. trav. chim.*, **68**, (1949), 649; *J. Polym. Sci.*, **12**, (1954), 1;
     J. Riseman and J. G. Kirkwood, *in:* F. Eirich, *Rheology*, Vol. I, pp. 495, New York (1956).

[8] J. E. Roberts, Proc. 2nd Intern. Congr. Rheology, Oxford 1953, London (1954), pp.91

[9] H. Markovitz and R. B. Williamson, *Trans. Soc. Rheol.*, **1**, (1957), 25.

[10] S. Prager, *Trans. Soc. Rheol.*, **1**, (1957), 53.

[11] W. Noll, *Arch. Rational Mech. Anal* **2** (1958), 197.

[12] A. J. M. Spencer and R. S. Rivlin, *Arch. Rational Mech. Anal.*,**2**, (1959), 309; **2**, (1959), 435; **4**, (1960), 214.

[13] T. Kotaka, *J. Chem. Phys.*, **30**, (1959), 1566.

[14] P. U. A. Grossman, *Kolloid.-Z.*, **174**, (1961), 97.

[15] W. Philippoff, *Rheol. Acta*, **1**, (1961), 371.

[16] W. Philippoff, *Trans. Soc. Rheol.*, **5**, (1961), 149.

[17] H. Giesekus, *Kolloid-Z.*, **147**, (1956), 29.

[18] H. Giesekus, *Rheol. Acta.* **1**, (1958), 2.

[19] H. Giesekus, *Rheol. Acta*, **1**, (1961), 395.

[20] H. Giesekus, *Rheol. Acta*, **1**, (1961), 404.

[21] H. Giesekus, *Rheol. Acta*, **2**, (1962), 50.

[22] H. Giesekus, *ZAMM* **42** (1962), 32.

[23] H. Giesekus, *Rheol. Acta*, **2**, (1962), 101.

[24] H. Giesekus, *Rheol. Acta*, **2**, (1962), 112.

[25] H. Giesekus, *Rheol. Acta*, **2**, (1962), 122.

[26] H. Giesekus, *ZAMM*, **42**, (1962), 259.

NORMAL STRESS MEASUREMENTS ON
A POLYISOBUTYLENE-CETANE SOLUTION IN
PARALLEL PLATE AND CONE-PLATE INSTRUMENTS

HERSHEL MARKOVITZ AND DAVID R. BROWN

Mellon Institute, Pittsburgh 13, Pennsylvania, U.S.A.

ABSTRACT

Normal stress measurements were obtained on a solution of polyisobutylene in cetane in steady torsional shearing between two parallel circular plates and between a cone and plate at shear rates from 0.3 to 300 sec^{-1}. At rates of shear below 2 sec^{-1}, a quadratic dependence of the normal stress behaviour on rate of shear is found and thus a zero shear normal stress coefficient can be determined. The comparison of the experimental results from the two geometries is not compatible with deductions based on the assumption of a simple laminar flow and any theory of the type that involves a simple proportionality between the normal stress functions.

A number of very general phenomenological theories of viscoelastic fluids have been discussed in the recent literature. Even for very general types of fluids the equations of motion can be solved for certain simple types of steady flow [1],[2],[3]. For such flows, three functions of the rate of shear are, in general, required to characterize the material [4],[5],[2]. One of these deals with the shearing stress and can be evaluated by one of the methods used in obtaining the shear rate dependence of the viscosity. The other two deal with the normal stresses. We have previously [4] indicated how they can be determined from measurements made in instruments of different geometries. In this paper we present data obtained by submitting a polymer solution to a continuous torsional deformation between parallel discs and between a cone and a plate.

Experimental.

The apparatus employed was, except for details, copied from that of Greensmith and Rivlin [6]. Following a technique suggested by Garner, Nissan and Wood [7], the pressure distribution over a surface was measured while the liquid was being sheared in a torsional type of flow. In the "parallel plate" mode, the liquid was sheared between the parallel flat bottoms of two coaxial cylindrical cups, the inner one of which was stationary while the outer one was driven at a constant speed. The surface tractions normal to the base of the stationary cup at various distances from the axis of rotation were measured by allowing the liquid to flow through holes in this base into glass manometer tubes where the height of liquid could be read by means of a cathetometer. In the "cone and plate" mode an accurate cone machined to fit snugly into the outer cup, was installed. The angle between the generator of the cone and the normal to axis was $\tan^{-1} .0352 = 2°1.0'$. The inner cup was positioned with the center of its bottom at the point where the apex of the cone would have been if the cone had not been truncated by 0.002". For most of the details of construction and operation we refer the reader to the article by Greensmith and Rivlin [6]. We give here only such details which might be of special interest or which differ to some degree from their instrument.

The outer cup was attached to the vertical shaft output of a worm gear speed reducer whose input shaft was coupled to a continuously variable speed transmission (Graham Transmissions, Inc., Menomenee Falls, Wisconsin) driven by a synchronous motor. For lower speeds a second speed reducer was inserted. Thus speeds of rotation of the cup, constant to $\pm 0.5\%$, from 0.25 to 125 rpm could be obtained. The direction of rotation could be reversed.

The holes in the base of the inner cup were of 1.5 mm diameter and arranged in a spiral pattern [6].

The temperature of the test liquid was controlled to $30.0° \pm 0.1°C$ by circulating water from a thermostat to the inside of the inner cup and the water-jacket surrounding the outer cup.

The liquid menisci in the manometer tubes were maintained at a convenient level for observation by connecting all of the tubes to a bulb which was maintained at a constant pressure somewhat below atmospheric by using a 100 ml hypodermic syringe as a dead weight gauge. The details of this manostat will be published separately. The pressure difference could be maintained constant over periods of hours to about ± 0.05 mm of solution. The levels of the menisci were determined with the outer cup at rest and with both directions of rotation at each speed. Because the bottoms of the two cylinders were not quite parallel to each other (deviation of about 0.001"), the steady-state levels were somewhat different in the two senses of rotation. The average of these two sets of readings is the quantity that is reported throughout this paper. Several hours were required to attain an equilibrium level of the menisci which were read to 0.01 mm by the cathetometer although the accuracy was estimated from the scatter of points to be less than 0.05 mm usually.

The solution was made by dissolving commercial polyisobutylene (Oppanol B100 from BASF) in cetane (99% minimum purity n-hexadecane obtained from Humphrey-Wilkinson, North Haven, Connecticut). The concentration was 6.86% by weight. R. E. Kerwin determined the viscosity average molecular weight, M, from the intrinsic viscosity, $[\eta]$, in cyclohexane at 30° to be 1.2×10^6 by use of the formula [8] $[\eta] = 2.7 \times 10^{-4} M^{0.70}$. The density of the solution was found to be 0.776 g/cm³. The zero shear viscosity was estimated to be 60.2 poises by the falling ball method. Two different size stainless steel balls (0.351 and 0.794 mm diameter) gave the same result to within ± 0.6%. Originally a considerable amount of data was obtained on solutions in decalin (decahydro-naphthalene) but the concentration increased slightly due to the evaporation of solvent during the several weeks it took to make the measurements and caused changes in the normal pressures to the extent of several per cent. It was then the change was made to the less volatile solvent, cetane.

Experimental results.

Figure 1 shows the data obtained in the parallel plate geometry with a gap of 0.638 cm at some of the speeds of rotation which were employed. They are displayed in two separate plots because of the range of the pressures covered. To avoid crowding, some of the runs have been omitted and curves been shifted vertically by arbitrary amounts. The abscissa, $\bar{h}$, represents the average of the height of the menisci for the two directions of rotation after corrections for the centrifugal effects (see below). On the curve for 123.6 rpm are the data for duplicate runs made on the same solution two weeks apart during which period most of the runs at the other speeds had been made. This served as a test for the stability of the solution and the precision of the data. As Greensmith and Rivlin point out, there is a considerable range of variables where $\bar{h}$ is linear in r but, at low values of r and ω the curves are concave to the r-axis while at high values of r and ω, the curves are convex to that axis. Here r is the distance from the axis of rotation and ω is the speed of rotation in radians per second. Data which were obtained with a gap of 0.324 cm are exhibited in a different form in a later graph.

Figure 2 shows the results obtained on the same solution with the instrument operated in the cone and plate mode. The abscissa has the same significance as in Figure 1. Here, however, the ordinate is the logarithm of r. The resulting plots are to a good approximation linear.

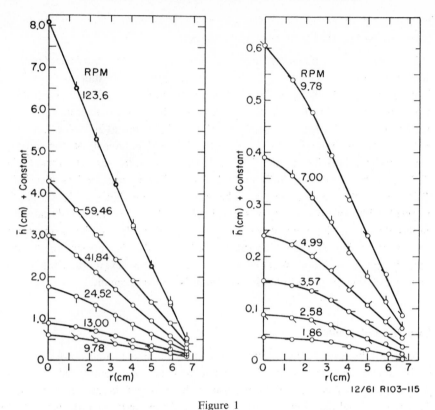

Figure 1

Pressure distribution in parallel plate experiments (gap of 0.638 cm) shown as the variation of $\bar{h}$ with r for various speeds of rotation as indicated. Runs made at 80.0 and 17.6 rpm are omitted to avoid crowding. For the same reason the curves have been shifted vertically by various amounts

Discussion.

The results of many of the phenomenological theories of incompressible fluids for certain types of laminar flow can be summarized in a rather simple way. Let us consider an infinitesimal volume of the fluid determined by the natural orthogonal coordinate surfaces: e.g. cylindrical coordinates in the torsional parallel disc, Couette, or Poiseuille flow and spherical coordinates in the cone and plate flow. Let us label the coordinate representing the direction of motion of a particle of fluid x^1, that perpendicular to the shearing surface x^2, and the remaining one x^3 in the "neutral" direction. (This notation, different from that in our previous paper [4], was adopted to bring it into conformity with that apparently almost unanimously preferred by others.) See Figure 3. Using such a coordinate system it turns out that, for all these cases, the *physical compo-*

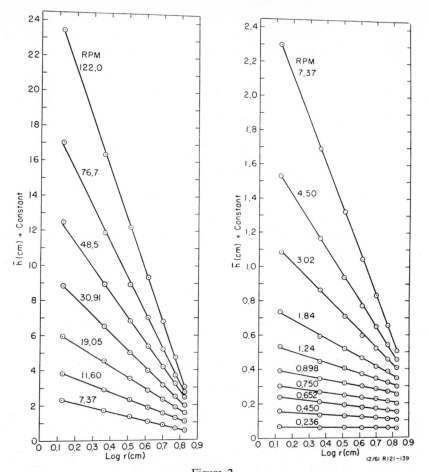

Figure 2

Pressure distribution in the cone and plate experiments shown as the variation of $\bar{h}$ with log r for various speeds of rotation are indicated. Curves have been shifted vertically by various amounts

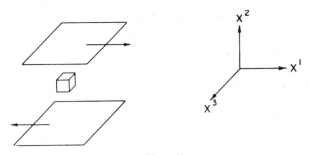

Figure 3

General coordinates used for description of flow

nents of the stress deviator, $- v_i$ are functions of the rate of shear, $\dot{\gamma}$, appropriate to each geometry. We summarize the results in terms of material functions $v_i(\dot{\gamma})$ and $\eta(\dot{\gamma})$ as defined in the following equations:

$$t_{11} - t = - v_I(\dot{\gamma}) \tag{1}$$

$$t_{22} - t = - v_{II}(\dot{\gamma}) \tag{2}$$

$$t_{33} - t = - v_{III}(\dot{\gamma}) \tag{3}$$

$$t_{12} = \dot{\gamma}\eta(\dot{\gamma}) \tag{4}$$

$$t_{13} = t_{23} = 0 \tag{5}$$

where the t_{ij} are the physical components of the stress tensor and t is the average of the normal stresses:

$$t_{11} + t_{22} + t_{33} = 3t \tag{6}$$

and therefore only two of the v_i are independent since:

$$v_I + v_{II} + v_{III} = 0. \tag{7}$$

The $v_i(\dot{\gamma})$ and $\eta(\dot{\gamma})$ are even functions of the rate of shear, $v_i(0) = 0$, and $\eta(\dot{\gamma})$ is the shear-dependent viscosity commonly used by rheologists. It is clear that differences between the physical components of the normal stresses, e.g., $t_{11} - t_{33}$, $t_{22} - t_{33}$, $t_{11} - t_{22}$ are also functions of the rate of shear and can be used as material functions to characterize the material.

Parallel plate torsional motion [1], [3], [4], [9]. In this case a cylindrical mass of the material is being sheared between two sufficiently large discs, the one at $z = 0$ being stationary while the one at $z = l$ is rotating with a speed ω. In the laminar flow visualized here, a particle of the fluid located at a distance of r from the axis of rotation has only a radial component of the velocity which is equal to $\omega r z/l$ and thus the rate of shear is $\omega r/l$. Such a flow is not compatible with the equations of motion unless the inertia of the fluid is neglected. In this case these equations yield the result that

$$\frac{\partial t_{zz}}{\partial r} = \frac{\partial}{\partial r}(v_{III} - v_{II}) + \frac{v_{III} - v_I}{r} \tag{8}$$

which can be rearranged to a form more convenient for some purposes:

$$\frac{\partial t_{zz}}{\partial \ln r} = 3v_{III} + (v_{III} - v_{II}) \left[\frac{\partial \ln(v_{III} - v_{II})}{\partial \ln r} - 1 \right] \tag{9}$$

or which can be integrated to give

$$t_{zz}(r) - t_{zz}(0) = \rho g(h_0 - \bar{h}) = v_{III} - v_{II} + \int_0^{\dot{\gamma}} \frac{(v_{III} - v_I)}{\dot{\gamma}'} d\dot{\gamma}' \tag{10}$$

Here h_0 is the level of the meniscus in the tube at the axis of rotation, ρ is the density of the fluid, g is the acceleration of gravity, t_{zz} is that component of the stress being measured in this experiment and the fact that $v_i(0) = 0$ was used. Thus, for a given fluid, $[t_{zz}(0) - t_{zz}(r)]$ or $(h_0 - \bar{h})$ is a function only of $\dot{\gamma}$ for all gap sizes and speeds of rotation.

It is expected that the inertia of the fluid will give rise to a centrifugal effect which will result in secondary flow. It has been pointed out [6] that the amount of this secondary flow will be greatly reduced in very viscous fluids and in small gaps. It has been suggested that the influence of this effect manifests itself as a pressure which was estimated to be

$$\bar{h}_c = A + Br^2 \tag{11}$$

where $B = \omega^2/6g = (1.70 \times 10^{-4} \, \text{sec}^2/\text{cm})\omega^2$ independent of whether the liquid is Newtonian or non-Newtonian. This expression was tested by Greensmith and Rivlin with some Newtonian liquids and found to be in satisfactory agreement with experiments on materials of sufficiently high viscosity. We have repeated this experiment with a viscous base lubricating oil. A linear plot is obtained when $\bar{h}$ is plotted against r^2 for each speed of rotation. The slope of this line B, is graphed against ω^2 in Figure 4. We have also included the data of Greensmith and Rivlin [6] for their lubricating oil. We find that $B = (1.5 \times 10^{-4} \, \text{sec}^2/\text{cm})\omega^2$ gives a better fit to both sets of data than the derived constant 1.70×10^{-4}. This expression was then used to calculate a corection which was applied to the data on polymer solutions. At the tube closest to the edge this correction amounted to less than 0.01 cm for speeds less than about 11 rpm and was about 1.1 cm at 120 rpm. This correction has been included in the data of Figure 1.

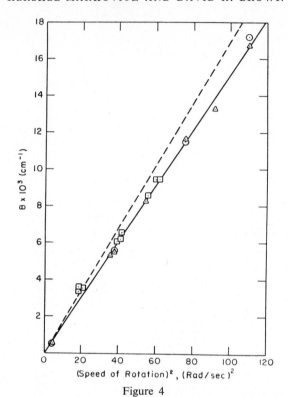

Figure 4

Centrifugal effect for a viscous Newtonian lubricating oil shown as the variation of B with the square of the speed of rotation. $-----$ calculated from approximate theory [6]. ⊡ Parallel plate data of Greensmith and Rivlin [6]. △ Present parallel plate data. ⊙ Cone and plate data

From equation (10) it is expected that all the data for a given liquid obtained at various gap sizes and speeds of rotation should produce a single curve when $(h_0 - \bar{h})$ is plotted as a function of the rate of shear $(\omega r/l)$. That this is true to a good approximation for this solution is seen in Figure 5 where data at 13 speeds from 1.9 to 120 rpm with the gap of 0.638 cm all fall rather well on a single curve. Almost all of the points lie within about 1% of the common curve except for the data from the lowest speeds. We also include in this figure the data obtained with a gap of 0.324 cm at 7 speeds from 8.5 to 120 rpm. (At the lower speeds with the smaller gap the data from the tube next to the center one are omitted because it was found later that an air bubble had been lodged in the solution beneath it. Apparently this also affected the center tube reading since a correction of 0.1 to 0.2 cm to the value of h_0 for each of the lower speed runs with the 0.324 cm gap would bring them within the small scatter of the 0.638 cm gap data.)

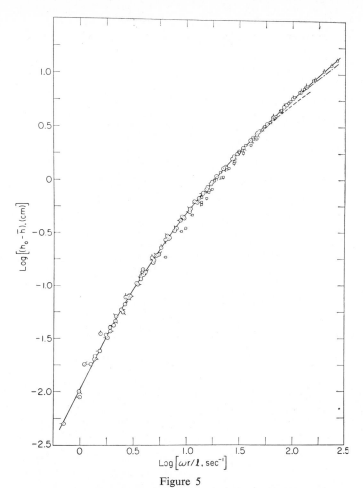

Figure 5

Summary of parallel plate normal stress data exhibited as the variation of log $(h_0 - \bar{h})$ with log $(\omega r/l)$. Circles indicate data obtained at a gap of 0.638 cm with the speed of rotation being indicated by the direction of the pip using the same code as in Figure 1. Squares indicate data from 0.324 cm gap with the pip on top indicating a speed of 123.2 rpm and pips rotating clockwise for the other speeds, respectively, 72.8, 48.3, 32.14, 21.26, 13.18, and 8.53 rpm. — — — — — 0.638 cm gap data without centrifugal correction. — — — - 0.324 cm gap data without centrifugal correction

The agreement also provides a test of the stability of the solution which had been used for the runs at the larger gap and of the reproducibility in reassembling the apparatus after it had been taken apart to change the gap size. The effect of applying the centrifugal correction is also exhibited in Figure 5. The dashed curves at the high rates of shear are plots of the data before this correc-

tion is applied. The data from the two gap sizes do not form a single curve
unless the centrifugal correction is applied.

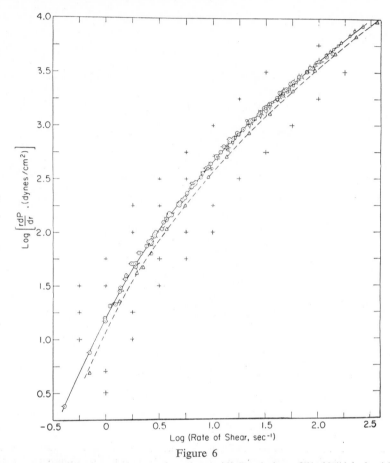

Figure 6

Summary of parallel plate and cone-plate data as the variation of $\log(dP/d\ln r)$ with log
$(\dot{\gamma})$. For parallel plate curve (——), $P = t_{zz}$. For cone and plate curve (— — —), $P = t_{\theta\theta}$.
Circles and squares with their pips have the same significance as in Figure 5. Triangles are
from cone and plate data. Crosses are coordinate markers inserted to assist in reading values
from the curves

The data are shown in Figure 6 in still another form: $\partial t_{zz}/\partial \ln r$ as a function
of the rate of shear. Plots of $\log(h_0 - \bar{h})$ vs. $\log \dot{\gamma}$ were made for each speed
of rotation and the slope determined at each experimental point as

$$\frac{\partial t_{zz}}{\partial \ln r} = \rho g(h_0 - \bar{h})\frac{\partial \log(h_0 - \bar{h})}{\partial \log \dot{\gamma}}$$

The va ues of $\partial t_{zz}/\partial \ln r$ obtained from the various runs are distinguished by different symbols. There is also good agreement among the data from the two different gaps. The small degree of scatter here is a rather good test of the consistency of the data since it depends on slopes of plots of the type shown in Figure 5.

Cone and plate torsional motion [3], [10-13]. Here it is envisaged that the material is sheared between a conical surface and a disc which passes through the apex of the cone and which is perpendicular to the axis of the cone. Thus, using a system of spherical coordinates with r the distance from the origin, θ the angle of colatitude, and ϕ the azimuth, the shearing surfaces are at $\theta = \pi/2$ and $\theta = \pi/2 + \beta$. (It will be clear from the context when r refers to a spherical coordinate as it does here, and when to a cylindrical coordinate as it does in the discussion of the parallel plate experiment.) In the laminar flow assumed here, the conical surfaces $\theta = $ constant are the surfaces of constant velocity. The only non-zero component of the velocity is that in the ϕ-direction, $v_\phi = r\omega^*$ where ω^* is a function of θ but not of r or ϕ. The rate of shear $(\dot{\gamma})$ varies somewhat with θ, but this variation is small if β is small. To a good approximation, $\dot{\gamma} = \omega/\beta$ where ω is the angular velocity of the rotating cone. If such a velocity distribution is assumed, the equations of motion can, in general, be solved only if the inertia of the fluid is neglected and if an appropriate distribution of body forces is supplied [3], [11], [12]. Under these conditions, the pressure distribution on the flat plate is given by

$$\frac{\partial t_{\theta\theta}}{\partial \ln r} = -\rho g \frac{\partial \bar{h}}{\partial \ln r} = 3v_{III} \tag{12}$$

where $t_{\theta\theta}$ is the physical component of the stress tensor that is being measured here. In the absence of these body forces, a secondary flow is expected. Arguments have been presented that these deviations from the simple flow should be small if β is made small [3].

The inertia is expected to produce an effect similar to that found in the parallel plate case. Experiments were performed on the Newtonian lubricating oil also with the cone and plate geometry. The results can be adequately described by equation (11). Values of B from the cone and plate experiments on this oil are also plotted in Figure 4. It is seen that the data from the two geometries fall on the same line. Therefore we used the same centrifugal correction for both. This correction has been included in the plots of Figure 2.

Attempts have been made in the past to determine experimentally whether secondary flow does take place to any great extent in the cone and plate geometry by measurements of the velocity distribution [10],[14],[15]. No deviations from the assumed simple laminar flow were detected except near the edges.

Since $\dot{\gamma}$ is independent of r, equation (12) implies that plots of h against $\log r$ should be linear. That this is true to a good approximation is seen in Figure 2. From the slopes of these lines one can find $\partial t_{\theta\theta}/\partial \ln r = -[\rho g/2.303] \times$ slope. These values are included in Figure 6. We also note that the two curves of Figure 6 can almost be superposed within the scatter of the experimental points by a horizontal shift along the $\log \dot{\gamma}$ axis corresponding to a factor of about 1.2 in $\dot{\gamma}$ (at various levels of the derivative, this factor varies from 1.15 to 1.25). We have no explanation at this time for this curious observation. Some less precise data on a more dilute solution do not appear to have this property.

Low shear rate behaviour. The normal stress functions $v_i(\dot{\gamma})$ are even functions of the rate of shear and vanish at $\dot{\gamma} = 0$. It is therefore expected that at low rates of shear the v_i will have a quadratic behaviour:

$$v_I \approx k_I \dot{\gamma}^2, \quad v_{II} \approx k_{II} \dot{\gamma}^2, \quad v_{III} \approx k_{III} \dot{\gamma}^2 \tag{13}$$

In this region of $\dot{\gamma}$, it can be shown from equation (10) that the traction distribution in the parallel plate experiment, will be given by

$$t_{zz}(r) - t_{zz}(0) = \rho g(h_0 - h) = (5k_{III} + k_I)\dot{\gamma}^2/2 \tag{14}$$

From equation (8), one can see that

$$\partial t_{zz}/\partial \ln r = \dot{\gamma}^2(5k_{III} + k_I) \tag{15}$$

Examination of Figures 5 and 6 indicate that at low rates of shear, the curves in these logarithmic plots have a slope of about 2 as expected from equations (14) and (15). This dependence is also seen in Figure 7 where the experimental points obtained in the parallel plate instrument are plotted against the square of the rate of shear. Although there is a considerable amount of scatter due to the relatively large error in the small pressure differences involved, there appears to be an appreciable region where this plot is linear. The slope has the value 15 g/cm. Unfortunately, our cone and plate data at the low values of $\dot{\gamma}$ are not sufficiently accurate or extensive to obtain a good approximation for the limiting value of $(\partial t_{\theta\theta}/\partial \ln r)/\dot{\gamma}^2$. For the curve which we have drawn in Figure 6, this quantity is about 11 g/cm.

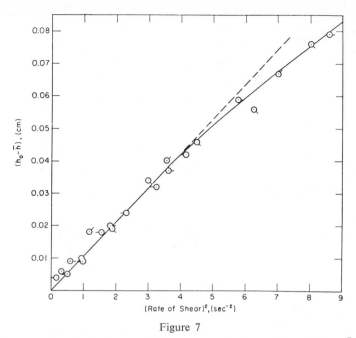

Figure 7

Low rate of shear behavior in the parallel plate geometry as the variation of $(h_0 - \bar{h})$ with $\dot{\gamma}^2$. Circles with pips have same significance as in Figure 1. Dashed line is the extrapolation of linear portion at low rates of shear

Normal stress coefficient. Just as one speaks of a *zero shear viscosity,* the limiting value of the ratio of the shearing stress to rate of shear as the latter approaches zero, it is convenient to speak of a *zero shear normal stress coefficient* as the limiting value of the ratio of the normal stress function (v_i) to the square of the shear rate. One can then also speak of the shear rate variation of a normal stress coefficient.

Rivlin has introduced such a coefficient which was defined in terms of his theory of viscous inelastic materials and labelled it Ψ. In the general case there will be two independent coefficients of this kind. We will here write $v_i/\dot{\gamma}^2 = \Psi_i$. We have plotted the normal stress coefficient Ψ_{III} in Figure 8 as obtained from the cone and plate data. It is seen that the quadratic dependence of v_{III} (or equivalently, the constancy of Ψ_{III}) seems to extend to about $2 \; \text{sec}^{-1}$ This is about the same range where our previous data [16] on polyisobutylene solutions leads us to expect the viscosity to be independent of $\dot{\gamma}$.

Special theories. As we have pointed out elsewhere [4], several of the special phenomenological theories which have been proposed involve a pro-

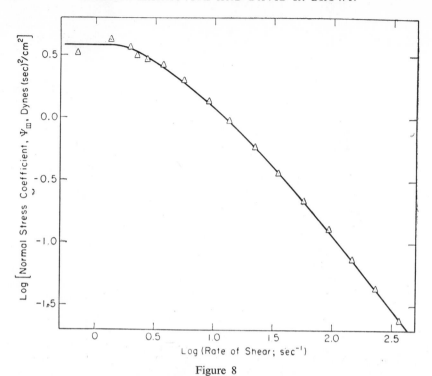

Figure 8

Rate of shear dependence of the normal stress coefficient Ψ_{III} shown in logarithmic plot. The line is calculated from the dashed curve of Figure 6. The triangles are calculated from the individual cone and plate experiments

portionality between the normal stress functions defined in equations 1–3. This we indicate by writing

$$v_I = k v_{III} \tag{16}$$

If such a relationship is valid, equation (9) can be rewritten [4] with the aid of equation (12) to give

$$\frac{\partial t_{zz}}{\partial \ln r} - \frac{\partial t_{\theta\theta}}{\partial \ln r} = v_{III}(2 + k)\left(\frac{\partial \ln v_{III}}{\partial \ln \dot{\gamma}} - 1\right). \tag{17}$$

This equation gives the prediction of these special theories with respect to the comparison of results from the two types of experiments we have been discussing. We have indicated [4] that the predictions of many of the theories would be difficult to distinguish from such data and therefore that considerable accuracy is needed to decide among the various theories with this method.

There are two special cases that equation (17) makes of special interest. If $k = -2$, as has been proposed by Weissenberg, the parallel plate data plotted in the form of $\partial t_{zz}/\partial \ln r$ and the cone and plate data plotted in the form $\partial t_{\theta\theta}/\partial \ln r$ should coincide. If equation (16) is an adequate description of the properties of the material for any value of k other than -2, we should expect from equation (17) that the curves representing $\partial t_{zz}/\partial \ln r$ and $\partial t_{\theta\theta}/\partial \ln r$ should cross at a value of $\dot{\gamma}$ where $\partial \ln v_{III}/\partial \ln \dot{\gamma}$ is 1.

For our particular polymer solution, the curves representing these derivatives as a function of the rate of shear are exhibited in Figure 6. They do not coincide. At a given rate of shear, the derivatives differ by about 35% at low rates of shear and 15% at high rates of shear. This difference lies outside our experimental error, we believe. Furthermore, $\partial \ln v_{III}/\partial \ln \dot{\gamma}$ (or equivalently from (12), $\partial[\partial t_{\theta\theta}/\partial \ln r]/\partial \dot{\gamma}$ is 1 near $\log \dot{\gamma} = 1.42$. The two curves do not cross at this point.

We are thus led to the conclusion that our experimental results are not compatible with the deductions based on any theory of this simple proportional type when the assumption of simple laminar flow lines is made. The direct observation of the flow lines and the linear semi-logarithmic pressure distribution in the cone and plate experiment, the correct scaling with speed and gap size in the parallel plate experiment lend confidence to, although they do not necessarily constitute proof of, the existence of a "sufficiently good" approximation to the simple flow pattern envisaged. The most likely conclusion then is that no theory of the kind typified by equation (17) is applicable here.

Theoretically, it is possible to calculate v_{II} from the present results. But the result of such a calculation would be extremely sensitive to small variations in the data as mentioned above. We therefore postpone the evaluation of v_{II} until we have obtained results from experiments in Couette flow which we are about to perform in our laboratory.

There have been a number of papers in which evidence favoring the Weissenberg relations has been presented. Some of this evidence has been based on some assumptions regarding the conditions which exist at the boundary between a Newtonian fluid and the test fluid [10],[14],[17]. Possible difficulties with such assumptions have been pointed out by Rivlin [12]. These are specially pertinent since observations of the flow lines have indicated deviations from the simple laminar pattern near the edges [10],[14]. That surface tension also plays a role has also been mentioned [10],[18] but not discussed very thoroughly.

In another paper [19], this evidence involves the pressure at the edge of the bob in a parallel plate experiment where some of the solution is present between the cylindrical surfaces. Here the flow pattern is so complicated that the interpretation of the significance of the level of the solution at the bob edge is not likely to be simple. Another approach [20] has been to draw conclusions from a comparison of normal stress data with the flow birefringence or the elastic behavior of the liquids. In this case still further assumptions have to be made and thus resulting deductions have a further degree of uncertainty.

It appears that objections can be raised against every experiment that has been reported and that unequivocal conclusions must await consistent results obtained from a sufficient number of different experiments.

Note on notation. Various authors who have discussed concepts similar to those discussed here have used different notations. To aid in translation a glossary is given here.

Many authors prefer to use normal stress differences as the relevant material functions. Coleman and Noll [2] use the symbols σ_i for some of these differences, the symbol τ for the shearing stress function, and $\bar{\tau}^1(\ )$ for the rate of shear. In this paper we have permuted the meaning of the numerical indices and use roman numerals for them to distinguish them from those we have previously written [4] as v_1, v_2, v_3. Thus:

$$\sigma_1 = t_{11} - t_{33} = v_1 - v_2 = v_{III} - v_I$$
$$\sigma_2 = t_{22} - t_{33} = v_1 - v_3 = v_{III} - v_{II}$$
$$\tau = t_{12}; \qquad {}^{-\frac{1}{\tau}}(\ ) = \dot{\gamma}$$

In Ericksen's [13] terminology:

$$3\Psi_I = 2(\beta_2 - \beta_3); \quad 3\Psi_{II} = -4\beta_2 + \beta_3; \quad 3\Psi_{III} = 2\beta_2 + \beta_3$$

$$\dot{\gamma} = \sqrt{X}$$

Kotaka, Kurata, and Tamura's symbol [19] $m = (2 + k)/(1 - k)$.

Acknowledgement.

The support of this work, in part, by the National Science Foundation is gratefully acknowledged.

REFERENCES

[1] R. S. RIVLIN, *J. Rational Mech. Anal.*, **5**, (1956), 179.

[2] B. D. COLEMAN AND W. NOLL, *Arch. Rational Mech. Anal*, **3**, (1959), 289.

[3] W. NOLL AND C. TRUESDELL in *Encyclopedia of Physics*, S. Flügge, ed., Springer, Berlin, Germany, to be published.

[4] HERSHEL MARKOVITZ, *Trans. Soc. Rheol.*, **1**, (1957), 37.

[5] W. O. CRIMINALE, Jr., J. L. ERICKSEN AND G. L. FILBEY, Jr., *Arch. Rational Mech. Anal.*, **1**, (1958), 410.

[6] H. W. GREENSMITH AND R. S. RIVLIN, *Trans. Roy. Soc. (London)*, **A245**, (1953), 399.

[7] F. H. GARNER, A. H. NISSAN AND G. F. WOOD, *Trans. Roy. Soc. (London)*, **A243**, (1950), 37.

[8] W. R. KRIGBAUM AND P. J. FLORY, *J. Am. Chem. Soc.*, **75**, (1953) 1775.

[9] R. S. RIVLIN, *Proc. Roy. Soc. (London)*, **A193**, (1948), 260.

[10] J. E. ROBERTS, The pressure distribution in liquids in laminar shearing motion and comparison with predictions from various theories, August, 1952. Unpublished Ministry of Supply report.

[11] J. G. OLDROYD, *Proc. Roy. Soc. (London)* **A245**, (1958), 278.

[11a] H. MARKOVITZ AND R. B. WILLIAMSON, *Trans. Soc. Rheology*, **1**, (1957), 25.

[12] R. S. RIVLIN, Flow of a visco-elastic fluid between coaxial cones, Unpublished Naval Research Laboratory report.

[13] J. L. Ericksen in *Viscoelasticity. Phenomenological Aspects*, J. T. Bergen, ed., Academic Press, New York, U. S. A., (1960), p. 77.

[14] J. E. ROBERTS, Proc. Second Intl. Congress on Rheology 91 (1954).

[15] A. JOBLING AND J. E. ROBERTS, *J. Polymer Sci.*, **36**, (1959), 421.

[16] T. W. DeWITT, H. MARKOVITZ, F. J. PADDEN, Jr. AND L. J. ZAPAS, *J. Colloid Sci.*, **10**, (1955), 174.

[17] A. JOBLING AND J. E. ROBERTS in *Rheology Theory and Applications*, F. R. Eirich, ed., Academic Press, Inc. New York, (1958), Vol. II, p. 503.

[18] A. JOBLING AND J. E. ROBERTS, *J. Polymer Sci.*, **36**, (1959), 433.

[19] T. KOTAKA, M. KURATA AND M. TAMURA, *J. Appl. Phys.*, **30**, (1959), 1705.

[20] WLADIMIR PHILIPPOFF, *Trans. Soc. Rheol.*, **5**, (1961), 163.

DISCUSSION

J.G. OLDROYD: Dr. Markovitz's contribution is one of considerable importance because it provides a way of deciding whether or not in a real liquid, Weissenberg's conjecture is true, namely that differences in the normal stresses perpendicular to the stream lines are absent, and that there is an extra simple tension along the streamlines. May I draw attention to two points on which the theoretician and experimentalist approach the problem rather differently. First, it is clear from the theory of flow of several idealized fluids that in cases when normal stress differences arise as an extra simple tension along the streamlines in steady simple shearing, they will not usually take this form in other types of flow, steady or nonsteady. Secondly, it is experimentally possible to measure the *differences* in the normal stresses, i.e. in effect the deviatoric stresses, but we must remember that we are not then measuring the whole of the stress associated with change of shape (as distinct from the stress associated with change of size of the material element) because the stress associated with change of shape is not usually deviatoric.

H. MARKOVITZ's reply: As we indicate in our introductory paragraph the various normal stress functions which we discuss in this paper arise from the treatment of a very restricted class of flows to which we refer as "certain simple types of steady flow." The precise definition is discussed in the papers cited in that paragraph and in a more recent paper by B. D. Coleman, Arch. Rational Mech. Anal. **9**, 273 (1962). These resulrs are valid for a very general class of fluids as is also indicated in these references. It is also clear that these functions will not, in general, be sufficient to characterize the the material in other types of flow. Furthermore, all of the special flows are isochoric so that they are volume preserving.

FLOW OF A NON-NEWTONIAN ELECTRICALLY CONDUCTING FLUID ALONG A CIRCULAR CYLINDER WITH UNIFORM SUCTION

M. N. L. Narasimhan

Department of Mathematics, Indian Institute of Technology, Bombay, India

ABSTRACT

An exact solution of the flow of a non-Newtonian electrically conducting fluid with an externally imposed magnetic field normal to the wall is obtained along a circular cylinder or a flat plate with uniform suction. Analytical results show that if the Alfvén wave velocity is smaller than the suction velocity, a physically possible solution is obtained under a given boundary condition, and that the applied magnetic field acts on the flow as a decelerating action, as expected from the general property of magnetic force. This decelerating action of the magnetic force is found to be more pronounced in the non-Newtonian flow past a cylinder than in the classical viscous fluid under similar flow conditions. The coefficient of skin friction and that of Maxwell's stress are calculated. The results are compared with those in the classical fluid case. It is found that the coefficient of skin friction for the flow past a cylinder is smaller than in the case of classical viscous fluid while the coefficient of Maxwell's stress is found to be the same as in the classical viscous fluid case under similar flow conditions. The coefficient of skin friction is reduced and that of Maxwell's stress is increased as the Alfvén wave velocity increases. Further, the solution reduces to that of the asymptotic suction flow of a non-conducting non-Newtonian fluid when the magnetic field tends to zero.

1. Introduction.

In recent years, effects of electro-magnetic field on the classical viscous fluid flow have been investigated with increasing interests from the practical needs of the astronautics, plasma physics and the aero-space engineering. In some of these investigations, the suction flow past solid bodies in the presence of magnetic fields have been considered. Since in the classical boundary layer theory, the aerodynamic suction is used to prevent the flow separation, these problems of suction flow in the presence of magnetic fields are of practical interest. The solution of the boundary layer over a circular cylinder with uniform suction has already been investigated for non-conducting flow by Wüst [1], Lew [2] and Yasuhara [3]. The problem of classical electrically conducting fluid flow past a cylinder or a flat plate with uniform suction, in the presence

of a transverse magnetic field has been solved by Yasuhara [4]. Thus these
workers have confined themselves only to the classical viscous fluid case. But
no work has been done so far on the flow of a non-Newtonian electrically conducting fluid in the presence of a magnetic field. Non-Newtonian liquids are
highly viscous liquids such as oils, certain paints, blood, high polymer solutions such as polyisobutylene and other organic liquids. In many astronautical
problems, biophysical problems and aero-space problems, such highly viscous
liquids are involved. Hence an investigation of the flow of such liquids in the
presence of magnetic fields are of practical interest.

The present paper therefore is devoted to the problem of steady flow of a
non-Newtonian electrically conducting fluid along a circular cylinder or a flat
plate with uniform suction in the presence of a magnetic field normal to the
wall. The main influence of electromagnetic field is caused by the interaction
between magnetic flux and fluid velocity and as in the case of the classical fluid,
the applied magnetic field acts on the non-Newtonian flow as a decelerating
action. This decelerating action on the flow past a cylinder is found to be
much more predominant in the case of non-Newtonian fluid than in the case
of classical viscous fluid. But for the flat plate, the velocity field for the non-
Newtonian flow is found to coincide with that of the classical viscous flow
under similar flow conditions and hence, the decelerating action is found to
be the same no matter whether it is Newtonian or non-Newtonian fluid, as
far as the conductiong flow past a flat plate with uniform suction is concerned.

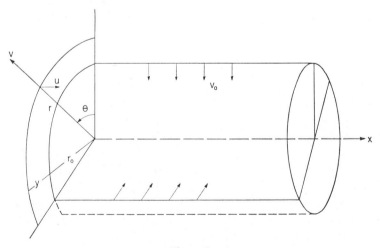

Figure 1
Cylindrical coordinates

2. Fundamental equations.

The steady continuous flow of a non-Newtonian electrically neutral fluid is considered, and the rationalized m.k.s. system of electromagnetic unit is used. The cylindrical flow is chosen as a typical problem in the present paper, because the flat plate case can be obtained as the limiting case where the radius of the cylinder becomes infinite. If the cylindrical coordinates (x, r, θ) is chosen as shown in Figure 1, and the asymptotic state in which all quantities are independent of x and θ is considered, then terms operated by $\partial/\partial x$ and $\partial/\partial\theta$ should vanish. It is assumed that the θ-component of velocity and magnetic field do not appear in the flow field. Then Maxwell's equations give:

$$e^{ikl}E_{l,k} = 0 \; : \; dE_x/dr = 0, \tag{1}$$

$$(1/r)\,d\,(rE_\theta)/dr = 0, \tag{2}$$

$$E^i_{,i} = 0 \quad : \; (1/r)\,d\,(rE_r)/dr = 0, \tag{3}$$

$$B^i_{,i} = 0 \quad : \; (1/r)\,d\,(rB_r)/dr = 0, \tag{4}$$

$$J^i = \sigma\,(E^i + e^{ikl}v_k B_l) = \frac{1}{\mu_e}\,e^{ikl}B_{l,k},$$

$$j_x = \sigma E_x = 0, \tag{5}$$

$$j_r = \sigma\,(E_y - uB_\theta) = 0, \tag{6}$$

$$j_\theta = \sigma\,(E_\theta + uB_r - vB_x) = -\frac{1}{\mu_e}\,\frac{dB_x}{dr}, \tag{7}$$

where e^{ikl} is the pemutation tensor which when expressed in terms of its physical components in any coordinate system, becomes

$$e^{ikl} = (1/\sqrt{g})\,\epsilon^{ikl}, \tag{8}$$

where g = determinant of the metric tensor of the coordinate system and

$$\epsilon^{ikl} = 1, \text{for an even permutation of } i, k, l$$

$$= -1, \text{ for an odd permutation of } i, k, l$$

$$= 0, \text{ for repetition of two or more indices.}$$

E^i represents the electric field intensity,

B^i magnetic flux density and v_k velocity field.

The physical components of these quantities in cylindrical coordinates are denoted by (E_x, E_r, E_θ), (B_x, B_r, B_θ) and $(u, v, 0)$ respectively, u being the component of velocity in the direction of the axis of the cylinder and v being radial component of velocity, μ_e the magnetic permeability and σ the electric conductivity.

We will now consider the fluid dynamical equations for the flow of a non-Newtonian liquid. Non-Newtonian liquids such as blood, thick oils, paints colloidal suspensions and high polymer solutions like polyisobutylene solution are highly viscous liquids. They exhibit certain types of phenomena which cannot be described by the stress-strain relations of the classical hydrodynamics. The rheological behaviour of the non-Newtonian liquids can be adequately studied by generalizing the stress-strain velocity relations of the classical hydrodynamics in the manner suggested by Reiner[5] and Rivlin[6]. This generalization is effected by introducing second order terms of the type $d_\alpha^i d_j^\alpha$ (where d_j^i is the rate of deformation tensor) in the classical stress-strain relations. We obtain the non-linear stress-strain velocity relations in the form

$$t_j^i = - p\delta_j^i + F_1 d_j^i + F_2 d_\alpha^i d_j^\alpha, \tag{9}$$

where p is the pressure of the liquid, F_1 and F_2 are in general functions of material invariants. But in our problem we restrict ourselves only to cases where F_1 and F_2 are constants known as the coefficients of viscosity and cross-viscosity respectively.

$$d_{ij} = \tfrac{1}{2}(v_{i,j} + v_{j,i}).$$

The equations of conservation of momentum are the well-known Eulerian hydrodynamical equations, modified so as to include terms representing the force field due to the interaction between fluid velocity field and the electromagnetic field. These equations for the steady flow in the tensor form are:

$$\rho v_{,j}^i v^j = t_{,j}^{ij} + e^{ikl} J_k B_l, \tag{10}$$

$$v_{,i}^i = 0, \tag{11}$$

where $e^{ikl} J_k B_l = \mathbf{J} \times \mathbf{B}$ is the ponderomotive force which represents the interaction between the fluid flow field and the electromagnetic field, e^{ikl} being the permutation tensor already explained in (8), ρ is the density of the liquid.

In our problem, in cylindrical coordinates these modified hydromagnetic equations become after taking $F_1 = 2\eta$ and $F_2 = 4\eta_1$ where η and η_1 are the coefficents of viscosity sand cross-viscosity respectively:

$$\rho v \frac{du}{dr} = \frac{\eta}{r} \frac{d}{dr}\left(r\frac{du}{dr}\right) + 4\eta_1 \left[\frac{1}{2}\frac{dv}{dr}\frac{d^2u}{dr^2} + \frac{1}{2}\frac{du}{dr}\frac{d^2v}{dr^2} + \frac{1}{2r}\frac{dv}{dr}\frac{du}{dr}\right] +$$
$$+ (j_r B_\theta - j_\theta B_r), \tag{12}$$

$$\rho v \frac{dv}{dr} = -\frac{dp}{dr} + 2\eta \frac{d}{dr}\left\{\frac{1}{r}\frac{d}{dr}(rv)\right\} +$$

$$+ 4\eta_1 \left[2\frac{dv}{dr}\frac{d^2v}{dr^2} + \frac{1}{2}\frac{du}{dr}\frac{d^2u}{dr^2} + \frac{1}{r}\left(\frac{dv}{dr}\right)^2 + \frac{1}{4r}\left(\frac{du}{dr}\right)^2 - \frac{v^2}{r^3}\right] +$$
$$+ (j_\theta B_x - j_x B_\theta), \tag{13}$$

$$\frac{1}{r}\frac{d}{dr}(vr) = 0. \tag{14}$$

From Maxwell's equations, it is deduced that $\mathbf{E}$, $\mathbf{B}$ and $\mathbf{J}$ must be of the forms

$$\mathbf{E} = (E_x, E_r, E_\theta) \equiv \left(0, \quad 0, \quad E_0 \frac{r_0}{r}\right),$$

$$\mathbf{B} = (B_x, B_r, B_\theta) \equiv \left(B_x, \quad B_0 \frac{r_0}{r}, \quad 0\right), \tag{15}$$

$$\mathbf{J} = (j_x, j_r, j_\theta) \equiv \left(0, 0, \quad -\frac{1}{\mu_e}\frac{dB_x}{dr}\right),$$

in our particular problem under initially given assumptions. In relation (15) r_0 represents the radius of cylinder and E_0 and B_0 are constant values of electric field intensity and magnetic flux density at the cylinder surface. Relations (15) represent that the electric field and the electric current have θ-component only, and further E_θ and B_r must be proportional to $1/r$, respectively. In the limiting flat plate case where $r_0 \rightarrow \infty$, these correspond to constant values of E_0 and B_0, respectively.

3. Boundary conditions.

The boundary conditions on the velocity field are imposed by fluid mechanical considerations. If the flow is of the boundary layer type and externally imposed magnetic field is normal to the wall, these are

$$u \rightarrow u_\infty, \; p \rightarrow p_\infty \; \text{and} \; B_x \rightarrow 0 \; \text{as} \; r \rightarrow \infty \left.\begin{array}{c} \\ \end{array}\right\}$$
$$u = 0 \; \text{and} \; v = v_0 \; \text{at} \; r = r_0 \qquad (16)$$

where v_0 represents the effective mean vertical suction velocity of fluid at the wall surface.

From electrodynamical considerations, the following relations must hold at the boundary between the fluid and solid wall:

$$\{\mathbf{E}_t\} = 0,$$
$$\{\mathbf{H}_t\} = \mathbf{j}_s \times \mathbf{n}, \qquad (17)$$
$$\{\mathbf{B}_n\} = 0,$$

where the bracket represents the jump of values between quantities in the fluid and the solid wall, $\mathbf{H}$ the magnetic field intensity which is equal to $\mathbf{B}/\mu_e$, suffix t and n the components tangential and normal to the wall surface respectively, $\mathbf{j}_s$ the surface current density and $\mathbf{n}$ the unit vector normal to the surface. If the electric conductivity of fluid and wall have finite values, there is no surface current and therefore $\mathbf{j}_s = 0$. In this case, above conditions reduce to:

$$E_{\theta 0} = E_{\theta w} = E_0, \qquad (18)$$

$$\frac{B_{x0}}{\mu_e} = \frac{B_{xw}}{\mu_{ew}}, \qquad (19)$$

$$B_{r0} = B_{rw} = B_0, \qquad (20)$$

where suffixes 0 and w represent values in fluid and in the wall next to the boundary surface, respectively.

Before proceeding to the flow solution, it is useful to study the electromagnetic field in the solid wall which is continued with that in the flow. In the solid wall it can be deduced that j_θ must vanish from Eqs. (12) and (15), as $u = 0$ there. Therefore Eq. (7) can be integrated to give

$$B_x = \text{const.} = B_{xw}, \qquad (21)$$

and similarly $E_\theta = vB_x$, which is reduced to

$$E_0 = v_0 B_{xw} \qquad (22)$$

with the aid of Eqs. (15), (21) and (23). From the above relations, it is known that the applied electric field E_θ induces the magnetic flux B_{xw} so as to cancel the electric current inside the wall.

4. Solution of the hydromagnetic equations.

In the present paper calculations are performed for the case in which the fluid is a non-Newtonian liquid and all coefficients such as σ $\mu_e, \eta, \eta_1, \rho$ are constants in the field. In this case the equations can be integrated analytically and the effect of magnetic field on the suction characteristics is easily evaluated. Equation (14) can be integrated to give

$$vr = v_0 r_0 = \text{constant.} \tag{23}$$

Rewriting eq. (12) with the aid of Eqs. (15) and (23), we obtain

$$\rho v_0 r_0 \frac{du}{dr} = \eta \frac{d}{dr}\left(r \frac{du}{dr}\right) - 2\eta_1 v_0 r_0 \frac{d}{dr}\left(\frac{1}{r}\frac{du}{dr}\right) + \frac{B_0 r_0}{\mu_e}\frac{dB_x}{dr}. \tag{24}$$

Also from Eqs. (7), (15) and (23), the following relation is obtained

$$-\frac{1}{\mu_e}\frac{dB_x}{dr} = \sigma\frac{r_0}{r}(E_0 + uB_0 - v_0 B_x). \tag{25}$$

Applying the boundary condition (16) on Eq. (24), it is deduced that dB_x/dr must vanish as $r \to \infty$ because $du/dr \to 0$ there. Formally this condition is automatically satisfied in Eq. (25) because the right-hand side tends to vanish at order $1/r$ as $r \to \infty$. However this condition is not always satisfied, for, in the limiting flat plate case, r_0/r tends to unity and therefore the right-hand side does not always vanish except when the terms in the brackets vanish. Thus, the plausible condition compatible for both cases is given by

$$E_0 + u_\infty B_0 = 0. \tag{26}$$

The above relation gives the electric field intensity. Mathematically, the condition (26) makes the right-hand side of Eq. (25) to approach zero most steeply as r increases, which is similar to the method of steepest descent used in the classical boundary layer theory. From Eqs. (19), (22) and (26), the following relation is obtained

$$\frac{B_{xw}}{B_0} = \frac{1}{\varepsilon}\frac{B_{x0}}{B_0} = -\frac{u_\infty}{v_0}, \tag{27}$$

where

$$\varepsilon = \frac{\mu_e}{\mu_{ew}}. \tag{28}$$

Under these boundary conditions the basic equations can be solved analytically as follows.

Now integrating (24) with the aid of the boundary condition (16) we obtain

$$B_x = \frac{\mu_e \rho v_0}{B_0}(u - u_\infty) - \frac{\mu_e \eta}{B_0 r_0} r \frac{du}{dr} + \frac{2\mu_e \eta_1 v_0}{B_0} \frac{1}{r} \frac{du}{dr}. \tag{29}$$

We eliminate B_x between (25) and (29) and we obtain after writing

$$u = u_\infty + u_1, \tag{30}$$

$$r^2 \frac{d^2 u_1}{dr^2}\left(1 + \frac{2v_1 R_e}{r^2}\right) + \left[(1 + R_e + R_m) - \frac{2v_1 R_e}{r^2}(1 - R_m)\right] r \frac{du_1}{dr} +$$

$$+ (R_e R_m - H^2)u_1 = 0, \tag{31}$$

where $v_1 = \eta_{1/\rho} =$ Kinematic coefficient of cross-viscosity.

The boundary conditions for u_1 now become

$$\left.\begin{array}{cc} r \to r_0, & u_1 \to -u_\infty \\ \\ r \to \infty, & u_1 \to 0 \end{array}\right\}, \tag{32}$$

and

where

$$\left.\begin{array}{c} R_e = -\dfrac{\rho v_0 r_0}{\eta}, \quad R_m = -\sigma\mu_e v_0 r_0, \\ \\ H = \sqrt{\dfrac{\sigma}{\eta}}\, B_0 r_0, \end{array}\right\} \tag{33}$$

H is the Hartmann number, R_e the Reynolds number and R_m the magnetic Reynolds number.

(a) General case

First, two conditions are required to obtain a physically possible solution. These are

$$\left.\begin{array}{c} v_0 < 0, \\ \\ |v_0| > V_a \equiv \dfrac{B_0}{\sqrt{\rho\mu_e}}, \end{array}\right\} \tag{34}$$

where V_n denotes the Alfvén wave velocity. We shall now employ Frobenius' method of solution for the system (31) and (32). Eq. (31) is found to be hypergeometric equation and we shall consider a particular case of the Frobenius' method when the roots of the indicial equation (*A treatise on Differential Equations* by A. R. Forsyth, sixth edition 1956, Macmillan and Co. Ltd. London, pp. 243–251) differ by a non-integer. Denoting the positive difference of the roots by G where G in our case is given by

$$G = \sqrt{(R_e - R_m)^2 + 4H^2}, \qquad (35)$$

we obtain the solution for the flow past a cylinder in terms of hypergeometric functions as follows :

$$1 - \frac{u}{u_\infty} = b_0 Y^{-2\alpha_1} F\left(\alpha_1, \beta_1, \gamma_1, \frac{K_0}{Y^2}\right) + b_1 Y^{-2\alpha_2} F\left(\alpha_2, \beta_2, \gamma_2, \frac{K_0}{Y^2}\right), \quad (36)$$

$$\frac{B_x}{B_0} = \frac{R_e R_m}{\delta}\left[b_0 Y^{2\alpha_1}\left\{ -\frac{2\alpha_2}{R_e}\left(1 - \frac{K_0}{Y^2}\right) + 1 \cdot F\left(\alpha_1, \beta_1, \gamma_1, \frac{K_0}{Y^2}\right) - \right.\right.$$

$$\left. - \frac{G}{R_e}\left(1 - \frac{K_0}{Y^2}\right) \cdot F\left(\alpha_1, \beta_1, \gamma_1 - 1, \frac{K_0}{Y^2}\right)\right\} + ,$$

$$+ b_1 Y^{-2\alpha_2}\left\{ \frac{-2\alpha_1}{R_e}\left(1 - \frac{K_0}{Y^2}\right) + 1 \cdot F\left(\alpha_2, \beta_2, \gamma_2, \frac{K_0}{Y^2}\right) + \right.$$

$$\left.\left. + \frac{G}{R_e}\left(1 - \frac{K_0}{Y^2}\right) \cdot F\left(\alpha_2, \beta_2, \gamma_2 - 1, \frac{K_0}{Y^2}\right)\right\}\right], \quad (37)$$

$$\frac{p_\infty - p}{\rho u_\infty^2/2} = \frac{\delta^2}{Y^2} + \frac{\delta^2 H^2}{R_e R_m}\left(\frac{B_x}{B_0}\right)^2 + \frac{4K_0}{R_e}\left[\frac{\delta^2}{Y^4} + \frac{f_1{}^2(Y)}{4Y^2} + \frac{f_2(Y)}{4}\right], \quad (38)$$

where

$$b_0 = -\frac{1}{\Delta}\left[F(\alpha_2,\beta_2,\gamma_2-1,K_0) + \frac{S-G+4\alpha_1 K_0}{2G(1-K_0)}F(\alpha_2,\beta_2,\gamma_2,K_0)\right],$$

$$b_1 = -\frac{1}{\Delta}\left[F(\alpha_1,\beta_1,\gamma_1-1,K_0) - \frac{S+G+4\alpha_2 K_0}{2G(1-K_0)}F(\alpha_1,\beta_1,\gamma_1,K_0)\right],$$

$$\Delta = F(\alpha_1,\beta_1,\gamma_1,K_0)\,F(\alpha_2,\beta_2,\gamma_2,K_0)\left[1 - \frac{F(\alpha_1,\beta_1,\gamma_1-1,K_0)}{F(\alpha_1,\beta_1,\gamma_1,K_0)} - \right.$$
$$\left. - \frac{F(\alpha_2,\beta_2,\gamma_2-1,K_0)}{F(\alpha_2,\beta_2,\gamma_2,K_0)}\right],$$

$$\alpha_1 = \frac{R_e+R_m+G}{4},\ \beta_1 = \frac{R_e-R_m+G+4}{4},\ \gamma_1 = \frac{G+2}{2},$$

$$\alpha_2 = \frac{R_e+R_m-G}{4},\ \beta_2 = \frac{R_e-R_m-G+4}{4},\ \gamma_2 = \frac{2-G}{2},$$

$$G = \sqrt{(R_e-R_m)^2+4H^2},\ S = R_e-R_m-\frac{2H^2\varepsilon}{R_m},$$

$$H = \sqrt{\frac{\sigma}{\eta}}\,B_0 r_0,\ Y = \frac{r}{r_0} = 1+\frac{y}{r_0},$$

$$\delta = -\frac{v_0}{u_\infty},\ K_0 = -\frac{2v_1 R_e}{r_0^2},\ \varepsilon = \frac{\mu_e}{\mu_{ew}},$$

$$f_1(Y) = b_0 Y^{-2\alpha_1}\left\{-2\alpha_2 F\left(\alpha_1,\beta_1,\gamma_1,\frac{K_0}{Y^2}\right) - GF\left(\alpha_1,\beta_1,\gamma_1-1,\frac{K_0}{Y^2}\right) + \right.$$
$$\left. + b_1 Y^{-2\alpha_2}\left\{-2\alpha_1 F\left(\alpha_2,\beta_2,\gamma_2,\frac{K_0}{Y^2}\right) + GF\left(\alpha_2,\beta_2,\gamma_2-1,\frac{K_0}{Y^2}\right)\right\}\right. ,$$

$$f_2(Y) = \int\frac{1}{Y}f_1^2(Y)\,dY,$$

$$\left.\rule{0pt}{60ex}\right\}\quad (39)$$

and

$$F(\alpha,\beta,\gamma,x) = 1 + \frac{\alpha\beta}{1\cdot\gamma}x + \frac{\alpha(\alpha+1)\beta(\beta+1)}{1\cdot 2\cdot\gamma(\gamma+1)}x^2 + \ldots\ldots\ .$$

Convergence of the solution.

For the case $v_0 < 0, |v_0| > V_a \equiv \dfrac{B_0}{\sqrt{\rho\mu_e}}$, the hypergeometric series obtained above converges if $\left| \dfrac{K_0}{Y^2} \right| < 1$ i.e.

$$\left| \frac{-2v_1 R_e}{r^2} \right| < 1 \quad \text{or} \quad 2v_1 R_e/r^2 < 1,$$

i.e. for convergence of the solution, we should have

$$r^2 > 2v_1 R_e.$$

In our problem, $r \geq r_0$, where r_0 is the radius of the cylinder and finally $r \to \infty$. In view of this, if we choose $r_0^2 > 2v_1 R_e$ the convergence condition is readily satisfied; then the region of convergence will be obtained as $0 < R_e < r_0^2/2v_1$. Hence our solution (36) to (38) will be convergent and hence will be valid for values of R_e in the range $0 < R_e < r_0^2/2v_1$. Since in most practical cases $r_0^2/2v_1$ will be a considerably large number, the solution will be valid over a wide range of values of R_e.

The coefficient of skin friction C_f and that of Maxwell's stress C_m are given for the case of the non-Newtonian flow past a cylinder, respectively by

$$C_f = \frac{\eta (du/dr)_{r=r_0}}{\rho u_\infty^2/2} = \frac{2\delta}{1 - K_0} \left\{ 1 - \left(\frac{V_a}{v_0} \right)^2 \varepsilon \right\}, \tag{40}$$

$$C_m = \frac{(B_0 B_x)_{r=r_0}/\mu_e}{\rho u_\infty^2/2} = 2\delta \left(\frac{V_a}{v_0} \right)^2 \varepsilon. \tag{41}$$

This completes the solution of the hydromagnetic equations for the flow past a cylinder in the non-Newtonian case. It may be noted that Yasuhara's (1960) solution for the classical viscous flow can be obtained as a particular case from our Eqs. (36), (37), (38), (40) and (41), by putting

$$v_1 = 0, \quad \text{or} \quad K_0 = 0.$$

It is found from (40) that the coefficient of skin friction C_f for flow past a cylinder in the non-Newtonian case is smaller than in the case of classical viscous fluid, since K_0 is negative, while the coefficient of Maxwell's stress

C_m is identical, no matter whether the flow is Newtonian or non-Newtonian. Further it is found that the coefficient of skin friction is decreased and that of Maxwell's stress is increased as V_a increases, as in the case of classical viscous fluid flowing past the cylinder.

(b) $B_0 = 0$, non-magnetic flow.

When there is no magnetic field, $B_0 = 0$ and the solution becomes

$$1 - \frac{u}{u_\infty} = \left\{ \frac{1 - K_0}{\left(1 + \dfrac{y}{r_0}\right)^2 - K_0} \right\}^{R_e/2}, \tag{42}$$

$$\frac{B_x}{B_0} = 0, \tag{43}$$

$$\frac{p_\infty - p}{\rho u_\infty^2/2} = \frac{\delta^2 r_0^2}{r^2} - v_1 \left[\frac{8\delta^2 r_0^2}{r^4} + \frac{R_e^2(1 - K_0)^{R_e}(1 + K + 2Re)\left(\dfrac{r_0}{r}\right)^{2R_e}}{r^2(R_e + 1)(1 - K)^{R_e + 2}} \right], \tag{44}$$

where $\delta = -\dfrac{v_0}{u_\infty}$, $v_1 = \eta_1/\rho$, $K_0 = -\dfrac{2v_1 R_e}{r_0^2}$ and $K = \dfrac{-2v_1 R_e}{r^2}$.

It is found that by putting $v_1 = 0$ or $K = 0$ in our equations (42), (43) and (44), we obtain as particular cases, the solution of asymptotic cylindrical suction flow of a classical viscous fluid obtained by Wüst[1], Lew[2], Yasuhara[3],[4].

(c) Two-dimensional case.

In the limiting case when r_0 tends to infinity, the solution gives the two-dimensional one. In this case, E_θ represents the component normal to x and y directions, and B_r and v the y component, and they have next forms

$$\left. \begin{array}{l} E_\theta = E_0, \\ B_r = B_0, \\ v = v_0. \end{array} \right\} \tag{45}$$

If the limiting relation

$$\lim_{r_0 \to \infty} r_0 \log\left(\frac{r_0 + y}{r_0}\right) = y$$

is applied on Eqs. (36), (37) and (38), these reduce to

$$1 - \frac{u}{u_\infty} = \left[\cosh\left(\frac{G'Y'}{2}\right) - \frac{S'}{G'}\sinh\left(\frac{G'Y'}{2}\right)\right]\exp\left(-\frac{R_e' + R_m'}{2}Y'\right), \quad (46)$$

$$\frac{B_x}{B_0} = \frac{1}{G'\delta}\left[\left\{2R_m' + (R_e' - R_m')\,\varepsilon\right\}\sinh\left(\frac{G'Y'}{2}\right) + \right.$$

$$\left. + G'\varepsilon\cosh\left(\frac{G'Y'}{2}\right)\right]\exp\left(-\frac{R_e' + R_m'}{2}Y'\right), \quad (47)$$

$$\frac{p_\infty - p}{\rho u_{\infty}^2/2} = \delta^2 + \frac{\delta^2 H'^2}{R_e' R_m'}\left(\frac{B_x}{B_0}\right)^2 - \frac{2v_1}{u_\infty^2}[\Phi_1^2(y) + \Psi_1(y)], \quad (48)$$

where

$$\Phi_1(y) = \lim_{r_0 \to \infty} \Phi(r_0 + y), \quad \Psi_1(y) = \lim_{r_0 \to \infty} \Psi(r_0 + y),$$

$$\Phi(r) = -\frac{b_0' u_\infty}{r}\left(\frac{r_0}{r}\right)^{2\alpha_1'}\left\{-2\alpha_2' F(\alpha_1', \beta_1', \gamma_1', K) - \right.$$

$$\left. - G'F(\alpha_1', \beta_1', \gamma_1' - 1, K)\right\} -$$

$$- \frac{b_1' u_\infty}{r}\left(\frac{r_0}{r}\right)^{2\alpha_2'}\left\{-2\alpha_1' F(\alpha_2', \beta_2', \gamma_2', K) + \right.$$

$$\left. + G'F(\alpha_2', \beta_2', \gamma_2' - 1, K)\right\}, \quad (49)$$

$$\Psi(r) = \int \frac{1}{r}\{\Phi(r)\}^2 dr,$$

and $$R_e' = -\frac{\rho v_0 L}{\eta}, \quad R_m' = -\sigma\mu_e v_0 L,$$

$$H' = \sqrt{\frac{\sigma}{\eta}}\cdot B_0 L, \quad G' = \sqrt{(R_e' - R_m')^2 + 4H'^2},$$

$$Y' = \frac{y}{L}, \quad S' = R_e' - R_m' - \frac{2H'^2}{R_m'}\varepsilon,$$

$b'_0, b'_1, \alpha'_1, \alpha'_2, \beta'_1, \beta'_2, \gamma'_1, \gamma'_2$ being obtained by replacing R_e, R_m, H, G and S by R'_e, R'_m, H', G' and S' respectively in the expressions for $b_0, b_1, \alpha_1, \alpha_2, \beta_1,$ $\beta_2, \gamma_1, \gamma_2$ in Eq. (39), and L is a reference length which, practically, has no influence on the solution. The coefficients of skin friction and that of Maxwell's stress become

$$C_f = 2\delta \left\{ 1 - \left(\frac{V_a}{v_0} \right)^2 \varepsilon \right\}, \tag{50}$$

$$C_m = 2\delta \left(\frac{V_a}{v_0} \right)^2 \varepsilon. \tag{51}$$

Thus (46) to (51) constitute the solution for the non-Newtonian suction flow past a flat plate. It is found that the velocity field and the magnetic field are the same as in the case of the classical viscous fluid flow solution obtained by Yasuhara [4]. But, however, the solution for the non-Newtonian flow past a flat plate differs from that of the classical viscous fluid flow in the pressure field. It may be noted that our solution for the non-Newtonian case yields the particular case of the classical viscous fluid flow [4] when we put $v_1 = 0$ or $K = 0$. While C_f and C_m are given by (50) and (51) and are found to be independent of cross-viscosity. Hence these coefficients are found to be the same for the flow past a flat plate, no matter whether it is classical viscous fluid flow or non-Newtonian fluid flow. Further it is found that C_f is decreased and C_m is increased as V_a increases, but the total drag $C_f + C_m$ is kept unchanged at a value of 2δ, which is the same as in the non-magnetic flow.

Further for non-magnetic flow, $B_0 = 0$ and (46) becomes

$$1 - \frac{u}{u_\infty} = e^{-R'_e Y'} = e^{\rho v_0 y / \eta}, \tag{52}$$

which coincides with the asymptotic flat plate suction flow of a classical viscous fluid [4].

5. Numerical calculations and discussions.

Velocity profiles calculated from the above results for cylindrical cases are shown in Figure 2 for several values of H in the cases of $R_e = 11$, $R_m = 10$, $K_0 = -\dfrac{2v_1 R_e}{r_0^2} = -0.02$. In this case, the condition $|v_0| > V_a$ corresponds

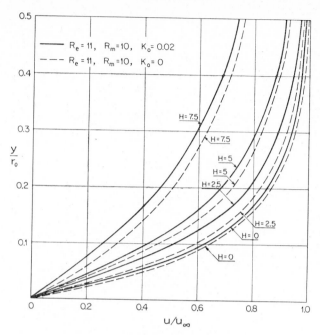

Figure 2
Velocity profiles for a circular cylinder

to $H < 10$. Further for this choice of R_e and R_m, $G = \sqrt{(R_e - R_m)^2 + 4H^2} =$ non-integer for each of the values of H, which is required for the validity of the solutions (36), (37) and (38). Similar results of the flat plate case are shown in Figure 2 for several values of H' in the case of $R'_e = 11$, $R'_m = 10$, $K_0 = -0.02$. The condition $|v_0| > V_a$ also corresponds to $H' < 10$. $C_f/2\delta$ and $C_m/2\delta$ are shown in Figure 4 as functions of $V_a/(-v_0)$ both for the cylindrical case and the flat plate case.

From these figures, it is found that the applied magnetic flux B_x acts on the flow as a decelerating action as in the classical viscous flow. This is an expected property of the magnetic force. But this decelerating action becomes more predominant in the non-Newtonian case than in the case of classical viscous fluid, for the flow past a cylinder under similar conditions of flow. In the above calculations, the electric field E_θ is determined so that its coefficient E_0 should satisfy (26). The physical meaning of this is as follows: — The above condition comes from the assumption that $u \to u_\infty$ as $r \to \infty$ and as a result of this condition, the induced electric current must vanish as $r \to \infty$, and in order to satisfy this condition, the electric field E_θ must be imposed on the flow so as to cancel the induced electric field. Practically such a model

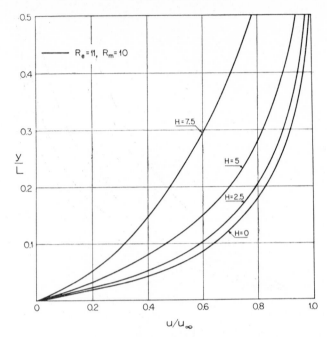

Figure 3
Velocity profiles for a flat plate

is equivalent to the one in which the imposed magnetic flux B_r is moving in the x-direction with uniform velocity u_∞. In this case there is no interacting motion between the velocity and the magnetic field in the flow field far distant from the wall.

6. Summary.

An exact solution of the flow of a non-Newtonian electrically conducting fluid with an externally imposed magnetic field normal to the wall is obtained for the flow past a circular cylinder or a flat plate with uniform suction. Analytical results show that if the Alfvén wave velocity is smaller than the suction velocity, a physically possible solution is obtained under a given boundary condition. The method of solution is illustrated for the case of G = a non-integer based on Frobenius' method. The following are the results obtained:

(i) The applied magnetic field acts on the non-Newtonian flow as a decelerating action as in the case of the classical viscous flow for the flow past a cylinder. But this decelrating action is found to be much more predominant in the non-Newtonian case than in the classical viscous flow case, for the flow past a cylinder under similar flow conditions.

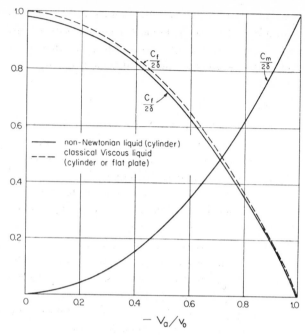

Figure 4

Curves of coefficients as functions of $- V_a/v_0$ for $e = 1$

(ii) The applied magnetic field acts on the non-Newtonian flow past a flat plate also as a decelerating action. But in this case the decelerating action is found to be quite independent of the cross viscous effects present in non-Newtonian liquids. Hence the decelerating action of the magnetic field is found to be the same for the case of the flat plate, no matter whether the fluid is classical viscous fluid or non-Newtonian liquid.

(iii) The coefficient of skin fraction decreases and that of Maxwell's stress increases in both the cases of non-Newtonian or classical viscous fluid, as the Alfvén wave velocity increases, no matter whether the flow is past a cylinder or flat plate.

(iv) The coefficient of skin friction is found to be smaller in the non-Newtonian case than in the classical viscous fluid case for the flow past a cylinder under similar conditions of flow. The coefficient of Maxwell's stress is found to be the same both for non-Newtonian and classical fluid cases under similar conditions of flow past a cylinder.

(v) Both the coefficients of skin friction and Maxwell's stress are found to be the same for the flat plate case, no matter whether the flow is of a non-

Newtonian fluid or classical viscous fluid under similar flow conditions. In this case the total drag is kept unchanged when the Alfvén wave velocity increases. Further, the solution in this case reduces to that of the asymptotic suction flow when the imposed magnetic fields tends to zero.

7.   List of Symbols.

(x, r, θ)	= the cylindrical coordinate system, in which x is the axial coordinate along the axis of the cylinder, r the radial coordinate, θ the circumferential coordinate.
r_0	= the radius of the cylinder.
L	= a characteristic dimension of the flat plate.
u	= component of fluid velocity in the direction parallel to the axis of the cylinder.
v	= radial component of velocity.
η, η_1	= coefficients of viscosity and cross-viscosity respectively.
ρ, p	= density and pressure respectively of the fluid.
$v_1 = \eta_1/\rho$	= kinematic coefficient of cross-viscosity.
v_0	= effective mean suction velocity of fluid at the wall surface.
$\mathbf{E}, E^i$	= the electric field intensity vector.
E_x, E_r, E_θ	= components of $\mathbf{E}$ in cylindrical coordinates.
$\mathbf{B}, B^i$	= the magnetic flux density vector.
B_x, B_r, B_θ	= the components of $\mathbf{B}$ in cylindrical coordinates.
$\mathbf{J}, J^i$	= the electric current density vector.
$x \ j_r, j_\theta$	= the components of $\mathbf{J}$ in cylindrical coordinates.
μ_e, μ_{ew}	= the magnetic permeability of the material of the fluid and the solid wall respectively.
ε	= μ_e/μ_{ew}.
σ	= the electric conductivity.
E_0, B_0	= constant values of the electric field intensity and magnetic flux density respectively at the cylinder surface.
u_∞	= velocity at infinity.
g	= the determinant of the metric tensor of the cylindrical coordinate system.

$$
\left.\begin{array}{l}
R_e = \dfrac{-\rho v_0 r_0}{\eta} \\[2em]
R'_e = \dfrac{-\rho v_0 L}{\eta}
\end{array}\right\} = \text{suction flow Reynolds numbers for the case of cylinder and flat plate respectively.}
$$

$R_m = -\sigma v_0 r_0 \mu_e$
$R'_m = -\sigma v L \mu_e$ $\Big\}$ = magnetic Reynolds numbers for the case of the cylinder and flat plate respectively.

$H = \sqrt{\dfrac{\sigma}{\eta}} B_0 r_0$
$H' = \sqrt{\dfrac{\sigma}{\eta}} B_0 L$ $\Big\}$ = Hartmann numbers for the case of the cylinder and flat plate respectively.

$V_a = \dfrac{B_0}{\sqrt{\rho \mu_e}}$ = Alfvén wave velocity.

$G = \sqrt{(R_e - R_m)^2 + 4H^2}$
$G' = \sqrt{(R'_e - R'_m)^2 + 4H'^2}$ $\Big\}$ = positive parameters of the hydromagnetic flow for the case of cylinder and flat plate respectively.

$S = R_e - R_m - \dfrac{2H^2 \varepsilon}{R_m}$
$S' = R'_e - R'_m - \dfrac{2H'^2 \varepsilon}{R'_m}$ $\Big\}$ = parameters of the hydromagnetic flow for the case of cylinder and flat plate respectively.

$Y = \dfrac{r}{r_0} = \dfrac{r_0 + y}{r_0}$
$Y' = \dfrac{y}{L}$ $\Big\}$ = non-dimensional distance parameters for the of cylinder and flat plate respectively.

$K_0 = \dfrac{-2v_1 R_e}{r_0^2}$ = a non-dimensional constant characterising the non-Newtonian flow.

$K = \dfrac{-2v_1 R_e}{r^2}$ = a non-dimensional parameter characterising the non-Newtonian flow.

$\delta = -\dfrac{v_0}{u_\infty}.$

$$\alpha_1 = \frac{R_e + R_m + G}{4}$$

$$\alpha_2 = \frac{R_e + R_m - G}{4}$$

$$\beta_1 = \frac{R_e - R_m + G + 4}{4}$$

$$\beta_2 = \frac{R_e - R_m - G + 4}{4}$$

$$\gamma_1 = \frac{G + 2}{2}$$

$$\gamma_2 = \frac{2 - G}{2}$$

= Hydromagnetic flow parameters.

C_f = coefficient of skin friction.
C_m = coefficient of Maxwell's stress.

REFERENCES

[1] W. Wüst, *Ing. Arch.*, **23,** (1955), 198.
[2] H. G. Lew, *J. Aero. Sci.*, **23,** (1956), 276.
[3] M. Yasuhara, *Rep. Inst. Sci. Technol. Univ. Tokyo,* **10,** (1956), 131.
[4] M. Yasuhara, *J. Phys. Soc. Japan,* **15,** (1960), 321.
[5] M. Reiner, *Quart. J. Mech. & Appl. Math.*, No. 1164 (1952), 16.
[6] R. S. Rivlin, *Proc. Roy. Soc. Lond.*, **A 193,** (1948), 260.

COLLOCATION METHOD TO STUDY
PROBLEMS OF CROSS-VISCOSITY

M. K. Jain

Indian Institute of Technology, Kharag-pur, India

ABSTRACT

In recent years the study of second order effects in fluid dynamics and in other branches of science has attracted, theoretically and practically, a considerable amount of attention. The general methods of solution available are mostly of theoretical character and do not in fact make it possible to actually find the solution of such problems. The equations of motion governing the second order effects are far more difficult than the Navier-Stokes equations and the exact solution of these problems can either not be found or has such a complicated structure that it is used only with difficulty in calculations.

Approximate methods of solving the problems of second order effects, particularly the asymptotic and the variational methods which have been developed in the first half of this century, have therefore been met with much interest on the part of the physicists and promptly obtained wide diffusion.

The collocation method has a very wide range of applicability, is simple to use and requires no special previous knowledge. The uncertainty in the choice of collocation points has discouraged physicists to apply this method to practical problems.

In this paper an attempt has been made to find a suitable choice of collocation points to study the second order effects in the following problems of hydrodynamics

1) Flow of non-Newtonian liquid near a stagnation point.

2) Flow of non-Newtonian liquid near a rotating disc.

3) Flow of non-Newtonian liquid against a disc with stagnation point at infinity.

4) Flow of non-Newtonian liquid with suction.

The cross-viscosity effect is found to depend on a non-dimensional number Re which is proportional to the coefficient of cross-viscosity. The cross-viscosity effect modifies the flow of viscous liquid and considerably affects the boundary layer thickness.

1. Introduction.

Most of the mathematical results obtained for the motion of viscous liquid are subjected to serious limitations. More often than not, we neglect the inertia terms. But even when it is possible not to neglect such terms, the ordinary theory does not give satisfactory results in the case of many liquids, we have to deal with in every day life; in fact non-Newtonian liquids in which cross-viscosity effect is present.

The equations governing the flow of non-Newtonian liquids are far more complicated than Navier-Stokes equations of motion and have been solved exactly only in a few cases. It seems almost impossible to obtain an exact analytical solution when the motion is three dimensional. Recourse is therefore made to solve them by numerical methods. Numerical difference procedures [1], [2] have been applied with good success to boundary layer flows, but the amount of numerical work involved is considerable. Apart from linearization methods, considerable efforts have been made in applying non-rigorous parameter methods to calculate boundary layer flows in general cases of interest. Such methods are unsatisfactory aside from the mathematical viewpoint. They are not only unreliable but also necessarily limited in accuracy.

The purpose of this paper is to describe a simple numerical method called 'Collocation method' to study problems of cross-viscosity. This method has a wide range of applicability and requires no special previous knowledge. In this method we are required to distribute uniformly, the error function, arising in satisfying the differential equation or boundary conditions over an interval $[a, b]$ or domain B.

To illustrate the application of this method, we have studied the effect of cross-viscosity in the following two examples from hydrodynamics

    1)   Flow near a stagnation point with suction,

    2)   Flow near a rotating disk.

It is found that cross-viscosity and suction effects depend on non-dimensional parameters R_c and K respectively. In both cases, the boundary layer thickness decreases when R_c increases. Furthermore, for flow near a stagnation point, we get that shearing at the wall increases with the increase of R_c, while the normal stress at the wall is independent of viscosity, cross-viscosity and suction. The dimensionless moment coefficient of the rotating disk increases with the increase of R_c.

2. Collocation method.

Consider the boundary-value problem in the form

$$M[u] = P[u], \tag{2.1}$$

$$R_\mu[u] = 0, \tag{2.2}$$

Where $M[u]$ and $P[u]$ are functions of x_j, u and its derivatives and R_μ are the boundary conditions given on the interval $[a, b]$ or on the $(n-1)$ dimensional hyper-surfaces of the x_j. The problem of finding an approximate solution of the boundary value problem (2.1) and (2.2) is often attacked by assuming as an approximation to the solution $u(x_1, x_2 \ldots x_n)$ or $y(x)$ an expression of the form

$$u \approx w(x_1, x_2, \ldots x_n, a_1, a_2, \ldots a_p), \qquad (2.3)$$

which depends on a number of parameters $a_1, a_2 \ldots a_p$ and is such that for arbitrary values of a_p, (a) the differential equation is already satisfied exactly, or (b) the boundary conditions are already satisfied exactly or (c) $w(x_1, x_2, \ldots x_n, a_1, a_2, \ldots a_p)$ satisfies neither the differential equation nor the boundary conditions. We then want to determine the parameters a_p such that $w(x_1, x_2, \ldots x_n, a_1, a_2, \ldots a_p)$ satisfies in case (a) the boundary conditions, in case (b) the differential equation, and in case (c) the boundary conditions and the differential equation, as accurately as possible.

We shall now describe the collocation method for ordinary differential equations defined in the interval $[a, b]$. In collocation method, we demand that the parameters a_p should be so determined that the Tchebyscheff condition namely

$$\underset{(a, b)}{\text{Max}} \ |\in(x)| = \min \qquad (2.4)$$

is satisfied as accurately as possible. $\in(x)$ being the defect in satisfying differential equation or boundary conditions.

Based on (2.4), we want that the defect $\in(x, a_p)$ should possess alternatively maximum and minimum values. We choose $(x_0^{(1)}, x_1^{(1)}, x_2^{(1)}, \ldots\ldots x_p^{(1)})$ points in the interval $[a, b]$ and set

$$\in(x_i^{(1)}, a_p) - (-1)^i \in(x_0^{(1)}, a_p) = 0, \quad i = 1, 2, \ldots p. \qquad (2.5)$$

Equation (2.5) represents a system of p-equations with a_p unknowns and will normally have a solution. Usually one takes symmetrical points $x_i^{(1)}$, or the points $x_k^{(n)} = \cos \dfrac{\pi k}{n}$ (the extremal points of the Tchebyscheff polynomial), then the error curve $\in(x)$ will be fairly uniform over the interval $[a, b]$. The points $x_k^{(n)}$ can be improved by using the iteration method

$$\in(x_i^{(v)}, a_p) - (-1)^i \in(x_0^{(v)}, a_p) = 0 \qquad (2.6)$$

where $x_i^{(v)}$ and $x_0^{(v)}$ represent the extremal points of $\in(x)$ obtained by computing and plotting the error curve at the v-th step.
A better and quicker result can be obtained by using

$$\in'(x_i^{(1)}) = 0, \tag{2.7}$$

where a dash denotes the differentiation with respect to x at $x = x_i{}^{(1)}$. The form (2.7) is suitable for electronic computers while (2.6) is convenient for hand computation. We shall now discuss two examples for illustration purpose.

3. Equations of motion.

Non-Newtonian liquids such as thick oils, paints, collodial suspensions and high polymer solutions like polyisobutylene solution are highly viscous liquids. They exhibit certain type of phenomena which cannot be described by stress-strain relations of classical hydrodynamics. The rheological behaviour of the non-Newtonian liquids can be adequately studied by the second order stress-strain velocity relations of the classical hydrodynamics as suggested in [3], [4] and [5].

The modified stress-strain velocity relationship is

$$S_{ij} = - p\delta_{ij} + k_1 f_{ij} + k_2 f_{i\alpha} f_{\alpha j} \tag{3.1}$$

$$2f_{ij} = v_{i,j} + v_j,i \tag{3.2}$$

The stress tensor (3.1) satisfies the equations of motion

$$\rho \left(\frac{\partial v_i}{\partial t} + v_{i,\alpha} v_\alpha \right) = S_{ij,j} + \rho f_i \tag{3.3}$$

Where ρ is density and f_i is the body force. The coefficients k_1 and k_2 are in general functions of material invariants. But in our problems we restrict ourselves only to cases where k_1 and k_2 are constants known as the coefficients of viscosity and cross-viscosity respectively.

4. Flow near a stagnation point with suction.

The flow near a stagnation point has been investigated by a number of workers [6], [7], [8], [9], [10] in the cases of Newtonian and non-Newtonian liquids.

A stagnation point occurs, when a stream of liquid impinges on a wall $z = 0$ at right angles to it and flows away radially in all directions. We take the stagnation point at the origin and the flow in the direction of the negative z-axis. We shall denote the radial and axial components of the velocity in the perfect flow by U and W respectively, whereas those in viscous flow will be denoted by $u = u(r, z)$ and $W = W(r, z)$.

The boundary conditions are

$$z = 0, \quad u = 0, \quad w = -w_0 \quad \Bigg\} \qquad (4.1)$$
$$z = \infty, \quad u = U$$

For frictionless flow, we can write

$$U = ar, \quad w = -2az,$$

where 'a' is a constant.

Assuming the similarity solution in the form

$$u = ar\Phi'(h), \quad w = -2\sqrt{av}\,\Phi(h) \qquad (4.2)$$

where

$$h = \sqrt{\frac{a}{v}}\,z.$$

We find that the equations of motion (3.3) and the boundary conditions (4.1) become

$$\phi''' + 2\phi\,\phi'' - \phi'^2 + 1 - R_c(2\phi'\,\phi''' + \phi''^2) = 0 \qquad (4.3)$$

$$h = 0, \quad \phi = K, \quad \phi' = 0 \quad \Bigg\} \qquad (4.4)$$
$$h = \infty, \quad \phi' = 1$$

where a dash denotes differentiation with respect to h.

We use for $\phi(h)$ an approximation function $g(h)$ satisfying the boundary conditions (4.4). Thus our approximating function $g(h)$ is of the form

$$\phi(h) \approx g(h) = K + (h - 1 + e^{-h}) + a_1(1 - 2e^{-h} + e^{-2h}) +$$
$$+ a_2(2 - 3e^{-h} + e^{-3h}) \qquad (4.5)$$

Substituting (4.5) into (4.3), it yields,

$$\in(h, ap) = g''' + 2gg'' - g'^2 + 1 - R_c(2g'g''' + g''^2) \tag{4.6}$$

where $\in(h, a_p)$ represents the defect in satisfying (4.3) and is function of a_1, a_2 and h.

In collocation method, we set

$$\in(h_0, a_p) + \in(h_1, a_p) = 0, \quad \in(h_1, a_p) + \in(h_2, a_p) = 0$$

and

$$\in'(h_j, a_p) = 0, \quad j = 0, 1, 2.$$

where h_0, h_1 and h_2 are extremal points of $\in(h)$ and a dash denotes differentiation with respect to h.

In order to compare the results with other known methods, we take $R_c = 0$, $K = 0$ and choose initially $h_0 = 0$, $h_1 = 0,5$, $h_2 = 1$.

The distribution of error function is shown in Figure 1 and we have for parameters and extremal points as

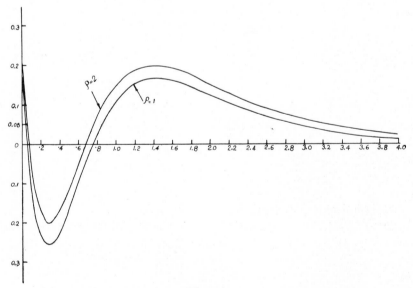

Figure 1

Error distribution function in case flow near a stagnation point

$$h_0 = 0, \quad h_1 = 0.283702, \quad h_2 = 1.41176$$

$$a_1 = 0.71722755, \quad a_2 = -0.18758077 \quad \text{Max} \, |\epsilon| = 0.19857$$

The value of $g''(0)$ compared with other methods is as follows:

	Exact solution	Collocation method	Pohlhausen method	Tomotika method
$g''(0)$	1.312	1.309	1.255	1.283

This shows that collocation method gives better results in comparison with other approximate methods. If we define the boundary layer thickness as that distance from the wall for which $u/U = 0.99$ and the shearing stress at the wall

$$\tau \phi''(0)/\mu U \sqrt{\frac{a}{v}} = (Srz)_{z=0},$$

the following results given below in Tables I and II are obtained.

TABLE I

Boundary layer thickness and shearing stress for different R_c and $K = O$

R_c	0	0.1	0.2	0.3
$\delta \sqrt{a/v}$	1.98	1.79	1.63	1.43
$\tau/\mu U \sqrt{a/v}$	1.3120	1.3154	1.3200	1.3271

TABLE II

Boundary layer thickness and shearing stress for different values of R_c and K

R_c	K	$\delta \sqrt{a/v}$	$\tau/\mu U \sqrt{a/v}$
0.1	0.3	1.55	1.7214
0.3	0.1	1.33	1.4720
0.3	0.3	1.18	1.7896
0	0.1	1.87	1.4351

For large suction, we define

$$\eta = K h$$

and

$$\phi = K + \frac{1}{K} \left[F_0(\eta) + \frac{1}{K^2} F_1(\eta) + \frac{1}{K^4} F_2(\eta) + \cdots \right] \qquad (4.7)$$

Substituting these in (4.3) and then equating to zero, the coefficients of various powers of K, we get a system of linear equations which can be solved without any difficulty. For large values of K and $R_c = 0, 0.5$, the shearing stress based on the expression (4.7) is given below

TABLE III

K	3	4	5	10
$\tau/\mu U \sqrt{a/v}, \quad R_c = 0$	6.38007	8.29356	10.29356	20.12355
$\tau/\mu U \sqrt{a/v} \ R_c = 0.5$	3.09797	4.06900	5.04092	10.00474

It is found that in both cases, the boundary layer thickness decreases and the shearing stress at the wall increases with the increase of R_c, while the normal stress at the wall is independent of viscosity, cross-viscosity and suction.

5. Flow near a rotating disk.

The steady flow of an incompressible viscous Newtonian and non-Newtonian liquids, due to an infinite rotating disk has been discussed in [11], [12], [13], [14], [15], [16]. Cylindrical polar coordinates r, θ, z are used with the disk in the plane $z = 0$ and the fluid occupies the region $z > 0$. The motion is rotationally symmetric and we assume the solution, with the dependent variable in the form

$$u = r \Omega F(h) \quad v = r \Omega G(h), \quad w = \sqrt{v \Omega} \, H(h) \qquad (5.1)$$

where u, v, w are the velocity component and Ω is the angular velocity of the disk, $h = \sqrt{\dfrac{\Omega}{v}} z$.

We find that the Navier–Stoke's equations of motion simplify to

$$F'' - F^2 + G^2 + HF' - R_c(2FF'' + F'^2 + 3G'^2) = 0 \tag{5.2}$$

$$G'' - 2FG - HG' - R_c(2FG'' - 2F'G') = 0 \tag{5.3}$$

$$H' + 2F = 0 \tag{5.4}$$

where a dash denotes differentiation with respect to h.

The boundary conditions are

$$\begin{array}{cccc} z = 0, & u = 0, & v = r\Omega, & w = 0 \\ z = \infty, & u = 0, & v = 0 \end{array}$$

and in view of (5.1), become

$$\left. \begin{array}{l} F(0) = 0, \quad G(0) = 1, \quad H(0) = 0 \\[2mm] F(\infty) = 0, \, G(\infty) = 0 \end{array} \right\} \tag{5.5}$$

We take a set of functions $F_1, F_2 \dots G_0, G_1, G_2 \dots H_1, H_2 \dots$ which fulfill all the boundary conditions of the problem and form a linear combination of these functions to obtain an approximate solution of (5.2 − 5.4). We set

$$F(h) \approx C_1 F_1(h) + C_2 F_2(h) \tag{5.6}$$

$$G(h) \approx G_0(h) + b_1 G_1(h) + b_2 G_2(h) \tag{5.7}$$

$$H(h) \approx C_1 H_1(h) + C_2 H_2(h) \tag{5.8}$$

where

$$F_1(h) = \frac{1}{2} h e^{-h}, \quad F_2(h) = 2h e^{-2h}$$

$$G_0(h) = e^{-3h}, \quad G_1(h) = e^{-h} - e^{-3h}, \quad G_2(h) = e^{-2h} - e^{-3h}$$

$$H_1(h) = -1 + (1 + h) e^{-h}, \quad H_2(h) = -1 + (1 + 2h) e^{-2h}$$

Substituting $(5.6 - 5.8)$ into (5.2) and (5.3), we get the defect functions D_F and D_G as

$$D_F = (C_1 F_1'' + C_2 F_2'') - (C_1 F_1 + C_2 F_2)^2 +$$

$$+ (G_0 + b_1 G_1 + b_2 G_2)^2 + (C_1 H_1 + C_2 H_2)(C_1 F_1' + C_2 F_2') -$$

$$- R_c [2(C_1 F_1 + C_2 F_2)(C_1 F_1'' + C_2 F_2'') + (C_1 F_1' + C_2 F_2')^2 +$$

$$+ 3(G_0' + b_1 G_1' + b_2 G_2')^2]$$

$$D_G = G_0'' + b_1 G_1'' + b_2 G_2'' -$$

$$- 2(C_1 F_1 + C_2 F_2)(G_0 + b_1 G_1 + b_2 G_2) -$$

$$- (C_1 H_1 + C_2 H_2)(G_0' + b_1 G_1' + b_2 G_2') -$$

$$- R_c [2(C_1 F_1 + C_2 F_2)(G_0'' + b_1 G_1'' + b_2 G_2'') -$$

$$- 2(C_1 F_1' + C_2 F_2')(G_0' + b_1 G_1' + b_2 G_2')]$$

The defect functions D_F and D_G are both functions of free parameters C_1 C_2, b_1, b_2 and h. We shall determine free parameters such that

$$\max |D_F| = \min, \quad \text{and} \quad \max |D_G| = \min$$

Let the trial extremal collocation points be

$$h = h_{11}, h_{12}, h_{13} \quad \text{and} \quad h = h_{21}, h_{22}, h_{23} \quad \text{for}$$

D_F and D_G respectively. We are then required to satisfy

$$D_{F_{11}} + D_{F_{12}} = 0, D_{F_{12}} + D_{F_{13}} = 0, \quad D_F'(h_{1j}) = 0 \quad j = 1, 2, 3.$$

$$D_{G_{21}} + D_{G_{22}} = 0, D_{G_{22}} + D_{G_{23}} = 0, \quad D_G'(h_{2j}) = 0, \quad j = 1, 2, 3.$$

These equations are solved by Newton's iteration process. The distribution of error functions D_F and D_G for $R_c = 0$ is shown in Figure 2. The free parameters for $R_c = 0.1$ are given below

$$C_1 = 0.97766073, \quad C_2 = -0.003478804, \quad \max|D_F| = 0.1434$$
$$b_1 = 1.42938658, \quad b_2 = -0.50133995, \quad \max|D_G| = 0.0097$$

The approximate solution for $R_c = 0.1$ becomes

$$F(h) \approx 0.488830365\, he^{-h} - 0.006957608\, he^{-2h}$$
$$G(h) \approx e^{-3h} + 1.42938658\,(e^{-h} - e^{-3h}) - 0.50133995\,(e^{-2h} - e^{-3h})$$
$$H(h) \approx 0.97766073\,[-1 + (1 + h)e^{-h}] - 0.003478804\,[-1 +$$
$$+ (1 + 2h)e^{-2h}]$$

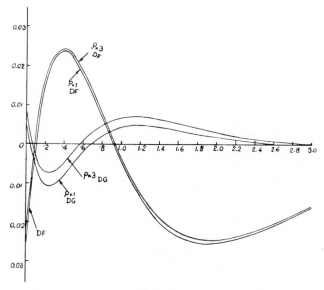

Figure 2

Error distribution function for flow near a rotating disk

The displacement thickness is given by

$$\overset{*}{\delta} = \sqrt{\frac{v}{\Omega}} \int_0^{\infty} G\,dh,$$

The momentum thickness by

$$\theta = \sqrt{\frac{v}{\Omega}} \int\limits_0^\infty G(1 - G)\,dh$$

and the dimensionless moment coefficient by

$$C_M = -2\pi\,G'(0)\,R^{-\frac{1}{2}}$$

where $R = \dfrac{a^2\Omega}{v}$ being the Reynold's number,

We get the following results given in Table IV.

TABLE IV

R_c	$\delta^* \sqrt{\dfrac{\Omega}{v}}$	$\theta \sqrt{\dfrac{\Omega}{v}}$	$R^{\frac{1}{2}} C_M/2\pi$	F_{max}
0	1.271	0.599	0.616	0.182
0.05	1.206	0.559	0.634	0.182
0.1	1.203	0.558	0.643	0.179

We find that the boundary layer thickness, momentum thickness and F_{max} decreases while the dimensionless moment coefficient C_M increases as R increases.

REFERENCES

[1]   H. Görtler, *Ang. Archiv.*, **16**, (1948), 173.
[2]   A. Witting, *Z.A.M.P.*, **4**, (1953), 376.
[3]   M. Reiner, *Amer. J. Math.*, **67**, (1945), 350.
[4]   M. Reiner and I. Braun, *Quart. Journ. Mech. & App. Math.*, **5**, (1952), 42.
[5]   R. S. Rivlin, *Proc. Roy. Soc. Lond.*, (A)**193**, (1948), 260.
[6]   F. Homann, *ZAMM*, **16**, (1936), 153.
[7]   N. Froessling, *Lunds, Univ. Arsskr. N.F.* Add.2, **35**, (1940), No. 4.
[8]   A. C. Srivastava, *ZAMP*, **9**, (1958), 80.
[9]   R. S. Nanda and M. K. Jain, *Jour. Sci. & Eng. Res.* **4**, (1961), 387.
[10] M. K. Jain, *Jour. Sci. Eng. Res.*, **5**, (1961), 81.
[11] Th. Von Karman, *ZAMM*, **1**, (1921), 233.
[12] W. G. Cochran, *Proc. Camb. Phil. Soc.*. **30**, (1934), 365.
[13] J. T. Stuart, *Quart. Journ. Mech. & App. Math.*, **7**, (1954), 446.
[14] A. C. Srivastava, *Bull. Cal. Math. Soc.*, **50**, (1958), 57.
[15] K. G. Mithal, *Ganita*, **9**, (1958), 95.
[16] M. K. Jain, *App. Sci Res. Sec. A.* **10**, (1962), (forthcoming).

DISCUSSION

H. GIESEKUS: To emphasize the importance of Reiner's formula (3.1) for the evolution of theoretical rheology at this place would mean "carrying coal to Newcastle." But in spite of this one can say today, that the general Reiner-Rivlin fluid is most likely not realised in nature. At least there is no doubt that systems which were examined experimentally till today as, e.g. high polymer solutions, colloidal suspensions etc., cannot be characterized by such a formula. An equation of state characterizing such materials must include not only f_{ik} but also its invariant time derivatives, cf., e.g., the papers by Oldroyd, Walters and Segawa. For the essential difference between real Newtonian and non-Newtonian fluids consists in the coaxiality respective non-coaxiallity of the stress and the rate of deformation tensors. The cross term of Reiner's formula describes the fact, that the two tensor ellipsoids are no more similar to each other, but rotation of axes must be described by time derivatives of the flow tensor (or, more generally, by the strain history).

If Prof. Jain succeeds in extending his method to elastico-viscous fluids, I think, this would be of great importance for the practical application.

THE HYDRODYNAMIC STABILITY OF A BINGHAM FLUID
IN COUETTE FLOW

W. P. GRAEBEL

*Department of Engineering Mechanics, The University of Michigan,
Ann Arbor, Michigan, U.S.A.*

ABSTRACT

Using a constitutive equation discussed by Oldroyd, the stability of a Bingham
fluid in rotational flow between two rotating cylinders is studied. The possibility
of the yield surface falling between the cylinders is analyzed and shown to have
little effect on the stability, although small waves may appear on the yield surface.
The conclusion is drawn that the non-Newtonian terms are always a stabilizing
factor, in that the critical Taylor number at which instability occurs is always
higher than for a Newtonian fluid. On the basis of the energy equation, it is shown
that for moderately large wave numbers the stability problem can be treated as
that for a Newtonian fluid with apparent viscosity $\mu(1+P)$, P being the Bingham
number. For low values of the wave number the disturbance shear stress parallel
to the primary flow alters the problem sufficiently so that this approximation is
not valid.

Perhaps the first non-Newtonian fluid to be investigated extensively was the
Bingham, or visco-plastic, fluid. Early researchers found that materials such
as oil-base paint, dough, cement paste, clay and sand-bitumen mixtures exhibit a yield stress[1]. For stress levels below the yield stress these materials
show no appreciable flow. As the stress level is increased to beyond the yield
stress, they behave much as Newtonian fluids do if the difference between
the actual stress and the yield stress is used in the constitutive equation of a
Newtonian fluid, i.e., that

$$\text{(shear stress)} - \text{(yield stress)} = \mu \times \text{(rate of shear deformation)}$$

for the one-dimensional case[2]. A simple one-dimensional mechanical model
for such a fluid is given by a spring in series with a dashpot-static friction

---

[1] See ref. [1] for approximate values of the yield stresses for these fluids.
[2] More recent work has cast serious doubt as to the actual behavior of these materials.
Several investigators believe only one true Bingham fluids is known, that being a plastic gel
composed of an aluminum soap dispersed in a petroleum fraction [2]. While the materials
mentioned do exhibit a yield stress, their behavior appears to be more complicated than
predicted by the simple Bingham model in that the apparent viscosity changes with shear
rate; the Bingham model does, however, provide a reasonable result within a limited range
of shear rates.

parallel combination as shown in Figure 1. For a three-dimensional stress state in such a fluid, the constitutive equation is given by

$$\tau_{ij} = \lambda e_{kk}\delta_{ij} + 2Ge_{ij} \tag{1}$$

before yield, and by

$$\tau_{ij} = \vartheta_{ij} - p\delta_{ij} + 2\mu d_{ij} \tag{2}$$

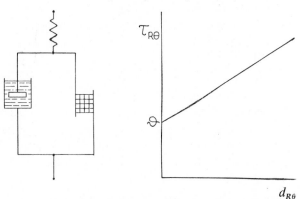

Figure 1
Mechanical model and stress-rate of deformation curve

after yield, where incompressibility has been assumed after yield occurs. Here G is the usual shear modulus of elasticity, λ the second Lamé constant, μ the absolute coefficient of viscosity, e_{ij} the strain tensor, d_{ij} the rate-of-deformation tensor, and ϑ_{ij} the yield-stress tensor. (The yield-stress tensor can be thought of as that part of the total stress causing elastic strain.) The summation convention is implied on repeated subscripts.

It remains to specify the yield-stress tensor and the yield criterion. Experimental evidence here is incomplete, as could be expected by analogy with similar problems in the field of solid mechanics. For the purpose of the present work, the assumption is made that the v. Mises criterion is valid, i.e., that

$$\tfrac{1}{2}\vartheta_{ij}\vartheta_{ij} = \vartheta^2 \tag{3}$$

where ϑ is the yield stress in pure shear. With the additional assumption that, for axes chosen such that $\tau_{ij} + p\delta_{ij} = 0$ $(i = j)$, $\vartheta_{ij}(i = j)$ will also be zero, it follows that [3]

$$\vartheta_{ij} = 2\vartheta(2d_{mn}d_{mn})^{-\frac{1}{2}}d_{ij}. \tag{4}$$

Then flow will occur when

$$\tfrac{1}{2}(\tau_{ij} + p\delta_{ij})(\tau_{ij} + p\delta_{ij}) \geqq \vartheta^2. \tag{5}$$

Eq. (2) can now be rewritten as

$$\tau_{ij} = -p\delta_{ij} + 2[\mu + \vartheta(2d_{mn}d_{mn})^{-\frac{1}{2}}]d_{ij}, \tag{6}$$

and it is understood to apply when Eq. (5) holds.[3]

A general problem in the flow of a Bingham fluid will thus possess non-linearities in the stress as well as the acceleration terms, and can be further complicated by the existence of a yield boundary whose location is not known a priori. It is not surprising, then, that only a few solutions to these problems exist [1], [5]. In an effort to contribute further to the understanding of these non-Newtonian effects, the present paper investigates the role which the yield stresses play in the stability of laminar flows. For definiteness, and because it allows comparison with well-known results for Newtonian fluids, rotational Couette flow is considered. Since this flow is present in one version of a plasto-meter used to measure the physical constants of such fluids, the present work should also provide basic information on the range in which such a plasto-meter is useful, and could also serve as a test in determining whether a given fluid was Bingham in nature.

The primary Couette flow is easily solved for in a semi-inverse manner. Using polar cylindrical coordinates and assuming that $d_{R\theta}$ is the only non-vanishing component of the rate-of-deformation tensor, the equilibrium equations show that $\tau_{R\theta}$ is proportional to R^{-2}, as is the case for a Newtonian fluid. If the inner cylinder of radius R_1 rotates with an angular velocity Ω_1 and the outer cylinder of radius R_2 rotates with angular velocity Ω_2, (see Figure 2), integration of the constitutive relationship along with the supposition of no slip on the boundary yields a tangential velocity given by

$$u_\theta \equiv V = [R_1\Omega_1/(1-R_1^2/R_2^2)] \; [N[(R/R_1) - R_1/R]\ln(R_2/R_1) -$$

$$- N(1 - R_1^2/R_2^2)(R/R_1)\ln(R/R_1) +$$

$$+ (R/R_1)[(\Omega_2/\Omega_1) - R_1^2/R_2^2] - (R_1/R)[(\Omega_2/\Omega_1) - 1]], \tag{7}$$

---

[3] To make the problem more general, μ could be regarded as being variable. An example of such a case would be

$$\mu = \mu_0 + \mu_1(2d_{mn}d_{mn})^{(p-1)/2},$$

which can be made to agree quite closely with one-dimensional experiments (see for example [4]). This has the effect in the mechanical model of putting nonlinear elements in parallel with the dashpot. However, since the mathematical generalization from the one-dimensional case is not unique and pertinent experimental data is not available to aid in a choice, and also since the effect of the yield stress is the main consideration in the present work, μ is taken to be constant.

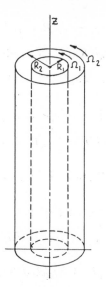

Figure 2
Coordinate system

where $N = \vartheta/\mu\Omega_1$ is the Bingham number (also referred to in the literature as the Oldroyd number). For convenience here, ϑ is considered as a signed quantity. The signs of $\tau_{r\theta}$ and $d_{r\theta}$ must be the same, and will determine the sign of ϑ. The shear stress and rate of deformation are

$$\tau_{R\theta} = 2\Omega_1\mu(1 - R_1^2/R_2^2)^{-1}(R_1^2/R^2)[N\ln(R_2/R_1) - 1 + \Omega_2/\Omega_1], \qquad (8)$$

$$d_{R\theta} = \Omega_1(1 - R_1^2/R_2^2)^{-1}\left[N[(R_1/R)^2\ln(R_2/R_1) - \tfrac{1}{2}(1 - R_1^2/R_2^2)] + \right.$$
$$\left. + (R_1/R)^2[\Omega_2/\Omega_1 - 1]\right]$$

If the yield surface should fall between the concentric cylinders, then in Eqs. (7) and (8) R_2 may be regarded as being the radius of the cylindrical yield surface and is determined from Eq. (8) by letting $R = R_2$, $\tau_{R\theta} = \vartheta$; thus

$$(R_2/R_1)^2 - \ln(R_2/R_1)^2 - 1 = (2/N)(\Omega_2/\Omega_1 - 1). \qquad (9)$$

The fluid outside of the yield surface is in rigid body rotation.

Before formulating the stability equations, it is desirable to write the general equations of motion for a Bingham fluid. These are exactly the Navier-Stokes equations for nonconstant viscosity, and in polar cylindrical form become

$$\rho[\partial u_R/\partial t + (\vec{u} \cdot \nabla)u_R - u_\theta^2/R] = -\partial p/\partial R + (\mu + \vartheta/I)[\nabla^2 u_R - u_R/R^2 -$$

$$- 2\partial u_\theta/R^2\partial\theta] + \vartheta[2(\partial u_R/\partial R)(\partial I^{-2}/\partial R) + (\partial u_\theta/\partial R - u_\theta/R +$$

$$+ \partial u_R/R\partial\theta)(\partial I^{-2}/R\partial\theta) + (\partial u_R/\partial z + \partial u_z/\partial R)(\partial I^{-1}/\partial z)], \qquad (10)$$

$$\rho[\partial u_\theta/\partial t + (\vec{u} \cdot \nabla)u_\theta + u_R u_\theta/R] = -\partial p/R\partial\theta + (\mu + \vartheta/I)[\nabla^2 u_\theta - u_\theta/R^2$$

$$+ 2\partial u_R/R^2\partial\theta] + \vartheta[(\partial u_\theta/\partial R - u_\theta/R + \partial u_R/R\partial\theta)(\partial I^{-1}/\partial R) +$$

$$+ 2(\partial u_\theta/R\partial\theta + u_R/R)(\partial I^{-1}/R\partial\theta) + (\partial u_\theta/\partial z + \partial u_z/R\partial\theta)(\partial I^{-1}/\partial z)], \quad (11)$$

$$\rho[\partial u_z/\partial t + (\vec{u} \cdot \nabla)u_z] = -\partial p/\partial z + (\mu + \vartheta/I)\nabla^2 u_z + \vartheta[(\partial u_z/\partial R + \partial u_R/\partial z) \cdot$$

$$(\partial I^{-1}/\partial R) + (\partial \mu_z/R\partial\theta + \partial u_\theta/\partial z)(\partial I^{-1}/R\partial\theta) + 2(\partial u_z/\partial z)(\partial I^{-1}/\partial z)], \quad (12)$$

$$\partial u_R/\partial R + u_R/R + \partial u_\theta/R\partial\theta + \partial u_z/\partial z = 0, \qquad (13)$$

where

$$I^2 = 2d_{ij}d_{ij}.$$

Upon assuming small rotationally symmetric disturbances and linearizing the resultant equations, Eqs. (10), (11), (12) and (13) become

$$\rho(\partial u_R'/\partial t - 2\bar{V}u_\theta'/R) = -\partial p'/\partial R + (\mu + \vartheta/I_p)(\nabla^2 u_R' - u_R'/R^2) +$$

$$+ 2\vartheta(\partial u_R'/\partial R)(dI_p^{-1}/dR), \qquad (14)$$

$$\rho[\partial u_\theta'/\partial t + (d\bar{V}/dR + \bar{V}/R)u_R'] = \mu(\nabla^2 u_\theta' - u_\theta'/R^2) + (\vartheta/I_p)\partial^2 u_\theta'/\partial z^2, \qquad (15)$$

$$\rho\partial u_z'/\partial t = -\partial p'/\partial z + (\mu + \vartheta/I_p)\nabla^2 u_z' + \vartheta(\partial u_z'/\partial R + \partial u_R'/\partial z)(dI_p^{-1}/dR), \qquad (16)$$

$$\partial u_R'/\partial R + u_r'/R + \partial u_z'/\partial z = 0 \qquad (17)$$

where

$$I_p = d\bar{V}/dR - \bar{V}/R$$

and primes indicate the disturbance quantities. After elimination of u_z' and p' and changing to dimensionless quantities, Eqs. (14), (15), (16) and (17) can be further reduced to

$$(L - \lambda^2)(L - \lambda^2 - \sigma\bar{R})u + NJ_p^{-1}\left[(L - \lambda^2)^2 u + (dJ_p^{-1}/dr)[2d(Lu)/dr - \right.$$

$$- 2\lambda^2 du/dr - r^{-1}(L - \lambda^2)u] + J_p^{-2}[2(dJ_p/dr)^2 - $$

$$\left. - J_p d^2 J_p/dr^2](L + \lambda^2)u\right] = 2\lambda^2\bar{R}\bar{V}v/r \tag{18}$$

and

$$(L - \lambda^2 - \sigma\bar{R} - N\lambda^2/J_p)v = \bar{R}(dV/dr + V/r)u$$

where the substitutions have been made that

$$u_r' = R_1\Omega_1 u(r)\sin(\lambda z/R_1)\exp(\sigma\Omega_1 t),$$

$$u_\theta' = R_1\Omega_1 v(r)\sin(\lambda z/R_1)\exp(\sigma\Omega_1 t),$$

$$I_p = \Omega_1 J_p, \qquad\qquad J_p = dV/dr - V/r,$$

$$\bar{V} = R_1\Omega_1 V, \qquad\qquad R = R_1 r,$$

$$\bar{R} = \rho R_1^2\Omega_1/\mu, \qquad\qquad \beta = (R_2 - R_1)/R_1,$$

$$L = d^2/dr^2 + d/rdr - 1/r^2.$$

When the yield surface does not occur between the cylinders, the boundary conditions are

$$u = v = du/dr = 0 \tag{20}$$

at $r = 1$ and $r = 1 + \beta$. If the yield surface does fall within the outer cylinder (at a radius determined by Eq. (9)), it is possible that the yield surface will be displaced by some (small) amount due to the disturbance quantities, and the conditions to be imposed at the yield surface are not as obvious. Since the radial and longitudinal velocities have to be continuous, u and du/dr still will be zero at $r = 1 + \beta$. Denoting the (dimensionless) displacement of the interface by η, continuity of the tangential velocity demands that

$$(v + V)_{r=1+\beta+\eta} = (1 + \beta + \eta)\Omega_2/\Omega_1.$$

Expanding the left side in a Taylor series about $r = 1 + \beta$, to the order of the first approximation,

$$(v + V + \eta dV/dr)_{r=1+\beta} = (1 + \beta + \eta)\Omega_2/\Omega_1.$$

But $(V)_{r=1+\beta} = (1 + \beta)\Omega_2/\Omega_1$ and, since this is to be satisfied at the yield surface, $dV/dr = V/r = \Omega_2/\Omega_1$. Hence the condition imposed is still

$(v)_{r=1+\beta} = 0$. Thus the boundary conditions are the same regardless of whether the yield surface occurs within the outer cylinder or not.

The displacement η can be computed from the yield condition. Thus

$$(\tau_{r\theta}^2 + 2\tau_{r\theta}\tau_{r\theta}')_{r=1+\beta+\eta} = \vartheta^2.$$

Again expanding about $r = 1 + \beta$,

$$(\tau_{r\theta}^2 + 2\tau_{r\theta}\eta d\tau_{r\theta}/dr + 2\tau_{r\theta}\tau_{r\theta}')_{r=1+\beta} = \vartheta^2$$

or

$$\eta = -[\tau_{r\theta}'/(d\bar{\tau}_{r\theta}/dr)]_{r=1+\beta}.$$

In terms of the perturbation velocities,

$$\eta = [(1+\beta)(dv/dr)_{r=1+\beta}/2N]\sin(\lambda z/R_1)\exp(\sigma\Omega_1 t). \tag{21}$$

Should the yield surface be at the outer cylinder, the above result is of interest only where it gives negative values of η.

The difficulty of solving the set of Eqs. (18), (19) can be greatly reduced by considering only the case of small spacing ($\beta \ll 1$). Letting

$$r = 1 + \beta\zeta, \qquad\qquad D = d/d\zeta,$$
$$k = \beta\lambda, \qquad\qquad R' = \beta^2\bar{R},$$
$$\alpha = \Omega_2/\Omega_1 - 1, \qquad\qquad T = -2\alpha(R')^2/\beta,$$
$$P = N\beta/\alpha = \vartheta\beta/\mu(\Omega_2 - \Omega_1),$$

and assuming $N\beta$ is of the order of 1, Eqs. (18) and (19) simplify to

$$(D^2 - k^2)(D^2 - k^2 - \sigma R')u + P(D^2 - k^2)^2 u = (1 + \alpha\zeta)v \tag{22}$$

$$(D^2 - k^2 - \sigma R' - k^2 P)v = -Tk^2 u. \tag{23}$$

The solution can now be carried out following Chandrasekhar [6]. Assuming

$$v = \sum_m A_m \sin m\pi\zeta$$

and considering the case of neutral stability ($\sigma = 0$), u is found from Eq. (22) to be given by

$$u = \sum_{m=1}^{\infty} \frac{A_m}{(m^2\pi^2 + k^2)}\left[(1 + \alpha\zeta)\sin m\pi\zeta + \frac{4\alpha m\pi}{m^2\pi^2 + k^2}\left[\cos m\pi\zeta - \cosh k\zeta +\right.\right.$$

$$+ \frac{(\cosh k - (-1)^m)(\sinh k\zeta - k\zeta\cosh k\zeta) + k\zeta\sinh k\sinh k\zeta}{\sinh k + (-1)^m k}\Big] +$$

$$+ \frac{m\pi}{\sinh^2 k - k^2}[k\sinh k\zeta + (\sinh k\cosh k - k)\zeta\sinh k\zeta - (\sinh k)^2\zeta\cosh k\zeta +$$

$$+ (-1)^m(1 + \alpha)(\sinh k\sinh k\zeta + k\zeta\cosh k\sinh k\zeta -$$

$$- \zeta\sinh k\sinh k\zeta - k\zeta\sinh k\cosh k\zeta)]\Big] \tag{24}$$

Substituting this into Eq. (23), multiplying by $\sin n\pi\zeta$, and integrating from zero to one, the result is obtained

$$\sum_m A_{mn}E_{mn}(m^2\pi^2 + k^2)^{-2} = 0, \qquad n = 1, 2, \dots \tag{25}$$

where

$$E_{mn} = -\delta_{mn}(1 + P)(m^2\pi^2 + k^2)^2(m^2\pi^2 + k^2 + k^2P)/2k^2T + a_{m.} + b_{mn}\alpha, \tag{26}$$

$$a_{mn} = \tfrac{1}{2}\delta_{mn} + 2mn\pi^2 k(n^2\pi^2 + k^2)^{-2}[1 + (-1)^{m+n}]\cdot$$

$$\cdot[\sinh k - (-1)^n k]^{-1}[(-1)^n - \cosh k], \tag{27}$$

$$b_{mn} = \tfrac{1}{4}\delta_{mn} + 2mn[1 - (-1)^{m+n}][-\pi^{-2}(m^2 - n^2 + \delta_{mn})^{-2} -$$

$$- 2\pi^2(m^2\pi^2 + k^2)^{-1}(n^2\pi^2 + k^2)^{-1} + 2(m^2\pi^2 + k^2)^{-1} \ .$$

$$\cdot(n^2 - m^2 + \delta_{mn})^{-1}] + 2kmn\pi^2(n^2\pi^2 + k^2)^{-2}[\sinh k - (-1)^n k]^{-1} \ .$$

$$\cdot[(-1)^{m+n}[(-1)^n - \cosh k] + [(-1)^{m+n} - 1]4k\sinh k/(m^2\pi^2 + k^2)]. \tag{28}$$

In order for a nontrivial solution to exist, the determinant of the E_{mn} must vanish; this condition then determines T. The neutral stability curves for $T/(1 + P)^2$ as a function of k, P and α are shown in Figures 3 through 6.

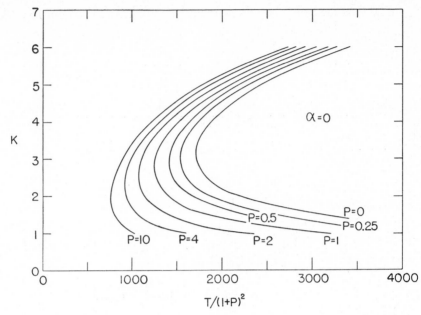

Figure 3
Neutral stability curves, $a = 0$

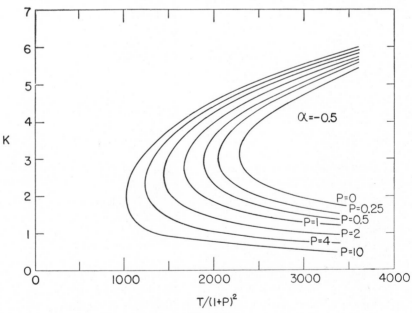

Figure 4
Neutral stability curves, $a = -0.5$

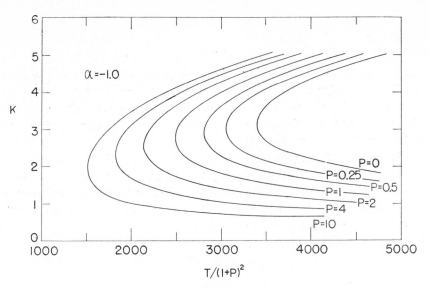

Figure 5
Neutral stability curves, $a = -1.0$

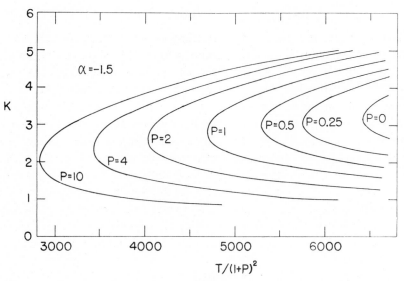

Figure 6
Neutral stability curves, $a = -1.5$

The fourth order determinant was used in the computation of the curves, the agreement with the results from the next higher approximation being well within one per cent. The sign of P has been restricted to be positive for the following reason: Ω_1 can always be made positive by a suitable choice of axes; hence, the sign of $\tau_{r\theta}$ and $d_{r\theta}$ for the primary flow is determined by the sign of α. Thus ϑ and α must have the same sign and, since the other quantities which make up P are always positive, P will always be positive. (This can also be seen directly from Eq. (9)).

An inspection of Eq. (26) reveals that the non-Newtonian components of this flow are always stabilizing in nature, in that a higher value of T is required for the onset of instability. The reason for this can be found by consideration of the energy of the disturbance flow. The energy equation association with Eqs. (14), (15), and (16) is readily found to be

$$\frac{dE'}{dt} = S - \Phi', \qquad (29)$$

where

$$E' = \int\int \rho[(u_R')^2 + (u_\theta')^2 + (u_z')^2]\, 2\pi R\, dR\, dz,$$

$$S = -\int\int \rho(dV/dR - V/R)u_R' u_\theta'\, 2\pi R\, dR\, dz,$$

$$\Phi' = 2\mu\int\int \left[(1 + \vartheta/\mu I_p)\left[(d_{RR}')^2 + (d_{\theta\theta}')^2 + (d_{zz}')^2 + \right.\right.$$

$$\left.\left. + 2(d_{Rz}')^2 + 2(d_{\theta z}')\,) + 2(d_{\theta R}')^2\right]\, 2\pi R\, dR\, dz,$$

the integration in each case being performed over a disturbance cell. S, the Reynolds' stress term, is not significantly affected by $\vartheta(dV/dR - V/R$, the rate of deformation for the primary flow, and u_R', u_θ' for the range of N considered here are essentially the same as in the Newtonian case). However, Φ', the dissipation function associated with the disturbance, is measurably increased due to the ϑ term, so that the fluid is now better able to dissipate the disturbance energy. For the neutrally stable case ($dE'/dt = 0$), then, the rate of deformation of the primary flow must be increased roughly by an amount $1 + P$ over that required in a Newtonian fluid to cause instability. In fact, the entire problem could be treated as the flow of a Newtonian fluid with viscosity $\mu(1 + P)$ were it not for $\tau_{r\theta}'$, which does not contain ϑ terms, When k is large compared with π, the effect of this defect in $\tau_{r\theta}'$ disappears as indicated by the neutral stability curves which for given α approach one another as k increases.

The parameter P in the present analysis is simply the Bingham number based on the difference in angular velocities, and so is the ratio of yield stress to Newtonian shear. While $P\alpha$ is of the order one, P may become large for small α, a case where the yield stress far outweighs the Newtonian stress. P is bounded, however, by Eq. (5). For the present problem, this demands that

$$P = 2\beta/[\beta(2 + \beta) - 2\ln(1 + \beta)] \approx 1/\beta.$$

Higher values of P will result in rigid body rotation of the fluid with no deformation present; the fluid then is essentially an elastic solid and the stability problem becomes meaningless.

The energy equation (Eq. (29)) for this problem affords both a physical interpretation of the role of the non-Newtonian terms and also a qualitative measure of their effect. It would be fortunate if this were possible for all non-Newtonian fluids so that insight into the mechanisms at work could be obtained with less numerical effort. That this cannot always be done is shown by determining the corresponding forms for S and Φ' for a Stokesian fluid [7]. For such a fluid S is of the same form (although V, u_R', u_θ' are different), but the expression for Φ' becomes

$$\Phi' = 2\mu \int\int \Big[(d_{RR}')^2 + (d_{\theta\theta}')^2 + (d_{zz}')^2 + 2(d_{R\theta}')^2 + 2(d_{Rz}')^2 + 2(d_{\theta z}')^2 +$$

$$+ (A^{(2)}/\mu)(dV/dR - V/R)[(d_{RR}' + d_{\theta\theta}')d_{R\theta}' + d_{\theta z}'d_{Rz}']\Big] 2\pi R\, dR\, dz.$$

Since the sign of the non-Newtonian terms is not clear a priori, a complete solution is necessary, and no help is gained from energy considerations.

In summary then, the non-Newtonian factors involved in the flow of a Bingham fluid can be generally expected to be a stabilizing influence. This is due to the fact that a higher stress level is necessary to produce a given rate of deformation. Since the dimensionless parameters which are used to formulate a criterion of stability (Taylor number, Reynolds' number) can be considered to be the ratio of inertia forces to dissipative forces, a higher value of such a parameter for the onset of instability in a non-Newtonian fluid is a simple statement that the inertia forces must be increased over that in a Newtonian fluid to overcome the increased dissipative forces.

The possible presence of a free (yield) surface, usually thought of as a destabilizing agent, here plays no role whatsoever in the stability criterion. This perhaps surprising result is due to the fact that the yield surface is not a material surface, so that even though the yield surface can move with a radial velocity, nevertheless the radial velocity of a fluid particle at the yield surface will be zero. The surface waves which can form are not able to re-distribute effectively the energies involved, and so cannot provide a mechanism for increasing the Reynolds' stress. Eq. (21) indicates that η, the perturbation of the yield surface, is of the order of β/P times the disturbance quantities, and so is very small. Its form is rather unusual, in that half of a cell will be pinched inwards while its remainder is bulged outward, so that the disturbed yield surface takes on somewhat the appearance of a corrugated metal culvert pipe.

The author is pleased to acknowledge the partial support of the Army Research Office.

REFERENCES

[1] M. REINER, *Handbuch der Physik*, VI, Springer-Verlag (1958), 457.
[2] E.L. MCMILLEN, *Chem. Eng. Prog.*, **44** (1948), 537.
[3] J.G. OLDROYD, *Proc. Cambridge Phil. Soc.*, **43** (1947), 100.
[4] A.W. SISKO, *Indust. and Eng. Chem.*, **50** (1958), 1789.
[5] J.G. OLDROYD, *Proc. Cambridge Phil. Soc.*, **43** (1947), 383, 396, 521.
[6] S. CHANDRASEKHAR, *Mathematika*, **1** (1954), 5.
[7] W. GRAEBEL, *Physics of Fluids*, **4** (1961), 362.

List of symbols.

τ_{ij}	$=$	stress tensor
e_{ij}	$=$	strain tensor
δ_{ij}	$=$	Kronecker delta
λ, G	$=$	elastic constants
ϑ_{ij}	$=$	yield stress tensor
ϑ	$=$	yield stress in pure shear
p	$=$	pressure
d_{ij}	$=$	rate of deformation tensor
μ	$=$	coefficient of viscosity
R_1, R_2	$=$	radii of cylinders
Ω_1, Ω_2	$=$	angular velocities of cylinders
N	$=$	Bingham (or Oldroyd) number
$\overline{V}$	$=$	velocity of primary flow
$\vec{u}$	$=$	velocity vector
I^2	$=$	second invariant of the rate of deformation tensor
I_p^2	$=$	second invariant of the rate of deformation tensor for primary flow
$\vec{u}', p'$	$=$	disturbance velocity and pressure
$\overline{R}$	$=$	Reynolds number

β =   dimensionless spacing
L =   Bessel operator
η =   disturbance of the yield surface
ζ =   dimensionless radius (variable)
λ =   dimensionless wave number
α =   dimensionless angular velocity
k =   modified wave number
R' =   modified Reynolds number
D =   differentiation with respect to
T =   Taylor number
P =   modified Bingham number
E' =   kinetic energy of disturbance
S =   Reynolds stress
Φ' =   rate of energy dissipation

DYNAMICS OF FLUID JETS: MEASUREMENT OF NORMAL STRESSES AT HIGH SHEAR RATES

A. B. Metzner, W. T. Houghton*, R. E. Hurd and C. C. Wolfe**

University of Delaware, Newark, Delaware, U.S.A.

ABSTRACT

This paper reports experimental measurements of normal stresses in fluids at high shear rates — to 10^5 sec^{-1}. The difference between the two deviatoric components $P_{11} - P_{22}$ (where 1 denotes the direction of the deformation or flow under condtions of simple shear) is obtained from measurements on a jet of fluid issuing from a round tube; no a priori assumptions concerning normal stress-deformation rate relationships are needed. Data are presented on polymeric solutions as well as on simpler (Newtonian) fluids and slurries.

1. Introduction.

Whereas rheologists have both predicted and measured normal stresses in some variety of materials, there has, in general, been very limited quantitative experimental support for any of the theoretical predictions. Furthermore, theoretical predictions of the magnitudes of the normal stress terms have usually been made in as general a manner as possible in the hope of thereby encompassing a greater number of real materials within the framework of a single theoretical approach. This greater degree of generality is manifested in a greater number of parameters or constants which must be evaluated experimentally. Under these conditions, therefore, it is evident that experimental measurements should be made over as wide a range of deformation rates as possible. On the one hand no determination of the large number of parameters or constants appearing in the theoretical predictions is possible unless precise data, over wide ranges of all the pertinent variables, are obtained. On the other hand, in the absence of any well-developed theoretical predictions of the magnitudes of these stresses any problem in fluid mechanics in which such normal stress terms appear cannot be solved explicitly unless experimental data giving the magnitudes of these stresses under the deformation rates of interest are available. For example, the addition

---

* Present address: Consolidated Paper Company, Grand'mere, Quebec, Canada.
** Present address: Esso Research & Engineering Company, Process Engineering Division, Florham Park, New Jersey. U.S.A.

of viscoelastic additives to fluids as a means of drag-reduction in fluid transport under turbulent flow conditions [1] has been widely exploited in the petroleum industry [2], [3] and some study of the application of these materials in naval architecture has been made [4]. Under such turbulent flow conditions, however, shear rates exceed 10^4 sec^{-1} in most instances and may reach a level of 5×10^5 sec^{-1} [1]. Similarly, many coating devices operate at shear rates of the order of 10^6 sec^{-1} and lubrication problems may involve shear rates which are greater still one or several orders of magnitude [5]. As is evident from these examples, measurements of normal stresses at a level of a few hundred reciprical seconds or below, as commonly reported using rotational devices, are of no value for application to the above engineering design problems and will probably be inadequate for distinguishing between various theoretical predictions. With the exception of the birefringence studies of Philippoff and co-workers [6], [7], [8], [9], which extend to shear rates of 6×10^4 sec $^{-1}$ for very dilute solutions and to 5×10^3 sec^{-1} for concentrated solutions, no measurements of normal stresses beyond 10^3 sec.$^{-1}$ have been reported using conventional techniques. Many of the limitations of the birefringence approach have been discussed by Philippoff [8]; additionally there is still some controversy over the assumed linearity between degree of birefringence and stress. Thus, this approach, while more versatile than force measurements in a rotational geometry in a number of important respects, retains several severe limitations.

The purpose of this paper is to exploit an analysis of the Barus effect, first suggested by Philippoff and Gaskins [9] as applicable to the measurement of normal stresses, for the measurement of normal stresses as a function of shear rate. In addition to enabling measurements at very high shear rates on polymeric solutions and similar systems of low viscosity the method has also been applied to the measurement of normal stresses in polymeric melts [10] which had heretofore been studied only over a very limited range of very low shear rates. The details of the development have recently been published elsewhere [11] and will not be repeated except insofar as necessary to discuss recent additions to the theory.

2. Development.

The equations for calculating normal stresses from measurements of the diameter of a fluid jet issuing from a smooth, round tube are based on a momentum balance over a portion of the jet [11]. The first control surface is taken across the end of the tube from which the jet is issuing; the second is taken sufficiently far downstream so that the elastic stresses imposed on the fluid in the tube will have relaxed completely (i.e. within the limit of experimental measurements). The assumptions employed are:

1. The flow is steady, laminar, and isothermal, and the tube from which the fluid is issuing is of a sufficiently great L/D ratio to ensure that a well-developed velocity profile, characteristic of the steady state shear stress-shear rate behavior of the fluid, has been developed at the downstream end of the tube (Section 1).

2. The equality of P_{22} and P_{33} is assumed.*

3. The fluid is assumed to be incompressible.

4. Gravitational effects, and drag of the air on the jet may be neglected. Experimentally, the jet will be found to droop and its diameter will decrease when gravitational effects become important. This will generally not occur at jet velocities above the order of 100–200cm/sec except downstream from Section 2, the point of measurement.

5. Effects of interfacial and surface tension, at the end of the tube and in the jet, respectively, are negligible. While the surface tension forces in the jet at the downstream control surface may be readily included (although a recent paper on the subject [13] has considered them incorrectly) the same is not true of the interfacial tension at the outlet of the tube: its magnitude is normally unknown and anti-wetting techniques, to reduce it, are frequently erratic. Fortunately, the entire problem of surface tension effects may be avoided by restricting the experiment to jet velocities of above about 150 cm/sec. Such a restriction also serves to render gravitational effects negligble, as they must be to avoid the addition of new stresses induced by elongation of elements of the fluid due to gravitational forces.

The following relation results from the above assumptions:

$$[P_{11} - P_{22}]_R = \frac{\rho V^2}{n'} \left\{ (n' + 1) \int_0^1 2\left(\frac{u}{V}\right)^2 \left(\frac{r}{R}\right) d\left(\frac{r}{R}\right) - \right.$$

$$\left. - \left(\frac{D}{d_j}\right)^2 \left[n' + 1 + \frac{d\left[\ln(D/d_j)\right]}{d\left[\ln 8V/D\right]} \right] \right\} \tag{1}$$

---

* It has recently been shown [12] that the equality of P_{22} and P_{33} need not be assumed if the geometry of a jet isssuing from between parallel flat plates, instead of from a round tube, is chosen. This is less convenient experimentally, however.

The shear rate at the wall of the tube, i.e. at the same position at which $P_{11}-P_{22}$ is evaluated in the above equation, is given by the usual Weissenberg-Rabinowitsch-Mooney relation:

$$(- du/dr)_R = [(3n' + 1)/4n'](8V/D) \tag{2}$$

To evaluate the integral remaining in Equation 1 it is necessary to evaluate the velocity profile. Any theoretical or empirical equation of adequate accuracy may be used. It has been shown [11] that even the empirical "power law" is adequate in almost all cases. This then gives, for the normal stress difference at the wall shear rate:

$$(P_{11} - P_{22})_R = \frac{\rho D^2}{64n'} \left(\frac{8V}{D}\right)^2 \left\{(n' + 1)\frac{3n + 1}{2n + 1} - \right.$$

$$\left. - \left(\frac{D}{d_j}\right)^2 \left[n' + 1 + \frac{d(\log D/d_j)}{d(\log 8V/D)}\right]\right\} \tag{3}$$

3. Experimental procedures.

Jets issuing from long tubes (L/D greater than 125 and usually above 240) were employed to ensure the complete development of the velocity profile, uninfluenced by entrance effects. The tube diameters ranged from 0.8 to 2.7 mm. Photographs of the jets were taken using slow speed Kodak "panatomic-X" film and a high intensity flash of short duration (approx. 0.5 to 1 millisecond) to obtain the sharpness and fine grain structure necessary for accurate measurement of the jet diameter. Measurements at several downstream positions showed that with all fluids employed the jet diameter had always become constant, within the experimental error of less than 1%, in a distance of less than 10 cm from the end of the tube. As jet velocities between 100 and 1400 cm/sec were employed, these data indicate higher rates of stress relaxation than expected in general, and for some materials longer relaxation times may be necessary.

Fluid densities and shear stress-shear rate data were obtained using conventional, accepted procedures. Complete details and the tabulated results are given in a number of theses [14], [15], [16] which are readily available.

4. Experimental results.

Newtonian fluids

For a purely Newtonian fluid ($P_{11} = P_{22} = 0$ and $n = n' = 1.00$) Eq. (3) predicts a jet- to tube-diameter ratio dj/D equal to 0.866, a value supported using early data on jets of water [11]. Middleman and Gavis [13] subsequently pointed out that the correctness of the first assumption employed in the theoretical development is not obvious: while the velocity profile may be well-developed within the tube itself, longitudinal accelerations must occur in the region downstream from the end of the tube in order to convert this well-developed tube-flow profile into the ultimately flat profile of the jet. It is not obvious that these accelerations are entirely confined to the region downstream from the first control surface at the end of the tube, and, unless this were the case, one of the terms in the momentum balance employed to derive Eqs. (1) and (3) would be incorrect. The analysis employed by Middleman and Gavis neglects a number of important aspects of the problem: if such longitudinal accelerations exist, radial accelerations of the same magnitude are required by continuity considerations. These in turn must result in radial pressure gradients and an attendant distortion of the velocity profile. While all these effects were neglected their semi-empirical final result, which may be derived more easily directly by dimensional analysis, is still valid: if such longitudinal accelerations exist in Newtonian fluids, d_j/D will not be equal to 0.866 and *must* be a unique function of Reynolds number, the only other pertinent dimensionless variable in the absence of surface or interfacial tension effects and accelerations induced by either gravitational or air-drag forces.

Figure 1 depicts experimental data on glycerine solutions obtained by Wolfe [16] to check this point. On the same figure, the band of earlier but somewhat less accurate data obtained by Middleman [17] and kindly made available by Professor Gavis, is also indicated. The trend is well-defined and is clearly independent of tube diameter, viscosity and jet velocity, all variables which would affect the data if experimental aberrations such as air-drag, surface and interfacial tensions or gravitational effects were present to measurable degrees. (In the case of the Middleman data only those regions are shown which include data at sufficiently high velocities to be free of surface and interfacial tension effects).

In contrast to the above correlation, calculations based on the assumption of the existence of normal stresses, using Eq. (3), resulted in no correlation of the results: for a given fluid at a fixed shear rate the calculated normal stresses varied systematically with tube diameter [16]. Thus, the phenomenon

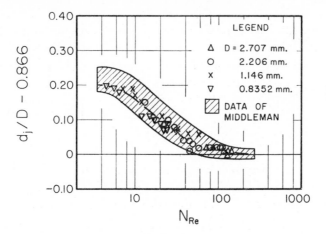

Figure 1

Data showing diameters of Newtonian jets: glycerine solutions having viscosities between 0.93 and 2.47 poise. The viscosities were shown to be independent of shear rate over the 2-decade range of shear rates studied, whithin the experimental accuracy of about ± 2%.

Data of Middleman [17] include 4 data points on mineral oil, and 19 points on syrup as well as glycerine data, using tube diameters between 1.4 and 2.4 mm

is clearly not due to normal stress effects under conditions where the assumed equality of P_{22} and P_{33} is valid. Similarly, jets of fluids possessing a "cross-viscosity", i.e. jets of Reiner-Rivlin fluids [18], [19] (for which $P_{11} = P_{22}$ and $P_{22} - P_{33} = \eta_c \, (- \, du/dr)^2$ in simple shearing flow) could show greater or lesser contractions than a Newtonian material, depending on the sign of the coefficient of cross viscosity, but the ratio d_j/D would be independent of flow rate, hence Reynolds number*. Thus it is clear that the fluids employed to date (oils and aqueous solutions) *either* exhibit the acceleration effects postulated by Middleman and Gavis or exhibit some normal stress effects which include the inequality of P_{22} and P_{33} in such a manner that the predicted jet diameter becomes a function of Reynolds number rather than of wall shear rate.

Another concomitant result of the acceleration effects postulated at the tube exit by Middleman and Gavis for Newtonian fluids must be an abnormal pressure gradient in that portion of the tube over which such accelerations occur. The integrated total pressure drop due to such abnormal pressure gradients may readily be computed by the means used to develop Eq. (1),

---

* While η_c need not be a constant it would only be a function of shear rate and not of flowrate or Reynolds number, under conditions of simple shear.

simply by moving the upstream control surface well back into the tube and allowing an additional term for such a pressure drop, ΔP excess. Expressing this quantity in terms of an "equivalent" length of tube which exhibits the same pressure drop, one obtains for a Newtonian fluid:

$$L_e/D = \frac{\dfrac{DV\rho}{\mu}\left[(4/3)(d_j/D)^2 - 1\right]}{32(d_j/D)^2} \tag{4}$$

Table I lists the values of the equivalent length ratio L_e/D computed using values for d_j/D taken from the curve of Figure 1. While these are small in magnitude their variation with Reynolds number is unusual.

TABLE I

Pressure drop requirements for exit acceleration terms, Newtonian fluids

N_{Re}	L_e/D
3	0.043
10	0.12
30	0.16
100	0.090
200	0.00

In summary, data taken on fluids exhibiting a clear linearity between shear stress and shear rate, and believed to be Newtonian, display a greater ratio of jet to tube diameter than predicted on the basis of a momentum balance which neglects acceleration effects. Empirically, this difference is found to be a function of the Reynolds number and carries with it the implication of an "exit pressure loss" which is seen to vary peculiarly with Reynolds number. These data cannot be interpreted as being due to either a coefficient of cross-viscosity or due to normal stresses unless very unusual relationships for the normal stress terms P_{22} and P_{33} are invoked. The effect is found to be restricted to a modest range of Reynolds numbers, hence may be of minor consequence in measurement of normal stresses in viscoelastic materials.

Non-Newtonian fluids

Figure 1 indicates that Eq. (1) or (3) may be used to evaluate $P_{11} - P_{22}$ provided the Reynolds number in the tube is maintained above a level of about 200 even if the fluid is only slightly viscoelastic. In more strongly viscoelastic systems d_j/D may exceed a value of 2.0 and even the use of Reynolds numbers as low as 30 would lead to only small errors under such conditions. The maximum error at any Reynolds number would not exceed about 25%. These statements pre-suppose that the curve of Figure 1 would not be a function of the flow behaviour index of the material but would be common to all "purely-viscous" fluids*. To check this point, extensive experimental measurements were carried out [15] using jets of clay slurries of various concentrations and solutions of "Carbopol", a partially cross-linked and carboxyated polymethylenic polymer. Studies of turbulence in non-Newtonian systems [1] have indicated these materials to be purely viscous or nearly so, although pronouncedly non-Newtonian. Data were obtained on 6 different fluid formulations. The results of these studies are summarized by the broad, crosshatched area of Figure 2. As expected, the data for these materials scatter considerably more than the experimental data shown on Figure 1 because of greater experimental difficulties.

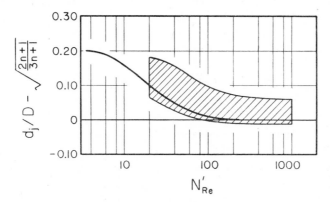

Figure 2

Expansion ratios of non-Newtonian fluids possessing only minor viscoelastic properties. Crosshatched area summarizes over 90 independent measurements; curve is taken from Figure 1

In Figure 2 the ordinate is so chosen that it would be equal to zero if $P_{11} - P_{22}$ were equal to zero and the abnormal accelerations (or other effects) found in Figure 1 were both absent. The Reynolds number used is the "ge-

---

* Purely viscous fluids are defined [5], [20], [22] as materials which exhibit no memory for their previous deformation history. That is, they exhibit no viscoelastic normal stresses, although the relationship between the stress tensor and the rate of deformation tensor may be markedly non-linear.

neralized" Reynolds number previously derived and shown to correlate ducted flow data on purely-viscous non-Newtonian systems [20], [21].

Most of the data in the cross-hatched area fall above the curve taken from Figure 1. This may be evidence of a weak effect of the degree of non-Newtonian behavior (flow behavior index) or, more likely, of the existence of small but finite normal stresses in these fluids. Interpretation of the data as normal stress effects, using Eq. (3), gave consistant results, independent of tube diameter, but with a great deal of experimental scatter [15].

An additional set of experimental data were obtained on glycerine-water solutions which were nearly saturated with lead nitrate to give a solution density of 1.676 g/ml. The purpose of these measurements was to ascertain even more conclusively whether or not the drag of the air on the jet was the cause of the non-zero values of the ordinates of Figures 1 and 2. The density of this fluid was 35% higher than that of any of the other fluids used; accordingly, the ordinate values would fall nearer zero if air drag were the principlle cause of positive values of the ordinate. This solution proved to be slightly non-Newtonian, having flow behavior indexes n' between 0.852 and 0.968, depending upon the shear rate used.

TABLE II

Results obtained using high-density fluid

N'_{Re}	Tube diameter, mm	Y^*, experimental	Y^*, curve of Figures 1 and 2
13.7	2.22	0.102	0.13
20.3	2.22	0.084	0.096
29.6	2.22	0.058	0.068
39.2	2.22	0.039	0.050
48.0	2.22	0.036	0.037
55.0	2.22	0.034	0.030
56.2	2.22	0.036	0.029
58.5	2.22	0.031	0.026
61.7	2.22	0.032	0.023
28.0	2.694	0.050	0.072
36.6	2.694	0.038	0.054
42.2	2.694	0.033	0.045
50.7	2.694	0.024	0.033
53.5	2.694	0.025	0.031
48.1	2.694	0.031	0.037

$$*Y = d_j/D - \sqrt{\frac{2n+1}{3n+1}}$$

As shown in Table II, the data for the two tube diameters employed are in agreement with each other and, except possibly at the lowest Reynolds numbers, any differences between the values obtained experimentally on this fluid and the curve from the low-density materials reported in Figure 1 are small and random. At the three lowest Reynolds numbers, the experimental value of d_j/D is lower than predicted from the data of Figure 1, but only by 3%. Thus, the possibility of significant experimental aberrations due to air drag are clearly ruled out and these data, being on a non-Newtonian fluid, further support the correctness of the curve through the data of Figure 1 for both Newtonian and non-Newtonian fluids which are free of normal stresses.

In summary, the curve through the data of Figure 1 appears to represent the behavior of both Newtonian and non-Newtonian fluids which are free of normal stress effects. The most significant conclusion to be drawn from all these results (Figures 1 and 2 and Table II) is that values of the ordinate are sufficiently close to zero at the higher Reynolds numbers to enable the calculation of normal stresses in more highly viscoelastic materials with a high degree of certainly: the 5–10% difference which would be caused by the finite value of the ordinate of Figure 2, above Reynolds numbers of about 100, is negligible in comparison to the gross inaccuracies or experimental scatter to be found in most normal stress measurements reported in the literature. At lower Reynolds numbers this technique may still be used without significant error on highly viscoelastic materials. An approximate correction may be derived from these figures to enable the use of this experimental technique with fluids exhibiting modest normal stresses at low Reynolds numbers.

Measurements on highly viscoelastic systems

Having established the applicability of Eqs. (1) and (3) to calculation of normal stresses as either an approximation or a highly accurate procedure, depending on the Reynolds number of the flow*, let us now turn to its application to measurements on highly viscoelastic substances.

Figure 3 gives extensive data on the ratio of jet to tube diameter at various values of $8V/D$, hence shear rate, on a 2% aqueous carboxymethylcellulose solution and Figures 4 and 5 give similar data on two different 5% solutions of polyisobutylene in decalin. The three solutions covered a wide range of

---

* This phrase is intended to refer only to the relatively small contributions by the abnormal accelerations or other effects depicted in Figure 1. The assumed equality of P_{22} and P_{33} must still be retained and the use of these circular jets is restricted to materials exhibiting such an equality.

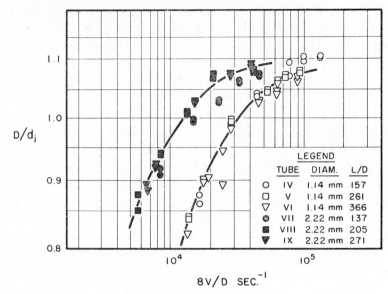

Figure 3
Expansion data: 2% C.M.C.

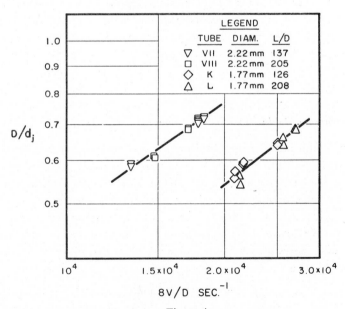

Figure 4
Expansion data: 5.0% polyisobutylene I

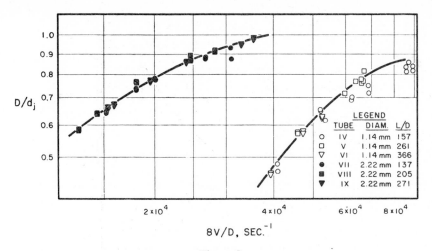

Figure 5
Expansion data: 5.0% polyisobutylene II

non-Newtonian behavior: the flow behavior index n' ranged between 0.288 and 0.618 for the CMC solution and between 0.500 and 0.922 for the polyisobutylenes, depending on the shear rate [14]. Figures 3–5 show that while most of the tubes employed were sufficiently long to ensure the absence of any entrance effects, some trends to lower values of D/d_j, attributable to an incompletely developed profile, are sometimes present in the data taken from tubes having L/D values of only 137 and 157. Such great values of the "entrance length", as compared to those for purely viscous fluids, have been studied and observed in much earlier work [20, 23] on viscoelastic materials and are not surprising. The data for tubes of differing diameters fall on separate curves in Figures 3–5, as required by Eqs. (1) and (3).

Figures 6 and 7 show the normal stress values for these solutions as a function of shear rate, calculated using Eqs. (3) and (2), respectively. It is seen that smooth curves, except for some experimental scatter in the case of one of the sets of data for CMC, are obtained in all cases. The polyisobutylene stresses are in approximate agreement with values extrapolated from the birefringence data of Philippoff and co-workers [6], although any more precise statement is impossible in view of the differences in the levels of shear rate employed. As measurements employing different tube diameters agree, the Reynolds number aberrations depicted by Figures 1 and 2 are negligible. Conversely, no correlation of the diameter ratio D/d_j as a function of Reynolds number is expected in these systems, a fact supported in Figure 8.

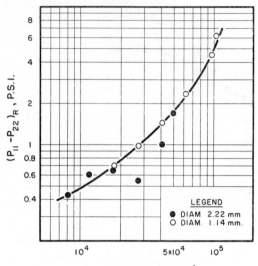

Figure 6
Normal stresses, 2.0% C.M.C.

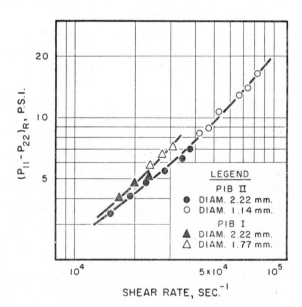

Figure 7
Normal stresses, 5.0% polyisobutylene

TABLE III

Tabulations of normal stress data

Shear rate sec^{-1}	Tube diameter, mm	D/d$_j$	P$_{11}$–P$_{22}$, psi	τ_{12}, psi	(P$_{11}$–P$_{22}$)/τ_{12}
		2.0% CMC solution			
0.810 × 10⁴	2.22	0.845	0.433	0.0778	5.56
1.16	2.22	0.929	0.616	0.0896	6.88
1.78	2.22	1.004	0.647	0.105	6.18
1.78	1.14	0.820	0.687	0.105	6.55
2.71	1.14	0.922	0.983	0.125	7.87
4.12	1.14	0.998	1.45	0.151	9.60
6.14	1.14	1.045	2.33	0.187	12.4
9.57	1.14	1.072	4.49	0.236	19.0
10.3 × 10⁴	1.14	1.076	6.20	0.250	24.8
		5.0% P. I. B. II			
4.22 × 10⁴	1.14	0.473	8.41	0.344	24.5
4.72	1.14	0.541	8.88	0.382	23.3
5.25	1.14	0.611	10.7	0.416	25.7
6.66	1.14	0.741	12.8	0.500	25.6
7.34	1.14	0.797	14.0	0.618	22.7
8.09	1.14	0.841	16.6	0.687	24.1
1.51	2.22	0.575	3.35	0.165	20.3
1.87	2.22	0.676	4.16	0.180	23.1
2.27	2.22	0.777	4.80	0.212	22.7
2.81	2.22	0.869	5.41	0.246	22.0
3.45	2.22	0.940	6.32	0.288	21.9
3.77 × 10⁴	2.22	0.968	6.91	0.316	21.9

Table III lists quantitative values of the shearing stress, shear rate and normal stress values for the two systems not reported on previously. The values of the ratio $(P_{11} - P_{22})/\tau_{12}$ (sometimes referred to as the "recoverable strain") are evidently higher than those previously obtained using other techniques on similar solutions, a fact which is not surprising in view of the much higher shear rates of the present work.

5. Conclusions.

1. The "exit effects" of Newtonian fluids and of purely-viscous non-Newtonian fluids issuing as jets from round tubes have been studied in some detail. They are shown not to be dependent on experimental aberrations such as tube diameter, surface tension effects or air drag upon the issuing jet of fluid.

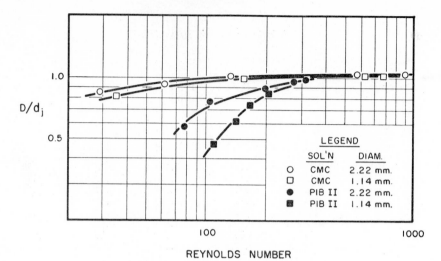

D/d$_j$

REYNOLDS NUMBER

Figure 8
Diameter ratio-Reynolds number relationship

Moreover, they appear to be identical functions of the Reynolds number in both Newtonian and purely-viscous non-Newtonian systems, within the accuracy of the experimental data.

Measurements of the jet to tube diameter ratio d_j/D in clay slurries and Carbopol solutions, materials previously believed to be virtually "purely viscous", give indications of measurable but small normal stresses.

2. The above "exit effects" do not interfere with normal stress measurements on viscoelastic materials provided simple precautions and limitations are observed. Data are given on two kinds of fluid systems, at shear rates of up to 10^5 sec^{-1}, or $1\frac{1}{2}$ to orders $2\frac{1}{2}$ of magnitude higher than any previously reported on similarly viscous fluids using prior-art techniques. In addition to extending considerably the range of permissible measurements this technique appears to be the first to clearly yield results within the range of shear rates required for application to engineering problems.

It is recommended that experimental measurements of normal stresses using the technique described employ, for the present, tubes having an L/D ratio in excess of 200 to ensure well-developed and stable velocity profiles at the downstream end of the tube.

3. Further work is required to determine the minimum permissible L/D values with which useful experimenta data may be obtained. It would ob-

viously also be desirable to obtain data using this as well as prior-art techniques in overlapping ranges of shear rate to assess any errors due to the assumed equality of P_{22} and P_{33}.

6. Acknowledgement.

Portions of this study were financed by the Army Research Office (Durham), the National Science Foundation and a University service scholarship to one of the authors. All three sources of support are gratefully acknowleded.

7. List of symbols.

d = differential operator.

d_j = jet diameter (after relaxation from stresses and velocity profile in tube is complete).

D = tube diameter.

K' = empirical constant in equation of tangent to the shear stress $- 8V/D$ curve at any given value of $8V/D$:

$$\tau_{12} = K' (8V/D)^{n'}$$

L = tube length.

L_e = length of tube which is equivalent, in magnitude of pressure drop, to exit effect.

n = power law exponent.

$$\tau_{12} = K(- du/dr)^n$$

n' = $[d \log (\tau_{12})_W]/[d \log (8V/D)]$.

N_{Re} = Reynolds number, $DV\rho/\mu$.

N'_{Re} = generalized Reynolds number of a non-Newtonian fluid

$$N'_{Re} = D^{n'} V^{2-n'} \rho/\gamma$$

P = deviatoric stress tensor having normal stress components P_{11}, P_{22} and P_{33}. The 1 direction is that of the simple shearing flow, the 2 direction is normal to this (the radial direction in the case of flow through a tube) and the 3 direction is normal to the other two. In the case of flow through a round tube 3 denotes the circumferential or angular co-ordinate direction

ΔP_{xs} = excess pressure loss near exit of tube.

r = distance in the radial coordinate direction.

R = tube radius.

u = longitudinal (axial) velocity at any radius r.

V = mean or bulk velocity.

γ = denominator of generalized Reynolds number.

$$\gamma = K' 8^{n'-}$$

η_e = coefficient of cross-viscosity.

μ = viscosity coefficient.

ρ = fluid density.

τ_{12} = shearing stress.

REFERENCES

[1] D. W. DODGE AND A. B. METZNER, *A.I.Ch.E. Journal*, **5**, (1959), 189.
[2] R. S. OUSTERHOUT AND C. D. HALL, Paper presented at Oct., 1960 meeting, Society of Petroleum Engineers.
[3] B. V. RANDALL, Private Communication (1960).
[4] A. G. FABULA, Unclassified Naval Ordanance Report (U.S.)(1961).
[5] J. L. WHITE AND A. B. METZNER, Second International Symposium on Thermophysical Properties, Princeton, N.J. (1962).
[6] J. G. BRODNYAN, F. H. GASKINS AND W. PHILIPPOFF, *Trans. Soc. Rheology*, **1**, (1957) 109.
[7] J. G. BRODNYAN, F. H. GASKINS, W. PHILIPPOFF AND E. G. LENDRAT, *Trans. Soc. Rheology*, **2**, (1958), 285.
[8] W. PHILIPPOFF, *Trans. Soc. Rheology*, **1**, (1957), 95; **4**, (1960), 159; **4**, (1960) 169, and Rheologica Acta **1**, 371 (1961).
[9] W. PHILIPPOFF AND F. H. GASKINS, *Trans. Soc. Rheology*, **2**, (1958), 263.
[10] A. B. METZNER, E. L. CARLEY AND I. K. PARK, *Modern Plastics*, **37**, (1960), 133, 11.
[11] A. B. METZNER, W. T. HOUGHTON, R. A. SAILOR AND J. L. WHITE, *Trans. Soc. Rheology*, **5**, (1961), 133.
[12] J. L. WHITE, M.Ch.E. thesis, Univ. of Delaware, Newark, Del. (1961).
[13] S. MIDDLEMAN AND J. GAVIS, *The Physics of Fluids*, **4**, (1961), 355.

[14] W. T. HOUGHTON, M.Ch.E. thesis, Univ. of Delaware Newark, Del. (1961).

[15] R. E. HURD, B.Ch.E. thesis, Univ. of Delaware, Newark, Del. (1962)

[16] C. C. WOLFE, B.Ch.E. thesis, Univ. of Delaware, Newark, Del. (1961).

[17] S. MIDDLEMAN, Ph.D. thesis, The Johns Hopkins Univ., Baltimore, Md. (1961).

[18] M. REINER, *A. J. Math* , **67**, (1945), 350. See also I. BRAUN AND M. REINER, *Quart. J. Mech. Appl. Math.* **5,** (1952), 42.

[19] R. S. RVLIN, *Proc. Royal. Soc.*, **A193**, (1948), 260.

[20] A. B. METZNER, in *Advances in Chem. Eng.*, T. B. Drew and J. W. Hoopes, Jr., editors. Academic Press, N. Y. (Vol. I, 1956). Also in *Hdbk. of Fluid Dynamics*, V. L. Streeter, ed. McGraw-Hill, N.Y. (1961).

[21] A. B. METNER AND J. C. REED, *A.I.Ch.E. Journal*, **1**, (1955), 434.

[22] D. W. DODGE, *Ind. Eng. Chem.*, **51**, (1959), 839.

[23] E. L. MCMILLEN, *Chem. Eng. Prog.*, **44** (1948), 537.

DISCUSSION

J.G. SAVINS: As a matter of interest we have computed P_{11} values from both the Metzner jet expansion method and the end correction method developed by Bagley, Philippoff and Gaskins, using the swelling and end correction data obtained by McIntosh on a two-percent solution of $N_A CMC$. The end correction method was applied only over the range of stress where the correction exhibited a linear dependence on stress. If one adopts Metzner's method, the range in P_{11} is 29—1.8×10^5 dynes/cm^2, while the end correction method predicts a range from 5.1×10^4 to 1.0×10^6 dynes/cm^2. These results suggest the need for further experimental intercomparisons of the type the author describes in this paper, in order to establish that method which yields the more realistic measure of normal stresses.

A. B. METZNER'S COMMENT: In reply to a question from the audience: If measurements can be made at very high shearing rates employing a parallel plate (centripetal pump) geometry, this should be done and you are encouraged to do so. Others have not considered this attractive, however.

The clearances you have cited in the rotational device which is operable at very high shear rates are of the same order of magnitude as the length of polymeric molecules. Other workers dealing with clearance about a hundred-fold greater, have encountered severe problems of temperature control. Therefore, it is not evident that high shear rate measurements can indeed be made using rotational devices.

SECOND AND HIGHER-ORDER THEORIES
FOR THE FLOW OF A VISCOELASTIC FLUID
IN A NON-CIRCULAR PIPE

R. S. RIVLIN

Brown University, Providence, R. I., U.S.A.

ABSTRACT

The flow of a viscoelastic fluid along a straight, non-circular pipe is discussed according to the first, second, third and fourth-order theories. It is shown that rectilinear flow is possible according to the first, second and third-order theories, but not according to the fourth-order theory.

1. Introduction.

Ericksen [1] showed that, in general, rectilinear flow of a viscoelastic fluid is not possible in a non-circular straight pipe unless some distribution of body forces is applied to the fluid. It was then shown by Green and Rivlin [2] that, for an incompressible slightly viscoelastic fluid obeying a particular constitutive equation. a transverse flow is superposed on the expected rectilinear flow. In the present paper, we discusss this earlier work as well as some recent work of Langlois and Rivlin [3] concerning the slow flow through a straight tube of non-circular cross-section, of an incompressible viscoelastic fluid obeying the general constitutive equation advanced by Rivlin and Ericksen [4].

2. Approximations to the constitutive equations for flow of an isotropic viscoelastic fluid.

We consider a mass of isotropic viscoelastic fluid to be in a steady state of flow. We denote by $v_i^{(1)} (=v_i)$, $v_i^{(2)}, ..., v_i^{(v)}$ the velocity, acceleration, ..., $(v-1)$th acceleration, referred to a rectangular Cartesian coordinate system x, at the point x_i and time t. Then,

$$v_i^{(\mu+1)} = D v_i^{(\mu)}/Dt, \qquad (2.1)$$

where D/Dt denotes the material time derivative.

It has been shown (Rivlin and Ericksen [4]) that if the stress components σ_{ij} at time t are assumed to be polynomial functions of the gradients $\partial v_p^{(\mu)}/\partial x_q$ ($\mu = 1, 2, ..., v$) at the point x and time t, then they must be expressible as polynomial functions of the components of v kinematic tensors $A_{ij}^{(\mu)}$ ($\mu = 1, 2, ..., v$) defined by

$$A_{ij}^{(\mu+1)} = \frac{DA_{ij}^{(\mu)}}{Dt} + A_{im}^{(\mu)} v_{m,j} + A_{jm}^{(\mu)} v_{m,i} \quad (\mu = 1, 2, ..., v-1),$$

$$A_{ij}^{(1)} = \tfrac{1}{2}(v_{i,j} + v_{j,i}), \tag{2.2}$$

where here and for the remainder of this paper $_{,i}$ denotes differentiation with respect to x_i. Thus,

$$\sigma_{ij} = f_{ij}(A_{pq}^{(1)}, A_{pq}^{(2)}, ..., A_{pq}^{(v)}). \tag{2.3}$$

If the fluid is incompressible, this relation must be modified by the introduction of a hydrostatic pressure p, which is arbitrary if the flow field is specified. We then have

$$\sigma_{ij} = -p\delta_{ij} + f_{ij}(A_{pq}^{(1)}, A_{pq}^{(2)}, ..., A_{pq}^{(v)}), \tag{2.4}$$

where δ_{ij} denotes the Kronecker delta.

If the flow is steady-state, equations (2.2) become

$$A_{ij}^{(\mu+1)} = v_m A_{ij,m}^{(\mu)} + A_{im}^{(\mu)} v_{m,j} + A_{jm}^{(\mu)} v_{m,i} \quad (\mu = 1, 2, ..., v-1),$$

$$A_{ij}^{(1)} = \tfrac{1}{2}(v_{i,j} + v_{j,i}). \tag{2.5}$$

We now consider that the flow is slow and write

$$v_i = \varepsilon u_i, \tag{2.6}$$

where ε is a small dimensionless constant. We obtain immediately from (2.5) that

$$A_{ij}^{(\mu)} = \varepsilon^\mu C_{ij}^{(\mu)},$$

where

$$C_{ij}^{(\mu+1)} = u_m C_{ij,m}^{(\mu)} + C_{im}^{(\mu)} u_{m,j} + C_{jm}^{(\mu)} u_{m,i}, \tag{2.7}$$

$$C_{ij}^{(1)} = \tfrac{1}{2}(u_{i,j} + u_{j,i}).$$

Then, if in (2.4) we wish to retain only terms of degree up to the fourth in ε, we can omit the arguments $A_{pq}^{(\nu)}$ for $\nu > 4$. Equation (2.4) then becomes

$$\sigma_{ij} = -p\delta_{ij} + f_{ij}(\varepsilon C_{pq}^{(1)}, \varepsilon^2 C_{pq}^{(2)}, \varepsilon^3 C_{pq}^{(3)}, \varepsilon^4 C_{pq}^{(4)}). \tag{2.8}$$

Since the material is isotropic f_{ij} must be an isotropic polynomial function of the four indicated argument tensors. A representation theorem for such functions has been obtained by Spencer and Rivlin [5]. Applying this theorem, at the same time omitting terms of higher degree than the fourth in ε, we obtain

$$\sigma_{ij} = -p\delta_{ij} + \varepsilon S_{ij}^{(1)} + \varepsilon^2 S_{ij}^{(2)} + \varepsilon^3 S_{ij}^{(3)} + \varepsilon^4 S_{ij}^{(4)}, \tag{2.9}$$

where, employing the notation

$$\mathbf{C} = \| C_{ij}^{(\mu)} \| \quad \text{and} \quad \mathbf{S}_\alpha = \| S_{ij}^{(\alpha)} \| \, (\alpha = 1,2,3,4), \tag{2.10}$$

we have

$$\mathbf{S}_1 = \alpha_1 \mathbf{C}_1, \quad \mathbf{S}_2 = \alpha_2 \mathbf{C}_2 + \alpha_3 \mathbf{C}_1^2,$$

$$\mathbf{S}_3 = (\beta_1 \text{ tr } \mathbf{C}_2) \mathbf{C}_1 + \beta_2 \mathbf{C}_3 + \beta_3 (\mathbf{C}_1 \mathbf{C}_2 + \mathbf{C}_2 \mathbf{C}_1),$$

and $\tag{2.11}$

$$\mathbf{S}_4 = (\gamma_1 \text{ tr } \mathbf{C}_1^3 + \gamma_2 \text{ tr } \mathbf{C}_1 \mathbf{C}_2 + \gamma_3 \text{ tr } \mathbf{C}_3) \mathbf{C}_1 +$$

$$+ (\gamma_4 \text{ tr } \mathbf{C}_2) \mathbf{C}_1^2 + (\gamma_5 \text{ tr } \mathbf{C}_2) \mathbf{C}_2 +$$

$$+ \gamma_6 \mathbf{C}_2^2 + \gamma_7 (\mathbf{C}_1^2 \mathbf{C}_2 + \mathbf{C}_2 \mathbf{C}_1^2) + \gamma_8 (\mathbf{C}_1 \mathbf{C}_3 + \mathbf{C}_3 \mathbf{C}_1) +$$

$$+ \gamma_9 \mathbf{C}_4,$$

where the α's, β's and γ's are constants. In deriving this result use is also made of the fact that for steady-state flow of an incompressible fluid

$$\text{tr } \mathbf{C}_1 = 0 \text{ and } 2 \text{ tr } \mathbf{C}_1^2 = \text{tr } \mathbf{C}_2. \tag{2.12}$$

We call (2.9) the fourth-order constitutive equation for flow of a visco-elastic fluid. We obtain the third, second and first order constitutive equations by omitting the terms of degree greater than the third, second and first respectively in ε.

3. Flow through a non-circular tube.

A few years ago, Ericksen [1] considered the steady-state flow, through a straight tube of uniform cross-section, under a uniform "pressure gradient", of an incompressible fluid for which the constitutive equation takes the form (Reiner [6], Rivlin [7])

$$\sigma_{ij} = -p\delta_{ij} + \varphi_1 A_{ij}^{(1)} + \varphi_2 A_{ik}^{(1)} A_{kj}^{(1)}, \tag{3.1}$$

where φ_1 and φ_2 are functions of

$$A_{pq}^{(1)} A_{qp}^{(1)} \quad \text{and} \quad A_{pq}^{(1)} A_{qr}^{(1)} A_{rp}^{(1)}. \tag{3.2}$$

He found, in accordance with the conclusion of Rivlin [8] that if the cross-section of the tube is circular, a possible solution of the problem is one in which the particles of fluid move in rectilinear paths parallel to the length of the tube, the precise radial distribution of the velocity being determined by the manner in which φ_1 depends on the quantities (3.2). Ericksen further found that if the tube has non-circular cross-section and the assumption is made that the flow is rectilinear, the equations of motion and boundary conditions, for the determination of the distribution over the cross-section of the longitudinal velocity, do not, in general, possess a solution, an exception arising only in the case when φ_2/φ_1 is constant. In an effort to understand the significance of this result, Green and Rivlin [2] considered the case when

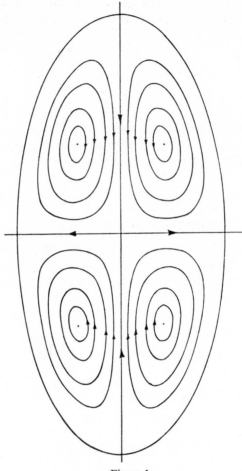

Figure 1

φ_1 in equation (3.1) is a constant and φ_2 departs only slightly from constancy, taking the form

$$\varphi_2 = \varepsilon(\theta_1 + \tfrac{1}{2} A_{pq}^{(1)} A_{qp}^{(1)}), \qquad (3.3)$$

where ε is a small dimensionless parameter.

In the case when $\varepsilon = 0$, the fluid is an incompressible, Newtonian fluid. The flow in which the particles of the fluid flow along rectilinear paths is then a possible one and the distribution of velocity over the cross-section of the tube can be determined for a wide variety of cross-sectional shapes. The components $\bar{v}_i$ of the velocity in the rectangular Cartesian coordinate system x, the x_3 axis of which is parallel to the length of the tube, are therefore given by

$$\bar{v}_1 = \bar{v}_2 = 0,$$

$$\bar{v}_3 = f(x_1, x_2).$$

(3.4)

In the case when the tube is the elliptical cylinder

$$b^2 x_1^2 + a^2 x_2^2 - a^2 b^2 = 0,$$

(3.5)

we have

$$\bar{v}_3 = \frac{G}{\varphi_1(a^2 + b^2)} \left(b^2 x_1^2 + a^2 x_2^2 - a^2 b^2 \right),$$

(3.6)

where G is the "pressure" gradient along the tube.

It was then assumed that if ε is not zero, but small compared with unity, the velocity components v_i may be written in the form

$$v_1 = \varepsilon u_1(x_1, x_2), \quad v_2 = \varepsilon u_2(x_1, x_2),$$

$$v_3 = \bar{v}_3 + \varepsilon u_3(x_1, x_2).$$

(3.7)

Systematically neglecting terms of higher degree than the first in ε, differential equations were derived for $u_1(x_1, x_2)$, $u_2(x_1, x_2)$, which could be solved subject to the appropriate boundary conditions ($u_1 = u_2 = 0$ on the surface (3.5)), leading to the result

$$v_1 = \varepsilon u_1 = -\varepsilon K \frac{(b^2 x_1^2 + a^2 x_2^2 - a^2 b^2)(b^2 x_1^2 + 5a^2 x_2^2 - a^2 b^2) x_1}{3\varphi_1(5a^4 + 6a^2 b^2 + 5b^4)},$$

(3.8)

$$v_2 = \varepsilon u_2 = \varepsilon K \frac{(b^2 x_1^2 + a^2 x_2^2 - a^2 b^2)(5b^2 x_1^2 + a^2 x_2^2 - a^2 b^2) x_2}{3\varphi_1(5a^4 + 6a^2 b^2 + 5b^4)},$$

where

$$K = \frac{3}{2} \left(\frac{G}{\varphi_1} \right)^4 \frac{a^2 b^2 (a^2 - b^2)}{(a^2 + b^2)^3}. \tag{3.9}$$

Thus, superimposed on the rectilinear flow, there is a transverse circulatory flow in each of the four quadrants of the ellipse, as shown in the Figure, where the arrows are in the directions relating to the case when $\varepsilon > 0$ and $a > b$.

Now, the constitutive equation (3.1) employed by Green and Rivlin appears to be a somewhat artifical one. Accordingly, more recently, Langlois and Rivlin [3] discussed the same problem in the context of the constitutive equation for incompressible viscoelastic fluids advanced by Rivlin and Ericksen [4]. In Sec. 2, we have seen how first, second, third and fourth-order approximations to this constitutive equation, for steady-state flows, may be obtained. Accordingly, taking the velocity field v_i for flow down the tube in the form

$$v_i = \varepsilon u_i^{(1)} + \varepsilon^2 u_i^{(2)} + \varepsilon^3 u_i^{(3)} + \varepsilon^4 u_i^{(4)}, \tag{3.10}$$

Langlois and Rivlin obtained successively the corrections $u_i^{(2)}, u_i^{(3)}, u_i^{(4)}$ to the first-order theory resulting from the inclusion of terms of second, third and fourth orders respectively in ε.

If terms of higher degree than the first in ε are neglected, the constitutive equation (2.9) becomes the constitutive equation for an incompressible Newtonian fluid and accordingly the flow field $\varepsilon u_i^{(1)}$ is given by

$$\varepsilon u_i^{(1)} = \bar{v}_i. \tag{3.11}$$

If terms of higher degree than the second in ε are neglected it is found that a flow field v_i, given by

$$v_i = \varepsilon u_i^{(1)} \equiv \bar{v}_i, \tag{3.12}$$

still satisfies the equations of motion and boundary conditions; the first-order solution for the flow field is also a second-order solution, i.e. $u_i^{(2)} = 0$.

If the constitutive equation (2.9) is used and terms of higher degree than the third in ε are consistently neglected, differential equations for the correction terms $u_i^{(3)}$ can be obtained, which may be solved, subject to the appropriate boundary conditions, $u_i^{(3)} = 0$ on the boundary of the tube, to yield, for the tube of elliptical cross-section (3.5),

$$u_1^{(3)} = u_2^{(3)} = 0$$

and

$$(3.13)$$

$$u_3^{(3)} = R(b^2 x_1^2 + a^2 x_2^2 - a^2 b^2)(A x_1^2 + B x_2^2 + C)$$

where

$$R = -8 \left[\frac{G}{\alpha_1(a^2 + b^2)} \right]^3 \frac{\beta_1 + \beta_3}{\alpha_1}$$

$$A = \frac{b^2}{12(a^4 + b^4 + 6a^2 b^2)} \left[b^2(a^2 + 3b^2)(b^2 + 6a^2) - a^4(b^2 + 3a^2) \right],$$

$$(3.14)$$

$$B = \frac{a^2}{12(a^4 + b^4 + 6a^2 b^2)} \left[a^2(b^2 + 3a^2)(a^2 + 6b^2) - b^4(a^2 + 3b^2) \right],$$

$$C = \frac{a^2 b^2(A + B)}{a^2 + b^2}.$$

Thus the flow given by the third-order theory is still rectilinear, but the velocity distribution is modified from that given by the first or second-order theories.

A similar procedure may be adopted to determine the correction $u_i^{(4)}$. It is then found that

$$u_1^{(4)} = -\frac{H(b^2 x_1^2 + a^2 x_2^2 - a^2 b^2)(b^2 x_1^2 + 5a^2 x_2^2 - a^2 b^2) x_1}{3\alpha_1(5a^4 + 6a^2 b^2 + 5b^4)},$$

and

$$(3.15)$$

$$u_2^{(4)} = \frac{H(b^2 x_1^2 + a^2 x_2^2 - a^2 b^2)(5b^2 x_1^2 + a^2 x_2^2 - a^2 b^2) x_2}{3\alpha_1(5a^4 + 6a^2 b^2 + 5b^4)},$$

where

$$H = -12 \left(\frac{G}{\alpha_1} \right)^4 \left[\frac{\beta_1 + \beta_3}{\alpha_1}(2\alpha_2 + \tfrac{1}{2}\alpha_3) - 2\gamma \right] \frac{a^2 b^2(a^2 - b^2)}{(a^2 + b^2)^3}$$

and

$$\gamma = \tfrac{1}{4}(\tfrac{1}{2}\gamma_4 + 4\gamma_5 + 4\gamma_6 + 2\gamma_7), \tag{3.16}$$

where the "pressure" gradient is now denoted εG. It can easily be shown that this result is in accord with that given in (3.8).

There may at first sight appear to be a discrepancy between the results just described and Ericksen's original conclusion that, for the constitutive equation (3.1), there can be no rectilinear flow in a tube of non-circular cross-section unless φ_2/φ_1 is constant. A particular case of the third-order constitutive equation, obtained by taking $\alpha_2 = \beta_2 = \beta_3 = 0$ in (2.11), is

$$\sigma_{ij} = -p\delta_{ij} + \varepsilon(\alpha_1 + \varepsilon^2\beta_1 C_{pq}^{(1)}C_{pq}^{(1)})C_{ij}^{(1)} + \varepsilon^2\alpha_3 C_{ik}^{(1)}C_{kj}^{(1)}. \tag{3.17}$$

According to Ericksen, rectilinear flow is not possible in a non-circular tube for a fluid for which this constitutive equation is valid, On the other hand, our third-order theory yields rectilinear flow. It must, however, be borne in mind that Ericksen's result is precise and it therefore remains possible that the constitutive equation (3.17) yields transverse components of velocity which are of fourth order in ε. That this is in fact the case can be seen by examining equations (3.15) and (3.16) from which it is seen that when $\beta_1 \neq 0$, a contribution is made to the transverse velocity given by the fourth-order theory, by the third-order terms in the constitutive equation.

Acknowledgement.

This paper was prepared under a grant DA-ARO(D)-31-124-G89 from the Office of Ordnance Research, U.S. Army.

REFERENCES

[1] J. L. ERICKSEN, *Q. Appl. Math.*, **14**, (1956), 318.
[2] A. E. GREEN AND R. S. RIVLIN, *Q. Appl. Math.*, **14**, (1956), 299.
[3] W. E. LANGLOIS AND R. S. RIVLIN, (1962), pending publication.
[4] R.S. RIVLIN AND J. L. ERICKSEN, *J. Rat'l. Mech. & Anal.*, **4**, (1955), 323.
[5] A. J. M. SPENCER AND R. S. RIVLIN, *Arch. Rat'l. Mech. & Anal.*, **4**, (1960), 214.
[6] M. REINER, *Amer. J. Math.*, **67**, (1945), 350.
[7] R. S. RIVLIN, *Proc. Roy. Soc.*, A **193**, (1948), 260.
[8] R. S. RIVLIN, *Proc. Camb. Phil. Soc.*, **45**, (1949), 88.

DISCUSSION

K. WALTERS: Your equations of state reduce to a very special form at small rates of shear in that they do not allow for stress relaxation. I believe this was pointed out this morning by Dr. Coleman. Is it to be expected that real materials can be characterized by such a special type of equation at small rates of shear?

Is there any reference in the literature to real materials that do not allow for stress relaxation at small rates of shear?

R.S. RIVLIN's reply: The constitutive equation I have used can only be expected to be valid for flows in which the velocity at an instant prior to that at which the stress is measured can be expressed in terms of the velocity and its time derivatives at the instant of measurement of stress by an absolutely convergent Taylor series. This is plainly not true for stress relaxation experiments. A material may exhibit stress relaxation and be describable by a constitutive equation of the type I have used for all flows satisfying the conditions stated above.

A similar situation exists in the classical visco-elastic theory in which the constitutive equation has the form of a linear relation between stress and its time derivatives and strain-velocity and its time derivatives. This constitutive equation does not allow the discussion of stress relaxation experiments. We have to add a special constitutive equation which tells us what happens as the result of a discontinuity in the strain-velocity or one of its time derivatives. The problem is not entirely avoided by interpreting the time derivatives in the wider sense of the theory of distributions. In doing this, we are merely saying that we regard our discontinuity as the limit, arrived at in a certain specified manner, of a continuous process.

The results I have obtained in the paper would be unaltered in character if I had taken my starting point a non-linear constitutive equation of the memory type. This can easily be seen from the fact that, for the flows obtained, the expansions as Taylor series, about the instant of measurement of stress, of the coordinates of a generic particle are absolutely convergent with an infinite radius of convergence. The non-linear constitutive equations of the memory type do, of course, allow the possibility of the discussion of stress relaxation. Thus from the point of view of the present paper no problem arises.

THE MECHANICAL EVOLUTION OF CLUSTERS BY BINARY ELASTIC COLLISIONS AND CONCEPTION OF A CRUCIAL EXPERIMENT ON TURBULENCE*

PAUL LIEBER

University of California, College of Engineering, Berkeley, U.S.A.

ABSTRACT

The mechanical evolution of clusters by binary elastic collisions is found to depend in a crucial manner on symmetry and uniformity used in a broad sense. Thus elements of symmetry and uniformity that can be identified in terms of collision attitude, the orientation of relative and resultant velocity vectors, mass distribution and body geometry are found to be fundamental to mechanical clustering. They play an equally fundamental role in the identification of a binary dissipation mechanism based on perfectly elastic collisions. Among the symmetry elements noted, body geometry plays a major role. These considerations led to the conception and design of a crucial experiment on turbulence in gas flows. The proposed experiment has been completed in its first phase and supports the ideas which led to its conception.

1. Introduction.

Although the evolution of clusters and aggregates in gases and dust clouds is characteristic of their phenomenological behavior, the specific processes by which they are made and organized are hardly known and even less understood. In 1953, I first contemplated the question concerning a possible explanation for the production of clusters on strictly *mechanical* grounds, without invoking the property of inelasticity for the interacting bodies. The question put and the answer sought are thus qualitative in nature, as they pertain directly to the problem of *how* clusters can be made and not to the calculation of their spatial-temporal distribution according to the Navier-Stokes equations; which in the case if air are usually purported to govern its behavior in all phenomenological manifestations.

Turbulence, and especially the specific elementary processes leading to its development, have defied identification and elucidation since they were first considered as subjects of scientific investigation. Most of what is factually

---

* This paper is an extension of ideas originally presented on March 8, 1954, as an invited lecture to the Institute De Mechanique, Faculte Des Sciences, University of Paris, France, entitled "A Study of Aggregation Related to Gas Flows."

known about turbulence is phenomenological in character, and is expressed by describables and measurables that refer to the macro-scale. Although phenomenological, these empirical facts must, of course, be accommodated by any admissible theory, and because of their universal and noncontroversial aspect, may be used as a point of departure for identifying the elementary processes operating in the production of turbulence.

A phenomenological fact and constant aspect of turbulence is the evolution of finitely extended short-lived macroscopic bodies, that move relative to the stream in which they are imbedded, from which they emerge and into which they decay. These bodies have short life spans and rapidly lose identity, by assimilating with the main stream. This phenomenological description of turbulence is equivalent to a descriptive definition given on a very elementary empirical level. It is so elementary and primitive in nature, that it appears to encompass turbulence in all its ramifications and on all scales of its occurrence. General agreement on this definition may be expected as it concerns description of indisputable facts rather than interpretation. Although steeped in empiricism and broad in scope, this descriptive definition of turbulence does not, however, identify or refer to the elementary processes leading to the production of clusters which are central to the description. Althlough there is considerable speculation and controversy concerning the mechanism of turbulence, I believe it correct to say that this descriptive definition, though incomplete, offers a point on which conflicting positions and views must converge and agree. It shall, therefore, be taken as a point of departure for what follows.

In so doing, I am choosing as point of departure certain observable and indisputable facts about turbulence, and evoking the self-evident axiom, that these phenomena necessarily have molecular counterparts; i.e., counterparts on a molecular scale of which they are but macroscopic manifestations. This paper is directed at the problem of elucidating some aspects of molecular organization which compulsively and directly follow from these facts and axiom. More specifically, those aspects which can be elucidated from strictly mechanical considerations as applied to binary collisions and molecular geometry; and from which all aspects of molecular organization are purported to evolve according to the kinetic theory of gases. In this way some questions are put and answered in precise terms by invoking only the most elementary principles of mechanics. From this information inferences are drawn concerning the relevance of molecular and particle geometry to the organization of clusters in gases and dust couds. These are qualitative in nature and lead to the conception and design of a crucial experiment on turbulence by which they may be tested. The question put by this experiment and the answer sought are therefore correspondingly qualitative in character. However, in order to test with confidence the prediction that clustering depends on molecular geometry, it is important to record some of the measurable attributes of the clusters and to ascertain the reproducibility of these measurements. The problem of calculating these measurable attributes from the standpoint of mechanics alone is, of course, analytically interactable at this time. However, a restricted n-body elastic collision problem which takes into consideration differences in molecular geometry should seriously be considered as a subject for numerical calculation, especially as the result of the experiment cited in the title supports the elementary mechanics and thinking that led to its conception.

The descriptive definition for turbulence given above is strictly empirical in character and according to it, the word turbulence is nothing but a label identified with the phenomena which it describes. According to this definition, therefore, the most direct answer to the question, what is turbulence, is found by referring to nature and pointing out what the definition describes. This must be distinguished from the question, how is it produced.

In summary, we shall in this paper consider the second question by referring only and directly to observables which appear beyond dispute and by introducing one self-evident hypothesis already noted. From this evolves reasoning and inference, having a rigorous and precise foundation in mechanics and leading to the conception and design of a crucial experiment (on turbulence) by which it can be tested. This proposed experiment on turbulence has been performed in part and the results support the theory and thinking that led to its conception.

I proposed this crucial experiment on turbulence to Professor Seymour Bogdonoff at Princeton University in 1955, as he had a facility for doing it. Mr. W. H. Webb, my former student decided to perform this experiment as the subject of his doctoral dissertation, to be carried out at Princeton under Professor Bogdonoff's guidance.

The experiment was in progress since 1956 at which time there were already indications that it may evolve into a positive experiment. The measurements were not, however, consistently reproducible and this was traced to erratic functioning of hot wire equipment used for these measurements. By acquiring increasing knowledge and skill of its operation, Mr. Webb systematically eliminated all sources of error and erratic functioning attributable to the apparatus used. The measurements are now consistently reproducible within two per cent error and show deviation of ten to twelve per cent in the quantities measured. These deviations should not exist, according to the Navier-Stokes equations if they indeed represent and condition turbulence in the gases used.

2. Mechanical clustering by binary elastic collisions as a function of molecular geometry.

Binary encounters play a central role in the kinetic theory of gases. There, it is tacitly assumed that all phenomena evolving on all scales are produced by a succession of spatially distributed binary encounters and which are in general space and time dependent. In particular then, the production and phenomenon of turbulence in all its manifestations must accordingly be attributed to a succession of binary encounters whose spatial distributions and initial conditions are functions of time.

The Maxwell model of a gas from which the Navier-Stokes equations can be derived by way of the Boltzman equation, represents the irreducible elements of the gas as smooth rigid elastic spheres, interacting only by collision. In terms of this model, we can put the following question. Do the principles of mechanics admit the production of a cluster consisting of two perfectly elastic smooth and rigid spheres, by a binary collision? To render the question precise, we shall define here a binary cluster, as two neighboring perfectly elastic bodies translating at zero relative velocity. With this definition, the question put can be precisely formulated and resolved, as a simple problem in mechanics. The answer to the question, as one might expect, is negative. That is, according to principles of mechanics a set of initial conditions that would produce such a binary cluster do not exist. This means that binary clusters, as defined, and consisting of smooth and elastic-rigid spheres, cannot have a mechanical basis. In fact they are mechanically inadmissible. The elementary analysis based on the principles of mechanics which renders this general conclusion is presented in the appendix.

This conslusion is however a consequence of the precise definition given for a binary cluster. This definition is indeed strict as compared to the descriptive and more realistic definition of a turbulent body, which calls for small rather than zero relative velocities in translation. Furthermore, the descriptive definition does not call for condensation; i.e., bodies maintaining virtual contact, which is indeed implied by the strict definition. Nevertheless, we shall see that the precise definition is useful for extracting from mechanics fundamental and general information bearing on the understanding of clustering in its more manifold and real aspects.

Although a binary cluster, as strictly defined, is mechanically impossible when the irreducible bodies are smooth rigid elastic spheres; we find that binary clusters are mechanically admissible when the bodies can support and transfer angular momentum. Smooth rigid and elastic spheres cannot transfer angular momentum by collision and consequently their initial angular momenta including zero values, are individually conserved under all collisions. The kinetic energy in translation always remains in translation; exchanges of kinetic energy between translatory and rotatory motions are excluded.

When smooth rigid and elastic bodies have less than spherical symmetry, then kinetic energy in translation can be transformed into kinetic energy in rotation and conversely. Under these conditions classes of initial conditions exist which indeed lead to binary clusters, as strictly defined.

This points up a *deep connection* on a binary level between symmetry, dissipation and aggregation. A connection between symmetry and dissipation was established on a binary level earlier in reference [1].

A physically meaningful and precise definition for binary dissipation is there established on strictly mechanical grounds. This is tantamount to the identification of a dissipation mechanism whose operation can be precisely described and calculated on the basis of mechanics alone, without invoking the notion of ergodicity, probability or thermodynamic concepts. This reveals a direct connection between symmetry and dissipation, cast in terms of binary collision.

Symmetry is used here in a comprehensive sense. Thus it refers to the geometrical symmetries of the individual bodies, their collision attitudes and to their relative and resultant velocity. Accordingly it was shown that when the bodies are smooth rigid elastic spheres, a *necessary* condition *for binary dissipation* is that their relative and resultant velocity vectors be obliquely oriented. In reference [1] I call these collision oblique as distinguished from direct. Direct collisions thus have more symmetry elements than do oblique collisions. In a direct collision the line normal to the contact surface and joining the centers, is parallel to both the relative and resultant velocity of the binary system. Thus used, the word symmetry has a geometrical-kinematic connotation and significance. When however either or both bodies are *not perfect* spheres then direct collisions can produce dissipation on the scale of a binary collision.

A *necessary* condition *for binary clustering* is however that the colliding bodies (at least one) have less than spherical symmetry. In other words, there *does not exist* a geometric-kinematic configuration to produce a binary cluster by collision, when both colliding bodies have maximum geometrical symmetry. This means that the necessary condition for binary clustering is more severe than it is for binary dissipation; which implies that it has a *lower apriori probability*.

As noted, the necessary condition for strict binary clustering need not be met, to produce a cluster in the sense of the descriptive definition given for a turbulent cluster. However, from the reasoning and conclusions set forth above it follows logically that the production, organization and dissipation of clusters in an actual gas or dust cloud, may depend significantly on whether or not their discrete bodies have a geometry which can accomodate strict binary aggregation. The principles of mechanics as used in the precise determination of necessary conditions for binary clustering, are given in the appendix.

3. The conception of a crucial experiment on turbulence.

The above led me to the conception and design of a crucial experiment bearing on the production and dissipation of turbulence in gases. This experiment is designed to determine in a crucial manner whether, as inferred, aspects of molecular geometry that are not represented by or implicit in the Navier-Stokes equations are relevant to the production and decay of turbulence. This inference which comes directly from reasoning outlined in **1** and **2**, can be tested experimentally by comparing *any* or *all* observable aspects of turbulent flow fields produced in two distinct gases, operating under conditions that are equivalent with respect to the Navier-Stokes equations.

The two gases are to be distinguished in their molecular geometry in a manner which takes cognizance of their representation by collision models. Thus for example in the case of the inert gas argon, the effect of "free" electrons upon the interaction of its elementary bodies (atoms in this case) does not have to be taken into consideration if one tries to represent their interaction by a collision model. Their atoms may be regarded as composed of full and stable electron shells which account for their inert properties and the absence of long range forces. Consequently, they are spherically symmetrical in their interactions and can with good approximation be represented by *smooth* rigid and elastic spheres, which interact by collision only. The short range forces are then approximated by the collision forces of the smooth rigid elastic spheres. In argon we thus find a counterpart in nature of a gas whose molecules behave under interaction in a manner well represented by a Maxwell gas. In particular then the conclusions drawn concerning binary clustering and binary dissipation with respect to a Maxwell gas should apply with good approximation to argon. They should consequently reveal themselves in some aspects of its phenomenological behavior — particularly those involving the production and disintegration of macro-clusters.

Conversely, the interaction of molecules of gases prominent in the composition of air is more realistically represented by a collision model, when the colliding bodies have *less than spherical symmetry*. As noted, this has immediate implications on the mechanical admissibility of binary clustering as strictly defined, as well as on the class of initial conditions that lead to binary dissipation. Thus in argon binary clusters are essentially mechanically inadmissible whereas in air they are admissible. Also the class of initial conditions that produce binary dissipation in argon and air, differ. Both of these factors are relevant to the production and disintegration of macro observable clusters that evolve in these gases and neither of these are given representation by the Navier-Stokes equations; as they are based on molecular geometry, which these equations neither explicitly or implicitly represent. Consequently, it is possible to conceive of an experiment in which air and argon flows are produced in the same environment and under conditions that are entirely equivalent from the standpoint of the Navier-Stokes equations. Under these conditions it would follow that if the Navier-Stokes equations are indeed complete and governing, then the two flows should be the same in *all* their significant and observable macroscopic manifestations.

The study of the mechanics of binary clustering and dissipation as a function of molecular geometry considered here and the inferences drawn therefrom, imply however that significant observable differences in their turbulent flow structure should appear. *This experiment is therefore crucial in at least two respects.* One, to test the qualitative theoretical result obtained here, according to which molecular geometry is relevant to the production, distribution and dissipation of turbulence. Two, to ascertain in a crucial manner whether the Navier-Stokes equations do indeed completely embody and condition turbulence in its significant observable manifestations.

In this experiment the gases used are to be distinguished first of all in their molecular geometry, insofar as it can enhance or deter binary clustering. In this regard we must keep in mind that although binary clusters (in the strict sense) are mechanically inadmissible in a Maxwell gas, this does not exclude the evolution there of finitely extended aggregates of short duration, consisting of a collection of neighboring molecules moving at small relative velocities. The evolution of such aggregates would then be a manifestation of laws peculiar to many body systems and their collective behavior, as individual binary collisions in this gas inevitably produce separation. In such cases the collective laws which produce aggregates extending over a small finite spatial domain and short time-interval must dominate their binary separations inherent in each individual binary collision. That is, these collective properties are in the case of the Maxwell model counteracted rather than supported by the binary collisions, when we regard them as isolated events.

We cannot of course refer directly to the production of aggregates in a Maxwell gas flow as a fact of nature nor to a solution of the Maxwell-Boltzman equation which implies such aggregation. We can do so only indirectly by noting examples wherein it provides a realistic model for an actual gas such as argon, in which aggregates can be observed in the laboratory. In other words though we cannot obtain direct experimental evidence for the production of turbulence in a Maxwell gas, indirectly it seems very plausible to assert that it can; by its success in depicting some observable behavior of actual gases. The Maxwell model has been used as a basis for deriving the Maxwell-Boltzman equation which in turn by an approximation due to Enskog renders the Navier-Stokes equations. This does not mean however that the class of gases and fluids whose macro-behavior are presumed well modeled by these equations, necessarily behave on a molecular level as a Maxwell gas — since they were originally obtained from considerations that are independent of their molecular representation and processes. This statement is of course consistent with the fact that the Navier-Stokes equations do not discern or give representation to such details of molecular geometry which are favorable and necessary for producing binary clusters as they are strictly defined. If however we choose to identify the Navier-Stokes equations with a particular collision model and molecular geometry by using the kinetic theory as a guide, then it follows that they indeed correspond to a Maxwell gas on a molecular level. Consequently they do not include, even implicitly, the elements of molecular geometry necessary for the production of binary clusters.

4. Description and design of proposed experiment.

The experiment consists of comparing two turbulent flows in all their observable manifestations produced in gases that give representation to the essential differences in molecular geometry considered above, under equivalent macroscopic conditions. By equivalent macroscopic conditions is meant here, conditions that are the same from the standpoint of the Navier-Stokes equations. Of course the physical environment in which the two flows are imbedded, and the conditions actuating the flows must be the same. This can be achieved experimentally under equivalent inflow and environmental conditions, by insuring that all the dimensionless parameters, in terms of which any and all solutions to the Navier-Stokes equations may be expressed, are numerically the same for the two gases.

At sufficiently small flow velocities, this condition is essentially met, when their Reynolds numbers are equal. This is for all practical purposes a sufficient condition, provided that the pressure gradients are everywhere small. Otherwise the Prandtl numbers must also be made essentially equal. At small flow speeds the effect of compressibility and Mach number may be neglected.

It was accordingly proposed to compare *all observable* aspects of two turbulent flow fields respectively produced in air and argon when subjected to the same physical environment and conditions equivalent in terms of the Navier-Stokes equations.

If therefore *any* reproducible differences in turbulence produced under these conditions are observed in air and argon, they are not in principle predictable by the Navier-Stokes theory. Furthermore, if as predicted, the result of this experiment is positive, it would follow that some important aspects of the mechanism which in general account for the production and decay of turbulence in nature, are not embodied in the Navier-Stokes equations. For this reason, this experiment may be regarded as a crucial one, and if positive would imply that the rotational degrees of freedom *may be* fundamental in the production and decay of turbulence.

From the above considerations, it follows that the reproducability of the experimental results is a sufficient criterion for guiding the experimental procedure. As long as the results are reproducible under equivalent conditions as noted, *each* and *every* aspect of turbulent motion is equally significant and useful for deriving the crucial implications of this experiment. Consequently, it is unnecessary to restrict measurements to locations where the turbulence is essentislly isotropic and homogeneous in structure.

Measurements of non-isotropic and non-homogenous turbulent motion close to the boundary of a flow channel provides a basis for comparing the rates of production of turbulence in these gases. Such measurements are as, if not more significant than measuring the decay of approximately homogenous-isotropic turbulence behind a grid. The important thing to emphasize, however, is that from the very nature of the experiment and its conceptual basis; all aspects of the turbulent flow fields are significant and useful for answering in a crucial manner the question put to it. Consequently, there is no theoretical reason for limiting measurements to locations where the turbulence is essentially isotropic and thus to restrict the experiment to decay measurements behind a grid. There is probably a practical advantage in first restricting the measurements to homogenous-isotropic turbulence, since here the pressure gradients and temperature gradients are minimal. Also since the spectrum of non-homogenous turbulence near solid boundaries is relatively rich in long period fluctuations the instrumentation must be more sophisticated to facilitate neasurememts at such locations.

Professor Bogdonoff understandably urged that we first restrict the proposed experiment to decay measurements of homogenous-isotropic turbulence behind a grid at which it is generated; and thus to compare experimentally the turbulence level as a function of distance behind the grid for the two macroscopically equivalent gas flows. I emphasized however that we are thus using but one of a number of observable manifestations to test the theory which led to the conception of the experiment. The theory predicts observable differences between the turbulent flow fields produced in the two gases under equivalent conditions as defined. This of course does not mean that should reproducible differences be observed; they would be equally prominent in all phenomenological manifestations. Thus deviations may be more prominent near solid boundaries than at distant locations.

Preliminary experiments initiated during the summer of 1956 at Princeton showed that the boundary joining the non-isotropic turbulence produced near the walls of a closed channel and the essentially isotropic turbulence produced behind the grid, is sharp and well defined for approximately 100 mesh lengths downstream. Experimentally delineating and comparing these boundaries in the two "Navier-Stokes equivalent" gas flows, thus constitutes another significant phenomenological manifestation of their flow fields, useful for crucially testing the existence of deviations as predicted.

It is appropriate to emphasize here again; that the concepts leading to this experiment, the questions put to it, and what it decides in a crucial manner, are all *qualitative* in nature; that they refer to qualitative (symmetry) aspects of molecular geometry of gases and to their *qualitative* implications on clustering and dissipation in gas flows; that these ideas have been identified here with turbulence by invoking one self-evident hypothesis, in fact so self-evident that it almost sounds trivial when enunciated; i.e., that in the context of this experiment, the numerical representation of the turbulent flow fields obtained by using hot wire equipment, is nothing but one of a number of indices in terms of which their *qualitative aspects* can be compared in a consistent and reproducible manner. The numbers thus rendered are subsidiary to the ideas behind the experiment and to the most fundamental implications of its result, which are indeed qualitative in character. Their importance from this point of view, resides in their representation of observable differences, if they do exist, and by providing a convenient method for testing their reproducibility in an accurate fashion. Accordingly, the question concerning whether or not the Navier-Stokes equations embody the essential mechanisms for the production and decay of the turbulence in all its significant and observable manifestations, is qualitative, and so is the answer which this experiment can render crucially.

Similarly, experiments conceived and performed by Professor Markus Reiner [2] have revealed in a crucial manner qualitative behaviour of fluids usually regarded as Newtonian, to be unaccountable for by the Navier-Stokes equations. Analogously, the question put by these experiments is indeed qualitative, and so are the fundamental implications of their results. Some reflection will show that the most fundamental and far reaching experiments of physics are generally qualitative rather than quantitative in character—the Michelson-Morley experiment being a case in point.

One phase of the proposed experiment was carried out at Princeton in a blow down tunnel, and the hot wire measurements were limited to locations

behind a turbulence generating grid at which the turbulence is presumed
isotropic. A deliberate effort was made to minimize in these measurements the
effects of the tunnel walls. However, at every position in the flow the turbulent
motion observed there may be regarded as the superposition of free stream
turbulence, turbulence generated at the grid and the inhomogenous noniso-
tropic turbulence produced in and near the boundary layers. In the context
and meaning of the proposed experiment, each and every aspect of turbulence,
whatever its source, is equally significant. In this regard, it is noted that although the level of turbulence connected with each source may differ in the
two gases, it does not necessarily follow that their superposition will lead to
observable differences at all locations. In order to insure that the results of
the experiment are conclusive it is essential therefore not to restrict the observations to a particular spatial domain of the flow. If however, differences
are observed in such a restricted domain, then they are sufficient to render
the experiment conclusive. The converse does not follow however. In particular, it follows that it is unnecessary to attenuate free stream turbulence or
any other source of turbulent motion which are usually regarded as undesirable in conventional experiments concerned with measuring decay of iso-
ropic turbulence behind a grid.

5. Experimental results.

Deviations between measurements of turbulent decay were first detected at
Princeton in 1956. However, the measurements were not consistently reproducible. This was eventually traced by Mr. Webb to the hot wire apparatus.
He systematically and carefully, rectified sources of its erratic behaviour in
the process of mastering its operation. The deviation thus became progres-
sively pronounced and consistently reproducible. Due to the fundamental
nature of their implications, extreme caution was exercised in checking and
rechecking the results. The existence of reproducible differences between the
decay curves in excess of ten per cent were thus definitely established, with
an experimental error of approximately 2% [3]. As noted, the numerical
representation of this deviation is subsidiary to the meaning and significance
of the experiment. What is fundamental is that it exists and that it is consistently reproducible. The magnitudes of deviations in the macro-observables
of the two gases is expected from the theory to vary significantly with location;
especially as the tunnel walls are approached. The experiment completed at
Princeton thus constitutes but a segment of the experiment originally proposed and outlined here. Nevertheless, it resolves in a positive and crucial
manner the qualitative question evolving from the theory leading to its conception.

6. Remarks and conclusions.

What logical inferences can be drawn from this experiment, bearing on the appropriateness of the Navier-Stokes equation for representing and conditioning turbulence in the gases tested?

If the Navier-Stokes equations give complete or at least adequate representation of turbulence for each and thus both gases, then the experiment would have been negative. That is, differences in turbulent structure, the existence of which were anticipated, would not occur. The fact that significant and reproducible differences are observed implies therefore that the Navier-Stokes equations do not govern significant observable aspects of turbulence in at least one of the two gases. The implication is probably much stronger: namely that these equations do not completely represent or condition turbulent motion in either gas. This however cannot be deduced as a logical consequence of the experiment alone. If however we postulate that, if they give adequate representation for one gas they do for both, then it follows directly from the experiment that they do not adequately govern turbulence in either gas.

The extent and magnitudes of observable deviations are significant for establishing experimentally the extent of the limitations of the Navier-Stokes equations in accounting for turbulence in the gases tested. Although obvious, it should be underlined that by this crucial experiment we are testing the appropriateness and completeness of these equations in their representation of turbulence, without solving them—a task which is of course beyond present capability. This again points up the inherently qualitative nature of the experiment and the ideas leading to it. It is of course much more conventional to regard important experiments to be quantitative in nature, by which numerical predictions based on analytical theory are compared to measurements of their experimental counterparts. Such an experiment for testing the appropriateness and completeness of the Navier-Stokes equations with respecs to turbulence, would indeed require the mathematical solutions, and this it precisely why it has not been performed. By putting a qualitative rather than qantitative question to the test of a crucial experiment, we can in depth investigate and resolve by experimentation this fundamental question, without solving the equations to which it refers.

The existence of observable differences in turbulent structure were predicted on the basis of geometrical molecular considerations which are neither explicitly or implicitly represented by the Navier-Stokes equations. The fact that the experiment so conceived is positive, does not however constitute proof that the observed differences are actually attributable to the specific molecular phenomena which led to its conception. It does however lend them strong inductive support.

The observed deviations may possibly still be accounted for in terms of a continuum model which embodies second-order effects, and if so, can possibly be related to the underlying molecular processes which account for the experimental results of reference [2]. The binary dissipation mechanism presented in ref. [1], strongly suggests that in sufficiently strong shock waves, the temperature as a measure of molecular motion in translation that does not contribute to the flow velocity, can indeed be anisotropic.* Thus, the temperature field in sufficiently shock waves and more generally in flows with sufficiently large velocity gradients may be polarized in this sense. The word "sufficiently" is used here in the context of existence; namely that there exist flow gradients sufficiently large, at which the temperature field would necessarily be polarized.

Professor Reiner has pointed out that the concept of a polarized temperature field, is consistent with his experimental results [2], and would enhance their physical interpretation. The velocity gradients produced in his experiments are exceedingly large. In such cases we may also expect, as in the case of strong shock waves, the kinetic energy in molecular rotation to be appreciable, provided of course the molecular geometry of a collision model for short range inter-molecular forces, readily admits transfer between translational and rotational energies. Here again we may expect that differences in molecular geometry can lead to significant differences in macroscopic behavior of their corresponding flows, under conditions equivalent from the standpoint of the Navier-Stokes equations.

There is reason to believe that the dissipation mechanism of reference [1] and its implications leading to concept of polarized temperature may help elucidate the physical meaning of the second viscosity coefficient (dilatational) which appears somewhat ambiguous within the framework of the Navier-Stokes theory, Its meaning is there established by identifying the thermodynamic pressure with the mean value of the three diagonal stress components. This yields the relation $2\mu + 3\lambda = 0$, between the two viscosity coefficients. There is some experimental evidence indicating that this relation is not satisfied by some fluids as for example carbon dioxide. In such cases the definition of thermodynamic pressure has been extended to include the term $(2/3\,\mu + \lambda)\dfrac{\partial u_i}{\partial x_i}$, but this step seems arbitrary and devoid of physical interpretation; especially

---

* That is, the temperature can then be thought of as a multiple-value scalar function of position which is direction dependent. The usual physical menaning ascribed to temperature, accordingly corresponds to the circumstance, where its value at a point is independent of the direction in which the point approached.

since the kinetic theory of the Maxwell gas indicates that this term is zero. The existence of such non-vanishing correction terms may therefore be inextricably linked to the nonspherical geometry of fluid molecules, not represented by the Maxwell model.

It is interesting to remark that the connection established here between the geometry of prefectly elastic bodies interacting by binary collisions, and the production of clusters, may be helpful in resolving a fundamental problem concerning the evolution of stars from interstellar dust clouds [4]. This problem concerns the evolution of critical masses in clouds following which their force of gravitation can account for their subsequent growth; and correspondingly increasing force of attraction. In this process the increasing gravitational forces can lead to dust particle velocities sufficiently large to initiate nuclear reactions operating in the stars. The suggested connection of particle geometry and the evolution of such critical masses by binary elastic and inelastic collisions, will be taken up further in a subsequent paper in which the mechanics of more general and sophisticated collision models are studied.

The model considered here is used simply to point up as simply as possible, the fundamental role of asymmetry in the geometry of the particles for mechanically admitting the formation of clusters by binary collisions. Although the collision attitude described in figure (1) on which the analysis is based is very restricted, it nevertheless reveals the fundamental role of geometrical symmetry with respect to molecular aggregation. A general binary collision model to which there corresponds a much larger class of initial conditions producing mechanical aggregation, will be presented in another (joint) paper. In this subsequent paper cosmological implications will be considered in greater detail. The extended collision model accounts for the connection between asymmetry and mechanical aggregation in a general way. It can therefore be used for programming on a computer a many body problem, for calculating its implications on their *collective* behavior. Such a study should be very revealing in lieu of the fundamental connections between symmetry, dissipation and aggregation already established and noted here on the basis of the mechanics of binary collisions.

In continuing to search for general information concerning these connections which may be further derived analytically from strictly mechanical considerations; it is now indicated that non-uniformity in the inertial as well as geometrical properties of colliding bodies may further enhance clustering and modify dissipation. This suggests that the experiments at Princeton be extended to investigate the effect on turbulence of mixing the argon in different proportions with another gas.

Acknowledgment.

Appreciation is extended to Professor S. Bogdonoff for his imaginative and courageous response in undertaking a most controversial experiment at his facility, to Mr. W. H. Webb for carrying it out in its first phase, and for assisting with the calculations in the appendix, and also to Professor M. Reiner and to Dr. K. S. Wan for helping me clarify ideas.

I also wish to thank the Office Of Naval Research USN for making the presentation of this paper possible.

APPENDIX

Introductory Remarks.

In order to gain further insight into the mechanics of aggregation, it is found helpful to consider the "Principle of Least Constraint" as established by Gauss. Although Gauss's principle is in a sense mathematically equivalent to other well known principles of analytical mechanics, it is found to be especially helpful for expressing and interpreting, in a simple way, an overall condition that governs the response of two particles confronted with a binary collision. This principle is adapted to our problem by asserting that the response of particles engaged in a binary collision is such as to minimize the constraints which they present to each other, the contraints being identified here with the condition of mutual impermeability of the particles treated as rigid.

The particles can, of course, minimize the constraints which they thus present to each other, by separating. Another way of relieving the constraints is for the particles to attain a zero relative velocity. Clearly, the second of these two possibilities leads to aggregation, whereas the first does not.

If the molecules are represented by material points, the constraints can be relieved only by separation, and consequently aggregation appears impossible in this fictitious system. If, however, finite dimensions are assigned to bodies having less than spherical symmetry, it is found that under suitable initial conditions the particles respond to an encounter by reducing their relative velocity in translation to zero. It follows, therefore, that admissible molecular rotation is a necessary condition for aggregation, and that the geometrical symmetry elements of the bodies are fundamental to mechanical aggregation.

For very special initial conditions, it is found that the rectilinear and rotational velocity vectors of both particles are equal following the encounter. This result leads to a natural definition for *perfect aggregation*.

The molecular encounters considered above are treated analytically in the foregoing section. An evaluation and interpretation of the results obtained from this treatment follows along with concluding remarks.

Analysis.

Figure 1 indicates the configuration of the collision model, the parallel motion of particles 1 and 2 being in the direction θ with respect to the tangent line of collision.

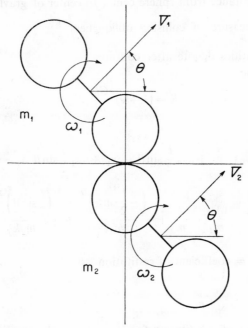

Figure 1
Collision model

The conversation of momentum requires that, for particle 1,

$$m_1(u_1' - u_1) = 0$$

$$m_1(v_1' - v_1) = R$$

$$I_1(\omega_1' - \omega_1) = -R\frac{l}{2}\sin\theta$$

and for particle 2,

$$m_2(u_2' - u_2) = 0$$

$$m_2(v_2' - v_2) = -R$$

$$I_2(\omega_2' - \omega_2) = -R\frac{l}{2}\sin\theta$$

where

m = mass
u = x-component of velocity
v = y-component of velocity

R = impulse

I = moment of inertia

ω = angular velocity in rotation (positive clockwise)

$\dfrac{l}{2}$ = distance from sphere center to center of gravity of dumbbell

θ = measure of collision obliqueness

The primed quantities denote after collision.

For the impulse,

$$R = (1 + e)\,\frac{C_0}{a'}$$

where

$$C_0 = v_2 + \omega_2 \frac{l}{2}\sin\theta - v_1 + \omega_1 \frac{l}{2}\sin\theta$$

$$a' = \frac{1}{m_1} + \frac{1}{m_2} + \frac{\left(-\dfrac{l}{2}\sin\theta\right)^2}{m_1 k_1^2} + \frac{\left(\dfrac{l}{2}\sin\theta\right)^2}{m_2 k_2^2}$$

e = coefficient of restitution

and

$$K = \sqrt{I/m}.$$

Letting e be unity and substituting for R gives, for the conditions after collision,

$$u_1' = u_1 = v_1 \cos\theta$$

$$u_2 = u_2 = v_2 \cos\theta$$

$$v_1' = \frac{2\left(v_2 + \omega_2 \dfrac{l}{2}\sin\theta + \omega_1 \dfrac{l}{2}\sin\theta - v_1\right)}{(m_1 + m_2)(1 + \sin^2\theta)} + v_1$$

$$v_2' = v_2 - \frac{2\left(v_2 + \omega_2 \dfrac{l}{2}\sin\theta + \omega_1 \dfrac{l}{2}\sin\theta - v_1\right)}{(m_1 + m_2)(1 + \sin^2\theta)}$$

$$\omega_1' = \frac{4m_2\sin\theta\left(v_1 - v_2 - \omega_2 \dfrac{l}{2}\sin\theta - \omega_1 \dfrac{l}{2}\sin\theta\right)}{l(m_1 + m_2)(1 + \sin^2\theta)} + \omega_1$$

$$\omega_2' = \frac{4m_2\sin\theta\left(v_1 - v_2 - \omega_2\frac{l}{2}\sin\theta - \omega_1\frac{l}{2}\sin\theta\right)}{l(m_1 + m_2)(1 + \sin^2\theta)} + \omega_2$$

The magnitudes of the resulting velocities are then of course given by

$$V_1' = \sqrt{u_1'^2 + v_1'^2}$$

$$V_2' = \sqrt{u_2'^2 + v_2'^2}$$

and the directions by

$$\theta_1' = \tan^{-1}\frac{v_1'}{u_1'}$$

$$\theta_2' = \tan^{-1}\frac{v_2'}{u_2'}$$

To determine the relations, between initial conditions necessary to produce perfect aggregation, let

$$V_1' = V_2'$$
$$\theta_1' = \theta_2'$$
$$\omega_1' = \omega_2'$$

Substitution for the above yields, where $c = m_2/m_1$

$$u_1 = u_2$$

$$\omega_2 + \omega_1 = \frac{(v_1 - v_2)\cos^2\theta}{l\sin\theta}$$

$$v_2 - v_1 = \frac{2\omega_1\frac{l}{2}\sin\theta(1 + c)}{(c-1)2\sin^2\theta - (c+1)\cos^2\theta}$$

Remarks.

To retain realism in the collision model, it is required for all cases that $\Delta V = V_2 - V_1$ be positive, where V_2 and V_1 are the velocities of the attacking and attacked particles respectively.

Initial conditions leading to *perfect aggregation* have been determined analytically above, by assigning to the variables θ, v, ω, and m values comparable to conditions occurring in gas flows, the curves of Figures 2 and 3 were obtained from the analysis. In the calculations, the initial rotation of particle 1 was maintained constant, the variation of the other conditions then yielding the effect of mass ratio on values of $v_2 - v_1$ and ω_2/ω_1, for contact angles from 0 to $\mu/2$.

If m_2 is slightly larger than m_1, the curves indicate that the mass ratio plays a predominant role in determing the velocity difference and rotation ratio required for perfect aggregation and that a small change in the mass ratio when it is near unity requires a large change in the other parameters to produce perfect aggregation. However, when the mass of the attacking particle is about fifty times the mass of the attacked particle or larger, the parameters required to produce perfect aggregation then become nearly independent of

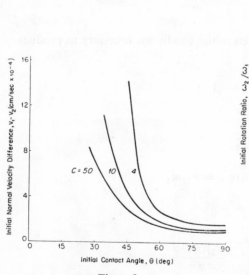

Figure 2

Initial normal velocity difference *vs*
Initial contact angle effect of mass ratio
(for perfect aggregation)

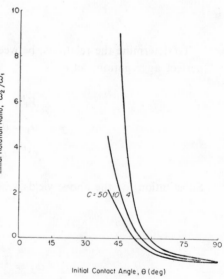

Figure 3

Initial rotation ratio *vs*
Initial contact angle effect of mass ratio
(for perfect aggregation)

differences in mass. Thus, if the probability of aggregation is measured by the degree to which the initial conditions are unrestricted, then as the mass of an aggregate increases and therefore the conditions necessary for aggregation become *less* restrictive, the chances for further growth of the aggregate are increased.

For collisions where the attacked particle has a higher mass than the attacking particles and also where the mass ratio is unity, perfect aggregation is not admissible by this restricted model. This indicates a limit to the growth of the aggregate, for when it has become of such a size that it no longer has a sufficient speed to overtake other particles, it will no longer be able to direct their velocities and will therefore cease to grow.

If the *masses are equal* in a normal collision, it is required by this model that the initial rotations be zero or that the velocity gradient be infinite. This condition may imply the necessity for non-homogeneity in rotational systems to produce an aggregate and indicates the strong effect of impurities in such systems. As applied to a macroscopic situation, i.e. a gas flow, the condition is satisfied by the admission of tertiary collisions which may occur near a boundary where there is a tendency for piling up of the fluid particles.

As noted in the body of the paper, the collision model analyzed here is very specialized as it represents the simplest model through which the fundamental connections between body symmetry and mechanical aggregation can be revealed and precisely established analytically. Consequently, the class of initial conditions producing aggregation according to this model are correspondingly and severely restricted. In a subsequent paper we shall consider a general model and demonstrate that the class of initial conditions leading to mechanical aggregation can indeed be very large. Correspondingly, new aspects of the connections between clustering, dissipation, and geometrico-dynamic symmetry, will be shown.

REFERENCES

[1] P. LIEBER, A dissipation mechanism in gas flows and similar physical systems, *Trans. N. Y. Acad. of Sci.*, March 1949.

[2] M. REINER, Cross stresses in the laminar flow of liquids, *The Physics of Fluids*, **3**, No. 3., May-June, 1960.

[3] W. H. WEBB, Turbulent decay in air, argon and helium. Preliminary Report, Princeton University, August 1961.

[4] L. SPITZER, Stars from interstellar clouds, *Journal of the Washington Accademy of Sciences*, **41**, (1951), No. 10.

DISCUSSION

L.J.F. Broer: 1.   Whereas the actual computation of the rate of formation of binary clusters would be very difficult, a calculation of the volume concentration of these clusters by means of sum-over-state methods seems quite feasible. It is to be expected that this concentration in air under normal conditions will turn out to be very small. In argon it will indeed be even less.

2. It is usual to assume that low-speed turbulence can be interpreted on the base of Reynolds' number only. I do not think the foundation of this belief, chiefly on friction coefficient data, very solid. A more detailed investigation therefore seems important. It seems preferable, however, to do this by purely mechanical means, e.g. using the static head fluctuations measuring technique as developed by de Haan and myself, as the dependence of hot wire response on heat conduction and specific heat may cause uncertainties in the interpretation of the results.

P. Lieber's reply: I established in the paper the fact that binary clusters formed by collisions between perfectly rigid and elastic bodies depends critically upon the geometric and kinematic symmetry properties of such collisions. In so doing, it was established on strictly mechanical grounds that binary clusters cannot *cannot* be prduct in this way sohen the individual bodies have maximum, that is, spherical symmetry. It was further established that a necessary condition for binary clusters to form by elastic collisions is for at least one body to have less than spherical symmetry.

1.   I believe that Professor Broer's remarks in his Item 1 are probably correct. They do not in any way conflict or put to question the ideas and results presented in the paper.

The reason for focusing attention on binary collisions is that they are assigned an exclusive role in the classical kinetic theory of gases according to which they are assumed to account for all changes produced by molecular interactions and for all phenomenological processes resulting therefrom.

2.   I believe that Professor Broer's Item 2 is pertinent and is indeed in accord with the ideas which led to the conception of the crucial experiment set forth in my paper and with experimental results which support these ideas. His suggestions concerning the use of mechanical measuring techniques as developed by him and de Haan sound very promising and may eliminate some of the inherent difficulties and uncertainties generally connected with hot wire work.

SURVEY ON SECOND-ORDER FLUID DYNAMICS

J. G. OLDROYD

University of Wales, Swansea, U. K.

The types of fluid that have been discussed in the present Symposium, those that show second-order stress effects, are of the kind that have some of the properties of ordinary fluids and also some of the properties more usually associated with solids — they have both viscosity and elasticity in varying degrees. We are in a field where the boundary between fluids and solids is not very sharp, in the sense that both fluids and solids with complicated rheological properties present somewhat similar difficulties to the experimentalist and the theoretician who are trying to understand them. Much of what I shall say, in attempting to outline a pattern into which the papers on fluids seem to fit, will apply equally well to fluid and to solid materials.

Rheology is a branch of physics, and we must not lose sight of the fact that it is a *real* flowing material that is ultimately of interest, in spite of the fact that it may be necessary to consider somewhat idealized theoretical models of it on the way to a complete understanding. It must be the aim of the rheologist to construct a precise, unambiguous statement of all the flow properties of the real physical material. This statement of properties (confining attention to a material that does not change irreversibly into a physical different material when it is deformed) should ideally describe the flow behaviour of the material under all conditions of motion, of stress and of temperature, each of which may have varied arbitrarily as a function of the time during the previous history of the material considered. It is very easy for a mathematician, when he starts writing down equations and proving theorems, to make this process of describing deformation and flow properties seem extremely complicated. But in the present lecture I shall try to strike a note of simplicity.

We may take comfort from the point that was made so effectively in the course of our discussion, that some real fluids were found to have the same odd rheological properties in Brussels in the autumn as they had exhibited here in Haifa in the previous spring. Even more reassuring is this corollary: the sequence of physical principles and mathematical ideas that are required for a completely general discussion of equations that describe rheological behaviour need be no more complicated in, say, America in 1955 than it was in Europe in 1950.

THE PATTERN OF RHEOLOGICAL INVESTIGATIONS

The headings under which it seems to me natural to discuss the ideas that have been presented at this Symposium are (i) Micro-rheology, (ii) Experiment, (iii) Formulation of equations of state, and (iv) Prediction of behaviour by simultaneous solution of the equations of state, motion, continuity, etc. These headings represent the stages in the cycle of operations which in practice have to be performed repeatedly in order to achieve a reasonbly complete statement of the rheological behaviour of a real material.

By micro-rheology, a term first used by our host Professor Reiner, we mean the deduction of the behaviour of a macroscopic element of material from what is known of its molecular or microscopic structure. Simple experiments provide in principle an alternative method of determining the general response of a small material sample to applied stress. Whichever method is adopted, the first statement of rheological properties is inevitably somewhat idealized, and appropriate only to certain conditions, e.g. to conditions of small rates of shear in a stationary material element. The formulation of equations of state, in a mathematical form suitable for use in all states of motion and of stress, is a process that will usually lead to several alternative forms of equations, all equally consistent with the limited amount of experimental data available. Even if the generalization of the first statement of properties is unambiguous, the resulting equations of state are at best an idealization of a real material (just as the concept of Newtonian liquid of constant viscosity is an over-simplification — an idealization of some ordinary liquids like water). To complete the cycle, the equations of state can in principle be solved, together with the equations of motion, continuity, heat transfer and appropriate boundary conditions, in order to predict theoretically what the behaviour of the material will be under conditions that have not yet been studied experimentally.

This is, however, not the end of the story, merely the beginning of a new cycle of operations. The prediction under heading (iv) should be capable of experimental verification, and should in fact be the basis on which a crucial experiment is planned to test the validity of the proposed equations of state. Any discrepancy between prediction and experiment requires a repetition of the cycle: re-formulation of equations of state, prediction, crucial experiment, re-formulation, and so on. This process demands the closest collaboration between experimentalist and theoretician at every stage, and especially in the detailed planning and interpretation of crucial experiments to test rival theories.

(i)   Micro-rheology.

Storer and Green have demonstrated, earlier in this Symposium, how rheological equations of state of some complexity can be deduced directly on the basis of the kinetic theory, starting from a phase-space distribution function for the (simple) molecules of a fluid. This is a most interesting development in the statistical mechanical field, and one is led to wonder whether work along these lines will provide an answer to the question: how simple must the molecular arrangements in a fluid be if second-order effects (however slight) are to be entirely absent?

This question has been posed, in effect, by the participants from Technion City who have sought an explanation of Reiner's air thrust bearing effect in terms of the kinetic theory of gases.

The presence of macro-molecules in solution is well known to be associated with rheological complications. Light has been thrown on the effect of molecular coiling by the contributions of Schurz and of Peterlin. In polymer-solvent systems we are still inevitably a long way from a full-scale statistical-mechanical theory.

Suspensions, in each of which the suspended particles have one of several different kinds of permanent anisotropy, have been studied by Giesekus, who concludes that such suspensions will show normal stress effects, not in general of the type associated with the name of Weissenberg (not, that is, consisting of only an extra simple tension along the streamlines).

"Mixtures" of two immiscible fluids have been studied by Hashin, who gives upper and lower limits for the viscosity of a mixture, valid provided the interfacial tension is negligibly small. This too comes under the heading of a micro-rheological study.

(ii)   Experiment.

The experimental papers on normal stress effects fall into two groups, those concerning air and simple liquids in which the existence of normal stress effects is highly controversial, and those setting out to measure normal-stress differences in polymer solutions that are known to be markedly elastico-viscous.

Foux and Reiner, investigating the centripetal pump effect in air, rare gases and toluene, conclude form experiments with air that the variation of thrust with ambient pressure supports an explanation in terms of some elasticity of shape in air, rather than the alternative explanation of Taylor and Saffman (in terms of ordinary viscosity and compressibility).

Bousso's accurate and systematic experiments with air are in accord with the Taylor-Saffman explanation of the thrust bearing effect when the two plates in relative rotation are deliberately misaligned. The elaborate precautions taken to ensure smooth surfaces in his apparatus suggest that, with the rotating plates parallel, a crucial experiment might be devised to test accurately whether the thrust in the air bearing varies with relative speed of rotation and gap between plates in a way that could be explained by elastico-viscosity.

Turning to the experiments on polymer solutions, those described by Markovitz and Brown on polyisobutylene solutions in cetane are especially interesting, as a crucial set of experiments designed to distinguish rival normal-stress-difference theories. Systematic observations on flow between parallel plates in relative rotation, and in the corresponding cone-and-plate apparatus, have been compared in such a way as to test Weissenberg's conjecture: that normal-stress differences consist of a simple extra tension along the streamlines, with stress isotropy perpendicular to the streamlines*. Subject to confirmation by further experiments with the same liquids in a Couette type of apparatus, the conclusion is that the conjecture is not true in these solutions. It is evident at least that Weissenberg's conjecture cannot be exactly true for all liquids.

The paper by Metzner and others presents a new method of measuring normal-stress differences at high rates of shear, deduced from observations of fluid jets issuing from a tube. The Weissenberg conjecture has been assumed approximately true in making the calculations.

(iii) Formulation of equations of state.

This subject has become a happy hunting ground for those of us who are mathematicians. A few years ago I was criticised by some rheologists for writing general papers that the physicists found difficult to understand. More recently there has been a tendency for pure mathematicians to write abstract papers about mathematical forms of stress, strain, rate-of-strain relations that even the applied mathematician (mathematical physicist) finds great difficulty in fitting into the physical scheme of real materials.

When Newton proposed in effect the first rheological equation of state for a real fluid, defining a single scalar coefficient, the *viscosity* (which might be dependent on temperature), it was accepted because it was *approximately* right

---

* In steady shearing flow. It is known that sets of equations of state consistent with the conjecture in steady shearing flow will in general give rise to more complicated stress-difference effects in other types of flow, steady and non-steady.

for some known materials and it was useful because it was so simple that important problems could be solved on the basis of it. It is still worth while to look for fairly simple equations of state that are something like correct for some real non-Newtonian fluids, even though they are imperfect. A general analysis of equations of state is, of course, necessary, up to the point where we can distinguish possible and impossible equations of state. Although we still do not understand precisely the restrictions imposed on sets of equations of state for flowing materials by the principles of thermodynamics, we have now known for more than a decade exactly what we must do to avoid writing down equations of state that represent different materials in different parts of an apparatus. Once this has been understood, it is surely some of the simpler non-Newtonian equations of state (that satisfy the known tests for physical possibility) which will be worth pursuing as most helpful to the physicist. There is in any case not much practical point in writing down equations of state that are so complicated that it is impossible to proceed to stage (iv), the prediction of material behaviour by solution of all the relevant equations.

A linear relationship between the rates of strain and the stresses associated with change of shape at sufficiently small strain rates (whether represented by linear differential equations or by a relaxation spectrum) has often been proposed as a simple representation of elastico-viscous behaviour. Two papers at the Symposium (by Walters and myself) and a paper by Markovitz, now in the press elsewhere, have made the point that a real material with such a "linear" response must be expected to show second-or higher-order effects if strain rates are not considered to be infinitesimal: second-order differences between the normal stresses are inevitable. It seems that only strictly Newtonian liquids could possibly fall outside the scope of this Symposium!

Attention has been drawn, in the paper by Rivlin, to the fact that non-Newtonian fluids exhibiting normal-stress-difference effects will not usually follow the simple flow patterns that are taken for granted in Newtonian flow, e.g. flow in straight lines down a pipe of non-circular section. An example is given of the secondary flow that must set in as a consequence of transverse pressure gradients.

The very different approach of Coleman and Noll is to be regarded as complementary to the above line of thought. These authors treat by modern mathematical analysis a type of equation of state they have proposed as a definition of a class of fluids, the "simple fluids". Briefly a "simple fluid" is one in which the stress in the material at the current instant can be expressed explicitly as a functional of a measure of the deformation, regarded as a function of the time throughout the previous history of the same piece of material.

(iv) Prediction of material behaviour by solution of the equations of state, motion, etc.

The solution of the simultaneous partial differential equations of state, motion, continuity and of heat transfer (unless explicit mention of the latter can be avoided by restricting attention, say, to isothermal conditions) presents an order of difficulty that is extremely sensitive to the initial and boundary conditions. One finds that with almost any non-Newtonian set of equations of state, a solution for the flow pattern can be obtained in closed form only when the boundary conditions are of the simplest, and when initial conditions are avoided by treating steady flow, or oscillatory flow with no transient element. Hence the scarcity of treatments of predicted flows other than simple shearing, Couette streaming, flow in narrow gaps between a cone and plate and flows in straight pipes.

In Jain's written contribution to the Symposium a novel numerical method of obtaining some solutions for some other flows is presented. Rintel illustrates how progress can be made by restricting attention to the first terms of power series expansions, e.g. in powers of a Reynolds number. Narasimhan has shown what elaboration is involved with even the simplest set of boundary conditions when a non-Newtonian fluid is electrically conducting and a magnetic field is present.

It has already been remarked that sometimes a non-Newtonian fluid will not be capable of following a simple flow pattern (such as rectilinear flow down a pipe), and that secondary flows are to be expected. Closely related to this possibility of simple non-Newtonian flow in circumstances where the same flow pattern in an ordinary Newtonian liquid is known to be stable. The study of stability is clearly of great practical importance; for example, the volume rate of flow down a pipe, calculated for a non-Newtonian fluid on the basis of rectilinear flow may be grossly over-estimated if that particular type of flow turns out to be unstable. In this context we must regard Graebel's contribution to the Symposium as an important one. He concludes that stability of steady flow in horizontal circles in a Couette apparatus should be enhanced if the material flow in horizontal circles in a Couette apparatus should be enhanced if the material has a yield value and flows as a Bingham plastic solid. Since this result is true whether or not there is a yield surface (separating the region of flow from material not stressed up to the yield point) present between the cylindrical boundaries, we can infer that the same conclusion applies to a purely viscous fluid with viscosity a decreasing function of rate or shear — since over a short range of stress this fluid is characterized by an extrapolated yield value and constant "plastic viscosity".

GENERAL CONCLUSIONS

We have now to ask ourselves what progress has been made in our understanding of non-linear effects in fluids, as revealed by the papers read, and by recorded and unrecorded discussion, during the Symposium in Haifa. How often can we now say with confidence "Here we have a non-Newtonian fluid, and these are its rheological equations of state, valid to a good approximation for all investigated conditions of flow?" If we mean equations describing quantitatively a particular specimen of non-Newtonian fluid, this hardly ever happens. We are much more likely to have equations giving only a fair, qualitative representation of the observed non-linear effects. There are serious gaps in our knowledge and we should do well to look critically at our use of the repetitive cycle of operations: experiment, formulation, prediction. (I omit here micro-rheological study as an alternative to basic experiment, on the grounds that it is in practice for a real liquid, the more difficult alternative.) I shall in conclusion venture to comment on the problems presented by each of these three stages of the cycle.

The Symposium has revealed, I think, that more work should be done on planning *decisive* experiments. There are several rival theories concerning the centripetal pump effect in air, and several theories of normal stress (Weissenberg) effects in polymer solutions, and in each case it is necessary to plan crucial experiments to decide between them. (The experiments of Bousso on air and of Markovitz and Brown on polymer solutions have already been cited as valuable contributions in this direction.) Moreover, we must expect such situations to be commonplace in rheological investigations, for at each reformulation of equations of state several alternative theoretical possibilities are likely to arise, all consistent with previous experiments; and only a carefully planned new set of experiments can distinguish between them. The value of predictions of what will happen, on a given theory, under new flow conditions, is much reduced if these are incapable of experimental test. Equally, little satisfaction can be gained from attempts to interpret observations made in an apparatus for which calculation of the theoretical flow presents insuperable difficulties. Crucial experiment and prediction of what is expected to happen must be integrated into one operation, demanding close collaboration on points of detail between experimental physicist and mathematician.

There is little one can say, in general terms, on the question of solving the partial differential equations and boundary conditions that are involved in the prediction of what will happen, on the basis of rival theories, in a crucial experiment. Each set of simultaneous equations has to be treated on its merits and may present formidable mathematical difficulties. More frequent recourse to high-speed computing techniques is clearly inevitable if progress is to be made.

There remains to be discussed one more stage in the repetitive cycle of operations, the formulation of rheological equations of state, and on this I feel I can usefully expand a little. What I have to say is not new, and my reason for spending the remaining few minutes of my time on this topic is that the physical simplicity and the generality of an approach [1] to this subject published in 1950 have not been understood by some later writers, who have made the subject appear extremely complicated. My remarks are aimed at showing that the formulation of the equations of state for materials with all sorts of rheological properties, in a form that can be used under all conditions of motion, is not one of prohibitive difficulty.

Whenever we are concerned with a physical concept of some complextiy — for example, the state of stress in a small piece of material (at a certain time), or the state of deformation of the same material in relation to a certain previous configuration (chosen arbitrarily for reference), or the way the state of stress (or of deformation) in that particular piece of material is changing with the time — then there are usually several alternative sets of mathematical symbols that one can define to measure this physical concept. From the purely mathematical point of view there is little to choose between the alternative ways of measuring the physical quantity; although one way might involve defining a small number of variables and operations, and another a larger number of variables and operations with certain fixed relationships between them. Our choice of representation of physical quantities should be governed by the physical problem we are discussing, since there is an advantage in choosing, if possible, a set of variables each of which has a physical significance directly relevant to the problem in hand, in preference to another set of variables only some combinations of which are strictly relevant to the problem in hand. This helps to give the equations we arrive at in the course of developing a theory a more immediate physical significance, since they are recognizable direct relationships between *relevant* physical variables.

It follows from this argument that the variables one needs for the simplest formulation of equations of state of a material will not necessarily be the same as those needed to express the equations of motion, and there may well be a different set of variables again in the most natural or the most concise mathematical expression of the laws of heat transfer in the same material. When all these equations have later to be brought together for simultaneous solution, we must of course then have them all expressed in terms of the same variables, and some purely mathematical transformation will be necessary in order to bring them into the right shape. But, for the immediate purpose of discussing general equations of state, where a certain amount of physical complexity must inevitably be contemplated, let us in the first instance avoid any unnecessary, additional, mathematical complexity by working in terms of the simplest possible representations of the relevant physical quantities. In this way we can discuss with ease the general continous physical material, solid or fluid, in a general state of deformation or flow and with a general stress-deformation-temperature history.

We assume, simply, that the rheological behaviour of any material element (a part of a moving continuum) is quite independent of the position and the motion of the element as a whole in space, and that the behaviour at any time t may depend on the previous rheological states through which that element has passed, but cannot depend directly on the corresponding states of neighbouring parts of the material. We therefore regard as irrelevant to the problem of formulating equations of state any variable measuring position or translatory or rotatory motion, of a material element in space, and any parameter labelling neighbouring material or labelling a time subsequent to the current time t. The easiest method of labelling particles of the material, in a way that does not require reference to where they are in space, is to consider a curvilinear coordinate system embedded in the material and convected with it as it flows or is deformed. If the coordinate surfaces are labelled ξ^j ($j = 1, 2, 3$), then any particle of material has the same coordinates ξ^j at all times. It follows from what has been said that the equations describing the behaviour at time t of a typical material element at ξ^j can most simply be expressed as relationships between functions of ξ^1, ξ^2, ξ^3 and previous times t' ($-\infty < t' \leq t$). It must be emphasized that ξ^1, ξ^2, ξ^3 occur only as three parameters labelling a point in the material, and a range of values of ξ^j would be irrelevant to the problem in hand and cannot occur

The simplest equation of state of all, $pv = RT$ for a perfect gas, relates a single dynamic variable p (the pressure), a single kinematic variable v (the specific volume), a thermodynamic variable T (the absolute temperature) and one scalar physical constant R; the variables involved can be functions of the time. For materials in general the relevant dynamic, kinematic and thermodynamic variables and physical constants will not all be scalars, but their definitions will involve reference to directions in the material, and they will most naturally be measured by tensors, in general varying with time. The usual tensor suffix notation allows us to write an equation of state, or a set of more than one equation, in a compact form independent of any coordinate system, as a relation between tensor variables; each tensor equation can be regarded as representing several component equations, each relating components of tensor variables that are all relevant to rheological behaviour. The tensor variables involved will be tensors at ξ^j, relating to conditions there at some time $t'\ (\leqq t)$, and will naturally be measured by their components in the ξ^j system of reference*. Then the operations of partial differentiation with respect to the time (regarding the material position labels ξ^j and the time as the independent variables), and addition or time integration of quantities associated with the same material at different times, are operations that can legitimately occur in the equations of state, i.e. they introduce no new factor that is irrelevant to the problem in hand. In contrast, an operation of partial differentiation with respect to a coordinate ξ^j, or of covariant differentiation in a spacial direction, cannot occur in the equations of state in the form we are considering, because its presence would imply some dependence of rheological behaviour at ξ^j on what has happened at a slightly different place in the material, and this we know to be irrelevant.

Now it is possible to enumerate all the variables that may be involved in the equations of state for the material at ξ^j in a flowing continuum, i.e., to be precise, the equations describing the rheological behaviour at the instant t of a small element at ξ^j.

Of the kinematic variables associated with the material at ξ^j at times $t'\ (\leqq t)$, all those referring to absolute motion in space may be excluded as irrelevant, so that only those defining the relative distances between parts of a material element (and the way these change with time are in the present context admissible. A knowledge of the distance $ds(t')$ between an arbitrary pair of neighbouring particles ξ^j and $\xi^j + d\xi^j$ at every instant $t'\ (\leqq t)$ therefore constitutes complete information about the relevant kinematics, and this information is given by the variable metric tensor of the coordinate system, $\gamma_{jl}(\xi,t')$, since

$$[ds(t')]^2 = \gamma_{jl}(\xi,t')\, d\xi^j d\xi^l.$$

In this equation, ξ is written for brevity in place of $(\xi^1,\ \xi^2,\ \xi^3)$, and the usual convention of summation over the values 1, 2, 3 applies when a suffix is repeated in the covariant and contravariant positions. We can now assert that all the kinematic quantities in the equations of state must be derivable from the tensor function

$$\gamma_{jl}(\xi,t')\ (t'\leqq t).$$

---

* There are substantial simplifications in the mathematical manipulation of tensors associated with a material element when these are represented by their components in a convected coordinate system. When a change of convected coordinates is made, from ξ^j to ξ'^i, the formulae for the new coordinates in terms of the old are time-independent. Hence the transformation law for components of tensors is time-independent. This means that tensors associated with the same material ξ^j at different times can be added together, component by component, to form a sum that is a tensor at ξ^j of the same type. As a corollary, time integration or differentiation of a tensor function of the time at ξ^j can be carried out, component by component, and results in another tensor at ξ^j of the same type as we started with.

The only dynamic quantities that may be involved in describing the rheological behaviour are the states of stress in the material during its previous history. (Body forces on a material element can always be made negligible compared with the surface forces, by letting the size of the element tend to zero.) The state of stress at ξ^j at time t' is measured by the stress tensor $\pi_{jl}(\xi,t')$, which is a symmetrical tensor in the absence of finite body couples per unit mass. We can write here the covariant absolute stress tensor without loss of generality, since we know that any other measure of stress at time t' can be expressed in terms of this and of the metric tensor $\gamma_{jl}(\xi,t')$. So all the dynamic and kinematic variables in the equations of state must be expressible in terms of the functions $\gamma_{jl}(\xi,t')$ and $\pi_{jl}(\xi,t')$ $(t' \leq t)$. At this stage we can say, thinking in terms of components, that the equations of state can be regarded as basically relationships between the six functions of time $\pi_{jl}(\xi,t')$ measuring stress history and the six functions $\gamma_{jl}(\xi,t')$ measuring deformation history, and we can therefore expect the number of independent component equations to be six. (This number of equations suffices, for example, to determine the stress history completely if the whole deformation history and initial conditions are known.)

The temperature history, measured by a scalar variable $T(\xi, t')$, the absolute temperature of the material element at the instant t' $(\leq t)$, will in general be an important factor in the description of rheological behaviour. The time-lag $(t-t')$ may also occur explicitly in the equations (functions of this variable being often thought of as "memory functions").

Having allowed explicitly for all the variables that can possibly occur in the equations of state we may reserve the term "physical constant" for a quantity associated with the material ξ^j that is independent of temperature and of time. Equations of state will in general involve universal constants, and physical constants of the material at ξ^j, that require reference to directions for their definitions, i.e. constant tensors

$$\kappa_n{}^{\cdots\cdots l\cdots}_{\cdot j\cdots}(\xi) \qquad (N = 1, 2, 3, \ldots),$$

satisfying $\partial\kappa_n{}^{\cdots\cdots l\cdots}_{\cdot j\cdots}/\partial t = 0$. In most fluids, with no inherent anisotropy in the equilibrium state (any preferred directions during flow being simply a consequence of the flow history), anisotropic physical constant tensors will not be involved, all constants being then combination of scalar physical constants and universal constant tensors.

We have now arrived by very simple arguments at the following conclusion. The equations of state, in a form suitable for use in a general state of flow, may be expressed as an invariant set of relationships between the variables

$$\gamma_{jl}(\xi, t'), \quad \pi_{jl}(\xi, t'), \quad T(\xi, t'), \quad \kappa_N{}^{\cdots\cdots l\cdots}_{\cdot j\cdots}(\xi), \ t)-)t' \qquad (N = 1, 2, 3, \ldots, \ t' \leq t);$$

the operations of integration and partial differentiation with respect to time may be present in these equations; ξ^1, ξ^2, ξ^3 (represented by ξ) occur only as three parameters labelling the material considered. Any equation of state written out in this way, however complicated the rheological-history dependence, can in principle be transformed — by mathematical rules that have been established once and for all — to a conventional reference system fixed in space, when that is found to be necessary in order to proceed to the making of predictions*.

The main advantage of the above approach is that it allows general equations of state of any liquid or solid to be regarded as a set of integro-differential relationships between a small number of time-dependent variables, each of which has a direct, easily understood, physical significance for the material element whose behaviour is being described — and this is true however complicated the dependence of current behaviour may be on previous stress-deformation-temperature history. No variables have been introduced that have not immediate relevance to the problem in hand. A secondary, but important, advantage is that a *physical constant of the material* is readily defined in this scheme, without presenting any conceptual difficulty, and is a tensor whose components are truly constant for a particular small piece of the material, quite independently of neighbouring pieces of material. This is true even in an anisotropic material in which there is arbitrary variation of preferred directions from place to place in some initial reference configuration; or in a material with qualitative anisotropy, i.e. different modes of behaviour when stressed in different directions. Usually the physical constants for different parts of a continuum of a single material will be simply related. Time does not permit me to go into detail in a single lecture, but I hope I have said enough to emphasize the simplicity and generality of the above physical approach, in contrast to some of the later analytical approaches to restricted classes of materials.

No discussion of formulation is complete without mention of the restrictions that must be imposed on the form of rheological equations of state by the laws of thermodynamics. The notation of the above approach to formulation allows the implication of these laws to be seen immediately in the case of anisotropic elastic solids (the general form the equations reduce to in equili-

---

* When the equations can be written without involving time integrals, the transformation to a fixed frame of reference is extremely easy and one can make the necessary transformations mentally and write everyhing in terms of a fixed coordinate system from the start. The simplest equations of state for fluids can be put in the form of differential equations relating $\pi_{ji}(\xi,t)$ and $\frac{1}{2}\partial\gamma_{ji}(\xi,t)/\partial t$, functions of the current time t only — or, in a fixed system of reference, between their transforms p_{ik} and e_{ik} (the conventional symbols for the fixed-components of the stres sand first rate-of-strain tensors). The transform of the partial time-derivative in the converted system of reference is the *convected derivative*, usually written $\mathfrak{D}/\mathfrak{D}t$, in a fixed system.

brium being then completely defined). In the case of fluid materials we have to admit that we do not yet know when we are writing down equations of state that conflict with thermodynamic principles. It is true that, guided by common sense, we have avoided developing theories of liquids of negative viscosity, and we refrain from using for example, the Reiner-Rivlin prototype equation of state with constant coefficients when the rate-of-strain tensor has a value that makes the rate of dissipation of energy negative. But a resoned separation of those theories of second-order effects that are compatible with the laws of thermodynamics from those that contradict them must await another symposium.

REFERENCE

[1]   J. G. OLDROYD, *Proc. Roy. Soc.*, A **200**, (1950), 523–541; **A202**, (1950), 345–358.

IV. PAPERS ACCEPTED
BUT NOT READ

ON THE UNIQUENESS OF SOLUTION IN STATICS OF CONTINUA WITH GENERAL DIFFERENTIAL STRESS–STRAIN RELATIONS

Leo Finzi

Polytechnic Institute of Milan, Italy

ABSTRACT

The problem of uniqueness of solution for bodies which obey generically holonomic* or non-holonomic stress-strain relations is discussed, without reference to the existence of a potential. It is shown how the uniqueness of solution is ensured when a quadratic form, having for coefficients the components of the tensor characterizing the mentioned relations, is defined in sign. The particular conditions ensuring the uniqueness of solution in finite terms for quasi-elastic and for Hencky's bodies are also deduced.

Finally, as a particular case of the general discussion, a demonstration is given of the uniqueness of solution in the differential range for Prandtl-Reuss elastic-plastic bodies.

1. Introduction.

Various demonstrations of the uniqueness of solution in the ordinary theory of elasticity are known; they are reported in [1] and [2].

These demonstrations may be extended to the case in which, in spite of the strains remaining infinitesimal, the stress-strain relation is one-one but not linear, as is the case for quasi-elastic bodies.

When the stress-strain relation is not holonomic, i.e. it is essentially differential, one should exclude the uniqueness of solution in finite terms of stress and strain, under equal conditions of connections and final loads, because the final state depends on the way in which the loads were successively applied and the connections imposed.

In this case one can only speak of uniqueness of solution in the differential range, i.e. uniqueness of increments of stresses and strains, with the same variation of forces and connections.

---

* That is to say an essentialy differential one.

715

The uniqueness of solution in such a range has been proved by Greenberg for the perfectly elastic-plastic bodies of Prandtl-Reuss [3], and by Bauer for bodies of the foregoing type having, however, a generic regular condition of plasticity [4]. Koiter [5] and Drucker [6] have discussed the case in which the condition of plasticity is of a discontinuous type like that of Tresca; Melan has considered elastic-plastic bodies with strain-hardening [7], [8].

The foregoing demonstrations apply to the uniqueness in the range o particular theories, and were evolved after the theories themselves in order to confirm them. Hill has discussed in a general way the problem of differential uniqueness assuming, however, the existence of a potential G in the form of a homogeneous quadratic function of the strain increment, whose derivatives gave the corresponding stress increments [9], [10], [11], [12]. These investigations extend the demonstration concerning elastic bodies (even if the strains are finite), substituting the stresses and strains by their differentials and the elastic potential, function of the strains, by a potential G being a function of the differentials of the above stresses and strains.

In this paper the problem of uniqueness is dealt with in a very general way referring to a generic holonomic or non-holonomic stress-strain relation; the latter type corresponds to finite or differential relations, such as those of generic continua which undergo strains or flow in the rheological range, without reference to the existence of a potential G.

With this end in view we resume the demonstration of uniqueness of solution for perfectly elastic, but generically anisotropic bodies, extending it to the case of quasi-elastic bodies.

We consider next the plastic bodies of Hencky in which the stress-strain relation is holonomic; the uniqueness of solution is demonstrated for equal connections and final forces, in the case for which unloading processes may be excluded.

The problem of differential uniqueness is then dealt with in the case where the stress-strain relation is a generic non-holonomic one:

$$d\xi_{rs} = \mu_{ikrs} dp^{ik} \quad (1)$$

where ξ_{rs} is the symmetrical tensor of strain, p_{ik} the symmetrical tensor of stress and μ_{ikrs} is a quadruple tensor depending upon the state of stress and strain throughout the conditions of state.

---

[1] As usual the summatory sign with respect to the saturated indices is omitted, the latter taking on values 1, 2, 3.

$$\phi^{jhpq}(\mu_{ikrs},\ p^{ik},\ \xi^{rs}) = 0 \tag{2}$$

When a potential G exists, $\mu_{ikrs} = \mu_{rsik}$, but this does not hold in general.

It is demonstrated how uniqueness will be ensured when a quadratic form having for coefficients the components of tensor μ_{ikrs} is defined in sign.

From the general formulation thus established, it is deduced that the uniqueness will subsist for a wide class of bodies comprising, as particular cases, those obeying the best known elastic-plastic theories.

2. Perfectly elastic bodies.

Consider a continuous body, generically not homogeneous and anisotropic, occupying the volume τ and limited by the surface σ.

Under equilibrium conditions, the stress tensor p_{ik} is related to the external force per unit volume F_i and to the superficial boundary forces f_i by the following equations:

$$\text{in } \tau \qquad p_{ik}^{/k} + F_i = 0^{(2)}; \quad p_{ik} = p_{ki} \tag{3}$$

$$\text{on } \sigma \qquad p_{ik}n^k + f_i = 0 \tag{4}$$

The tensile stresses and elongations are considered positive, n_k being the versor normal to σ and directed towards the outside.

Let s_r be the displacement, which we will consider infinitesimal, corresponding in the strain tensor ξ_{rs} and related to it by the relation:

$$\text{in } \tau \qquad \xi^{rs} = \tfrac{1}{2}(s^{r/s} + s^{s/r}) \tag{5}$$

At the boundary we assume:

$$\text{on } \sigma \qquad s_r = \bar{s}_r \tag{6}$$

Let us consider two solutions of the same equilibrium problem, for equal volume τ, boundary surface σ and equal distribution of forces over such a volume and along such a surface. If r_{ik} be the difference between the two stresses p'_{ik} and p_{ik}, z_{rk} the difference between the strains ξ'_{rs} and ξ_{rs}, and t_r the difference between the displacements s'_r and s_r:

---

(2) The indices preceded by a solidus denote derivation.

$$r_{ik} = p'_{ik} - p_{ik}; \quad z_{rs} = \xi'_{rs} - \xi_{rs}; \quad t_r = s'_r - s_r \tag{7}$$

From (3) and (4) we obtain:

$$\text{in } \tau \qquad r^{/k}_{ik} = 0; \quad r_{ik} = r_{ki} \tag{8}$$

$$\text{on } \sigma \qquad r_{ik}n^k = 0 \tag{9}$$

while (5) gives:

$$\text{in } \tau \qquad z^{rs} = \tfrac{1}{2}(t^{r/s} + t^{s/r}). \tag{10}$$

From (8) we deduce:

$$\int_\tau r^{/k}_{ik}t^i d\tau = 0 \tag{11}$$

Integrating by parts the left-hand side of (11) and keeping in mind relation (10), we obtain:

$$\int_\tau (r_{ik}t^i)^{/k}d\tau - \int_\tau r_{ik}t^{i/k}d\tau = \int_\tau (r_{ik}t^i)^{/k}d\tau - \int_\tau r_{ik}z^{ik}d\tau = 0 \tag{12}$$

Under conditions of regularity, applying Green's lemma we deduce:

$$\int_\sigma r_{ik}t^i n^k d\sigma - \int_\tau r_{ik}z^{ik}d\tau = 0 \tag{13}$$

But the first integral in (13) is zero whether the boundary forces be pre-fixed, (for (9)), the displacements be prefixed (as in such a case $t \equiv 0$), or whether the forces be given on one part of the boundary and the displacements on the remaining part. In any case hence:

$$\int_\tau r_{ik}z^{ik}d\tau = 0 \tag{14}$$

Taking into account the fact that the body is perfectly elastic, the stress-strain relation is therefore of type:

$$p_{ik} = c_{ikrs}\zeta^{rs}. \tag{15}$$

where the elastic tensor c_{ikrs} possesses besides the symmetries $c_{ikrs} = c_{kirs}$ $c_{ikrs} = c_{iksr}$, also the symmetry $c_{ikrs} = c_{rsik}$; the latter derives from the existence of a density of strain energy which is essentially positive

$$U = \tfrac{1}{2} c_{ikrs} \zeta^{ik} \zeta^{rs} > 0 \text{ for } \zeta^{ik} \neq 0 \tag{16}$$

From (15), taking into account (7), we deduce:

$$r_{ik} = c_{ikrs} z^{rs} \tag{17}$$

and (14) becomes:

$$\int_{\tau} c_{ikrs} z^{ik} z^{rs} d\tau = 0 \tag{18}$$

But for equation (16) the quadratic form constituted by the integrand is always positive for $z_{ik} \neq 0$, and the left-hand side of (18) becomes zero only if everywhere $z_{ik} = 0$, i.e. when the two solutions of the elastic problem coincide (differing at the most by one rigid displacement, if the connections allow it).

3.   Quasi-elastic bodies.

In a quasi-elastic body, subject to small strains, the stress–strain relation is a one to one finite relation of the type:

$$p_{ik} = p_{ik}(\zeta^{rs}) \tag{19}$$

where, however, as there is still a density of strain energy U, we have:

$$p_{ik} = \frac{\partial U}{\partial \zeta^{ik}} \text{ and hence } \frac{\partial p_{ik}}{\partial \zeta^{rs}} = \frac{\partial p_{rs}}{\partial \zeta_{ik}} \tag{20}$$

Relation (14), which follows from the equilibrium conditions, holds true and leads one to state that uniqueness of solution subsists also for a quasi-elastic body if the invariant $r_{ik} z^{ik}$ is defined in sign, i.e. when the direct work corresponding to the passage from one state of stress to another (for equal applied forces) is defined in sign.

When there is a single component of stress depending upon a single component of strain, the preceding condition corresponds to the circumstance in which the stress-strain relation is monotonous and hence one-one.

In general, from the formula of finite increment, we derive:

$$r_{ik} = \left(\frac{\partial p_{ik}}{\partial \zeta^{rs}}\right)^{*} z^{rs} = \left(\frac{\partial^2 U}{\partial \zeta^{ik} \partial \zeta^{rs}}\right)^{*} z^{rs} \tag{21}$$

where the asterisk denotes that the derivatives are calculated at a point of the interval $[\xi_{ik},\ \xi'_{ik}]$.

Condition (14) therefore becomes:

$$\int_{\tau}\left(\frac{\partial^2 U}{\partial \xi^{ik}\ \partial \xi^{rs}}\right)^* z^{ik}z^{rs}d\tau = 0 \tag{22}$$

The left-hand side of (22) is defined in sign when the increment undergone by the strain energy on passing from one equilibrium configuration to another is also defined in sign.

The problem of stability of equilibrium leads to an analogous analysis.

In fact the total energy corresponding to constant external forces is:

$$V = \int_{\tau} U\, d\tau + \int_{\tau} F_i s^i d\tau + \int_{\sigma} f_i s^i d\sigma$$

and hence the increment it undergoes on passing from a state of equilibrium to another generic $\xi + z$, is (for Taylor's formula):

$$\Delta V = \int_{\tau}\frac{dU}{\partial \xi^{ik}}z^{ik}d\tau - \int_{\tau} F_i t^i\, d\tau - \int_{\sigma} f_i t^i d\sigma + \frac{1}{2}\int_{\tau}\left(\frac{\partial U}{\partial \xi^{ik}\ \partial \xi^{rs}}\right)^* z^{ik}z^{rs}d\tau$$

But:

$$\int_{\tau}\frac{\partial U}{\partial \xi^{ik}}z^{ik}d\tau - \int_{\tau} F_i t^i d\tau - \int_{\sigma} f_i t^i d\tau = \int_{\tau} p_{ik}t^{i/k}\, d\tau -$$

$$- \int_{\tau} F_i t^i d\tau - \int_{\sigma} f_i t^i d\sigma = - \int_{\tau}(p_{ik}^{/k}+F_i)\,t^i d\tau + \int_{\sigma}(p_{ik}n^k-f_i)\,t^i d\sigma$$

is null in a state of equilibrium (for (1) and (21)). Therefore

$$\Delta V = \frac{1}{2}\int_{\tau}\left(\frac{\partial^2 U}{\partial \xi^{ik}\ \partial \xi^{rs}}\right)^* z^{ik}z^{rs}\, d\tau$$

The discussion on stability of equilibrium which, as well known, is centered upon the sign of ΔV and the discussion on uniqueness, centered upon the sign of the left-hand side of (22), thus appear evidently interconnected.

4. Plastic bodies of Hencky.

A discussion will now follow on the problem of uniqueness of solution for the case where relation (1) is holonomic so that (1) itself may be substituted by a finite relation.

Such is the case for the quasi-elastic bodies examined in section 3, and such is also the case for Hencky's plastic bodies when unloading processes do not occur.

I shall now discuss the latter case as it is the most important and significant.

In Hencky's theory the pressure $\frac{1}{3}p$ is related to the mean normal strain $\frac{1}{3}\xi$ as in the ordinary theory of elasticity, while the relation between the stress deviator q_{ik} and the strain deviator η_{ik} is the following:

$$d\eta_{ik} = \mu dq_{ik} + q_{ik}d\lambda \tag{23}$$

where λ and μ are two scalars and

$$\eta_{ik} = \xi_{ik} - \tfrac{1}{3}\xi a_{ik}; \quad \xi = a^{ik}\xi_{ik} \tag{24}$$

$$q_{ik} = p_{ik} - \tfrac{1}{3}p a_{ik}; \quad p = a^{ik}p_{ik} \tag{25}$$

(in Cartesian orthogonal coordinates $a_{ik} = 0$ for $i \neq k$; $a_{ik} = 1$ for $i = k$).

The conditions of state are two:

$$\lambda = \mu \tag{26}$$

and the condition of plasticity (von Mises):

$$q_{ik}q^{ik} = 2h^2 \tag{27}$$

where h is the plasticity constant.

Taking into account (26), equation (23) assumes, by integration, the finite form:

$$\eta_{ik} = \lambda q_{ik} \tag{28}$$

Equation (14) holds true, but it must be written inserting the differences of deviators, i.e. introducing:

$$\chi_{ik} = \eta'_{ik} - \eta_{ik}; \quad z = \xi' - \xi; \quad g_{ik} = q'_{ik} - q_{ik} \tag{29}$$

$$r = p' - p \qquad \omega = \lambda' - \lambda$$

It follows, (noting that $g_{ik}a^{ik} = \chi_{ik}a^{ik} = 0$):

$$r_{ik}z^{ik} = (\tfrac{1}{3}ra_{ik} + g_{ik})(\tfrac{1}{3}za^{ik} + \chi^{ik}) = \tfrac{1}{3}rz + g_{ik}\chi^{ik}$$

and (14) becomes:

$$\tfrac{1}{3}\int_\tau rzd\tau + \int_\tau g_{ik}\chi^{ik}d\tau = 0 \tag{30}$$

Now the first integral here is the same which we have in the elastic range and it may be null or positive. It will be shown that such a circumstance occurs also for the second integral.

In fact:

$$g_{ik}\chi^{ik} = g^{ik}(\lambda'q'_{ik} - \lambda q_{ik}) = \lambda'g_{ik}g^{ik} + \omega q_{ik}g^{ik} \tag{31}$$

while, from the condition of plasticity (27), we derive:

$$(q_{ik} + g_{ik}) \cdot (q^{ik} + g^{ik}) = 2h^2 \tag{32}$$

hence:

$$2q_{ik}g^{ik} + g_{ik}g^{ik} = 0 \tag{33}$$

From (31) and (33) we therefore deduce:

$$g_{ik}\chi^{ik} = \frac{\lambda' + \lambda}{2}g_{ik}g^{ik} \tag{34}$$

Now $g_{ik}g^{ik}$ is positive and null only for $g_{ik} = 0$. Therefore the sign of the left-hand side of (34) will be given by the sign of the λ's. But the latter are always positive, because the density of strain energy connected to the variation of form:

$$dW = q_{ik}d\eta^{ik} = q_{ik}d(\lambda q^{ik}) = q_{ik}dq^{ik} + d\lambda q_{ik}q^{ik} = 2h^2 d\lambda \tag{35}[3]$$

is also positive, Therefore $d\lambda$ will always be positive and, as initially λ is equal to the positive elastic constant $1/2G$, λ will also be positive.

In conclusion therefore, the second integral, which appears on the left-hand side in (30), is also always positive or null for $g_{ik} = 0$ like the first integral.

In order that (30) be satisfied it is hence necessary that the differences between stresses should be null.

Therefore, for Hencky's plastic bodies, in the absence of unloading processes, the uniqueness of solution is ensured for equal loads and final connections.

---

[3] Note that equation (27) by differentiation gives $q_{ik}\,dq^{ik} = 0$.

5. Bodies having a general differential stress-strain relation.

Assume that the stress-strain relation is that given by (1) and let us carry out our considerations in differential terms, i.e. referring to the increments of load, stress, displacement and strain.

The equation analogous to (14) is the following:

$$\int_\tau dr_{ik}dz^{ik}d\tau = 0 \tag{36}$$

Starting from the same state of stress and strain, let us consider two different increments of stress dp'_{ik} and dp_{ik} and also of strain $d\xi'_{rs}$ and $d\xi_{rs}$ produced by the same variation of load.

We shall hence have:

$$dp'_{ik} = dp_{ik} + dr_{ik}; \quad d\xi'_{rs} = d\xi_{rs} + dz_{rs} \tag{37}$$

while:

$$\mu'_{ikrs} = \mu_{ikrs} \tag{38}$$

because tensor μ_{ikrs} depends upon the state of stress and strain and not upon their increments.

From (1) we shall hence derive:

$$dz_{ik} = \mu_{ikrs}dr^{rs} \tag{39}$$

Substituting this in (36) the latter becomes:

$$\int_\tau \mu_{ikrs}dr^{ik}dr^{rs}d\tau = 0 \tag{40}$$

When the quadratic differential form

$$d^*\psi = \mu_{ikrs}dr^{ik}dr^{rs} \tag{41}$$

which appears under the integral sign in (40), is defined in sign, the differential uniqueness of solution subsists.

Having in mind the symmetry of tensor r_{ik} and that of tensor μ_{ikrs}, we shall be able to mark the components with only two indices α and β, which assume values from 1 to 6.

The quadratic form (41) will therefore be written as follows:

$$d*\psi = \mu_{\alpha\beta}dr^\alpha dr^\beta \quad (\alpha, \beta = 1, 2, \dots 6) \tag{42}$$

As an example we shall show that (42) is always defined in sign in the case of elastic isotropic bodies.

In an elastic isotropic body, if E, G and γ are the usual three elastic constants (positive), the matrix of the coefficients $\mu_{\alpha\beta}$ is:

$$
\begin{vmatrix}
\dfrac{1}{E} & -\dfrac{v}{E} & -\dfrac{v}{E} & 0 & 0 & 0 \\[2mm]
-\dfrac{v}{E} & \dfrac{1}{E} & -\dfrac{v}{E} & 0 & 0 & 0 \\[2mm]
-\dfrac{v}{E} & -\dfrac{v}{E} & \dfrac{1}{E} & 0 & 0 & 0 \\[2mm]
0 & 0 & 0 & \dfrac{1}{G} & 0 & 0 \\[2mm]
0 & 0 & 0 & 0 & \dfrac{1}{G} & 0 \\[2mm]
0 & 0 & 0 & 0 & 0 & \dfrac{1}{G}
\end{vmatrix}
$$

The conditions for (42) to be defined in sign are the following:

$$
\begin{vmatrix} \dfrac{1}{E} & -\dfrac{v}{E} \\[2mm] -\dfrac{v}{E} & \dfrac{1}{E} \end{vmatrix}^2 - \begin{vmatrix} -\dfrac{v}{E} & -\dfrac{v}{E} \\[2mm] \dfrac{1}{E} & -\dfrac{v}{E} \end{vmatrix} \times \begin{vmatrix} -\dfrac{v}{E} & \dfrac{1}{E} \\[2mm] -\dfrac{v}{E} & -\dfrac{v}{E} \end{vmatrix} > 0; \quad \begin{vmatrix} \dfrac{1}{E} & -\dfrac{v}{E} \\[2mm] -\dfrac{v}{E} & \dfrac{1}{E} \end{vmatrix} > 0
$$

viz.:

$$\frac{1}{E^4}\left[(1 - v^2)^2 - (v^2 + v)^2\right] = \frac{1}{E}(1 - 3v^2 - 2v^3) > 0; \quad \frac{1}{E^2}(1 + v^2) > 0$$

The second condition is always satisfied and the first one is satisfied for $0 \leq v \leq 0.5$, as it is known it should be in the elastic case.

6. Application to elastic-plastic bodies.

The elastic-plastic bodies considered by the best known theories are special cases among those for which tensor μ_{ikrs} is the sum of the isotropic tensor $\frac{1-2v}{3E} a_{ik} a_{rs}$ which gives the elastic variation in volume corresponding to the pressure, and of a quadruple tensor characterizing the plastic nature of the material:

$$\bar{\mu}_{ikrs} = \mu(a_{ir}a_{ks} - \frac{1}{3} a_{ik}a_{rs}) + v a_{ik}q_{rs} \tag{43}$$

where μ and v are scalars [13].

Using the notations introduced in the preceding section, we have:

$$\bar{\mu}_{\alpha\beta} = \mu(a_{\alpha\beta} - \frac{1}{3} a_\alpha a_\beta) + v a_\alpha q_\beta \tag{44}$$

where $a_\alpha = 1$ for $a = 1, 2, 3$ and $a_a = 0$ for $a = 4, 5, 6$.

Substituting the above in (1) which we write in the form:

$$d\xi_\beta = \mu_{\alpha\beta} dp^\alpha \tag{45}$$

we obtain, (having (24) and (25) in mind):

$$d\xi_\beta = d\eta_\beta + \frac{1}{3} d\xi a_\beta = \mu(dp_\beta - \frac{1}{3} dp a_\beta) + v \, dp \, q_\beta + \frac{1-2v}{3E} dp a_\beta \tag{46}$$

But, as in the elastic range,

$$d\xi = \frac{1-2v}{3E} \cdot dp \tag{47}$$

hence (46) becomes:

$$d\eta_\beta = \mu dq_\beta + q_\beta d\lambda \tag{48}$$

where:

$$d\lambda = v \, dp \tag{49}$$

Consider the quadratic form defined by (42). We shall transform it by introducing the deviators and taking into account (44).

Note first of all that:

$$dr_\alpha = dp'_\alpha - dp_\alpha = \frac{1}{3} dp'a_\alpha + d'q_\alpha - \frac{1}{3} dpa_\alpha - dq_\alpha = \frac{1}{3} dra_\alpha + dg_\alpha \qquad (50)$$

where:

$$dr = dp' - dp ; \quad dg_\alpha = dq'_\alpha - dq_\alpha \qquad (51)$$

If the volume variation of the body, which gives always a positive contribution $\frac{1-2v}{3E}(dr)^2$, as in the elastic case, is eliminated from equation (42) the latter becomes:

$$d^*\psi = \bar{\mu}_{\alpha\beta}\left(\frac{1}{3} dra^\alpha + dg^\alpha\right)\left(\frac{1}{3} dra^\beta + dg^\beta\right) = \qquad (52)$$

$$=\left[\mu\left(a_{\alpha\beta} - \frac{1}{3} a_\alpha a_\beta\right) + va_\alpha q_\beta\right] \cdot \left[\frac{1}{9}(dr)^2 a^\alpha a^\beta + \frac{1}{3} dra^\alpha dg^\beta + \right.$$

$$\left. + \frac{1}{3} dra^\beta dg^\alpha + dg^\alpha dg^\beta \right].$$

Having in mind that:

$$a_\alpha dg^\alpha = 0 \qquad (53)$$

and that, for the condition of plasticity:

$$q^\beta dg_\beta = q^\beta(dq'_\beta - dq_\beta) = 0^{(4)} \qquad (54)$$

we find:

$$d^*\psi = \mu dg_\alpha dg^\alpha. \qquad (55)$$

The quadratic form $d^*\psi$ is therefore defined in sign if the coefficient μ is also defined in sign.

For bodies having a generic relation (43), the uniqueness of solution (in terms of stress) subsists whenever the coefficient μ is defined in sign.

---

(4) It must be remembered that by differentiating the condition of plasticity (27), one obtains not only $q^\beta dq_\beta = 0$, but also $q^\beta dq'_\beta = 0$.

This occurs in particular in the Prandtl-Reuss theory in which μ is equal to the positive elastic constant $\dfrac{1}{2G}$ and also in Mises limit-theory where $\mu \to 0$, because $G \to +\infty$. It occurs also in Hencky's theory, in which $\mu = \lambda$ and as we saw λ is a positive quantity. It must be noted however, as shown previously, that in Hencky's theory the uniqueness of solution subsists not only in the differential range, but also in finite terms if unloading processes are excluded.

7. Cases of discontinuity.

Cases of discontinuity may occur either due to the simultaneous presence of an elastic region τ_e and a plastic region τ_p, separated by an interface σ_f, or due to possible discontinuities which may occur in the plastic range, in correspondence to characteristic surfaces σ_c or to their envelopes.

The forces transmitted through these surfaces must be equal and opposite on one side and on the other. Therefore it is still justified to deduce (14) from (12), even if a σ_f or a σ_c is present in τ.

All is therefore reduced once again to the discussion of the sign of the quadratic form $d^*\psi$. The latter is positive in elastic regions, and also in plastic regions, under the conditions specified in the preceding sections.

In the differential range one moves from the same physical state, comparing variations in stress and strain which start from the same state of stress, and the same state of strain, and hence from the same surfaces σ_f and σ_c. The uniqueness of solution is thus ensured whatever are the elastic constants and the scalar μ, provided only that the latter is positive.

In the finite range, when the body is wholly elastic or quasi-elastic (the characteristics not being real and there being no interfaces), no discontinuities can exist unless they are pre-constituted through the association of different bodies. Nevertheless the uniqueness of solution always subsists.

Hencky's elastic-plastic bodies constitute instead a typical case.

Here there are two solutions to be compared and accordingly it will be possible to distinguish three regions in the volume τ, an elastic region τ_e, for both solutions, a plastic region τ_b for both solutions and a region τ_{ep} plastic for the first solution and elastic for the second or vice-versa.

In the region τ_e, the invariant $g_{ik}\chi^{ik}$ is, as in the elastic case, always positive; this holds true also in τ_p as shown in section 4. In τ_{ep} we have:

$$g_{ik}\chi^{ik} = \frac{\lambda' + \dfrac{1}{2G}}{2} g_{ik}g^{ik} \tag{56}$$

and, as $\lambda' > \dfrac{1}{2G} > 0$, the invariant is positive also in τ_{ep}.

The uniqueness of solution in terms of stresses is therefore ensured.

REFERENCES

[1] A. E. H. Love, *A Treatise on the Mathematical Theory of Elasticity*, Dover publications, New York, p. 170–172 (1927).

[2] R. Marcolongo, *Teoria matematica dell'equilibrio dei corpi elastici*, Hoepli, Milano (1904). p. 194–198.

[3] H. J. Greenberg, Complementary minimum principles for an elastic-plastic material. *Quart. Appl. Math.*, **7**, (1949), 85–95.

[4] F. B. Bauer, Brown University Report A 11–27 (1949).

[5] W. T. Koiter, Stress-strain relations, uniqueness and variational theorems for elastic-plastic material with a singular yield surface, *Quart. Appl. Math.*, **11**, (1953), 350–353.

[6] D. C. Drucker, On uniqueness in the theory of plasticity, *Quart. Appl. Math.*, **14**, (1956), 35–42.

[7] E. Melan, Zur Plastizität des räumlichen Kontinuums, *Ingenieur-Archiv*, **9**, (1938), 116–126.

[8] R. Hill, *The Mathematical Theory of Plasticity*, Clarendon Press, Oxford, (1950), 53–60.

[9] R. Hill, A general theory of uniqueness and stability in elastic-plastic solids, *Jour. Mech. Phys. of Solids*, **6**, (1958), 236–249.

[10] R. Hill, Some basic principles in the mechanics of solids without a natural time, *Jour. Mech. Phys. of Solids* **7**, (1959), 209-225.

[11] R. Hill, Uniqueness in general boundary-value problems for elastic or inelastic solids, *Jour. Mech. Phys. of Solids* **9**, (1960), 114–130.

[12] R. Hill, Bifurcation and uniqueness in non-linear mechanics of continua. *Problem of Continuum Mechanics*, Philadelphia, (1961), p. 155–164.

[13] L. Finzi, Formulazioni variazionali della congruenza nei corpi elasto-plastici, *Rend. Sem. Mat. e Fis. di Milano*, **26**, (1955), 25–44.

STRAIN HISTORY EFFECTS IN PLASTIC DEFORMATION OF METALS

Y. Yoshimura

Aeronautical Research Institute, University of Tokyo, Japan

AND

Y. Takenaka

National Aeronautical Laboratory, Tokyo, Japan

ABSTRACT

As an extension of the Mises' theory of plasticity for isotropic work-hardening, a theory is proposed in this paper in which the strain history effects in plastic deformation, as anisotropy and the Bauschinger effect, as well as work-hardening, are correlated with the previous strain history, and it is then compared with some fundamental experiments. It is shown that the deviations of these experimental results from the predictions of the Mises' theory are well explained by this theory. Practically, the theory serves to predict the anisotropy of the yield strength produced in metals by a certain process of working.

1. Introduction.

While elastic deformation is due to the change in the distances among constituent atoms, their topological relations being preserved, plastic deformation is due to the change in the topological relations among atoms, i.e. the slip in metal crystals, for example, resulting from the motion of dislocations. In consequence of this, most metals undergo by plastic deformation certain changes in micro-structural state, represented mainly by the group pattern of dislocations, that is dependent on the previous history of the deformation. It is for this reason that metals reveal strain history effects such as work-hardening, anisotropy and the Bauschinger effect in plastic deformation. Physically, work-hardening is considered to be brought about by a change in density of the dislocations, plastic anisotropy by the directional deviation of the way of their grouping, and the Bauschinger effect by the difference of the pattern when viewed from the loading and from the opposite directions. Besides these, there might exist some factors, for example, the structural change in grain boundaries and the preferred orientation of grains, which influence more or less these plastic properties. At any rate, all of these micro-structural states are to be uniquely determined when the previous strain history of the material is given.

In the present paper, we will first introduce the strain representing this strain history, and therefore regarded as corresponding to the current micro-structural state. This will be done by generalizing the so-called logarithmic strain to the three dimensional deformation.

By means of such a strain, which corresponds to the micro-structural state, it becomes conceptually possible to describe the strain history effects as anisotropy, and the Bauschinger effect as certain functions of the strain. An attempt to solve this problem will be given in this paper. The yield function, that was hitherto defined as a function of stress alone for the ficticious case of isotropic work-hardening, will now be generalized so as to be a function of both stress and strain for the case of real metals, in which anisotropy and the Bauschinger effect coexist with work-hardening. Thus all strain history effects, work-hardening, anisotropy and the Bauschinger effect, are seen to be incorporated simultaneously into a mathematical frame work of the plasticity theory.

In order to examine the validity of this theory, experiments were made on the yielding of circular tubes, made of mild steel and of brass respectively, for the combined stress state of tension-torsion after they had been subjected to the respective strain histories of axial elongation and twist, and the results were then compared with the theory. Other experimental facts already published concerning anisotropy effects were also examined in the light of this theory.

The present paper's main object is to describe the fundamental features of our ideas on this problem, and will not enter into all its details.

2. History-dependent strain.

As was mentioned in the Introduction, plastic deformation caused by a change in the topological relations among constituent particles is accompanied by a change in the micro-structural state. The final micro-structural state after deformation, by which the mechanical state under the strain of a deformed body should be identified, arises from the accumulation of successive infinitesimal changes in the micro-structural state, due to successive incremental deformations. Accordingly, it depends on the path of deformation for the same final geometrical configuration of the body. By this reason the strain, representing the mechanical state of the deformed body, is an integral, along the given deformation path, of incremental strains, properly defined, and is regarded as dependent on the path

Incremental strain is defined, based on the essential character of plastic deformation, as such that the current deformed state is, at the same time, regarded as an undeformed initial state. Let the Lagrangian coordinates be indicated by $x^\lambda (\lambda = 1, 2, 3)$ with Greek index, and the Eulerian coordinates by $x^i (i = 1, 2, 3)$ with Roman index, then the incremental strain is defined as [1]

$$
\begin{aligned}
D\mathbf{E} &= (D\varepsilon)_{\lambda\mu}\mathbf{e}^\lambda \mathbf{e}^\mu = (D\varepsilon)_{ij}\mathbf{e}^i \mathbf{e}^j = (D\overset{\circ}{\varepsilon})_{\lambda\mu}\overset{\circ}{\mathbf{e}}^\lambda \overset{\circ}{\mathbf{e}}^\mu \\
(D\varepsilon)_{\lambda\mu} &= \tfrac{1}{2}Dg_{\lambda\mu} = \tfrac{1}{2}\left[\nabla_\lambda (Du)_\mu + \nabla_\mu (Du)_\lambda\right] \\
(D\varepsilon)_{ij} &= \tfrac{1}{2}x^\lambda_{,i}x^\mu_{,j}Dg_{\lambda\mu} = \tfrac{1}{2}[\nabla_i (Du)_j - \nabla_j (Du)_i] \\
(D\overset{\circ}{\varepsilon})_{\lambda\mu} &= \overset{*}{J}^\nu_\lambda \overset{*}{J}^\kappa_\mu (D\varepsilon)_{\nu\kappa}
\end{aligned}
\right\} \tag{2.1}
$$

where

$$
\begin{aligned}
\nabla_\lambda (Du)_\mu &= (Du)_{\mu,\lambda} - (Du)_\alpha \Gamma^\alpha_{\lambda\mu} \\
\Gamma^\alpha_{\lambda\mu} &= \tfrac{1}{2}g^{\alpha\nu}(g_{\mu\nu,\lambda} + g_{\nu\lambda,\mu} - g_{\lambda\mu,\nu})
\end{aligned}
\right\} \tag{2.2}
$$

and $\overset{*}{J}^\lambda_\mu$ is the reduced cofactor of

$$
J^\mu_\lambda = \delta^\mu_\lambda + \overset{\circ}{\nabla}_\lambda \overset{\circ}{u}^\mu \tag{2.3}
$$

in the determinant $J = \left| J^\mu_\lambda \right|$, and

$$
\overset{\circ}{\nabla}_\lambda \overset{\circ}{u}^\mu = \overset{\circ}{u}^\mu_{,\lambda} + \overset{\circ}{u}^\alpha \overset{\circ}{\Gamma}^\mu_{\alpha\lambda}, \quad \overset{\circ}{\Gamma}^\alpha_{\lambda\mu} = \tfrac{1}{2}\overset{\circ}{g}^{\alpha\nu}(\overset{\circ}{g}_{\mu\nu,\lambda} + \overset{\circ}{g}_{\nu\lambda\ \mu} - \overset{\circ}{g}_{\lambda\mu,\nu}) \tag{2.4}
$$

$\mathbf{e}^\lambda$ and $\overset{\circ}{\mathbf{e}}^\lambda$ are the vectors reciprocal to the Lagrangian base vectors $\mathbf{e}_\lambda$ and $\overset{\circ}{\mathbf{e}}_\lambda$ for the deformed and undeformed states respectively, $\mathbf{e}^i$ the vectors reciprocal to the Eulerian base vectors $\mathbf{e}_i$ for the deformed position of a material point, and $g_{\lambda\mu} = \mathbf{e}_\lambda \cdot \mathbf{e}_\mu$ and $\overset{\circ}{g}_{\lambda\mu} = \overset{\circ}{\mathbf{e}}_\lambda \cdot \overset{\circ}{\mathbf{e}}_\mu$ the Lagrangian metric fundamental tensors for the deformed and undeformed states respectively. The Hill's definition [2] of the incremental strain $d\varepsilon_{ij}$, given for the special case when the coordinate system is rectangular Cartesian, is not clear for which of the two coordinate systems, Lagrangian or Eulerian, it holds.

The strain tensor, representing the previous strain history up to the current state, is obtained by the integration

$$\mathbf{E} = \int_0^t D\mathbf{E} \tag{2.5}$$

along a given deformation path, t denoting the time or a parameter representing extent of deformation. Putting $\mathbf{E} = \varepsilon_{\lambda\mu}\mathbf{e}^\lambda\mathbf{e}^\mu$, (2.5) is rewritten in the form of the differential equation

$$D\varepsilon_{\lambda\mu} - g^{\kappa\rho}[\varepsilon_{\kappa\mu}\nabla_\lambda(Du)_\rho + \varepsilon_{\lambda\kappa}\nabla_\mu(Du)_\rho] = (D\varepsilon)_{\lambda\mu} \tag{2.6}$$

whose solution $\varepsilon_{\lambda\mu}$ is dependent on the deformation path, i.e.

$$\oint D\mathbf{E} \neq 0 \tag{2.7}$$

because of the fact that the coefficients $\nabla_\lambda(Du)_\rho$, $\nabla_\mu(Du)_\rho$ and $(D\varepsilon)_{\lambda\mu}$ are path-dependent. For example, the strain of a thin circular tube subjected to a combined axial elongation and twist is different according to the deformation path, i.e., for instance, twist after elongation or elongation after twist, even if the final geometrical configuration is identical. The difference, however, is a small quantity of the second order, when the deformation is small. Thus the history-dependent strain $\mathbf{E}$ is considered to correspond to the mechanical state of the body specified by the history-dependent micro-structural state, and it can therefore serve for the description of the strain history effects such as anisotropy, and the Bauschinger effect.

On the other hand, the history-dependent strain $\mathbf{E}$ is shown to become the so-called logarithmic strain, in the case of simple elongation. This is rather natural when viewed from the process of its derivation. That a logarithmic strain is reasonable for describing plastic deformation has been verified by many people since P. Ludwik [3], and it is sure from a theoretical view-point too. This fact means that the history-dependent strain $\mathbf{E}$ as a generalization of the logarithmic strain serves not only for describing the special effects as anisotropy, but also for all the phenomena of plastic deformation. This is because plastic deformation in itself is essentially a history-dependent phenomenon.

3. The Mises' criterion as that for the initial isotropic state.

The sharp yielding of mild steel is excluded from our subject, because it results from a particular process of unstable character. With the exception of this case, one cannot know experimentally the yield stress or the yield condition in the initial isotropic state of most metals, because yielding in the annealed state is not clear in them, taking place gradually, and further, the work-hardening range of mild steel is preceded by the sharp yielding process. For this reason, experiments on yielding are usually made for a certain state work-hardened by a strain history (pre-strain), as seen in the experiments of Taylor and Quinney [4] and of W. Lode [5]. The experimental results thus obtained on yield condition, and others, are considered to be effected by anisotropy due to the strain history, and therefore the form of yield function for the isotropic state is not accessible, unless the material revealed isotropic work-hardening in particular.

Among many metals, those of higher purity seem to show less hardening and anisotropy. The result for *Cu* in Taylor-Quinney's experiments [4] seems to correspond to this case of nearly isotropic hardening. In the light of this result, and the calculation based on slip systems by J.F.W. Bishop and R. Hill [6] concerning face-centered cubic crystals, it seems probable that the yield surface for the isotropic state, particularly of that crystal form, is located very close to Mises' criterion, between it and that of Tresca's. But since its discrepancy from the Mises' is very small, one may be allowed to choose the Mises' criterion as a good approximation for the initial isotropic state.

4. Yield function in the presence of anisotropy and the Bauschinger effect due to strain history.

Before proceeding to the main subject, we need to consider the Mises' yield function, which was assumed to hold for the initial isotropic state. Since the following arguments hold for any coordinate system (x^λ or x^i) and reference frame ($\mathbf{e}_\lambda$ or $\mathring{\mathbf{e}}_\lambda$ for x^λ), we will now make use of the Lagrangian system in the deformed state (the basic vectors are $\mathbf{e}_\lambda$), as an example. Then the Mises' yield function is written as [7]

$$f(\sigma^{\lambda\mu}) = \frac{1}{2}\sigma'^{\lambda\mu}\sigma'_{\lambda\mu} \tag{4.1}$$

or alternatively as [8]

$$f(\sigma^{\lambda\mu}) = \frac{1}{2}g'_{\lambda\mu\nu\kappa}\sigma'^{\lambda\mu}\sigma'^{\nu\kappa} \tag{4.2}$$

where

$$g'_{\lambda\mu\nu\kappa} = \frac{1}{2}(g_{\lambda\nu}g_{\mu\kappa} + g_{\lambda\kappa}g_{\mu\nu}) \tag{4.3}$$

Here the metric tensor $g_{\lambda\mu}$ is nothing but the components of the unit tensor $\mathfrak{I} = g_{\lambda\mu}e^{\lambda}e^{\mu}$ which is of spherical symmetry with isotropic property. And the Mises' function (4.2) is seen to be constructed, by the rule (4.2) and (4.3), from the stress deviator $\sigma'^{\lambda\mu}$ and the spherically symmetric (isotropic) tenstor $g_{\lambda\mu}$. It is due to the isotropic character of $g_{\lambda\mu}$ that the Mises' function represents a yield function corresponding to the isotropic state. Of course, yield functions other than the Mises' are also theoretically possible for the isotropic state, and they are all to be constructed from $\sigma'^{\lambda\mu}$ and $g_{\lambda\mu}$, although this may not be by rules as simple as (4.2) and (4.3).

Now we will come back to our subject. Since $\varepsilon_{\lambda\mu}$ is regarded as corresponding to the change in the micro-structural state, so that the mechanical state, from the undeformed isotropic state, represented by $g_{\lambda\mu}$, changes to the deformed state, it is very natural to consider that the deformed state is expressed by

$$g_{\lambda\mu} + A\varepsilon_{\lambda\mu} \tag{4.4}$$

A being generally a scalar function of $\varepsilon_{\lambda\mu}$. Then it is also natural to consider that the yield function for the anisotropic state resulting from the strain history $\varepsilon_{\lambda\mu}$ is obtained from $\sigma'^{\lambda\mu}$ and $g_{\lambda\mu} + A\varepsilon_{\lambda\mu}$ by the same rule, (4.2) and (4.3) as the Mises' yield function was obtained for the isotropic state from $\sigma'^{\lambda\mu}$ and $g_{\lambda\mu}$. That is, we obtain the result

$$f(\sigma^{\lambda\mu}, \varepsilon_{\lambda\mu}) = \frac{1}{2}c'_{\lambda\mu\nu\kappa}\sigma'^{\lambda\mu}\sigma'^{\nu\kappa} - B\varepsilon_{\lambda\mu}\sigma'^{\lambda\mu} \tag{4.5}$$

$$c'_{\lambda\mu\nu\kappa} = \frac{1}{2}[(g_{\lambda\nu} + A\varepsilon_{\lambda\nu})(g_{\mu\kappa} + A\varepsilon_{\mu\kappa}) + (g_{\lambda\kappa} + A\varepsilon_{\lambda\kappa})(g_{\mu\nu} + A\varepsilon_{\mu\nu})] \tag{4.6}$$

including the Bauschinger effect, which is considered to be introduced into the yield function as a scalar invariant dependent on $\varepsilon_{\lambda\mu}$ and linear with respect to $\sigma'^{\lambda\mu}$. Expanding (4.6) with regard to A, we have

$$C'_{\lambda\mu\nu\kappa} = g'_{\lambda\mu\nu\kappa} + AL'_{\lambda\mu\nu\kappa} + A^2M'_{\lambda\mu\nu\kappa} \tag{4.7}$$

$$L'_{\lambda\mu\nu\kappa} = \frac{1}{2}(g_{\lambda\nu}\varepsilon_{\mu\kappa} + g_{\mu\kappa}\varepsilon_{\lambda\nu} + g_{\lambda\kappa}\varepsilon_{\mu\nu} + g_{\mu\nu}\varepsilon_{\lambda\kappa}) \tag{4.8}$$

$$M'_{\lambda\mu\nu\kappa} = \frac{1}{2}(\varepsilon_{\lambda\nu}\varepsilon_{\mu\kappa} + \varepsilon_{\lambda\kappa}\varepsilon_{\mu\nu}) \tag{4.9}$$

where $g'_{\lambda\mu\nu\kappa}$ is given by (4.3)

Another, more special, hypothesis for deriving the yield function in anisotropic state is that the part of the function representing the deviation from isotropy is constructed from $\sigma'^{\lambda\mu}$ and $A\varepsilon_{\lambda\mu}$ by the same rule, (4.2) and (4.3), as the Mises' yield function was constructed for the isotropic state from $\sigma'^{\lambda\mu}$ and $g_{\lambda\mu}$. In this case, we have

$$f(\sigma^{\lambda\mu}, \varepsilon_{\lambda\mu}) = \frac{1}{2}(g'_{\lambda\mu\nu\kappa} + a'_{\lambda\mu\nu\kappa})\sigma'^{\lambda\mu}\sigma'^{\nu\kappa} - B\varepsilon_{\lambda\mu}\sigma'^{\lambda\mu} \tag{4.10}$$

$$a'_{\lambda\mu\nu\kappa} = A^2 M'_{\lambda\mu\nu\kappa} = A^2 \frac{1}{2}(\varepsilon_{\lambda\nu}\varepsilon_{\mu\kappa} + \varepsilon_{\lambda\kappa}\varepsilon_{\mu\nu}) \tag{4.11}$$

This result is seen to be a special case of the result (4.7) when $L'_{\lambda\mu\nu\kappa} = 0$.

5. Stress-strain relations.

For the case of anisotropic work-hardening with the Bauschinger effect, we can put $f(\sigma^{\lambda\mu}, \varepsilon_{\lambda\mu})$ of (4.5) or (4.10) in the relation

$$f(\sigma^{\lambda\mu}, \varepsilon_{\lambda\mu}) = F(W) \tag{5.1}$$

as against the plastic work

$$W = \int_0^t \sigma^{\lambda\mu}(D\varepsilon)_{\lambda\mu} \tag{5.2}$$

From the principle of maximum plastic work, we have

$$(D\varepsilon)_{\lambda\mu} = \frac{\partial f}{\partial \sigma^{\lambda\mu}} D\lambda \tag{5.3}$$

where $D\lambda$ is obtained from (5.1) and (5.3) as

$$D\lambda = \frac{Df}{F'\sigma^{\lambda\mu}\dfrac{\partial f}{\partial \sigma^{\lambda\mu}}} \tag{5.4}$$

F' indicating DF/DW.

From (4.5), in general, and (5.3), we have the stress-strain relations

$$(D\varepsilon)_{\lambda\mu} = \left\{ \left[g'_{\lambda\mu\nu\kappa} + A \left(L'_{\lambda\mu\nu\kappa} - \frac{2}{3} g_{\lambda\mu}\varepsilon_{\nu\kappa} \right) + \right. \right.$$
$$\left. \left. + A^2 \left(M'_{\lambda\mu\nu\kappa} - \frac{1}{3} M'_{\alpha\beta\nu\kappa} g^{\alpha\beta} g_{\lambda\mu} \right) \right] \sigma'^{\nu\kappa} - B\varepsilon_{\lambda\mu} \right\} D\lambda \tag{5.5}$$

The terms with A and A^2 on the right side represent anisotropy effect and that with B the Bauschinger effect. For the special yield function (4.10), the terms with A are omitted in (5.5).

6. Strain history effects of thin tubes due to axial elongation and twist.

In order to examine whether our theory, which lies on a purely theoretical basis, is valid or not, we will now compare its results with the fundamental experiments, i.e. those on the yielding of thin circular tubes under the combined stress states of axial tension and torsion after having been subjected to strain histories of axial elongation and twist respectively.

Let x^1, x^2, x^3 be the axes of a rectangular Cartesian coordinate system with its origin on the wall of the tube be taken in the radial, circumferential and axial directions of the tube respectively, and the coordinates x^1, x^2, x^3 be Lagrangian (Fig. 1). Of the two kinds of base vectors e_λ and $\overset{\circ}{e}_\lambda$ ($\lambda = 1, 2, 3$) we now choose the latter more suitable for practical problems*. Then, if the tube is subjected to the strain history both of axial elongation and twist, i.e.

$$\left. \begin{array}{ll} \varepsilon_{11} = \varepsilon_{22} = -\dfrac{1}{2}\varepsilon_0, & \varepsilon_{33} = \varepsilon_0 \\[3mm] \varepsilon_{23} = \dfrac{1}{2}\gamma_0, & \varepsilon_{31} = \varepsilon_{12} = 0 \end{array} \right\} \tag{6.1}$$

---

* The Lagrangian expressions in Sections 4 and 5 hold in the same form for the vectors $\overset{\circ}{e}_\lambda$ as for e_λ.

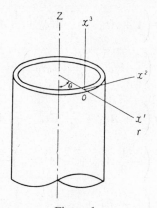

Figure 1
Coordinates axes for a circular tube.

where

$$\varepsilon_0 = \log(l/l_0) \qquad (6.2)$$

(l_0 and l are the lengths of the tube before and after the elongation), the yield function (4.5) assumes the form

$$f = \frac{1}{3}\sigma^2 \left(1 + A\varepsilon_0 + \frac{3}{4}A^2\varepsilon_0^2 - \frac{1}{6}A^2\gamma_0^2\right) + \tau^2 \left(1 + \frac{1}{2}A\varepsilon_0 - \frac{1}{2}A^2\varepsilon_0^2 + \right.$$

$$\left. + \frac{1}{4}A^2\gamma_0^2\right) + \frac{1}{3}\sigma\tau\left(\frac{1}{2}A\gamma_0 + \frac{5}{2}A^2\varepsilon_0\gamma_0\right) - B\left(\varepsilon_0\sigma + \frac{1}{2}\gamma_0\tau\right) \quad (6.3)$$

for the combined stress state of tension-torsion

$$\sigma_{33} = \sigma, \quad \sigma_{23} = \tau, \quad \text{the other } \sigma_{\lambda\mu} = 0 \qquad (6.4)$$

and the stress-strain relations under the same stress state are read from (5.5) as

$$
\left.
\begin{aligned}
D\varepsilon_{11} &= -\left[\frac{1}{3}\sigma\left(1 + A\varepsilon_0 + \frac{3}{4}A^2\varepsilon_0^2 + \frac{1}{12}A^2\gamma_0^2\right) + \right.\\
&\qquad + \tau\left(\frac{2}{3}A\gamma_0 + \frac{1}{6}A^2\varepsilon_0\gamma_0\right) - \frac{1}{2}B\varepsilon_0 \Bigg] D\lambda\\[6pt]
D\varepsilon_{22} &= -\left[\frac{1}{3}\sigma\left(1 + A\varepsilon_0 + \frac{3}{4}A^2\varepsilon_0^2 - \frac{5}{12}A^2\gamma_0^2\right) + \right.\\
&\qquad + \tau\left(-\frac{1}{3}A\gamma_0 + \frac{2}{3}A^2\varepsilon_0\gamma_0\right) - \frac{1}{2}B\varepsilon_0 \Bigg] D\lambda\\[6pt]
D\varepsilon_{33} &= \left[\frac{2}{3}\sigma\left(1 + A\varepsilon_0 + \frac{3}{4}A^2\varepsilon_0^2 - \frac{1}{6}A^2\gamma_0^2\right) + \right.\\
&\qquad + 2\tau\left(\frac{1}{6}A\gamma_0 + \frac{5}{12}A^2\varepsilon_0\gamma_0\right) - B\varepsilon_0 \Bigg] D\lambda\\[6pt]
D\varepsilon_{23} &= \left[\tau\left(1 + \frac{1}{2}A\varepsilon_0 - \frac{1}{2}A^2\varepsilon_0^2 + \frac{1}{4}A^2\lambda_0^2\right) + \right.\\
&\qquad + \sigma\left(-\frac{1}{6}A\gamma_0 + \frac{5}{12}A^2\varepsilon_0\gamma_0\right) - \frac{1}{2}B\gamma_0 \Bigg] D\lambda\\[6pt]
D\varepsilon_{31} &= D\varepsilon_{12} = 0
\end{aligned}
\right\} \quad (6.5)
$$

Although the tubes in our experiments were annealed enough in order to remove initial anisotropy, we can suppose that more or less might have remained even after the annealing. Since the anisotropy, if it exists, is due to a surviving effect of a drawing of the bars, from which the tubes were machined in the process of production, it may be equivalent to the anisotropy due to a certain axial elongation. Accordingly, the strain history of pre-elongated tubes is given by ε_0, $\gamma_0 = 0$ as the results, while that of pre-twisted by $\varepsilon_0 = \varepsilon_i$ and γ_0 (ε_i = small initial elongation).

Thus the yield function and the stress-strain relations for the stress state of combined tension-torsion of a pre-elongated tube are given, by putting $\gamma_0 = 0$ in (6.3) and (6.5) respectively, as

$$
f = \frac{1}{3}\sigma^2\left(1 + A\varepsilon_0 + \frac{3}{4}A^2\varepsilon_0^2\right) + \tau^2\left(1 + \frac{1}{2}A\varepsilon_0 - \frac{1}{2}A^2\varepsilon_0^2\right) - B\varepsilon_0\sigma \quad (6.6)
$$

and

$$D\varepsilon_{33} = D\varepsilon = \left[\frac{2}{3}\sigma \left(1 + A\varepsilon_0 + \frac{3}{4}A^2\varepsilon_0^2 \right) - B\varepsilon_0 \right] D\lambda$$

$$D\varepsilon_{11} = D\varepsilon_{22} = -\frac{1}{2}D\varepsilon_{33}$$

$$D\varepsilon_{23} = \frac{1}{2}D\gamma = \tau \left(1 + \frac{1}{2}A\varepsilon_0 - \frac{1}{2}A^2\varepsilon_0^2 \right) D\lambda$$

(6.7)

If the tensile stress was $\sigma_{33} = \sigma = \sigma_0$ when the tube was first elongated by ε_0, then (6.6) must be satisfied also by the stress state $\sigma = \sigma_0$ and $\tau = 0$, and therefore we have the relation

$$f = \frac{1}{3}\sigma^2 \left(1 + A\varepsilon_0 + \frac{3}{4}A^2\varepsilon_0^2 \right) + \tau^2 \bigg) 1 + \frac{1}{2}A\varepsilon_0 - \frac{1}{2}A^2\varepsilon_0^2 \bigg) - B\varepsilon_0\sigma$$

$$= \frac{1}{3}\sigma_0^2 \left(1 + A\varepsilon_0 + \frac{3}{4}A^2\varepsilon_0^2 \right) - B\varepsilon_0\sigma_0 = \frac{1}{3}\sigma_{iso}^2 = F(W_{\varepsilon_0})$$

(6.8)

taking account of (5.1), where W_{ε_0} indicates the plastic work done up to the state ε_0, and σ_{iso} the ficticious tensile stress for the strain ε_0 when the tube is assumed to perform isotropic work-hardening.

On the other hand, the yield function and the stress-strain relations for the pre-twisted tube are given, from what was mentioned above, by (6.3) and (6.5) themselves, replacing ε_0 by the strain ε_i corresponding to the initial anisotropy. Hence, indicating the stress at the strain $\varepsilon_{23} = \frac{1}{2}\gamma_0$ by τ_0, the yield criterion for the pre-twisted case is written

$$f = \frac{1}{3}\sigma^2 \left(1 + A\varepsilon_i + \frac{3}{4}A^2\varepsilon_i^2 - \frac{1}{6}A^2\gamma_0^2 \right) + \tau^2 \left(1 + \frac{1}{2}A\varepsilon_i - \frac{1}{2}A^2\varepsilon_i^2 + \right.$$

$$\left. + \frac{1}{4}A^2\gamma_0^2 \right) + \frac{1}{3}\sigma\tau \left(\frac{1}{2}A\gamma_0 + \frac{5}{2}A^2\varepsilon_i\gamma_0 \right) - B \left(\varepsilon_i\sigma + \frac{1}{2}\gamma_0\tau \right)$$

$$= \tau_0^2 \left(1 + \frac{1}{2}A\varepsilon_i - \frac{1}{2}A^2\varepsilon_i^2 + \frac{1}{4}A^2\gamma_0^2 \right) - \frac{1}{2}B\gamma_0\tau_0$$

$$= \tau_{iso}^2 = F(W_{\gamma_0})$$

(6.9)

where $\varepsilon_i \ll \gamma_0$. If the tube is completely isotropic initially, in particular, then we can put $\varepsilon_i = 0$ in (6.9) and (6.5), and have

$$f = \frac{1}{3}\sigma^2 \left(1 - \frac{1}{6}A^2\gamma_0^2 \right) + \tau^2 \left(1 + \frac{1}{4}A^2\gamma_0^2 \right) + \frac{1}{3}\sigma\tau \frac{1}{2}A\gamma_0 - B\frac{1}{2}\gamma_0\tau$$

$$= \tau_0^2 \left(1 + \frac{1}{4}A^2\gamma_0^2 \right) - \frac{1}{2}B\gamma_0\tau_0 = \tau_{iso}^2 = F(W_{\gamma_0}) \tag{6.10}$$

The above results were all deduced for the general case when (4.5) holds as yield function. For the case when yield function is given by (4.10) all the terms linear with respect to A are dropped in the results in this section, and only the terms with A^2 being reserved.

Experiments were first made on mild steel tubes with 0.11 %C. First, a strain history of axial elongation $\varepsilon_0 = 0.078$, where $\sigma_0 = 35.57$ kg/mm², is given to the specimen. After unloading the tensile stress, the specimen is then subjected to the combined stress of axial tension and torsion along the loading path shown in Figure 2. The effective stress $\bar{\sigma}$—effective strain $\bar{\varepsilon}$ curves for some of the paths are indicated in Figure 3, and the yield points for each loading path are determined by the method, as shown in the figure, of drawing the tangents to each curve parallel to that to the standard curve for simple extension. The yield points thus obtained for the combined stress state of tension-torsion after the strain history of axial elongation are plotted in Figure 4, in ratio to the stress σ_0.

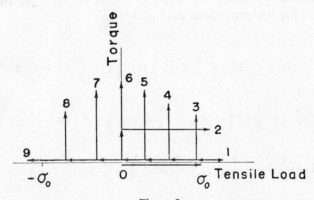

Figure 2

Loading paths after the strain history of axial elongation.

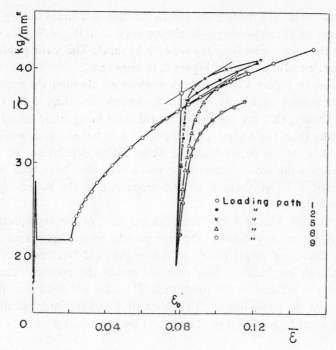

Figure 3
Effective stress—effective strain curves for each loading paths in the case
of the strain history of axial elongation.

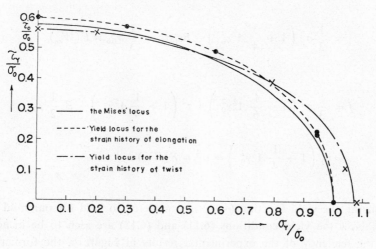

Figure 4
Yield loci for the respective strain histories of axial elongation and twist
in mild steel tubes.

The same procedure is followed also in the case of a strain history of twist. The amount of the pre-twist γ_0 is chosen such that $W_{\gamma_0} = W_{\varepsilon_0}$ ($\varepsilon_0 = 0.078$), for which the shear stress is $\sqrt{3}\tau_0 = 34.70$ kg/mm². The yield point stresses for this case are also plotted in Figure 4, in ratio to σ_0.

We can see in Figure 4 that the curves which go through the experimental yield point stresses have quite opposite tendencies according to the two cases of strain history, that for the pre-elongated state being more round, though only a little, than the Mises' yield locus $\sigma^2 + 3\tau^2 = $ constant, whereas that for the pre-twisted is flatter than the Mises'. This dependence of the yield limit curves on the strain histories, to which the tubes have been subjected, is considered to be attributable to anisotropy and to the Bauschinger effect, due to the histories.

It is seen from Figure 4 that the principal axes of the experimental yield limit curve for the pre-twisted tubes are parallel to the stress axes (σ—and τ—axes). Therefore we are forced to choose the yield condition (6.9) lacking the terms with $\sigma\tau$, because their presence makes the principal axes of the yield condition inclined to the stress axes. Thus, for our mild steel tubes, we are led to put the terms linear with respect to A and the initial strain ε, after annealing equal to zero, and (6.8) and (6.9) are replaced by

$$f = \frac{1}{3}\sigma^2\left(1 + \frac{3}{4}A^2\varepsilon_0^2\right) + \tau^2\left(1 - \frac{1}{2}A^2\varepsilon_0^2\right) - B\varepsilon_0\sigma$$

$$= \frac{1}{3}\sigma_0^2\left(1 + \frac{3}{4}A^2\varepsilon_0^2\right) - B\varepsilon_0\sigma_0 = \frac{1}{3}\sigma_{iso}^2 = F(W_{\varepsilon_0}) \qquad (6.11)$$

and

$$f = \frac{1}{3}\sigma^2\left(1 - \frac{1}{6}A^2\gamma_0^2\right) + \tau^2\left(1 + \frac{1}{4}A^2\gamma_0^2\right) - B\frac{1}{2}\gamma_0\tau$$

$$= \tau_0^2\left(1 + \frac{1}{4}A^2\gamma_0^2\right) = \tau_{iso}^2 = F(W_{\gamma_0}) \qquad (6.12)$$

In general, the yield function (4.10) is considered to hold for our mild steel tubes. Now the yield conditions (6.11) and (6.12) are seen to be in accord with the tendency of the experimental results in Figure 4, the former representing a locus more round than the Mises' and the latter one flatter than the Mises', no matter what the value of A may be, positive or negative. In order to approximate to the experimental results, as shown by the curves in Figure 4, A and B are determined as

$$A^2 = 21.69, \quad B = 16.37$$

for the strain history of the axial elongation of the amount $\varepsilon_0 = 0.078$, and

$$A^2 = 36.16, \quad B = 17.27$$

for that of the twist, so that $W_{\gamma_0} = W_{\varepsilon_0}$, where $\varepsilon_0 = 0.078$. These results show that the anisotropy and the Bauschinger effect are nearly equal for the two cases of strain history, though somewhat larger for that of the twist.

The ficticious stresses σ_{iso} and $\sqrt{3}\,\tau_{iso}$ for isotropic work-hardening are obtained as

$$\sigma_{iso} = 35.4 \text{ kg/mm}^2, \quad \sqrt{3}\,\tau_{iso} = 35.5 \text{ kg/mm}^2$$

This is in accord with our assumption that the tubes obey the Mises' criterion if they should remain isotropic when work-hardened.

As for brass tubes in contrast with mild steel ones, the circumstances are somewhat different, and the principal axes of the experimental yield limit curve for pre-twisted tubes is tilted a little to the stresses axes (Figure 5). But the inclination is too small to be interpreted by (6.10) for the case with no initial elongation, in which the inclination coefficient $A\gamma_0$ is determined uniquely from $A^2\gamma_0^2$ specified by the magnitudes of the axes of the ellipse representing the yield locus.

It seems that there exist two possibilities for the explanation of the experimental results on brass tubes. One is the complex of the two mechanisms of development of anisotropy, i.e. those with and without the terms of A, (6.8), (6.10) and (6.11), (6.12). Indicating by A_1 the coefficient in the former mechanism, (6.8) and (6.10), and by A_2 that in the latter, (6.11) and (6.12), we obtain the result

$$A_1 = 0.712, \quad A_2 = \pm 4.21, \quad B = 8.57$$

for the strain history of twist $\gamma_0/\sqrt{3} = 0.10$, and then, under the assumption $\sigma_{iso} = \sqrt{3}\,\tau_{iso}$, the result

$$A_1 = -0.372, \quad A_2 = \pm 3.91, \quad B = 10.37$$

for the strain history of elongation of the same order $(\varepsilon_0 \doteqdot 0.10)$. The dissimilarity of the values of A_1 for the two histories is considered to suggest some inconsistency of this idea.

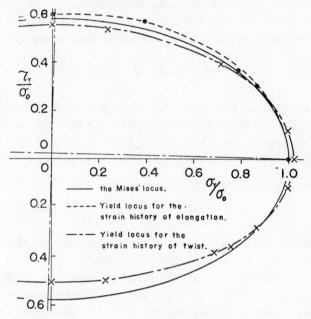

Figure 5

Yield loci for the respective strain histories of axial elongation and twist in brass tubes.

The other possibility, which seems more natural, is that the inclination of the principal axes of the experimental yield locus is due to the term $\frac{5}{6}\sigma\tau A^2\varepsilon_i\gamma_0$ in (6.9), arising from the initial strain history of elongation ε_i, but not to the term $\frac{1}{6}\sigma\tau A\gamma_0$. In this case, the yield condition (6.9) for the pre-twisted case is reduced to

$$
f = \frac{1}{3}\sigma^2\left(1 + \frac{3}{4}A^2\varepsilon_i^2 - \frac{1}{6}A^2\gamma_0^2\right) + \tau^2\left(1 - \frac{1}{2}A^2\varepsilon_i^2 + \frac{1}{4}A^2\gamma_0^2\right) +
$$

$$
+ \frac{5}{6}\sigma\tau A^2\varepsilon_i\gamma_0 - B\left(\varepsilon_i\sigma + \frac{1}{2}\gamma_0\tau\right)
$$

$$
= \tau_0^2\left(1 - \frac{1}{2}A^2\varepsilon_i^2 + \frac{1}{4}A^2\gamma_0^2\right) - \frac{1}{2}B\gamma_0\tau_0
$$

$$
= \tau_{iso}^2 = F(W_{\gamma 0}) \tag{6.13}
$$

The yield condition for the pre-elongated case is given by (6.11). By endowing A, B and ε_i with adequate values, an unifying interpretation will be given to the yield loci for the respective strain histories of axial elongation and twist.

So far as our experiments are concerned, it would seem probable that the yield function (4.10) holds in general without the linear terms of A in (4.5). But one cannot hastily draw the conclusion, without carrying out many more experiments with other materials, that the strain history effects governed by (4.5) do not ever occur.

7. Length changes in twisted tubes.

It has been ascertained by some authors [9] that a cylindrical specimen shows a small permanent increase of length when twisted plastically. This phenomenon has been treated by R. Hill as based on his theory of anisotropy [10]. For the explanation of this phenomenon our theory is seen to be suitable, insofar as it correlates anisotropy to strain history as its cause.

Under the assumption that there remains in a tube, even after annealing, a certain initial strain of axial elongation ε_i, we obtain from (6.5), being $\sigma = 0$

$$
\left.
\begin{aligned}
D\varepsilon_{11} &= -\left[\tau\left(\frac{2}{3}A\gamma + \frac{1}{6}A^2\varepsilon_i\gamma\right) - \frac{1}{2}B\varepsilon_i\right]D\lambda \\[2mm]
D\varepsilon_{22} &= -\left[\tau\left(-\frac{1}{3}A\gamma + \frac{2}{3}A^2\varepsilon_i\gamma\right) - \frac{1}{2}B\varepsilon_i\right]D\lambda \\[2mm]
D\varepsilon_{33} &= \left[2\tau\left(\frac{1}{6}A\gamma + \frac{5}{12}A^2\varepsilon_i\gamma\right) - B\varepsilon_i\right]D\lambda \\[2mm]
D\varepsilon_{23} &= \left[\tau\left(1 + \frac{1}{2}A\varepsilon_i - \frac{1}{2}A^2\varepsilon_i^2 + \frac{1}{4}A^2\gamma^2\right) - \frac{1}{2}B\gamma\right]D\lambda \\[2mm]
D\varepsilon_{31} &= \quad D\varepsilon_{12} = 0
\end{aligned}
\right\} \quad (7.1)
$$

It is clear from the third equation (7.1) that a certain axial elongation $D\varepsilon_{33}$ occurs owing to the pure shear stress τ and the twisting strain $\varepsilon_{23} = \frac{1}{2}\gamma$ arising from τ. Here also we confront the problem of to which as the terms $\frac{1}{6}A\gamma$ or $\frac{5}{12}A^2\varepsilon_i\gamma$, or both of them, the elongation is attributable. Although this point is not certain without further experiments for various amounts of initial strain ε_i, it is preferable to consider the term $\frac{5}{12}A^2\varepsilon_i\gamma$ as being responsible for the axial elongation, in view of the results for yield condition. From this point of view, the exceptional materials, such as lead, which shortens when twisted, are considered to have a certain initial compressive strain $(\varepsilon_i < 0)$.

8. Direction dependence of yield stress of a plate extended in one direction.

Let the rectangular Cartesian axes x^1, x^2, x^3 be taken as in Figure 6, and the plate be extended by $\varepsilon_{33} = \varepsilon_0$ in the x^3 direction, where $\sigma_{33} = \sigma_0$. The strain history in this case is

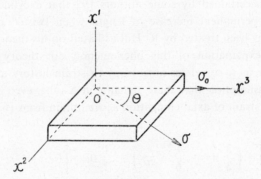

Figure 6
Coordinate axes in a pre-extended plate.

$$\left.\begin{array}{l} \varepsilon_{33} = \varepsilon_0, \quad \varepsilon_{11} = \varepsilon_{22} = -\dfrac{1}{2}\varepsilon_0 \\[2mm] \text{the other} \quad \varepsilon_{\lambda\mu} = 0 \end{array}\right\} \tag{8.1}$$

If we denote by σ the tensile stress in a direction tilted by θ from the initial direction x^3 in which the tensile yield stress is σ_0, then

$$\left.\begin{array}{l} \sigma_{33} = \dfrac{1}{2}\sigma(1 + \cos 2\theta) \\[4mm] \sigma_{22} = \dfrac{1}{2}\sigma(1 - \cos 2\theta) \\[4mm] \sigma_{23} = \dfrac{1}{2}\sigma \sin 2\theta \\[4mm] \text{the other} \ \sigma_{\lambda\mu} = 0 \end{array}\right\} \tag{8.2}$$

Substituting (8.1) and (8.2) into the yield function (4.10) without the linear terms of A, and considering that it also holds for $\sigma = \sigma_0$, $\theta = 0$, we obtain the yield condition

$$f = \frac{1}{3}\sigma^2 \left[1 + \frac{3}{8} A^2 \varepsilon_0^2 \left(-\frac{3}{4} + \frac{1}{2} \cos 2\theta + \frac{9}{4} \cos^2 2\theta \right) \right] -$$

$$- \frac{1}{4} B \varepsilon_0 \sigma (1 + 3 \cos 2\theta)$$

$$= \frac{1}{3} \sigma_0^2 \left(1 + \frac{3}{4} A^2 \varepsilon_0^2 \right) - B \varepsilon_0 \sigma_0 \tag{8.3}$$

If we take the values of ε_0 and σ_0 and the corresponding values of A and B in (8.3) equal to those for our mild steel tubes in the previous section, that is, as

$$\varepsilon_0 = 0.078, \qquad \sigma_0 = 35.57 \text{ kg/mm}^2$$

$$A = 21.69, \qquad B = 16.37$$

then the tensile yield stress σ in ratio to σ_0 as against the direction θ is calculated from (8.3) as shown in Figure 7. The curve is shown between the range from 0° to 90°, and that between 90° and 180° is of symmetrical form.

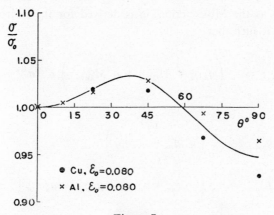

Figure 7
Direction dependence of the tensile yield stress
in a plate pre-extended in one direction.

It is found that the yield stress σ_0 in the initial direction is a minimum, but not the smallest value, it being in the direction $\theta = 90°$, and that the maximum (the largest) is in the direction somewhat smaller than $\theta = 45°$. This tendency is seen for other values of A and B, only the extremum values being different.

We have no experiments of this kind for mild steel plates, but we have those for brass and alminium plates [11], in which ε_0 is 0.08. The experimental results plotted in Figure 7 are seen to be in good agreement, considering that the materials are different from mild steel. This is probably because the anisotropy and the Bauschinger effects which grow in brass and aluminium are of the same order of magnitude as those in mild steel.

9. Conclusion.

For the purpose of explaining the strain history effects, such as anisotropy and the Bauschinger effect accompanying work-hardening, which cannot be interpreted by the Mises' theory valid for isotropic work-hardening, a theory was proposed, in which anisotropy and the Bauschinger effect as well as work-hardening are correlated with the previous strain history represented by a history-dependent strain tensor $\varepsilon_{\lambda\mu}$.

There exist two possibilities as to the way of the correlation, considering that the isotropic state is represented by a fundamental metric tensor $g_{\lambda\mu}$, which is the unit tensor of spherical symmetry and that any deviation of the anisotropic state, resulting from the strain history $\varepsilon_{\lambda\mu}$, from the initial isotropic state, is represented by $A\varepsilon_{\lambda\mu}$, A being a scalar function of $\varepsilon_{\lambda\mu}$. One is such that the yield function for the anisotropic state resulting from the strain history $\varepsilon_{\lambda\mu}$ is derived from $g_{\lambda\mu} + A\varepsilon_{\lambda\mu}$ and the stress deviator $\sigma'^{\lambda\mu}$ in the same way as the Mises' criterion is derived for the isotropic state from $g_{\lambda\mu}$ and $\sigma'^{\lambda\mu}$, i.e. such that

$$f(\sigma^{\lambda\mu}, \varepsilon_{\lambda\mu}) = \frac{1}{2}\left(g'_{\lambda\mu\nu\kappa} + AL'_{\lambda\mu\nu\kappa} + A^2 M'_{\lambda\mu\nu\kappa} \right) \sigma'^{\lambda\mu}\sigma'^{\nu\kappa} - B\varepsilon_{\lambda\mu}\sigma'^{\lambda\mu}$$

where

$$g'_{\lambda\mu\nu\kappa} = \frac{1}{2}\left(g_{\lambda\nu}g_{\mu\kappa} + g_{\lambda\kappa}g_{\mu\nu} \right)$$

$$L'_{\lambda\mu\nu\kappa} = \frac{1}{2}\left(g_{\lambda\nu}\varepsilon_{\mu\kappa} + g_{\mu\kappa}\varepsilon_{\lambda\nu} + g_{\lambda\kappa}\varepsilon_{\mu\nu} + g_{\mu\nu}\varepsilon_{\lambda\kappa} \right)$$

$$M'_{\lambda\mu\nu\kappa} = \frac{1}{2}\left(\varepsilon_{\lambda\nu}\varepsilon_{\mu\kappa} + \varepsilon_{\lambda\kappa}\varepsilon_{\mu\nu} \right)$$

The other, which is also a special case of the former, is such that the part of the yield function corresponding to the anisotropy resulting from $\varepsilon_{\lambda\mu}$ is derived from $A\varepsilon_{\lambda\mu}$ and $\sigma'^{\lambda\mu}$ in the same way as its isotropic part, i.e. the Mises' criterion, is derived from $g_{\lambda\mu}$ and $\sigma'^{\lambda\mu}$, namely such that

$$f(\sigma^{\lambda\mu}, \varepsilon_{\lambda\mu}) = \frac{1}{2}\left(g'_{\lambda\mu\nu\kappa} + A^2 M'_{\lambda\mu\nu\kappa}\right)\sigma'^{\lambda\mu}\sigma'^{\nu\kappa} - B\varepsilon_{\lambda\mu}\sigma'^{\lambda\mu}$$

where $g'_{\lambda\mu\nu\kappa}$ and $M'_{\lambda\mu\nu\kappa}$ are the same as the above. The stress-strain relations are deduced from the respective yield functions according to the relation

$$(D\varepsilon)_{\lambda\mu} = \frac{\partial f}{\partial \sigma^{\lambda\mu}} D\lambda$$

By comparing this theory with experiments on the yielding of mild steel and brass tubes under the combined stress state of tension and torsion, after having been subjected to respective strain histories of axial elongation and twist, and also with those on length changes of tubes due to twisting, and further on the direction dependence of the tensile yield stress of a plate pre-extended in a certain direction, it was concluded that the theory, based on the latter form of yield function holds true. But this conclusion is not necessarily final, because it might be that the former function holds for some other kinds of materials and other strain histories.

REFERENCES

[1] Y. YOSHIMURA, Theory of Plasticity for Small and Finite Deformations based on Legitimate Concept of Strain, *Aeron. Res. Inst.*, Univ. of Tokyo, Report No. 348 (September ,1959).

[2] R. Hill, *Mathematical Theory of Plasticity*, Oxford, (1951), p.25.

[3] P. LUDWIK, Elemente der technologischen Mechanik, Springer, Berlin (1909).

[4] G. I. TAYLOR AND H. QUINNEY, The Plastic Distorsion of Metals, *Phil. Trans. Roy. Soc. London*, **A230,** (1931), 323-362.

[5] W. LODE, Versche über Einfluss der mittleren Hauptspannung auf die Fliessgrenze, *Z.A.M.M.*, **5,** (1925), 142.

[6] J. F. W. BISHOP AND R. HILL, A Theoretical Derivation of the Plastic Properties of a Polycrystalline Face-centered Metal, *Phil. Mag.* (7), 42 (1951), 1298-1307.

[7] von Mises; Mechanik der festen Körper im plastisch-deformablen Zustand, *Gettinger Nachrichten* (1913), p. 582.

[8] Y. YOSHIMURA, Hypothetical Theory of Anisotropy and the Bauschinger Effect due to Plastic Strain History, *Aeron. Res. Inst.*, Univ. of Tokyo, Report No. 349,(1959).

[9] H. W. SWIFT, Length Changes in Metals under Torsional Overstrain, *Engineering*, **158,** (1947), 253-257.

[10] R. HILL, *Mathematical Theory of Plasticly*, Oxford, (1951), p. 325.

[11] K. SAITO, Anisotropy Produced by Plastic Deformation, Part 1, *Trans. J.S.M.E.*, **20,** 1954), 771.

RELAXATION OF STRESSES IN FLANGED JOINTS
OF HIGH-PRESSURE STEAM PIPING

J. Dvořák

The National Research Institute of Heat Engineering, Prague, Czechoslovakia

The use of high-temperature steam compels us to respect the phenomenon of creep of material, which affects the correct function of equipment subjected to such temperatures. The shape and grouping of curves obtained in creep tests form the basis for a mathematical formulation of relations between the relative elongation, stress and time. The formulation is empirical and represents a certain starting point for the investigation of creep phenomena and relaxation of material of component parts stressed in a complex manner. The study of diffusion and dislocations brings ever new results in this field and thus helps to elucidate the problem of the dependnce of creep properties of the material upon its chemical composition, temperature and the magnitude of applied stress.

The calculation of the relaxation of stresses in a flanged joint is based on the so-called theory of ageing which uses the following integral expression for formulating the relation between the stress and deformation

$$\varepsilon = \frac{\sigma}{E} + \sigma \int_0^t \sigma^{n-1}(t) \cdot B(t)\, dt \tag{1}$$

where n is a constant depending upon the temperature at which the test was performed, and upon the composition of steel. It ranges between 1.2 and 10 and is read from the diagram of creep curves. $B(t) = \dfrac{d\Omega(t)}{dt} =$ rate of change of the time function, $t =$ time.

Tightening a symmetrical flange joint is represented in the schematic diagram as a motion of point I lying in the centre of the bolt stem by Δy in the downward direction. By prestressing, the bolts having an initial length of $2\bar{l}$ are elongated by $2\Delta l(0)$ to $2l(0)$; it is evident that

$$\Delta l(0) + \bar{l} = l(0)$$

751

Argument zero indicates that the values pertain to a condition immediately following the tightening. Simultaneously, the flange ring is tilted by angle $\psi(0)$. Then

$$\Delta l(0) + e\psi(0) = \Delta y$$

where e is the distance of the ring collar from the bolt centreline. After time t the initial quantities change to $\Delta l(t)$, $l(t)$ and $\psi(t)$, but the condition of compatibility

$$\Delta l(t)\, e\psi\,(t) = \Delta y = \text{const}$$

is still applicable.

The section of the flange ring stressed by tilting moment rotates by angle

$$\psi(0) = \frac{P(0) \cdot e}{2E_f \cdot J_f}$$

and the bolts are elongated by

$$\Delta l(0) = \frac{P(0)}{mE_b \cdot F_b}\, l,$$

E_f, (E_b) denote the modulus of elasticvity of the flange and bolt materials, respectively, at an operating temperature

$$I_f = \int_{F_f}^{1} \frac{z^2}{r+y}\, dF_f$$

F_f, (F_b) are the areas of transverse cross-sections of the flange and bolt, respectively, m is the number of bolts and $P(0) =$ the total force in all bolts.

The relative elongation of the circumferential filaments of the ring is

$$\varepsilon_f(0) = \frac{z}{r+y}\psi(0)$$

and the circumferential stress

$$\sigma_f(0) = E_f \frac{z}{r+y}\psi(0)$$

From the condition of equilibrium of an element of the ring with a centre angle $d\varphi$ follows that

$$d\varphi \, \frac{P}{2\pi} e = d\varphi \int_{F_f} \sigma_f \cdot z dF_f$$

By differentiating and rearranging the accepted formulation (1) of the law of creep we obtain Bernouilli's differential equation

$$\frac{d\sigma}{dt} - \frac{d\varepsilon}{dt} \frac{\sigma}{\varepsilon} + \frac{B(t)}{\varepsilon} \sigma^{n+1} = 0$$

and by its solution an explicit expression of the stress

$$\sigma = \left\{ -\frac{n}{\varepsilon^n} \left[C - \int_0^t B(t)\varepsilon^{n-1} \right] dt \right\}^{-1/n}$$

The foregoing indicates that for $t = 0$

$$\sigma(0) = -\frac{n}{\varepsilon^n(0)} \cdot C$$

and since $\dfrac{\sigma(0)}{\varepsilon(0)} = E$, $\qquad C = -\dfrac{1}{nE^n}$.

Thus for the bolt

$$\sigma_b(t) = \varepsilon_b(t) \left[\frac{1}{E_b^{n_b}} + n_b \int_0^t B_b(t)\varepsilon_b^{n_b-1}(t)dt \right]^{-1/n_b}$$

and for the flange

$$\sigma_f(t) = \varepsilon_f(t) \left[\frac{1}{E_f^{n_f}} + n_f \int_0^t B_f(t)\varepsilon_f(t)^{n_f-1}dt \right]^{-1/n_f}$$

Introducing a new variable $\beta(t) = \dfrac{\psi(t)}{\psi(0)}$, we can write the condition of compatibility

$$\varepsilon_b(t) = \frac{\Delta y}{l} \left[1 - \frac{e\psi(0)}{\Delta y} \beta(t) \right]$$

and the relative elongation of the ring filaments

$$\varepsilon_f(t) = \frac{z}{r+y} \psi(0)\beta(t)$$

Inserting into the condition of force equilibrium

$$F_b \cdot m \cdot \sigma_b(t) \cdot e = 2\pi \int_{F_f} \sigma_f(t) \cdot z \cdot dF_f$$

the above four expressions for the relative elongation and stress, we obtain the equation for the sought-for function β as follows:

$$\frac{\Delta y - e\psi(0) \cdot \beta}{\beta\psi(0)} = \frac{2\pi l E_f}{m F_b e E_b} \left\{ 1 + \frac{n_b E_b^{n_b}}{l^{-n_b-1}} \int_0^t B_b(t) \left[\Delta y - e\beta\psi(0) \right]^{n_b-1} dt \right\}^{1/n_b} \cdot$$

$$\cdot \int_{F_f} \frac{z^2}{r+y} \left[1 + n_f E_f^{n\cdot} \left(\frac{z}{r+y} \right)^{n_f-1} \psi(0)^{n_f-1} \cdot \int_0^t B_f(t)\beta^{n_f-1} dt \right]^{-(1[n_f])} dF_f$$

Its analytical solution is not possible mainly because the nucleus of the equation, function $(B(t)$, is obtained experimentally. For this reason the calculation is carried out by iterations. Assuming that for a brief interval of time, β is constant we can write the previous equation as follows:

$$\frac{\Delta y - e\beta_{i+1}\psi(0)}{\beta_{i+1}\psi(0)} = \frac{2\pi l}{m F_b \cdot e} \frac{E_f}{E_b} C(t_i)$$

and after expressing

$$\beta_{i+1} = \frac{\Delta y}{e\psi(0) + \frac{2\pi l}{m F_b \cdot e} \psi(0) C(t_i) \frac{E_f}{E_b}}$$

where

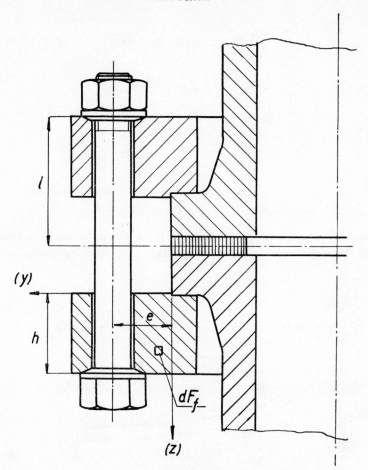

Figure 1

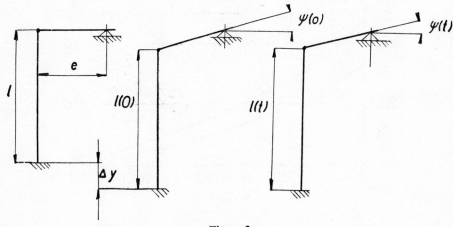

Figure 2

$$C(t_i) \left\{ 1 + \frac{n_b E_b^{n_b}}{l^{n_b-1}} \sum_{k=0}^{i} [\Delta y - e\beta_k \psi(0)]^{n_b-1} \cdot [\Omega_b(t_{k+1}) - \Omega_f(t_k)] \right\}^{1/n_b} \cdot$$

$$\cdot \int_{F_f} \frac{z^2}{r+y} \left[1 + \left(\frac{z}{r+y} \right)^{n_f-1} A(t_i) \right]^{-1/n_f} dF_f \quad ,$$

$$A(t_i) = n_f E_f^{n_f} \psi(0)^{n_f-1} \sum_{k=0}^{i} \beta_k^{n_f-1} [\Omega_f(t_{k+1}) - \Omega_f(t_k)]$$

Immediately after tightening, $A(0) = 0$ and $C(0) = I_f$.

Numerical calculation was performred for a flange having dimensions in accordance with the Czechoslovak standard and working under nominal

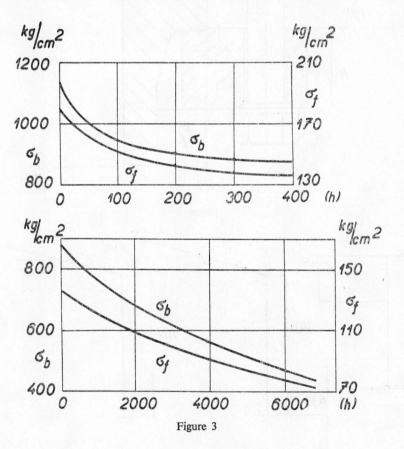

Figure 3

pressure of 96 ata and 510°C. The composition of the steel used for the bolts and the flange was 0.28% C, 0.58% Mn, 0.24% Si, 1.55% Cr, 0.38% Mo, 0.16% Va and 0.12% Ni.

The time function is given in Table I.

TABLE I

$t(h)$	$10^9.\Omega(t)$	$t(h)$	$10^9.\Omega(t)$	$t(h)$	$10^9.\Omega(t)$	$t(h)$	$10^9.\Omega(t)$
0	0.000	100	0.374	400	0.582	2000	1.366
20	0.180	150	0.440	600	0.680	3000	1.856
40	0.250	200	0.480	800	0.778	5000	2.836
60	0.304	250	0.510	1000	0.876	7000	3.816
80	0.340	300	0.536	1500	1.121	9000	4.796

The value of coefficient $n_b = n_f = 1.83$, the modulus of elasticity at 500°C was 1.8×10^6 kg/cm².

Table II summarizes the results of a numerical calculation of the above example; the diagram of Figure 3 indicates the time dependence of the maximum stress in the flange and bolts.

TABLE II

$t(h)$	$A(t)$	$\dfrac{C(t)}{R^2}$	$\beta_b(t)$	$\sigma(t)$
0	0.0000	0.1823	1.000	1138
20	0.0826	0.1983	0.927	1034
40	0.1124	0.2040	0.902	1000
60	0.1349	0.2090	0.884	976
80	0.1496	0.2110	0.873	963
100	0.1634	0.2140	0.863	947
150	0.1905	0.2190	0.844	924
200	0.2070	0.2210	0.835	909
250	0.2190	0.2230	0.829	899
300	0.2290	0.2250	0.822	890
400	0.2470	0.2280	0.813	885
600	0.2850	0.2340	0.792	854
800	0.3210	0.2400	0.775	826
1000	0.3580	0.2460	0.758	800
1500	0.4490	0.2580	0.724	745
2000	0.5340	0.2680	0.698	701
3000	0.7000	0.2850	0.659	630
5000	0.9860	0.3090	0.612	534
7000	1.2840	0.3170	0.595	438

For a given minimum permissible force in the bolts, the time of operation between two successive tightenings of the flange can be read from these diagrams.

RHEOLOGICAL EQUATIONS OF GENERALIZED MAXWELL MODEL AND VOIGT MODEL IN THREE-DIMENSIONAL, NON-LINEAR DEFORMATION

Wataru Segawa

College of Humanities and Sciences, Nihon, University Tokyo, Japan

ABSTRACT

Rheological equations of generalized Maxwell model and Voigt model which are valid for three-dimensional, non-linear deformation have been obtained. It has been also shown that, the conditions of small deformation being introduced, each of the two sets are reduced to three-dimensional extensions of the corresponding classical equations.

1. Introduction.

Recently, phenomenological theories [1], [2], [3] of three-dimensional, non-linear elastico-viscosity and visco-elasticity based on Maxwell model and Voigt model have been developed in Japan. In these treatments, one-dimensional, classical equations have been extended so as to be applicable to three-dimensional, non-linear deformations. Especially in the previous paper [3] we have derived Maxwell's formula for general deformation utilizing strain-stress relation and strain rate-stress relation which was derived by Reiner [4].

As is well known, in the classical theory of visco-elasticity we considered the generalized Maxwell model and Voigt model having the distribution of relaxation times and retardation times, respectively, and the former is the parallel combination of Maxwell element and the latter is the series combination of Voigt elements.

In this paper, under the similar considerations of the previous paper [3] we will derive the rheological equations of the generalized models for the general deformation and, moreover, we will make clear how the above equations will be reduced to the corresponding classical formulae. In this article, we need not discriminate between contravariant, mixed and covariant components of a tensor, because we will be mainly concerned with tensors defined in a rectangular coordinate system fixed in deformed state.

This article is substantially equivalent to the preceding [5] having the same title, although new symbols will be employed.

2. Generalized Maxwell model.

Let the quantities relating to p-th Maxwell element be denoted by subscript p. In analogy with classical model, the generalized Maxwell model in the three-dimensional case will be specified by the condition

$$s^{ij} = \sum_{p=1}^{n} s_p^{ij} \qquad (2.1)$$

where s^{ij} is the component of stress tensor in a rectangular coordinate system (referred to the deformed state) and S_p^{ij} is the component of stress tensor in p-th Maxwell element.

Let the initial coordinates and the final coordinates due to elastic deformation of a material particle be denoted by a^i and y_p^i respectively, in a rectangular coordinate system fixed in space. Then, considering the assumption that the actual strain rate is a sum of the elastic strain rate and the viscous strain rate, the strain rate-stress relation in the p-th Maxwell element may be represented by

$$f^{ij} = \frac{\partial y_p^i}{\partial a^\lambda} \frac{\partial y_p^j}{\partial a^\mu} \frac{d}{dt} \left\{ \frac{\partial a^\lambda}{\partial y_p^\alpha} \frac{\partial a^\mu}{\partial y_p^\beta} (A_p \delta^{\alpha\beta} + B_p S_p^{\alpha\beta} + C_p S_p^{\alpha\gamma} S_p^{\gamma\beta}) \right\} + \qquad (2.2)\,[3]$$

$$+ D_p \delta^{ij} + E_p S_p^{ij} + F_p S_p^{i\gamma} S_p^{\gamma j}$$

where f^{ij} is the component of the (actual) strain rate tensor and A_p, B_p, C_p D_p, E_p, F_p, are the functions of stress invariants, for instance, defined by

$$\mathrm{I}_{sp} = S_p^{\lambda\lambda}, \quad \mathrm{II}_{sp} = \tfrac{1}{2} S_p S_p^{\mu\lambda}, \quad \mathrm{III}_{sp} = \tfrac{1}{3} S_p^{\lambda\nu} S_p^{\nu\mu} S_p^{\mu\lambda} \qquad (2.3)$$

A component of elastic strain tensor in the p-th Maxwell element will be given by

$$e_p^{ij} = \frac{1}{2} \left(\frac{\partial y_p^i}{\partial a^\lambda} \frac{\partial y_p^j}{\partial a^\lambda} - \delta^{ij} \right) \qquad (2.4)$$

which is the Green measure in a strained state [6,7]. The elastic strain-stress relation in the p-th Maxwell element is written as follows:

$$e_p^{ij} = A_p \delta^{ij} + B_p S_p^{ij} + C_p S_p^{i\gamma} S_p^{\gamma j} \qquad (2.5)$$

which has appeared in Eq. (2.2).

By virtue of Eq. (2.4) and (2.5), we can decide $\partial y_p/\partial a^j$ (and accordingly $\partial a^i/\partial y_p^j$) as functions of S_p^{ij} then Eq. (2.2) becomes the relation between f^{ij} and S_p^{ij}. Thus, Eq. (2.1) and (2.2) express the rheological equation of the generalized Maxwell model for the material which is isotropic in its natural state.

When deformation is sufficiently small, we can use the relation

$$\frac{\partial y_p^i}{\partial a^\lambda} \frac{\partial y_p^j}{\partial a^\mu} = \delta_\lambda^i \delta_\mu^j \ , \quad \frac{\partial a^\lambda}{\partial y_p^\alpha} \frac{\partial a^\mu}{\partial y_p^\beta} = \delta_\alpha^\lambda \delta_\beta^\mu, \qquad (2.6)$$

and the strain-stress relation and the strain rate-stress relation will become linear. Substituting these conditions into Eq. (2.2), we have

$$f^{ij} = \frac{d}{dt}(A_p \delta^{ij} + B_p S_p{}^{ij}) + D_p \delta^{ij} + E_p S_p^{ij} \qquad (2.7)$$

where, denoting the shear modulus by μ_p and the coefficient of shear viscosity by η_p

$$A_p = -\frac{1}{6\mu_p} I_{sp}, \quad B_p = \frac{1}{2\mu_p} \qquad D_p = -\frac{1}{\partial\eta_p} I_{sp}, \quad E_p = \frac{1}{2\eta_p} \quad (2.8)$$

if the material is incompressible and isotropic.

Eq. (2.1) and (2.7), together with Eq. (2.8), are the three-dimensional extension of the classical equation of the generalized Maxwell model.

3. Generalized Voigt model.

In analogy with the classical model, we assume that in a Voigt element of a generalized Voigt model, the elastic strain rate (or elastic strain) is equal to the viscous strain rate (or viscous strain), so we need not discriminate between the two, and moreover we assume that

$$f^{ij} = \sum f_p^{ij} \qquad (3.1)$$

where f_p^{ij} represents the component of the strain rate tensor in the p-th Voigt element.

Considering the assumption that actual stress is a sum of elastic stress and viscous stress, the rheological equation for the p-th element of Voigtian material which is isotropic in its natural state will be represented by

$$S^{ij} = L_p\delta^{ij} + M_p e_p^{ij} + N_p e_p^{i\gamma} e_p^{\gamma j} + P_p\delta^{ij} + Q_p f_p^{ij} + R_p f_p^{i\gamma} f_p^{\gamma j},\qquad (3.2)$$

where S^{ij} is a component of stress tensor and L_p, M_p, N_p and P_p, Q_p, R_p are functions of the strain invariants and strain rate invariants, respectively, defined by

$$\left. \begin{array}{lll} \mathrm{I}_{ep} = e_p^{\lambda\lambda}, & \mathrm{II}_{ep} = \tfrac{1}{2}e_p^{\lambda\mu}e_p^{\mu\lambda}, & \mathrm{III}_{ep} = \tfrac{1}{3}e_p^{\lambda\nu}e_p^{\nu\mu}e_p^{\mu\lambda} \\[6pt] \mathrm{I}_{fp} = f_p^{\lambda\lambda}, & \mathrm{II}_{fp} = \tfrac{1}{2}f_p^{\lambda\mu}f_p^{\mu\lambda}, & \mathrm{III}_{fp} = \tfrac{1}{3}f_p^{\lambda\nu}f_p^{\nu\mu}f_p^{\mu\lambda} \end{array} \right\} \qquad (3.3)$$

If the material is incompressible, L_p will be reduced to an undetermined coefficient ϕ, and I_{fp} will become zero.

The strain component in the p-th Voigt element may be defined by

$$e_p^{ij} = \frac{1}{2}\left(\frac{\partial y_p^i}{\partial a^\lambda}\frac{\partial y_p^j}{\partial a^\lambda} - \delta^{ij}\right) \qquad (3.4)$$

where the elastic final position y_p^i is equivalent to the viscous final position. Moreover, strain components and strain rate components are related to each other as follows:

$$e_p^{ij} = \frac{\partial y_p^i}{\partial a^\lambda}\frac{\partial y_p^j}{\partial a^\mu}\int \frac{\partial a^\lambda}{\partial y_p^\alpha}\frac{\partial a^\mu}{\partial y_p^\beta} f_p^{\alpha\beta}\, dt \qquad (3.5)$$

or

$$f_p^{ij} = \frac{\partial y_p^i}{\partial a^\lambda}\frac{\partial y_p^j}{\partial a^\mu}\frac{d}{dt}\left(\frac{\partial a^\lambda}{\partial y_p^\alpha}\frac{\partial a^\mu}{\partial y_p^\beta} e_p^{\alpha\beta}\right) \qquad (3.5)\,[3]$$

which has appeared in Eq. (2.2). Then, we can express e_p^{ij} as a function of f_p^{ij} by virtue of Eq. (3.4) and (3.5), or vice versa. Thus, Eq. (3.1), Eq. (3.2), together with Eq. (3.4) and (3.5), constitute the rheological equation of the generalized Voigt model for the material which is isotropic in natural state.

When the deformation is sufficiently small, Eq. (3.2) will become linear and, using the relation corresponding to Eq. (2.6), Eq. (3.5) and (3.5) will be reduced to

$$e_p^{ij} = \int f_p^{ij}\, dt \quad \text{and} \quad f_p^{ij} = \frac{d}{dt}e_p^{ij} \qquad (3.6)$$

respectively. Thus, Eq. (3.2) will be reduced to

$$S^{ij} = L_p\delta^{ij} + M_p e_p^{ij} + P_p\delta^{ij} + Q_p f_p^{ij} \tag{3.7}$$

where, denoting the shear modulus by μ_p and the coefficient of shear viscosity by η_p

$$M_p = 2\mu_p \quad , \quad Q_p = 2\eta_p \tag{3.8}$$

and L_p and P_p are linear functions of I_{ep} and I_{fp}, respectively. Moreover, if the material is incompressible, Eq. (3.7) will be reduced to

$$s^{ij} = \phi\delta^{ij} + 2\mu_p e_p^{ij} + 2\eta_p f_p^{ij} \tag{3.9}$$

Eq. (3.1) and (3.9) express the three-dimensional extension of the classical rheological equation of the generalized Voigt model.

4. Discussion.

In the preceeding, we have derived two sets of rheological equations for the generalized Maxwell and Voigt model in the case of three-dimensional, non-linear deformation, utilizing the most general relations between stress, strain and strain rate which was initially derived by Reiner and Rivlin.

In this paper, the Green measure of strain in a strained state [6, 7] has been employed. We can easily show that similar rheological equations as in this paper can be derived, based on the Almansi measure in a strained state [6, 7]. Such derivation in the case of a single Maxwell element has been done in a previous paper [3].

In this article, rheological equations have been described in a rectangular coordinate system. Their description in a general coordinate system is not difficult but very involved.

5. List of symbols.

p = subscript denoting p-th Maxwell or p-th Voigt element

$\alpha, \beta, \ldots \lambda, \mu, \ldots$ = dummy indices

δ^{ij} or δ_j^i = Kronecker's delta

a^i = initial coordinate

y_p^i = final coordinate due to elastic deformation in p-th element

e_p^{ij} = strain tensor (due to elastic deformation) in p-th element

f^{ij} = actual strain rate (or flow) tensor

f_p^{ij} = strain rate (or flow) tensor in p-th element

S^{ij} = actual stress tensor

S_p^{ij} = stress tensor in p-th element

μ_p = shear modulus in p-th element

η_p = coefficients of shear viscosity in p-th element

I_a, II_a, III_a = invariants of tensor a.

REFERENCES

[1] M. YAMAMOTO, *J. Phy. Soc. Japan*, **14,** (1959), 313; *Suppl. Prog. Theor. Phys.* **10,** (1959) 19.

[2] W. SEGAWA, *J. Phys. Soc. Japan*, **14,** (1959), 1102.

[3] W. SEGAWA, *J. Phys. Soc. Japan*, **15,** (1960), 339.

[4] M. REINER, *Amer. J. Math.*, **67,** (1945), 350.

[5] W. SEGAWA, *J. Phys. Soc. Japan*, **16,** (1961), 320.

[6] W. SEGAWA, *J. Phys. Soc. Japan*, **15,** (1960), 518.

[7] Z. KARNI AND M. REINER, *Bull. Res. Counc. of Israel*, **8C,** (1960), 89.

MICRO-RHEOLOGICAL CLASSIFICATION AND ANALYSIS OF COMPLEX MULTIPHASE SUSPENSIONS

LEOPOLD DINTENFASS

Department of Medicine, Sydney, Australia

ABSTRACT

Suspensions of pigments and powders in Newtonian and non-Newtonian liquids may be classified on the basis of their rheological curves. The shape of these curves depends on the rheological characteristics of the component phases. Each particular phase, would it be solid or liquid, shows one or more of the typical modes of flow: Newtonian, thixotropic, and dilatant.

These modes of flow are intimately related to the colloidal structures of the respective phases. Flocculation of pigment particles causes the thixotropy of suspensions; the presence of thixotropy in suspensions indicates a presence of flocculated pigment particles. A formation of a dynamic network by polymer molecules results in the dilatant characteristics; dilatancy in polymer solutions indicates a presence of polymer network; dilatancy in a pigment suspension may be due either to the solid or to the liquid phase.

The micro-rheological classification is based on a two-term nomenclature, in which the first term refers to the rheological characteristics of the solid (dispersed, discontinuous) phase, and the second term describes the rheological characteristics of the liquid (continuous) phase. The latter phase may contain two sub-phases.

On the basis of micro-rheological classification it is possible to interpret the rheological curves in the terms of pigments degree of flocculation, sedimentation volumes, the apparent molecular weight of the polymer, the degree of coiling and aggregation of polymers, and so on.

1. Introduction.

A realistic approach to the rheological problems requires a recognition of the fact that such multiphase systems as paints, inks, protoplasm, polymer solutions, lubricants, etc., are colloids and that their flow behaviour is directly related to their respective colloidal structures.

While macro-rheology regards all materials as homogeneous and devoid of structure, micro-rheology takes account of their structure.

Micro-rheology has two main tasks [1]. It either aims of getting a picture of the structure of the investigated material from the observed flow curves, or it aims to explain the rheological behaviour of a complex material from the known rheological behaviour of its components. The first task is called *structural analysis* and the second one *structural theory*.

764

This paper is intended to present a classification of multiphase suspensions on the basis of their flow curves and their colloidal structures; it intends to show a correlation of such colloidal structures with the specific types of flow.

Only three typical modes of flow can be observed: Newtonian, Thixotropic, and Dilatant (Figure 1). In a multiphase system each of the component phases may show a different type of flow: consequently, the flow type of a multiphase system is of a very complex nature and may show simultaneously some or all of these typical modes of flow.

The following discussion will be concerned with colloidal states, terminology, classification and analysis. The flow curves of the tested materials are determined under equilibrium conditions and plotted as log viscosity against the log rate of shear. A large span of rates of shear has to be used; at least it should be between 0.01 and 100 sec^{-1}.

2. Colloidal states.

Fluid multiphase systems may be characterized by terms reflecting the colloidal states of their component phases.

The possible states of the dispersed (solid) phase are: a. total dispersion or de-flocculation, b. flocculation. In deflocculated pigment suspensions the molecules of the surface active agents (polar-nonpolar compounds, resins, etc.) are adsorbed onto the pigment surface forming an envelope (a partial or total monolayer) around the pigment particles and satisfying the forces existing on pigment surfaces. Such totally dispersed (deflocculated) pigment particles retain their individuality. When the adhesion of the pigment particles against each other is larger than against the liquid phase (vehicle), the pigment particles are flocculated, that is, a number of individual pigment particles adhere to each other. There exists an intimate relationship between the adsorption, flocculation and sedimentation phenomena, based on the selective polar adsorption and the heterogeneous nature of pigment surfaces [2]. A selective adsorption may be followed by a selective deflocculation if more than one specific type of pigment is present.

Flocculation may be due either to the primary forces (van der Waals attraction), then we speak about *primary flocculation;* or it may be induced by some multi-polar agents (citric acid, triethanolamine) which are capable of linking two pigment particles together and cause a *secondary flocculation.* It is possible to flocculate pigment particles by precipitating the polymer present in the liquid phase; such precipitated polymer acts as a glue and agglutinates pigment particles. This third type of flocculation, described as *tertiary flocculation*, or more commonly as *agglutination*, is not a completely reversible one.

The possible states of the liquid phase (polymer solution, oils, etc.) are: a. dispersed (peptised), b. aggregated. While simple liquids, such as toluene, ether, glycerol, etc., belong to the first type only, the solutions of resins or polymers may be in either of these states. Polymers as well as soaps may show a continuous transition from dispersed (or solvated) molecules, through small aggregates and micelles, to linear and network structures containing hundreds of individual molecules. When the values of the cohesive energy density and effective polarity [3] of the solvent or solvent mixtures correspond to the same values of the polymer, the polymer molecules will be monodisperse. When, however, these values do not correspond to each other, being either too low or too high, aggregation and coiling of the macromolecules will take place; in this way an attempt is made to orientate the chain portions of widely differing polarities in order to reduce the interfacial tension.

The degree of aggregation and coiling of the macromolecules will be influenced by their molecular weight distribution; as the adsorption of a lower molecular weight fraction onto the pigment particles is quite common, an addition of pigment to polymer solution is usually followed by a decrease in the solubility, and an increase of the aggregation, of the macromolecules remaining in the bulk of the liquid phase. The polymeric aggregates are capable of forming dynamic three-dimensional networks. In some cases the precipitated fraction may have a form of highly coiled and compact solid-like aggregates.

3. Terminology of the typical modes of flow.

A characteristic rheological flow type corresponds to the each of the above described colloidal states.

The term *Newtonian* describes a system in which viscosity is independent of time and rate of shear. The "Newtonian" pigment suspension is composed of totally dispersed (deflocculated) pigment particles; any attractive forces between these particles being effectively eliminated by protective and stabilizing layers. The contribution of the pigment (solid phase) to the viscosity of suspension is due only to its presence as such ("crowding effect"). The "Newtonian" liquid is either of a simple liquid type, such as toluene, ethanol, etc., or it is a solution of a polymer (resin) in the solvent of the optimum solubilizing and peptising powers.

The term *dilatant* describes a system in which viscosity increases with the rate of shear. With regard to pigment suspensions (solid phase) it means one containing dispersed pigment particles with a minimum amount of liquid; the action of stress changes in pigment configuration and packing, increases the effective pigment volume, and induces a formation of the surface and voids. With regard to the liquid phase, dilatancy means an aggregated poly-

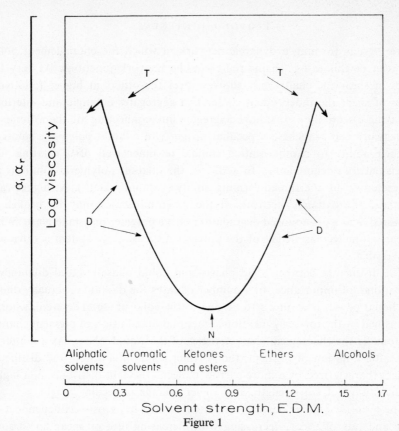

Figure 1

The viscosity and rheology of a polymer solution as a function of the solvent strength. T, D and N indicate the three regions of flow: thixotropic, dilatant and Newtonian. For legend see text

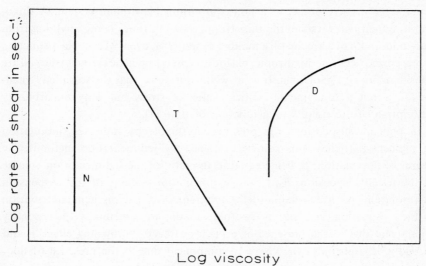

Figure 2

The three typical modes of flow. N–Newtonian, T–thixotropic, D–dilatant

meric system forming a dynamic network in which the entanglement points between neighbouring chains represent the network junctions. At very low rates of shear the chains may slip one over the other; at higher (relatively) rates of shear the independent chains and aggregates entangle and interlock, behaving essentially as one huge aggregate interconnecting all the volume by its network and branches. A peculiar property of dilatant polymeric solutions is their ability to climb rotating spindle or inner wall of a rotating tube (Weissenberg phenomenon). In addition, the dilatant polymeric solutions are characterized by the thread-forming ability ("Spinnbarkeit"). At higher rates of shear the dynamic network of the macromolecules may be broken or ruptured, and a pronounced degradation of the polymer may take place. When the actual molecular weight of the polymer decreases, the system is obviously irreversible.

The distinction between solid phase- and liquid phase-induced dilatancy is of paramount importance. In a number of cases the dilatancy, actually due to the liquid phase, is assumed to be due to the solid phase. These confusion is intensified by the formerly mentioned fact that an addition of pigment changes profoundly the rheological characteristics of the liquid phase. As a matter of fact, after addition of pigment, the polymer solution is a new and distinctive system characterized by a more narrow molecular weight distribution, a higher sensitivity to solvent strength, and higher average molecular weight.

The term *thixotropic* describes a system in which viscosity is dependent on time and rate of shear, decreasing with increasing rate of shear up to some critical rate of shear value; above this critical value the viscosity remains constant and independent of any further increase of rate of shear. At this latter stage it corresponds to a non-equilibrium Newtonian system. A thixotropic system is reversible, the thixotropic recovery times being anything from one-thousandth of a second till a number of hours or, even, weeks. No distinction is recognized between thixotropic, plastic and pseudo-plastic systems; they all are considered to be thixotropic. It is, as well, considered that the so-called "yield-value" is not a fundamental critical value of stress but only an arbitrary description of the rigidity as a function of time [4].

In pigment suspensions the presence of thixotropy indicates flocculation of pigment particles. This can be evaluated by sedimentation methods, the degree of flocculation, β, being equal to the ratio of the sedimentation volume of the tested suspension, F_0, to the sedimentation volume of this suspension at absolute pigment dispersion (deflocculation), F_∞. The pigment contribution to the suspension viscosity is twofold: firstly, it contributes the viscosity component due to the presence of particles as such ("crowding effect"), and secondly, it contributes the viscosity component due to the presence of flocculated pigment structure; the latter component is called *structural viscosity*. The structural viscosity depends on the rate of shear and corresponds to the existence of a dynamic and reversible network structure formed by the pigment flocculate. A slight pseudo-thixotropic effect may be observed in dispersed suspensionsof rod-like particles, and is due to the orientation of these otherwise deflocculated particles.

It is the basic characteristic of a thixotropic system that its flow curve, when plotted in a log-log scale, is formed by two straight lines intersecting at the point described formerly as the critical rate of shear value. If the arms of the flow curve are not straight lines, it indicates that the continuous phase is not of a Newtonian type. A "hysteresis loop" does not exist under equilibrium conditions.

In systems containing only a polymer solution thixotropy indicates the presence of highly coiled and compact resin aggregates; it may be due, as well, to very strong hydrogen bondings existing between polymer molecules or aggregates.

4. Micro-rheological classification.

The micro-rheological type of a multi-phase system is described by a two-term classification. The first term relates to the solid phase (discontinuous phase) and the second term relates to the liquid phase (continuous phase) [5]. (See Figures 2 and 3.)

I. *Newtonian-Newtonian:* The system contains totally dispersed (deflocculated) pigment (solid phase) and non-aggregated polymer solution (or, alternatively, a simple liquid). There is no change of viscosity with the rate of shear. It is possible to find a pseudo-Newtonian-Newtonian systems when only a narrow range of shear rates is used (Figure 5). This "pseudo" system is a special case of the thixotropic-dilatant system, and is due to the compensating effects of the simultaneous thixotropy of the solid phase and dilatancy of the liquid phase. Measurement of viscosity at very low rates of shear, or measurements of viscosity at two different temperatures, can be used for identification.

II. *Thixotropic-Newtonian*: (Figures 3.2 and 4.2) The system contains flocculated pigment and a simple or non-aggregated liquid phase. The viscosity decreases with increasing rates of shear, up to the point of the critical rate of shear. When temperature increases, the degree of flocculation increases, and thus the structural viscosity increases; simultaneously, the viscosity of the liquid phase decreases. Depending on the contribution of these components, the over-all viscosity of suspension may either increase or decrease with an increase in temperature.

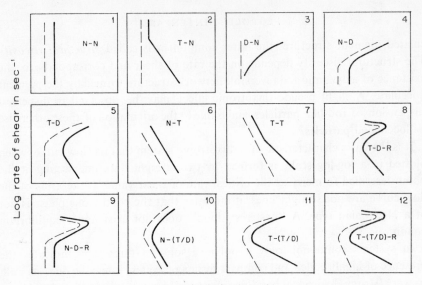

Figure 3

Micro-rheological classification of suspensions of rigid particles in Newtonian and non-Newtonian liquid (continuous) media. The full lines represent the flow curves of suspensions; the dotted lines indicate a contribution of the liquid medium to the suspension viscosity. N–Newtonian, T–thixotropic, D–dilatant, R–rupture. For legend see text

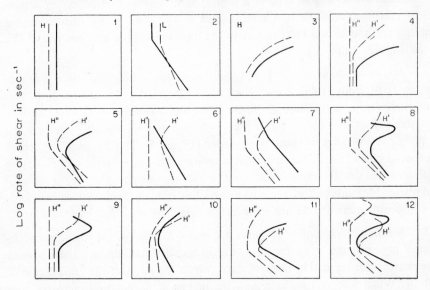

Figure 4

Effect of temperature on the rheological flow types. The full lines show the typical flow types as illustrated by Fig. 5. The dotted lines show transitions flow in the types induced by a lower temperature (L), a higher and a very high temperatures (H′, H″). L ≧ 10°C; H″ ≦ 60°C. For legend see text

III. *Dilatant-Newtonian*: (Figures 3.3 and 4.3) Such system is generally illustrated by an example of sand and water. Suspension contains dispersed pigment or powder in a simple or non-aggregated liquid. An application of stress changes configuration and orientation of pigment particles and, consequently, its effective volume increases. Formation of voids and internal surface causes a drying out effect. The viscosity is rapidly increasing with the rate of shear.

IV. *Newtonian-Dilatant:* (Figures 3.4 and 4.4) The system contains dispersed (deflocculated) pigment in aggregated polymeric solution. The polymeric aggregates remain independent at very low rates of shear, their chains being capable of slipping one over another; at increasing rates of shear the chains entangle, aggregates interlock and form a dynamic network. Such suspensions show Weissenberg effect. An increase of temperature increases the solubility of the polymeric species, and the dilatant effect is reduced. At very high temperatures the suspension may undergo a transition into a Newtonian-Newtonian system. Effects similar to the ones induced by temperature changes may be caused by additions or replacements of stronger or weaker solvents (Figure 1).

V. *Thixotropic-Dilatant:* (Figures 3.5 and 4.5) The suspension contains a flocculated pigment and aggregated polymer solution. At low rates of shear the thixotropic component is predominant, at higher rates of shear the dilatant component is more evident. An increase in temperature will magnify the thixotropic component and decrease the dilatant effect due to the liquid phase. A decrease in temperature may cause a partial precipitation of the polymer, the system becoming much more complex.

VI. *Newtonian-Thixotropic:* (Figures 3.6 and 4.6) Such system contains deflocculated (dispersed) pigment in a thixotropic liquid phase. An increase of temperature, or an addition of a strong solvent, will change the liquid phase rheological type into dilatant or even Newtonian.

VII. *Thixotropic-Thixotropic:* (Figures 3.7 and 4.7) Such system contains flocculated pigment in thixotropic fluid. This fluid may be either designed to be thixotropic, as is the case with the so-called "thixotropic" alkyds, or it may be due to the precipitation of polymer molecules in a form of highly-coiled aggregates. The flocculation of pigment particles may be due to the agglutination of the otherwise, perhaps, dispersed particles by the precipitated polymer. An increase of temperature may solubilize the precipitated polymer and the liquid phase may become dilatant or Newtonian.

VIII. and IX. *Thixotropic-Dilatant with Rupture* and *Newtonian-Dilatant with Rupture*, respectively. (Figures 3.8, 3.9, 4.8 and 4.9) The formerly described systems IV and V can be characterized by *rupture*. This means that under high rates of shear a mechanical breakdown of aggregates and of the network take place. These are accompanied by a decrease in the apparent, or even in the real molecular weight of the polymer, and by a corresponding decrease in the viscosity of the liquid phase. A temperature increase could change the rheological type of the liquid phase ito dilatant or Newtonian.

X. and XI. *Newtonian-(Thixotropic/Dilatant)* and *Thixotropic-(Thixotropic/ Dilatant)*: (Figures 3.10, 3.11, 4.10, and 4.11) The rheology of such systems is very complex. In the case when a fraction of the polymer is precipitated while another fraction is in solution and capable to form a dynamic network (two sub-phases in the liquid phase), the liquid phase itself will have the characteristics of a thixotropic-dilatant system. If a pigment is incorporated in such liquid, the flow curve of the suspension can follow closely that of the liquid (when the pigment particles are deflocculated), or the thixotropic characteristics can be magnified (when the pigment particles are flocculated). An increase of temperature, or an addition of stronger solvent, will cause a solubilization of the precipitated polymer fraction and the liquid phase will tend to become dilatant or Newtonian.

XII. Both above systems, XI and X may show *rupture* at higher rates of shear, that is, a sudden decrease of viscosity at higher rates of shear may be observed. (Figures 3.12 and 4.12) This phenomenon was already explained as being due to the breakdown of the aggregates and polymeric network. The proper term for the system illustrated the on Figure 3.12 will be thus *Thixotropic-(Thixotropic/Dilatant)* *with Rupture*. It is actually suspected that systems showing *rupture* are of a more general type and that, under suitable testing conditions, rupture would be observed in all systems containing a dilatant liquid phase.

5. Analysis.

A determination of flow curves at two temperatures permits recognition of the micro-rheological class of the tested suspension. Once this is known and the flow curve is plotted, a semi-quantitative determination and estimation of such parameters as pigments degree of flocculation, sedimentation volume, polymer aggregation and coiling, may follow.

The solid phase contributes to the viscosity of suspension by a two-fold mechanism. Firstly, by the presence of pigment particles as such, that is the so-called crowding effect. While a number of equations are in existence, the author uses a recently suggested equation [4], [6] which relates the sedimentation volume at total deflocculation (which corresponds to the sedimentation

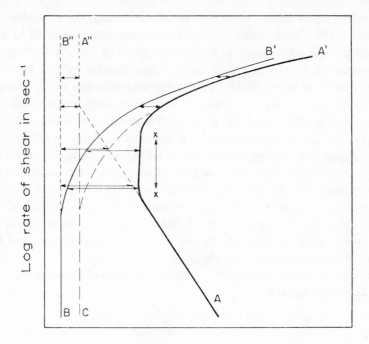

Log viscosity

Figure 5

Analysis of a Thixotropic-Dilatant system. The curve A — A′ corresponds to the flow curve of suspension; the curve B — B′ represents a contribution of the liquid medium to the viscosity of suspension. The viscosity of suspension is always directly proportional to the viscosity of the liquid phase. The curve C — A′ represents a contribution of the "crowding effect" of the pigment in the tested suspension. The area between curves C — A′ and A — A′ corresponds to the structural viscosity caused by flocculation of the pigment particles. The region indicated by arrows X — X corresponds to a pseudo-Newtonian-Newtonian flow type. For legend see text

volume or the hydrodynamic volume of the solid phase at infinite rate of shear), F_∞, and the relative viscosity, η_r, the latter being a ratio of the suspension viscosity in kinematic units to the viscosity of the liquid phase in the kinematic units.

$$\log \frac{\eta_\infty}{\eta_v} = \log \eta_{r,\infty} = \frac{F_\infty}{1 - F_\infty}$$

When F_∞ is estimated by sedimentation tests, the contribution of the crowding effect may be determined. The degree of aggregation and coiling, as measured by the hydrodynamic coeffient α, of the polymeric solution may be then calculated [3].

When the liquid phase shows dilatant characteristics, the respective contributions of the liquid phase, pigments crowding effect and the structural viscosity may be represented as on the Figure 5. The curve A—A' represents the experimentally-obtained flow curve. Determination of F_∞ and the η_v of the supernatant liquid (B—B″) permits the determination of the position of C—A″ curve and A—A″ curve. While the former corresponds to the contribution of the crowding effect, the latter gives the flow curve of an analogous suspension in which the structural viscosity is identical as in the tested suspension but the liquid phase is Newtonian and equal in viscosity to the actual liquid phase when measured at very low rates of shear. As the contribution of the crowding effect and the structural viscosity is always directly proportional to the viscosity of the liquid phase, it is possible to graph the position of B—B' and C—A' curves. It may be observed that at identical values for rate of shear, the distances between curves B—B″ and A—A″, on the one hand, and B—B' and A—A', on the other hand, are equal.

The viscosity of suspension, below the critical rate of shear, at the rate of shear D, will be equal to:

$$\log \eta_D = k.(F^{1/3} - F_\infty^{1/3}) + \frac{F_\infty}{1 - F_\infty} + \log \eta_v$$

where F is the sedimentation volume of suspensions,

k is the coefficient corresponding to the rate of shear D;

The slope of the thixotropic arm of the flow curve, if given as an S-fold increase in viscosity at tenfold decrease of the rate of shear, may be also related to the sedimentation volume and the hydrodynamic volume of the solid phase [4] by a following expression:

$$S = [24.5 \, (F^{1/3} - F_\infty^{1/3}) + 1]^{k'}$$

the value of k' depending on the fact if the suspension is of "compressed" or "expanded" type; that is, if the sedimentation volume is larger or smaller than unity.

Flocculation, sedimentation and thixotropy of suspensions are highly influenced by the structures and properties of the continuous phase. The rheological characteristics of the continuous phase depend on the concentration, molecular weight and molecular weight distribution of the polymer; and on the configuration, coiling and aggregation of polymer molecules. The latter phenomena depend, in their turn, on the solvent strength of a solvent or a thinner employed, and on the polymer-solvent interactions. The size of macromolecular aggregates is influenced mainly by the solvent strength and temperature; the effect of concentration is negligible above a certain critical value.

The following equation illustrates a relationship between the relative viscosity of a polymer solution (η_r), solvent strength in *EDM* units [3], and the hydrodynamic coefficient α_r which indicates the degree of coiling and aggregation of polymer molecules.

$$\alpha_r = \frac{\log \eta_r}{1.9 \, C_v} = 1/B \cdot (X/A - A/X) \cdot \log X/A + \alpha_{r,\,min}.$$

where: X — solvent effective polarity (3);

A — value of X corresponding to the minimum of the curve; it is equal to the effective polarity of the polymer solution;

B — a constant which is a function of the molecular weight distribution;

$\alpha_{r,min}$ — a value of α_r corresponding to the minimum of the curve and to the total dispersion (peptisation) of polymer molecules.

C_v — volume fraction of polymer

The estimation of molecular weights and degree of aggregations of polymeric systems is limited, so far, to the solutions showing Newtonian and dilatant characteristics. No method was found yet for thixotropic polymeric systems. In the liquid systems showing both thixotropy and dilatancy it is possible to approximate the fraction responsible for the thixotropic component; the methods analogous to the ones employed in the case of suspensions may be applied.

The discussion of analytical methods is not complete and the readers are referred to the original papers. While the techniques described are not exact, they should permit a qualitative and semi-quantitative determination of the colloidal and rheological parameters.

REFERENCES

[1] M. REINER, *Twelve Lectures on Theoretical Rheology*, (1949), Amsterdam.
[2] L. DINTENFASS, *Kolloid Z.*, **151**, (1957), 154; **155**, 121; **161**, (1958), 60, 70.
[3] L. DINTENFASS, *J. Oil and Colour Chem. Assoc.*, **40**, (1957), 761; **41**, (1958), 125, 333; **42**, (1959), 849; **43**, (1960), 46.
[4] L. DINTENFASS, *Kolloid Z.*, **163**, (1959), 48.
[5] L. DINTENFASS, *J. Appl. Chem.*, **8**, (1958), 349; *Kolloid Z.*, **170**, (1960), 1.
[6] L. DINTENFASS, *Chem. and Ind.*, (1957), 141.

NON-NEWTONIAN INTRINSIC VISCOSITY
AND STREAMING BIREFRINGENCE
OF POLYMER SOLUTIONS

ANTON PETERLIN

Camille Dreyfus Laboratory, Research Triangle Institute, Durham, N. C., U.S.A.

ABSTRACT

With increasing gradient perfectly soft macromolecular coils expand in laminar flow. As a consequence of the expansion the hydrodynamic interaction decreases. Due to the opposite sign of movement of both ends of the macromolecules this decrease first reduces the intrinsic viscosity. The specific interaction between the solute and the solvent substantially influences the initial drop. With higher gradient the viscosity ought to increase again. This effect in most cases does not appear because the coil expansion is limited by the finite length of macromolecular chain. Actual macromolecules also have a finite rigidity which in normal solvents substantially limits coil expansion. But the rigidity does not matter very much in extremely viscous solvents where indeed such an increase of intrinsic viscosity at high shearing stress was observed. Coil expansion and the consequent changes in hydrodynamic interaction also influence the streaming birefringence and to a lesser extent the extinction angle.

The intrinsic viscosity number of polymer solutions measures the additional shearing stress due to the presence of isolated macromolecules in the laminar flow field $(0,Gx,0)$. With linear macromolecules it mainly depends on the root mean gyration radius R or the *r.m.s.* end-to-end distance h and the hydrodynamic permeability of the corresponding statistical coil.

In the limit of zero gradient the coil dimensions equal those in the solutions at rest. With a given macromolecule they still depend on the solvent. At the Flory's θ-temperature the coil dimensions obey the random-walk rules, i.e.. the mean square of the gyration radius R_0^2 is proportional to molecular weight M

$$R_0^2 = A_0 M$$
$$h_0^2 = A_0 M/6. \tag{1}$$

In good solvents the coil is more expanded

$$h' = \alpha h_0 \quad , \qquad \alpha \geqslant 1 \tag{2}$$

As a consequence the better the solvent the higher the intrinsic viscosity.

With non-vanishing gradient G the intrinsic viscosity changes. As a rule it drops and very likely asymptotically approaches a new, lower, non-vanishing value at infinite gradiant. Some cases, however, indicate an increase (dilatancy) after the initial drop.

In order to explain this behavior the shape change and orientation of macro-molecular coil in laminar flow have to be considered. Streaming birefringence measurements indicate the existence of both effects. The extinction angle χ, i.e., the direction of preferential coil orientation, being 45° at $G = 0$, steadily decreases with G indicating that the coils get more and more oriented in the flow direction. The accompanying coil extension yields a more than linear increase of the amount of birefringence with gradient.

A perfectly flexible random coil with constant and isotropic hydrodynamic interaction[1] ("ideal" coil) yields a constant intrinsic viscosity independent on gradient. The increased contribution to shearing stress as a consequence of coil expansion is just compensated by orientation which reduces the number of contributing molecules per unit area. In order to obtain the experimentally established gradient dependence the following three effects were considered: 1. partial chain rigidity 2. anisotropy of hydrodynamic interaction and 3. change of hydrodynamic interaction as a consequence of coil deformation.

1. The stress field in laminar flow tends to expand the macromolecular coil at 45° and to compress at −45° to the flow direction. Because due to the rotational part $(G/2)(-y, x, o)$ of the flow field the macromolecule rotates with the mean angular velocity $G/2$, it has to be twice subsequently compressed and expanded during one full turn which is completed in $t = 4\pi/G$. The shape resistance of the actual coil opposes such fast changes and results in sub-stantially smaller mean expansion than that of a perfectly flexible coil. As a consequence the contribution of coil expansion increases less than in the "ideal" case. The reduction of shearing stress due to coil orientation, however, remains nearly unchanged. Hence the intrinsic viscosity drops with increasing gradient. Kuhn and Kuhn [3] performed the calculation for the case of completely rigid macromolecular coil (dumbbell model, two-dimensional motion) and concluded that actual polymer solutions may exhibit a gradient dependence between this limiting case and that of perfectly soft coil. Cerf [4] used Rose's model and obtained explicit results for different degrees of coil resistance to fast shape changes.

2. At any given end-to-end distance and orientation the average monomer distribution of all possible coil conformations is anisotropic leading to an anisotropy of hydrodynamic resistance for displacement of the free ends of the

---

[1] The free draining coil (no hydrodynamic interaction, dumbbell model) [1] and the coil with constant interaction proportional to the inverse r.m.s. distance between any two chain elements in solution at rest (Rouse's model) [2] have been investigated in this connection.

macromolecule. The radial resistance is smaller than the tangential one. As a consequence the coils are better oriented and less expanded than in the "ideal" coil, the intrinsic viscosity drops with increasing gradient [5], [6].

3. The coil extension in laminar flow increases the intrachain distances and thence decreases the hydrodynamic interaction between any two chain elements. But due to the fact that on the average one half of the macromolecule has just the opposite movement to that of the other half the first effect of expansion is a decrease of intrinsic viscosity in agreement with the main body of experimental evidence. At higher expansion however, it rises again [7]. Such a dilatancy was only found in extremely viscous solutions [8] (lubricating oils containing a small amount of polymer silicon as improver). In such a case the strong hydrodynamic forces are very likely sufficient to expand the macromolecular coil in spite of its shape resistance. The latter is substantially reduced by the relatively low speed or rotation since due to the high solvent viscosity the non-Newtonian behavior is already observable at rather small gradients.

In all three cases the initial drop of relative intrinsic viscosity

$$[\eta]_{rel} = \frac{[\eta]_G}{[\eta]_0} = 1 - B\beta_0^2 + \dots \tag{3}$$

is proportional to the square of the parameter β_0

$$\beta_0 = \frac{M[\eta]_0\eta_0}{N_A kT} \cdot G \tag{4}$$

η_0 viscosity of the solvent, N_A Avogardo's number, k Boltzmann's constant, T absolute temperature.

The proportionality factor B is still a function of M and α. The relative contribution of different effects may be seen in Figure 1. In actual polymer solution these contributions are superimposed. Effect 2 is independent on coil flexibility. Contribution 1, however, vanishes with perfectly soft molecules where 3 is maximum and vice versa with rigid molecules reaches its maximum at vanishing effect 3. No attempt of combining the three effects was yet made mainly due to the fact that even the experimental data are not sufficiently well established for a definitive check of the proposed theories. In addition the recently observed linear decrease of relative intrinsic viscosity with β_0

$$[\eta]_{rel} = 1 - B'\beta_0 + \dots \tag{5}$$

in cellulose nitrate solutions [9] cannot be explained by any existing theoretical approach.

Since both effects 1 and 2 were already reviewed on many occasions let us concentrate on the third effect, and in addition to non-Newtonian viscosity, also consider the closely related streaming birefringence.

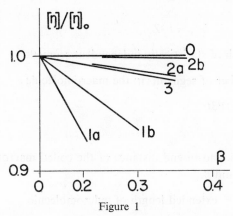

Figure 1

Initial decrease of relative intrinsic viscosity as function of β_0^2. The slope yields B. 0. perfectly flexible coil with constant hydrodynamic interaction ($B = 0$). 1a. rigid coil, two-dimensional movement, dumb-bell model (Kuhn and Kuhn [3], $B = 2$). 1c. rather rigid coil, Rouse's model (Cerf [4], $B = 0.72$). 2. anisotropy of hydrodynamic interaction: a. (Čopič, Peterlin [5], $B = 0.148$;) b. (Ikeda, $B = 0.020$). 3. change of hydrodynamic interaction as consequence of coil expansion ($B = 0.152e/(1 + e)$)

The variation of hydrodynamic interaction and its influence on viscosity and streaming birefringence was treated on the basis of the simple dumb-bell model [7], but taking into account the cooperation of all the statistically independent segments of the macromopecule. Such a treatment corresponds to limiting Rouse's model to the first deformation mode. This affects the numerical constants, e.g., the ratio of intrinsic orientation and intrinsic viscosity, and the intrinsic viscosity behaviour at high G, but does not change basically the character of the gradient dependence. The simplicity of the model, however, permits the explicit consideration of the effects of solvent [10] and of finite chain length [11]. In agreement with Zimm's treatment [2] of Rouse's model at any β value average values of hydrodynamic interaction and coil expansion are introduced, their variation with coil orientation and actual end-to-end distance of single configurations being neglected

With these assumptions the solution of diffusion equation of the free end of the macromolecule, the other end being fixed at the origin, reads [10],

$$\phi(x_1\,y_1\,z) = \frac{(\mu/\pi)^{3/2}}{(1+\beta^2)^{\frac{1}{2}}}\,\exp\left\{-\frac{\mu}{(1+\beta^2)}\,[(1+2\beta^2)x^2 - 2\beta xy + y^2 + \right.$$

$$\left. + (1+\beta^2)z^2]\right\} \tag{6}$$

$\mu \quad = \mu'E/E'$

$\mu' \quad = 3/2h'^2$

$h \quad = \alpha h_0 \qquad h^2{}_0 = b^2 Z$

$b \quad = $ length of statistically independent segment

$Z \quad = $ number of segments in the macromolecule

$E(t) \quad = \mathscr{L}^{-1}(t)/3t$

$t \quad = h/L$

$h \quad = $ r.m.s. end-to-end distance of the coiled macromolecule at given α and β.

$L \quad = bZ = $ extended length of macromolecule

$\mathscr{L}^{-1} \quad = $ inverse Langevin function

$\beta \quad = G/4\mu D = (M[\eta]\eta_0/N_A kT)\,G$

$D \quad = kT/\eta_0 W = (6kT/\eta_0 Z\Lambda)(1 + eSf) = $ diffusion constant of the free end

$e \quad = (\Lambda/b)(Z/6\pi^3)^{\frac{1}{2}}$

$\Lambda \quad = $ hydrodynamic resistance coefficient of single segment

$$S \quad = S_Z(t) = \left[\sum_{m=1}^{Z/2}\left(\frac{m}{Z}\right)^{-1/2} - 2\sum_{1}^{Z}\left(\frac{m}{Z}\right)^{1/2} - 2\sum_{1}^{Z/2}\left(\frac{m}{Z}\right)^{3/2} + \right.$$

$$\left. + 2\sum_{Z/2+1}^{Z}\left(\frac{m}{Z}\right)^{3/2}\right]\cdot\left[1 + \frac{m-1}{Z-1}\left(t^2 Z - 1\right)\right]^{-1/2}\cdot Z^{-1}$$

$f \quad = f(\beta) = F(k,\varphi)[(1+2\beta^2/3)/2\beta(1+\beta^2)^{1/2}]^{1/2}$

$F \quad = $ incomplete elliptic integral of the first kind

$k^2 \quad = \frac{1}{2}[1 + \beta/(1+\beta^2)^{1/2}]$

$\sin^2\varphi = 2\beta[(1+\beta^2)^{1/2} - \beta].$

The function E measures the more than linear increase in restoring force with the end-to-end distance h approaching to extended length L. The dashed quantities refer to the solution at rest.

The distribution function $\emptyset$ yields for relative intrinsic viscosity

$$[\eta]_{rel} = \frac{E'}{E} \cdot \frac{1 + eS'}{1 + eSf}, \tag{7}$$

for the amount of streaming birefringence[2]

$$\frac{\Delta n}{nc} = \frac{4\pi}{5} \left(\frac{n^2 + 2}{3n}\right)^2 \frac{N_A}{M}(\alpha_1 - \alpha_2)\beta(1 + \beta^2)^{1/2}\gamma\alpha^2/E$$

$$\gamma = \frac{5}{3}(1 - 1/E) \tag{8}$$

$\alpha_1 - \alpha_2$ = apparent optical anisotropy of segment in the actual solvent, and for the extinction angle

$$\cot 2\chi = \beta. \tag{9}$$

The corresponding curves are plotted in Figures 2, 3, 4, 5, as functions of

$$\beta_0 = \beta/[\eta]_{rel} = \text{const. } G. \tag{10}$$

The number of segments Z is 10^2, 10^3, and 10^4 respectively. The values of ε correspond to $\alpha = 1.000, 1.414, 2.000, 2.828, 4.000$ at $Z = 10^4$, to $\alpha = 1.000, 1.260, 1.589, 2.005, 2.524$ at $Z = 10^3$, and to $\alpha = 1.000, 1.123, 1.262, 1.416, 1.592$ at $Z = 10^2$. Ideal solution is characterized by $\varepsilon = 0$.[3]

Initial drop of $[\eta]_{rel}$ as function of β_0 is reduced and even nearly completely disappears at $Z = 10^4$ and $\varepsilon = 0.4$. With smaller Z the effects are less conspicuous due to the correspondigly smaller α values. A comparison with the experimentally obtained dilatancy [8] (Figure 6) seems to indicate that the added polymer had a Z between 10^3 and 10^4 and an α between 1.5 and 2.5 provided that the effects of chain rigidity and of hydrodynamic anisotropy may be neglected.

---

[2] The shape anisotropy [12] is completely neglected. Lorenz-Lorentz optical inner field is assumed.

[3] The actual choice of ε and α as function of Z means that at $Z = 10$ the coil dimensions coincide regardless of solvent quality: $\alpha = h'/ho = (Z/10)^{\varepsilon/2}$. This assumption is rather arbitrary. As a consequence one has to attach more significance to α than to ε.

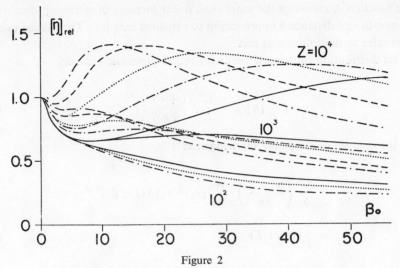

Figure 2

Relative intrinsic viscosity as function of β_0. For explanation see Figure 3

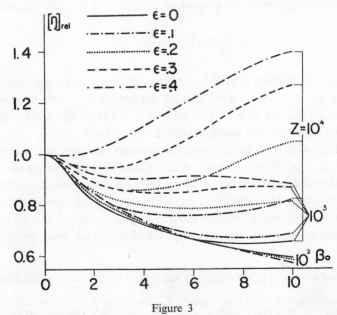

Figure 3

Relative intrinsic viscosity as function of β_0 in the range $0 < \beta_0 < 10$

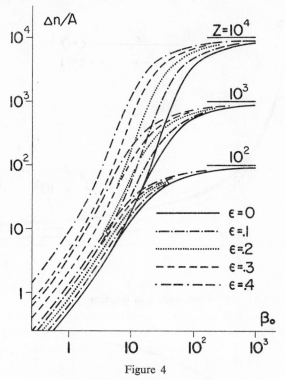

Figure 4

Relative streaming birefringence

$$\Delta n : A = \frac{\Delta n}{cn} : 2\pi \left(\frac{n^2 + 2}{3n}\right)^2 \frac{N_A}{M}(\alpha_1 - \alpha_2)$$

as function of β_0 with limiting values for $\beta_0 = \infty$

The streaming birefringence is displaced to lower β_0 with increasing α or ε. The displacement is nearly constant in the bilogarithmic plot and rather a function of α than of ε. The limiting amount at $\beta_0 = \infty$ is of course independent on α since it corresponds to completely extended macromolecules.

The extinction angle is the least sensitive to Z and α or ε when plotted over β_0. That means that especially the initial drop from $45°$ with G (intrinsic orientation) is mainly proportional to $[\eta]_0$ which of course very markedly varies with coil dimensions, i.e., with α or ε. But, at least in the limits of the dumb-bell model, the initial slope is insensitive to the change of hydro-dynamic interaction as a consequence of coil expansion in flow.

More extended experiments on dilute polymer solutions in a very viscous solvent are needed for checking the validity of the presented theory. Intrinsic

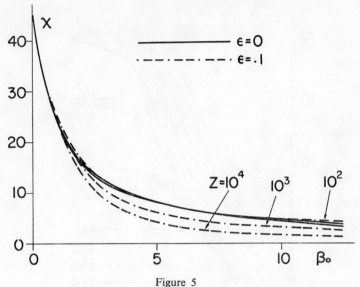

Figure 5

Extinction angle χ as function of β_0.

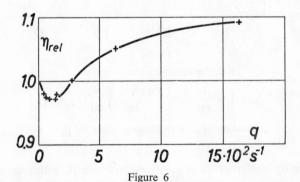

Figure 6

Relative viscosity of silicon improved lubricating oil as function of G^7.

viscosity measurements seem to be the most promising. In addition they are
the least requiring. We hope soon to be able to start with experiments of this
kind. Streaming birefringence measurements are intriguing by the fact that
the coil expansion in good solvents is immediately projected in the initial slope
(specific Maxwell constant)

$$M_{sp} = \left(\frac{\Delta n}{cn\eta_0 G} \right)_{G=0} = \frac{4\pi}{5} \left(\frac{n^2 + 2}{3n} \right)^2 (\alpha_1 - \alpha_2)\frac{[\eta]_0}{kT} \cdot \frac{\gamma'\alpha^2}{E'}. \qquad (11)$$

All the factors may be independently determined — $(\alpha_1-\alpha_2)$ for instance from measurements at low M when α is close to unity, γ'/E' nearly equals unity in all cases of interest — so that α^2 can be derived from combination of M_{sp} and $[\eta]_0$.

Very likely the method can be easily extended to include higher deformation modes of Rouse's model. Again all the parameters of hydrodynamic interaction and limited coil expansion have to be assumed independent on coordinates, but functions of β, i.e. of the mean coil dimension and orientation.

In order to get a complete theory of intrinsic viscosity and streaming birefringence all the three effects, as mentioned in the introduction, have to be considered simultaneously. The inclusion of shape resistance and of anisotropy of hydrodynamic interaction can be achieved by a series expansion as suggested by Cerf [4] since both have the same tensor character, i.e. rotational and radial deformation motion have to be separated.

REFERENCES

[1] J. J. HERMANS, *Physica*, **70**, (1943), 777.

[2] B. H. ZIMM, *J. Chem. Phys.*, **24**, (1956), 269.

[3] W. KUHN AND H. KUHN, *Helv. Chim. Acta*, **28**, (1945), 1533; **29**, (1946), 72, 609, 830.

[4] R. CERF, *J. Phys. Radium*, **19**, (1958), 122.

[5] M. ČOPIČ, *J. Chem. Phys.*, **53**, (1956), 440; A. PETERLIN AND M. ČOPIČ, *J. Appl. Phys.*, **27**, (1956), 434.

[6] Y. IKEDA, *J. Phys. Soc. Japan*, **12**, (1957), 378.

[7] A. PETERLIN, *J. Chem. Phys.*, **33**, (1960), 1799.

[8] T. W. SELBY AND N. A. HUNSTAD: paper presented at ASTM Symposium on non-Newtonian viscosity, Washington, D. C., October 1960.

[9] S. CLAESSON AND U. LOHMANDER, *Makromol. Chem.*, **44–46**, (1961), 461.

[10] A. PETERLIN, *Kolloid. Z.* (in press).

[11] A. PETERLIN, *Makromol. Chem.*, **44–46**, (1961), 338; *Polymer*, **2**, (1961), 257.

[12] M. ČOPIČ, *J. Chem. Phys.*, **26**, (1957), 1382; R. K. BULLOUGH, *J. Polymer Sci.*, **46**, (1960), 517.

NORMAL PRESSURE EFFECTS IN THE SHEARING
OF VISCOUS LIQUIDS

R. D. BELL AND R. C. L. BOSWORTH

The University of New South Wales, Sydney, Australia

ABSTRACT

A viscous fluid in a slowly revolving vessel may give rise to pressure differences in a stationary tube held parallel to the axis of the rotation with its open end kept slightly clear from the revolving bottom. The pressures, which do not necessarily arise from Weissenberg phenomena, may be of the order of one atmosphere, and arise from relaxational phenomena and changing velocities of flow past the open end of the tube. The changing velocity is due to slight imperfections in the surface of the platen and may be eliminated with associated pressure differences by using plane surfaces.

1. Introduction.

The peculiar phenomena exhibited by the Weissenberg effect in sheared liquids consist in the production of pressure differences resulting from the application of strain and strain velocity components which normally give rise only to tangential (or shear) stress components. As such, these phenomena may be compared with the behaviour of "dilatancy" in which purely elastic phenomena give rise to a change in volume as a result of the application of pure static shears, alone, and thus a change in static pressure as the result of shearing strains. However, there are instances in which pressure changes which may result from the operation of non-uniform stresses of a purely shear type even when the medium concerned is what Weissenberg has called a general fluid. If the strain velocities are not truly uniform then the fluid behaves as though the rheological characteristics are more complicated than that of a simple fluid.

For example, if certain viscous fluids are treated in a normal glass beaker which is rotated, then a stationary tube held close to the rotating surface of the bottom shows that a pressure difference, as manifested by a rise in the level in the stationary tube, is developed as long as the tube is not placed in an axial position. For example, if golden syrup contained in a 2 litre beaker is placed on a slowly rotated platform such as a gramophone turn-table then a glass tube is placed with the free end close to the bottom and held vertical, the free liquid surface is observed to rise in the tube as long as that tube is

786

not placed along the axis of rotation. The faster the rate of rotation or smaller the clearance, i.e. the difference between the stationary tube and the bottom of the beaker (the rotating platen), and the greater the distance from the axis of the tube to the axis of the beaker, the greater will be the rise of the liquid in the tube and, accordingly, the greater is the pressure developed by the act of shearing the viscous fluid between the stationary end of the tube and the rotating bottom of the beaker. Rheological properties of golden syrup are approximately those of a general fluid in the Weissenberg sense with a viscosity at operating temperature of 200 poises. The rate of rotation of the beaker was of the order of 50 R.P.M., the distance of clearance of the order of 0.1 mm and hydrostatic pressure developed was of the order of 2 meters of golden syrup. The phenomenon observed is thus by no means insignificant, and a more comprehensive treatment was obviously worthy of investigation.

2. The effects of physical parameters on the magnitude of the pressure effects observed.

The magnitude of the pressure difference developed increases rapidly with the decrease in the clearance between the end of the tube and the rotating platen. It is, accordingly, necessary to know accurately the magnitude of this clearance. The surface of a chemical beaker is by no means true. The clearance between the bottom and the end of the tube is not only indeterminate but varies with the angle of rotation. The beaker used was accordingly built up from a ring screwed or riveted to a flat plate consisting of a machined or horizontal plane of metal or polymer.

The rotating vessel consisted of a horizontal turned platen some 19 cms in diameter and rotated at a speed adjustable from 7.5 to 75 R.P.M., by means of a robust gear box. The vertical glass tube, which had an internal diameter of 10 mm, was arranged above the horizontal platen and the free end was connected to a U-tube manometer for measuring the pressure in the vertical tube. A diagram of the rotating vessel and stationary tube connected to the manometer is given in the left-hand side of Figure 1.

The clearance between the vertical tube above the platen was measured by a cathetometer. By noting the position of a fixed mark on the tube when resting on the platen and when raised above the platen, the distance between the end of the tube and the platen could be determined. The planarity of the platen was assessed by recording the cathetometer reading at different positions on that platen with the tube resting on the surface.

Vertical pressure was mesured by allowing the liquid in the U-tube to rise in that tube until equilibrium was reached. Depending on conditions, the times for equilibrium varied from four minutes to half an hour.

Figure 1

In the second instrument constructed, the platen was machined from aluminium. This was presumed to be initially plane, but on checking after use the surface was found to be irregular, probably due to distortion of the platen and the shaft. The clearance distances at selected points 120° apart at two radii are shown in Figure 2.

This instrument was a considerable improvement on earlier instruments of perspex platens which distort irregularly under stress. Distortion in the aluminium instrument mentioned above arises principally from bending the shaft carrying the level gears, and the only solution was to build an instrument with a more robust transmission.

To overcome the problem of the shaft bending under load, a half-inch diameter shaft was used for the bevel gear. To overcome irregularity in the platen, a glass plate was cemented to the metal base with Araldite cement. Before the cement set, the glass was levelled with a dial gauge to ensure that the platen was perfectly horizontal with respect to vertical position of the upright driving shaft.

The instrument was mounted on a cast aluminium base. By packing the base with shims, the rotating platen could then be set in a horizontal position by checking with a spirit level.

A, B & C are points of measurement by the cathetometer.

Radius = 7.5 cm

1/3 Circum. = 15.1 cm.

Angles between points are:

tan Θ	Θ radians	Θ minutes
0.0002	0.0002	0.7
0.0006	0.0006	2.0
0.0008	0.0008	2.7

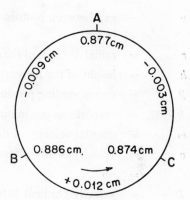

Radius = 3.2 cm.

1/3 Circum. = 6.7 cm.

Angles between points are:

tan Θ	Θ radians	Θ minutes
0.00045	0.00045	1.5
0.00090	0.00090	3.0

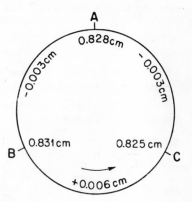

Figure 2
2nd Instrument. Uneven nature of aluminium platen

The vertical position of the tube was checked as for the second instrument. The pressure was recorded from the manometer and the clearance was again measured by the cathetometer.

3. Results.

The following symbols were used:

y = gap between bottom of the tube and the platen (or the clearance) in cm

r = radial distance of the centre of the tube to the centre of platen in cm

h = height of the mercury manometer in cm

P = corresponding pressure in dynes cm^{-2} or $= 1.333 \times 10^4 h$

$R.P.M.$ = revolutions per minute of the platen

ω = angular velocity of the platen in radians sec^{-1}, $= R.P.M. \times 2\pi/60$

v = velocity of the platen past a point in cm sec^{-1},

= $r\omega$

D = velocity gradient between the clearance of the tube and the rotating platen in sec^{-1}

= v/y

α = angle of the tube from the vertical in radians.

The viscosities of the various liquids used at various flow rates were examined on a model H. B. T. Brookfield Viscometer at 25°C. The results of such examination were recorded in Table I.

TABLE I

Brookfield viscosity at 25°C

Material:	Golden syrup	SAE 50 oil	2.5% Methyl cellulose soln.	Glycerine	Polyiso-butylene in mineral oil
Spindle No.:	4	1	2	1	1
R.P.M.	Poise	Poise	Poise	Poise	Poise-
100	—	3.6	24.8	5.9	4.4
50	187	3.6	30.4	5.9	3.0
20	190	3.5	37.1	5.8	2.6
10	192	3.7	40.6	5.9	2.8
5	192	3.8	44.8	6.1	2.9

The pressures developed from the aluminium platen with the operating fluid as golden syrup and the operating temperature as 25.6°C (and the radius $r = 3.2$ cm) are reported in Figure 3.

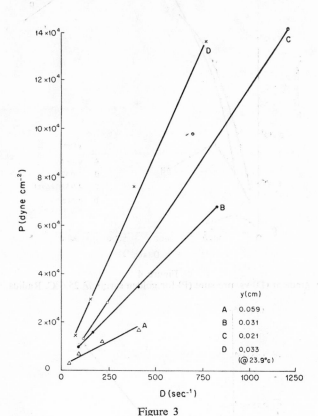

Figure 3

Velocity gradiant (D) vs pressure (P) for golden syrup @ 25.6°C. Radius $r = 3.2$ cm.

A corresponding set of figures at $r = 7.5$ cm is recorded in Figure 4.

With the operating fluid being SAE 50 grade lubricating oil and $r = 3.2$ cm, the corresponding data are given in Figure 5, and with $r = 7.5$ cm in Figure 6.

Data with the methyl cellulose solution as the operating fluid are given in Figure 7.

Data with glycerine as the operating fluid are shown in Figure 8.

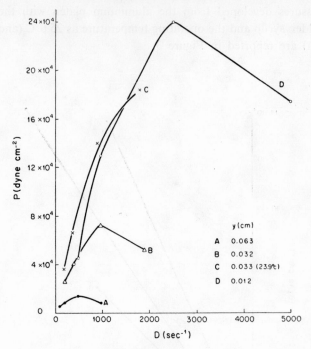

Figure 4
Velocity gradient (D) vs. pressure (P) for golden syrup @ 25.6°C. Radius = 7.5 cm

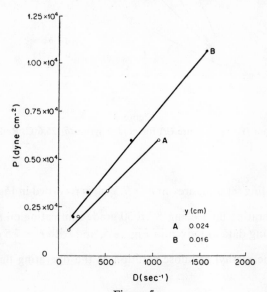

Figure 5
Velocity gradient (D) vs pressure (P) for SAE 50 motor oil @ 24.4°C. r = 3.2 cm.

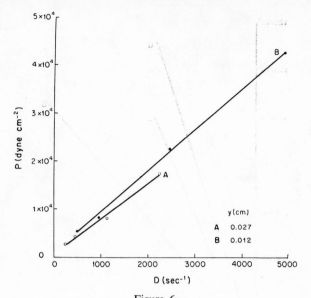

Figure 6

Velocity gradient (D) vs pressure (P) for SAE 50 motor oil @ 24.4°C. $r = 7.5$ cm

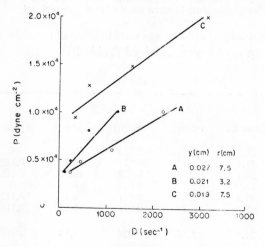

Figure 7

Velocity gradient (D) vs. pressure (P) for 2.3 % methyl cellulose solution @ 21.2°C

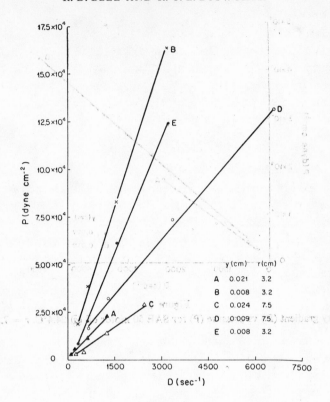

Figure 8

Velocity gradient (D) vs. pressure(P) for glycerine @ 23.9°C. A-B-C-D-E refer to order of experiments to show effect of moisture pick-up

When the horizontal glass platen was used in place of the distorted aluminium plate, the following results were obtained (Table II):

TABLE II

Substance	Temp°C.	r(cms)	y(cms)	v cm sec^{-1}	a(radians)	$P \times 10^4$ dynes cm^2
Golden syrup	21.1	5.35	0.024	10.25	0	0
Golden syrup	21.1	5.35	0.024	10.25	0.112	4.0
Golden syrup	21.1	5.35	0.024	10.25	0.118	34.0
Golden syrup	19.5	3.2	0.027	6.13	0	0
Golden syrup	19.5	3.2	0.027	6.13	0.112	0.53
Golden syrup	19.5	3.2	0.027	6.13	0.118	4.53
Polyisobutylene solution	21.4	5.35	0.024	6.13	0	0
Polyisobutylene solution	21.4	5.35	0.024	6.13	0.133	0

4. Discussion.

The most striking feature of the results is the difference between true planar platens and platens which were slightly irregular. In the former instance the act of shearing produces no measurable pressure differences unless the measuring tube is inclined quite steeply towards the direction of motion of the viscous fluid. This suggests quite strongly that the recorded pressure differences are the result of Pitot effects or inertial effects.

$$\Delta p = \Delta(pv^2)$$

In the case of the irregular platen, the velocity of flow is increasing when the clearance is decreasing and a positive (Pitot) pressure is expected to develop. A corresponding negative pressure is expected to be developed when the clearance is increasing, so that the nett pressure averaged over a complete rotation of the platen is expected to be zero, provided the physical properties of the fluid take the same values with the stream velocity v positive as with the stream velocity negative. If, however, the physical properties of the fluid are subject to relaxational phenomena, the act of taking v through a cyclical range of values could give an average of P which could take a positive value. The fluids tested with the (non-uniform) aluminium platen appear, therefore, to be such as subject the relaxation times to the same order of magnitude as the rotational times of the platen. In this respect, the decrease in effective pressure at high rates of shear, noted in particular in Figure 4, are particularly significant.

Below shear rates at which this phenomenon occurs, the values of P are directly proportional to ΔD. This is noted in Figures 3 to 8. Where values are studied at different values of the clearance, the pressure at any particular value of D is inversely proportional to the clearance. It may also be noted that the pressure is increased by a decrease in temperature and, accordingly, appears to rise with an increase in viscosity. This conclusion is also reached by comparison of the ratios of P to D in Figures 3 to 8.